SOLUTIONS TO EXERCISES

ROXY WILSON

University of Illinois, Urbana–Champaign

TWELFTH EDITION

CHEMISTRY
THE CENTRAL SCIENCE

BROWN LeMAY BURSTEN MURPHY WOODWARD

Prentice Hall

Boston Columbus Indianapolis New York San Francisco Upper Saddle River
Amsterdam Cape Town Dubai London Madrid Milan Munich Paris Montréal Toronto
Delhi Mexico City São Paulo Sydney Hong Kong Seoul Singapore Taipei Tokyo

Editor in Chief, Chemistry: Adam Jaworski
Acquisitions Editor: Terry Haugen
Marketing Manager: Erin Gardner
Senior Project Editor: Jennifer Hart
Managing Editor, Chemistry and Geosciences: Gina M. Cheselka
Project Manager, Science: Shari Toron
Operations Specialist: Maura Zaldivar
Supplement Cover Designer: Paul Gourhan
Cover Credit: Graphene by Dr. Jannik C. Meyer of the University of Ulm, Germany

© 2012, 2009, 2006, 2003, 2000, 1997, 1994, 1991, 1988, 1985, 1981, 1977

Pearson Education, Inc.

Pearson Prentice Hall

Upper Saddle River, NJ 07458

Printed in the United States of America

10 9 8 7 6 5 4 3 2 1

ISBN-13:   978-0-321-70500-6

ISBN-10:   0-321-70500-9

Prentice Hall
is an imprint of

www.pearsonhighered.com

Contents

Introduction

Chemistry: The Central Science, 12th edition, contains more than 2600 end-of-chapter exercises. Considerable attention has been given to these exercises because one of the best ways for students to master chemistry is by solving problems. Grouping the exercises according to subject matter is intended to aid the student in selecting and recognizing particular types of problems. Within each subject matter group, similar problems are arranged in pairs. This provides the student with an opportunity to reinforce a particular kind of problem. There are also a substantial number of general exercises in each chapter to supplement those grouped by topic. Integrative exercises, which require students to integrate concepts from several chapters, are a continuing feature of the 12th edition. Answers to the odd numbered topical exercises plus selected general and integrative exercises, about 1200 in all, are provided in the text. These appendix answers help to make the text a useful self-contained vehicle for learning.

This manual, **Solutions to Exercises in Chemistry: The Central Science, 12th edition,** was written to enhance the end-of-chapter exercises by providing documented solutions. The manual assists the instructor by saving time spent generating solutions for assigned problem sets and aids the student by offering a convenient independent source to check their understanding of the material. Most solutions have been worked in the same detail as the in-chapter sample exercises to help guide students in their studies.

To reinforce the '*Analyze, Plan, Solve, Check*' problem-solving method used extensively in the text, this strategy has also been incorporated into the Solution Manual. Solutions to most red paired exercises and selected Additional and Integrative exercises feature this four-step approach. We strongly encourage students to master this powerful and totally general method.

When using this manual, keep in mind that the numerical result of any calculation is influenced by the precision of the numbers used in the calculation. In this manual, for example, atomic masses and physical constants are typically expressed to four significant figures, or at least as precisely as the data given in the problem. If students use slightly different values to solve problems, their answers will differ slightly from those listed in the appendix of the text or this manual. This is a normal and a common occurrence when comparing results from different calculations or experiments.

Rounding methods are another source of differences between calculated values. In this manual, when a solution is given in steps, intermediate results will be rounded to the correct number of significant figures; however, unrounded numbers will be used in subsequent calculations. By following this scheme, calculators need not be cleared to re-enter rounded intermediate results in the middle of a calculation sequence. The final answer will appear with the correct number of significant figures. This may result in a small discrepancy in the last significant digit between student-calculated answers and those given in this manual. Variations due to rounding can occur in any analysis of numerical data.

The first step in checking your solution and resolving differences between your answer and the listed value is to look for similarities and differences in problem-solving methods. Ultimately, resolving the small numerical differences described above is less important than understanding the general method for solving a problem. The goal of this manual is to provide a reference for sound and consistent problem-solving methods in addition to accurate answers to text exercises.

Extraordinary efforts have been made to keep this manual as error-free as possible. All exercises were worked and proof-read by at least three chemists to ensure clarity in methods and accuracy in mathematics. The work and advice of Ms. Rene Musto, Ms. Kate Vigor, Dr. Christopher Musto and Dr. Timothy Kucharski have been invaluable to this project. In any written work as technically challenging as this manual, typos and errors inevitably creep in, despite our combined efforts. Please help us find and eliminate them. We hope that both instructors and students will find this manual accurate, helpful and instructive.

Roxy B. Wilson, Ph.D.
1829 Maynard Dr.
Champaign, IL 61822
rbwilson@illinois.edu

1 Introduction: Matter and Measurement

Visualizing Concepts

1.1 *Pure elements* contain only one kind of atom. Atoms can be present singly or as tightly bound groups called molecules. *Compounds* contain two or more kinds of atoms bound tightly into molecules. *Mixtures* contain more than one kind of atom and/or molecule, not bound into discrete particles.

    (a)   pure element: i

    (b)   mixture of elements: v, vi

    (c)   pure compound: iv

    (d)   mixture of an element and a compound: ii, iii

1.2 After a *physical change*, the identities of the substances involved are the same as their identities before the change. That is, molecules retain their original composition. During a *chemical change*, at least one new substance is produced; rearrangement of atoms into new molecules occurs.

The diagram represents a chemical change, because the molecules after the change are different than the molecules before the change.

1.3 To brew a cup of coffee, begin with ground coffee beans, a heterogeneous mixture, and water, a pure substance. Hot water contacts the coffee grounds and dissolves components of the coffee bean that are water-soluble. This creates a new heterogeneous mixture of undissolved coffee bean solids and liquid coffee solution; this mixture is separated by filtration. Undissolved grounds are left on the filter paper and liquid coffee, itself a homogeneous mixture, drips into the container below.

Overall, two separations occur. Chemical differences among the components of the coffee bean allow certain compounds to dissolve in water, while other components remain insoluble. This kind of separation based on solubility differences is called *extraction*. The insoluble grounds are then separated from the coffee solution by *filtration*.

1.4   (a)   time   (b) mass   (c) temperature   (d) area   (e) length

    (f)   area   (g) temperature   (h) density   (i) volume

1.5 Density is the ratio of mass to volume. For a sphere, size is like volume; both are determined by the radius of the sphere.

    (a)   For spheres of the same size or volume, the denominator of the density relationship is the same. The denser the sphere, the heavier it is. A list from lightest to heaviest is in order of increasing density and mass. The aluminum sphere (density = 2.70 g/cm³) is lightest, then nickel (density = 8.90 g/cm³), then silver (density = 10.409 g/cm³).

(b)   For spheres of equal mass, the numerator of the density relationship is the same. The denser the sphere, the smaller its volume or size. A list from smallest to largest is in order of decreasing density. The platinum sphere (density = 21.45 g/cm³) is smallest, then gold (density = 19.30 g/cm³), then lead (density = 11.35 g/cm³).

1.6   Measurements (darts) that are close to each other are *precise*. Measurements that are close to the "true value" (the bull's eye) are *accurate*.

(a)   Figure ii represents data that are both accurate and precise. The darts are close to the bull's eye and each other.

(b)   Figure i represents data that are precise but inaccurate. The darts are near each other but their center point (average value) is far from the bull's eye.

(c)   Figure iii represents data that are imprecise but their average value is accurate. The darts are far from each other, but their average value, or geometric center point, is close to the bull's eye.

1.7   (a)   7.5 cm. There are two significant figures in this measurement; the number of cm can be read precisely, but there is some estimating (uncertainty) required to read tenths of a centimeter. Listing two significant figures is consistent with the convention that measured quantities are reported so that there is uncertainty in only the last digit.

(b)   The speed is 72 mi/hr (inner scale, two significant figures) or 115 km/hr (outer scale, three significant figures). Both scales are read with certainty in the "hundreds" and "tens" place, and some uncertainty in the "ones" place. The km/hr speed has one more significant figure because its magnitude is in the hundreds.

1.8   (a)   Volume = length × width × height. Because the operation is multiplication, the dimension with fewest significant figures (sig figs) determines the number of sig figs in the result. The dimension "2.5 cm" has 2 sig figs, so the volume is reported with 2 sig figs.

(b)   Density = mass/volume. Because the operation is division, again the datum with fewer significant figures determines the number of sig figs in the result. While mass, 104.72 g, has 5 sig figs, volume [from (a)] has 2 sig figs, so density is also reported to 2 sig figs.

1.9   When converting units, arrange the conversion factor so that the given unit cancels and the desired unit is in the correct position. For example, suppose a quantity is expressed in terms of centimeters, but the desired result is expressed in inches. If the given unit has 'cm' in the numerator, then the conversion factor must have 'cm' in its denominator. However, if the original unit has 'cm' in the denominator, the conversion factor must have 'cm' in the numerator. Ideally, this will lead to the desired units in the appropriate location, numerator or denominator. However, the inverse of the answer can be taken when necessary.

1.10   Given: m/s Find: mi/hr.   Both the given and desired units have distance in the numerator and time in the denominator. Use appropriate conversion factors to change 'm' to 'mi' in the numerator and 's' to 'hr' in the denominator.

Classification and Properties of Matter (sections 1.2 and 1.3)

1.11   (a)   heterogeneous mixture

        (b)   homogeneous mixture (If there are undissolved particles, such as sand or decaying plants, the mixture is heterogeneous.)

        (c)   pure substance

        (d)   pure substance

1.12   (a)   homogeneous mixture

        (b)   heterogeneous mixture (particles in liquid)

        (c)   pure substance

        (d)   heterogeneous mixture

1.13   (a)   S   (b) Au   (c) K   (d) Cl   (e) Cu   (f) uranium

        (g)   nickel   (h) sodium (i) aluminum   (j) silicon

1.14   (a)   C   (b) N   (c) Ti   (d) Zn   (e) Fe   (f) phosphorus

        (g)   calcium (h) helium (i) lead   (j) silver

1.15   A(s)   →   B(s) + C(g)

        When solid carbon is burned in excess oxygen gas, the two elements combine to form a gaseous compound, carbon dioxide. Clearly substance C is this compound.   Since C is produced when A is heated in the absence of oxygen (from air), both the carbon and oxygen in C must have been present in A originally. A is, therefore, a compound composed of two or more elements chemically combined. Without more information on the chemical or physical properties of B, we cannot determine absolutely whether it is an element or a compound. However, few if any elements exist as white solids, so B is probably also a compound.

1.16   Gold, Au, is an element and "fool's gold", FeS_2, is a compound; both are solids and pure substances.   Take advantage of differences in physical and or chemical properties between the two substances. Density and melting point measurements are often used to identify solids. For these two substances, melting points are very high, but densities are easy to measure. Gold is much denser than "fool's gold". Gold is much less chemically reactive than FeS_2, so relative reactivity with acids and bases can be observed. Of these experiments, density measurement is the most definitive and does not destroy the sample. (Note that neither substance is attracted to a magnet, so this test will not identify the gold.)

1.17   *Physical properties*: silvery white (color); lustrous; melting point = 649°C; boiling point = 1105°C; density at 20°C = 1.738 g/cm^3; pounded into sheets (malleable); drawn into wires (ductile); good conductor. *Chemical properties*: burns in air to give intense white light; reacts with Cl_2 to produce brittle white solid.

1.18   *Physical properties*: silver-gray (color); melting point = 420°C; hardness = 2.5 Mohs; density = 7.13 g/cm^3 at 25°C. *Chemical properties*: metal; reacts with sulfuric acid to produce hydrogen gas; reacts slowly with oxygen at elevated temperatures to produce ZnO.

1.19   (a) chemical   (b) physical   (c) physical   (d) chemical   (e) chemical

1.20   (a)   chemical

        (b)   physical

        (c)   physical (The production of H_2O is a chemical change, but its *condensation* is a physical change.)

        (d)   physical (The production of soot is a chemical change, but its *deposition* is a physical change.)

1.21   (a)   Take advantage of the different water solubilities of the two solids. Add water to dissolve the sugar; filter this mixture, collecting the sand on the filter paper and the sugar water in the flask. Evaporate water from the flask to recover solid sugar.

        (b)   Take advantage of the different solubilities and densities of the two liquids. Allow the mixture to settle so that there are two distinct layers. Vinegar (a water solution) is denser and on the bottom; oil (the organic layer) is less dense and on top. Carefully pour off most of the top layer. After the layers reform, use a dropper to remove any remaining oil. Vinegar is in the original vessel and oil is in a second container.

1.22   First heat the liquid in each beaker to 100°C to evaporate the water. The beaker with no residue contained pure water. The other two beakers have a solid, white residue. Measure the melting point of each solid. Sugar has a much lower melting point than salt, so the beaker with the lower-melting residue contained sugar water and that with the higher-melting residue contained salt water. (If confirmation is required, measure the densities of the two white residues.)

Units and Measurement (section 1.4)

1.23   (a) 1×10^{-1} (b) 1×10^{-2} (c) 1×10^{-15} (d) 1×10^{-6} (e) 1×10^{6}

        (f) 1×10^{3} (g) 1×10^{-9} (h) 1×10^{-3} (i) 1×10^{-12}

1.24   (a) $2.3 \times 10^{-10} \, L \times \dfrac{1 \, nL}{1 \times 10^{-9} \, L} = 0.23 \, nL$

(b) $4.7 \times 10^{-6}\,g \times \dfrac{1\,\mu g}{1 \times 10^{-6}\,g} = 4.7\,\mu g$

(c) $1.85 \times 10^{-12}\,m \times \dfrac{1\,pm}{1 \times 10^{-12}\,m} = 1.85\,pm$

(d) $16.7 \times 10^{6}\,s \times \dfrac{1\,Ms}{1 \times 10^{6}\,s} = 16.7\,Ms$

(e) $15.7 \times 10^{3}\,g \times \dfrac{1\,kg}{1 \times 10^{3}\,g} = 15.7\,kg$

(f) $1.34 \times 10^{-3}\,m \times \dfrac{1\,mm}{1 \times 10^{-3}\,m} = 1.34\,mm$

(g) $1.84 \times 10^{2}\,cm \times \dfrac{1\,m}{1 \times 10^{2}\,cm} = 1.84\,m$

1.25   (a)   °C = 5/9 (°F – 32°); 5/9 (72 – 32) = 22°C

(b)   °F = 9/5 (°C) + 32°; 9/5 (216.7) + 32 = 422.1°F

(c)   K = °C + 273.15; 233°C + 273.15 = 506 K

(d)   °C = 315 K – 273.15 = 41.85 = 42°C; °F = 9/5 (41.85°C) + 32 = 107°F

(e)   °C = 5/9 (°F – 32°); 5/9 (2500 – 32) = 1371°C; K = 1371°C + 273.15 = 1644 K
      (assuming 2500 °F has 4 sig figs)

(f)   °C = 0 K – 273.15 = –273.15°C; °F = 9/5 (–273.15°C) + 32 = –459.67°F
      (assuming 0 K has infinite sig figs)

1.26   (a)   °C = 5/9 (87°F – 32°) = 31°C

(b)   K = 25°C + 273.15 = 298 K; °F = 9/5 (25°C) + 32 = 77°F

(c)   °C = 5/9 (400°F – 32°) = 204.444 = 204°C

      K = °C + 273.15 = 204.444°C + 273.15 = 478 K

(d)   °C = 77 K – 273.15 = –196.15 = –196°C; °F = 9/5 (–196.15°C) + 32 = –321°F

1.27   (a)   density $= \dfrac{mass}{volume} = \dfrac{40.55\,g}{25.0\,mL} = 1.62\,g/mL$ or $1.62\,g/cm^{3}$

(The units cm^{3} and mL will be used interchangeably in this manual.)

Tetrachloroethylene, 1.62 g/mL, is more dense than water, 1.00 g/mL; tetrachloroethylene will sink rather than float on water.

(b) $25.0\,cm^{3} \times 0.469\,\dfrac{g}{cm^{3}} = 11.7\,g$

1.28   (a)   volume = length^{3} (cm^{3}); density = mass/volume (g/cm^{3})

      volume = $(1.500)^{3}\,cm^{3} = 3.375\,cm^{3}$

      density $= \dfrac{76.31\,g}{3.375\,cm^{3}} = 22.61\,g/cm^{3}$ osmium

(b) $125.0 \text{ mL} \times \dfrac{1 \text{ cm}^3}{1 \text{ mL}} \times \dfrac{4.51 \text{ g}}{1 \text{ cm}^3} = 563.75 = 564 \text{ g titanium}$

(c) $0.1500 \text{ L} \times \dfrac{1 \text{ mL}}{1 \times 10^{-3} \text{ L}} \times \dfrac{0.8787 \text{ g}}{1 \text{ mL}} = 131.8 \text{ g benzene}$

1.29   (a) $\text{density} = \dfrac{38.5 \text{ g}}{45 \text{ mL}} = 0.86 \text{ g/mL}$

The substance is probably toluene, density = 0.866 g/mL.

(b) $45.0 \text{ g} \times \dfrac{1 \text{ mL}}{1.114 \text{ g}} = 40.4 \text{ mL ethylene glycol}$

(c) $(5.00)^3 \text{ cm}^3 \times \dfrac{8.90 \text{ g}}{1 \text{ cm}^3} = 1.11 \times 10^3 \text{ g } (1.11 \text{ kg}) \text{ nickel}$

1.30   (a) $\dfrac{21.95 \text{ g}}{25.0 \text{ mL}} = 0.878 \text{ g/mL}$

The tabulated value has four significant figures, while the experimental value has three. The tabulated value rounded to three figures is 0.879. The values agree within one in the last significant figure of the experimental value; the two results agree. The liquid could be benzene.

(b) $15.0 \text{ g} \times \dfrac{1 \text{ mL}}{0.7781 \text{ g}} = 19.3 \text{ mL cyclohexane}$

(c) $r = d/2 = 5.0 \text{ cm}/2 = 2.5 \text{ cm}$

$V = 4/3 \, \pi \, r^3 = 4/3 \times \pi \times (2.5)^3 \text{ cm}^3 = 65.4498 = 65 \text{ cm}^3$

$65.4498 \text{ cm}^3 \times \dfrac{11.34 \text{ g}}{\text{cm}^3} = 7.4 \times 10^2 \text{ g}$

(The answer has two significant figures because the diameter had only two significant figures.)

Note: This is the first exercise where "intermediate rounding" occurs. In this manual, when a solution is given in steps, the intermediate result will be rounded to the correct number of significant figures. However, the **unrounded** number will be used in subsequent calculations. The final answer will appear with the correct number of significant figures. That is, calculators need not be cleared and new numbers entered in the middle of a calculation sequence. This may result in a small discrepancy in the last significant digit between student-calculated answers and those given in the manual. These variations occur in any analysis of numerical data.

For example, in this exercise the volume of the sphere, 65.4498 cm^3, is rounded to 65 cm^3, but 65.4498 is retained in the subsequent calculation of mass, 7.4×10^2 g. In this case, 65 cm^3 × 11.34 g/cm^3 also yields 7.4×10^2 g. In other exercises, the correctly rounded results of the two methods may not be identical.

1.31   31 billion tons $\times \dfrac{1 \times 10^9 \text{ tons}}{1 \text{ billion tons}} \times \dfrac{2000 \text{ lb}}{1 \text{ ton}} \times \dfrac{453.59 \text{ g}}{1 \text{ lb}} = 2.8 \times 10^{16}$ g

The metric prefix for 1×10^{15} is peta, abbreviated P.

2.8×10^{16} g $\times \dfrac{1 \text{ Pg}}{1 \times 10^{15} \text{ g}} = 28 \text{ Pg}$

1.32   (a)   The wafers have the same diameter as the boule, so the question becomes 'how many 0.75 mm wafers can be cut from the 2 m boule?'

$\dfrac{2.0 \text{ m}}{\text{boule}} \times \dfrac{1 \text{ mm}}{1 \times 10^{-3} \text{ m}} \times \dfrac{1 \text{ wafer}}{0.75 \text{ mm}} = 2667 = 2.7 \times 10^3$ wafers

(b)   Calculate the volume of the wafer in cm^3. $V = \pi r^2 h$

$r = \dfrac{d}{2} = \dfrac{300 \text{ mm}}{2} \times \dfrac{1 \text{ cm}}{10 \text{ mm}} = 15 \text{ cm};$ $h = 0.75 \text{ mm} \times \dfrac{1 \text{ cm}}{10 \text{ mm}} = 7.5 \times 10^{-2}$ cm

$V = \pi r^2 h = \pi(15 \text{ cm})^2(7.5 \times 10^{-2} \text{ cm}) = 53.0144 = 53 \text{ cm}^3$

Density = mass / V;   mass = density $\times$ V

$\dfrac{2.33 \text{ g}}{cm^3} \times 53.0144 \text{ cm}^3 = 123.52 = 1.2 \times 10^2$ g

Uncertainty in Measurement (section 1.5)

1.33   Exact: (c), (d), and (f) (All others depend on measurements and standards that have margins of error, e.g., the length of a week as defined by the earth's rotation.)

1.34   Exact: (b), (e) (The number of students is exact on any given day.)

1.35   (a)   3   (b) 2   (c) 5   (d) 3   (e) 5   (f) 1 [See Sample Exercise 1.6 (c)]

1.36   (a)   4   (b) 3   (c) 4   (d) 5   (e) 6   (f) 2

1.37   (a) 1.025×10^2 (b) 6.570×10^5 (c) 8.543×10^{-3}

(d) 2.579×10^{-4} (e) -3.572×10^{-2}

1.38   (a) 7.93×10^3 mi   (b) 4.001×10^4 km

1.39   (a)   14.3505 + 2.65 = 17.0005 = 17.00 (For addition and subtraction, the minimum number of decimal places, here two, determines decimal places in the result.)

(b)   952.7 – 140.7389 = 812.0

(c) $(3.29 \times 10^4)(0.2501) = 8.23 \times 10^3$ (For multiplication and division, the minimum number of significant figures, here three, determines sig figs in the result.)

(d)   0.0588/0.677 = 8.69×10^{-2}

1.40 (a) $[320.5 - 6104.5/2.3] = -2.3 \times 10^3$ (The intermediate result has two significant figures, so only the thousand and hundred places in the answer are significant.)

(b) $[285.3 \times 10^5 - 0.01200 \times 10^5] \times 2.8954 = 8.260 \times 10^7$ (Since subtraction depends on decimal places, both numbers must have the same exponent to determine decimal places/sig figs. The intermediate result has 1 decimal place and 4 sig figs, so the answer has 4 sig figs.)

(c) $(0.0045 \times 20,000.0)$ + (2813×12) = 3.4×10^4
2 sig figs / 0 dec pl   2 sig figs / first 2 digits

(d)   863   × [1255   − $(3.45 \times 108)]$ = 7.62×10^5
(3 sig figs / 0 dec pl)

3 sig figs   ×   [0 dec pl/3 sig figs]   = 3 sig figs

1.41 The mass 21.427 g has 5 significant figures.

1.42 The volume in the graduated cylinder is 19.5 mL. Liquid volumes are read at the bottom of the meniscus, so the volume is slightly less than 20 mL. Volumes in this cylinder can be read with certainty to 1 mL, and with some uncertainty to 0.1 mL, so this measurement has 3 sig figs.

Dimensional Analysis (section 1.6)

1.43 In each conversion factor, the old unit appears in the denominator, so it cancels, and the new unit appears in the numerator.

(a) $mm \rightarrow nm$: $\dfrac{1 \times 10^{-3}\,m}{1\,mm} \times \dfrac{1\,nm}{1 \times 10^{-9}\,m} = 1 \times 10^6\ nm/mm$

(b) $mg \rightarrow kg$: $\dfrac{1 \times 10^{-3}\,g}{1\,mg} \times \dfrac{1\,kg}{1000\,g} = 1 \times 10^{-6}\ kg/mg$

(c) $km \rightarrow ft$: $\dfrac{1000\,m}{1\,km} \times \dfrac{1\,cm}{1 \times 10^{-2}\,m} \times \dfrac{1\,in}{2.54\,cm} \times \dfrac{1\,ft}{12\,in} = 3.28 \times 10^3\ km/ft$

(d) $in^3 \rightarrow cm^3$: $\dfrac{(2.54)^3\,cm^3}{1^3\,in^3} = 16.4\ cm^3/in^3$

1.44 In each conversion factor, the old unit appears in the denominator, so it cancels, and the new unit appears in the numerator.

(a) $\mu m \rightarrow mm$: $\dfrac{1 \times 10^{-6}\,m}{1\,\mu m} \times \dfrac{1\,mm}{1 \times 10^{-3}\,m} = 1 \times 10^{-3}\ mm/\mu m$

(b) $ms \rightarrow ns$: $\dfrac{1 \times 10^{-3}\,s}{1\,ms} \times \dfrac{1\,ns}{1 \times 10^{-9}\,s} = 1 \times 10^6\ ns/ms$

(c) $mi \rightarrow km$: 1.6093 km/mi

(d) $ft^3 \rightarrow L$: $\dfrac{(12)^3\,in^3}{1\,ft^3} \times \dfrac{(2.54)^3\,cm^3}{1\,in^3} \times \dfrac{1\,L}{1000\,cm^3} = 28.3\ L/ft^3$

1.45   (a) $\dfrac{15.2\,m}{s} \times \dfrac{1\,km}{1000\,m} \times \dfrac{60\,s}{1\,min} \times \dfrac{60\,min}{1\,hr} = 54.7\,km/hr$

       (b) $5.0 \times 10^3\,L \times \dfrac{1\,gal}{3.7854\,L} = 1.3 \times 10^3\,gal$

       (c) $151\,ft \times \dfrac{1\,yd}{3\,ft} \times \dfrac{1\,m}{1.0936\,yd} = 46.025 = 46.0\,m$

       (d) $\dfrac{60.0\,cm}{d} \times \dfrac{1\,in}{2.54\,cm} \times \dfrac{1\,d}{24\,hr} = 0.984\,in/hr$

1.46   (a) $\dfrac{2.998 \times 10^8\,m}{s} \times \dfrac{1\,km}{1000\,m} \times \dfrac{1\,mi}{1.6093\,km} \times \dfrac{60\,s}{1\,min} \times \dfrac{60\,min}{1\,hr} = 6.707 \times 10^8\,mi/hr$

       (b) $1454\,ft \times \dfrac{1\,yd}{3\,ft} \times \dfrac{1\,m}{1.0936\,yd} = 443.18 = 443.2\,m$

       (c) $3,666,500\,m^3 \times \dfrac{1^3\,dm^3}{(1 \times 10^{-1})^3\,m^3} \times \dfrac{1\,L}{1\,dm^3} = 3.6665 \times 10^9\,L$

       (d) $\dfrac{242\,mg\ cholesterol}{100\,mL\ blood} \times \dfrac{1\,mL}{1 \times 10^{-3}\,L} \times 5.2\,L \times \dfrac{1 \times 10^{-3}\,g}{1\,mg} = 12.58 = 13\,g\ cholesterol$

1.47   (a) $5.00\,days \times \dfrac{24\,hr}{1\,day} \times \dfrac{60\,min}{1\,hr} \times \dfrac{60\,s}{1\,min} = 4.32 \times 10^5\,s$

       (b) $0.0550\,mi \times \dfrac{1.6093\,km}{mi} \times \dfrac{1000\,m}{1\,km} = 88.5\,m$

       (c) $\dfrac{\$1.89}{gal} \times \dfrac{1\,gal}{3.7854\,L} = \dfrac{\$0.499}{L}$

       (d) $\dfrac{0.510\,in}{ms} \times \dfrac{2.54\,cm}{1\,in} \times \dfrac{1 \times 10^{-2}\,m}{1\,cm} \times \dfrac{1\,km}{1000\,m} \times \dfrac{1\,ms}{1 \times 10^{-3}\,s} \times \dfrac{60\,s}{1\,min} \times \dfrac{60\,min}{1\,hr} = 46.6\,\dfrac{km}{hr}$

       Estimate: $0.5 \times 2.5 = 1.25;\ 1.25 \times 0.01 \approx 0.01;\ 0.01 \times 60 \times 60 \approx 36\,km/hr$

       (e) $\dfrac{22.50\,gal}{min} \times \dfrac{3.7854\,L}{gal} \times \dfrac{1\,min}{60\,s} = 1.41953 = 1.420\,L/s$

       Estimate: $20 \times 4 = 80;\ 80/60 \approx 1.3\,L/s$

       (f) $0.02500\,ft^3 \times \dfrac{12^3\,in^3}{1\,ft^3} \times \dfrac{2.54^3\,cm^3}{1\,in^3} = 707.9\,cm^3$

       Estimate: $10^3 = 1000;\ 3^3 = 27;\ 1000 \times 27 = 27,000;\ 27,000/0.04 \approx 700\,cm^3$

1.48   (a) $0.105\,in \times \dfrac{2.54\,cm}{in} \times \dfrac{1 \times 10^{-2}\,m}{cm} \times \dfrac{1\,mm}{1 \times 10^{-3}\,m} = 2.667 = 2.67\,mm$

       (b) $0.650\,qt \times \dfrac{1\,L}{1.057\,qt} \times \dfrac{1\,mL}{1 \times 10^{-3}\,L} = 614.94 = 615\,mL$

       (c) $\dfrac{8.75\,\mu m}{s} \times \dfrac{1 \times 10^{-6}\,m}{1\,\mu m} \times \dfrac{1\,km}{1 \times 10^3\,m} \times \dfrac{60\,s}{1\,min} \times \dfrac{60\,min}{1\,hr} = 3.15 \times 10^{-5}\,km/hr$

(d) $\quad 1.955 \text{ m}^3 \times \dfrac{(1.0936)^3 \text{ yd}^3}{1 \text{ m}^3} = 2.55695 = 2.557 \text{ yd}^3$

(e) $\quad \dfrac{\$3.99}{\text{lb}} \times \dfrac{2.205 \text{ lb}}{1 \text{ kg}} = 8.798 = \$8.80/\text{kg}$

(f) $\quad \dfrac{8.75 \text{ lb}}{\text{ft}^3} \times \dfrac{453.59 \text{ g}}{1 \text{ lb}} \times \dfrac{1 \text{ ft}^3}{12^3 \text{ in}^3} \times \dfrac{1 \text{ in}^3}{2.54^3 \text{ cm}^3} \times \dfrac{1 \text{ cm}^3}{1 \text{ mL}} = 0.140 \text{ g/mL}$

1.49 (a) $\quad 31 \text{ gal} \times \dfrac{4 \text{ qt}}{1 \text{ gal}} \times \dfrac{1 \text{ L}}{1.057 \text{ qt}} = 1.2 \times 10^2 \text{ L}$

Estimate: $(30 \times 4)/1 \approx 120 \text{ L}$

(b) $\quad \dfrac{6 \text{ mg}}{\text{kg (body)}} \times \dfrac{1 \text{ kg}}{2.205 \text{ lb}} \times 185 \text{ lb} = 5 \times 10^2 \text{ mg}$

Estimate: $6/2 = 3; 3 \times 180 = 540 \text{ mg}$

(c) $\quad \dfrac{400 \text{ km}}{47.3 \text{ L}} \times \dfrac{1 \text{ mi}}{1.6093 \text{ km}} \times \dfrac{1 \text{ L}}{1.057 \text{ qt}} \times \dfrac{4 \text{ qt}}{1 \text{ gal}} = \dfrac{19.9 \text{ mi}}{\text{gal}}$

$(2 \times 10^1 \text{ mi/gal for 1 sig fig})$

Estimate: $400/50 = 8; 8/1.6 = 5; 5/1 = 5; 5 \times 4 \approx 20 \text{ mi/gal}$

(d) $\quad \dfrac{50 \text{ cups}}{1 \text{ lb}} \times \dfrac{1 \text{ qt}}{4 \text{ cups}} \times \dfrac{1 \text{ L}}{1.057 \text{ qt}} \times \dfrac{1000 \text{ mL}}{1 \text{ L}} \times \dfrac{1 \text{ lb}}{453.6 \text{ g}} = \dfrac{26 \text{ mL}}{\text{g}}$

$(3 \times 10^1 \text{ mL/L for 1 sig fig})$

Estimate: $50/4 = 12; 1000/500 = 2; (12 \times 2)/1 \approx 24 \text{ mL/g}$

1.50 (a) $\quad 1257 \text{ mi} \times \dfrac{1 \text{ km}}{0.62137 \text{ mi}} \times \dfrac{\text{charge}}{225 \text{ km}} = 8.99 \text{ charges}$

Since charges are integral events, 9 total charges are required. The trip begins with a full charge, so 8 additional charges during the trip are needed.

(b) $\quad \dfrac{14 \text{ m}}{\text{s}} \times \dfrac{1 \text{ km}}{1 \times 10^3 \text{ m}} \times \dfrac{1 \text{ mi}}{1.6093 \text{ km}} \times \dfrac{60 \text{ s}}{1 \text{ min}} \times \dfrac{60 \text{ min}}{1 \text{ hr}} = 31 \text{ mi/hr}$

(c) $\quad 450 \text{ in}^3 \times \dfrac{(2.54)^3 \text{ cm}^3}{1 \text{ in}^3} \times \dfrac{1 \text{ mL}}{1 \text{ cm}^3} \times \dfrac{1 \times 10^{-3} \text{ L}}{1 \text{ mL}} = 7.37 \text{ L}$

(d) $\quad 2.4 \times 10^5 \text{ barrels} \times \dfrac{42 \text{ gal}}{1 \text{ barrel}} \times \dfrac{4 \text{ qt}}{1 \text{ gal}} \times \dfrac{1 \text{ L}}{1.057 \text{ qt}} = 3.8 \times 10^7 \text{ L}$

1.51 $\quad 14.5 \text{ ft} \times 16.5 \text{ ft} \times 8.0 \text{ ft} = 1914 = 1.9 \times 10^3 \text{ ft}^3$ (2 sig figs)

$1914 \text{ ft}^3 \times \dfrac{(1 \text{ yd})^3}{(3 \text{ ft})^3} \times \dfrac{(1 \text{ m})^3}{(1.0936)^3 \text{ yd}^3} \times \dfrac{10^3 \text{ dm}^3}{1 \text{ m}^3} \times \dfrac{1 \text{ L}}{1 \text{ dm}^3} \times \dfrac{1.19 \text{ g}}{\text{L}} \times \dfrac{1 \text{ kg}}{1000 \text{ g}} = 64.4985 = 64 \text{ kg air}$

Estimate: $1900/27 \approx 60; (60 \times 1)/1 \approx 60 \text{ kg}$

1.52 $11.0 \text{ ft} \times 11.5 \text{ ft} \times 20.5 \text{ ft} = 2593.25 = 2.59 \times 10^3 \text{ ft}^3$

$$2593.25 \text{ ft}^3 \times \frac{(1 \text{ yd})^3}{(3 \text{ ft})^3} \times \frac{(1 \text{ m})^3}{(1.0936 \text{ yd})^3} \times \frac{48 \text{ μg CO}}{1 \text{ m}^3} \times \frac{1 \times 10^{-6} \text{ g}}{1 \text{ μg}} = 3.5 \times 10^{-3} \text{ g CO}$$

1.53   Select a common unit for comparison, in this case the cm.

1 in ≈ 2.5 cm, 1 m = 100 cm

57 cm = 57 cm

14 in ≈ 35 cm

1.1 m = 110 cm

The order of length from shortest to longest is 14-in shoe < 57-cm string < 1.1-m pipe.

1.54   Select a common unit for comparison, in this case the kg.

1 kg > 2 lb, 1 L ≈ 1 qt

5 lb potatoes < 2.5 kg

5 kg sugar = 5 kg

1 gal = 4 qt ≈ 4 L; 1 mL H_2O = 1 g H_2O; 1 L = 1000 g, 4 L = 4000 g = 4 kg

The order of mass from lightest to heaviest is 5 lb potatoes < 1 gal water < 5 kg sugar.

1.55   Strategy: 1) Calculate volume of gold (Au) in cm^3 in the sheet

   2) Mass = density × volume

   3) Change g → troy oz and $

$$100 \text{ ft} \times 82 \text{ ft} \times \frac{(12)^2 \text{ in}^2}{1 \text{ ft}^2} \times 5 \times 10^{-6} \text{ in} \times \frac{(2.54)^3 \text{ cm}^3}{1 \text{ in}^3} = 96.75 = 1 \times 10^2 \text{ cm}^3 \text{ Au}$$

$$96.75 \text{ cm}^3 \text{ Au} \times \frac{19.32 \text{ g}}{1 \text{ cm}^3} \times \frac{1 \text{ troy oz}}{31.1034768 \text{ g}} \times \frac{\$953}{\text{troy oz}} = \$57,272 = \$6 \times 10^4$$

(Strictly speaking, the datum 100 ft has 1 sig fig, so the result has 1 sig fig.)

1.56   A wire is a very long, thin cylinder of volume, $V = \pi r^2 h$, where h is the length of the wire and πr^2 is the cross-sectional area of the wire.

Strategy: 1) Calculate total volume of copper in cm^3 from mass and density

   2) h (length in cm) = $\dfrac{V}{\pi r^2}$

   3) Change cm → ft

$$150 \text{ lb Cu} \times \frac{453.6 \text{ g}}{1 \text{ lb Cu}} \times \frac{1 \text{ cm}^3}{8.94 \text{ g}} = 7610.7 = 7.61 \times 10^3 \text{ cm}^3$$

$$r = d/2 = 7.50 \text{ mm} \times \frac{1 \text{ cm}}{10 \text{ mm}} \times \frac{1}{2} = 0.375 \text{ cm}$$

$$h = \frac{V}{\pi r^2} = \frac{7610.7 \text{ cm}^3}{\pi(0.375)^2 \text{ cm}^2} = 1.7227 \times 10^4 = 1.72 \times 10^4 \text{ cm}$$

$$1.7227 \times 10^4 \text{ cm} \times \frac{1 \text{ in}}{2.54 \text{ cm}} \times \frac{1 \text{ ft}}{12 \text{ in}} = 565 \text{ ft}$$

(too difficult to estimate)

Additional Exercises

1.57   (a)   A gold coin is probably a *solid solution*. Pure gold (element 79) is too soft and too valuable to be used for coinage, so other metals are added. However, the simple term "gold coin" does not give a specific indication of the other metals in the mixture.

                    A cup of coffee is a *solution* if there are no suspended solids (coffee grounds). It is a heterogeneous mixture if there are grounds. If cream or sugar is added, the homogeneity of the mixture depends on how thoroughly the components are mixed.

                    A wood plank is a *heterogeneous mixture* of various cellulose components. The different domains in the mixture are visible as wood grain or knots.

     (b)   The ambiguity in each of these examples is that the name of the substance does not provide a complete description of the material. We must rely on mental images, and these vary from person to person.

1.58   (a)   A *hypothesis* is a possible explanation for certain phenomena based on preliminary experimental data. A *theory* may be more general, and has a significant body of experimental evidence to support it; a theory has withstood the test of experimentation.

     (b)   A scientific *law* is a summary or statement of natural behavior; it tells how matter behaves. A *theory* is an explanation of natural behavior; it attempts to explain why matter behaves the way it does.

1.59   Any sample of vitamin C has the same relative amount of carbon and oxygen; the ratio of oxygen to carbon in the isolated sample is the same as the ratio in synthesized vitamin C.

$$\frac{2.00 \text{ g O}}{1.50 \text{ g C}} = \frac{x \text{ g O}}{6.35 \text{ g C}}; \quad x = \frac{(2.00 \text{ g O})(6.35 \text{ g C})}{1.50 \text{ g C}} = 8.47 \text{ g O}$$

This calculation assumes the law of constant composition.

1.60   (a)   I.   (22.52 + 22.48 + 22.54)/3 = 22.51

                II.   (22.64 + 22.58 + 22.62)/3 = 22.61

                Based on the average, set I is more accurate. That is, it is closer to the true value of 22.52%.

(b)   Average deviation $= \sum |\text{value} - \text{average}|/3$

I. $|22.52 - 22.51| + |22.48 - 22.51| + |22.54 - 22.51|/3 = 0.02$

II. $|22.64 - 22.61| + |22.58 - 22.61| + |22.62 - 22.61|/3 = 0.02$

The two sets display the same precision, even though set I is more accurate.

1.61   (a)   Appropriate. The number 22,727,000 implies a precision of one part per thousand, or 0.1%. This is an appropriate level of precision for the accounting records of a company like Apple Computer.

(b)   Appropriate. Rainfall data can be measured to a precision of at least one decimal place. Calculating annual rainfall and average annual rainfall involves addition, which dictates that significant figures are determined by the least number of decimal places in the data being summed.

(c)   Appropriate. The percentage has three significant figures. In a population as large as the United States, the number of people named Brown can surely be counted by census data or otherwise to a precision of three significant figures.

(d)   Inappropriate. Letter grades are posted at most to two decimal places and three significant figures (if plus and minus modifiers are quantified). The grade-point-average, obtained by addition and division, cannot have more decimal places or significant figures than the numbers being averaged.

1.62   (a)   volume   (b) area   (c) volume   (d) density

(e)   time   (f) length   (g) temperature

1.63   (a) $\dfrac{m}{s^2}$ (b) $\dfrac{kg-m}{s^2}$ (c) $\dfrac{kg-m}{s^2} \times m = \dfrac{kg-m^2}{s^2}$

(d) $\dfrac{kg-m}{s^2} \times \dfrac{1}{m^2} = \dfrac{kg}{m-s^2}$ (e) $\dfrac{kg-m^2}{s^2} \times \dfrac{1}{s} = \dfrac{kg-m^2}{s^3}$

(f) $\dfrac{m}{s}$ (g) $kg \times \left(\dfrac{m}{s}\right)^2 = \dfrac{kg-m^2}{s^2}$

1.64   (a) $2.4 \times 10^5 \, mi \times \dfrac{1.609 \, km}{1 \, mi} \times \dfrac{1000 \, m}{1 \, km} = 3.862 \times 10^8 = 3.9 \times 10^8 \, m$

(b) $2.4 \times 10^5 \, mi \times \dfrac{1.609 \, km}{1 \, mi} \times \dfrac{1 \, hr}{350 \, km} \times \dfrac{60 \, min}{1 \, hr} \times \dfrac{60 \, s}{1 \, min} = 4.0 \times 10^6 \, s$

(c) $3.862 \times 10^8 \, m \times 2 \times \dfrac{1 \, s}{3.00 \times 10^8 \, m} = 2.574 = 2.6 \, s$

(d) $\dfrac{29.783 \, km}{s} \times \dfrac{1 \, mi}{1.6093 \, km} \times \dfrac{60 \, s}{1 \, min} \times \dfrac{60 \, min}{1 \, hr} = 6.6624 \times 10^4 \, mi/hr$

1.65   (a) $575 \, ft \times \dfrac{12 \, in}{1 \, ft} \times \dfrac{2.54 \, cm}{1 \, in} \times \dfrac{10 \, mm}{1 \, cm} \times \dfrac{1 \, quarter}{1.55 \, mm} = 1.1307 \times 10^5 = 1.13 \times 10^5 \, quarters$

(b) 1.1307×10^5 quarters $\times \dfrac{5.67\,g}{1\,quarter} = 6.41 \times 10^5$ g (641 kg)

(c) 1.1307×10^5 quarters $\times \dfrac{1\,dollar}{4\,quarters} = \$28{,}268 = \$2.83 \times 10^4$

(d) $\$11{,}687{,}233{,}914{,}811.11 \times \dfrac{1\,stack}{\$28{,}268} = 4.13 \times 10^8$ stacks

1.66   (a)

$$\dfrac{\$1950}{acre-ft} \times \dfrac{1\,acre}{4840\,yd^2} \times \dfrac{3\,ft}{1\,yd} \times \dfrac{(1.094\,yd)^3}{(1\,m)^3} \times \dfrac{(1\,m)^3}{(10\,dm)^3} \times \dfrac{(1\,dm)^3}{1\,L} =$$

$\$1.583 \times 10^{-3}/L$ or 0.1583 ¢/L   (0.158 ¢/L to 3 sig figs)

(b)

$$\dfrac{\$1950}{acre-ft} \times \dfrac{1\,acre-ft}{2\,households-year} \times \dfrac{1\,year}{365\,days} \times 1\,household = \dfrac{\$2.671}{day} = \dfrac{\$2.67}{day}$$

1.67   There are 347 degrees between the freezing and boiling points on the oleic acid (O) scale and 100 degrees on the celsius (C) scale. Also, 13°C = 0°O. By analogy with °F and °C,

$$^{\circ}O = \frac{100}{347}(^{\circ}C - 13) \quad or \quad ^{\circ}C = \frac{347}{100}(^{\circ}O) + 13$$

These equations correctly relate the freezing point (and boiling point) of oleic acid on the two scales.

f.p. of H_2O: $^{\circ}O = \dfrac{100}{347}\,(0^{\circ}C - 13) = -3.746 = -4^{\circ}O$

1.68   The most dense liquid, Hg, will sink; the least dense, cyclohexane, will float; H_2O will be in the middle.

1.69   Density is the ratio of mass and volume. For samples with the same volume, in this case spheres with the same diameter, the denser ball will have a greater mass. The heavier ball, the red one on the right in the diagram is more dense.

1.70   The mass of water in the bottle does not change with temperature, but the density (ratio of mass to volume) does. That is, the amount of volume occupied by a certain mass of water changes with temperature. Calculate the mass of water in the bottle at 25°C, and then the volume occupied by this mass at –10°C.

(a)   25°C: $1.50\,L\,H_2O \times \dfrac{1000\,cm^3}{1\,L} \times \dfrac{0.997\,g\,H_2O}{1\,cm^3} = 1.4955 \times 10^3 = 1.50 \times 10^3$ g H_2O

$$-10°C:\ 1.4955 \times 10^3 \text{ g H}_2\text{O} \times \frac{1 \text{ cm}^3}{0.917 \text{ g H}_2\text{O}} \times \frac{1 \text{ L}}{1000 \text{ cm}^3} = 1.6309 = 1.63 \text{ L}$$

(b) No. If the soft-drink bottle is completely filled with 1.50 L of water, the 1.63 L of ice **cannot** be contained in the bottle. The extra volume of ice will push through any opening in the bottle, or crack the bottle to create an opening.

1.71 mass of toluene = 58.58 g – 32.65 g = 25.93 g

$$\text{volume of toluene} = 25.93 \text{ g} \times \frac{1 \text{ mL}}{0.864 \text{ g}} = 30.0116 = 30.0 \text{ mL}$$

volume of solid = 50.00 mL – 30.0116 mL = 19.9884 = 20.0 mL

$$\text{density of solid} = \frac{32.65 \text{ g}}{19.9884 \text{ mL}} = 1.63 \text{ g/mL}$$

1.72 (a) $V = 4/3\ \pi\ r^3 = 4/3\ \pi\ (28.9 \text{ cm})^3 = 1.0111 \times 10^5 = 1.01 \times 10^5 = 1.01 \times 10^5 \text{ cm}^3$

$$1.0111 \times 10^5 \text{ cm}^3 \times \frac{19.3 \text{ g}}{\text{cm}^3} \times \frac{1 \text{ lb}}{453.59 \text{ g}} = 4,302 = 4.30 \times 10^3 \text{ lb}$$

(b) No. The sphere weighs 4300 pounds, more than two tons. The student is unlikely to be able to carry the it without asssistance.

1.73 $1.00 \text{ gal battery acid} \times \dfrac{4 \text{ qt}}{1 \text{ gal}} \times \dfrac{1000 \text{ mL}}{1.0567 \text{ qt}} \times \dfrac{1.28 \text{ g}}{\text{mL}} = 4,845.3 = 4.85 \times 10^3 \text{ g battery acid}$

$$4.8453 \times 10^3 \text{ g battery acid} \times \frac{38.1 \text{ g sulfuric acid}}{100 \text{ g battery acid}} = 1846 = 1.85 \times 10^3 \text{ g sulfuric acid}$$

1.74 (a) $\dfrac{40 \text{ lb peat}}{14 \times 20 \times 30 \text{ in}^3} \times \dfrac{1 \text{ in}^3}{(2.54)^3 \text{ cm}^3} \times \dfrac{453.6 \text{ g}}{1 \text{ lb}} = 0.13 \text{ g/cm}^3 \text{ peat}$

$$\frac{40 \text{ lb soil}}{1.9 \text{ gal}} \times \frac{1 \text{ gal}}{4 \text{ qt}} \times \frac{1.057 \text{ qt}}{1 \text{ L}} \times \frac{1 \times 10^{-3} \text{ L}}{1 \text{ mL}} \times \frac{1 \text{ mL}}{1 \text{ cm}^3} \times \frac{453.6 \text{ g}}{1 \text{ lb}} = 2.5 \text{ g/cm}^3 \text{ soil}$$

No. Volume must be specified in order to compare mass. The densities tell us that a certain volume of peat moss is "lighter" (weighs less) than the same volume of top soil.

(b) 1 bag peat = $14 \times 20 \times 30 = 8.4 \times 10^3 \text{ in}^3$

$$15.0 \text{ ft} \times 20.0 \text{ ft} \times 3.0 \text{ in} \times \frac{12^2 \text{ in}^2}{\text{ft}^2} = 129,600 = 1.3 \times 10^5 \text{ in}^3 \text{ peat needed}$$

$$129,600 \text{ in}^3 \times \frac{1 \text{ bag}}{8.4 \times 10^3 \text{ in}^3} = 15.4 = 15 \text{ bags (Buy 16 bags of peat.)}$$

1.75 $8.0 \text{ oz} \times \dfrac{1 \text{ lb}}{16 \text{ oz}} \times \dfrac{453.6 \text{ g}}{\text{lb}} \times \dfrac{1 \text{ cm}^3}{2.70 \text{ g}} = 84.00 = 84 \text{ cm}^3$

$$\frac{84 \text{ cm}^3}{50 \text{ ft}^2} \times \frac{1^2 \text{ ft}^2}{12^2 \text{ in}^2} \times \frac{1^2 \text{ in}^2}{2.54^2 \text{ cm}^2} \times \frac{10 \text{ mm}}{1 \text{ cm}} = 0.018 \text{ mm}$$

1.76 $15\text{TW} \times \dfrac{1 \times 10^{12}\,\text{W}}{1\,\text{TW}} \times \dfrac{1\,\text{kW}}{1 \times 10^3\,\text{W}} \times \dfrac{1^2\,\text{m}^2}{1.336\,\text{kW}} = 1.1228 \times 10^{10} = 1.1 \times 10^{10}\,\text{m}^2$

Collection is 10% efficient, so 10 times this area is needed, $1.1 \times 10^{11}\,\text{m}^2$.

$1.97 \times 10^8\,\text{mi}^2 \times \dfrac{1.6093^2\,\text{km}^2}{1^2\,\text{mi}^2} \times \dfrac{1000^2\,\text{m}^2}{1^2\,\text{km}^2} = 5.1020 \times 10^{14}\,\text{m}^2 = 5.10 \times 10^{14}\,\text{m}^2$

$\dfrac{1.1228 \times 10^{11}\,\text{m}^2\ \text{needed}}{5.1020 \times 10^{14}\,\text{m}^2\ \text{total surface Earth}} \times 100 = 0.02201 = 0.022\%\ \text{Earth's surface needed}$

1.77 $11.86\,\text{g ethanol} \times \dfrac{1\,\text{cm}^3}{0.789\,\text{g ethanol}} = 15.0317 = 15.03\,\text{cm}^3,\ \text{volume of cylinder}$

$V = \pi r^2 h;\ r = (V/\pi h)^{1/2} = \left[\dfrac{15.0317\,\text{cm}^3}{\pi \times 15.0\,\text{cm}}\right]^{1/2} = 0.5648 = 0.565\,\text{cm}$

$d = 2r = 1.13\,\text{cm}$

1.78   (a)   Let x = mass of Au in jewelry

9.85 - x = mass of Ag in jewelry

The total volume of jewelry = volume of Au + volume of Ag

$0.675\,\text{cm}^3 = x\,\text{g} \times \dfrac{1\,\text{cm}^3}{19.3\,\text{g}} + (9.85 - x)\text{g} \times \dfrac{1\,\text{cm}^3}{10.5\,\text{g}}$

$0.675 = \dfrac{x}{19.3} + \dfrac{9.85 - x}{10.5}$ (To solve, multiply both sides by (19.3)(10.5))

$0.675\,(19.3)(10.5) = 10.5\,x + (9.85 - x)(19.3)$

$136.79 = 10.5\,x + 190.105 - 19.3\,x$

$-53.315 = -8.8\,x$

x = 6.06 g Au; 9.85 g total – 6.06 g Au = 3.79 g Ag

$\text{mass \% Au} = \dfrac{6.06\,\text{g Au}}{9.85\,\text{g jewelry}} \times 100 = 61.5\%\ \text{Au}$

(b)   24 carats × 0.615 = 15 carat gold

1.79   The separation with distinctly separated red and blue spots is more successful. The procedure that produced the purple blur did not separate the two dyes. To quantify the characteristics of the separation, calculate a reference value for each spot that is

$$\dfrac{\text{distance travelled by spot}}{\text{distance travelled by solvent}}$$

If the values for the two spots are fairly different, the separation is successful. (One could measure the distance between the spots, but this would depend on the length of paper used and be different for each experiment. The values suggested above are independent of the length of paper.)

1.80   The densities are:

carbon tetrachloride (methane, tetrachloro) – 1.5940 g/cm^3

hexane – 0.6603 g/cm^3

benzene – 0.87654 g/cm^3

methylene iodide (methane, diiodo) – 3.3254 g/cm^3

Only methylene iodide will separate the two granular solids. The undesirable solid (2.04 g/cm^3) is less dense than methylene iodide and will float; the desired material is more dense than methylene iodide and will sink. The other three liquids are less dense than both solids and will not produce separation.

1.81   (a) $10.0 \text{ mg} \times \dfrac{1 \times 10^{-3} \text{ g}}{1 \text{ mg}} \times \dfrac{1 \text{ cm}^3}{0.20 \text{ g}} = 0.050 \text{ cm}^3 = 0.050 \text{ mL}$ volume

(b) $10.0 \text{ mg} \times \dfrac{1 \times 10^{-3} \text{ g}}{1 \text{ mg}} \times \dfrac{1242 \text{ m}^2}{1 \text{ g}} = 12.42 = 12.4 \text{ m}^2$ surface area

(c)   7.748 mg Hg initial – 0.001 mg Hg remain = 7.747 mg Hg removed

$\dfrac{7.747 \text{ mg Hg removed}}{7.748 \text{ mg Hg initial}} \times 100 = 99.99\% \text{ Hg removed}$

(d)   10.0 mg "spongy" initial + 7.747 mg Hg removed=17.747=17.7 mg after exposure

1.82   Study (a) is likely to be both precise and accurate, because the errors are carefully controlled. The secondary weight standard will be resistant to chemical and physical changes, the balance is carefully calibrated, and weighings are likely to be made by the same person. The relatively large number of measurements is likely to minimize the effect of random errors on the average value. The accuracy and precision of study (b) depend on the veracity of the participants' responses, which cannot be carefully controlled. It also depends on the definition of "comparable lifestyle." The percentages are not precise, because the broad definition of lifestyle leads to a range of results (scatter). The relatively large number of participants improves the precision and accuracy. In general, controlling errors and maximizing the number of data points in a study improves precision and accuracy.

2 Atoms, Molecules, and Ions

Visualizing Concepts

2.1   (a)   The path of the charged particle bends because the particle is repelled by the negatively charged plate and attracted to the positively charged plate.

(b)   Like charges repel and opposite charges attract, so the sign of the electrical charge on the particle is negative.

(c)   The greater the magnitude of the charges, the greater the electrostatic repulsion or attraction. As the charge on the plates is increased, the bending will increase.

(d)   As the mass of the particle increases and speed stays the same, linear momentum (mv) of the particle increases and bending decreases. (See **A Closer Look**: The Mass Spectrometer.)

2.2   (a) $\% \text{ abundance} = \dfrac{\# \text{ of mass number} \times \text{particles}}{\text{total number of particles}} \times 100$

12 red ^{293}Nv particles

8 blue ^{295}Nv particles

20 total particles

$\% \text{ abundance } ^{293}\text{Nv} = \dfrac{12}{20} \times 100 = 60\%$

$\% \text{ abundance } ^{295}\text{Nv} = \dfrac{8}{20} \times 100 = 40\%$

(b)   Atomic weight (AW) is the same as average atomic mass.

Atomic weight (average atomic mass) = $\sum$ fractional abundance $\times$ mass of isotope

AW of Nv = 0.60(293.15) + 0.40(295.15) = 293.95 amu

(Since % abundance was calculated by counting exact numbers of particles, assume % abundance is an exact number. Then, the number of significant figures in the AW is determined by the number of sig figs in the masses of the isotopes.)

2.3   In general, metals occupy the left side of the chart, and nonmetals the right side.

metals: red and green   *nonmetals*: blue and yellow

alkaline earth metal: red   *noble gas*: yellow

2.4   Since the number of electrons (negatively charged particles) does not equal the number of protons (positively charged particles), the particle is an ion. The charge on the ion is 2-.

Atomic number = number of protons = 16. The element is S, sulfur.

Mass number = protons + neutrons = 32

$^{32}_{16}\text{S}^{2-}$

2.5   In a solid, particles are close together and their relative positions are fixed. In a liquid, particles are close but moving relative to each other. In a gas, particles are far apart and moving. All ionic compounds are solids because of the strong forces among charged particles. Molecular compounds can exist in any state: solid, liquid, or gas.

Since the molecules in *ii* are far apart, *ii* must be a molecular compound. The particles in *i* are near each other and exist in a regular, ordered arrangement, so *i* is likely to be an ionic compound.

2.6   Formula: IF_5 Name: iodine pentafluoride
Since the compound is composed of elements that are all nonmetals, it is molecular.

2.7   See Figure 2.20. yellow box: 1+ (group 1A); blue box: 2+ (group 2A)

black box: 3+ (a metal in Group 3A); red box: 2- (a nonmetal in group 6A);

green box: 1- (a nonmetal in group 7A)

2.8   Cations (red spheres) have positive charges; anions (blue spheres) have negative charges. There are twice as many anions as cations, so the formula has the general form CA_2. Only $Ca(NO_3)_2$, calcium nitrate, is consistent with the diagram.

Atomic Theory and the Discovery of Atomic Structure (sections 2.1-2.2)

2.9   Postulate 4 of the atomic theory is the *law of constant composition*. It states that the relative number and kinds of atoms in a compound are constant, regardless of the source. Therefore, 1.0 g of pure water should always contain the same relative amounts of hydrogen and oxygen, no matter where or how the sample is obtained.

2.10   (a)   6.500 g compound – 0.384 g hydrogen = 6.116 g sulfur

(b)   *Conservation of mass*

(c)   According to postulate 3 of the atomic theory, atoms are neither created nor destroyed during a chemical reaction. If 0.384 g of H are recovered from a compound that contains only H and S, the remaining mass must be sulfur.

2.11　(a)　$\dfrac{17.60\,\text{g oxygen}}{30.82\,\text{g nitrogen}} = \dfrac{0.5711\,\text{g O}}{1\,\text{g N}}; \quad 0.5711/0.5711 = 1.0$

$\dfrac{35.20\,\text{g oxygen}}{30.82\,\text{g nitrogen}} = \dfrac{1.142\,\text{g O}}{1\,\text{g N}}; \quad 1.142/0.5711 = 2.0$

$\dfrac{70.40\,\text{g oxygen}}{30.82\,\text{g nitrogen}} = \dfrac{2.284\,\text{g O}}{1\,\text{g N}}; \quad 2.284/0.5711 = 4.0$

$\dfrac{88.00\,\text{g oxygen}}{30.82\,\text{g nitrogen}} = \dfrac{2.855\,\text{g O}}{1\,\text{g N}}; \quad 2.855/0.5711 = 5.0$

(b)　These masses of oxygen per one gram nitrogen are in the ratio of 1:2:4:5 and thus obey the *law of multiple proportions*. Multiple proportions arise because atoms are the indivisible entities combining, as stated in Dalton's theory. Since atoms are indivisible, they must combine in ratios of small whole numbers.

2.12　(a)　1:　$\dfrac{3.56\,\text{g fluorine}}{4.75\,\text{g iodine}} = 0.749\,\text{g fluorine/1 g iodine}$

2:　$\dfrac{3.43\,\text{g fluorine}}{7.64\,\text{g iodine}} = 0.449\,\text{g fluorine/1 g iodine}$

3:　$\dfrac{9.86\,\text{g fluorine}}{9.41\,\text{g iodine}} = 1.05\,\text{g fluorine/1 g iodine}$

(b)　To look for integer relationships among these values, divide each one by the smallest.

If the quotients aren't all integers, multiply by a common factor to obtain all integers.

1: 0.749/0.449 = 1.67; 1.67 × 3 = 5

2: 0.449/0.449 = 1.00; 1.00 × 3 = 3

3: 1.05/0.449 = 2.34; 2.34 × 3 = 7

The ratio of g fluorine to g iodine in the three compounds is 5:3:7. These are in the ratio of small whole numbers and, therefore, obey the *law of multiple proportions*. This integer ratio indicates that the combining fluorine "units" (atoms) are indivisible entities.

2.13　Evidence that cathode rays were negatively charged particles was (1) that electric and magnetic fields deflected the rays in the same way they would deflect negatively charged particles and (2) that a metal plate exposed to cathode rays acquired a negative charge.

2.14　Since the unknown particle is deflected in the opposite direction from that of a negatively charged beta (β) particle, it is attracted to the (–) plate and repelled by the (+) plate. The unknown particle is positively charged. The magnitude of the deflection is less than that of the β particle, or electron, so the unknown particle has greater mass than the electron. The unknown is a positively charged particle of greater mass than the electron.

2.15   (a)   Most of the volume of an atom is empty space in which electrons move. Most alpha particles passed through this space. The path of the massive alpha particle would not be significantly altered by interaction with a "puny" electron.

        (b)   Most of the mass of an atom is contained in a very small, dense area called the nucleus. The few alpha particles that hit the massive, positively charged gold nuclei were strongly repelled and essentially deflected back in the direction they came from.

        (c)   The Be nuclei have a much smaller volume and positive charge than the Au nuclei; the charge repulsion between the alpha particles and the Be nuclei will be less, and there will be fewer direct hits because the Be nuclei have an even smaller volume than the Au nuclei. Fewer alpha particles will be scattered in general and fewer will be strongly back scattered.

2.16   (a)   The droplets carry different total charges because there may be 1, 2, 3, or more electrons on the droplet.

        (b)   The electronic charge is likely to be the lowest common factor in all the observed charges.

        (c)   Assuming this is so, we calculate the apparent electronic charge from each drop as follows:

            A: $1.60 \times 10^{-19} / 1 = 1.60 \times 10^{-19}$ C

            B: $3.15 \times 10^{-19} / 2 = 1.58 \times 10^{-19}$ C

            C: $4.81 \times 10^{-19} / 3 = 1.60 \times 10^{-19}$ C

            D: $6.31 \times 10^{-19} / 4 = 1.58 \times 10^{-19}$ C

The reported value is the average of these four values. Since each calculated charge has three significant figures, the average will also have three significant figures.

$(1.60 \times 10^{-19}$ C $+ 1.58 \times 10^{-19}$ C $+ 1.60 \times 10^{-19}$ C $+ 1.58 \times 10^{-19}$ C$) / 4 = 1.59 \times 10^{-19}$ C

Modern View of Atomic Structure; Atomic Weights (sections 2.3-2.4)

2.17   (a) $1.35 \, \text{Å} \times \dfrac{1 \times 10^{-10} \, \text{m}}{1 \, \text{Å}} \times \dfrac{1 \, \text{nm}}{1 \times 10^{-9} \, \text{m}} = 0.135 \, \text{nm}$

             $1.35 \, \text{Å} \times \dfrac{1 \times 10^{-10} \, \text{m}}{1 \, \text{Å}} \times \dfrac{1 \, \text{pm}}{1 \times 10^{-12} \, \text{m}} = 1.35 \times 10^2$ or $135 \, \text{pm}$ (1 Å = 100 pm)

        (b)   Aligned Au atoms have **diameters** touching. d = 2r = 2(1.35 Å) = 2.70 Å

             $1.0 \, \text{mm} \times \dfrac{1 \, \text{m}}{1000 \, \text{mm}} \times \dfrac{1 \, \text{Å}}{1 \times 10^{-10} \, \text{m}} \times \dfrac{1 \, \text{Au atom}}{2.70 \, \text{Å}} = 3.70 \times 10^6$ Au atoms

        (c) $V = 4/3 \, \pi r^3$. $r = 1.35 \, \text{Å} \times \dfrac{1 \times 10^{-10} \, \text{m}}{1 \, \text{Å}} \times \dfrac{100 \, \text{cm}}{\text{m}} = 1.35 \times 10^{-8} \, \text{cm}$

             $V = (4/3)(\pi)(1.35 \times 10^{-8})^3 \, \text{cm}^3 = 1.03 \times 10^{-23} \, \text{cm}^3$

2.18   (a) $r = d/2; r = \dfrac{2.7 \times 10^{-8} \text{ cm}}{2} \times \dfrac{1\,\text{Å}}{1 \times 10^{-8} \text{ cm}} = 1.35 = 1.4\,\text{Å}$

          $r = \dfrac{2.7 \times 10^{-8} \text{ cm}}{2} \times \dfrac{1\,\text{m}}{100\,\text{cm}} = 1.35 \times 10^{-10} = 1.4 \times 10^{-10}\,\text{m}$

     (b)   Aligned Rh atoms have **diameters** touching. $d = 2.7 \times 10^{-8} \text{ cm} = 2.7 \times 10^{-10}\,\text{m}$

          $6.0\,\mu\text{m} \times \dfrac{1 \times 10^{-6}\,\text{m}}{1\,\mu\text{m}} \times \dfrac{1\,\text{Rh atom}}{2.7 \times 10^{-10}\,\text{m}} = 2.2 \times 10^{4}\,\text{Rh atoms}$

     (c) $V = 4/3\,\pi\,r^{3}; r = 1.35 \times 10^{-10} = 1.4 \times 10^{-10}\,\text{m}$

          $V = (4/3)[(\pi(1.35 \times 10^{-10})^{3}]\,\text{m}^{3} = 1.031 \times 10^{-29} = 1.0 \times 10^{-29}\,\text{m}^{3}$

2.19   (a)   proton, neutron, electron

     (b)   proton = +1, neutron = 0, electron = –1

     (c)   The neutron is most massive. (The neutron and proton have very similar masses).

     (d)   The electron least massive.

2.20   (a)   The nucleus has most of the mass **but occupies very little** of the volume of an atom.

     (b)   True

     (c)   The number of electrons in a neutral atom is equal to the number of **protons** in the atom.

     (d)   True

2.21   (a)   *Atomic number* is the number of protons in the nucleus of an atom. *Mass number* is the total number of nuclear particles, protons plus neutrons, in an atom.

     (b)   The mass number can vary without changing the identity of the atom, but the atomic number of every atom of a given element is the same.

2.22   (a) $^{31}_{16}\text{X}$ and $^{32}_{16}\text{X}$ are isotopes of the same element, because they have identical atomic numbers.

     (b)   These are isotopes of the element sulfur, S, atomic number = 16.

2.23   p = protons, n = neutrons, e = electrons

     (a) ^{40}Ar has 18 p, 22 n, 18 e   (b) ^{65}Zn has 30 p, 35 n, 30 e

     (c) ^{70}Ga has 31 p, 39 n, 31 e   (d) ^{80}Br has 35 p, 45 n, 35 e

     (e) ^{184}W has 74 p, 110 n, 74 e   (f) ^{243}Am has 95 p, 148 n, 95 e

2.24   (a) ^{32}P has 15 p, 17 n   (b) ^{51}Cr has 24 p, 27 n

     (c) ^{60}Co has 27 p, 33 n   (d) ^{99}Tc has 43 p, 56 n

     (e) ^{131}I has 53 p, 78 n   (f) ^{201}Tl has 81 p, 120 n

2.25

Symbol	^{52}Cr	^{55}Mn	^{112}Cd	^{222}Rn	^{207}Pb
Protons	24	25	48	86	82
Neutrons	28	30	64	136	125
Electrons	24	25	48	86	82
Mass no.	52	55	112	222	207

2.26

Symbol	^{65}Zn	^{96}Sr	^{87}Sr	^{81}Kr	^{235}U
Protons	30	38	38	36	92
Neutrons	35	58	49	45	143
Electrons	30	38	38	36	92
Mass No.	65	96	87	81	235

2.27   (a) $^{196}_{78}$Pt   (b) $^{84}_{36}$Kr   (c) $^{75}_{33}$As   (c) $^{24}_{12}$Mg

2.28   Since the two nuclides are atoms of the same element, by definition they have the same number of protons, 54. They differ in mass number (and mass) because they have different numbers of neutrons. ^{129}Xe has 75 neutrons and ^{130}Xe has 76 neutrons.

2.29   (a) $^{12}_{6}$C

      (b)   Atomic weights are really average atomic masses, the sum of the mass of each naturally occurring isotope of an element times its fractional abundance. Each B atom will have the mass of one of the naturally occurring isotopes, while the "atomic weight" is an average value. The naturally occurring isotopes of B, their atomic masses, and relative abundances are:

           ^{10}B, 10.012937, 19.9%; ^{11}B, 11.009305, 80.1%.

2.30   (a)   12 amu

      (b)   The atomic weight of carbon reported on the front-inside cover of the text is the abundance-weighted average of the atomic masses of the two naturally occurring isotopes of carbon, ^{12}C, and ^{13}C. The mass of a ^{12}C atom is exactly 12 amu, but the atomic weight of 12.011 takes into account the presence of some ^{13}C atoms in every natural sample of the element.

2.31   Atomic weight (average atomic mass) = Σ fractional abundance × mass of isotope

       Atomic weight = 0.6917(62.9296) + 0.3083(64.9278) = 63.5456 = 63.55 amu

2.32   Atomic weight (average atomic mass) = Σ fractional abundance × mass of isotope

       Atomic weight = 0.7215(84.9118) + 0.2785(86.9092) = 85.4681 = 85.47 amu

       (The result has 2 decimal places and 4 sig figs because each term in the sum has 4 sig figs and 2 decimal places.)

2.33   (a)   Compare Figures 2.4 and 2.12, referring to Solution 2.14. In Thomson's cathode ray experiments and in mass spectrometry a stream of charged particles is passed through a magnetic field. The charged particles are deflected by the magnetic field according to their mass and charge. For a constant magnetic field strength and speed of the particles, the lighter particles experience a greater deflection.

        (b)   The x-axis label (independent variable) is atomic weight and the y-axis label (dependent variable) is signal intensity.

        (c)   Uncharged particles are not deflected in a magnetic field. The effect of the magnetic field on moving, *charged* particles is the basis of their separation by mass.

2.34   (a)   The purpose of the magnet in the mass spectrometer is to change the path of the moving ions. The magnitude of the deflection is inversely related to mass, which is the basis of the discrimination by mass.

        (b)   The atomic weight of Cl, 35.5, is an average atomic mass. It is the average of the masses of two naturally occurring isotopes, weighted by their abundances.

        (c)   The single peak at mass 31 in the mass spectrum of phosphorus indicates that the sample contains a single isotope of P, and the mass of this isotope is 31 amu.

2.35   (a)   Average atomic mass = 0.7899(23.98504) + 0.1000(24.98584) + 0.1101(25.98259)

                 = 24.31 amu

        (b)

        The relative intensities of the peaks in the mass spectrum are the same as the relative abundances of the isotopes. The abundances and peak heights are in the ratio ^{24}Mg: ^{25}Mg: ^{26}Mg as 7.8 : 1.0 : 1.1.

2.36   (a)   Three peaks: ^{1}H – ^{1}H, ^{1}H – ^{2}H, ^{2}H – ^{2}H

        (b) ^{1}H – ^{1}H = 2(1.00783) = 2.01566 amu

               ^{1}H – ^{2}H = 1.00783 + 2.01410 = 3.02193 amu

$^2H - {}^2H = 2(2.01410) = 4.02820$ amu

The mass ratios are $1 : 1.49923 : 1.99845$ or $1 : 1.5 : 2$.

(c) $^1H - {}^1H$ is largest, because there is the greatest chance that two atoms of the more abundant isotope will combine.

$^2H - {}^2H$ is the smallest, because there is the least chance that two atoms of the less abundant isotope will combine.

The Periodic Table; Molecules and Ions (sections 2.5-2.7)

2.37   (a)   Cr, 24 (metal)   (b) He, 2 (nonmetal)   (c) P, 15 (nonmetal)

(d)   Zn, 30 (metal)   (e) Mg, 12 (metal)   (f) Br, 35 (nonmetal)

(g)   As, 33 (metalloid)

2.38   (a)   lithium, 3 (metal)   (b)   scandium,21 (metal)

(c)   germanium, 32 (metalloid)   (d)   ytterbium, 70 (metal)

(e)   manganese, 25 (metal)   (f)   antimony, 51 (metalloid)

(g)   xenon, 54 (nonmetal)

2.39   (a)   K, alkali metals (metal)   (b)   I, halogens (nonmetal)

(c)   Mg, alkaline earth metals (metal)   (d)   Ar, noble gases (nonmetal)

(e)   S, chalcogens (nonmetal)

2.40   C, carbon, nonmetal; Si, silicon, metalloid; Ge, germanium, metalloid; Sn, tin, metal; Pb, lead, metal

2.41   An *empirical formula* shows the simplest ratio of the different atoms in a molecule. A *molecular formula* shows the exact number and kinds of atoms in a molecule. A *structural formula* shows how these atoms are arranged.

2.42   Compounds with the same empirical but different molecular formulas differ by the integer number of empirical formula units in the respective molecules. Thus, they can have very different molecular structure, size, and mass, resulting in very different physical properties.

2.43   (a) $AlBr_3$ (b) C_4H_5 (c) C_2H_4O (d) P_2O_5

(e) C_3H_2Cl (f) BNH_2

2.44   A molecular formula contains all atoms in a molecule. An empirical formula shows the simplest ratio of atoms in a molecule or elements in a compound.

(a)   molecular formula: C_6H_6; empirical formula: CH

(b)   molecular formula: $SiCl_4$; empirical formula: $SiCl_4$ (1:4 is the simplest ratio)

(c)   molecular: B_2H_6; empirical: BH_3

(d)   molecular: $C_6H_{12}O_6$; empirical: CH_2O

2.45   (a)   6   (b) 6   (c) 12

2.46   (a)   4   (b) 8   (c) 9

2.47   (a) C_2H_6O

H—C—O—C—H (with H above and below each C)

(b) C_2H_6O

H—C—C—O—H (with H above and below each C)

(c) CH_4O H—C—O—H (with H above and below C)

(d) PF_3 F—P—F (with F below P)

2.48   (a) C_2H_5Br H—C—C—Br (with H above and below each C)

(b) C_2H_7N H—C—N—C—H (with H above and below C's and H above/below N)

(c) CH_2Cl_2 H—C—Cl (with H above and Cl below)

(d) NH_2OH H—N—O (with H below N and H below O)

2.49

Symbol	$^{59}Co^{3+}$	$^{80}Se^{2-}$	$^{192}Os^{2+}$	$^{200}Hg^{2+}$
Protons	27	34	76	80
Neutrons	32	46	116	120
Electrons	24	36	74	78
Net Charge	3+	2–	2+	2+

2.50

Symbol	$^{31}P^{3-}$	$^{79}Se^{2-}$	$^{119}Sn^{4+}$	$^{197}Au^{3+}$
Protons	15	34	50	79
Neutrons	16	45	69	118
Electrons	18	36	46	76
Net Charge	3–	2–	4+	3+

2.51   (a) Mg^{2+} (b) Al^{3+} (c) K^+ (d) S^{2-} (e) F^-

2.52   (a) Ga^{3+} (b) Sr^{2+} (c) As^{3-} (d) Br^- (e) Se^{2-}

2.53   (a) GaF_3, gallium(III) fluoride   (b)   LiH, lithium hydride

(c) AlI_3, aluminum iodide   (d) K_2S, potassium sulfide

2.54   (a) ScI_3 (b) Sc_2S_3 (c)   ScN

2.55   (a) $CaBr_2$ (b) K_2CO_3 (c) $Al(CH_3COO)_3$ (d) $(NH_4)_2SO_4$ (e) $Mg_3(PO_4)_2$

2.56   (a) $CrBr_3$ (b) Fe_2O_3 (c) Hg_2CO_3 (d) $Ca(ClO_3)_2$ (e) $(NH_4)_3PO_4$

2.57

Ion	K^+	NH_4^+	Mg^{2+}	Fe^{3+}
Cl^-	KCl	NH_4Cl	$MgCl_2$	$FeCl_3$
OH^-	KOH	NH_4OH^*	$Mg(OH)_2$	$Fe(OH)_3$
CO_3^{2-}	K_2CO_3	$(NH_4)_2CO_3$	$MgCO_3$	$Fe_2(CO_3)_3$
PO_4^{3-}	K_3PO_4	$(NH_4)_3PO_4$	$Mg_3(PO_4)_2$	$FePO_4$

*Equivalent to $NH_3(aq)$.

2.58

Ion	Na^+	Ca^{2+}	Fe^{2+}	Al^{3+}
O^{2-}	Na_2O	CaO	FeO	Al_2O_3
NO_3^-	$NaNO_3$	$Ca(NO_3)_2$	$Fe(NO_3)_2$	$Al(NO_3)_3$
SO_4^{2-}	Na_2SO_4	$CaSO_4$	$FeSO_4$	$Al_2(SO_4)_3$
AsO_4^{3-}	Na_3AsO_4	$Ca_3(AsO_4)_2$	$Fe_3(AsO_4)_2$	$AlAsO_4$

2.59   Molecular (all elements are nonmetals):

(a) B_2H_6 (b) CH_3OH (f) NOCl   (g) NF_3

Ionic (formed by a cation and an anion, usually contains a metal cation):

(c) $LiNO_3$ (d) Sc_2O_3 (e)   CsBr   (h) Ag_2SO_4

2.60   Molecular (all elements are nonmetals):

(a) PF_5 (c) SCl_2 (h) N_2O_4

Ionic (formed from ions, usually contains a metal cation):

(b)   NaI   (d) $Ca(NO_3)_2$ (e) $FeCl_3$ (f)   LaP   (g) $CoCO_3$

Naming Inorganic Compounds; Organic Molecules (sections 2.8-2.9)

2.61   (a) ClO_2^- (b) Cl^- (c) ClO_3^- (d) ClO_4^- (e) ClO^-

2.62   (a)   selenate   (b)   selenide   (c)   hydrogen selenide (biselenide)

(d)   hydrogen selenite (biselenite)

2.63   (a)   calcium, 2+; oxide, 2–   (b)   sodium, 1+; sulfate, 2–

     (c)   potassium, 1+; perchorate, 1–   (d)   iron, 2+; nitrate, 1–

     (e)   chromium, 3+; hydroxide, 1–

2.64   (a)   copper, 2+; sulfide, 2–   (b)   silver, 1+; sulfate, 2–

     (c)   aluminum, 3+; chlorate, 1–   (d)   cobalt, 2+; hydroxide, 1–

     (e)   lead, 2+; carbonate, 2–

2.65   (a)   lithium oxide   (b)   iron(III) chloride (ferric chloride)

     (c)   sodium hypochlorite   (d)   calcium sulfite

     (e)   copper(II) hydroxide (cupric hydroxide)   (f)   iron(II) nitrate (ferrous nitrate)

     (g)   calcium acetate   (h)   chromium(III) carbonate (chromic carbonate)

     (i)   potassium chromate   (j)   ammonium sulfate

2.66   (a)   potassium cyanide   (b)   sodium bromite

     (c)   strontium hydroxide   (d)   cobalt(II) sulfide (cobaltous sulfide)

     (e)   iron(III) carbonate (ferric carbonate)

     (f)   chromium(III) nitrate (chromic nitrate)

     (g)   ammonium sulfite   (h)   sodium dihydrogen phosphate

     (i)   potassium permanganate   (j)   silver dichromate

2.67   (a) $Al(OH)_3$ (b) K_2SO_4 (c) Cu_2O (d) $Zn(NO_3)_2$

     (e) $HgBr_2$ (f) $Fe_2(CO_3)_3$ (g) $NaBrO$

2.68   (a) Na_3PO_4 (b) $Zn(NO_3)_2$ (c) $Ba(BrO_3)_2$ (d) $Fe(ClO_4)_2$

     (e) $Co(HCO_3)_2$ (f) $Cr(CH_3COO)_3$ (g) $K_2Cr_2O_7$

2.69   (a)   bromic acid   (b)   hydrobromic acid   (c)   phosphoric acid

     (d) $HClO$ (e) HIO_3 (f) H_2SO_3

2.70   (a) HI (b) $HClO_3$ (c) HNO_2

     (d)   carbonic acid   (e)   perchloric acid   (f)   acetic acid

2.71   (a)   sulfur hexafluoride   (b)   iodine pentafluoride   (c)   xenon trioxide

     (d) N_2O_4 (e) HCN (f) P_4S_6

2.72   (a)   dinitrogen monoxide   (b)   nitrogen monoxide   (c)   nitrogen dioxide

     (d)   dinitrogen pentoxide   (e)   dinitrogen tetroxide

2.73   (a) $ZnCO_3$, ZnO, CO_2 (b) HF, SiO_2, SiF_4, H_2O (c) SO_2, H_2O, H_2SO_3

     (d) PH_3 (e) $HClO_4$, Cd, $Cd(ClO_4)_2$ (f) VBr_3

2.74   (a) $NaHCO_3$ (b) $Ca(ClO)_2$ (c) HCN

(d) $Mg(OH)_2$ (e) SnF_2 (f) CdS, H_2SO_4, H_2S

2.75   (a)   A hydrocarbon is a compound composed of the elements hydrogen and carbon only.

       (b)

          molecular: C_4H_{10}

          empirical: C_2H_5

2.76   (a)   *-ane*

       (b)   **Hex**ane has 6 carbons in its chain.

          molecular: C_6H_{14}

          empirical: C_3H_7

2.77   (a)   *Functional groups* are groups of specific atoms that are constant from one molecule to the next. For example, the alcohol functional group is an –OH. Whenever a molecule is called an alcohol, it contains the -OH group.

       (b)   —OH   (c)

2.78   (a)   They both have two carbon atoms in their molecular backbone, or chain.

       (b)   In 1-propanol one of the H atoms on an outer (terminal) C atom has been replaced by an −OH group.

2.79   (a)

       (b)   1-chloropropane   2-chloropropane

2.80

Additional Exercises

2.81 (a) Droplet D would fall most slowly. It carries the most negative charge, so it would be most strongly attracted to the upper (+) plate and most strongly repelled by the lower (–) plate. These electrostatic forces would provide the greatest opposition to gravity.

(b) Calculate the lowest common factor.

A: $3.84 \times 10^{-8} / 2.88 \times 10^{-8} = 1.33$; $1.33 \times 3 = 4$

B: $4.80 \times 10^{-8} / 2.88 \times 10^{-8} = 1.67$; $1.67 \times 3 = 5$

C: $2.88 \times 10^{-8} / 2.88 \times 10^{-8} = 1.00$; $1.00 \times 3 = 3$

D: $8.64 \times 10^{-8} / 2.88 \times 10^{-8} = 3.00$; $3.00 \times 3 = 9$

The total charge on the drops is in the ratio of 4:5:3:9. Divide the total charge on each drop by the appropriate integer and average the four values to get the charge of an electron in warmombs.

A: $3.84 \times 10^{-8} / 4 = 9.60 \times 10^{-9}$ wa

B: $4.80 \times 10^{-8} / 5 = 9.60 \times 10^{-9}$ wa

C: $2.88 \times 10^{-8} / 3 = 9.60 \times 10^{-9}$ wa

D: $8.64 \times 10^{-8} / 9 = 9.60 \times 10^{-9}$ wa

The charge on an electron is 9.60×10^{-9} wa

(c) The number of electrons on each drop are the integers calculated in part (b). A has 4 e^-, B has 5 e^-, C has 3 e^- and D has 9 e^-.

(d) $\dfrac{9.60 \times 10^{-9} \text{ wa}}{1 e^-} \times \dfrac{1 e^-}{1.60 \times 10^{-16} \text{ C}} = 6.00 \times 10^7$ wa/C

2.82 (a) ^{3}He has 2 protons, 1 neutron, and 2 electrons.

(b) ^{3}H has 1 proton, 2 neutrons, and 1 electron.

^{3}He: $2(1.672621673 \times 10^{-24}$ g$) + 1.674927211 \times 10^{-24}$ g $+ 2(9.10938215 \times 10^{-28}$ g$)$

$$= 5.021992 \times 10^{-24} \text{ g}$$

^{3}H: $1.672621673 \times 10^{-24}$ g $+ 2(1.674927211 \times 10^{-24}$ g$) + 9.10938215 \times 10^{-28}$ g

$$= 5.023387 \times 10^{-24} \text{ g}$$

Tritium, ^{3}H, is more massive.

(c)   The masses of the two particles differ by 0.0014×10^{-24} g. Each particle loses 1 electron to form the +1 ion, so the difference in the masses of the ions is still 1.4×10^{-27}. A mass spectrometer would need precision to 1×10^{-27} g to differentiate ^{3}He$^+$ and ^{3}H.

2.83   (a)   Calculate the mass of a single gold atom, then divide the mass of the cube by the mass of the gold atom.

$$\frac{197.0 \text{ amu}}{\text{gold atom}} \times \frac{1 \text{ g}}{6.022 \times 10^{23} \text{ amu}} = 3.2713 \times 10^{-22} = 3.271 \times 10^{-22} \text{ g/gold atom}$$

$$\frac{19.3 \text{ g}}{\text{cube}} \times \frac{1 \text{ gold atom}}{3.271 \times 10^{-22} \text{ g}} = 5.90 \times 10^{22} \text{ Au atoms in the cube}$$

(b)   The shape of atoms is spherical; spheres cannot be arranged into a cube so that there is no empty space. The question is, how much empty space is there? We can calculate the two limiting cases, no empty space and maximum empty space. The true diameter will be somewhere in this range.

No empty space: volume cube/number of atoms = volume of one atom

$V = 4/3\pi r^3$; $r = (3\pi V/4)^{1/3}$; $d = 2r$

$$\text{vol. of cube} = (1.0 \times 1.0 \times 1.0) = \frac{1.0 \text{ cm}^3}{5.90 \times 10^{22} \text{ Au atoms}} = 1.695 \times 10^{-23}$$

$$= 1.7 \times 10^{-23} \text{ cm}^3$$

$r = [\pi (1.695 \times 10^{-23} \text{ cm}^3)/4]^{1/3} = 3.4 \times 10^{-8}$ cm; $d = 2r = 6.8 \times 10^{-8}$ cm

Maximum empty space: assume atoms are arranged in rows in all three directions so they are touching across their diameters. That is, each atom occupies the volume of a cube, with the atomic diameter as the length of the side of the cube. The number of atoms along one edge of the gold cube is then

$(5.90 \times 10^{22})^{1/3} = 3.893 \times 10^7 = 3.89 \times 10^7$ atoms/1.0 cm.

The diameter of a single atom is 1.0 cm/3.89×10^7 atoms $= 2.569 \times 10^{-8}$

$$= 2.6 \times 10^{-8} \text{ cm.}$$

The diameter of a gold atom is between 2.6×10^{-8} cm and 6.8×10^{-8} cm (2.6 – 6.8 Å).

(c)   Some atomic arrangement must be assumed, since none is specified. The solid state is characterized by an orderly arrangement of particles, so it isn't surprising that atomic arrangement is required to calculate the density of a solid. A more detailed discussion of solid-state structure and density appears in Chapter 11.

2.84   (a)   In arrangement A the number of atoms in 1 cm^2 is just the square of the number that fit linearly in 1 cm.

$$1.0 \text{ cm} \times \frac{1 \text{ atom}}{4.95 \text{ Å}} \times \frac{1 \times 10^{10} \text{ Å}}{1 \text{ m}} \times \frac{1 \text{ m}}{100 \text{ cm}} = 2.02 \times 10^7 = 2.0 \times 10^7 \text{ atoms/cm}$$

$$1.0 \text{ cm}^2 = (2.02 \times 10^7)^2 = 4.081 \times 10^{14} = 4.1 \times 10^{14} \text{ atoms/cm}^2$$

(b)   In arrangement B, the atoms in the horizontal rows are touching along their diameters, as in arrangement A. The number of Rb atoms in a 1.0 cm row is then 2.0×10^7 Rb atoms. Relative to arrangement A, the vertical rows are offset by 1/2 of an atom. Atoms in a "column" are no longer touching along their vertical diameter. We must calculate the vertical distance occupied by a row of atoms, which is now less than the diameter of one Rb atom.

Consider the triangle shown below. This is an isosceles triangle (equal side lengths, equal interior angles) with a side-length of 2d and an angle of 60°. Drop a bisector to the uppermost angle so that it bisects the opposite side.

The result is a right triangle with two known side lengths. The length of the unknown side (the angle bisector) is 2h, two times the vertical distance occupied by a row of atoms. Solve for h, the "height" of one row of atoms.

$$(2h)^2 + d^2 = (2d)^2; \; 4h^2 = 4d^2 - d^2 = 3d^2; \; h^2 = 3d^2/4$$

$$h = (3d^2/4)^{1/2} = (3(4.95 \text{ Å})^2/4)^{1/2} = 4.2868 = 4.29 \text{ Å}$$

The number of rows of atoms in 1 cm is then

$$1.0 \text{ cm} \times \frac{1 \text{ row}}{4.2868 \text{ Å}} \times \frac{1 \times 10^{10} \text{ Å}}{1 \text{ m}} \times \frac{1 \text{ m}}{100 \text{ cm}} = 2.333 \times 10^7 = 2.3 \times 10^7$$

The number of atoms in a 1.0 cm^2 square area is then

$$\frac{2.020 \times 10^7 \text{ atoms}}{1 \text{ row}} \times 2.333 \times 10^7 \text{ rows} = 4.713 \times 10^{14} = 4.7 \times 10^{14} \text{ atoms}$$

Note that we have ignored the loss of "1/2" atom at the end of each horizontal row. Out of 2.0×10^7 atoms per row, one atom is not significant.

(c)   The ratio of atoms in arrangement B to arrangement A is then 4.713×10^{14} atoms/$4.081 \times 10^{14} = 1.555 = 1.2:1$. Clearly, arrangement B results in less empty space per unit area or volume. If extended to three dimensions, arrangement B would lead to a greater density for Rb metal.

2.85   (a)   diameter of nucleus = 1×10^{-4} Å; diameter of atom = 1 Å

$V = 4/3 \pi r^3$; $r = d/2$; $r_n = 0.5 \times 10^{-4}$ Å; $r_a = 0.5$ Å

volume of nucleus = $4/3 \pi (0.5 \times 10^{-4})^3$ Å^3

volume of atom = $4/3 \pi (0.5)^3$ Å^3

volume fraction of nucleus = $\dfrac{\text{volume of nucleus}}{\text{volume of atom}} = \dfrac{4/3 \pi (0.5 \times 10^{-4})^3 \text{ Å}^3}{4/3 \pi (0.5)^3 \text{ Å}^3} = 1 \times 10^{-12}$

diameter of atom = 5 Å, $r_a = 2.5$ Å

volume fraction of nucleus = $\dfrac{4/3 \pi (0.5 \times 10^{-4})^3 \text{ Å}^3}{4/3 \pi (2.5)^3 \text{ Å}^3} = 8 \times 10^{-15}$

Depending on the radius of the atom, the volume fraction of the nucleus is between 1×10^{-12} and 8×10^{-15}, that is, between 1 part in 10^{12} and 8 parts in 10^{15}.

(b)   mass of proton = 1.0073 amu

1.0073 amu $\times$ 1.66054 $\times 10^{-24}$ g/amu = 1.6727 $\times 10^{-24}$ g

diameter = 1.0×10^{-15} m, radius = 0.50×10^{-15} m $\times \dfrac{100 \text{ cm}}{1 \text{ m}} = 5.0 \times 10^{-14}$ cm

Assuming a proton is a sphere, $V = 4/3 \pi r^3$.

density $= \dfrac{g}{\text{cm}^3} = \dfrac{1.6727 \times 10^{-24} \text{ g}}{4/3 \pi (5.0 \times 10^{-14})^3 \text{ cm}^3} = 3.2 \times 10^{15}$ g/cm^3

2.86   The integer on the lower left of a nuclide is the atomic number; it is the number of protons in any atom of the element and gives the element's identity. The number of neutrons is the mass number (upper left) minus atomic number.

(a)   As, 33 protons, 41 neutrons

(b)   I, 53 protons, 74 neutrons

(c)   Eu, 63 protons, 89 neutrons

(d)   Bi, 83 protons, 126 neutrons

2.87   (a) $^{16}_{8}O$, $^{17}_{8}O$, $^{18}_{8}O$

       (b)   All isotopes are atoms of the same element, oxygen, with the same atomic number (Z = 8), 8 protons in the nucleus and 8 electrons. Elements with similar electron arrangements have similar chemical properties (Section 2.5). Since the 3 isotopes all have 8 electrons, we expect their electron arrangements to be the same and their chemical properties to be very similar, perhaps identical. Each has a different number of neutrons (8, 9, or 10), a different mass number (A = 16, 17, or 18) and thus a different atomic mass.

2.88 $F = k\, Q_1 Q_2/d^2$; $k = 9.0 \times 10^9\, N\, m^2/C^2$; $d = 0.53 \times 10^{-10}\, m$;

       Q (electron) $= -1.6 \times 10^{-19}\, C$; Q (proton) $= -Q$ (electron) $= 1.6 \times 10^{-19}\, C$

$$F = \dfrac{\dfrac{9.0 \times 10^9\, N\, m^2}{C^2} \times -1.6 \times 10^{-19}\, C \times 1.6 \times 10^{-19}\, C}{(0.53 \times 10^{-10})^2\, m^2} = -8.202 \times 10^{-8} = -8.2 \times 10^{-8}\, N$$

2.89   Atomic weight (average atomic mass) $= \Sigma$ fractional abundance $\times$ mass of isotope

       Atomic weight $= 0.014(203.97302) + 0.241(205.97444) + 0.221(206.97587) +$
                                          $0.524(207.97663) = 207.22 = 207\, amu$

(The result has 0 decimal places and 3 sig figs because the fourth term in the sum has 3 sig figs and 0 decimal places.)

2.90   (a)   The 68.926 amu isotope has a mass number of 69, with 31 protons, 38 neutrons and the symbol $^{69}_{31}Ga$. The 70.925 amu isotope has a mass number of 71, 31 protons, 40 neutrons, and symbol $^{71}_{31}Ga$. (All Ga atoms have 31 protons.)

       (b)   The average mass of a Ga atom is 69.72 amu. Let x = abundance of the lighter isotope, 1–x = abundance of the heavier isotope. Then x(68.926) + (1–x)(70.925) = 69.72; x = 0.6028 = 0.603, $^{69}Ga = 60.3\%$, $^{71}Ga = 39.7\%$.

2.91   (a)   There are 24 known isotopes of Ni, from ^{51}Ni to ^{74}Ni.

       (b)   The five most abundant isotopes are

             ^{58}Ni, 57.935346 amu, 68.077%

             ^{60}Ni, 59.930788 amu, 26.223%

             ^{62}Ni, 61.928346 amu, 3.634%

             ^{61}Ni, 60.931058 amu, 1.140%

             ^{64}Ni, 63.927968 amu, 0.926%

             Data from *Handbook of Chemistry and Physics*, 74th Ed. [Data may differ slightly in other editions.]

2.92   (a)   A Br_2 molecule could consist of two atoms of the same isotope or one atom of each of the two different isotopes. This second possibility is twice as likely as the first. Therefore, the second peak (twice as large as peaks 1 and 3) represents a Br_2 molecule containing different isotopes. The mass numbers of the two isotopes are determined from the masses of the two smaller peaks. Since $157.836 \approx 158$, the first peak represents a $^{79}Br - {}^{79}Br$ molecule. Peak 3, $161.832 \approx 162$, represents a $^{81}Br - {}^{81}Br$ molecule. Peak 2 then contains one atom of each isotope, $^{79}Br - {}^{81}Br$, with an approximate mass of 160 amu.

(b)   The mass of the lighter isotope is 157.836 amu/2 atoms, or 78.918 amu/atom. For the heavier one, 161.832 amu/2 atoms = 80.916 amu/atom.

(c)   The relative size of the three peaks in the mass spectrum of Br_2 indicates their relative abundance. The average mass of a Br_2 molecule is

$0.2569(157.836) + 0.4999(159.834) + 0.2431(161.832) = 159.79$ amu.

(Each product has four significant figures and two decimal places, so the answer has two decimal places.)

(d) $\dfrac{159.79 \text{ amu}}{\text{avg. } Br_2 \text{ molecule}} \times \dfrac{1 \, Br_2 \text{ molecule}}{2 \, Br \text{ atoms}} = 79.895 \text{ amu}$

(e)   Let x = the abundance of ^{79}Br, 1 – x = abundance of ^{81}Br. From (b), the masses of the two isotopes are 78.918 amu and 80.916 amu, respectively. From (d), the mass of an average Br atom is 79.895 amu.

$x(78.918) + (1 - x)(80.916) = 79.895, \; x = 0.5110$

$^{79}Br = 51.10\%, \; {}^{81}Br = 48.90\%$

2.93   (a)   Five significant figures. $^{1}H^{+}$ is a bare proton with mass 1.0073 amu. ^{1}H is a hydrogen atom, with 1 proton and 1 electron. The mass of the electron is 5.486×10^{-4} or 0.0005486 amu. Thus the mass of the electron is significant in the fourth decimal place or fifth significant figure in the mass of ^{1}H.

(b)   Mass of ^{1}H = 1.0073 amu   (proton)

            <u>0.0005486 amu</u>   (electron)

            1.0078 amu   (We have not rounded up to 1.0079 since 49 < 50 in the final sum.)

$\text{Mass \% of electron} = \dfrac{\text{mass of } e^{-}}{\text{mass of } {}^{1}H} \times 100 = \dfrac{5.486 \times 10^{-4} \text{ amu}}{1.0078 \text{ amu}} \times 100 = 0.05444\%$

2.94   (a)   an alkali metal: K   (b) an alkaline earth metal: Ca   (c) a noble gas: Ar

(d)   a halogen: Br   (e) a metalloid: Ge   (f) a nonmetal in 1A: H

(g)   a metal that forms a 3+ ion: Al   (h) a nonmetal that forms a 2– ion: O

(i)   an element that resembles Al: Ga

2.95   (a) $^{266}_{106}$Sg has 106 protons, 160 neutrons and 106 electrons

(b)   Sg is in Group 6B (or 6) and immediately below tungsten, W. We expect the chemical properties of Sg to most closely resemble those of W.

2.96   Strontium is an alkaline earth metal, similar in chemical properties to calcium and magnesium. Calcium is ubiquitous in biological organisms, humans included. It is a vital nutrient required for formation and maintenance of healthy bones and teeth. As such, there are efficient pathways for calcium uptake and distribution in the body, pathways that are also available to chemically similar strontium. Harmful strontium imitates calcium and then behaves badly when the body tries to use it as it uses calcium.

2.97   (a)   chlorine gas, Cl_2: ii   (b)   propane, C_3H_8: v   (c)   nitrate ion, NO_3^- : i

            (d)   sulfur trioxide, SO_3: iii   (e)   methylchloride, CH_3Cl: iv

2.98   (a)   nickel(II) oxide, 2+   (b)   manganese(IV) oxide, 4+

            (c)   chromium(III) oxide, 3+   (d)   molybdenium(VI) oxide, 6+

2.99

Cation	Anion	Formula	Name
Li^+	O^{2-}	Li_2O	Lithium oxide
Fe^{2+}	PO_4^{3-}	$Fe_3(PO_4)_2$	Iron(II) phosphate
Al^{3+}	SO_4^{2-}	$Al_3(SO_4)_2$	Aluminum sulfate
Cu^{2+}	NO_3^-	$Cu(NO_3)_2$	Copper(II) nitrate
Cr^{3+}	I^-	CrI_2	Chromium(III) iodide
Mn^{2+}	ClO_2^-	$MnClO_2$	Manganese(I) chlorite
NH_4^+	CO_3^{2-}	$(NH_4)_2CO_3$	Ammonium carbonate
Zn^{2+}	ClO_4^-	$Zn(ClO_4)_2$	Zinc perchlorate

2.100   (a) IO_3^- (b) IO_4^- (c) IO^- (d) HIO (e) HIO_4 or (H_5IO_6)

2.101   (a)   perbromate ion   (b)   selenite ion

            (c) AsO_4^{3-} (d) $HTeO_4^-$

2.102   Carbonic acid: H_2CO_3; the cation is H^+ because it is an acid; the anion is carbonate because the acid reacts with lithium hydroxide to form lithium carbonate.
        Lithium hydroxide: $LiOH$; lithium carbonate: Li_2CO_3

2.103   (a)   sodium chloride   (b) sodium bicarbonate (or sodium hydrogen carbonate)

            (c)   sodium hypochlorite   (d) sodium hydroxide

            (e)   ammonium carbonate   (f) calcium sulfate

2.104   (a)   potassium nitrate   (b) sodium carbonate   (c) calcium oxide

            (d)   hydrochloric acid   (e) magnesium sulfate   (f) magnesium hydroxide

2.105   (a) CaS, $Ca(HS)_2$ (b) HBr, $HBrO_3$ (c) AlN, $Al(NO_2)_3$ (d) FeO, Fe_2O_3

          (e) NH_3, NH_4^+ (f) K_2SO_3, $KHSO_3$ (g) Hg_2Cl_2, $HgCl_2$ (h) $HClO_3$, $HClO_4$

2.106   (a)   In an alkane, all C atoms have 4 single bonds, so each C in the partial structure needs 2 more bonds. All alkanes are hydrocarbons, so 2 H atoms will bind to each C atom in the ring.

          (b)   The molecular formula of cyclohexane is C_6H_{12}; the molecular formula of *n*-hexane is C_6H_{14} (see Solution 2.76(b)). Cyclohexane can be thought of as *n*-hexane in which the two outer (terminal) C atoms are joined to each other. In order to form this C—C bond, each outer C atom must lose 1 H atom. The number of C atoms is unchanged, and each C atom still has 4 single bonds. The resulting molecular formula is $C_6H_{14-2} = C_6H_{12}$.

          (c)   On the structure in part (a), replace 1 H atom with an OH group.

3 Stoichiometry: Calculations with Chemical Formulas and Equations

Visualizing Concepts

3.1 Reactant A = blue, reactant B = red

Overall, 4 blue A_2 molecules + 4 red B atoms → 4 A_2B molecules

Since 4 is a common factor, this equation reduces to equation (a).

3.2

Write the balanced equation for the reaction.

$$2H_2 + CO \rightarrow CH_3OH$$

The combining ratio of H_2: CO is 2:1. If we have 8 H_2 molecules, 4 CO molecules are required for complete reaction. Alternatively, you could examine the atom ratios in the formula of CH_3OH, but the balanced equation is most direct.

3.3 (a) There are twice as many O atoms as N atoms, so the empirical formula of the original compound is NO_2.

(b) No, because we have no way of knowing whether the empirical and molecular formulas are the same. NO_2 represents the simplest ratio of atoms in a molecule but not the only possible molecular formula.

3.4 The box contains 4 C atoms and 16 H atoms, so the empirical formula of the hydrocarbon is CH_4.

3.5 (a) *Analyze.* Given the molecular model, write the molecular formula.

Plan. Use the colors of the atoms (spheres) in the model to determine the number of atoms of each element.

Solve. Observe 2 gray C atoms, 5 white H atoms, 1 blue N atom, 2 red O atoms. $C_2H_5NO_2$

(b) *Plan.* Follow the method in Sample Exercise 3.9. Calculate formula weight in amu and molar mass in grams.

$$2 \text{ C atoms} = 2(12.0 \text{ amu}) = 24.0 \text{ amu}$$

$$5 \text{ H atoms} = 5(1.0 \text{ amu}) = 5.0 \text{ amu}$$

$$1 \text{ N atoms} = 1(14.0 \text{ amu}) = 14.0 \text{ amu}$$

$$2 \text{ O atoms} = 2(16.0 \text{ amu}) = \underline{32.0 \text{ amu}}$$

$$75.0 \text{ amu}$$

Formula weight = 75.0 amu, molar mass = 75.0 g/mol

(c)   *Plan.* The molar mass of a substance provides the factor for converting moles to grams (or grams to moles).

Solve. $3 \text{ mol glycine} \times \dfrac{75.0 \text{ g glycine}}{\text{mol}} = 225 \text{ g glycine}$

(d)   *Plan.* Use the definition of mass % and the results from parts (a) and (b) above to find mass % N in glycine.

Solve. $\text{mass} \% \text{ N} = \dfrac{\text{g N}}{\text{g C}_2\text{H}_5\text{NO}_2} \times 100$

Assume 1 mol $C_2H_5NO_2$. From the molecular formula of glycine [part (a)], there is 1 mol N/mol glycine.

$$\text{mass} \% \text{ N} = \dfrac{1 \times (\text{molar mass N})}{\text{molar mass glycine}} \times 100 = \dfrac{14.0 \text{ g}}{75.0 \text{ g}} \times 100 = 18.7\%$$

3.6   *Analyze.* Given: 4.0 mol CH_4. Find: mol CO and mol H_2

Plan. Examine the boxes to determine the CH_4:CO mol ratio and CH_4:H_2O mole ratio.

Solve. There are 2 CH_4 molecules in the reactant box and 2 CO molecules in the product box. The mole ratio is 2:2 or 1:1. Therefore, 4.0 mol CH_4 can produce 4.0 mol CO. There are 2 CH_4 molecules in the reactant box and 6 H_2 molecules in the product box. The mole ratio is 2:6 or 1:3. So, 4.0 mol CH_4 can produce 12:0 mol H_2.

Check. Use proportions. 2 mol CH_4/2 mol CO = 4 mol CH_4/4 mol CO; 2 mol CH_4/6 mol H_2 = 4 mol CH_4/12 mol H_2.

3.7   *Analyze.* Given a box diagram and formulas of reactants, draw a box diagram of products.

Plan. Write and balance the chemical equation. Determine combining ratios of elements and decide on limiting reactant. Draw a box diagram of products, containing the correct number of product molecules and only excess reactant.

Solve. $N_2 + 3H_2 \longrightarrow 3NH_3$. $N_2 = $, $NH_3 = $

Each N atom (1/2 of an N_2 molecule) reacts with 3 H atoms (1.5 H_2 molecules) to form an NH_3 molecule. Eight N atoms (4 N_2 molecules) require 24 H atoms (12 H_2 molecules) for complete reaction. Only 9 H_2 molecules are available, so H_2 is the limiting reactant. Nine H_2 molecules (18 H atoms) determine that 6 NH_3 molecules are produced. One N_2 molecule is in excess.

Check. Verify that mass is conserved in your solution, that the number and kinds of atoms are the same in reactant and product diagrams. In this example, there are 8 N atoms and 18 H atoms in both diagrams, so mass is conserved.

3.8   (a) $2NO + O_2 \rightarrow 2NO_2$, $O_2 =$, $NO_2 =$

Each NO molecule reacts with 1 O atom (1/2 of an O_2 molecule) to produce 1 NO_2 molecule. Eight NO molecules react with 8 O atoms (4 O_2 molecules) to produce 8 NO_2 molecules. One O_2 molecule doesn't react (is in excess). NO is the limiting reactant.

(b)   % yield $= \dfrac{\text{actual yield}}{\text{theoretical yield}} \times 100$;   actual yield $= \dfrac{\% \text{ yield}}{100} \times$ theoretical yield

The theoretical yield from part (a) is 8 NO_2 molecules. If the percent yield is 75%, then 0.75(8) = 6 NO_2 would appear in the products box.

Balancing Chemical Equations (section 3.1)

3.9   (a)   In balancing chemical equations, the law of conservation of mass, that atoms are neither created nor destroyed during the course of a reaction, is observed. This means that the **number** and **kinds** of atoms on both sides of the chemical equation must be the same.

(b)   Subscripts in chemical formulas should not be changed when balancing equations, because changing the subscript changes the identity of the compound (law of constant composition).

(c)   liquid water = $H_2O(l)$;   water vapor = $H_2O(g)$; aqueous sodium chloride = NaCl(aq); solid sodium chloride = NaCl(s)

3.10   (a)   In a CO molecule, there is one O atom bound to C. 2CO indicates that there are **two CO molecules**, each of which contains one C and one O atom. Adding a subscript 2 to CO to form CO_2 means that there are **two O atoms** bound to one C in a CO_2 molecule. The composition of the different molecules, CO_2 and CO, is different and the physical and chemical properties of the two compounds they constitute are very different. The subscript 2 changes molecular composition and thus properties of the compound. The prefix 2 indicates how many molecules (or moles) of the original compound are under consideration.

(b)   Yes. There are the same number and kinds of atoms on the reactants side and the products side of the equation.

3.11   (a) $2CO(g) + O_2(g) \rightarrow 2CO_2(g)$

         (b) $N_2O_5(g) + H_2O(l) \rightarrow 2HNO_3(aq)$

         (c) $CH_4(g) + 4Cl_2(g) \rightarrow CCl_4(l) + 4HCl(g)$

         (d) $Al_4C_3(s) + 12H_2O(l) \rightarrow 4Al(OH)_3(s) + 3CH_4(g)$

         (e) $2C_5H_{10}O_2(l) + 13O_2(g) \rightarrow 10CO_2(g) + 10H_2O(g)$

         (f) $2Fe(OH)_3(s) + 3H_2SO_4(aq) \rightarrow Fe_2(SO_4)_3(aq) + 6H_2O(l)$

         (g) $Mg_3N_2(s) + 4H_2SO_4(aq) \rightarrow 3MgSO_4(aq) + (NH_4)_2SO_4(aq)$

3.12   (a) $6Li(s) + N_2(g) \rightarrow 2Li_3N(s)$

         (b) $TiCl_4(l) + 2H_2O(l) \rightarrow TiO_2(s) + 4HCl(aq)$

         (c) $2NH_4NO_3(s) \rightarrow 2N_2(g) + O_2(g) + 4H_2O(g)$

         (d) $Ca_3P_2(s) + 6H_2O(l) \rightarrow 3Ca(OH)_2(aq) + 2PH_3(g)$

         (e) $2Al(OH)_3(s) + 3H_2SO_4(aq) \rightarrow Al_2(SO_4)_3(aq) + 6H_2O(l)$

         (f) $2AgNO_3(aq) + Na_2CO_3(aq) \rightarrow Ag_2CO_3(s) + 2NaNO_3(aq)$

         (g) $4C_2H_5NH_2(g) + 15O_2(g) \rightarrow 8CO_2(g) + 14H_2O(g) + 2N_2(g)$

3.13   (a) $CaC_2(s) + 2H_2O(l) \rightarrow Ca(OH)_2(aq) + C_2H_2(g)$

         (b) $2KClO_3(s) \overset{\Delta}{\rightarrow} 2KCl(s) + 3O_2(g)$

         (c) $Zn(s) + H_2SO_4(aq) \rightarrow H_2(g) + ZnSO_4(aq)$

         (d) $PCl_3(l) + 3H_2O(l) \rightarrow H_3PO_3(aq) + 3HCl(aq)$

         (e) $3H_2S(g) + 2Fe(OH)_3(s) \rightarrow Fe_2S_3(s) + 6H_2O(g)$

3.14   (a) $SO_3(g) + H_2O(l) \rightarrow H_2SO_4(aq)$

         (b) $B_2S_3(s) + 6H_2O(l) \rightarrow 2H_3BO_3(aq) + 3H_2S(g)$

         (c) $4PH_3(g) + 8O_2(g) \rightarrow P_4O_{10}(s) + 6H_2O(g)$

         (d) $2Hg(NO_3)_2(s) \overset{\Delta}{\rightarrow} 2HgO(s) + 4NO_2(g) + O_2(g)$

         (e) $Cu(s) + 2H_2SO_4(aq) \rightarrow CuSO_4(aq) + SO_2(g) + 2H_2O(l)$

Patterns of Chemical Reactivity (section 3.2)

3.15   (a)   When a metal reacts with a nonmetal, an ionic compound forms. The combining ratio of the atoms is such that the total positive charge on the metal cation(s) is equal to the total negative charge on the nonmetal anion(s). Determine the formula by balancing the positive and negative charges in the ionic product. All ionic compounds are solids. $2 Na(s) + Br_2(l) \rightarrow 2NaBr(s)$

       (b)   The second reactant is oxygen gas from the air, $O_2(g)$. The products are $CO_2(g)$ and $H_2O(l)$. $2C_6H_6(l) + 15O_2(g) \rightarrow 12CO_2(g) + 6H_2O(l)$.

3.16   (a)   Neutral Al atom loses $3e^-$ to form Al^{3+}. Neutral Br_2 molecule gains $2e^-$ to form $2Br^-$. The formula of the product will be $AlBr_3$, because the cationic and anionic charges balance. $2Al(s) + 3Br_2(l) \rightarrow 2\,AlBr_3(s)$

       (b)   The products are $CO_2(g)$ and $H_2O(l)$. $C_3H_6O(l) + 4O_2(g) \rightarrow 3CO_2(g) + 3H_2O(l)$

3.17   (a) $Mg(s) + Cl_2(g) \rightarrow MgCl_2(s)$

       (b) $BaCO_3(s) \overset{\Delta}{\rightarrow} BaO(s) + CO_2(g)$

       (c) $C_8H_8(l) + 10O_2(g) \rightarrow 8CO_2(g) + 4H_2O(l)$

       (d) CH_3OCH_3 is C_2H_6O. $C_2H_6O(g) + 3O_2(g) \rightarrow 2CO_2(g) + 3H_2O(l)$

3.18   (a) $2Ca(s) + O_2(g) \rightarrow 2CaO$

       (b) $Cu(OH)_2(s) \overset{\Delta}{\rightarrow} CuO(s) + H_2O(g)$

       (c) $C_7H_{16}(l) + 11O_2(g) \rightarrow 7CO_2(g) + 8H_2O(l)$

       (d) $2C_5H_{12}O(l) + 15O_2(g) \rightarrow 10CO_2(g) + 12H_2O(l)$

3.19   (a) $2C_3H_6(g) + 9O_2(g) \rightarrow 6CO_2(g) + 6H_2O(g)$ combustion

       (b) $NH_4NO_3(s) \rightarrow N_2O(g) + 2H_2O(g)$ decomposition

       (c) $C_5H_6O(l) + 6O_2(g) \rightarrow 5CO_2(g) + 3H_2O(g)$ combustion

       (d) $N_2(g) + 3H_2(g) \rightarrow 2NH_3(g)$ combination

       (e) $K_2O(s) + H_2O(l) \rightarrow 2KOH(aq)$ combination

3.20   (a) $PbCO_3(s) \rightarrow PbO(s) + CO_2(g)$ decomposition

       (b) $C_2H_4(g) + 3O_2(g) \rightarrow 2CO_2(g) + 2H_2O(g)$ combustion

       (c) $3Mg(s) + N_2(g) \rightarrow Mg_3N_2(s)$ combination

       (d) $C_7H_8O_2(l) + 8O_2(g) \rightarrow 7CO_2(g) + 4H_2O(g)$ combustion

       (e) $2Al(s) + 3Cl_2(g) \rightarrow 2AlCl_3(s)$ combination

Formula Weights (section 3.3)

3.21   *Analyze.* Given molecular formula or name, calculate formula weight.

       Plan. If a name is given, write the correct molecular formula. Then, follow the method in Sample Exercise 3.5.   *Solve.*

(a) HNO_3: $1(1.0) + 1(14.0) + 3(16.0) = 63.0$ amu

(b) $KMnO_4$: $1(39.1) + 1(54.9) + 4(16.0) = 158.0$ amu

(c) $Ca_3(PO_4)_2$: $3(40.1) + 2(31.0) + 8(16.0) = 310.3$ amu

(d) SiO_2: $1(28.1) + 2(16.0) = 60.1$ amu

(e) Ga_2S_3: $2(69.7) + 3(32.1) = 235.7$ amu

(f) $Cr_2(SO_4)_3$: $2(52.0) + 3(32.1) + 12(16.0) = 392.3$ amu

(g) PCl_3: $1(31.0) + 3(35.5) = 137.5$ amu

3.22   Formula weight in amu to 1 decimal place.

(a) N_2O: FW $= 2(14.0) + 1(16.0) = 44.0$ amu

(b) $HC_7H_5O_2$: $7(12.0) + 6(1.0) + 2(16.0) = 122.0$ amu

(c) $Mg(OH)_2$: $1(24.3) + 2(16.0) + 2(1.0) = 58.3$ amu

(d) $(NH_2)_2CO$: $2(14.0) + 4(1.0) + 1(12.0) + 1(16.0) = 60.0$ amu

(e) $CH_3CO_2C_5H_{11}$: $7(12.0) + 14(1.0) + 2(16.0) = 130.0$ amu

3.23   *Plan.* Calculate the formula weight (FW), then the mass % oxygen in the compound. *Solve.*

(a) $C_{17}H_{19}NO_3$: FW $= 17(12.0) + 19(1.0) + 1(14.0) + 3(16.0) = 285.0$ amu

$$\% O = \frac{3(16.0)\,amu}{285.0\,amu} \times 100 = 16.842 = 16.8\%$$

(b) $C_{18}H_{21}NO_3$: FW $= 18(12.0) + 21(1.0) + 1(14.0) + 3(16.0) = 299.0$ amu

$$\% O = \frac{3(16.0)\,amu}{299.0\,amu} \times 100 = 16.054 = 16.1\%$$

(c) $C_{17}H_{21}NO_4$: FW $= 17(12.0) + 21(1.0) + 1(14.0) + 4(16.0) = 303.0$ amu

$$\% O = \frac{4(16.0)\,amu}{303.0\,amu} \times 100 = 21.122 = 21.1\%$$

(d) $C_{22}H_{24}N_2O_8$: FW $= 22(12.0) + 24(1.0) + 2(14.0) + 8(16.0) = 444.0$ amu

$$\% O = \frac{8(16.0)\,amu}{444.0\,amu} \times 100 = 28.829 = 28.8\%$$

(e) $C_{41}H_{64}O_{13}$: FW $= 4(12.0) + 64(1.0) + 13(16.0) = 764.0$ amu

$$\% O = \frac{13(16.0)\,amu}{764\,amu} \times 100 = 27.225 = 27.2\%$$

(f) $C_{66}H_{75}Cl_2N_9O_{24}$: FW $= 66(12.0)+75(1.0)+2(35.5)+9(14.0)+24(16.0) = 1448.0$ amu

$$\% O = \frac{24(16.0)\,amu}{1448.0\,amu} \times 100 = 26.519 = 26.5\%$$

3.24   (a) C_2H_2: FW $= 2(12.0) + 2(1.0) = 26.0$ amu

$$\% C = \frac{2(12.0)\,amu}{26.0\,amu} \times 100 = 92.3\%$$

(b) $HC_6H_7O_6$: FW $= 6(12.0) + 8(1.0) + 6(16.0) = 176.0$ amu

$$\% H = \frac{8(1.0)\,amu}{176.0\,amu} \times 100 = 4.5\%$$

(c) $(NH_4)_2SO_4$: FW = 2(14.0) + 8(1.0) + 1(32.1) + 4(16.0) = 132.1 amu

$$\% \, H = \frac{8(1.0)\,amu}{132.1\,amu} \times 100 = 6.1\%$$

(d) $PtCl_2(NH_3)_2$: FW = 1(195.1) + 2(35.5) + 2(14.0) + 6(1.0) = 300.1 amu

$$\% \, Pt = \frac{1(195.1)\,amu}{300.1\,amu} \times 100 = 65.01\%$$

(e) $C_{18}H_{24}O_2$: FW = 18(12.0) + 24(1.0) + 2(16.0) = 272.0 amu

$$\% \, O = \frac{2(16.0)\,amu}{272.0\,amu} \times 100 = 11.8\%$$

(f) $C_{18}H_{27}NO_3$: FW = 18(12.0) + 27(1.0) + 1(14.0) + 3(16.0) = 305.0 amu

$$\% \, C = \frac{18(12.0)\,amu}{305.0\,amu} \times 100 = 70.8\%$$

3.25   *Plan.* Follow the logic for calculating mass % C given in Sample Exercise 3.6.   *Solve.*

(a) C_7H_6O: FW = 7(12.0) + 6(1.0) + 1(16.0) = 106.0 amu

$$\% \, C = \frac{7(12.0)\,amu}{106.0\,amu} \times 100 = 79.2\%$$

(b) $C_8H_8O_3$: FW = 8(12.0) + 8(1.0) + 3(16.0) = 152.0 amu

$$\% \, C = \frac{8(12.0)\,amu}{152.0\,amu} \times 100 = 63.2\%$$

(c) $C_7H_{14}O_2$: FW = 7(12.0) + 14(1.0) + 2(16.0) = 130.0 amu

$$\% \, C = \frac{7(12.0)\,amu}{130.0\,amu} \times 100 = 64.6\%$$

3.26   (a) CO_2: FW = 1(12.0) + 2(16.0) = 44.0 amu

$$\% \, C = \frac{12.0\,amu}{44.0\,amu} \times 100 = 27.3\%$$

(b) CH_3OH: FW = 1(12.0) + 4(1.0) + 1(16.0) = 32.0 amu

$$\% \, C = \frac{12.0\,amu}{32.0\,amu} \times 100 = 37.5\%$$

(c) C_2H_6: FW = 2(12.0) + 6(1.0) = 30.0 amu

$$\% \, C = \frac{2(12.0)\,amu}{30.0\,amu} \times 100 = 80.0\%$$

(d) $CS(NH_2)_2$: FW = 1(12.0) + 1(32.1) + 2(14.0) + 4(1.0) = 76.1 amu

$$\% \, C = \frac{12.0\,amu}{76.1\,amu} \times 100 = 15.8\%$$

Avogadro's Number and the Mole (section 3.4)

3.27   (a) 6.022×10^{23}. This is the number of objects in a mole of anything.

       (b)   The formula weight of a substance in amu has the same numerical value as the molar mass expressed in grams.

3.28   (a)   <u>exactly</u> 12 g   (b) 6.0221421×10^{23}, Avogadro's number

3.29   *Plan.* Since the mole is a counting unit, use it as a basis of comparison; determine the total moles of atoms in each given quantity.   *Solve.*

23 g Na contains 1 mol of atoms

0.5 mol H_2O contains (3 atoms × 0.5 mol) = 1.5 mol atoms

6.0×10^{23} N_2 molecules contains (2 atoms × 1 mol) = 2 mol atoms

3.30   16 g O_2 contains (2 atoms × 0.5 mol) = 1 mol atoms

9.0×10^{23} H_2O_2 molecules contains (4 atoms × 1.5 mol) = 6 mol atoms

2.0 mol CH_4 contains (5 atoms × 2 mol) = 10 mol atoms

3.31   *Analyze.* Given: 160 lb/person; Avogadro's number of people, 6.022×10^{23} people. Find: mass in kg of Avogadro's number of people; compare with mass of Earth.

Plan. people → mass in lb → mass in kg; mass of people /mass of Earth

Solve. 6.022×10^{23} people $\times \dfrac{160\,\text{lb}}{\text{person}} \times \dfrac{1\,\text{kg}}{2.2046\,\text{lb}} = 4.370 \times 10^{25} = 4.37 \times 10^{25}$ or 4.4×10^{25} kg

$\dfrac{4.370 \times 10^{25}\,\text{kg of people}}{5.98 \times 10^{24}\,\text{kg Earth}} = 7.31$ or 7.3

One mole of people weighs 7.31 times as much as Earth.

Check. This mass of people is reasonable since Avogadro's number is large.

Estimate: 160 lb ≈ 70 kg; $6 \times 10^{23} \times 70 = 420 \times 10^{23} = 4.2 \times 10^{25}$ kg

3.32   300 million = $300 \times 10^6 = 3.00 \times 10^8$ or 3×10^8 people

(The number 300 million has an ambiguous number of sig figs.)

$\dfrac{6.022 \times 10^{23}\,\text{¢}}{3.00 \times 10^8\,\text{people}} \times \dfrac{\$1}{100\,\text{¢}} = \dfrac{\$6.022 \times 10^{21}}{3.00 \times 10^8\,\text{people}} = 2.007 \times 10^{13} = \$2.01 \times 10^{13}$/person

$\$14.4\ \text{trillion} = \$1.44 \times 10^{13}$ $\dfrac{\$2.007 \times 10^{13}}{\$1.44 \times 10^{13}} = 1.394 = 1.39$ or 1

Each person would receive an amount that is 1.39 (or 1) times the dollar amount of the national debt.

3.33   (a)   *Analyze.* Given: 0.105 mol sucrose, $C_{12}H_{22}O_{11}$. Find: mass in g.

       Plan. Use molar mass (g/mol) of $C_{12}H_{22}O_{11}$ to find g $C_{12}H_{22}O_{11}$.

       Solve. molar mass = 12(12.0107) + 22(1.00794) + 11(15.9994) = 342.296 = 342.30

       0.105 mol sucrose $\times \dfrac{342.30\,\text{g}}{1\,\text{mol}} = 35.942 = 35.9$ g $C_{12}H_{22}O_{11}$

       Check. 0.1(342) = 34.2 g. The calculated result is reasonable.

     (b)   *Analyze.* Given: mass. Find: moles. *Plan.* Use molar mass of $Zn(NO_3)_2$.

       Solve. molar mass = 1(65.39) + 2(14.0067) + 6(15.9994) = 189.3998 = 189.40

       143.50 g $Zn(NO_3)_2$ $\times \dfrac{1\,\text{mol}}{189.40\,\text{g}\ Zn(NO_3)_2} = 0.75766$ mol $Zn(NO_3)_2$

       Check. 140/180 ≈ 7/9 = 0.78 mol

(c)   *Analyze.* Given: moles. Find: molecules. *Plan.* Use Avogadro's number.

     Solve. 1.0×10^{-6} mol $CH_3CH_2OH \times \dfrac{6.022 \times 10^{23} \text{ molecules}}{1 \text{ mol}} = 6.022 \times 10^{17}$

$$= 6.0 \times 10^{17} \, CH_3CH_2OH \text{ molecules}$$

     Check. $(1.0 \times 10^{-6})(6 \times 10^{23}) = 6 \times 10^{17}$

(d)   *Analyze.* Given: mol NH_3. Find: N atoms.

     Plan. mol $NH_3 \rightarrow$ mol N atoms $\rightarrow$ N atoms

     Solve. 0.410 mol $NH_3 \times \dfrac{1 \text{ mol N atoms}}{1 \text{ mol } NH_3} \times \dfrac{6.022 \times 10^{23} \text{ atoms}}{1 \text{ mol}}$

$$= 2.47 \times 10^{23} \text{ N atoms}$$

     Check. $(0.4)(6 \times 10^{23}) = 2.4 \times 10^{23}$.

3.34   (a)   molar mass = $1(112.41) + 1(32.07) = 144.48$ g

        1.50×10^{-2} mol CdS $\times \dfrac{144.48 \text{ g}}{1 \text{ mol}} = 2.17$ g CdS

     (b)   molar mass = $1(14.01) + 4(1.008) + 1(35.45) = 53.49$ g/mol

        86.6 g $NH_4Cl \times \dfrac{1 \text{ mol}}{53.49 \text{ g}} = 1.6190 = 1.62$ mol NH_4Cl

     (c) 8.447×10^{-2} mol $C_6H_6 \times \dfrac{6.02214 \times 10^{23} \text{ molecules}}{1 \text{ mol}} = 5.087 \times 10^{22} \, C_6H_6$ molecules

     (d) 6.25×10^{-3} mol $Al(NO_3)_3 \times \dfrac{9 \text{ mol O}}{1 \text{ mol } Al(NO_3)_3} \times \dfrac{6.022 \times 10^{23} \text{ O atoms}}{1 \text{ mol}}$

$$= 3.39 \times 10^{22} \text{ O atoms}$$

3.35   *Analyze/Plan.* See Solution 3.33 for stepwise problem-solving approach.   *Solve.*

     (a) $(NH_4)_3PO_4$ molar mass = $3(14.007) + 12(1.008) + 1(30.974) + 4(16.00) = 149.091$

$$= 149.1 \text{ g/mol}$$

        2.50×10^{-3} mol $(NH_4)_3PO_4 \times \dfrac{149.1 \text{ g } (NH_4)_3PO_4}{1 \text{ mol}} = 0.373$ g $(NH_4)_3PO_4$

     (b) $AlCl_3$ molar mass = $26.982 + 3(35.453) = 133.341 = 133.34$ g/mol

        0.2550 g $AlCl_3 \times \dfrac{1 \text{ mol}}{133.34 \text{ g } AlCl_3} \times \dfrac{3 \text{ mol } Cl^-}{1 \text{ mol } AlCl_3} = 5.737 \times 10^{-3}$ mol Cl^-

     (c) $C_8H_{10}N_4O_2$ molar mass = $8(12.01) + 10(1.008) + 4(14.01) + 2(16.00) = 194.20$

$$= 194.2 \text{ g/mol}$$

        7.70×10^{20} molecules $\times \dfrac{1 \text{ mol}}{6.022 \times 10^{23} \text{ molecules}} \times \dfrac{194.2 \text{ g } C_8H_{10}N_4O_2}{1 \text{ mol caffeine}}$

$$= 0.248 \text{ g } C_8H_{10}N_4O_2$$

     (d) $\dfrac{0.406 \text{ g cholesterol}}{0.00105 \text{ mol}} = 387$ g cholesterol/mol

3.36   (a) $Fe_2(SO_4)_3$ molar mass = 2(55.845) + 3(32.07) + 12(16.00) = 399.900 = 399.9 g/mol

$$1.223 \text{ mol } Fe_2(SO_4)_3 \times \frac{399.9 \text{ g } Fe_2(SO_4)_3}{1 \text{ mol}} = 489.077 = 489.1 \text{ g } Fe_2(SO_4)_3$$

(b) $(NH_4)_2CO_3$ molar mass = 2(14.007) + 8(1.008) + 12.011 + 3(15.9994) = 96.0872

$$= 96.087 \text{ g/mol}$$

$$6.955 \text{ g } (NH_4)_2CO_3 \times \frac{1 \text{ mol}}{96.087 \text{ g } (NH_4)_2CO_3} \times \frac{2 \text{ mol } NH_4^+}{1 \text{ mol } (NH_4)_2CO_3} = 0.1448 \text{ mol } NH_4^+$$

(c) $C_9H_8O_4$ molar mass = 9(12.01) + 8(1.008) + 4(16.00) = 180.154 = 180.2 g/mol

$$1.50 \times 10^{21} \text{ molecules} \times \frac{1 \text{ mol}}{6.022 \times 10^{23} \text{ molecules}} \times \frac{180.2 \text{ g } C_9H_8O_4}{1 \text{ mol aspirin}} = 0.449 \text{ g } C_9H_8O_4$$

(d) $\dfrac{15.86 \text{ g Valium}}{0.05570 \text{ mol}} = 284.7$ g Valium/mol

3.37   (a) $C_6H_{10}OS_2$ molar mass = 6(12.01) + 10(1.008) + 1(16.00) + 2(32.07) = 162.28

$$= 162.3 \text{ g/mol}$$

(b)   *Plan.* mg → g → mol   *Solve.*

$$5.00 \text{ mg allicin} \times \frac{1 \times 10^{-3} \text{ g}}{1 \text{ mg}} \times \frac{1 \text{ mol}}{162.3 \text{ g}} = 3.081 \times 10^{-5} = 3.08 \times 10^{-5} \text{ mol allicin}$$

Check. 5.00 mg is a small mass, so the small answer is reasonable.

$(5 \times 10^{-3})/200 = 2.5 \times 10^{-5}$

(c)   *Plan.* Use mol from part (b) and Avogadro's number to calculate molecules.

$$\text{Solve. } 3.081 \times 10^{-5} \text{ mol allicin} \times \frac{6.022 \times 10^{23} \text{ molecules}}{\text{mol}} = 1.855 \times 10^{19}$$

$$= 1.86 \times 10^{19} \text{ allicin molecules}$$

Check. $(3 \times 10^{-5})(6 \times 10^{23}) = 18 \times 10^{18} = 1.8 \times 10^{19}$

(d)   *Plan.* Use molecules from part (c) and molecular formula to calculate S atoms.

$$\textit{Solve. } 1.855 \times 10^{19} \text{ allicin molecules} \times \frac{2 \text{ S atoms}}{1 \text{ allicin molecule}} = 3.71 \times 10^{19} \text{ S atoms}$$

Check. Obvious.

3.38   (a) $C_{14}H_{18}N_2O_5$ molar mass = 14(12.01) + 18(1.008) + 2(14.01) + 5(16.00)

$$= 294.30 \text{ g/mol}$$

(b) $1.00 \text{ mg aspartame} \times \dfrac{1 \times 10^{-3} \text{ g}}{1 \text{ mg}} \times \dfrac{1 \text{ mol}}{294.3 \text{ g}} = 3.398 \times 10^{-6} = 3.40 \times 10^{-6}$ mol aspartame

(c) $3.398 \times 10^{-6} \text{ mol aspartame} \times \dfrac{6.022 \times 10^{23} \text{ molecules}}{1 \text{ mol}} = 2.046 \times 10^{18}$

$$= 2.05 \times 10^{18} \text{ aspartame molecules}$$

(d) 2.046×10^{18} aspartame molecules $\times \dfrac{18\,\text{H atoms}}{1\,\text{aspartame molecule}} = 3.68 \times 10^{19}$ H atoms

3.39 (a) *Analyze.* Given: $C_6H_{12}O_6$, 1.250×10^{21} C atoms. Find: H atoms.

Plan. Use molecular formula to determine number of H atoms that are present with 1.250×10^{21} C atoms. *Solve.*

$$\frac{12\,\text{H atoms}}{6\,\text{C atoms}} = \frac{2\,\text{H}}{1\,\text{C}} \times 1.250 \times 10^{21}\,\text{C atoms} = 2.500 \times 10^{21}\,\text{H atoms}$$

Check. $(2 \times 1 \times 10^{21}) = 2 \times 10^{21}$

(b) *Plan.* Use molecular formula to find the number of glucose molecules that contain 1.250×10^{21} C atoms. *Solve.*

$$\frac{1\,C_6H_{12}O_6\,\text{molecule}}{6\,\text{C atoms}} \times 1.250 \times 10^{21}\,\text{C atoms} = 2.0833 \times 10^{20}$$

$$= 2.083 \times 10^{20}\ C_6H_{12}O_6\,\text{molecules}$$

Check. $(12 \times 10^{20}/6) = 2 \times 10^{20}$

(c) *Plan.* Use Avogadro's number to change molecules → mol. *Solve.*

$$2.0833 \times 10^{20}\ C_6H_{12}O_6\,\text{molecules} \times \frac{1\,\text{mol}}{6.022 \times 10^{23}\,\text{molecules}}$$

$$= 3.4595 \times 10^{-4} = 3.460 \times 10^{-4}\,\text{mol}\ C_6H_{12}O_6$$

Check. $(2 \times 10^{20})/(6 \times 10^{23}) = 0.33 \times 10^{-3} = 3.3 \times 10^{-4}$

(d) *Plan.* Use molar mass to change mol → g. *Solve.*

1 mole of $C_6H_{12}O_6$ weighs 180.0 g (Sample Exercise 3.9)

$$3.4595 \times 10^{-4}\,\text{mol}\ C_6H_{12}O_6 \times \frac{180.0\,\text{g}\ C_6H_{12}O_6}{1\,\text{mol}} = 0.06227\,\text{g}\ C_6H_{12}O_6$$

Check. $3.5 \times 180 = 630$; $630 \times 10^{-4} = 0.063$

3.40 (a) 3.88×10^{21} H atoms $\times \dfrac{19\,\text{C atoms}}{28\,\text{H atoms}} = 2.63 \times 10^{21}$ C atoms

(b) 3.88×10^{21} H atoms $\times \dfrac{1\,C_{19}H_{28}O_2\,\text{molecule}}{28\,\text{H atoms}} = 1.3857 \times 10^{20}$

$$= 1.39 \times 10^{20}\ C_{19}H_{28}O_2\,\text{molecules}$$

(c) $1.3857 \times 10^{20}\ C_{19}H_{28}O_2$ molecules $\times \dfrac{1\,\text{mol}}{6.022 \times 10^{23}\,\text{molecules}} = 2.301 \times 10^{-4}$

$$= 2.30 \times 10^{-4}\,\text{mol}\ C_{19}H_{28}O_2$$

(d) $C_{19}H_{28}O_2$ molar mass $= 19(12.01) + 28(1.008) + 2(16.00) = 288.41 = 288.4$ g/mol

$$2.301 \times 10^{-4}\,\text{mol}\ C_{19}H_{28}O_2 \times \frac{288.4\,\text{g}\ C_{19}H_{28}O_2}{1\,\text{mol}} = 0.0664\,\text{g}\ C_{19}H_{28}O_2$$

3.41   *Analyze.* Given: $g\ C_2H_3Cl/L$.   Find: mol/L, molecules/L.

         Plan. The /L is constant throughout the problem, so we can ignore it. Use molar mass for g → mol, Avogadro's number for mol → molecules.   *Solve.*

$$\frac{2.0\times10^{-6}\ g\ C_2H_3Cl}{1\,L}\times\frac{1\,mol\ C_2H_3Cl}{62.50\,g\ C_2H_3Cl}=3.20\times10^{-8}=3.2\times10^{-8}\ mol\ C_2H_3Cl/L$$

$$\frac{3.20\times10^{-8}\ mol\ C_2H_3Cl}{1\,L}\times\frac{6.022\times10^{23}\ molecules}{1\,mol}=1.9\times10^{16}\ molecules/L$$

         Check. $(200\times10^{-8})/60=2.5\times10^{-8}\ mol$

                 $(2.5\times10^{-8})\times(6\times10^{23})=15\times10^{15}=1.5\times10^{16}$

3.42 $25\times10^{-6}\ g\ C_{21}H_{30}O_2\times\dfrac{1\,mol\ C_{21}H_{30}O_2}{314.5\,g\ C_{21}H_{30}O_2}=7.95\times10^{-8}=8.0\times10^{-8}\ mol\ C_{21}H_{30}O_2$

         $7.95\times10^{-8}\ mol\ C_{21}H_{30}O_2\times\dfrac{6.022\times10^{23}\ molecules}{1\,mol}=4.8\times10^{16}\ C_{21}H_{30}O_2\ molecules$

Empirical Formulas (section 3.5)

3.43   (a)   *Analyze.* Given: moles. Find: empirical formula.

             Plan. Find the **simplest ratio of moles** by dividing by the smallest number of moles present.

             Solve. 0.0130 mol C / 0.0065 = 2

                         0.0390 mol H / 0.0065 = 6

                         0.0065 mol O / 0.0065 = 1

             The empirical formula is C_2H_6O.

             Check. The subscripts are simple integers.

   (b)   *Analyze.* Given: grams. Find: empirical formula.

             Plan. Calculate the moles of each element present, then the simplest ratio of moles.

             Solve. $11.66\,g\ Fe\times\dfrac{1\,mol\ Fe}{55.85\,g\ Fe}=0.2088\ mol\ Fe;\ 0.2088/0.2088=1$

             $5.01\,g\ O\times\dfrac{1\,mol\ O}{16.00\,g\ O}=0.3131\ mol\ O;\ 0.3131/0.2088\approx1.5$

             Multiplying by two, the integer ratio is 2 Fe : 3 O; the empirical formula is Fe_2O_3.

             Check. The subscripts are simple integers.

   (c)   *Analyze.* Given: mass %. Find: empirical formulas.

             Plan. Assume 100 g sample, calculate moles of each element, find the simplest ratio of moles.

Solve. $40.0 \text{ g C} \times \dfrac{1 \text{ mol C}}{12.01 \text{ g C}} = 3.33 \text{ mol C}; \ 3.33 / 3.33 = 1$

$6.7 \text{ g H} \times \dfrac{1 \text{ mol H}}{1.008 \text{ mol H}} = 6.65 \text{ mol H}; \ 6.65 / 3.33 \approx 2$

$53.3 \text{ g O} \times \dfrac{1 \text{ mol O}}{16.00 \text{ mol O}} = 3.33 \text{ mol O}; \ 3.33 / 3.33 = 1$

The empirical formula is CH_2O.

Check. The subscripts are simple integers.

3.44   (a)   Calculate the simplest ratio of moles.

$0.104 \text{ mol K} / 0.052 = 2$

$0.052 \text{ mol C} / 0.052 = 1$

$0.156 \text{ mol O} / 0.052 = 3$

The empirical formula is K_2CO_3.

(b)   Calculate moles of each element present, then the simplest ratio of moles.

$5.28 \text{ g Sn} \times \dfrac{1 \text{ mol Sn}}{118.7 \text{ g Sn}} = 0.04448 \text{ mol Sn}; \ 0.04448 / 0.04448 = 1$

$3.37 \text{ g F} \times \dfrac{1 \text{ mol F}}{19.00 \text{ g FSn}} = 0.1774 \text{ mol F}; \ 0.1774 / 0.04448 \approx 4$

The integer ratio is $1 \text{ Sn} : 4 \text{ F}$; the empirical formula is SnF_4.

(c)   Assume 100 g sample, calculate moles of each element, find the simplest ratio of moles.

$87.5\% \text{ N} = 87.5 \text{ g N} \times \dfrac{1 \text{ mol N}}{14.01 \text{ g}} = 6.25 \text{ mol N}; \ 6.25 / 6.25 = 1$

$12.5\% \text{ H} = 12.5 \text{ g H} \times \dfrac{1 \text{ mol}}{1.008 \text{ g}} = 12.4 \text{ mol H}; \ 12.4 / 6.25 \approx 2$

The empirical formula is NH_2.

3.45   *Analyze/Plan.* The procedure in all these cases is to assume 100 g of sample, calculate the number of moles of each element present in that 100 g, then obtain the ratio of moles as smallest whole numbers.   *Solve.*

(a) $10.4 \text{ g C} \times \dfrac{1 \text{ mol C}}{12.01 \text{ g C}} = 0.866 \text{ mol C}; \ 0.866 / 0.866 = 1$

$27.8 \text{ g S} \times \dfrac{1 \text{ mol S}}{32.07 \text{ g S}} = 0.867 \text{ mol S}; \ 0.867 / 0.866 \approx 1$

$61.7 \text{ g Cl} \times \dfrac{1 \text{ mol Cl}}{35.45 \text{ g Cl}} = 1.74 \text{ mol Cl}; \ 1.74 / 0.866 \approx 2$

The empirical formula is $CSCl_2$.

(b) $21.7 \text{ g C} \times \dfrac{1 \text{ mol C}}{12.01 \text{ g C}} = 1.81 \text{ mol C}; \ 1.81 / 0.600 \approx 3$

$9.6 \text{ g O} \times \dfrac{1 \text{ mol O}}{16.00 \text{ g O}} = 0.600 \text{ mol O}; \ 0.600 / 0.600 = 1$

$$68.7 \text{ g F} \times \frac{1 \text{ mol F}}{19.00 \text{ g F}} = 3.62 \text{ mol F}; \quad 3.62 / 0.600 \approx 6$$

The empirical formula is C_3OF_6.

(c)   The mass of F is [100 g total – (32.79 g Na + 13.02 Al)] = 54.19 g F

$$32.79 \text{ g Na} \times \frac{1 \text{ mol Na}}{22.99 \text{ g Na}} = 1.426 \text{ mol Na}; \quad 1.426 / 0.4826 \approx 3$$

$$13.02 \text{ g Al} \times \frac{1 \text{ mol Al}}{26.98 \text{ g Al}} = 0.4826 \text{ mol Al}; \quad 0.4826 / 0.4826 = 1$$

$$54.19 \text{ g F} \times \frac{1 \text{ mol F}}{19.00 \text{ g F}} = 2.852 \text{ mol F}; \quad 2.852 / 0.4826 \approx 6$$

The empirical formula is Na_3AlF_6.

3.46   See Solution 3.45 for stepwise problem-solving approach.

(a) $55.3 \text{ g K} \times \dfrac{1 \text{ mol K}}{39.10 \text{ g K}} = 1.414 \text{ mol K}; 1.414/0.4714 \approx 3$

$14.6 \text{ g P} \times \dfrac{1 \text{ mol P}}{30.97 \text{ g P}} = 0.4714 \text{ mol P}; \ 0.4714/0.4714 = 1$

$30.1 \text{ g O} \times \dfrac{1 \text{ mol O}}{16.00 \text{ g O}} = 1.881 \text{ mol O}; \ 1.881/0.4714 \approx 4$

The empirical formula is K_3PO_4.

(b) $24.5 \text{ g Na} \times \dfrac{1 \text{ mol Na}}{22.99 \text{ g Na}} = 1.066 \text{ mol Na}; \ 1.066/0.5304 \approx 2$

$14.9 \text{ g Si} \times \dfrac{1 \text{ mol Si}}{28.09 \text{ Si}} = 0.5304 \text{ mol si}; \ 0.5304/0.5304 = 1$

$60.6 \text{ g F} \times \dfrac{1 \text{ mol F}}{19.00 \text{ g F}} = 3.189 \text{ mol F}; 3.189/0.5304 \approx 6$

The empirical formula is Na_2SiF_6.

(c)   The mass of O is [100 g total – (62.1 g C + 5.21 g H + 12.1 g N)] = 20.59 = 20.6 g O

$62.1 \text{ g C} \times \dfrac{1 \text{ mol C}}{12.01 \text{ g C}} = 5.17 \text{ mol C}; \ 5.17 / 0.864 \approx 6$

$5.21 \text{ g H} \times \dfrac{1 \text{ mol H}}{1.008 \text{ g H}} = 5.17 \text{ mol O}; \ 5.17 / 0.864 \approx 6$

$12.1 \text{ g N} \times \dfrac{1 \text{ mol N}}{14.01 \text{ g N}} = 0.864 \text{ mol N}; \ 0.864 / 0.864 = 1$

$20.6 \text{ g O} \times \dfrac{1 \text{ mol O}}{16.00 \text{ g O}} = 1.29 \text{ mol O}; \ 1.29 / 0.864 \approx 1.5$

Multiplying by two, the empirical formula is $C_{12}H_{12}N_2O_3$.

3.47   *Analyze.* Given: mass% F; empirical formula XF_3 implies 3:1 ratio of mol F to mol X. Find: atomic mass (AM) of X.

   Plan. Calculate mol F. This is 3 times mol X. mol X = 35 g X/AM X. mol F/3 = 35 g X/AM X. Solve for AM X.

   Solve. Mol F = 65/19.0 = 3.421 = 3.4; mol X = 3.421/3 = 1.14035 = 1.1

   1.14035 mol X = 35 g X/AM X; AM X = 35 g X/1.14035 mol X = 30.69 = 31 g/mol

3.48   Follow the logic in Exercise 3.47. Match the calculated atomic mass to that of an element.

   mol Cl = 75.0/35.453 = 2.1155 = 2.12; mol X = 2.1155/4 = 0.52887 = 0.529

   0.52887 mol X = 25.0 g X/AM X; AM X = 25.0 g X/0.52887 mol X = 47.271 = 47.3 g/mol

   The element with atomic mass closest to 47.3 is **Ti**, atomic mass = 47.867 g/mol.

3.49   *Analyze.* Given: empirical formula, molar mass. Find: molecular formula.

   Plan. Calculate the empirical formula weight (FW); divide FW by molar mass (MM) to calculate the integer that relates the empirical and molecular formulas. Check. If FW/MM is an integer, the result is reasonable. *Solve.*

   (a)   FW CH_2 = 12 + 2(1) = 14. $\dfrac{MM}{FW} = \dfrac{84}{14} = 6$

   The subscripts in the empirical formula are multiplied by 6. The molecular formula is C_6H_{12}.

   (b)   FW NH_2Cl = 14.01 + 2(1.008) + 35.45 = 51.48. $\dfrac{MM}{FW} = \dfrac{51.5}{51.5} = 1$

   The empirical and molecular formulas are NH_2Cl.

3.50   (a)   FW HCO_2 = 12.01 + 1.008 + 2(16.00) = 45.0 $\dfrac{MM}{FW} = \dfrac{90.0}{45.0} = 2$

   The molecular formula is $C_2H_2O_4$.

   (b)   FW C_2H_4O = 2(12) + 4(1) + 16 = 44. $\dfrac{MM}{FW} = \dfrac{88}{44} = 2$

   The molecular formula is $C_4H_8O_2$.

3.51   *Analyze.* Given: mass %, molar mass. Find: molecular formula.

   Plan. Use the plan detailed in Solution 3.45 to find an empirical formula from mass % data. Then use the plan detailed in 3.47 to find the molecular formula. Note that some indication of molar mass must be given, or the molecular formula cannot be determined. *Check.* If there is an integer ratio of moles and MM/ FW is an integer, the result is reasonable.   *Solve.*

   (a) $92.3 \text{ g C} \times \dfrac{1 \text{ mol C}}{12.01 \text{ g C}} = 7.685 \text{ mol C}$; 7.685/7.639 = 1.006 ≈ 1

   $7.7 \text{ g H} \times \dfrac{1 \text{ mol H}}{1.008 \text{ g H}} = 7.639 \text{ mol H}$; 7.639/7.639 = 1

   The empirical formula is CH, FW = 13.

$$\frac{MM}{FW} = \frac{104}{13} = 8; \text{ the molecular formula is } C_8H_8.$$

(b) $49.5 \, g \, C \times \dfrac{1 \, mol \, C}{12.01 \, g \, C} = 4.12 \, mol \, C; \quad 4.12/1.03 \approx 4$

$5.15 \, g \, H \times \dfrac{1 \, mol \, H}{1.008 \, g \, H} = 5.11 \, mol \, H; \quad 5.11/1.03 \approx 5$

$28.9 \, g \, N \times \dfrac{1 \, mol \, N}{14.01 \, g \, N} = 2.06 \, mol \, N; \quad 2.06/1.03 \approx 2$

$16.5 \, g \, O \times \dfrac{1 \, mol \, O}{16.00 \, g \, O} = 1.03 \, mol \, O; \quad 1.03/1.03 = 1$

Thus, $C_4H_5N_2O$, FW = 97. If the molar mass is about 195, a factor of 2 gives the molecular formula $C_8H_{10}N_4O_2$.

(c) $35.51 \, g \, C \times \dfrac{1 \, mol \, C}{12.01 \, g \, C} = 2.96 \, mol \, C; \quad 2.96/0.592 = 5$

$4.77 \, g \, H \times \dfrac{1 \, mol \, H}{1.008 \, g \, H} = 4.73 \, mol \, H; \quad 4.73/0.592 = 7.99 \approx 8$

$37.85 \, g \, O \times \dfrac{1 \, mol \, O}{16.00 \, g \, O} = 2.37 \, mol \, O; \quad 2.37/0.592 = 4$

$8.29 \, g \, N \times \dfrac{1 \, mol \, N}{14.01 \, g \, N} = 0.592 \, mol \, N; \quad 0.592/0.592 = 1$

$13.60 \, g \, Na \times \dfrac{1 \, mol \, Na}{22.99 \, g \, Na} = 0.592 \, mol \, Na; \quad 0.592/0.592 = 1$

The empirical formula is $C_5H_8O_4NNa$, FW = 169 g. Since the empirical formula weight and molar mass are approximately equal, the empirical and molecular formulas are both $NaC_5H_8O_4N$.

3.52 Assume 100 g in the following problems.

(a) $75.69 \, g \, C \times \dfrac{1 \, mol \, C}{12.01 \, g \, C} = 6.30 \, mol \, C; \quad 6.30/0.969 = 6.5$

$8.80 \, g \, H \times \dfrac{1 \, mol \, H}{1.008 \, g \, H} = 8.73 \, mol \, H; \quad 8.73/0.969 = 9.0$

$15.51 \, g \, O \times \dfrac{1 \, mol \, O}{16.00 \, g \, O} = 0.969 \, mol \, O; \quad 0.969/0.969 = 1$

Multiply by 2 to obtain the integer ratio 13:18:2. The empirical formula is $C_{13}H_{18}O_2$, FW = 206 g. Since the empirical formula weight and the molar mass are equal (206 g), the empirical and molecular formulas are $C_{13}H_{18}O_2$.

(b) $58.55 \, g \, C \times \dfrac{1 \, mol \, C}{12.01 \, g \, C} = 4.875 \, mol \, C; \quad 4.875/1.956 \approx 2.5$

$$13.81\,\text{g H} \times \frac{1\,\text{mol H}}{1.008\,\text{g H}} = 13.700\,\text{mol H}; \quad 13.700/1.956 \approx 7.0$$

$$27.40\,\text{g N} \times \frac{1\,\text{mol N}}{14.01\,\text{g N}} = 1.956\,\text{mol N}; \quad 1.956/1.956 = 1.0$$

Multiply by 2 to obtain the integer ratio 5:14:2. The empirical formula is $C_5H_{14}N_2$; FW = 102. Since the empirical formula weight and the molar mass are equal

(102 g), the empirical and molecular formulas are $C_5H_{14}N_2$.

(c) $\quad 59.0\,\text{g C} \times \dfrac{1\,\text{mol C}}{12.01\,\text{g C}} = 4.91\,\text{mol C}; \quad 4.91/0.550 \approx 9$

$$7.1\,\text{g H} \times \frac{1\,\text{mol H}}{1.008\,\text{g H}} = 7.04\,\text{mol H}; \quad 7.04/0.550 \approx 13$$

$$26.2\,\text{g O} \times \frac{1\,\text{mol O}}{16.00\,\text{g O}} = 1.64\,\text{mol O}; \quad 1.64/0.550 \approx 3$$

$$7.7\,\text{g N} \times \frac{1\,\text{mol N}}{14.01\,\text{g N}} = 0.550\,\text{mol N}; \quad 0.550/0.550 = 1$$

The empirical formula is $C_9H_{13}O_3N$, FW = 183 amu (or g). Since the molecular weight is approximately 180 amu, the empirical formula and molecular formula are the same, $C_9H_{13}O_3N$.

3.53 (a) *Analyze.* Given: mg CO_2, mg H_2O Find: empirical formula of hydrocarbon, C_xH_y

Plan. Upon combustion, all $C \rightarrow CO_2$, all $H \rightarrow H_2O$.

mg $CO_2 \rightarrow$ g $CO_2 \rightarrow$ mol C; mg $H_2O \rightarrow$ g H_2O, mol H

Find simplest ratio of moles and empirical formula. *Solve.*

$$5.86 \times 10^{-3}\,\text{g CO}_2 \times \frac{1\,\text{mol CO}_2}{44.01\,\text{g CO}_2} \times \frac{1\,\text{mol C}}{1\,\text{mol CO}_2} = 1.33 \times 10^{-4}\,\text{mol C}$$

$$1.37 \times 10^{-3}\,\text{g H}_2\text{O} \times \frac{1\,\text{mol H}_2\text{O}}{18.02\,\text{g H}_2\text{O}} \times \frac{2\,\text{mol H}}{1\,\text{mol H}_2\text{O}} = 1.52 \times 10^{-4}\,\text{mol H}$$

Dividing both values by 1.33×10^{-4} gives C:H of 1:1.14. This is not "close enough" to be considered 1:1. No obvious multipliers (2, 3, 4) produce an integer ratio. Testing other multipliers (trial and error!), the correct factor seems to be 7. The empirical formula is C_7H_8.

Check. See discussion of C:H ratio above.

(b) *Analyze.* Given: g of menthol, g CO_2, g H_2O, molar mass. Find: molecular formula.

Plan/Solve. Calculate mol C and mol H in the sample.

$$0.2829\,\text{g CO}_2 \times \frac{1\,\text{mol CO}_2}{44.01\,\text{g CO}_2} \times \frac{1\,\text{mol C}}{1\,\text{mol CO}_2} = 0.0064281 = 0.006428\,\text{mol C}$$

$$0.1159 \, \text{g H}_2\text{O} \times \frac{1 \, \text{mol H}_2\text{O}}{18.02 \, \text{g H}_2\text{O}} \times \frac{2 \, \text{mol H}}{1 \, \text{mol H}_2\text{O}} = 0.012863 = 0.01286 \, \text{mol H}$$

Calculate g C, g H and get g O by subtraction.

$$0.0064281 \, \text{mol C} \times \frac{12.01 \, \text{g C}}{1 \, \text{mol C}} = 0.07720 \, \text{g C}$$

$$0.012863 \, \text{mol H} \times \frac{1.008 \, \text{g H}}{1 \, \text{mol H}} = 0.01297 \, \text{g H}$$

mass O = 0.1005 g sample – (0.07720 g C + 0.01297 g H) = 0.01033 g O

Calculate mol O and find integer ratio of mol C: mol H: mol O.

$$0.01033 \, \text{g O} \times \frac{1 \, \text{mol O}}{16.00 \, \text{g O}} = 6.456 \times 10^{-4} \, \text{mol O}$$

Divide moles by 6.456×10^{-4}.

$$\text{C:} \, \frac{0.006428}{6.456 \times 10^{-4}} \approx 10; \quad \text{H:} \, \frac{0.01286}{6.456 \times 10^{-4}} \approx 20; \quad \text{O:} \, \frac{6.456 \times 10^{-4}}{6.456 \times 10^{-4}} = 1$$

The empirical formula is $C_{10}H_{20}O$.

$$\text{FW} = 10(12) + 20(1) + 16 = 156; \quad \frac{M}{\text{FW}} = \frac{156}{156} = 1$$

The molecular formula is the same as the empirical formula, $C_{10}H_{20}O$.

Check. The mass of O wasn't negative or greater than the sample mass; empirical and molecular formulas are reasonable.

3.54   (a)   *Plan.* Calculate mol C and mol H, then g C and g H; get g O by subtraction.

Solve.

$$6.32 \times 10^{-3} \, \text{g CO}_2 \times \frac{1 \, \text{mol CO}_2}{44.01 \, \text{g CO}_2} \times \frac{1 \, \text{mol C}}{1 \, \text{mol CO}_2} = 1.436 \times 10^{-4} = 1.44 \times 10^{-4} \, \text{mol C}$$

$$2.58 \times 10^{-3} \, \text{g H}_2\text{O} \times \frac{1 \, \text{mol H}_2\text{O}}{18.02 \, \text{g H}_2\text{O}} \times \frac{2 \, \text{mol H}}{1 \, \text{mol H}_2\text{O}} = 2.863 \times 10^{-4} = 2.86 \times 10^{-4} \, \text{mol H}$$

$$1.436 \times 10^{-4} \, \text{mol C} \times \frac{12.01 \, \text{g C}}{1 \, \text{mol C}} = 1.725 \times 10^{-3} \, \text{g C} = 1.73 \, \text{mg C}$$

$$2.863 \times 10^{-4} \, \text{mol H} \times \frac{1.008 \, \text{g H}}{1 \, \text{mol H}} = 2.886 \times 10^{-4} \, \text{g H} = 0.289 \, \text{mg H}$$

mass of O = 2.78 mg sample – (1.725 mg C + 0.289 mg H) = 0.77 mg O

$$0.77 \times 10^{-3} \, \text{g O} \times \frac{1 \, \text{mol O}}{16.00 \, \text{g O}} = 4.81 \times 10^{-5} \, \text{mol O}. \quad \text{Divide moles by } 4.81 \times 10^{-5}.$$

$$\text{C:} \, \frac{1.44 \times 10^{-4}}{4.81 \times 10^{-5}} \approx 3; \quad \text{H:} \, \frac{2.86 \times 10^{-4}}{4.81 \times 10^{-5}} \approx 6; \quad \text{O:} \, \frac{4.81 \times 10^{-5}}{4.81 \times 10^{-5}} = 1$$

The empirical formula is C_3H_6O.

   (b)   *Plan.* Calculate mol C and mol H, then g C and g H. In this case, get N by subtraction.   *Solve.*

$$14.242 \times 10^{-3} \text{ g CO}_2 \times \frac{1 \text{ mol CO}_2}{44.01 \text{ g CO}_2} \times \frac{1 \text{ mol C}}{1 \text{ mol CO}_2} = 3.2361 \times 10^{-4} \text{ mol C}$$

$$4.083 \times 10^{-3} \text{ g H}_2\text{O} \times \frac{1 \text{ mol H}_2\text{O}}{18.02 \text{ g H}_2\text{O}} \times \frac{2 \text{ mol H}}{1 \text{ mol H}_2\text{O}} = 4.5316 \times 10^{-4} = 4.532 \times 10^{-4} \text{ mol H}$$

$$3.2361 \times 10^{-4} \text{ g mol C} \times \frac{12.01 \text{ g C}}{1 \text{ mol H}} = 3.8866 \times 10^{-3} \text{ g C} = 3.8866 \text{ mg C}$$

$$4.532 \times 10^{-4} \text{ mol H} \times \frac{1.008 \text{ g H}}{1 \text{ mol H}} = 0.45683 \times 10^{-3} \text{ g H} = 0.4568 \text{ mg H}$$

mass of N = 5.250 mg sample – (3.8866 mg C + 0.4568 mg H) = 0.9066

$$= 0.907 \text{ mg N}$$

$$0.9066 \times 10^{-3} \text{ g N} \times \frac{1 \text{ mol N}}{14.01 \text{ g N}} = 6.47 \times 10^{-5} \text{ mol N. Divide moles by } 6.47 \times 10^{-5}.$$

$$\text{C}: \frac{3.24 \times 10^{-4}}{6.47 \times 10^{-5}} \approx 5; \quad \text{H}: \frac{4.53 \times 10^{-4}}{6.47 \times 10^{-5}} \approx 7; \quad \text{N}: \frac{6.47 \times 10^{-5}}{6.47 \times 10^{-5}} = 1$$

The empirical formula is C_5H_7N, FW = 81. A molar mass of 160 ± 5 indicates a factor of 2 and a molecular formula of $C_{10}H_{14}N_2$.

3.55   *Analyze.* Given: mass gain in H_2O absorber = mass of H_2O; mass gain in CO_2 absorber = mass CO_2; molecular model of valproic acid. Find: empirical formula of valproic acid from combustion data and compare to molecular formula from model.

Plan. Calculate mol C and mol H, then g C and g H; get g O by subtraction.

Solve.

$$0.403 \text{ g CO}_2 \times \frac{1 \text{ mol CO}_2}{44.01 \text{ g CO}_2} \times \frac{1 \text{ mol C}}{1 \text{ mol CO}_2} = 9.157 \times 10^{-3} = 9.16 \times 10^{-3} \text{ mol C}$$

$$0.166 \text{ g H}_2\text{O} \times \frac{1 \text{ mol H}_2\text{O}}{18.02 \text{ g H}_2\text{O}} \times \frac{2 \text{ mol H}}{1 \text{ mol H}_2\text{O}} = 0.018424 = 0.0184 \text{ mol H}$$

$$9.157 \times 10^{-3} \text{ mol C} \times \frac{12.01 \text{ g C}}{1 \text{ mol C}} = 0.10998 \text{ g C} = 0.110 \text{ g C}$$

$$0.018424 \text{ mol H} \times \frac{1.008 \text{ g H}}{1 \text{ mol H}} = 0.01857 \text{ g H} = 0.0186 \text{ g H}$$

mass of O = 0.165 mg sample – (0.10998 g C + 0.01857 mg H) = 0.03645 = 0.036 g O

$$0.03645 \text{ g O} \times \frac{1 \text{ mol O}}{16.00 \text{ g O}} = 2.278 \times 10^{-3} = 2.3 \times 10^{-3} \text{ mol O. Divide moles by } 2.278 \times 10^{-3}.$$

$$\text{C}: \frac{9.157 \times 10^{-3}}{2.278 \times 10^{-3}} \approx 4; \quad \text{H}: \frac{0.018424}{2.278 \times 10^{-3}} \approx 8; \quad \text{O}: \frac{2.278 \times 10^{-3}}{2.278 \times 10^{-3}} = 1$$

The empirical formula is C_4H_8O.

On the molecular model, there are 8 grey C atoms, 16 white H atoms, and 2 red O atoms. The molecular formula is $C_8H_{16}O_2$. Dividing by the common factor 2, the empirical formula is C_4H_8O, which matches the empirical formula derived from combustion data.

3.56   Follow the logic in Exercise 3.55.

$$0.374 \, g \, CO_2 \times \frac{1 \, mol \, CO_2}{44.01 \, g \, CO_2} \times \frac{1 \, mol \, C}{1 \, mol \, CO_2} = 8.498 \times 10^{-3} = 8.50 \times 10^{-3} \, mol \, C$$

$$0.102 \, g \, H_2O \times \frac{1 \, mol \, H_2O}{18.02 \, g \, H_2O} \times \frac{2 \, mol \, H}{1 \, mol \, H_2O} = 0.01132 = 0.0113 \, mol \, H$$

$$8.498 \times 10^{-3} \, mol \, C \times \frac{12.01 \, g \, C}{1 \, mol \, C} = 0.10206 \, g \, C = 0.102 \, g \, C$$

$$0.01132 \, mol \, H \times \frac{1.008 \, g \, H}{1 \, mol \, H} = 0.01141 \, g \, H = 0.0114 \, g \, H$$

mass of O = 0.2033 mg sample – (0.10206 g C + 0.01141 mg H) = 0.08983 = 0.090 g O

$$0.08983 \, g \, O \times \frac{1 \, mol \, O}{16.00 \, g \, O} = 5.614 \times 10^{-3} = 5.6 \times 10^{-3} \, mol \, O.$$ Divide moles by 5.614×10^{-3}.

$$C: \frac{8.498 \times 10^{-3}}{5.614 \times 10^{-3}} \approx 1.5; \quad H: \frac{0.01132}{5.614 \times 10^{-3}} \approx 2; \quad O: \frac{5.614 \times 10^{-3}}{5.614 \times 10^{-3}} = 1$$

Multiplying these ratios by 2 to obtain whole number subscripts. The empirical formula is $C_3H_4O_2$.

On the molecular model, there are 3 grey C atoms, 4 white H atoms, and 2 red O atoms. The molecular and empirical formulas are $C_3H_4O_2$.. The results from this combustion analysis support the conclusion that the material in the flask is propenoic acid.

3.57   *Analyze.* Given 2.558 g $Na_2CO_3 \cdot xH_2O$, 0.948 g Na_2CO_3. Find: x.

Plan. The reaction involved is $Na_2CO_3 \cdot xH_2O(s) \rightarrow Na_2CO_3(s) + xH_2O(g)$.

Calculate the mass of H_2O lost and then the mole ratio of Na_2CO_3 and H_2O.

Solve. g H_2O lost = 2.558 g sample – 0.948 g Na_2CO_3 = 1.610 g H_2O

$$0.948 \, g \, Na_2CO_3 \times \frac{1 \, mol \, Na_2CO_3}{106.0 \, g \, Na_2CO_3} = 0.00894 \, mol \, Na_2CO_3$$

$$1.610 \, g \, H_2O \times \frac{1 \, mol \, H_2O}{18.02 \, g \, H_2O} = 0.08935 \, mol \, H_2O$$

The formula is $Na_2CO_3 \cdot \underline{\mathbf{10}} \, H_2O$.

Check. x is an integer.

3.58   The reaction involved is $MgSO_4 \cdot xH_2O(s) \rightarrow MgSO_4(s) + xH_2O(g)$. First, calculate the number of moles of product $MgSO_4$; this is the same as the number of moles of starting hydrate.

$$2.472 \, g \, MgSO_4 \times \frac{1 \, mol \, MgSO_4}{120.4 \, g \, MgSO_4} \times \frac{1 \, mol \, MgSO_4 \cdot xH_2O}{1 \, mol \, MgSO_4} = 0.02053 \, mol \, MgSO_4 \cdot xH_2O$$

Thus, $$\frac{5.061 \, g \, MgSO_4 \cdot xH_2O}{0.02053} = 246.5 \, g/mol = FW \, of \, MgSO_4 \cdot xH_2O$$

FW of $MgSO_4 \cdot xH_2O$ = FW of $MgSO_4$ + x(FW of H_2O).

246.5 = 120.4 + x(18.02). x = 6.998. The hydrate formula is $MgSO_4 \cdot \underline{7}H_2O$.

Alternatively, we could calculate the number of moles of water represented by weight loss: (5.061 – 2.472) = 2.589 g H_2O lost.

$$2.589 \text{ g } H_2O \times \frac{1 \text{ mol } H_2O}{18.02 \text{ g } H_2O} = 0.1437 \text{ mol } H_2O; \quad \frac{\text{mol } H_2O}{\text{mol } MgSO_4} = \frac{0.1437}{0.02053} = 7.000$$

Again the correct formula is $MgSO_4 \cdot \underline{7}H_2O$.

Calculations Based on Chemical Equations (section 3.6)

3.59   The mole ratios implicit in the coefficients of a balanced chemical equation express the fundamental relationship between amounts of reactants and products. If the equation is not balanced, the mole ratios will be incorrect and lead to erroneous calculated amounts of products.

3.60   The **integer coefficients** immediately preceding each molecular formula in a chemical equation give information about relative numbers of moles of reactants and products involved in a reaction.

3.61 $Na_2SiO_3(s) + 8HF(aq) \rightarrow H_2SiF_6(aq) + 2NaF(aq) + 3H_2O(l)$

(a)   *Analyze.* Given: mol Na_2SiO_3. Find: mol HF. *Plan.* Use the mole ratio 8HF:1Na_2SiO_3 from the balanced equation to relate moles of the two reactants. *Solve.*

$$0.300 \text{ mol } Na_2SiO_3 \times \frac{8 \text{ mol HF}}{1 \text{ mol } Na_2SiO_3} = 2.40 \text{ mol HF}$$

Check. Mol HF should be greater than mol Na_2SiO_3.

(b)   *Analyze.* Given: mol HF. Find: g NaF. *Plan.* Use the mole ratio 2NaF:8HF to change mol HF to mol NaF, then molar mass to get NaF.   *Solve.*

$$0.500 \text{ mol HF} \times \frac{2 \text{ mol NaF}}{8 \text{ mol HF}} \times \frac{41.99 \text{ g NaF}}{1 \text{ mol NaF}} = 5.25 \text{ g NaF}$$

Check. (0.5/4) = 0.125; 0.13 × 42 > 4 g NaF

(c)   *Analyze.* Given: g HF Find: g Na_2SiO_3.

Plan. g HF $\rightarrow$ mol HF $\left(\dfrac{\text{mol}}{\text{ratio}}\right) \rightarrow$ mol $Na_2SiO_3 \rightarrow$ g Na_2SiO_3

The mole ratio is at the heart of every stoichiometry problem. Molar mass is used to change to and from grams.   *Solve.*

$$0.800 \text{ g HF} \times \frac{1 \text{ mol HF}}{20.01 \text{ g HF}} \times \frac{1 \text{ mol } Na_2SiO_3}{8 \text{ mol HF}} \times \frac{122.1 \text{ g } Na_2SiO_3}{1 \text{ mol } Na_2SiO_3} = 0.610 \text{ g } Na_2SiO_3$$

Check. 0.8 (120/160) < 0.75 mol

3.62 $4KO_2 + 2CO_2 \rightarrow 2K_2CO_3 + 3O_2$

(a) $0.400 \text{ mol } KO_2 \times \dfrac{3 \text{ mol } O_2}{4 \text{ mol } KO_2} = 0.300 \text{ mol } O_2$

(b) $7.50 \text{ g O}_2 \times \dfrac{1 \text{ mol O}_2}{32.00 \text{ g O}_2} \times \dfrac{4 \text{ mol KO}_2}{3 \text{ mol O}_2} \times \dfrac{71.10 \text{ g KO}_2}{1 \text{ mol KO}_2} = 22.2 \text{ g KO}_2$

(c) $7.50 \text{ g O}_2 \times \dfrac{1 \text{ mol O}_2}{32.00 \text{ g O}_2} \times \dfrac{2 \text{ mol CO}_2}{3 \text{ mol O}_2} \times \dfrac{44.01 \text{ g CO}_2}{1 \text{ mol CO}_2} = 6.88 \text{ g CO}_2$

3.63   (a) $Al(OH)_3(s) + 3HCl(aq) \rightarrow AlCl_3(aq) + 3H_2O(l)$

       (b)   *Analyze.* Given mass of one reactant, find stoichiometric mass of other reactant and products.

           Plan. Follow the logic in Sample Exercise 3.16. Calculate mol $Al(OH)_3$ in 0.500 g $Al(OH_3)_3$ separately, since it will be used several times.

           Solve. $0.500 \text{ g Al(OH)}_3 \times \dfrac{1 \text{ mol Al(OH)}_3}{78.00 \text{ g Al(OH)}_3} = 6.410 \times 10^{-3} = 6.41 \times 10^{-3} \text{ mol Al(OH)}_3$

           $6.410 \times 10^{-3} \text{ mol Al(OH)}_3 \times \dfrac{3 \text{ mol HCl}}{1 \text{ mol Al(OH)}_3} \times \dfrac{36.46 \text{ g HCl}}{1 \text{ mol HCl}} = 0.7012 = 0.701 \text{ g HCl}$

       (c) $6.410 \times 10^{-3} \text{ mol Al(OH)}_3 \times \dfrac{1 \text{ mol HCl}}{1 \text{ mol Al(OH)}_3} \times \dfrac{133.34 \text{ g AlCl}_3}{1 \text{ mol AlCl}_3} = 0.8547$

                                                                              $= 0.855 \text{ g AlCl}_3$

           $6.410 \times 10^{-3} \text{ mol Al(OH)}_3 \times \dfrac{3 \text{ mol H}_2\text{O}}{1 \text{ mol Al(OH)}_3} \times \dfrac{18.02 \text{ g H}_2\text{O}}{1 \text{ mol H}_2\text{O}} = 0.3465 = 0.347 \text{ g H}_2\text{O}$

       (d)   Conservation of mass: mass of products = mass of reactants

           reactants: $Al(OH)_3$ + HCl, 0.500 g + 0.701 g = 1.201 g

           products: $AlCl_3$ + H_2O, 0.855 g + 0.347 g = 1.202 g

           The 0.001 g difference is due to rounding (0.8547 + 0.3465 = 1.2012). This is an excellent *check* of results.

3.64   (a) $Fe_2O_3(s) + 3CO(g) \rightarrow 2Fe(s) + 3CO_2(g)$

       (b) $0.350 \text{ kg Fe}_2\text{O}_3 \times \dfrac{1000 \text{ g}}{1 \text{ kg}} \times \dfrac{1 \text{ mol Fe}_2\text{O}_3}{159.688 \text{ g Fe}_2\text{O}_3} = 2.1918 = 2.19 \text{ mol Fe}_2\text{O}_3$

           $2.1918 \text{ mol Fe}_2\text{O}_3 \times \dfrac{3 \text{ mol CO}}{1 \text{ mol Fe}_2\text{O}_3} \times \dfrac{28.01 \text{ g CO}}{1 \text{ mol CO}} = 184.17 = 184 \text{ g CO}$

       (c) $2.1918 \text{ mol Fe}_2\text{O}_3 \times \dfrac{2 \text{ mol Fe}}{1 \text{ mol Fe}_2\text{O}_3} \times \dfrac{55.845 \text{ g Fe}}{1 \text{ mol Fe}} = 244.80 = 245 \text{ g Fe}$

           $2.1918 \text{ mol Fe}_2\text{O}_3 \times \dfrac{3 \text{ mol CO}_2}{1 \text{ mol Fe}_2\text{O}_3} \times \dfrac{44.01 \text{ g CO}_2}{1 \text{ mol CO}_2} = 289.38 = 289 \text{ g CO}_2$

       (d)   reactants: 350 g Fe_2O_3 + 184.17 g CO = 534.17 = 534 g

           products: 244.80 g Fe + 289.38 g CO_2 = 534.18 = 534 g

           Mass is conserved.

3.65   (a) $Al_2S_3(s) + 6H_2O(l) \rightarrow 2Al(OH)_3(s) + 3H_2S(g)$

         (b)   *Plan.* g A $\rightarrow$ mol A $\rightarrow$ mol B $\rightarrow$ g B. See Solution 3.61 (c).   *Solve.*

$$14.2 \text{ g } Al_2S_3 \times \frac{1 \text{ mol } Al_2S_3}{150.2 \text{ g } Al_2S_3} \times \frac{2 \text{ mol } Al(OH)_3}{1 \text{ mol } Al_2S_3} \times \frac{78.00 \text{ g } Al(OH)_3}{1 \text{ mol } Al(OH)_3} = 14.7 \text{ g } Al(OH)_3$$

               Check. $14\left(\dfrac{2 \times 78}{150}\right) \approx 14(1) \approx 14 \text{ g } Al(OH)_3$

3.66   (a) $CaH_2(s) + 2H_2O(l) \rightarrow Ca(OH)_2(aq) + 2H_2(g)$

         (b) $4.500 \text{ g } H_2 \times \dfrac{1 \text{ mol } H_2}{2.016 \text{ g } H_2} \times \dfrac{1 \text{ mol } CaH_2}{2 \text{ mol } H_2} \times \dfrac{42.10 \text{ g } CaH_2}{1 \text{ mol } CaH_2} = 46.99 \text{ g } CaH_2$

3.67   (a)   *Analyze.* Given: mol NaN_3. Find: mol N_2.

               Plan. Use mole ratio from balanced equation.   *Solve.*

$$1.50 \text{ mol } NaN_3 \times \frac{3 \text{ mol } N_2}{2 \text{ mol } NaN_3} = 2.25 \text{ mol } N_2$$

               Check. The resulting mol N_2 should be greater than mol NaN_3, (the $N_2:NaN_3$ ratio is > 1), and it is.

         (b)   *Analyze.* Given: g N_2 Find: g NaN_3.

               Plan. Use molar masses to get from and to grams, mol ratio to relate moles of the two substances.   *Solve.*

$$10.0 \text{ g } N_2 \times \frac{1 \text{ mol } N_2}{28.01 \text{ g } N_2} \times \frac{2 \text{ mol } NaN_3}{3 \text{ mol } N_2} \times \frac{65.01 \text{ g } NaN_3}{1 \text{ mol } NaN_3} = 15.5 \text{ g } NaN_3$$

               Check. Mass relations are less intuitive than mole relations. Estimating the ratio of molar masses is sometimes useful. In this case, 65 g NaN_3/28 g $N_2 \approx 2.25$ Then, $(10 \times 2/3 \times 2.25) \approx 15$ g NaN_3. The calculated result looks reasonable.

         (c)   *Analyze.* Given: vol N_2 in ft^3, density N_2 in g/L. Find: g NaN_3.

               Plan. First determine how many g N_2 are in 10.0 ft^3, using the density of N_2. Then proceed as in part (b).

               Solve.

$$\frac{1.25 \text{ g}}{1 \text{ L}} \times \frac{1 \text{ L}}{1000 \text{ cm}^3} \times \frac{(2.54)^3 \text{ cm}^3}{1 \text{ in}^3} \times \frac{(12)^3 \text{ in}^3}{1 \text{ ft}^3} \times 10.0 \text{ ft}^3 = 354.0 = 354 \text{ g } N_2$$

$$354.0 \text{ g } N_2 \times \frac{1 \text{ mol } N_2}{28.01 \text{ g } N_2} \times \frac{2 \text{ mol } NaN_3}{3 \text{ mol } N_2} \times \frac{65.01 \text{ g } NaN_3}{1 \text{ mol } NaN_3} = 548 \text{ g } NaN_3$$

               Check. 1 $ft^3 \sim$ 28 L; 10 $ft^3 \sim$ 280 L; 280 L $\times$ 1.25 $\sim$ 350 g N_2

               Using the ratio of molar masses from part (b), $(350 \times 2/3 \times 2.25) \approx 525$ g NaN_3

3.68 $2C_8H_{18}(l) + 25O_2(g) \rightarrow 16CO_2(g) + 18H_2O(l)$

         (a) $1.50 \text{ mol } C_8H_{18} \times \dfrac{25 \text{ mol } O_2}{2 \text{ mol } C_8H_{18}} = 18.75 = 18.8 \text{ mol } O_2$

(b) $10.0 \, g \, C_8H_{18} \times \dfrac{1 \, mol \, C_8H_{18}}{114.2 \, g \, C_8H_{18}} \times \dfrac{25 \, mol \, O_2}{2 \, mol \, C_8H_{18}} \times \dfrac{32.00 \, g \, O_2}{1 \, mol \, O_2} = 35.0 \, g \, O_2$

(c) $15.0 \, gal \, C_8H_{18} \times \dfrac{3.7854 \, L}{1 \, gal} \times \dfrac{1000 \, mL}{1 \, L} \times \dfrac{0.692 \, g}{1 \, mL} = 39{,}292 = 3.93 \times 10^4 \, g \, C_8H_{18}$

$3.9292 \times 10^4 \, g \, C_8H_{18} \times \dfrac{1 \, mol \, C_8H_{18}}{114.2 \, g \, C_8H_{18}} \times \dfrac{25 \, mol \, O_2}{2 \, mol \, C_8H_{18}} \times \dfrac{32.00 \, g \, O_2}{1 \, mol \, O_2} = 137{,}627 \, g$

$= 1.38 \times 10^5 \, g \, O_2$

(d) $3.9292 \times 10^4 \, g \, C_8H_{18} \times \dfrac{1 \, mol \, C_8H_{18}}{114.2 \, g \, C_8H_{18}} \times \dfrac{16 \, mol \, CO_2}{2 \, mol \, C_8H_{18}} \times \dfrac{44.01 \, g \, O_2}{1 \, mol \, O_2} = 121{,}139 \, g$

$= 1.21 \times 10^5 \, g \, CO_2$

3.69   (a)   *Analyze.* Given: dimensions of Al foil. Find: mol Al.

Plan. Dimensions $\rightarrow$ vol $\xrightarrow{\text{density}}$ mass $\xrightarrow{\frac{\text{molar}}{\text{mass}}}$ mol Al

Solve. $1.00 \, cm \times 1.00 \, cm \times 0.550 \, mm \times \dfrac{1 \, cm}{10 \, mm} = 0.0550 \, cm^3 \, Al$

$0.0550 \, cm^3 \, Al \times \dfrac{2.699 \, g \, Al}{1 \, cm^3} \times \dfrac{1 \, mol \, Al}{26.98 \, g \, Al} = 5.502 \times 10^{-3} = 5.50 \times 10^{-3} \, mol \, Al$

Check. $2.699 / 26.98 \approx 0.1$; $(0.055 \, cm^3 \times 0.1) = 5.5 \times 10^{-3} \, mol \, Al$

(b)   *Plan.* Write the balanced equation to get a mole ratio; change mol Al $\rightarrow$ mol $AlBr_3 \rightarrow$ g $AlBr_3$.

Solve. $2Al(s) + 3Br_2(l) \rightarrow 2AlBr_3(s)$

$5.502 \times 10^{-3} \, mol \, Al \times \dfrac{2 \, mol \, AlBr_3}{2 \, mol \, Al} \times \dfrac{266.69 \, g \, AlBr_3}{1 \, mol \, AlBr_3} = 1.467 = 1.47 \, g \, AlBr_3$

Check. $(0.006 \times 1 \times 270) \approx 1.6 \, g \, AlBr_3$

3.70   (a)   *Plan.* Calculate a "mole ratio" between nitroglycerine and total moles of gas produced. $(12 + 6 + 1 + 10) = 29$ mol gas; 4 mol nitro: 29 total mol gas.   *Solve.*

$2.00 \, mL \, nitro \times \dfrac{1.592 \, g}{mL} \times \dfrac{1 \, mol \, nitro}{227.1 \, g \, nitro} \times \dfrac{29 \, mol \, gas}{4 \, mol \, nitro} = 0.10165 = 0.102 \, mol \, gas$

(b) $0.10165 \, mol \, gas \times \dfrac{55 \, L}{mol} = 5.5906 = 5.6 \, L$

(c) $2.00 \, mL \, nitro \times \dfrac{1.592 \, g}{mL} \times \dfrac{1 \, mol \, nitro}{227.1 \, g \, nitro} \times \dfrac{6 \, mol \, N_2}{4 \, mol \, nitro} \times \dfrac{28.01 \, g \, N_2}{1 \, mol \, N_2} = 0.589 \, g \, N_2$

Limiting Reactants; Theoretical Yields (section 3.7)

3.71   (a)   The *limiting reactant* determines the maximum number of product moles resulting from a chemical reaction; any other reactant is an *excess reactant*.

(b)   The limiting reactant regulates the amount of products, because it is completely used up during the reaction; no more product can be made when one of the reactants is unavailable.

(c)   Combining ratios are molecule and mole ratios. Since different molecules have different masses, equal masses of different reactants will not have equal numbers of molecules. By comparing initial moles, we compare numbers of available reactant molecules, the fundamental combining units in a chemical reaction.

3.72   (a)   *Theoretical yield* is the maximum amount of product possible, as predicted by stoichiometry, assuming that the limiting reactant is converted entirely to product.

                Actual yield is the amount of product actually obtained, less than or equal to the theoretical yield. *Percent yield* is the ratio of (actual yield to theoretical yield) × 100.

      (b)   No reaction is perfect. Not all reactant molecules come together effectively to form products; alternative reaction pathways may produce secondary products and reduce the amount of desired product actually obtained, or it might not be possible to completely isolate the desired product from the reaction mixture. In any case, these factors reduce the actual yield of a reaction.

      (c)   No, 110% actual yield is not possible. Theoretical yield is the maximum possible amount of pure product, assuming all available limiting reactant is converted to product, and that all product is isolated. If an actual yield of 110% if obtained, the product must contain impurities which increase the experimental mass.

3.73   (a)   Each bicycle needs 2 wheels, 1 frame, and 1 set of handlebars. A total of 4815 wheels corresponds to 2407.5 pairs of wheels. This is more than the number of frames or handlebars. The 2255 handlebars determine that 2255 bicycles can be produced.

      (b)   2305 frames – 2255 bicycles = 50 frames left over

                2407.5 pairs of wheels – 2255 bicycles = 152.5 pairs of wheels left over 2(152.5) = 305 wheels left over

      (c)   The handlebars are the "limiting reactant" in that they determine the number of bicycles that can be produced.

3.74   (a) $48{,}775 \text{ L beverage} \times \dfrac{1 \text{ bottle}}{0.355 \text{ L}} = 137{,}394.37 = 1.37 \times 10^5 \text{ portions of beverage}$

                (The uncertainty in 355 mL limits the precision of the number of portions we can reasonably expect to deliver to three significant figures.)

                126,515 bottles; 108,500 caps; 1.09×10^5 bottles can be filled and capped.

      (b)   126,515 empty bottles – 108,500 caps = 18,015 bottles remain

                137,394 portions – 108,500 caps =28,894 = 2.89×10^4 portions remain

                (Uncertainty in the number of portions available limits the results to 3 sig fig.)

      (c)   The caps limit production.

3.75   *Analyze.* Given: 1.85 mol NaOH, 1.00 mol CO_2. Find: mol Na_2CO_3.

Plan. Amounts of more than one reactant are given, so we must determine which reactant regulates (limits) product. Then apply the appropriate mole ratio from the balanced equation.

Solve. The mole ratio is $2NaOH:1CO_2$, so 1.00 mol CO_2 requires 2.00 mol NaOH for complete reaction. Less than 2.00 mol NaOH are present, so NaOH is the limiting reactant.

$$1.85 \text{ mol NaOH} \times \frac{1 \text{ mol } Na_2CO_3}{2 \text{ mol NaOH}} = 0.925 \text{ mol } Na_2CO_3 \text{ can be produced}$$

The $Na_2CO_3:CO_2$ ratio is 1:1, so 0.925 mol Na_2CO_3 produced requires 0.925 mol CO_2 consumed. (Alternately, 1.85 mol NaOH × 1 mol CO_2/2 mol NaOH = 0.925 mol CO_2 reacted). 1.00 mol CO_2 initial – 0.925 mol CO_2 reacted = 0.075 mol CO_2 remain.

Check.	$2NaOH(s)$	$+$	$CO_2(g)$	$\rightarrow$	$Na_2CO_3(s)$	$+$	$H_2O(l)$
initial	1.85 mol		1.00 mol		0 mol		
change (reaction)	–1.85 mol		–0.925 mol		+0.925 mol		
final	0 mol		0.075 mol		0.925 mol		

Note that the "change" line (but not necessarily the "final" line) reflects the mole ratios from the balanced equation.

3.76 $$0.500 \text{ mol Al(OH)}_3 \times \frac{3 \text{ mol } H_2SO_4}{2 \text{ mol Al(OH)}_3} = 0.750 \text{ mol } H_2SO_4 \text{ needed for complete reaction}$$

Only 0.500 mol H_2SO_4 available, so H_2SO_4 limits.

$$0.500 \text{ mol } H_2SO_4 \times \frac{1 \text{ mol } Al_2(SO_4)_3}{3 \text{ mol } H_2SO_4} = 0.1667 = 0.167 \text{ mol } Al_2(SO_4)_3 \text{ can form}$$

$$0.500 \text{ mol } H_2SO_4 \times \frac{2 \text{ mol Al(OH)}_3}{3 \text{ mol } H_2SO_4} = 0.3333 = 0.333 \text{ mol Al(OH)}_3 \text{ react}$$

0.500 mol Al(OH)$_3$ initial – 0.333 mol react = 0.167 mol Al(OH)$_3$ remain

3.77 $3NaHCO_3(aq) + H_3C_6H_5O_7(aq) \rightarrow 3CO_2(g) + 3H_2O(l) + Na_3C_6H_5O_7(aq)$

(a)   *Analyze/Plan.* Abbreviate citric acid as H_3Cit. Follow the approach in Sample Exercise 3.19. *Solve.*

$$1.00 \text{ g NaHCO}_3 \times \frac{1 \text{ mol NaHCO}_3}{84.01 \text{ g NaHCO}_3} = 1.190 \times 10^{-2} = 1.19 \times 10^{-2} \text{ mol NaHCO}_3$$

$$1.00 \text{ g } H_3C_6H_5O_7 \times \frac{1 \text{ mol } H_3Cit}{192.1 \text{ g } H_3Cit} = 5.206 \times 10^{-3} = 5.21 \times 10^{-3} \text{ mol } H_3Cit$$

But $NaHCO_3$ and H_3Cit react in a 3:1 ratio, so 5.21×10^{-3} mol H_3Cit require $3(5.21 \times 10^{-3}) = 1.56 \times 10^{-2}$ mol $NaHCO_3$. We have only 1.19×10^{-2} mol $NaHCO_3$, so $NaHCO_3$ is the limiting reactant.

(b) 1.190×10^{-2} mol $NaHCO_3 \times \dfrac{3\,mol\,CO_2}{3\,mol\,NaHCO_3} \times \dfrac{44.01\,g\,CO_2}{1\,mol\,CO_2} = 0.524\,g\,CO_2$

(c) 1.190×10^{-2} mol $NaHCO_3 \times \dfrac{1\,mol\,H_3Cit}{3\,mol\,NaHCO_3} = 3.968 \times 10^{-3}$

$$= 3.97 \times 10^{-3} \text{ mol } H_3Cit \text{ react}$$

$$5.206 \times 10^{-3} \text{ mol } H_3Cit - 3.968 \times 10^{-3} \text{ mol react} = 1.238 \times 10^{-3}$$

$$= 1.24 \times 10^{-3} \text{ mol } H_3Cit \text{ remain}$$

$$1.238 \times 10^{-3} \text{ mol } H_3Cit \times \dfrac{192.1\,g\,H_3Cit}{mol\,H_3Cit} = 0.238 \text{ g } H_3Cit \text{ remain}$$

3.78 $4NH_3(g) + 5O_2(g) \rightarrow 4NO(g) + 6H_2O(g)$

(a)   Follow the approach in Sample Exercise 3.19.

$$2.00 \text{ g } NH_3 \times \dfrac{1\,mol\,NH_3}{17.03\,g\,NH_3} = 0.11744 = 0.117 \text{ mol } NH_3$$

$$2.50 \text{ g } O_2 \times \dfrac{1\,mol\,O_2}{32.00\,g\,O_2} = 0.07813 = 0.0781 \text{ mol } O_2$$

$$0.07813 \text{ mol } O_2 \times \dfrac{4\,mol\,NH_3}{5\,mol\,O_2} = 0.06250 = 0.0625 \text{ mol } NH_3 \text{ required}$$

More than 0.0625 mol NH_3 is available, so O_2 is the limiting reactant.

(b) 0.07813 mol $O_2 \times \dfrac{4\,mol\,NO}{5\,mol\,O_2} \times \dfrac{30.01\,g\,NO}{1\,mol\,NO} = 1.8756 = 1.88 \text{ g NO produced}$

$$0.07813 \text{ mol } O_2 \times \dfrac{6\,mol\,H_2O}{5\,mol\,O_2} \times \dfrac{18.02\,g\,H_2O}{1\,mol\,H_2O} = 1.6894 = 1.69 \text{ g } H_2O \text{ produced}$$

(c) 0.11744 mol $NH_3 - 0.0625$ mol NH_3 reacted $= 0.05494 = 0.0549$ mol NH_3 remain

$$0.05494 \text{ mol } NH_3 \times \dfrac{17.03\,g\,NH_3}{1\,mol\,NH_3} = 0.93563 = 0.936 \text{ g } NH_3 \text{ remain}$$

(d)   mass products = 1.8756 g NO + 1.6894 g H_2O + 0.9356 g NH_3 remaining = 4.50g products

mass reactants = 2.00 g NH_3 + 2.50 g O_2 = 4.50 g reactants

(For comparison purposes, the mass of excess reactant can be either added to the products, as above, or subtracted from reactants.)

3.79   *Analyze.* Given: initial g Na_2CO_3, g $AgNO_3$. Find: final g Na_2CO_3, $AgNO_3$, Ag_2CO_3, $NaNO_3$

Plan. Write balanced equation; determine limiting reactant; calculate amounts of excess reactant remaining and products, based on limiting reactant.

Solve. $2AgNO_3(aq) + Na_2CO_3(aq) \rightarrow Ag_2CO_3(s) + 2NaNO_3(aq)$

$$3.50 \text{ g Na}_2\text{CO}_3 \times \frac{1 \text{ mol Na}_2\text{CO}_3}{106.0 \text{ g Na}_2\text{CO}_3} = 0.03302 = 0.0330 \text{ mol Na}_2\text{CO}_3$$

$$5.00 \text{ g AgNO}_3 \times \frac{1 \text{ mol AgNO}_3}{169.9 \text{ g AgNO}_3} = 0.02943 = 0.0294 \text{ mol AgNO}_3$$

$$0.02943 \text{ mol AgNO}_3 \times \frac{1 \text{ mol Na}_2\text{CO}_3}{2 \text{ mol AgNO}_3} = 0.01471 = 0.0147 \text{ mol Na}_2\text{CO}_3 \text{ required}$$

$AgNO_3$ is the limiting reactant and Na_2CO_3 is present in excess.

	$2AgNO_3(aq)$	+	$Na_2CO_3(aq)$	$\rightarrow$	$Ag_2CO_3(s)$	+	$2NaNO_3(aq)$
initial	0.0294 mol		0.0330 mol		0 mol		0 mol
reaction	–0.0294 mol		–0.0147 mol		+0.0147 mol		+0.0294 mol
final	0 mol		0.0183 mol		0.0147 mol		0.0294 mol

$0.01830 \text{ mol Na}_2\text{CO}_3 \times 106.0 \text{ g/mol} = 1.940 = 1.94 \text{ g Na}_2\text{CO}_3$

$0.01471 \text{ mol Ag}_2\text{CO}_3 \times 275.8 \text{ g/mol} = 4.057 = 4.06 \text{ g Ag}_2\text{CO}_3$

$0.02943 \text{ mol NaNO}_3 \times 85.00 \text{ g/mol} = 2.502 = 2.50 \text{ g NaNO}_3$

Check. The initial mass of reactants was 8.50 g, and the final mass of excess reactant and products is 8.50 g; mass is conserved.

3.80   *Plan.* Write balanced equation; determine limiting reactant; calculate amounts of excess reactant remaining and products, based on limiting reactant.

Solve. $H_2SO_4(aq) + Pb(C_2H_3O_2)_2(aq) \rightarrow PbSO_4(s) + 2HC_2H_3O_2(aq)$

$$5.00 \text{ g H}_2\text{SO}_4 \times \frac{1 \text{ mol H}_2\text{SO}_4}{98.09 \text{ g H}_2\text{SO}_4} = 0.05097 = 0.0510 \text{ mol H}_2\text{SO}_4$$

$$5.00 \text{ g Pb(C}_2\text{H}_3\text{O}_2)_2 \times \frac{1 \text{ mol Pb(C}_2\text{H}_3\text{O}_2)_2}{325.3 \text{ g Pb(C}_2\text{H}_3\text{O}_2)_2} = 0.015370 = 0.0154 \text{ mol Pb(C}_2\text{H}_3\text{O}_2)_2$$

1 mol H_2SO_4:1 mol $Pb(C_2H_3O_2)_2$, so $Pb(C_2H_3O_2)_2$ is the limiting reactant.

0 mol $Pb(C_2H_3O_2)_2$, (0.05097 – 0.01537) = 0.0356 mol H_2SO_4, 0.0154 mol $PbSO_4$,

(0.01537 × 2) = 0.0307 mol $HC_2H_3O_2$ are present after reaction

$0.03560 \text{ mol H}_2\text{SO}_4 \times 98.09 \text{ g/mol} = 3.4920 = 3.49 \text{ g H}_2\text{SO}_4$

$0.01537 \text{ mol PbSO}_4 \times 303.3 \text{ g/mol} = 4.6619 = 4.66 \text{ g PbSO}_4$

$0.03074 \text{ mol HC}_2\text{H}_3\text{O}_2 \times 60.05 \text{ g/mol} = 1.8460 = 1.85 \text{ g HC}_2\text{H}_3\text{O}_2$

Check. The initial mass of reactants was 10.00 g; and the final mass of excess reactant and products is 10.00 g; mass is conserved.

3.81   *Analyze.* Given: amounts of two reactants. Find: theoretical yield.

Plan. Determine the limiting reactant and the maximum amount of product it could produce. Then calculate % yield.   *Solve.*

(a) $30.0 \text{ g C}_6\text{H}_6 \times \dfrac{1 \text{ mol C}_6\text{H}_6}{78.11 \text{ g C}_6\text{H}_6} = 0.3841 = 0.384 \text{ mol C}_6\text{H}_6$

$65.0 \text{ g Br}_2 \times \dfrac{1 \text{ mol Br}_2}{159.8 \text{ g Br}_2} = 0.4068 = 0.407 \text{ mol Br}_2$

Since C_6H_6 and Br_2 react in a 1:1 mole ratio, C_6H_6 is the limiting reactant and determines the theoretical yield.

$0.3841 \text{ mol C}_6\text{H}_6 \times \dfrac{1 \text{ mol C}_6\text{H}_5\text{Br}}{1 \text{ mol C}_6\text{H}_6} \times \dfrac{157.0 \text{ g C}_6\text{H}_5\text{Br}}{1 \text{ mol C}_6\text{H}_5\text{Br}} = 60.30 = 60.3 \text{ g C}_6\text{H}_5\text{Br}$

Check. $30/78 \sim 3/8$ mol C_6H_6. $65/160 \sim 3/8$ mol Br_2. Since moles of the two reactants are similar, a precise calculation is needed to determine the limiting reactant. $3/8 \times 160 \approx 60$ g product

(b) $\% \text{ yield} = \dfrac{42.3 \text{ g C}_6\text{H}_5\text{Br actual}}{60.3 \text{ g C}_6\text{H}_5\text{Br theoretical}} \times 100 = 70.149 = 70.10\%$

3.82   (a) $C_2H_6 + Cl_2 \rightarrow C_2H_5Cl + HCl$

$125 \text{ g C}_2\text{H}_6 \times \dfrac{1 \text{ mol C}_2\text{H}_6}{30.07 \text{ g C}_2\text{H}_6} = 4.157 = 4.16 \text{ mol C}_2\text{H}_6$

$255 \text{ g Cl}_2 \times \dfrac{1 \text{ mol Cl}_2}{70.91 \text{ g Cl}_2} = 3.596 = 3.60 \text{ mol Cl}_2$

Since the reactants combine in a 1:1 mole ratio, Cl_2 is the limiting reactant. The theoretical yield is:

$3.596 \text{ mol Cl}_2 \times \dfrac{1 \text{ mol C}_2\text{H}_5\text{Cl}}{1 \text{ mol Cl}_2} \times \dfrac{64.51 \text{ g C}_2\text{H}_5\text{Cl}}{1 \text{ mol C}_2\text{H}_5\text{Cl}} = 231.98 = 232 \text{ g C}_2\text{H}_5\text{Cl}$

(b) $\% \text{ yield} = \dfrac{206 \text{ g C}_2\text{H}_5\text{Cl actual}}{232 \text{ g C}_2\text{H}_5\text{Cl theoretical}} \times 100 = 88.8\%$

3.83   *Analyze.* Given: g of two reactants, % yield. Find: g S_8.

Plan. Determine limiting reactant and theoretical yield. Use definition of % yield to calculate actual yield.   *Solve.*

$30.0 \text{ g H}_2\text{S} \times \dfrac{1 \text{ mol H}_2\text{S}}{34.08 \text{ g H}_2\text{S}} = 0.8803 = 0.880 \text{ mol H}_2\text{S}$

$50.0 \text{ g O}_2 \times \dfrac{1 \text{ mol O}_2}{32.00 \text{ g H}_2\text{S}} = 1.5625 = 1.56 \text{ mol O}_2$

$0.8803 \text{ mol H}_2\text{S} \times \dfrac{4 \text{ mol O}_2}{8 \text{ mol H}_2\text{S}} = 0.4401 = 0.440 \text{ mol O}_2 \text{ required}$

Since there is more than enough O_2 to react exactly with 0.880 mol H_2S, O_2 is present in excess and H_2S is the limiting reactant.

$0.8803 \text{ mol H}_2\text{S} \times \dfrac{1 \text{ mol S}_8}{8 \text{ mol H}_2\text{S}} \times \dfrac{256.56 \text{ g S}_8}{1 \text{ mol S}_8} = 28.231 = 28.2 \text{ g S}_8 \text{ theoretical yield}$

Check. $30/34 \approx 1$ mol H_2S; $50/32 \approx 1.5$ mol O_2. Twice as many mol H_2S as mol O_2 are required, so H_2S limits. $1 \times (260/8) \approx 30$ g S_8 theoretical.

$$\% \text{ yield} = \frac{\text{actual}}{\text{theoretical}} \times 100; \quad \frac{\% \text{ yield} \times \text{theoretical}}{100} = \text{actual yield}$$

$$\frac{98\%}{100} \times 28.231 \text{ g } S_8 = 27.666 = 28 \text{ g } S_8 \text{ actual}$$

3.84 $H_2S(g) + 2NaOH(aq) \rightarrow Na_2S(aq) + 2H_2O(l)$

$$1.25 \text{ g } H_2S \times \frac{1 \text{ mol } H_2S}{34.08 \text{ g } H_2S} = 0.03668 = 0.0367 \text{ mol } H_2S$$

$$2.00 \text{ g NaOH} \times \frac{1 \text{ mol NaOH}}{40.00 \text{ g NaOH}} = 0.0500 \text{ mol NaOH}$$

By inspection, twice as many mol NaOH as H_2S are needed for exact reaction, but mol NaOH given is less than twice mol H_2S, so NaOH limits.

$$0.0500 \text{ mol NaOH} \times \frac{1 \text{ mol } Na_2S}{2 \text{ mol NaOH}} \times \frac{78.05 \text{ g } Na_2S}{1 \text{ mol } Na_2S} = 1.95125 = 1.95 \text{ g } Na_2S \text{ theoretical}$$

$$\frac{92.0\%}{100} \times 1.95125 \text{ g } Na_2S \text{ theoretical} = 1.7951 = 1.80 \text{ g } Na_2S \text{ actual}$$

Additional Exercises

3.85   (a) $CH_3COOH = C_2H_4O_2$. At room temperature and pressure, pure acetic acid is a liquid. $C_2H_4O_2(l) + 2 O_2(g) \rightarrow 2 CO_2(g) + 2 H_2O(l)$

(b) $Ca(OH)_2(s) \rightarrow CaO(s) + H_2O(g)$

(c) $Ni(s) + Cl_2(g) \rightarrow NiCl_2(s)$

3.86 $C_2H_5OH(l) + 3O_2(g) \rightarrow 2CO_2(g) + 3H_2O(g)$

$C_3H_8(g) + 5O_2(g) \rightarrow 3CO_2(g) + 4H_2O(g)$

$CH_3CH_2COCH_3(l) + 11/2 \, O_2(g) \rightarrow 4CO_2(g) + 4H_2O(l)$

In a combustion reaction, all H in the fuel is transformed to H_2O in the products. The reactant with most mol H/mol fuel will produce the most H_2O. C_3H_8 and $CH_3CH_2COCH_3$ (C_4H_8O) both have 8 mol H/mol fuel, so 1.5 mol of either fuel will produce the same amount of H_2O. 1.5 mol C_2H_5OH will produce less H_2O.

3.87   The formulas of the fertilizers are NH_3, NH_4NO_3, $(NH_4)_2SO_4$ and $(NH_2)_2CO$. Qualitatively, the more heavy, non-nitrogen atoms in a molecule, the smaller the mass % of N. By inspection, the mass of NH_3 is dominated by N, so it will have the greatest % N, $(NH_4)_2SO_4$ will have the least. In order of increasing % N:

$(NH_4)_2SO_4 < NH_4NO_3 < (NH_2)_2CO < NH_3$.

Check by calculation:

$(NH_4)_2SO_4$: FW = $2(14.0) + 8(1.0) + 1(32.1) + 4(16.0) = 132.1$ amu

% N = $[2(14.0)/132.1] \times 100 = 21.2\%$

NH_4NO_3: FW = 2(14.0) + 4(1.0) + 3(16.0) = 80.0 amu

% N = [2(14.0)/80.0] × 100 = 35.0%

$(NH_2)_2CO$: FW = 2(14.0) + 4(1.0) = 1(12.0) + 1(16.0) = 60.0 amu

% N = [2(14.0)/60.0] × 100 = 46.7% N

NH_3: FW = 1(14.0) + 3(1.0) = 17.0

% N = [14.0/17.0] × 100 = 82.4 % N

3.88   (a) $0.500 \text{ g } C_9H_8O_4 \times \dfrac{1 \text{ mol } C_9H_8O_4}{180.2 \text{ g } C_9H_8O_4} = 2.7747 \times 10^{-3} = 2.77 \times 10^{-3} \text{ mol } C_9H_8O_4$

       (b) $0.0027747 \text{ mol } C_9H_8O_4 \times \dfrac{6.022 \times 10^{23} \text{ molecules}}{1 \text{ mol}} = 1.67 \times 10^{21} \; C_9H_8O_4 \text{ molecules}$

       (c) $1.67 \times 10^{21} \; C_9H_8O_4 \text{ molecules} \times \dfrac{9 \text{ C atoms}}{1 C_9H_8O_4 \text{ molecule}} = 1.50 \times 10^{22} \text{ C atoms}$

3.89   (a)   *Analyze.* Given: diameter of Si sphere (dot), density of Si. Find: mass of dot.

           Plan. Calculate volume of sphere in cm³, use density to calculate mass of the sphere (dot).

           Solve. V = 4/3π r³; r = d/2

           $\text{radius of dot} = \dfrac{4 \text{ nm}}{2} \times \dfrac{1 \times 10^{-9} \text{ m}}{1 \text{ nm}} \times \dfrac{1 \text{ cm}}{1 \times 10^{-2} \text{ m}} = 2 \times 10^{-7} \text{ cm}$

           volume of dot = $(4/3) \times \pi \times (2 \times 10^{-7})^3 = 3.35 \times 10^{-20} = 3 \times 10^{-20}$ cm³

           $3.35 \times 10^{-20} \text{ cm}^3 \times \dfrac{2.3 \text{ g Si}}{\text{cm}^3} = 7.707 \times 10^{-20} = 8 \times 10^{-20} \text{ g Si in dot}$

       (b)   *Plan.* Change g Si to mol Si using molar mass, then mol Si to atoms Si using Avogadro's number. *Solve.*

           $7.707 \times 10^{-20} \text{ g Si} \times \dfrac{1 \text{ mol Si}}{28.0855 \text{ g Si}} \times \dfrac{6.022 \times 10^{23} \text{ Si atoms}}{\text{mol Si}} = 1.653 \times 10^3$

                                                       $= 2 \times 10^3$ Si atoms

       (c)   *Plan.* A 4 nm quantum dot of Ge also has a volume of 3×10^{-20} cm³. Use density of Ge and Avogadro's number to calculate the number of Ge atoms in a 4 nm spherical quantum dot.

           $3.35 \times 10^{-20} \text{ cm}^3 \times \dfrac{5.325 \text{ g Ge}}{\text{cm}^3} \times \dfrac{1 \text{ mol Ge}}{72.64 \text{ g Ge}} \times \dfrac{6.022 \times 10^{23} \text{ Ge atoms}}{\text{mol Ge}}$

                                                     $= 1.479 \times 10^3 = 1 \times 10^3 \text{ Ge atoms}$

       Strictly speaking, the result has 1 sig fig (from 4 nm). A more meaningful comparison might be 1700 Si atoms vs. 1500 Ge atoms. Although Ge has greater molar mass, it is also more than twice as dense as Si, so the numbers of atoms in the Si and Ge dots are similar.

3.90   (a) $$\frac{5.342 \times 10^{-21}\,g}{1\,\text{molecule penicillin G}} \times \frac{6.0221 \times 10^{23}\,\text{molecules}}{1\,\text{mol}} = 3217\,\text{g/mol penicillin G}$$

     (b)   1.00 g hemoglobin (hem) contains 3.40×10^{-3} g Fe.

$$\frac{1.00\,g\,\text{hem}}{3.40 \times 10^{-3}\,g\,Fe} \times \frac{55.85\,g\,Fe}{1\,\text{mol Fe}} \times \frac{4\,\text{mol Fe}}{1\,\text{mol hem}} = 6.57 \times 10^{4}\,\text{g/mol hemoglobin}$$

3.91   *Plan.* Assume 100 g, calculate mole ratios, empirical formula, then molecular formula from molar mass.   *Solve.*

$$68.2\,g\,C \times \frac{1\,\text{mol C}}{12.01\,g\,C} = 5.68\,\text{mol C};\ 5.68/0.568 \approx 10$$

$$6.86\,g\,H \times \frac{1\,\text{mol H}}{1.008\,g\,H} = 6.81\,\text{mol H};\ 6.81/0.568 \approx 12$$

$$15.9\,g\,N \times \frac{1\,\text{mol N}}{14.01\,g\,N} = 1.13\,\text{mol N};\ 1.13/0.568 \approx 2$$

$$9.08\,g\,O \times \frac{1\,\text{mol O}}{16.00\,g\,O} = 0.568\,\text{mol O};\ 0.568/0.568 = 1$$

The empirical formula is $C_{10}H_{12}N_2O$, FW = 176 amu (or g). Since the molar mass is 176, the empirical and molecular formula are the same, $C_{10}H_{12}N_2O$.

3.92   *Plan.* Assume 1.000 g and get mass O by subtraction.   *Solve.*

     (a) $$0.7787\,g\,C \times \frac{1\,\text{mol C}}{12.01\,g\,C} = 0.06484\,\text{mol C}$$

$$0.1176\,g\,H \times \frac{1\,\text{mol H}}{1.008\,g\,H} = 0.1167\,\text{mol H}$$

$$0.1037\,g\,O \times \frac{1\,\text{mol C}}{16.00\,g\,O} = 0.006481\,\text{mol O}$$

Dividing through by the smallest of these values we obtain $C_{10}H_{18}O$.

     (b)   The formula weight of $C_{10}H_{18}O$ is 154. Thus, the empirical formula is also the molecular formula.

3.93   Since all the C in the vanillin must be present in the CO_2 produced, get g C from g CO_2.

$$2.43\,g\,CO_2 \times \frac{1\,\text{mol CO}_2}{44.01\,g\,CO_2} \times \frac{12.01\,g\,C}{1\,\text{mol C}} = 0.6631 = 0.663\,g\,C$$

Since all the H in vanillin must be present in the H_2O produced, get g H from g H_2O.

$$0.50\,g\,H_2O \times \frac{1\,\text{mol H}_2O}{18.02\,g\,H_2O} \times \frac{2\,\text{mol H}}{1\,\text{mol H}_2O} \times \frac{1.008\,g\,H}{1\,\text{mol H}} = 0.0559 = 0.056\,g\,H$$

Get g O by subtraction. (Since the analysis was performed by combustion, an unspecified amount of O_2 was a reactant, and thus not all the O in the CO_2 and H_2O produced came from vanillin.) 1.05 g vanillin – 0.663 g C – 0.056 g H = 0.331 g O

$$0.6631 \text{ g C} \times \frac{1 \text{ mol C}}{12.01 \text{ g C}} = 0.0552 \text{ mol C}; \quad 0.0552 / 0.0207 = 2.67$$

$$0.0559 \text{ g H} \times \frac{1 \text{ mol H}}{1.008 \text{ g H}} = 0.0555 \text{ mol C}; \quad 0.0555 / 0.0207 = 2.68$$

$$0.331 \text{ g O} \times \frac{1 \text{ mol O}}{16.00 \text{ g O}} = 0.0207 \text{ mol O}; \quad 0.0207 / 0.0207 = 1.00$$

Multiplying the numbers above by **3** to obtain an integer ratio of moles, the empirical formula of vanillin is $C_8H_8O_3$.

3.94   *Plan.* Because different sample sizes were used to analyze the different elements, calculate mass % of each element in the sample.

i.   Calculate mass % C from g CO_2.

ii.   Calculate mass % Cl from AgCl.

iii.   Get mass % H by subtraction.

iv.   Calculate mole ratios and the empirical formulas.

Solve.

i. $$3.52 \text{ g CO}_2 \times \frac{1 \text{ mol CO}_2}{44.01 \text{ g CO}_2} \times \frac{1 \text{ mol C}}{1 \text{ mol CO}_2} \times \frac{12.01 \text{ g C}}{1 \text{ mol C}} = 0.9606 = 0.961 \text{ g C}$$

$$\frac{0.9606 \text{ g C}}{1.50 \text{ g sample}} \times 100 = 64.04 = 64.0\% \text{ C}$$

ii. $$1.27 \text{ g AgCl} \times \frac{1 \text{ mol AgCl}}{143.3 \text{ g AgCl}} \times \frac{1 \text{ mol Cl}}{1 \text{ mol AgCl}} \times \frac{35.45 \text{ g Cl}}{1 \text{ mol Cl}} = 0.3142 = 0.314 \text{ g Cl}$$

$$\frac{0.3142 \text{ g Cl}}{1.00 \text{ g sample}} \times 100 = 31.42 = 31.4\% \text{ Cl}$$

iii.   % H = 100.0 – (64.04% C + 31.42% Cl) = 4.54 = 4.5% H

iv.   Assume 100 g sample.

$$64.04 \text{ g C} \times \frac{1 \text{ mol C}}{12.01 \text{ g C}} = 5.33 \text{ mol C}; \quad 5.33 / 0.886 = 6.02$$

$$31.42 \text{ g Cl} \times \frac{1 \text{ mol Cl}}{35.45 \text{ g Cl}} = 0.886 \text{ mol Cl}; \quad 0.886 / 0.886 = 1.00$$

$$4.54 \text{ g H} \times \frac{1 \text{ mol H}}{1.008 \text{ g H}} = 4.50 \text{ mol H}; \quad 4.50 / 0.886 = 5.08$$

The empirical formula is probably C_6H_5Cl.

The subscript for H, 5.08, is relatively far from 5.00, but C_6H_5Cl makes chemical sense. More significant figures in the mass data are required for a more accurate mole ratio.

3.95 The mass percentage is determined by the relative number of atoms of the element times the atomic weight, divided by the total formula mass. Thus, the mass percent of bromine in $KBrO_x$ is given by $0.5292 = \dfrac{79.91}{39.10 + 79.91 + x(16.00)}$. Solving for x, we obtain x = 2.00. Thus, the formula is $KBrO_2$.

3.96 (a) Let AW = the atomic weight of X.

According to the chemical reaction, moles XI_3 reacted = moles XCl_3 produced

$0.5000 \, g \, XI_3 \times 1 \, mol \, XI_3 \, / \, (AW + 380.71) \, g \, XI_3$

$$= 0.2360 \, g \, XCl_3 \times \dfrac{1 \, mol \, XCl_3}{(AW + 106.36) \, g \, XCl_3}$$

$0.5000 \, (AW + 106.36) = 0.2360 \, (AW + 380.71)$

$0.5000 \, AW + 53.180 = 0.2360 \, AW + 89.848$

$0.2640 \, AW = 36.67; \quad AW = 138.9 \, g$

(b) X is lanthanum, La, atomic number 57.

3.97 $O_3(g) + 2NaI(aq) + H_2O(l) \rightarrow O_2(g) + I_2(s) + 2NaOH(aq)$

(a) $5.95 \times 10^{-6} \, mol \, O_3 \times \dfrac{2 \, mol \, NaI}{1 \, mol \, O_3} = 1.19 \times 10^{-5} \, mol \, NaI$

(b) $1.3 \, mg \, O_3 \times \dfrac{1 \times 10^{-3} \, g}{1 \, mg} \times \dfrac{1 \, mol \, O_3}{48.00 \, g \, O_3} \times \dfrac{2 \, mol \, NaI}{1 \, mol \, O_3} \times \dfrac{149.9 \, g \, NaI}{1 \, mol \, NaI}$

$$= 8.120 \times 10^{-3} = 8.1 \times 10^{-3} \, g \, NaI = 8.1 \, mg \, NaI$$

3.98 $2NaCl(aq) + 2H_2O(l) \rightarrow 2NaOH(aq) + H_2(g) + Cl_2(g)$

Calculate mol Cl_2 and relate to mol H_2, mol NaOH.

$1.5 \times 10^6 \, kg \times \dfrac{1000 \, g}{1 \, kg} \times \dfrac{1 \, mol \, Cl_2}{70.91 \, g \, Cl_2} = 2.115 \times 10^7 = 2.1 \times 10^7 \, mol \, Cl_2$

$2.115 \times 10^7 \, mol \, Cl_2 \times \dfrac{1 \, mol \, H_2}{1 \, mol \, Cl_2} \times \dfrac{2.016 \, g \, H_2}{1 \, mol \, H_2} = 4.26 \times 10^7 \, g \, H_2 = 4.3 \times 10^4 \, kg \, H_2$

$4.3 \times 10^7 \, g \times \dfrac{1 \, metric \, ton}{1 \times 10^6 \, g \, (1 \, Mg)} = 43 \, metric \, tons \, H_2$

$2.115 \times 10^7 \, mol \, Cl_2 \times \dfrac{2 \, mol \, NaOH}{1 \, mol \, Cl_2} \times \dfrac{40.0 \, g \, NaOH}{1 \, mol \, NaOH} = 1.69 \times 10^9 = 1.7 \times 10^9 \, g \, NaOH$

$1.7 \times 10^9 \, g \, NaOH = 1.7 \times 10^6 \, kg \, NaOH = 1.7 \times 10^3 \, metric \, tons \, NaOH$

3.99 $2C_{57}H_{110}O_6 + 163O_2 \rightarrow 114CO_2 + 110H_2O$

molar mass of fat = 57(12.01) + 110(1.008) + 6(16.00) = 891.5

$1.0 \, kg \, fat \times \dfrac{1000 \, g}{1 \, kg} \times \dfrac{1 \, mol \, fat}{891.5 \, g \, fat} \times \dfrac{110 \, mol \, H_2O}{2 \, mol \, fat} \times \dfrac{18.02 \, g \, H_2O}{1 \, mol \, H_2O} \times \dfrac{1 \, kg}{1000 \, g} = 1.1 \, kg \, H_2O$

3.100   (a)   *Plan.* Calculate the total mass of C from g CO and g CO_2. Calculate the mass of H from g H_2O. Calculate mole ratios and the empirical formula.   *Solve.*

$$0.467 \text{ g CO} \times \frac{1 \text{ mol CO}}{28.01 \text{ g CO}} \times \frac{1 \text{ mol C}}{1 \text{ mol CO}} \times 12.01 \text{ g C} = 0.200 \text{ g C}$$

$$0.733 \text{ g CO}_2 \times \frac{1 \text{ mol CO}_2}{44.01 \text{ g CO}_2} \times \frac{1 \text{ mol C}}{1 \text{ mol CO}_2} \times 12.01 \text{ g C} = 0.200 \text{ g C}$$

Total mass C is 0.200 g + 0.200 g = 0.400 g C.

$$0.450 \text{ g H}_2\text{O} \times \frac{1 \text{ mol H}_2\text{O}}{18.02 \text{ g H}_2\text{O}} \times \frac{2 \text{ mol H}}{1 \text{ mol H}_2\text{O}} \times \frac{1.008 \text{ g H}}{1 \text{ mol H}} = 0.0503 \text{ g H}$$

(Since hydrocarbons contain only the elements C and H, g H can also be obtained by subtraction: 0.450 g sample – 0.400 g C = 0.050 g H.)

$$0.400 \text{ g C} \times \frac{1 \text{ mol C}}{12.01 \text{ g C}} = 0.0333 \text{ mol C}; \quad 0.0333 / 0.0333 = 1.0$$

$$0.0503 \text{ g H} \times \frac{1 \text{ mol H}}{1.008 \text{ g H}} = 0.0499 \text{ mol H}; \quad 0.0499 / 0.0333 = 1.5$$

Multiplying by a factor of 2, the empirical formula is C_2H_3.

  (b)   Mass is conserved. Total mass products – mass sample = mass O_2 consumed.

0.467 g CO + 0.733 g CO_2 + 0.450 g H_2O – 0.450 g sample = 1.200 g O_2 consumed

  (c)   For complete combustion, 0.467 g CO must be converted to CO_2.

$2CO(g) + O_2(g) \rightarrow 2CO_2(g)$

$$0.467 \text{ g CO} \times \frac{1 \text{ mol CO}}{28.01 \text{ g CO}} \times \frac{1 \text{ mol O}_2}{2 \text{ mol CO}} \times \frac{32.00 \text{ g O}_2}{1 \text{ mol O}_2} = 0.267 \text{ g O}_2$$

The total mass of O_2 required for complete combustion is
1.200 g + 0.267 g = 1.467 g O_2.

3.101 $N_2(g) + 3H_2(g) \rightarrow 2NH_3(g)$

Determine the moles of N_2 and H_2 required to form the 3.0 moles of NH_3 present after the reaction has stopped.

$$3.0 \text{ mol NH}_3 \times \frac{3 \text{ mol H}_2}{2 \text{ mol NH}_3} = 4.5 \text{ mol H}_2 \text{ reacted}$$

$$3.0 \text{ mol NH}_3 \times \frac{1 \text{ mol N}_2}{2 \text{ mol NH}_3} = 1.5 \text{ mol N}_2 \text{ reacted}$$

mol H_2 initial = 3.0 mol H_2 remain + 4.5 mol H_2 reacted = 7.5 mol H_2

mol N_2 initial = 3.0 mol N_2 remain + 1.5 mol N_2 reacted = 4.5 mol N_2

In tabular form:	$N_2(g)$	+	$3H_2(g)$	→	$2NH_3(g)$
initial	4.5 mol		7.5 mol		0 mol
reaction	–1.5 mol		–4.5 mol		+3.0 mol
final	3.0 mol		3.0 mol		3.0 mol

(Tables like this will be extremely useful for solving chemical equilibrium problems in Chapter 15.)

3.102 All of the O_2 is produced from $KClO_3$; get g $KClO_3$ from g O_2. All of the H_2O is produced from $KHCO_3$; get g $KHCO_3$ from g H_2O. The g H_2O produced also reveals the g CO_2 from the decomposition of $KHCO_3$. The remaining CO_2 (13.2 g CO_2– g CO_2 from $KHCO_3$) is due to K_2CO_3 and g K_2CO_3 can be derived from it.

$$4.00 \text{ g } O_2 \times \frac{1 \text{ mol } O_2}{32.00 \text{ g } O_2} \times \frac{2 \text{ mol } KClO_3}{3 \text{ mol } O_2} \times \frac{122.6 \text{ g } KClO_3}{1 \text{ mol } KClO_3} = 10.22 = 10.2 \text{ g } KClO_3$$

$$1.80 \text{ g } H_2O \times \frac{1 \text{ mol } H_2O}{18.02 \text{ g } H_2O} \times \frac{2 \text{ mol } KHCO_3}{1 \text{ mol } H_2O} \times \frac{100.1 \text{ g } KHCO_3}{1 \text{ mol } KHCO_3} = 20.00 = 20.0 \text{ g } KHCO_3$$

$$1.80 \text{ g } H_2O \times \frac{1 \text{ mol } H_2O}{18.02 \text{ g } H_2O} \times \frac{2 \text{ mol } CO_2}{1 \text{ mol } H_2O} \times \frac{44.01 \text{ g } CO_2}{1 \text{ mol } CO_2} = 8.792 = 8.79 \text{ g } CO_2 \text{ from } KHCO_3$$

13.20 g CO_2 total – 8.792 CO_2 from $KHCO_3$ = 4.408 = 4.41 g CO_2 from K_2CO_3

$$4.408 \text{ g } CO_2 \times \frac{1 \text{ mol } CO_2}{44.01 \text{ g } CO_2} \times \frac{1 \text{ mol } K_2CO_3}{1 \text{ mol } CO_2} \times \frac{138.2 \text{ g } K_2CO_3}{1 \text{ mol } K_2CO_3} = 13.84 = 13.8 \text{ g } K_2CO_3$$

100.0 g mixture – 10.22 g $KClO_3$ – 20.00 g $KHCO_3$ – 13.84 g K_2CO_3 = 55.9 g KCl

3.103 (a) $2C_2H_2(g) + 5O_2(g) \rightarrow 4CO_2(g) + 2H_2O(g)$

(b) Following the approach in Sample Exercise 3.18,

$$10.0 \text{ g } C_2H_2 \times \frac{1 \text{ mol } C_2H_2}{26.04 \text{ g } C_2H_2} \times \frac{5 \text{ mol } O_2}{2 \text{ mol } C_2H_2} \times \frac{32.00 \text{ g } O_2}{1 \text{ mol } O_2} = 30.7 \text{ g } O_2 \text{ required}$$

Only 10.0 g O_2 are available, so O_2 limits.

(c) Since O_2 limits, 0.0 g O_2 remain.

Next, calculate the g C_2H_2 consumed and the amounts of CO_2 and H_2O produced by reaction of 10.0 g O_2.

$$10.0 \text{ g } O_2 \times \frac{1 \text{ mol } O_2}{32.00 \text{ g } O_2} \times \frac{2 \text{ mol } C_2H_2}{5 \text{ mol } O_2} \times \frac{26.04 \text{ g } C_2H_2}{1 \text{ mol } C_2H_2} = 3.26 \text{ g } C_2H_2 \text{ consumed}$$

10.0 g C_2H_2 initial – 3.26 g consumed = 6.74 = 6.7 g C_2H_2 remain

$$10.0 \text{ g } O_2 \times \frac{1 \text{ mol } O_2}{32.00 \text{ g } O_2} \times \frac{4 \text{ mol } CO_2}{5 \text{ mol } O_2} \times \frac{44.01 \text{ g } CO_2}{1 \text{ mol } CO_2} = 11.0 \text{ g } CO_2 \text{ produced}$$

$$10.0 \text{ g } O_2 \times \frac{1 \text{ mol } O_2}{32.00 \text{ g } O_2} \times \frac{2 \text{ mol } H_2O}{5 \text{ mol } O_2} \times \frac{18.02 \text{ g } H_2O}{1 \text{ mol } H_2O} = 2.25 \text{ g } H_2O \text{ produced}$$

3.104   (a) $1.5 \times 10^5 \text{ g } C_9H_8O_4 \times \dfrac{1 \text{ mol } C_9H_8O_4}{180.2 \text{ g } C_9H_8O_4} \times \dfrac{1 \text{ mol } C_7H_6O_3}{1 \text{ mol } C_9H_8O_4} \times \dfrac{138.1 \text{ g } C_7H_6O_3}{1 \text{ mol } C_7H_6O_3}$

$$= 1.1496 \times 10^5 \text{ g} = 1.1 \times 10^2 \text{ kg } C_7H_6O_3$$

(b)   If only 80 percent of the acid reacts, then we need $1/0.80 = 1.25$ times as much to obtain the same mass of product: $1.25 \times 1.15 \times 10^2 \text{ kg} = 1.4 \times 10^2 \text{ kg } C_7H_6O_3$

(c)   Calculate the number of moles of each reactant:

$$1.85 \times 10^5 \text{ g } C_7H_6O_3 \times \dfrac{1 \text{ mol } C_7H_6O_3}{138.1 \text{ g } C_7H_6O_3} = 1.340 \times 10^3 = 1.34 \times 10^3 \text{ mol } C_7H_6O_3$$

$$1.25 \times 10^5 \text{ g } C_4H_6O_3 \times \dfrac{1 \text{ mol } C_4H_6O_3}{102.1 \text{ g } C_4H_6O_3} = 1.224 \times 10^3 = 1.22 \times 10^3 \text{ mol } C_4H_6O_3$$

We see that $C_4H_6O_3$ limits, because equal numbers of moles of the two reactants are consumed in the reaction.

$$1.224 \times 10^3 \text{ mol } C_4H_6O_3 \times \dfrac{1 \text{ mol } C_9H_8O_4}{1 \text{ mol } C_7H_6O_3} \times \dfrac{180.2 \text{ g } C_9H_8O_4}{1 \text{ mol } C_9H_8O_4} = 2.206 \times 10^5$$

$$= 2.21 \times 10^5 \text{ g} C_9H_8O_4$$

(d) $\text{percent yield} = \dfrac{1.82 \times 10^5 \text{ g}}{2.206 \times 10^5 \text{ g}} \times 100 = 82.5\%$

Integrative Exercises

3.105   *Plan.* Volume cube $\xrightarrow{\text{density}}$ mass $CaCO_3 \rightarrow$ moles $CaCO_3 \rightarrow$ moles $O \rightarrow O$ atoms

Solve. $(2.005)^3 \text{ in}^3 \times \dfrac{(2.54)^3 \text{ cm}^3}{1 \text{ in}^3} \times \dfrac{2.71 \text{ g } CaCO_3}{1 \text{ cm}^3} \times \dfrac{1 \text{ mol } CaCO_3}{100.1 \text{ g } CaCO_3} \times \dfrac{3 \text{ mol } O}{1 \text{ mol } CaCO_3}$

$$\times \dfrac{6.022 \times 10^{23} \text{ O atoms}}{1 \text{ mol } O} = 6.46 \times 10^{24} \text{ O atoms}$$

3.106   (a)   *Plan.* volume of Ag cube $\xrightarrow{\text{density}}$ mass of $Ag \rightarrow$ mol $Ag \rightarrow Ag$ atoms

Solve. $(1.000)^3 \text{ cm}^3 \text{ Ag} \times \dfrac{10.5 \text{ g } Ag}{1 \text{ cm}^3 \text{ Ag}} \times \dfrac{1 \text{ mol } Ag}{107.87 \text{ g } Ag} \times \dfrac{6.022 \times 10^{23} \text{ atoms}}{1 \text{ mol}}$

$$= 5.8618 \times 10^{22} = 5.86 \times 10^{22} \text{ Ag atoms}$$

(b) 1.000 cm^3 cube volume, 74% is occupied by Ag atoms

$0.74 \text{ cm}^3 = $ volume of 5.86×10^{22} Ag atoms

$$\dfrac{0.7400 \text{ cm}^3}{5.8618 \times 10^{22} \text{ Ag atoms}} = 1.2624 \times 10^{-23} = 1.3 \times 10^{-23} \text{ cm}^3 \text{ / Ag atom}$$

Since atomic dimensions are usually given in Å, we will show this conversion.

$$1.2624 \times 10^{-23} \text{ cm}^3 \times \dfrac{(1 \times 10^{-2})^3 \text{ m}^3}{1 \text{ cm}^3} \times \dfrac{1 \text{ Å}^3}{(1 \times 10^{-10})^3 \text{ m}^3} = 12.62 = 13 \text{ Å}^3 \text{ / Ag atom}$$

(c) $V = 4/3 \, \pi \, r^3; \; r^3 = 3V/4\pi; \; r = (3V/4\pi)^{1/3}$

          $r_A = (3 \times 12.62 \, \text{Å}^3 \, / \, 4\pi)^{1/3} = 1.444 = 1.4 \, \text{Å}$

3.107   (a)   *Analyze.* Given: gasoline = C_8H_{18}, density = 0.69 g/mL, 20.5 mi/gal, 225 mi.

         Find: kg CO_2.

         Plan. Write and balance the equation for the combustion of octane. Change mi $\rightarrow$ gal octane $\rightarrow$ mL $\rightarrow$ g octane. Use stoichiometry to calculate g and kg CO_2 from g octane.

         Solve. $2C_8H_{18}(l) + 25O_2(g) \rightarrow 16CO_2(g) + 18H_2O(l)$

$$225 \, \text{mi} \times \frac{1 \, \text{gal}}{20.5 \, \text{mi}} \times \frac{3.7854 \, \text{L}}{1 \, \text{gal}} \times \frac{1 \, \text{mL}}{1 \times 10^{-3} \, \text{L}} \times \frac{0.69 \, \text{g octane}}{1 \, \text{mL}} = 2.8667 \times 10^4 \, \text{g}$$

$$= 29 \, \text{kg octane}$$

$$2.8667 \times 10^4 \, \text{g} \, C_8H_{18} \times \frac{1 \, \text{mol} \, C_8H_{18}}{114.2 \, \text{g} \, C_8H_{18}} \times \frac{16 \, \text{mol} \, CO_2}{2 \, \text{mol} \, C_8H_{18}} \times \frac{44.01 \, \text{g} \, CO_2}{1 \, \text{mol} \, CO_2} = 8.8382 \times 10^4 \, \text{g}$$

$$= 88 \, \text{kg} \, CO_2$$

         Check. $\left(\dfrac{225 \times 4 \times 0.7}{20} \right) \times 10^3 = (45 \times 0.7) \times 10^3 = 30 \times 10^3 \, \text{g} = 30 \, \text{kg octane}$

         $\dfrac{44}{114} \approx \dfrac{1}{3}; \; \dfrac{30 \, \text{kg} \times 8}{3} \approx 80 \, \text{kg} \, CO_2$

   (b)   *Plan.* Use the same strategy as part (a). *Solve.*

$$225 \, \text{mi} \times \frac{1 \, \text{gal}}{5 \, \text{mi}} \times \frac{3.7854 \, \text{L}}{1 \, \text{gal}} \times \frac{1 \, \text{mL}}{1 \times 10^{-3} \, \text{L}} \times \frac{0.69 \, \text{g octane}}{1 \, \text{mL}} = 1.1754 \times 10^5$$

$$= 1 \times 10^2 \, \text{kg octane}$$

$$1.1754 \times 10^5 \, \text{g} \, C_8H_{18} \times \frac{1 \, \text{mol} \, C_8H_{18}}{114.2 \, \text{g} \, C_8H_{18}} \times \frac{16 \, \text{mol} \, CO_2}{2 \, \text{mol} \, C_8H_{18}} \times \frac{44.01 \, \text{g} \, CO_2}{1 \, \text{mol} \, CO_2} =$$

$$3.624 \times 10^5 \, \text{g} = 4 \times 10^2 \, \text{kg} \, CO_2$$

Check. Mileage of 5 mi/gal requires ~4 times as much gasoline as mileage of 20.5 mi/gal, so it should produce ~4 times as much CO_2. 90 kg CO_2 [from (a)] × 4 = 360 = 4×10^2 kg CO_2 [from (b)].

3.108   Structural isomers, like 1-propanol and 2-propanol, have the sa me number and kinds of atoms, but different arrangements of these atoms. Since molecular weight is the sum of atomic weights, and number and kinds of atoms are the same, the molecular weights of structural isomers are the same. Again, because number and kinds of atoms are the same, percent composition and therefore combustion analysis results will be the same. Physical properties, like boiling point and density, are influenced by structure as well as molecular weight, and are different for structural isomers.

        The properties (a) boiling point and (d) density will distinguish between 1-propanol and 2-propanol. This is confirmed by comparing these properties from either Wolfram Alpha (WA) or the CRC Handbook of Chemistry and Physics (CRC).

Compound	Boiling Point (WA)	Boiling Point (CRC)	Density (WA)	Density (CRC)
1-propanol	97°C	97.4°C	0.804 g/cm³	0.8035 g/cm³
2-propanol	82°C	82.4°C	0.785 g/cm³	0.7855 g/cm³

3.109   (a) $S(s) + O_2(g) \rightarrow SO_2(g)$; $SO_2(g) + CaO(s) \rightarrow CaSO_3(s)$

       (b)   If the coal contains 2.5% S, then 1 g coal contains 0.025 g S.

$$\frac{2000 \text{ tons coal}}{\text{day}} \times \frac{2000 \text{ lb}}{1 \text{ ton}} \times \frac{1 \text{ kg}}{2.20 \text{ lb}} \times \frac{1000 \text{ g}}{1 \text{ kg}} \times \frac{0.025 \text{ g S}}{1 \text{ g coal}} \times \frac{1 \text{ mol S}}{32.07 \text{ g S}}$$

$$\times \frac{1 \text{ mol SO}_2}{1 \text{ mol S}} \times \frac{1 \text{ mol CaO}}{1 \text{ mol SO}_2} \times \frac{56.08 \text{ g CaO}}{1 \text{ mol CaO}} \times \frac{1 \text{ kg CaO}}{1000 \text{ g CaO}} =$$

$$79,485 = 7.9 \times 10^4 \text{ kg CaO or } 7.9 \times 10^7 \text{ g CaO}$$

       (c)   1 mol CaO = 1 mol $CaSO_3$

$$7.9485 \times 10^7 \text{ g CaO} \times \frac{1 \text{ mol CaO}}{56.08 \text{ g CaO}} \times \frac{1 \text{ mol CaSO}_3}{1 \text{ mol CaO}} \times \frac{120.14 \text{ g CaSO}_3}{1 \text{ mol CaSO}_3}$$

$$= 1.703 \times 10^8 = 1.7 \times 10^8 \text{ g CaSO}_3$$

          This corresponds to about 190 tons of $CaSO_3$ per day as a waste product.

3.110   *Analyze.* Given: 2.0 in × 3.0 in boards, 5000 boards, 0.65 mm thick Cu; 8.96 g/cm³ Cu; 85% Cu removed; 97% yield for reaction. Find: mass $Cu(NH_3)_4Cl_2$, mass NH_3.

       Plan. vol Cu/board × density → mass Cu/board → 5000 boards × 85% = total Cu removed = actual yield; actual yield/0.97 = theoretical yield Cu.

       mass Cu → mol Cu → mol $Cu(NH_3)_4$ Cl or NH_3 → desired masses.

       Solve. $2.0 \text{ in} \times 3.0 \text{ in} \times \dfrac{(2.54)^2 \text{ cm}^2}{\text{in}^2} \times 0.65 \text{ mm} \times \dfrac{1 \text{ cm}}{10 \text{ mm}} = 2.516 = 2.5 \text{ cm}^3 \text{ Cu/board}$

$$\frac{2.516 \text{ cm}^3 \text{ Cu}}{\text{board}} \times \frac{8.96 \text{ g}}{\text{cm}^3} \times 5000 \text{ boards} \times 0.85 \text{ removed} = 95,814 \text{ g} = 96 \text{ kg Cu removed}$$

$$\frac{95,814 \text{ g Cu actual yield}}{0.97} = 98,777 \text{ g} = 99 \text{ kg Cu theoretical}$$

$$98,777 \text{ g Cu} \times \frac{1 \text{ mol Cu}}{63.546 \text{ g Cu}} \times \frac{1 \text{ mol Cu(NH}_3)_4\text{Cl}_2}{1 \text{ mol Cu}} \times \frac{202.575 \text{ g}}{1 \text{ mol Cu(NH}_3)_4\text{Cl}_2} = 314,887 \text{ g}$$

$$= 3.1 \times 10^2 \text{ kg Cu(NH}_3)_4\text{Cl}_2$$

$$98,777 \text{ g Cu} \times \frac{1 \text{ mol Cu}}{63.546 \text{ g Cu}} \times \frac{4 \text{ mol NH}_3}{1 \text{ mol Cu}} \times \frac{17.03 \text{ g NH}_3}{\text{mol NH}_3} = 105,891 \text{ g} = 1.1 \times 10^2 \text{ kg NH}_3$$

3.111   (a)   *Plan.* Calculate the kg of air in the room and then the mass of HCN required to produce a dose of 300 mg HCN/kg air.   *Solve.*

          12 ft × 15 ft × 8.0 ft = 1440 = 1.4×10^3 ft³ of air in the room

$$1440\,ft^3\,air \times \frac{(12\,in)^3}{1\,ft^3} \times \frac{(2.54\,cm)^3}{1\,in^3} \times \frac{0.00118\,g\,air}{1\,cm^3\,air} \times \frac{1\,kg}{1000\,g} = 48.12 = 48\,kg\,air$$

$$48.12\,kg\,air \times \frac{300\,mg\,HCN}{1\,kg\,air} \times \frac{1\,g}{1000\,mg} = 14.43 = 14\,g\,HCN$$

(b) $2NaCN(s) + H_2SO_4(aq) \rightarrow Na_2SO_4(aq) + 2HCN(g)$

The question can be restated as: What mass of NaCN is required to produce 14 g of HCN according to the above reaction?

$$14.43\,g\,HCN \times \frac{1\,mol\,HCN}{27.03\,g\,HCN} \times \frac{2\,mol\,NaCN}{2\,mol\,HCN} \times \frac{49.01\,g\,NaCN}{1\,mol\,NaCN} = 26.2 = 26\,g\,NaCN$$

(c)
$$12\,ft \times 15\,ft \times \frac{1\,yd^2}{9\,ft^2} \times \frac{30\,oz}{1\,yd^2} \times \frac{1\,lb}{16\,oz} \times \frac{454\,g}{1\,lb} = 17,025$$

$$= 1.7 \times 10^4\,g\,acrilan\,in\,the\,room$$

50% of the carpet burns, so the starting amount of CH_2CHCN is
$0.50(17,025) = 8,513 = 8.5 \times 10^3$ g

$$8,513\,g\,CH_2CHCN \times \frac{50.9\,g\,HCN}{100\,g\,CH_2CHCN} = 4333 = 4.3 \times 10^3\,g\,HCN\,possible$$

If the actual yield of combustion is 20%, actual g HCN = 4,333(0.20) = 866.6 $= 8.7 \times 10^2$ g HCN produced. From part (a), 14 g of HCN is a lethal dose. The fire produces much more than a lethal dose of HCN.

3.112   (a) $N_2(g) + O_2(g) \rightarrow 2NO(g);\ 2NO(g) + O_2(g) \rightarrow 2NO_2(g)$

(b)   1 million = 1×10^6

$$22 \times 10^6\,tons\,NO_2 \times \frac{2000\,lb}{1\,ton} \times \frac{453.6\,g}{1\,lb} = 1.996 \times 10^{13} = 2.0 \times 10^{13}\,g\,NO_2$$

(c)   *Plan.* Calculate g O_2 needed to burn 500 g octane. This is 85% of total O_2 in the engine. 15% of total O_2 is used to produce NO_2, according to the second equation in part (a).

Solve. $2C_8H_{18}(l) + 25O_2(g) \rightarrow 16CO_2(g) + 18H_2O(l)$

$$500\,g\,C_8H_{18} \times \frac{1\,mol\,C_8H_{18}}{114.2\,g\,C_8H_{18}} \times \frac{25\,mol\,O_2}{2\,mol\,C_8H_{18}} \times \frac{32.00\,g\,O_2}{mol\,O_2} = 1751 = 1.75 \times 10^3\,g\,O_2$$

$$\frac{1751\,g\,O_2}{total\,g\,O_2} = 0.85;\ 2060 = 2.1 \times 10^3\,g\,O_2\,total\,in\,engine$$

2060 g O_2 total × 0.15 = 309.1 = 3.1×10^2 g O_2 used to produce NO_2. One mol O_2 produces 2 mol NO. Then 2 mol NO react with a second mol O_2 to produce 2 mol NO_2. Two mol O_2 are required to produce 2 mol NO_2; one mol O_2 per mol NO_2.

$$309.1\,g\,O_2 \times \frac{1\,mol\,O_2}{32.00\,g} \times \frac{1\,mol\,NO_2}{1\,mol\,O_2} \times \frac{46.01\,g\,NO_2}{1\,mol\,O_2} = 444.4 = 4.4 \times 10^2\,g\,NO_2$$

4 Reactions in Aqueous Solution

Visualizing Concepts

4.1   *Analyze.* Correlate the formula of the solute with the charged spheres in the diagrams.

Plan. Determine the electrolyte properties of the solute and the relative number of cations, anions, or neutral molecules produced when the solute dissolves.

Solve. Li_2SO_4 is a strong electrolyte, a soluble ionic solid that dissociates into separate Li^+ and SO_4^{2-} when it dissolves in water. There are twice as many Li^+ cations as SO_4^{2-} anions. Diagram (c) represents the aqueous solution of a 2:1 electrolyte.

4.2   *Analyze/Plan.* Correlate the neutral molecules, cations, and anions in the diagrams with the definitions of strong, weak, and nonelectrolytes.   *Solve.*

(a)   AX is a nonelectrolyte, because no ions form when the molecules dissolve.

(b)   AY is a weak electrolyte because a few molecules ionize when they dissolve, but most do not.

(c)   AZ is a strong electrolyte because all molecules break up into ions when they dissolve.

4.3   *Analyze/Plan.* From the molecular representations, write molecular formulas for the compounds. Using Table 4.2 and molecular formulas (there are no ionic compounds in this exercise), classify the compounds as strong acid, strong base, weak acid, weak base (NH_3) or nonelectrolyte. Strong acids and bases are strong electrolytes, weak acids and bases are weak electrolytes. *Solve.*

(a)   HCOOH.   The molecule has a –COOH group; it is a weak acid and weak electrolyte (it is not one of the strong acids listed in Table 4.2).

(b) HNO_3. The molecule is a strong acid (Table 4.2) and a strong electrolyte.

(c) CH_3CH_2OH. The molecule is neither an acid nor a base; it is a nonelectrolyte.

4.4   The brightness of the bulb in Figure 4.2 is related to the number of ions per unit volume of solution. If 0.1 M CH_3COOH has about the same brightness of 0.001 M HBr, the two solutions have about the same number of ions. Since 0.1 M CH_3COOH has 100 times more solute than 0.001 M HBr, HBr must be dissociated to a much greater extent than CH_3COOH. HBr is one of the few molecular acids that is a strong electrolyte. CH_3COOH is a weak electrolyte; if it were a nonelectrolyte, the bulb in Figure 4.2 wouldn't glow.

4.5   *Analyze/Plan.* From the names and/or formulas of the three possible solids, determine which exhibits the described solubility properties. Use Table 4.1.

        Solve. The three possible compounds are $BaCl_2$, $PbCl_2$, and $ZnCl_2$. $PbCl_2$ does not dissolve in water to give a clear solution, so it can be eliminated. Of the remaining possibilities, Ba^{2+} has a sulfate precipitate, but Zn^{2+} does not. The compound is indeed $BaCl_2$.

4.6   Certain pairs of ions form precipitates because their attraction is so strong that they cannot be surrounded and separated by solvent molecules. That is, the attraction between solute particles is greater than the stabilization offered by interaction of individual ions with solvent molecules. These precipitates are insoluble ionic solids.

4.7   *Analyze.* Given the formulas of some ions, determine whether these ions ever form precipitates in aqueous solution. *Plan.* Use Table 4.1 to determine if the given ions can form precipitates. If not, they will always be spectator ions.   *Solve.*

        (a) Cl^- can form precipitates with Ag^+, Hg_2^{2+}, Pb^{2+}.

        (b) NO_3^- never forms precipitates, so it is always a spectator.

        (c) NH_4^+ never forms precipitates, so it is always a spectator.

        (d) S^{2-} usually forms precipitates.

        (e) SO_4^{2-} can form precipitates with Sr^{2+}, Ba^{2+}, Hg_2^{2+}, Pb^{2+}.

        Check. NH_4^+ is a soluble exception for sulfides, phosphates, and carbonates, which usually form precipitates, so all rules indicate that it is a perpetual spectator.

4.8   *Analyze/Plan.* Given three metal powders and three 1 *M* solutions, use Table 4.5, the activity series of metals, to find a scheme to distinguish the metals.

        Solve. In the activity series, any metal on the list can be oxidized by the ions of elements below it. The nitric acid solution contains $H^+(aq)$. This solution will oxidize and thus dissolve $Zn(s)$ and $Pb(s)$, which appear above $H_2(g)$ on the list. Platinum, $Pt(s)$, is distinguished by its lack of reaction with nitric acid.

        To distinguish between Zn and Pb, use a metal ion that occurs between them on the list. We have such an ion, $Ni^{2+}(aq)$ in the nickel nitrate solution. $Ni^{2+}(aq)$ will oxidize and thus dissolve $Zn(s)$, which is above it on the list. $Ni^{2+}(aq)$ will not oxidize or dissolve $Pb(s)$, which is below it on the list.

        To summarize, $Pt(s)$ will neither be oxidized by nor dissolve in any of the three available solutions. $Pb(s)$ is oxidized by and will dissolve in the nitric acid solution, but not the nickel nitrate solution. $Zn(s)$ is oxidized by and will dissolve in both nitric acid and nickel nitrate solutions.

4.9   In a redox reaction, one reactant loses electrons and a different reactant gains electrons; electrons are transferred. Acids ionize in aqueous solution to produce (donate) hydrogen ions (H^+, protons). Bases are substances that react with or accept protons (H^+). In an acid-base reaction, protons are transferred from an acid to a base. We characterize redox reactions by tracking electron transfer using oxidation numbers. We characterize acid-base reactions by tracking H^+ (proton) transfer via molecular formulas of reactants and products.

4.10   Concentration is a ratio of amount of solute to amount of solution or solvent. Thus there are two ways to double the concentration of a solution: double the amount of solute, keeping volume constant or reduce the volume of solution by half, keeping the amount of solute the same.

General Properties of Aqueous Solutions (section 4.1)

4.11   No. Electrolyte solutions conduct electricity because the dissolved ions carry charge through the solution (from one electrode to the other).

4.12   When CH_3OH dissolves, neutral CH_3OH molecules are dispersed throughout the solution. These electrically neutral particles do not carry charge and the solution is nonconducting. When CH_3COOH dissolves, mostly neutral molecules are dispersed throughout the solution. A few of the dissolved molecules ionize to form $H^+(aq)$ and $CH_3COO^-(aq)$. These few ions carry some charge and the solution is weakly conducting.

4.13   Although H_2O molecules are electrically neutral, there is an unequal distribution of electrons throughout the molecule. There are more electrons near O and fewer near H, giving the O end of the molecule a partial negative charge and the H end of the molecule a partial positive charge. Ionic compounds are composed of positively and negatively charged ions. The partially positive ends of H_2O molecules are attracted to the negative ions (anions) in the solid, while the partially negative ends are attracted to the positive ions (cations). Thus, both cations and anions in an ionic solid are surrounded and separated (dissolved) by H_2O molecules.

     We do not expect ionic compounds to be soluble in molecular liquids such as $Br_2(l)$ or $Hg(l)$. There is a symmetrical charge distribution in Hg atoms and Br_2 molecules. There is no permanent full or partial charge on these solvent atoms or molecules, no attractive forces to stabilize the separated ions of an ionic solid.

4.14   Generally, dissolved particles are solvated when they are surrounded by solvent molecules. In aqueous solution, dissolved ions are solvated when they are surrounded by H_2O molecules.

4.15   *Analyze/Plan.* Given the solute formula, determine the separate ions formed upon dissociation. *Solve.*

         (a) $ZnCl_2(aq) \rightarrow Zn^{2+}(aq) + 2Cl^-(aq)$

         (b) $HNO_3(aq) \rightarrow H^+(aq) + NO_3^-(aq)$

         (c) $(NH_4)_2SO_4(aq) \rightarrow 2NH_4^+(aq) + SO_4^{2-}(aq)$

         (d) $Ca(OH)_2(aq) \rightarrow Ca^{2+}(aq) + 2OH^-(aq)$

4.16   (a) $MgI_2(aq) \rightarrow Mg^{2+}(aq) + 2I^-(aq)$

         (b) $Al(NO_3)_3(aq) \rightarrow Al^{3+}(aq) + 3NO_3^-(aq)$

         (c) $HClO_4(aq) \rightarrow H^+(aq) + ClO_4^-(aq)$

         (d) $NaCH_3COO(aq) \rightarrow Na^+(aq) + CH_3COO^-(aq)$

4.17   *Analyze/Plan.* Apply the definition of a weak electrolyte to HCOOH.

         Solve. When HCOOH dissolves in water, neutral HCOOH molecules, H^+ ions and $HCOO^-$ ions are all present in the solution. $HCOOH(aq) \rightleftharpoons H^+(aq) + HCOO^-(aq)$

4.18   (a)   acetone (nonelectrolyte): $CH_3COCH_3(aq)$ molecules only; hypochlorous acid (weak electrolyte): $HClO(aq)$ molecules, $H^+(aq)$, ClO^- (aq); ammonium chloride (strong electrolyte): $NH_4^+(aq)$, $Cl^-(aq)$

         (b) NH_4Cl, 0.2 mol solute particles; HClO, between 0.1 and 0.2 mol particles; CH_3COCH_3, 0.1 mol of solute particles

Precipitation Reactions (section 4.2)

4.19   *Analyze.* Given: formula of compound. Find: solubility.

         Plan. Follow the guidelines in Table 4.1, in light of the anion present in the compound and notable exceptions to the "rules."   *Solve.*

         (a) $MgBr_2$: soluble

         (b) PbI_2: insoluble, Pb^{2+} is an exception to soluble iodides

         (c) $(NH_4)_2CO_3$: soluble, NH_4^+ is an exception to insoluble carbonates

         (d) $Sr(OH)_2$: soluble, Sr^{2+} is an exception to insoluble hydroxides

         (e) $ZnSO_4$: soluble

4.20   According to Table 4.1:

         (a)   AgI: insoluble

         (b) Na_2CO_3: soluble, Na^+ is an exception to insoluble carbonates

         (c) $BaCl_2$: soluble

         (d) $Al(OH)_3$: insoluble

         (e) $Zn(CH_3COO)_2$: soluble

4.21   *Analyze.* Given: formulas of reactants. Find: balanced equation including precipitates.

         Plan. Follow the logic in Sample Exercise 4.3.

         Solve. In each reaction, the precipitate is in bold type.

         (a) $Na_2CO_3(aq) + 2AgNO_3(aq) \rightarrow \mathbf{Ag_2CO_3(s)} + 2NaNO_3(aq)$

         (b)   No precipitate (all nitrates and most sulfates are soluble).

         (c) $FeSO_4(aq) + Pb(NO_3)_2(aq) \rightarrow \mathbf{PbSO_4(s)} + Fe(NO_3)_2(aq)$

4.22   In each reaction, the precipitate is in bold type.

         (a)   No precipitate. [CH_3COO^- gains H^+ to form $CH_3COOH(aq)$, which is soluble.]

         (b) $Cu(NO_3)_2(aq) + 2KOH(aq) \rightarrow \mathbf{Cu(OH)_2(s)} + 2KNO_3(aq)$

         (c) $Na_2S(aq) + CdSO_4(aq) \rightarrow \mathbf{CdS(s)} + Na_2SO_4(aq)$

4.23   *Analyze/Plan.* Follow the logic in Sample Exercise 4.4. From the complete ionic equation, identify the ions that don't change during the reaction; these are the spectator ions. *Solve.*

         (a) $2Na^+(aq) + CO_3^{2-}(aq) + Mg^{2+}(aq) + SO_4^{2-}(aq) \rightarrow MgCO_3(s) + 2Na^+(aq) + SO_4^{2-}(aq)$

             Spectators: Na^+, SO_4^{2-}

(b) $Pb^{2+}(aq) + 2NO_3^-(aq) + 2Na^+(aq) + S^{2-}(aq) \rightarrow PbS(s) + 2Na^+(aq) + 2NO_3^-(aq)$
      Spectators: Na^+, NO_3^-

(c) $6NH_4^+(aq) + 2PO_4^{3-}(aq) + 3Ca^{2+}(aq) + 6Cl^-(aq) \rightarrow Ca_3(PO_4)_2(s) + 6NH_4^+(aq) +$
      $6Cl^-(aq)$ Spectators: NH_4^+, Cl^-

4.24   Spectator ions are those that do not change during reaction.

(a) $2Cr^{3+}(aq) + 3CO_3^{2-}(aq) \rightarrow Cr_2(CO_3)_3(s)$; spectators: NH_4^+, SO_4^{2-}

(b) $Ba^{2+}(aq) + SO_4^{2-}(aq) \rightarrow BaSO_4(s)$; spectators: K^+, NO_3^-

(c) $Fe^{2+}(aq) + 2OH^-(aq) \rightarrow Fe(OH)_2(s)$; spectators: K^+, NO_3^-

4.25   *Analyze.* Given: reactions of unknown with HBr, H_2SO_4, NaOH. Find: The unknown contains a single salt. Is K^+ or Pb^{2+} or Ba^{2+} present?

Plan. Analyze solubility guidelines for Br^-, SO_4^{2-} and OH^- and select the cation that produces a precipitate with each of the anions.

Solve. K^+ forms no precipitates with any of the anions. $BaSO_4$ is insoluble, but $BaCl_2$ and $Ba(OH)_2$ are soluble. Since the unknown forms precipitates with all three anions, it must contain Pb^{2+}.

Check. $PbBr_2$, $PbSO_4$, and $Pb(OH)_2$ are all insoluble according to Table 4.1, so our process of elimination is confirmed by the insolubility of the Pb^{2+} compounds.

4.26 Br^- and NO_3^- can be ruled out because the $BaBr_2$ is soluble and all NO_3^- salts are soluble. CO_3^{2-} forms insoluble salts with the three cations given; it must be the anion in question.

4.27   *Analyze.* Given: three possible salts in an unknown solution react with $Ba(NO_3)_2$ and then NaCl. Find: Can the results identify the unknown salt? Do the three possible unknowns give distinctly different results with $Ba(NO_3)_2$ and NaCl?

Plan. Using Table 4.1, determine whether each of the possible unknowns will form a precipitate with $Ba(NO_3)_2$ and NaCl. *Solve.*

Compound	$Ba(NO_3)_2$ result	NaCl result
$AgNO_3(aq)$	no ppt	AgCl ppt
$CaCl_2(aq)$	no ppt	no ppt
$Al_2(SO_4)_3$	$BaSO_4$ ppt	no ppt

This sequence of tests would definitively identify the contents of the bottle, because the results for each compound are unique.

4.28   (a) $Pb(CH_3COO)_2(aq) + Na_2S(aq) \rightarrow PbS(s) + 2NaCH_3COO(aq)$
      net ionic: $Pb^{2+}(aq) + S^{2-}(aq) \rightarrow PbS(s)$
      $Pb(CH_3COO)_2(aq) + CaCl_2(aq) \rightarrow PbCl_2(s) + Ca(CH_3COO)_2(aq)$
      net ionic: $Pb^{2+}(aq) + 2Cl^-(aq) \rightarrow PbCl_2(s)$

$Na_2S(aq) + CaCl_2(aq) \rightarrow CaS(aq) + 2NaCl(aq)$

net ionic: no reaction

(b)   Spectator ions: Na^+, Ca^{2+}, CH_3COO^-

Acids, Bases, and Neutralization Reactions (section 4.3)

4.29   *Analyze.* Given: solute and concentration of three solutions. Find: solution with greatest concentration of solvated protons.

        Plan: See Sample Exercise 4.6. Determine whether solutes are strong or weak acids or bases or nonelectrolytes. For solutions of equal concentration, strong acids will have greatest concentration of solvated protons. Take varying concentration into consideration when evaluating the same class of solutions.

        Solve. LiOH is a strong base, HI is a strong acid, CH_3OH is a molecular compound and nonelectrolyte. The strong acid HI will have the greatest concentration of solvated protons.

        Check. The solution concentrations weren't needed to answer the question.

4.30 $NH_3(aq)$ is a weak base, while KOH and $Ba(OH)_2$ are strong bases. $NH_3(aq)$ is only slightly ionized, so even (a) 0.6 M NH_3 is less basic than (b) 0.150 M KOH. $Ba(OH)_2$ has twice as many OH^- per mole as KOH, so (c) 0.100 M $Ba(OH)_2$ is more basic than (b) 0.150 M KOH. The most basic solution is (c) 0.100 M $Ba(OH)_2$.

4.31   (a)   A *monoprotic acid* has one ionizable (acidic) H and a *diprotic acid* has two.

         (b)   A *strong acid* is completely ionized in aqueous solution, whereas only a fraction of *weak acid* molecules are ionized.

         (c)   An *acid* is an H^+ donor, a substance that increases the concentration of H^+ in aqueous solution. A *base* is an H^+ acceptor and thus increases the concentration of OH^- in aqueous solution.

4.32   (a) NH_3 produces OH^- in aqueous solution by reacting with H_2O (hydrolysis): $NH_3(aq) + H_2O(l) \rightleftharpoons NH_4^+(aq) + OH^-(aq)$. The OH^- causes the solution to be basic.

         (b)   The term "weak" refers to the tendency of HF to dissociate into H^+ and F^- in aqueous solution, not its reactivity toward other compounds.

         (c) H_2SO_4 is a **diprotic** acid; it has two ionizable hydrogens. The first hydrogen completely ionizes to form H^+ and HSO_4^-, but HSO_4^- only **partially** ionizes into H^+ and SO_4^{2-} (HSO_4^- is a weak electrolyte). Thus, an aqueous solution of H_2SO_4 contains a mixture of H^+, HSO_4^- and SO_4^{2-}, with the concentration of HSO_4^- greater than the concentration of SO_4^{2-}.

4.33   When each of the strong acids in Table 4.2 dissociates, the anions formed are the same ones that normally form soluble ionic compounds (Table 4.1). Although ClO_3^- and ClO_4^- don't appear in Table 4.1, their ionic compounds are typically water soluble, but less common than compounds containing anions that do appear in the table. The one anion that typically forms soluble compounds that is not the anion of a strong acid is acetate, CH_3COO^-; it is the anion of a weak acid.

4.34   All soluble ionic hydroxides from Table 4.1 are listed as strong bases in Table 4.2. Insoluble hydroxides like $Cd(OH)_2$ are not listed as strong bases. "Insoluble" means that less than 1% of the base molecules exist as separated ions and are dissolved. Thus, insoluble hydroxide salts produce too few $OH^-(aq)$ to be considered strong bases.

4.35   *Analyze.* Given: chemical formulas. Find: classify as acid, base, salt; strong, weak, or nonelectrolyte.

        Plan. See Table 4.3. Ionic or molecular? Ionic, soluble: OH^-, strong base and strong electrolyte; otherwise, salt, strong electrolyte. Molecular: NH_3, weak base and weak electrolyte; H-first, acid; strong acid (Table 4.2), strong electrolyte; otherwise weak acid and weak electrolyte.   *Solve.*

        (a)   HF: acid, mixture of ions and molecules (weak electrolyte)

        (b) CH_3CN: none of the above, entirely molecules (nonelectrolyte)

        (c) $NaClO_4$: salt, entirely ions (strong electrolyte)

        (d) $Ba(OH)_2$: base, entirely ions (strong electrolyte)

4.36   Since the solution does conduct some electricity, but less than an equimolar NaCl solution (a strong electrolyte), the unknown solute must be a weak electrolyte. The weak electrolytes in the list of choices are NH_3 and H_3PO_3; since the solution is acidic, the unknown must be H_3PO_3.

4.37   *Analyze.* Given: chemical formulas. Find: electrolyte properties.

        Plan. In order to classify as electrolytes, formulas must be identified as acids, bases, or salts as in Solution 4.35.   *Solve.*

        (a) H_2SO_3: H first, so acid; not in Table 4.2, so weak acid; therefore, weak electrolyte

        (b) C_2H_5OH: not acid, not ionic (no metal cation), contains OH group, but not as anion so not a base; therefore, nonelectrolyte

        (c) NH_3: common weak base; therefore, weak electrolyte

        (d) $KClO_3$: ionic compound, so strong electrolyte

        (e) $Cu(NO_3)_2$: ionic compound, so strong electrolyte

4.38   (a) $LiClO_4$: strong   (b) HClO: weak   (c) $CH_3CH_2CH_2OH$: non

        (d) $HClO_3$: strong   (e) $CuSO_4$: strong   (f) $C_{12}H_{22}O_{11}$: non

4.39   *Plan.* Follow Sample Exercise 4.7.   *Solve.*

        (a) $2HBr(aq) + Ca(OH)_2(aq) \rightarrow CaBr_2(aq) + 2H_2O(l)$

                 $H^+(aq) + OH^-(aq) \rightarrow H_2O(l)$

        (b) $Cu(OH)_2(s) + 2HClO_4(aq) \rightarrow Cu(ClO_4)_2(aq) + 2H_2O(l)$

                 $Cu(OH)_2(s) + 2H^+(aq) \rightarrow 2H_2O(l) + Cu^{2+}(aq)$

        (c) $Al(OH)_3(s) + 3HNO_3(aq) \rightarrow Al(NO_3)_3(aq) + 3H_2O(l)$

                 $Al(OH)_3(s) + 3H^+(aq) \rightarrow 3H_2O(l) + Al^{3+}(aq)$

4.40   (a) $2CH_3COOH(aq) + Ba(OH)_2(aq) \rightarrow Ba(CH_3COO)_2(aq) + 2H_2O(l)$

$CH_3COOH(aq) + OH^-(aq) \rightarrow CH_3COO^-(aq) + H_2O(l)$

(b) $Cr(OH)_3(s) + 3HNO_2(aq) \rightarrow Cr(NO_2)_3(aq) + 3H_2O(l)$

$Cr(OH)_3(s) + 3HNO_2(aq) \rightarrow 3H_2O(l) + Cr^{3+}(aq) + 3NO_2^-(aq)$

(c) $HNO_3(aq) + NH_3(aq) \rightarrow NH_4NO_3(aq)$

$H^+(aq) + NH_3(aq) \rightarrow NH_4^+(aq)$

4.41   *Analyze.* Given: names of reactants. Find: gaseous products.

Plan. Write correct chemical formulas for the reactants, complete and balance the metathesis reaction, and identify either H_2S or CO_2 products as gases.   *Solve.*

(a) $CdS(s) + H_2SO_4(aq) \rightarrow CdSO_4(aq) + H_2S(g)$

$CdS(s) + 2H^+(aq) \rightarrow H_2S(g) + Cd^{2+}(aq)$

(b) $MgCO_3(s) + 2HClO_4(aq) \rightarrow Mg(ClO_4)_2(aq) + H_2O(l) + CO_2(g)$

$MgCO_3(s) + 2H^+(aq) \rightarrow H_2O(l) + CO_2(g) + Mg^{2+}(aq)$

4.42   (a) $FeO(s) + 2H^+(aq) \rightarrow H_2O(l) + Fe^{2+}(aq)$

(b) $NiO(s) + 2H^+(aq) \rightarrow H_2O(l) + Ni^{2+}(aq)$

4.43   *Analyze.* Given the formulas or names of reactants, write balanced molecular and net ionic equations for the reactions.

Plan. Write correct chemical formulas for all reactants. Predict products of the neutralization reactions by exchanging ion partners. Balance the complete molecular equation, identify spectator ions by recognizing strong electrolytes, write the corresponding net ionic equation (omitting spectators).   *Solve.*

(a) $MgCO_3(s) + 2HCl(aq) \rightarrow MgCl_2(aq) + H_2O(l) + CO_2(g)$

$MgCO_3(s) + 2H^+(aq) \rightarrow Mg^{2+}(aq) + H_2O(l) + CO_2(g)$

$MgO(s) + 2HCl(aq) \rightarrow MgCl_2(aq) + H_2O(l)$

$MgO(s) + 2H^+(aq) \rightarrow Mg^{2+}(aq) + H_2O(l)$

$Mg(OH)_2(s) + 2HCl(aq) \rightarrow MgCl_2(aq) + 2H_2O(l)$

$Mg(OH)_2(s) + 2H^+(aq) \rightarrow Mg^{2+}(aq) + 2H_2O(l)$

(b)   Yes. The reaction involving magnesium carbonate, $MgCO_3(s)$, produces $CO_2(g)$ which appears as bubbles. The other two reactions are calm.

(c)   If excess $HCl(aq)$ is added in each case, the identity of the ions in the clear product solution is the same. Each different reaction produces $Mg^{2+}(aq)$, along with Cl^- (aq) spectator ions. There will be $H^+(aq)$ [and more $Cl^-(aq)$] from the excess acid.

4.44 $K_2O(aq) + H_2O(l) \rightarrow 2KOH(aq)$, molecular; $O^{2-}(aq) + H_2O(l) \rightarrow 2OH^-(aq)$, net ionic

base: (H^+ ion acceptor) $O^{2-}(aq)$; acid: (H^+ ion donor) $H_2O(aq)$; spectator: K^+

Oxidation-Reduction Reactions (section 4.4)

4.45   (a)   In terms of electron transfer, *oxidation* is the loss of electrons by a substance, and *reduction* is the gain of electrons (LEO says GER).

           (b)   Relative to oxidation numbers, when a substance is oxidized, its oxidation number increases. When a substance is reduced, its oxidation number decreases.

4.46   Oxidation is loss of electrons; it can occur in the presence of any electron acceptor, not just oxygen.

           Oxidation and reduction can only occur together, not separately. When a substance is oxidized, it loses electrons, but free electrons do not exist under normal conditions. If electrons are lost by one substance they must be gained by another, and vice versa.

4.47   *Analyze.* Given the labeled periodic chart, determine which region is most readily oxidized and which is most readily reduced.

           Plan. Review the definition of oxidation and apply it to the properties of elements in the indicated regions of the chart.

           Solve. Oxidation is loss of electrons. Elements readily oxidized form positive ions; these are metals. Elements not readily oxidized tend to gain electrons and form negative ions; these are nonmetals. Elements in regions A, B, and C are metals, and their ease of oxidation is shown in Table 4.5. Metals in region A, Na, Mg, K, and Ca are most easily oxidized. Elements in region D are nonmetals and are least easily oxidized.

4.48   (a) $BaSO_4$; +6   (b) H_2SO_3; +4   (c) SrS; –2   (d) H_2S; –2

           (e)   Based on these compounds, the range of oxidation numbers for sulfur is +6 to –2. Sulfur is a nonmetal, and positive as well as negative oxidation numbers are possible. It is located in group 6A, and 6 is the maximum positive oxidation number for it.

4.49   *Analyze.* Given the chemical formula of a substance, determine the oxidation number of a particular element in the substance.

           Plan. Follow the logic in Sample Exercise 4.8. *Solve.*

           (a)   +4   (b) +4   (c) +7   (d) +1   (e) 0   (f) –1 (O_2^{2-} is peroxide ion)

4.50   (a)   +3   (b) +3   (c) –2   (d) –3   (e) +3   (f) +6

4.51   *Analyze.* Given: chemical reaction. Find: element oxidized or reduced. *Plan.* Assign oxidation numbers to all species. The element whose oxidation number increases (becomes more positive) is oxidized; the one whose oxidation number decreases (becomes more negative) is reduced.   *Solve.*

           (a) $N_2(g)$ [N, 0] → $2NH_3(g)$ [N, –3], N is reduced; $3H_2(g)$ [H, 0] → $2NH_3(g)$ [H, +1], H is oxidized.

           (b) Fe^{2+} → Fe, Fe is reduced; Al → Al^{3+}, Al is oxidized

           (c) Cl_2 → $2Cl^-$, Cl is reduced; $2I^-$ → I_2, I is oxidized

           (d) S^{2-} → SO_4^{2-} (S, +6), S is oxidized; H_2O_2 (O, –1) → H_2O (O, –2); O is reduced

4.52   (a)   oxidation-reduction reaction; P is oxidized, Cl is reduced

         (b)   oxidation-reduction reaction; K is oxidized, Br is reduced

         (c)   oxidation-reduction reaction; C is oxidized, O is reduced

         (d)   precipitation reaction

4.53   *Analyze.* Given: reactants. Find: balanced molecular and net ionic equations.

        Plan. Metals oxidized by H^+ form cations. Predict products by exchanging cations and balance. The anions are the spectator ions and do not appear in the net ionic equations. *Solve.*

         (a) $Mn(s) + H_2SO_4(aq) \rightarrow MnSO_4(aq) + H_2(g)$; $Mn(s) + 2H^+(aq) \rightarrow Mn^{2+}(aq) + H_2(g)$

               Products with the metal in a higher oxidation state are possible, depending on reaction conditions and acid concentration.

         (b) $2Cr(s) + 6HBr(aq) \rightarrow 2CrBr_3(aq) + 3H_2(g)$; $2Cr(s) + 6H^+(aq) \rightarrow 2Cr^{3+}(aq) + 3H_2(g)$

         (c) $Sn(s) + 2HCl(aq) \rightarrow SnCl_2(aq) + H_2(g)$; $Sn(s) + 2H^+(aq) \rightarrow Sn^{2+}(aq) + H_2(g)$

         (d) $2Al(s) + 6HCOOH(aq) \rightarrow 2Al(HCOO)_3(aq) + 3H_2(g)$;

               $2Al(s) + 6HCOOH(aq) \rightarrow 2Al^{3+}(aq) + 6HCOO^-(aq) + 3H_2(g)$

4.54   (a) $2HCl(aq) + Ni(s) \rightarrow NiCl_2(aq) + H_2(g)$; $Ni(s) + 2H^+(aq) \rightarrow Ni^{2+}(aq) + H_2(g)$

         (b) $H_2SO_4(aq) + Fe(s) \rightarrow FeSO_4(aq) + H_2(g)$; $Fe(s) + 2H^+(aq) \rightarrow Fe^{2+}(aq) + H_2(g)$

               Products with the metal in a higher oxidation state are possible, depending on reaction conditions and acid concentration.

         (c) $2HBr(aq) + Mg(s) \rightarrow MgBr_2(aq) + H_2(g)$; $Mg(s) + 2H^+(aq) \rightarrow Mg^{2+}(aq) + H_2(g)$

         (d) $2CH_3COOH(aq) + Zn(s) \rightarrow Zn(CH_3COO)_2(aq) + H_2(g)$;

               $Zn(s) + 2CH_3COOH(aq) \rightarrow Zn^{2+}(aq) + 2CH_3COO^-(aq) + H_2(g)$

4.55   *Analyze.* Given: a metal and an aqueous solution. Find: balanced equation.

        Plan. Use Table 4.5. If the metal is above the aqueous solution, reaction will occur; if the aqueous solution is higher, NR. If reaction occurs, predict products by exchanging cations (a metal ion or H^+), then balance the equation.   *Solve.*

         (a) $Fe(s) + Cu(NO_3)_2(aq) \rightarrow Fe(NO_3)_2(aq) + Cu(s)$

         (b) $Zn(s) + MgSO_4(aq) \rightarrow NR$

         (c) $Sn(s) + 2HBr(aq) \rightarrow SnBr_2(aq) + H_2(g)$

         (d) $H_2(g) + NiCl_2(aq) \rightarrow NR$

         (e) $2Al(s) + 3CoSO_4(aq) \rightarrow Al_2(SO_4)_3(aq) + 3Co(s)$

4.56   (a) $Ni(s) + Cu(NO_3)_2(aq) \rightarrow Ni(NO_3)_2(aq) + Cu(s)$

         (b) $Zn(NO_3)_2(aq) + MgSO_4(aq) \rightarrow NR$

         (c) $Au(s) + HCl(aq) \rightarrow NR$

    (d) $2Cr(s) + 3CoCl_2(aq) \rightarrow 2CrCl_3(aq) + 3Co(s)$

    (e) $H_2(g) + 2AgNO_3(aq) \rightarrow 2Ag(s) + 2HNO_3(aq)$

4.57   (a)   i. $Zn(s) + Cd^{2+}(aq) \rightarrow Cd(s) + Zn^{2+}(aq)$

                ii. $Cd(s) + Ni^{2+}(aq) \rightarrow Ni(s) + Cd^{2+}(aq)$

    (b)   According to Table 4.5, the most active metals are most easily oxidized, and Zn is more active than Ni. Observation (i) indicates that Cd is less active than Zn; observation (ii) indicates that Cd is more active than Ni. Cd is between Zn and Ni on the activity series.

    (c)   Place an iron strip in $CdCl_2(aq)$. If Cd(s) is deposited, Cd is less active than Fe; if there is no reaction, Cd is more active than Fe. Do the same test with Co if Cd is less active than Fe or with Cr if Cd is more active than Fe.

4.58   (a) $Br_2 + 2NaI \rightarrow 2NaBr + I_2$ indicates that Br_2 is more easily reduced than I_2.

             $Cl_2 + 2NaBr \rightarrow 2NaCl + Br_2$ shows that Cl_2 is more easily reduced than Br_2.

             The order for ease of reduction is $Cl_2 > Br_2 > I_2$. Conversely, the order for ease of oxidation is $I^- > Br^- > Cl^-$.

    (b)   Since the halogens are nonmetals, they tend to form anions when they react chemically. Nonmetallic character decreases going down a family and so does the tendency to gain electrons during a chemical reaction. Thus, the ease of reduction of the halogen, X_2, decreases going down the family and the ease of oxidation of the halide, X^-, increases going down the family.

    (c) $Cl_2 + 2KI \rightarrow 2KCl + I_2$; $Br_2 + LiCl \rightarrow$ no reaction

Concentrations of Solutions (section 4.5)

4.59   (a)   *Concentration* is an *intensive* property; it is the **ratio** of the amount of solute present in a certain quantity of solvent or solution. This ratio remains constant regardless of how much solution is present.

    (b)   The term *0.50 mol HCl* defines an amount (~18 g) of the pure substance HCl. The term 0.50 *M* HCl is a ratio; it indicates that there are 0.50 mol of HCl solute in 1.0 liter of solution. This same ratio of moles solute to solution volume is present regardless of the volume of solution under consideration.

4.60   (a)   The concentration of the remaining solution is unchanged, assuming the original solution was thoroughly mixed. Molar concentration is a **ratio** of moles solute to liters solution. Although there are fewer moles solute remaining in the flask, there is also less solution volume, so the ratio of moles solute/solution volume remains the same.

    (b)   The concentration of the remaining solution is increased. The moles solute remaining in the flask are unchanged, but the solution volume decreases after evaporation. The ratio of moles solute/solution volume increases.

(c) The second solution is five times as concentrated as the first. An equal volume of the more concentrated solution will contain five times as much solute (five times the number of moles and also five times the mass) as the 0.50 *M* solution. Thus, the mass of solute in the 2.50 *M* solution is 5×4.5 g = 22.5 g.

Mathematically:

$$\frac{\dfrac{2.50 \text{ mol solute}}{1 \text{ L solution}}}{\dfrac{0.50 \text{ mol solute}}{1 \text{ L solution}}} = \frac{x \text{ grams solute}}{4.5 \text{ g solute}}$$

$$\frac{2.50 \text{ mol solute}}{0.50 \text{ mol solute}} = \frac{x \text{ g solute}}{4.5 \text{ g solute}}; \; 5.0(4.5 \text{ g solute}) = 23 \text{ g solute}$$

The result has 2 sig figs; 22.5 rounds to 23 g solute.

4.61 *Analyze/Plan.* Follow the logic in Sample Exercises 4.11 and 4.13. *Solve.*

(a) $M = \dfrac{\text{mol solute}}{\text{L solution}}; \; \dfrac{0.175 \text{ mol ZnCl}_2}{150 \text{ mL}} \times \dfrac{1000 \text{ mL}}{1 \text{ L}} = 1.17 \, M \text{ ZnCl}_2$

Check. (0.175 / 0.150) > 1.0 *M*

(b) $\text{mol} = M \times \text{L}; \dfrac{4.50 \text{ mol HNO}_3}{1 \text{ L}} \times 0.0350 \text{ L} = 0.158 \text{ mol HNO}_3$

Check. $(4.5 \times .04) \approx 0.16$ mol

(c) $\text{L} = \dfrac{\text{mol}}{M}; \; \dfrac{0.325 \text{ mol NaOH}}{6.00 \text{ mol NaOH/L}} = 0.0542 \text{ L or } 54.2 \text{ mL of } 6.00 \, M \text{ NaOH}$

Check. (0.325/6.0) > 0.50 L.

4.62 (a) $M = \dfrac{\text{mol solute}}{\text{L solution}}; \; \dfrac{12.5 \text{ g Na}_2\text{CrO}_4}{0.550 \text{ L}} \times \dfrac{1 \text{ mol Na}_2\text{CrO}_4}{161.97 \text{ g Na}_2\text{CrO}_4} = 0.140 \, M \text{ Na}_2\text{CrO}_4$

(b) $\text{mol} = M \times \text{L}; \dfrac{0.275 \text{ mol KBr}}{1 \text{ L}} \times 0.150 \text{ L} = 4.13 \times 10^{-2} \text{ mol KBr}$

(c) $\text{L} = \dfrac{\text{mol}}{M}; \; \dfrac{0.100 \text{ mol HCl}}{6.1 \text{ mol HCl/L}} = 1.6 \times 10^{-2} \text{ L or } 16 \text{ mL}$

4.63 *Analyze.* Given molarity, *M*, and volume, L, find mass of Na^+(aq) in the blood.

Plan. Calculate moles Na^+(aq) using the definition of molarity: $M = \dfrac{\text{mol}}{\text{L}}$; mol = $M \times$ L.

Calculate mass Na^+(aq) using the definition moles: mol = g/MM; g = mol × MM. (MM is the symbol for molar mass in this manual.)

Solve. $\dfrac{0.135 \text{ mol}}{\text{L}} \times 5.0 \text{ L} \times \dfrac{23.0 \text{ g Na}^+}{\text{mol Na}^+} = 15.525 = 16 \text{ g Na}^+\text{(aq)}$

Check. Since there are more than 0.1 mol/L and we have 5.0 L, there should be more than half a mol (11.5 g) of Na^+. The calculation agrees with this estimate.

4.64   Calculate the mol of Na^+ at the two concentrations; the difference is the mol NaCl required to increase the Na^+ concentration to the desired level.

$$\frac{0.118\,mol}{L} \times 4.6\,L = 0.5428 = 0.54\,mol\,Na^+$$

$$\frac{0.138\,mol}{L} \times 4.6\,L = 0.6348 = 0.63\,mol\,Na^+$$

(0.6348 − 0.5428) = 0.092 = 0.09 mol NaCl (2 decimal places and 1 sig fig)

$$0.092\,mol\,NaCl \times \frac{58.5\,g\,NaCl}{mol} = 5.38 = 5\,g\,NaCl$$

4.65   *Analyze.* Given: g alcohol/100 mL blood; molecular formula of alcohol. Find: molarity (mol/L) of alcohol. *Plan.* Use the molar mass (MM) of alcohol to change (g/100) mL to (mol/100 mL) then mL to L.

Solve. MM of alcohol = 2(12.01) + 6(1.1008) + 1(16.00) = 46.07 g alcohol/mol

$$BAC = \frac{0.08\,g\,alcohol}{100\,mL\,blood} \times \frac{1\,mol\,alcohol}{46.07\,g\,alcohol} \times \frac{1000\,mL}{1\,L} = 0.0174 = 0.02\,M\,alcohol$$

4.66   *Analyze.* Given: BAC (definition from Exercise 4.65), vol of blood. Find: mass alcohol in bloodstream.

Plan. Change BAC (g/100 mL) to (g/L), then times vol of blood in L.

Solve. BAC = 0.10 g/100 mL

$$\frac{0.10\,g\,alcohol}{100\,mL\,blood} \times \frac{1000\,mL}{1\,L} \times 5.0\,L\,blood = 5.0\,g\,alcohol$$

4.67   *Plan.* Proceed as in Sample Exercises 4.11 and 4.13.

$$M = \frac{mol}{L}; \quad mol = \frac{g}{MM} \quad \text{(MM is the symbol for molar mass in this manual.)}$$

Solve.

(a) $$\frac{0.175\,M\,KBr}{1\,L} \times 0.250\,L \times \frac{119.0\,g\,KBr}{1\,mol\,KBr} = 5.21\,g\,KBr$$

Check. (0.25 × 120) ≈ 30; 30 × 0.18 ≈ 5.4 g KBr

(b) $$14.75\,g\,Ca(NO_3)_2 \times \frac{1\,mol\,Ca(NO_3)_2}{164.09\,g\,Ca(NO_3)_2} \times \frac{1}{1.375\,L} = 0.06537\,M\,Ca(NO_3)_2$$

Check. (15/1.5) ≈ 10; 10/160 = 5/80 ≈ 0.06 M $Ca(NO_3)_2$

(c) $$2.50\,g\,Na_3PO_4 \times \frac{1\,mol\,Na_3PO_4}{163.9\,g\,Na_3PO_4} \times \frac{1\,L}{1.50\,mol\,Na_3PO_4} \times \frac{1000\,mL}{1\,L}$$
$$= 10.2\,mL\,solution$$

Check. [25/(160 × 1.5)] ≈ 2.5/240 ≈ 1/100 ≈ 0.01 L = 10 mL

4.68 $M = \dfrac{mol}{L}$; $mol = \dfrac{g}{MM}$ (MM is the symbol for molar mass in this manual.)

(a) $\dfrac{0.736 \text{ mol } K_2Cr_2O_7}{1\,L} \times 15.0 \text{ mL} \times \dfrac{1\,L}{1000 \text{ mL}} \times \dfrac{294.2 \text{ g } K_2Cr_2O_7}{1 \text{ mol } K_2Cr_2O_7} = 3.25 \text{ g } K_2Cr_2O_7$

(b) $14.00 \text{ g } (NH_4)_2SO_4 \times \dfrac{1 \text{ mol } (NH_4)_2SO_4}{132.2 \text{ g } (NH_4)_2SO_4} \times \dfrac{1}{250 \text{ mL}} \times \dfrac{1000 \text{ mL}}{1\,L}$

$$= 0.424 \ M \ (NH_4)_2SO_4$$

(c) $3.65 \text{ g } CuSO_4 \times \dfrac{1 \text{ mol } CuSO_4}{159.6 \text{ g } CuSO_4} \times \dfrac{1\,L}{0.0455 \text{ mol } CuSO_4} \times \dfrac{1000 \text{ mL}}{1L} = 503 \text{ mL solution}$

4.69   *Analyze.* Given: formula and concentration of each solute. Find: concentration of K^+ in each solution. *Plan.* Note mol K^+/mol solute and compare concentrations or total moles. *Solve.*

(a) $KCl \rightarrow K^+ + Cl^-$; $0.20 \ M$ KCl = $0.20 \ M \ K^+$

      $K_2CrO_4 \rightarrow \mathbf{2}\,K^+ + CrO_4{}^{2-}$; $0.15 \ M \ K_2CrO_4 = 0.30 \ M \ K^+$

      $K_3PO_4 \rightarrow \mathbf{3}\,K^+ + PO_4{}^{3-}$; $0.080 \ M \ K_3PO_4 = 0.24 \ M \ K^+$

      $0.15 \ M \ K_2CrO_4$ has the highest K^+ concentration.

(b) K_2CrO_4: $0.30 \ M \ K^+ \times 0.0300 \ L = 0.0090 \text{ mol } K^+$

      K_3PO_4: $0.24 \ M \ K^+ \times 0.0250 \ L = 0.0060 \text{ mol } K^+$

      30.0 mL of $0.15 \ M \ K_2CrO_4$ has more K^+ ions.

4.70   (a) $0.10 \ M \ BaI_2 = 0.2 \ M \ I^-$; $0.25 \ M$ KI = $0.25 \ M \ I^-$

            $0.25 \ M$ KI has the higher I^- concentration.

      (b) $0.10 \ M$ KI = $0.1 \ M \ I^-$; $0.040 \ M \ ZnI_2 = 0.080 \ M \ I^-$; $0.10 \ M$ KI has a higher I^- concentration than $0.040 \ M \ ZnI_2$. Total volume does not affect concentration.

      (c) $3.2 \ M$ HI = $3.2 \ M \ I^-$

         $145 \text{ g NaI} \times \dfrac{1 \text{ mol NaI}}{149.9 \text{ g NaI}} \times \dfrac{1}{0.150 \ L} = 6.45 \ M \text{ NaI} = 6.45 \ M \ I^-$

         The NaI solution has the higher I^- concentration.

4.71   *Analyze.* Given: molecular formula and solution molarity. Find: concentration (M) of each ion.

         Plan. Follow the logic in Sample Exercise 4.12.

         Solve.

(a) $NaNO_3 \rightarrow Na^+, NO_3{}^-$; $0.25 \ M \ NaNO_3 = 0.25 \ M \ Na^+$, $0.25 \ M \ NO_3{}^-$

(b) $MgSO_4 \rightarrow Mg^{2+}, SO_4^{2-}$; $1.3 \times 10^{-2}\ M\ MgSO_4 = 1.3 \times 10^{-2}\ M\ Mg^{2+}$, $1.3 \times 10^{-2}\ M\ SO_4^{2-}$

(c) $C_6H_{12}O_6 \rightarrow C_6H_{12}O_6$ (molecular solute); $0.0150\ M\ C_6H_{12}O_6 = 0.0150\ M\ C_6H_{12}O_6$

(d)   *Plan.* There is no reaction between $NaCl$ and $(NH_4)_2CO_3$, so this is just a dilution problem, $M_1V_1 = M_2V_2$. Then account for ion stoichiometry.

        Solve. 45.0 mL + 65.0 mL = 110.0 mL total volume

$$\frac{0.272\ M\ NaCl \times 45.0\ mL}{110.0\ mL} = 0.111\ M\ NaCl;\ 0.111\ M\ Na^+, 0.111\ M\ Cl^-$$

$$\frac{0.0247\ M\ (NH_4)_2CO_3 \times 65.0\ mL}{110.0\ mL} = 0.0146\ M\ (NH_4)_2CO_3$$

$$2 \times (0.0146\ M) = 0.0292\ M\ NH_4^+, 0.0146\ M\ CO_3^{2-}$$

        Check. By adding the two solutions (with no common ions or chemical reaction), we have approximately doubled the solution volume, and reduced the concentration of each ion by approximately a factor of two.

4.72   (a)   *Plan.* These two solutions have common ions. Find the ion concentration resulting from each solution, then add.

        Solve. total volume = 42.0 mL + 37.6 mL = 79.6 mL

$$\frac{0.170\ M\ NaOH \times 42.0\ mL}{79.6\ mL} = 0.08970 = 0.0897\ M\ NaOH;$$

        $0.0897\ M\ Na^+,\ 0.0897\ M\ OH^-$

$$\frac{0.400\ M\ NaOH \times 37.6\ mL}{79.6\ mL} = 0.18894 = 0.189\ M\ NaOH;$$

        $0.189\ M\ Na^+,\ 0.189\ M\ OH^-$

        $M\ Na^+ = 0.08970\ M + 0.18894\ M = 0.27864 = 0.2786\ M\ Na^+$

        $M\ OH^- = M\ Na^+ = 0.2786\ M\ OH^-$

(b)   *Plan.* No common ions; just dilution.

        Solve. 44.0 mL + 25.0 mL = 69.0 mL

$$\frac{0.100\ M\ Na_2SO_4 \times 44.0\ mL}{69.0\ mL} = 0.06377 = 0.0638\ M\ Na_2SO_4$$

        $2 \times (0.06377\ M) = 0.1275 = 0.128\ M\ Na^+;\ 0.0638\ M\ SO_4^{2-}$

$$\frac{0.150\ M\ KCl \times 25.0\ mL}{69.0\ mL} = 0.054348 = 0.0543\ M\ KCl$$

$0.0543\ M\ K^+$, $0.0543\ M\ Cl^-$

(c)   *Plan.* Calculate concentration of K^+ and Cl^- due to the added solid. Then sum to get total concentration of Cl^-.

Solve. $\dfrac{3.60\ g\ KCl}{75.0\ mL\ so\ln} \times \dfrac{1\ mol\ KCl}{74.55\ g\ KCl} \times \dfrac{1000\ mL}{1\ L} = 0.6439 = 0.644\ M\ KCl$

$0.250\ M\ CaCl_2$; $2(0.250\ M) = 0.500\ M\ Cl^-$

total $Cl^- = 0.644\ M + 0.500\ M = 1.144\ M\ Cl^-$, $0.644\ M\ K^+$, $0.250\ M\ Ca^{2+}$

4.73   *Analyze/Plan.* Follow the logic of Sample Exercise 4.14.

Solve.

(a) $V_1 = M_2V_2/M_1$; $\dfrac{0.250\ M\ NH_3 \times 1000.0\ mL}{14.8\ M\ NH_3} = 16.89 = 16.9\ mL\ 14.8\ M\ NH_3$

Check. $250/15 \approx 15\ M$

(b) $M_2 = M_1V_1/V_2$; $\dfrac{14.8\ M\ NH_3 \times 10.0\ mL}{500\ mL} = 0.296\ M\ NH_3$

Check. $150/500 \approx 0.30\ M$

4.74   (a) $V_1 = M_2V_2/M_1$; $\dfrac{0.500\ M\ HNO_3 \times 0.110\ L}{6.0\ M\ HNO_3} = 0.00917\ L = 9.2\ mL\ 6.0\ M\ HNO_3$

(b) $M_2 = M_1V_1/V_2$; $\dfrac{6.0\ M\ HNO_3 \times 10.0\ mL}{250\ mL} = 0.240\ M\ HNO_3$

4.75   (a)   *Plan/Solve.* Follow the logic in Sample Exercise 4.13. The number of moles of sucrose needed is $\dfrac{0.250\ mol}{1\ L} \times 0.250\ L = 0.06250 = 0.0625\ mol$

Weigh out $0.0625\ mol\ C_{12}H_{22}O_{11} \times \dfrac{342.3\ g\ C_{12}H_{22}O_{11}}{1\ mol\ C_{12}H_{22}O_{11}} = 21.4\ g\ C_{12}H_{22}O_{11}$

Add this amount of solid to a 250 mL volumetric flask, dissolve in a small volume of water, and add water to the mark on the neck of the flask. Agitate thoroughly to ensure total mixing.

(b)   *Plan/Solve.* Follow the logic in Sample Exercise 4.14. Calculate the moles of solute present in the final 350.0 mL of $0.100\ M\ C_{12}H_{22}O_{11}$ solution:

moles $C_{12}H_{22}O_{11} = M \times L = \dfrac{0.100\ mol\ C_{12}H_{22}O_{11}}{1\ L} \times 0.3500\ L = 0.0350\ mol\ C_{12}H_{22}O_{11}$

Calculate the volume of $1.50\ M$ glucose solution that would contain $0.0350\ mol$ $C_{12}H_{22}O_{11}$:

$$L = moles/M; \ 0.0350 \ mol \ C_{12}H_{22}O_{11} \times \frac{1 \ L}{1.50 \ mol \ C_{12}H_{22}O_{11}} = 0.02333 = 0.0233 \ L$$

$$0.02333 \ L \times \frac{1000 \ mL}{1 \ L} = 23.3 \ mL$$

Thoroughly rinse, clean, and fill a 50 mL buret with the 1.50 M $C_{12}H_{22}O_{11}$. Dispense 23.3 mL of this solution into a 350 mL volumetric container, add water to the mark, and mix thoroughly. (23.3 mL is a difficult volume to measure with a pipette.)

4.76   (a)   The amount of $AgNO_3$ needed is:
              0.150 M × 0.1750 L = 0.02625 = 0.263 mol $AgNO_3$

$$0.02625 \ mol \ AgNO_3 \times \frac{169.88 \ g \ AgNO_3}{1 \ mol \ AgNO_3} = 4.4594 = 4.46 \ g \ AgNO_3$$

Add this amount of solid to a 175 mL volumetric container, dissolve in a small amount of water, bring the total volume to exactly 175 mL, and agitate well.

       (b)   Dilute the 3.6 M HNO_3 to prepare 100 mL of 0.50 M HNO_3. To determine the volume of 3.6 M HNO_3 needed, calculate the moles HNO_3 present in 100 mL of 0.50 M HNO_3 and then the volume of 3.6 M solution that contains this number of moles.

              0.100 L × 0.50 M = 0.050 mol HNO_3 needed;

$$L = \frac{mol}{M}; \ L \ of \ 3.6 \ M \ HNO_3 = \frac{0.050 \ mol \ needed}{3.6 \ M} = 0.01389 \ L = 14 \ mL$$

Thoroughly clean, rinse, and fill a buret with the 3.6 M HNO_3, taking precautions appropriate for working with a relatively concentrated acid. Dispense 14 mL of the 3.6 M acid into a 100 mL volumetric flask, add water to the mark, and mix thoroughly.

4.77   *Analyze.* Given: density of pure acetic acid, volume pure acetic acid, volume new solution. Find: molarity of new solution. *Plan.* Calculate the mass of acetic acid, CH_3COOH, present in 20.0 mL of the pure liquid.   *Solve.*

$$20.00 \ mL \ acetic \ acid \times \frac{1.049 \ g \ acetic \ acid}{1 \ mL \ acetic \ acid} = 20.98 \ g \ acetic \ acid$$

$$20.98 \ g \ CH_3COOH \times \frac{1 \ mol \ CH_3COOH}{60.05 \ g \ CH_3COOH} = 0.349375 = 0.3494 \ mol \ CH_3COOH$$

$$M = mol/L = \frac{0.349375 \ mol \ CH_3COOH}{0.2500 \ L \ solution} = 1.39750 = 1.398 \ M \ CH_3COOH$$

Check. (20 × 1) ≈ 20 g acid; (20/60) ≈ 0.33 mol acid; (0.33/0.25 = 0.33 × 4) ≈ 1.33 M

4.78 $50.000 \ mL \ glycerol \times \dfrac{1.2656 \ g \ glycerol}{1 \ mL \ glycerol} = 63.280 \ g \ glycerol$

$$63.280 \text{ g C}_3\text{H}_8\text{O}_3 \times \frac{1 \text{ mol C}_3\text{H}_8\text{O}_3}{92.094 \text{ g C}_3\text{H}_8\text{O}_3} = 0.687124 = 0.68712 \text{ mol C}_3\text{H}_8\text{O}_3$$

$$M = \frac{0.687124 \text{ mol C}_3\text{H}_8\text{O}_3}{0.25000 \text{ L solution}} = 2.7485 \, M \text{ C}_3\text{H}_8\text{O}_3$$

Solution Stoichiometry and Chemcial Analysis (section 4.6)

4.79   *Analyze.* Given: volume and molarity $AgNO_3$. Find: mass KCl.

Plan. $M \times L$ = mol $AgNO_3$ = mol Ag^+; balanced equation gives ratio mol KCl/mol $AgNO_3$; mol KCl → g KCl.   *Solve.*

$$\frac{0.200 \text{ mol AgNO}_3}{1 \text{ L}} \times 0.0150 \text{ L} = 3.00 \times 10^{-3} \text{ mol AgNO}_3 \text{(aq)}$$

$AgNO_3\text{(aq)} + KCl\text{(aq)} \rightarrow AgCl\text{(s)} + KNO_3\text{(aq)}$

mol KCl = mol $AgNO_3$ = 3.00×10^{-3} mol KCl

$$3.00 \times 10^{-3} \text{ mol KCl} \times \frac{74.55 \text{ g KCl}}{1 \text{ mol KCl}} = 0.224 \text{ g KCl}$$

Check. $(0.2 \times 0.015) = 0.003$ mol; $(0.003 \times 75) \approx 0.225$ g KCl

4.80   *Plan.* $M \times L$ = mol $Cd(NO_3)_2$; balanced equation → mol ratio → mol NaOH → g NaOH

Solve. $\dfrac{0.500 \text{ mol Cd(NO}_3)_2}{1 \text{ L}} \times 0.0350 \text{ L} = 0.0175 \text{ mol Cd(NO}_3)_2$

$Cd(NO_3)_2\text{(aq)} + 2NaOH\text{(aq)} \rightarrow Cd(OH)_2\text{(s)} + 2NaNO_3\text{(aq)}$

$$0.0175 \text{ mol Cd(NO}_3)_2 \times \frac{2 \text{ mol NaOH}}{1 \text{ mol Cd(NO}_3)_2} \times \frac{40.00 \text{ g NaOH}}{1 \text{ mol NaOH}} = 1.40 \text{ g NaOH}$$

4.81   (a)   *Analyze.* Given: M and vol base, M acid. Find: vol acid

Plan/Solve. Write the balanced equation for the reaction in question:

$HClO_4\text{(aq)} + NaOH\text{(aq)} \rightarrow NaClO_4\text{(aq)} + H_2O\text{(l)}$

Calculate the moles of the known substance, in this case NaOH.

$$\text{moles NaOH} = M \times L = \frac{0.0875 \text{ mol NaOH}}{1 \text{ L}} \times 0.0500 \text{ L} = 0.004375 = 0.00438 \text{ mol NaOH}$$

Apply the mole ratio (mol unknown/mol known) from the chemical equation.

$$0.004375 \text{ mol NaOH} \times \frac{1 \text{ mol HClO}_4}{1 \text{ mol NaOH}} = 0.004375 \text{ mol HClO}_4$$

Calculate the desired quantity of unknown, in this case the volume of 0.115 M $HClO_4$ solution.

$$L = \text{mol}/M; \; L = 0.004375 \text{ mol HClO}_4 \times \frac{1 \text{ L}}{0.115 \text{ mol HClO}_4} = 0.0380 \text{ L} = 38.0 \text{ mL}$$

Check. $(0.09 \times 0.05) = 0.0045$ mol; $(0.0045/0.11) \approx 0.040$ L ≈ 40 mL

(b)   Following the logic outlined in part (a):

$$2HCl(aq) + Mg(OH)_2(s) \rightarrow MgCl_2(aq) + 2H_2O(l)$$

$$2.87 \text{ g Mg(OH)}_2 \times \frac{1 \text{ mol Mg(OH)}_2}{58.32 \text{ g Mg(OH)}_2} = 0.049211 = 0.0492 \text{ mol Mg(OH)}_2$$

$$0.0492 \text{ mol Mg(OH)}_2 \times \frac{2 \text{ mol HCl}}{1 \text{ mol Mg(OH)}_2} = 0.0984 \text{ mol HCl}$$

$$L = \text{mol}/M = 0.09840 \text{ mol HCl} \times \frac{1 \text{ L HCl}}{0.128 \text{ mol HCl}} = 0.769 \text{ L} = 769 \text{ mL}$$

(c) $AgNO_3(aq) + KCl(aq) \rightarrow AgCl(s) + KNO_3(aq)$

$$785 \text{ mg KCl} \times \frac{1 \times 10^{-3} \text{ g}}{1 \text{ mg}} \times \frac{1 \text{ mol KCl}}{74.55 \text{ g KCl}} \times \frac{1 \text{ mol AgNO}_3}{1 \text{ mol KCl}} = 0.01053 = 0.0105 \text{ mol AgNO}_3$$

$$M = \text{mol}/L = \frac{0.01053 \text{ mol AgNO}_3}{0.0258 \text{ L}} = 0.408 \text{ } M \text{ AgNO}_3$$

(d) $HCl(aq) + KOH(aq) \rightarrow KCl(aq) + H_2O(l)$

$$\frac{0.108 \text{ mol HCl}}{1 \text{ L}} \times 0.0453 \text{ L} \times \frac{1 \text{ mol KOH}}{1 \text{ mol HCl}} \times \frac{56.11 \text{ g KOH}}{1 \text{ mol KOH}} = 0.275 \text{ g KOH}$$

4.82   (a) $2HCl(aq) + Ba(OH)_2(aq) \rightarrow BaCl_2(aq) + 2H_2O(l)$

$$\frac{0.101 \text{ mol Ba(OH)}_2}{1 \text{ L Ba(OH)}_2} \times 0.0500 \text{ L Ba(OH)}_2 \times \frac{2 \text{ mol HCl}}{1 \text{ mol Ba(OH)}_2} \times \frac{1 \text{ L HCl}}{0.120 \text{ mol HCl}}$$
$$= 0.0842 \text{ L or } 84.2 \text{ mL HCl soln}$$

(b) $H_2SO_4(aq) + 2NaOH(aq) \rightarrow Na_2SO_4(aq) + 2H_2O(l)$

$$0.200 \text{ g NaOH} \times \frac{1 \text{ mol NaOH}}{40.00 \text{ g NaOH}} \times \frac{1 \text{ mol H}_2SO_4}{2 \text{ mol NaOH}} \times \frac{1 \text{ L H}_2SO_4}{0.125 \text{ mol H}_2SO_4}$$
$$= 0.0200 \text{ L or } 20.0 \text{ mL H}_2SO_4 \text{ soln}$$

(c) $BaCl_2(aq) + Na_2SO_4(aq) \rightarrow BaSO_4(s) + 2NaCl(aq)$

$$752 \text{ mg} = 0.752 \text{ g Na}_2SO_4 \times \frac{1 \text{ mol Na}_2SO_4}{142.1 \text{ g Na}_2SO_4} \times \frac{1 \text{ mol BaCl}_2}{1 \text{ mol Na}_2SO_4} \times \frac{1}{0.0558 \text{ L}}$$
$$= 0.0948 \text{ M BaCl}_2$$

(d) $2HCl(aq) + Ca(OH)_2(aq) \rightarrow CaCl_2(aq) + 2H_2O(l)$

$$0.0427 \text{ L HCl} \times \frac{0.208 \text{ mol HCl}}{1 \text{ L HCl}} \times \frac{1 \text{ mol Ca(OH)}_2}{2 \text{ mol HCl}} \times \frac{74.10 \text{ g Ca(OH)}_2}{1 \text{ mol Ca(OH)}_2} = 0.329 \text{ g Ca(OH)}_2$$

4.83   *Analyze/Plan.* See Exercise 4.81(a) for a more detailed approach.   *Solve.*

$$\frac{6.0 \text{ mol H}_2SO_4}{1 \text{ L}} \times 0.027 \text{ L} \times \frac{2 \text{ mol NaHCO}_3}{1 \text{ mol H}_2SO_4} \times \frac{84.01 \text{ g NaHCO}_3}{1 \text{ mol NaHCO}_3} = 27 \text{ g NaHCO}_3$$

4.84   See Exercise 4.81(a) for a more detailed approach.

$$\frac{0.115\,\text{mol NaOH}}{1\,\text{L}} \times 0.0425\,\text{L} \times \frac{1\,\text{mol CH}_3\text{COOH}}{1\,\text{mol NaOH}} \times \frac{60.05\,\text{g CH}_3\text{COOH}}{1\,\text{mol CH}_3\text{COOH}}$$

$$= 0.29349 = 0.293\,\text{g CH}_3\text{COOH in 3.45 mL}$$

$$1.00\,\text{qt vinegar} \times \frac{1\,\text{L}}{1.057\,\text{qt}} \times \frac{1000\,\text{mL}}{1\,\text{L}} \times \frac{0.29349\,\text{g CH}_3\text{COOH}}{3.45\,\text{mL vinegar}} = 80.5\,\text{g CH}_3\text{COOH/qt}$$

4.85   *Analyze.* Given: M and vol HCl. Find: MM of base, an alkali metal hydroxide.

Plan. Alkali metal ions have a 1+ charge, so the general mormula of an alkali metal hydroxide is MOH. One mol of MOH requires one mol of HCl for neutralization.

(a) $M \times \text{L} = \text{mol HCl} = \text{mol MOH}$. $\text{MM} = \dfrac{\text{g MOH}}{1\,\text{mol MOH}}$. *Solve.*

$$\frac{2.50\,\text{mol HCl}}{1\,\text{L}} \times 0.0170\,\text{L} = 0.0425\,\text{mol HCl} = 0.0425\,\text{mol MOH}$$

$$\text{MM of MOH} = \frac{4.36\,\text{g MOH}}{0.0425\,\text{mol MOH}} = 102.59 = 103\,\text{g/mol}$$

(b)   MM of alkali metal = MM of MOH – (17.01 g)   *Solve.*

MM of alkali metal = (102.59 g/mol – 17.01 g/mol) = 85.58 = 86 g/mol

The experimental molar mass most closely fits that of Rb^+, 85.47 g/mol

Check. The experimental molar mass matches one of the alkali metals.

4.86   *Analyze/Plan.* Follow the logic in Exercise 4.85. The unknown is a group 2A metal hydroxide, general formula $M(OH)_2$. Two mol HCL are required to neutralize 1 mol $M(OH)_2$. *Solve.*

(a) $\dfrac{2.50\,\text{mol HCl}}{1\,\text{L}} \times 0.0569\,\text{L} \times \dfrac{1\,\text{mol M(OH)}_2}{2\,\text{mol HCl}} = 0.071125 = 0.0711\,\text{mol M(OH)}_2$

$$\text{MM of M(OH)}_2 = \frac{8.65\,\text{g M(OH)}_2}{0.071125\,\text{mol M(OH)}_2} = 121.62 = 122\,\text{g/mol}$$

(b)   MM of group 2A metal = MM of $M(OH)_2$ – 2(17.01 g)   *Solve.*

MM of group 2A metal = (121.62 g/mol – 34.02 g/mol) = 87.60 = 88 g/mol

The experimental molar mass most closely fits that of Sr^{2+}, 87.62 g/mol

Check. The experimental molar mass matches one of the group 2A metals.

4.87   (a) $NiSO_4(aq) + 2KOH(aq) \rightarrow Ni(OH)_2(s) + K_2SO_4(aq)$

(b)   The precipitate is $Ni(OH)_2$.

(c)   *Plan.* Compare mol of each reactant; mol = $M \times$ L

Solve. 0.200 M KOH × 0.1000 L KOH = 0.0200 mol KOH

0.150 M $NiSO_4$ × 0.2000 L KOH = 0.0300 mol $NiSO_4$

1 mol $NiSO_4$ requires 2 mol KOH, so 0.0300 mol $NiSO_4$ requires 0.0600 mol KOH. Since only 0.0200 mol KOH is available, KOH is the limiting reactant.

(d)   *Plan.* The amount of the limiting reactant (KOH) determines amount of product, in this case $Ni(OH)_2$.

Solve. $0.0200 \text{ mol KOH} \times \dfrac{1 \text{ mol Ni(OH)}_2}{2 \text{ mol KOH}} \times \dfrac{92.71 \text{ g Ni(OH)}_2}{1 \text{ mol Ni(OH)}_2} = 0.927 \text{ g Ni(OH)}_2$

(e)   *Plan/Solve.* Limiting reactant: OH^-: no excess OH^- remains in solution.

Excess reactant: Ni^{2+}: M Ni^{2+} remaining = mol Ni^{2+} remaining/L solution

$0.0300 \text{ mol Ni}^{2+}$ initial – $0.0100 \text{ mol Ni}^{2+}$ reacted = $0.0200 \text{ mol Ni}^{2+}$ remaining

$0.0200 \text{ mol Ni}^{2+}/0.3000 \text{ L} = 0.0667 \ M \ Ni^{2+}(aq)$

Spectators: SO_4^{2-}, K^+. These ions do not react, so the only change in their concentration is dilution. The final volume of the solution is 0.3000 L.

$M_2 = M_1V_1/V_2$: $0.200 \ M \ K^+ \times 0.1000 \text{ L}/0.3000 \text{ L} = 0.0667 \ M \ K^+(aq)$

$0.150 \ M \ SO_4^{2-} \times 0.2000 \text{ L}/0.3000 \text{ L} = 0.100 \ M \ SO_4^{2-}(aq)$

4.88   (a) $2HNO_3(aq) + Sr(OH)_2(s) \rightarrow Sr(NO_3)_2(aq) + 2H_2O(l)$

(b)   Determine the limiting reactant, then the identity and concentration of ions remaining in solution. Assume that the $H_2O(l)$ produced by the reaction does **not** increase the total solution volume.

$15.0 \text{ g Sr(OH)}_2 \times \dfrac{1 \text{ mol Sr(OH)}_2}{121.64 \text{ g Sr(OH)}_2} = 0.1233 = 0.123 \text{ mol Sr(OH)}_2$

$\text{mol } OH^- = 2(0.1233) \text{ mol Sr(OH)}_2 = 0.2466 = 0.247 \text{ mol } OH^-$

$0.200 \ M \ HNO_3 \times 0.0550 \text{ L HNO}_3 = 0.0110 \text{ mol HNO}_3.$

Two mol HNO_3 react with one mol $Sr(OH)_2$, so HNO_3 is the limiting reactant. No excess H^+ remains in solution. The remaining ions are OH^- (excess reactant), Sr^{2+}, and NO_3^- (spectators).

OH^-: $0.2466 \text{ mol } OH^-$ initial – $0.0110 \text{ mol } OH^-$ react = $0.2356 = 0.236 \text{ mol } OH^-$ remain

$0.2356 \text{ mol } OH^-/0.0550 \text{ L soln} = 4.28 \ M \ OH^-(aq)$

Sr^{2+}: $0.123 \text{ mol Sr}^{2+}/0.0550 \text{ L soln} = 2.24 \ M \ Sr^{2+}(aq)$

NO_3^-: $0.0110 \text{ mol NO}_3^-/0.0550 \text{ L} = 0.200 \ M \ NO_3^-(aq)$

(c)   The resulting solution is **basic** because of the large excess of $OH^-(aq)$.

4.89   *Analyze.* Given: mass impure $Mg(OH)_2$; M and vol **excess** HCl; M and vol NaOH.

Find: mass % $Mg(OH)_2$ in sample. *Plan/Solve.* Write balanced equations.

$Mg(OH)_2(s) + 2HCl(aq) \rightarrow MgCl_2(aq) + 2H_2O(l)$

$HCl(aq) + NaOH(aq) \rightarrow NaCl(aq) + H_2O(l)$

Calculate total moles HCl = M HCl × L HCl

$\dfrac{0.2050 \text{ mol HCl}}{1 \text{ L soln}} \times 0.1000 \text{ L} = 0.02050 \text{ mol HCl total}$

mol excess HCl = mol NaOH used = M NaOH × L NaOH

$$\frac{0.1020 \text{ mol NaOH}}{1 \text{ L soln}} \times 0.01985 \text{ L} = 0.0020247 = 0.002025 \text{ mol NaOH}$$

mol HCl reacted with $Mg(OH)_2$ = total mol HCl – excess mol HCl

0.02050 mol total – 0.0020247 mol excess = 0.0184753 = 0.01848 mol HCl reacted

(The result has 5 decimal places and 4 sig. figs.)

Use mol ratio to get mol $Mg(OH)_2$ in sample, then molar mass of $Mg(OH)_2$ to get g pure $Mg(OH)_2$.

$$0.0184753 \text{ mol HCl} \times \frac{1 \text{ mol Mg(OH)}_2}{2 \text{ mol HCl}} \times \frac{58.32 \text{ g Mg(OH)}_2}{1 \text{ mol Mg(OH)}_2} = 0.5387 \text{ Mg(OH)}_2$$

$$\text{mass \% Mg(OH)}_2 = \frac{\text{g Mg(OH)}_2}{\text{g sample}} \times 100 = \frac{0.5388 \text{ g Mg(OH)}_2}{0.5895 \text{ g sample}} \times 100 = 91.40\% \text{ Mg(OH)}_2$$

4.90   *Plan.* $CaCO_3(s) + 2HCl(aq) \rightarrow CaCl_2(aq) + H_2O(l) + CO_2(g)$

$\qquad\qquad$ $HCl(aq) + NaOH(aq) \rightarrow NaCl(aq) + H_2O(l)$

total mol HCl – excess mol HCl = mol HCl reacted; mol $CaCO_3$ = (mol HCl)/2;

g $CaCO_3$ = mol $CaCO_3$ × molar mass; mass % = (g $CaCO_3$/g sample) × 100

Solve:

$$\frac{1.035 \text{ mol HCl}}{1 \text{ L soln}} \times 0.03000 \text{ L} = 0.031050 = 0.03105 \text{ mol HCl total}$$

$$\frac{1.010 \text{ mol NaOH}}{1 \text{ L soln}} \times 0.01156 \text{ L} = 0.011676 = 0.01168 \text{ mol HCl excess}$$

0.031050 total – 0.011676 excess = 0.019374 = 0.01937 mol HCl reacted

$$0.019374 \text{ mol HCl} \times \frac{1 \text{ mol CaCO}_3}{2 \text{ mol HCl}} \times \frac{100.09 \text{ g CaCO}_3}{1 \text{ mol CaCO}_3} = 0.96959 = 0.9696 \text{ g CaCO}_3$$

$$\text{mass \% CaCO}_3 = \frac{\text{g CaCO}_3}{\text{g rock}} \times 100 = \frac{0.96959}{1.248} \times 100 = 77.69\% \text{ CaCO}_3$$

Additional Exercises

4.91   Gold is one of the least active metals, and it is extremely dense. These two properties make it possible to find gold by panning. Inactivity means that gold is not oxidized in air and does not react with water, so it exists in its elemental state in nature. High density means that the gold nuggets sink to the bottom of the pan where they can be observed and physically separated from other materials in the pan.

4.92   The precipitate is CdS(s). $Na^+(aq)$ and $NO_3^-(aq)$ are spectator ions and remain in solution. Any excess reactant ions also remain in solution. The net ionic equation is:

$Cd^{2+}(aq) + S^{2-}(aq) \rightarrow CdS(s)$.

4.93 The two precipitates formed are due to AgCl(s) and $SrSO_4$(s). Since no precipitate forms on addition of hydroxide ion to the remaining solution, the other two possibilities, Ni^{2+} and Mn^{2+}, are absent.

4.94 (a,b) Expt. 1 No reaction

Expt. 2 $2Ag^+$(aq) + $CrO_4{}^{2-}$(aq) → Ag_2CrO_4(s) red precipitate

Expt. 3 Ca^{2+}(aq) + $CrO_4{}^{2-}$(aq) → $CaCrO_4$(s) yellow precipitate

Expt. 4 $2Ag^+$(aq) + $C_2O_4{}^{2-}$(aq) → $Ag_2C_2O_4$(s) white precipitate

Expt. 5 Ca^{2+}(aq) + $C_2O_4{}^{2-}$(aq) → CaC_2O_4(s) white precipitate

Expt. 6 Ag^+(aq) + Cl^-(aq) → AgCl(s) white precipitate

4.95 (a) $Al(OH)_3$(s) + $3H^+$(aq) → Al^{3+}(aq) + $3H_2O$(l)

(b) $Mg(OH)_2$(s) + $2H^+$(aq) → Mg^{2+}(aq) + $2H_2O$(l)

(c) $MgCO_3$(s) + $2H^+$(aq) → Mg^{2+}(aq) + H_2O(l) + CO_2(g)

(d) $NaAl(CO_3)(OH)_2$(s) + $4H^+$(aq) → Na^+(aq) + Al^{3+}(aq) + $3H_2O$(l) + CO_2(g)

(e) $CaCO_3$(s) + $2H^+$(aq) → Ca^{2+}(aq) + H_2O(l) + CO_2(g)

[In (c), (d) and (e), one could also write the equation for formation of bicarbonate, e.g., $MgCO_3$(s) + H^+(aq) → Mg^{2+} + $HCO_3{}^-$(aq).]

4.96 $4NH_3$(g) + $5O_2$(g) → $4NO$(g) + $6H_2O$(g).
N = –3 O = 0 N = +2 O = –2

(a) redox reaction (b) N is oxidized, O is reduced

$2NO$(g) + O_2(g) → $2NO_2$(g).
N = +2 O = 0 N = +4, O = –2

(a) redox reaction (b) N is oxidized, O is reduced

$3NO_2$(g) + H_2O(l) → HNO_3(aq) + NO(g).
N = +4 N = +5 N = +2

(a) redox reaction

(b) N is oxidized (NO_2 → HNO_3), N is reduced (NO_2 → NO). A reaction where the same element is both oxidized and reduced is called disproportionation.

4.97 A metal on Table 4.5 can be oxidized by ions of the elements below it. Or, a metal on the table is able to displace the (metal) cations below it from their compounds.

(a) Zn(s) + $2HNO_3$(aq) → $Zn(NO_3)_2$(aq) + H_2(g)

The substance that inflates the balloon is H_2(g). Of Zn, Cu and Hg, only Zn is above H on Table 4.5, so only Zn can displace H from HCl.

(b) $35.0 \text{ g Zn} \times \dfrac{1 \text{ mol Zn}}{65.39 \text{ g Zn}} = 0.53525 = 0.535 \text{ mol Zn}$

$$\frac{3.00 \text{ mol HNO}_3}{\text{L}} \times 0.150 \text{ L} = 0.450 \text{ mol HNO}_3$$

One mol Zn reacts with 2 mol HNO_3, so HNO_3 is the limiting reactant.

$$0.450 \text{ mol HNO}_3 \times \frac{1 \text{ mol H}_2}{2 \text{ mol HNO}_3} \times \frac{2.016 \text{ g H}_2}{1 \text{ mol H}_2} = 0.4536 = 0.454 \text{ g H}_2$$

(c)   Both Zn and Cu are above Ag on Table 4.5, so both Zn and Cu can displace Ag from $AgNO_3$. Note that $H_2(g)$ would also displace Ag, but $H^+(aq)$ will not.

$Zn(s) + 2AgNO_3(aq) \rightarrow 2Ag(s) + Zn(NO_3)_2(aq)$; $Zn^{2+}(aq)$ and $NO_3^-(aq)$ remain

$Cu(s) + 2AgNO_3(aq) \rightarrow 2Ag(s) + Cu(NO_3)_2(aq)$; $Cu^{2+}(aq)$ and $NO_3^-(aq)$ remain

(d)   0.535 mol Zn [from part (b)]; $42.0 \text{ g Zn} \times \dfrac{1 \text{ mol Zn}}{63.546 \text{ g Cu}} = 0.6609 = 0.661 \text{ mol Cu}$

$$\frac{0.750 \text{ mol AgNO}_3}{\text{L}} \times 0.150 \text{ L} = 0.1125 = 0.113 \text{ mol AgNO}_3$$

One mol metal reacts with 2 mol $AgNO_3$, so $AgNO_3$ is the limiting reactant for both Zn and Cu.

$$0.1125 \text{ mol AgNO}_3 \times \frac{107.87 \text{ g Ag}}{1 \text{ mol Ag}} = 12.135 = 12.1 \text{ g Ag in both reactions}$$

4.98   (a) $A : La_2O_3$ Metals often react with the oxygen in air to produce metal oxides.

                     $B : La(OH)_3$ When metals react with water (HOH) to form H_2, OH^- remains.

                     $C : LaCl_3$ Most chlorides are soluble.

                     $D : La_2(SO_4)_3$ Sulfuric acid provides SO_4^{2-} ions.

     (b) $4La(s) + 3O_2(g) \rightarrow 2La_2O_3(s)$

           $2La(s) + 6 H_2O(l) \rightarrow 2La(OH)_3(s) + 3H_2(g)$

           (There are no spectator ions in either of these reactions.)

           molecular: $La_2O_3(s) + 6HCl(aq) \rightarrow 2LaCl_3(aq) + 3H_2O(l)$

           net ionic: $La_2O_3(s) + 6H^+(aq) \rightarrow 2La^{3+}(aq) + 3H_2O(l)$

           molecular: $La(OH)_3(s) + 3HCl(aq) \rightarrow LaCl_3(aq) + 3H_2O(l)$

           net ionic: $La(OH)_3(s) + 3H^+(aq) \rightarrow La^{3+}(aq) + 3H_2O(l)$

           molecular: $2LaCl_3(aq) + 3H_2SO_4(aq) \rightarrow La_2(SO_4)_3(s) + 6HCl(aq)$

           net ionic: $2La^{3+}(aq) + 3SO_4^{2-}(aq) \rightarrow La_2(SO_4)_3(s)$

     (c)   La metal is oxidized by water to produce $H_2(g)$, so La is definitely above H_2 on the activity series. In fact, since an acid is not required to oxidize La, it is probably one of the more active metals.

4.99   *Plan.* Calculate moles KBr from the two quantities of solution (mol = $M \times$ L), then new molarity (M = mol/L). KBr is nonvolatile, so no solute is lost when the solution is evaporated to reduce the total volume. *Solve.*

$1.00\,M$ KBr $\times$ 0.0350 L = 0.0350 mol KBr; $0.600\,M$ KBr $\times$ 0.060 L = 0.0360 mol KBr

0.0350 mol KBr + 0.0360 mol KBr = 0.0710 mol KBr total

$$\frac{0.0710\text{ mol KBr}}{0.0500\text{ L soln}} = 1.42\,M\text{ KBr}$$

4.100   (a) $\dfrac{50\text{ pg}}{1\text{ mL}} \times \dfrac{1\times10^{-12}\text{ g}}{1\text{ pg}} \times \dfrac{1\times10^{3}\text{ mL}}{\text{L}} \times \dfrac{1\text{ mol Na}}{23.0\text{ g Na}} = 2.17\times10^{-9} = 2.2\times10^{-9}\,M\text{ Na}^{+}$

           (b) $\dfrac{2.17\times10^{-9}\text{ mol Na}}{1\text{ L soln}} \times \dfrac{1\text{ L}}{1\times10^{3}\text{ cm}^{3}} \times \dfrac{6.02\times10^{23}\text{ Na atom}}{1\text{ mol Na}}$

$$= 1.3\times10^{12}\text{ atom or Na}^{+}\text{ ions/cm}^{3}$$

4.101   (a)   Na^{+} must replace the total positive (+) charge due to Ca^{2+} and Mg^{2+}. Think of this as moles of charge rather than moles of particles.

$$\frac{0.020\text{ mol Ca}^{2+}}{1\text{ L water}} \times 1.5\times10^{3}\text{ L} \times \frac{2\text{ mol + change}}{1\text{ mol Ca}^{2+}} = 60\text{ mol of + charge}$$

$$\frac{0.0040\text{ mol Mg}^{2+}}{1\text{ L water}} \times 1.5\times10^{3}\text{ L} \times \frac{2\text{ mol + charge}}{1\text{ mol Mg}^{2+}} = 12\text{ mol of + charge}$$

72 moles of + charge must be replaced; 72 mol Na^{+} are needed.

           (b) $72\text{ mol Na}^{+} \times \dfrac{1\text{ mol Na}^{+}}{1\text{ mol NaCl}} \times \dfrac{58.44\text{ g NaCl}}{1\text{ mol NaCl}} = 4208\text{ g} = 4.2\times10^{3}\text{ g Ag}$

4.102 $H_2C_4H_4O_6 + 2OH^{-}(aq) \rightarrow C_4H_4O_6{}^{2-}(aq) + 2H_2O(l)$

         $0.02465\text{ L NaOH soln} \times \dfrac{0.2500\text{ mol NaOH}}{1\text{ L}} \times \dfrac{1\text{ mol }H_2C_4H_4O_6}{2\text{ mol NaOH}} \times \dfrac{1}{0.0500\text{ L }H_2C_4H_4O_6}$

$$= 0.06163\,M\,H_2C_4H_4O_6\text{ soln}$$

4.103   (a) $10.45\text{ g Sr(OH)}_2 \times \dfrac{1\text{ mol Sr(OH)}_2}{121.64\text{ g Sr(OH)}_2} \times \dfrac{1}{0.05000\text{ L}} = 1.7182 = 1.718\,M\text{ Sr(OH)}_2$

           (b) $2\,HNO_3(aq) + Sr(OH)_2(s) \rightarrow Sr(NO_3)_2(aq) + 2H_2O(l)$

           (c)   *Plan.* mol Sr(OH)$_2$ = $M \times$ L $\rightarrow$ mol ratio $\rightarrow$ mol HNO$_3$ $\rightarrow$ M HNO$_3$.   *Solve.*

$$\frac{1.7182\text{ mol Sr(OH)}_2}{\text{L}} \times 0.0239\text{ L Sr(OH)}_2 \times \frac{2\text{ mol HNO}_3}{1\text{ mol Sr(OH)}_2} \times \frac{1}{0.0315\text{ L HNO}_3}$$

$$= 2.6073 = 2.61\,M\text{ HNO}_3$$

4.104   mol OH^{-} from NaOH(aq) + mol OH^{-} from Zn(OH)$_2$(s) = mol H^{+} from HBr

         mol H^{+} = M HBr $\times$ L HBr = $0.500\,M$ HBr $\times$ 0.350 L HBr = 0.175 mol H^{+}

         mol OH^{-} from NaOH = M NaOH $\times$ L NaOH = $0.500\,M$ NaOH $\times$ 0.0885 L NaOH

$$= 0.04425 = 0.0443\text{ mol OH}^{-}$$

$$\text{mol OH}^- \text{ from Zn(OH)}_2\text{(s)} = 0.175 \text{ mol H}^+ - 0.04425 \text{ mol OH}^- \text{ from NaOH} = 0.13075$$

$$= 0.131 \text{ mol OH}^- \text{ from Zn(OH)}_2$$

$$0.13075 \text{ mol OH}^- \times \frac{1 \text{ mol Zn(OH)}_2}{2 \text{ mol OH}^-} \times \frac{99.41 \text{ g Zn(OH)}_2}{1 \text{ mol Zn(OH)}_2} = 6.50 \text{ g Zn(OH)}_2$$

Integrative Exercises

4.105 (a) A metal can be oxidized by ions of the elements below it on Table 4.5. Of the three substances given, K^+(aq) is above Mg(s), but Ag^+(aq) is below it, so $AgNO_3$(aq) will react with Mg(s).

(b) $Mg(s) + 2Ag^+(aq) \rightarrow Mg^{2+}(aq) + 2Ag(s)$

(c) g Mg $\rightarrow$ mol Mg $\rightarrow$ [via mole ratio] mol Ag^+ $\rightarrow$ [via (mol/M)] vol $AgNO_3$(aq)

$$5.00 \text{ g Mg} \times \frac{1 \text{ mol Mg}}{24.305 \text{g Mg}} = 0.2057 = 0.206 \text{ mol Mg}$$

$$0.2057 \text{ mol Mg} \times \frac{2 \text{ mol AgNO}_3}{1 \text{ mol Mg}} \times \frac{1.00 \text{ L}}{2.00 \text{ mol AgNO}_3} = 0.2057 = 0.206 \text{ L AgNO}_3\text{(aq)}$$

(d) $\dfrac{0.2057 \text{ mol Mg}^{2+}}{0.2057 \text{ L soln}} = 1.00 \ M \ \text{Mg}^{2+}\text{(aq)}$

4.106 (a) At the equivalence point of a titration, mol NaOH added = mol H^+ present

$$M_{\text{NaOH}} \times L_{\text{NaOH}} = \frac{\text{g acid}}{\text{MM acid}} \text{ (for an acid with 1 acidic hydrogen)}$$

$$\text{MM acid} = \frac{\text{g acid}}{M_{\text{NaOH}} \times L_{\text{NaOH}}} = \frac{0.2053 \text{ g}}{0.1008 \ M \times 0.0150 \text{ L}} = 136 \text{ g/mol}$$

(b) Assume 100 g of acid.

$$70.6 \text{ g C} \times \frac{1 \text{ mol C}}{12.01 \text{g C}} = 5.88 \text{ mol C}; \ 5.88 / 1.47 \approx 4$$

$$5.89 \text{ g H} \times \frac{1 \text{ mol H}}{1.008 \text{ g H}} = 5.84 \text{ mol H}; \ 5.84 / 1.47 \approx 4$$

$$23.5 \text{ g O} \times \frac{1 \text{ mol O}}{16.00 \text{ g O}} = 1.47 \text{ mol O}; \ 1.47 / 1.47 = 1$$

The empirical formula is C_4H_4O.

$$\frac{\text{MM}}{\text{FW}} = \frac{136}{68.1} = 2; \text{ the molecular formula is } 2 \times \text{ the empirical formula.}$$

The molecular formula is $C_8H_8O_2$.

4.107 $Ba^{2+}(aq) + SO_4{}^{2-}(aq) \rightarrow BaSO_4(s)$

$$0.2815 \text{ g BaSO}_4 \times \frac{137.3 \text{ g Ba}}{233.4 \text{ g BaSO}_4} = 0.16560 = 0.1656 \text{ g Ba}$$

$$\text{mass \%} = \frac{\text{g Ba}}{\text{g sample}} \times 100 = \frac{0.16560 \text{ g Ba}}{3.455 \text{ g sample}} \times 100 = 4.793 \text{ \% Ba}$$

4.108   *Plan.* Write balanced equation.

mass H_2SO_4 soln $\xrightarrow{\text{mass \%}}$ mass $H_2SO_4 \rightarrow$ mol $H_2SO_4 \rightarrow$ mol $Na_2CO_3 \rightarrow$ mass Na_2CO_3

Solve. $H_2SO_4(aq) + Na_2CO_3(s) \rightarrow Na_2SO_4(aq) + H_2O(l) + CO_2(g)$

$$5.0 \times 10^3 \text{ kg conc. } H_2SO_4 \times \frac{0.950 \text{ kg } H_2SO_4}{1.00 \text{ kg conc. } H_2SO_4} = 4.75 \times 10^3 = 4.8 \times 10^3 \text{ kg } H_2SO_4$$

$$4.75 \times 10^3 \text{ kg } H_2SO_4 \times \frac{1 \times 10^3 \text{ g}}{1 \text{ kg}} \times \frac{1 \text{ mol } H_2SO_4}{98.08 \text{ g } H_2SO_4} \times \frac{1 \text{ mol } Na_2CO_3}{1 \text{ mol } H_2SO_4}$$

$$\times \frac{105.99 \text{ g } NaHCO_3}{1 \text{ mol } NaHCO_3} \times \frac{1 \text{ kg}}{1 \times 10^3 \text{ g}} = 5.133 \times 10^3 = 5.1 \times 10^3 \text{ kg } Na_2CO_3$$

4.109   (a) $Mg(OH)_2(s) + 2HNO_3(aq) \rightarrow Mg(NO_3)_2(aq) + 2H_2O(l)$

(b) $5.53 \text{ g } Mg(OH)_2 \times \dfrac{1 \text{ mol } Mg(OH)_2}{58.32 \text{ g } Mg(OH)_2} = 0.09482 = 0.0948 \text{ mol } Mg(OH)_2$

$0.200 \, M \, HNO_3 \times 0.0250 \text{ L} = 0.00500 \text{ mol } HNO_3$

The 0.00500 mol HNO_3 would neutralize 0.00250 mol $Mg(OH)_2$ and much more $Mg(OH)_2$ is present, so HNO_3 is the limiting reactant.

(c)   Since HNO_3 limits, 0 mol HNO_3 is present after reaction.

0.00250 mol $Mg(NO_3)_2$ is produced.

0.09482 mol $Mg(OH)_2$ initial – 0.00250 mol $Mg(OH)_2$ react

$$= 0.0923 \text{ mol } Mg(OH)_2 \text{ remain}$$

4.110   (a) $Na_2SO_4(aq) + Pb(NO_3)_2(s) \rightarrow PbSO_4(s) + 2NaNO_3(aq)$

(b)   Calculate mol of each reactant and compare.

$$1.50 \text{ g } Pb(NO_3)_2 \times \frac{1 \text{ mol } Pb(NO_3)_2}{331.2 \text{ g } Pb(NO_3)_2} = 0.004529 = 4.53 \times 10^{-3} \text{ mol } Pb(NO_3)_2$$

$0.100 \, M \, Na_2SO_4 \times 0.125 \text{ L} = 0.0125 \text{ mol } Na_2SO_4$

Since the reactants combine in a 1:1 mol ratio, $Pb(NO_3)_2$ is the limiting reactant.

(c) $Pb(NO_3)_2$ is the limiting reactant, so no Pb^{2+} remains in solution. The remaining ions are: SO_4^{2-} (excess reactant), Na^+ and NO_3^- (spectators).

SO_4^{2-}:   0.0125 mol SO_4^{2-} initial – 0.00453 mol SO_4^{2-} reacted

$$= 0.00797 = 0.0080 \text{ mol } SO_4^{2-} \text{ remain}$$

0.00797 mol SO_4^{2-} / 0.125 L soln = 0.064 $M \, SO_4^{2-}$

Na^+:   Since the total volume of solution is the volume of $Na_2SO_4(aq)$ added, the concentration of Na^+ is unchanged.

$0.100 \, M \, Na_2SO_4 \times (2 \text{ mol } Na^+ / 1 \text{ mol } Na_2SO_4) = 0.200 \, M \, Na^+$

NO_3^-: 4.53×10^{-3} mol $Pb(NO_3)_2 \times 2$ mol NO_3^- / 1 mol $Pb(NO_3)_2$

$$= 9.06 \times 10^{-3} \text{ mol } NO_3^-$$

$$9.06 \times 10^{-3} \text{ mol } NO_3^- / 0.125 \text{ L} = 0.0725 \, M \, NO_3^-$$

4.111   *Plan.* $M = \dfrac{\text{mol } Br^-}{\text{L seawater}}$; mg $Br^- \rightarrow$ g $Br^- \rightarrow$ mol Br^-;

1 kg seawater $\rightarrow$ g $\xrightarrow{\text{density}}$ mL water $\rightarrow$ L seawater

Solve. 65 mg $Br^- \times \dfrac{1 \text{ g } Br^-}{1000 \text{ mg } Br^-} \times \dfrac{1 \text{ mol } Br^-}{79.90 \text{ g } Br^-} = 8.135 \times 10^{-4} = 8.1 \times 10^{-4}$ mol Br^-

1 kg seawater $\times \dfrac{1000 \text{ g}}{1 \text{ kg}} \times \dfrac{1 \text{ mL water}}{1.025 \text{ g water}} \times \dfrac{1 \text{ L}}{1000 \text{ mL}} = 0.9756$ L

$M \, Br^- = \dfrac{8.135 \times 10^{-4} \text{ mol } Br^-}{0.9756 \text{ L seawater}} = 8.3 \times 10^{-4} \, M \, Br^-$

4.112 $Ag^+(aq) + Cl^-(aq) \rightarrow AgCl(s)$

$\dfrac{0.2997 \text{ mol } Ag^+}{1 \text{ L}} \times 0.04258 \text{ L} \times \dfrac{1 \text{ mol } Cl^-}{1 \text{ mol } Ag^+} \times \dfrac{35.453 \text{ g } Cl^-}{1 \text{ mol } Cl^-} = 0.45242 = 0.4524$ g Cl^-

25.00 mL seawater $\times \dfrac{1.025 \text{ g}}{\text{mL}} = 25.625 = 25.63$ g seawater

mass % $Cl^- = \dfrac{0.45242 \text{ g } Cl^-}{25.625 \text{ g seawater}} \times 100 = 1.766\% \, Cl^-$

4.113   (a) $AsO_4{}^{3-}$; +5

(b) Ag_3PO_4 is silver phosphate; Ag_3AsO_4 is silver arsenate

(c)   0.0250 L soln $\times \dfrac{0.102 \text{ mol } Ag^+}{1 \text{ L soln}} \times \dfrac{1 \text{ mol } Ag_3AsO_4}{3 \text{ mol } Ag^+} \times \dfrac{1 \text{ mol As}}{1 \text{ mol } Ag_3AsO_4} \times \dfrac{74.92 \text{ g As}}{1 \text{ mol As}}$

$$= 0.06368 = 0.0637 \text{ g As}$$

mass percent $= \dfrac{0.06368 \text{ g As}}{1.22 \text{ g sample}} \times 100 = 5.22\%$ As

4.114   *Analyze.* Given 10 ppb $AsO_4{}^{3-}$, find mass Na_3AsO_4 in 1.00 L of drinking water.

Plan. Use the definition of ppb to calculate g $AsO_4{}^{3-}$ in 1.0 L of water. Convert g

$AsO_4{}^{3-} \rightarrow$ g Na_3AsO_4 using molar masses. Assume the density of H_2O is 1.00 g/mL.

Solve. 1 billion $= 1 \times 10^9$; 1 ppb $= \dfrac{1 \text{ g solute}}{1 \times 10^9 \text{ g solution}}$

$\dfrac{1 \text{ g solute}}{1 \times 10^9 \text{ g solution}} \times \dfrac{1 \text{ g solution}}{1 \text{ mL solution}} \times \dfrac{1 \times 10^3 \text{ mL}}{1 \text{ L solution}} = \dfrac{\text{g } AsO_4{}^{3-}}{1 \times 10^6 \text{ L } H_2O}$

$$10 \text{ ppb AsO}_4{}^{3-} = \frac{10 \text{ g AsO}_4}{1 \times 10^6 \text{ L H}_2\text{O}} \times 1 \text{ L H}_2\text{O} = 1.0 \times 10^{-5} \text{ g As/L}.$$

$$1.0 \times 10^{-5} \text{ g AsO}_4{}^{3-} \times \frac{1 \text{ mol AsO}_4{}^{3-}}{138.92 \text{ g AsO}_4{}^{3-}} \times \frac{1 \text{ mol Na}_3\text{AsO}_4}{1 \text{ mol As}} \times \frac{207.89 \text{ g Na}_3\text{AsO}_4{}^{3-}}{1 \text{ mol Na}_3\text{AsO}_4}$$

$$= 1.5 \times 10^{-5} \text{ g Na}_3\text{AsO}_4 \text{ in } 1.00 \text{ L H}_2\text{O}$$

4.115   (a)   mol HCl initial − mol NH$_3$ from air = mol HCl remaining

$$= \text{mol NaOH required for titration}$$

mol NaOH = 0.0588 M × 0.0131 L = 7.703×10^{-4} = 7.70×10^{-4} mol NaOH

$$= 7.70 \times 10^{-4} \text{ mol HCl remain}$$

mol HCl initial − mol HCl remaining = mol NH$_3$ from air

(0.0105 M HCl × 0.100 L) − 7.703×10^{-4} mol HCl = mol NH$_3$

10.5×10^{-4} mol HCl − 7.703×10^{-4} mol HCl = 2.80×10^{-4} = 2.8×10^{-4} mol NH$_3$

$$2.8 \times 10^{-4} \text{ mol NH}_3 \times \frac{17.03 \text{ g NH}_3}{1 \text{ mol NH}_3} = 4.77 \times 10^{-3} = 4.8 \times 10^{-3} \text{ g NH}_3$$

(b)   ppm is defined as molecules of NH$_3$/1×10^6 molecules in air.

Calculate molecules NH$_3$ from mol NH$_3$.

$$2.80 \times 10^{-4} \text{ mol NH}_3 \times \frac{6.022 \times 10^{23} \text{ molecules}}{1 \text{ mol}} = 1.686 \times 10^{20}$$

$$= 1.7 \times 10^{20} \text{ NH}_3 \text{ molecules}$$

Calculate total volume of air processed, then g air using density, then molecules air using molar mass.

$$\frac{10.0 \text{ L}}{1 \text{ min}} \times 10.0 \text{ min} \times \frac{1.20 \text{ g air}}{1 \text{ L air}} \times \frac{1 \text{ mol air}}{29.0 \text{ g air}} \times \frac{6.022 \times 10^{23} \text{ molecules}}{1 \text{ mol}}$$

$$= 2.492 \times 10^{24} = 2.5 \times 10^{24} \text{ air molecules}$$

$$\text{ppm NH}_3 = \frac{1.686 \times 10^{20} \text{ NH}_3 \text{ molecules}}{2.492 \times 10^{24} \text{ air molecules}} \times 1 \times 10^6 = 68 \text{ ppm NH}_3$$

(c)   68 ppm > 50 ppm. The manufacturer is **not** in compliance.

5 Thermochemistry

Visualizing Concepts

5.1   The book's potential energy is due to the opposition of gravity by an object of mass m at a distance d above the surface of the earth. Kinetic energy is due to the motion of the book. As the book falls, d decreases and potential energy changes into kinetic energy.

The first law states that the total energy of a system is conserved. At the instant before impact, all potential energy has been converted to kinetic energy, so the book's total kinetic energy is 71 J, assuming no transfer of energy as heat.

For an object under the influence of gravity, both potential (E_p = mgd) and kinetic energy (E_k = ½ mv²) are directly proportional to mass of the object. A heavier book falling from the same shelf has greater kinetic energy when it hits the floor.

5.2   (a)   The caterpillar uses energy produced by its metabolism of food to climb the twig and increase its potential energy.

(b)   Heat, q, is the energy transferred from a hotter to a cooler object. Without knowing the temperature of the caterpillar and its surroundings, we cannot predict the sign of q. It is likely that q is approximately zero, since a small creature like a caterpillar is unlikely to support a body temperature much different from its environmental temperature.

(c)   Work, w, is the energy transferred when a force moves an object. When the caterpillar climbs the twig, it does work as its body moves against the force of gravity.

(d)   No. The amount of work is independent of time, and therefore independent of speed (assuming constant caterpillar speed).

(e)   No. Potential energy depends only on the caterpillar's position, so the change in potential energy depends only on the distance climbed, not on the speed of the climb.

5.3   (a)   The internal energy, E, of the products is greater than that of the reactants, so the diagram represents an increase in the internal energy of the system.

(b)   ΔE for this process is positive, +.

(c)   If no work is associated with the process, it is endothermic.

5.4   (a)   For an endothermic process, the sign of q is positive; the system gains heat. This is true only for system (iii).

(b)   In order for ΔE to be less than 0, there is a net transfer of heat or work from the system to the surroundings. The magnitude of the quantity leaving the system is

107

greater than the magnitude of the quantity entering the system. In system (i), the magnitude of the heat leaving the system is less than the magnitude of the work done on the system. In system (iii), the magnitude of the work done by the system is less than the magnitude of the heat entering the system. None of the systems has $\Delta E < 0$.

(c)   In order for ΔE to be greater than 0, there is a net transfer of work or heat to the system from the surroundings. In system (i), the magnitude of the work done on the system is greater than the magnitude of the heat leaving the system. In system (ii), work is done on the system with no change in heat. In system (iii) the magnitude of the heat gained by the system is greater than the magnitude of the work done on the surroundings. $\Delta E > 0$ for all three systems.

5.5   (a).   No. This distance traveled to the top of a mountain depends on the path taken by the hiker. Distance is a path function, not a state function.

(b)   Yes. Change in elevation depends only on the location of the base camp and the height of the mountain, not on the path to the top. Change in elevation is a state function, not a path function.

5.6   (a)   State B

(b) ΔE_{AB} = energy difference between State A and State B.

$\Delta E_{AB} = \Delta E_1 + \Delta E_2$ or $\Delta E_{AB} = \Delta E_3 + \Delta E_4$

(c) ΔE_{CD} = energy difference between State C and State D.

$\Delta E_{CD} = \Delta E_2 - \Delta E_4$ or $\Delta E_{DC} = \Delta E_3 - \Delta E_1$

(Note that the sign of ΔE depends on the definition of initial and final state, but the magnitude is the absolute value of the difference in energy.)

(d)   The energy of State E is $\Delta E_1 + \Delta E_4$, while the energy of State B is $\Delta E_1 + \Delta E_2$. Since $\Delta E_4 > \Delta E_2$, State E is above State B on the diagram; State E would be the highest energy on the diagram.

5.7   (a)   You, part of the surroundings, do work on the air, part of the system. Energy is transferred to the system via work and the sign of w is (+).

(b)   The body of the pump (the system) is warmer than the surroundings. Heat is transferred from the warmer system to the cooler surroundings and the sign of q is (−).

(c)   The sign of w is positive and the sign of q is negative, so we cannot absolutely determine the sign of ΔE. It is likely that the heat lost is much smaller than the work done on the system, so the sign of ΔE is probably positive.

5.8   (a) $w = -P\Delta V$. Since ΔV for the process is (−), the sign of w is (+).

(b) $\Delta E = q + w$. At constant pressure, $\Delta H = q$. If the reaction is endothermic, the signs of ΔH and q are (+). From (a), the sign of w is (+), so the sign of ΔE is (+). The internal energy of the system increases during the change. (This situation is described by the diagram (ii) in Exercise 5.4.)

5.9   (a)   The temperature of the system and surroundings will equalize, so the temperature of the hotter system will decrease and the temperature of the colder surroundings will increase. The system loses heat by decreasing its temperature, so the sign of q_{sys} is (–). The surrounding gains heat by increasing its temperature, so the sign of q_{surr} is (+). From the system's perspective, the process is exothermic because it loses heat.

(b)   If neither volume nor pressure of the system changes, $w = 0$ and $\Delta E = q = \Delta H$. The change in internal energy is equal to the change in enthalpy.

5.10   (a) $N_2(g) + O_2(g) \rightarrow 2NO(g)$. Since $\Delta V = 0$, $w = 0$.

        (b) $\Delta H = \Delta H_f = 90.37$ kJ for production of 1 mol of NO(g). The definition of a formation reaction is one where elements combine to form one mole of a single product. The enthalpy change for such a reaction is the enthalpy of formation.

5.11   (a) $\Delta H_A = \Delta H_B + \Delta H_C$. The net enthalpy change associated with going from the initial state to the final state does not depend on path. The diagram shows that the change can be accomplished via reaction A, or via two successive reactions, B then C, with the same net enthalpy change. $\Delta H_A = \Delta H_B + \Delta H_C$ because ΔH is a state function, independent of path.

        (b) $\Delta H_Z = \Delta H_X + \Delta H_Y$. The diagram indicates that Reaction Z can be written as the sum of reactions X and Y.

        (c)   Hess's law states that the enthalpy change for a net reaction is the sum of the enthalpy changes of the component steps, regardless of whether the reaction actually occurs via this path. The diagrams are a visual statement of Hess's law.

5.12   Since mass must be conserved in the reaction A $\rightarrow$ B, the component elements of A and B must be the same. Further, if $\Delta H_f^\circ > 0$ for both A and B, the energies of both A and B are above the energies of their component elements on the energy diagram.

        (a)   The bold arrow shows the reaction as written; combination of the two thin arrows shows an alternate route from A to B.

        (b) $\Delta H_{rxn}^\circ = \Delta H_f^\circ \, B - \Delta H_f^\circ \, A$. If the overall reaction is exothermic, the sign of ΔH is (–) and $\Delta H_f^\circ \, A > \Delta H_f^\circ \, B$. This means that the enthalpy of A is the highest energy level on the diagram. This is the situation pictured in the diagram above, but nothing in the given information requires this arrangement. If the reaction is endothermic, $\Delta H_f^\circ \, B > \Delta H_f^\circ \, A$ and the enthalpy of B would be the highest energy level on the diagram.

The Nature of Energy (section 5.1)

5.13   An object can possess energy by virtue of its motion or position. Kinetic energy, the energy of motion, depends on the mass of the object and its velocity. Potential energy, stored energy, depends on the position of the object relative to the body with which it interacts.

5.14   (a)   The kinetic energy of the ball **decreases** as it moves higher. As the ball moves higher and opposes gravity, kinetic energy is changed into potential energy.

        (b)   The potential energy of the ball **increases** as it moves higher.

        (c)   The heavier ball would go **half as high** as the tennis ball. At the apex of the trajectory, all initial kinetic energy has been changed into potential energy. The magnitude of the change in potential energy is $m\,g\,d$, which is equal to the energy initially imparted to the ball. If the same amount of energy is imparted to a ball with twice the mass, m doubles so d is half as large.

5.15   (a)   *Plan.* $E_k = 1/2\,mv^2$; $m = 1{,}200$ kg; $v = 18$ m/s; 1 kg-m^2/s$^2 = 1$ J

               Solve. $E_k = 1/2 \times 1{,}200$ kg $\times (18)^2$ m^2/s$^2 = 1.944 \times 10^5 = 1.9 \times 10^5$ J

        (b) 1 cal $= 4.184$ J; 1.944×10^5 J $\times \dfrac{1\,\text{cal}}{4.184\,\text{J}} = 4.646 \times 10^4$ cal $= 4.6 \times 10^4$ cal

        (c)   As the automobile brakes to a stop, its speed (and hence its kinetic energy) drops to zero. Brakes stop a moving vehicle, so the kinetic energy of the automobile is primarily transferred to friction between brakes and wheels, and somewhat to deformation of the tire and friction between the tire and road.

5.16   (a)   *Analyze.* Given: mass and speed of ball.   Find: kinetic energy.

               Plan. Since $1\,\text{J} = 1\,\text{kg} \cdot \text{m}^2/\text{s}^2$, convert oz $\rightarrow$ kg and mph to m/s to obtain E_k in J.

               Solve. $5.13\,\text{oz} \times \dfrac{1\,\text{lb}}{16\,\text{oz}} \times \dfrac{1\,\text{kg}}{2.205\,\text{lb}} = 0.14541 = 0.145$ kg

$$\dfrac{95.0\,\text{mi}}{1\,\text{hr}} \times \dfrac{1.6093\,\text{km}}{1\,\text{mi}} \times \dfrac{1000\,\text{m}}{1\,\text{km}} \times \dfrac{1\,\text{hr}}{60\,\text{min}} \times \dfrac{1\,\text{min}}{60\,\text{sec}} = 42.468 = 42.5\,\text{m/s}$$

$$E_k = 1/2\,mv^2 = 1/2 \times 0.14541\,\text{kg} \times \left(\dfrac{42.468\,\text{m}}{1\,\text{s}}\right)^2 = \dfrac{131\,\text{kg} \cdot \text{m}^2}{1\,\text{s}^2} = 131\,\text{J}$$

               Check. $1/2(0.15 \times 1600) \approx 1/2(160+80) \approx 120$ J

        (b)   Kinetic energy is related to velocity squared (v^2); if the speed of the ball decreases to 55.0 mph, the kinetic energy of the ball will decrease by a factor of $(55.0/95.0)^2$. (The conversion factors to m/s apply to both speeds and will cancel in the ratio.) The numerical multiplier is $(55/95)^2 = 0.335$. The kinetic energy decreases by approximately a factor of 3.

        (c)   As the ball hits the catcher's glove, its speed (and hence its kinetic energy) drops to zero. Some of the kinetic energy is transferred to the glove, which deforms when the ball lands. Some is transferred to the catcher's body (mostly the arm), which recoils while catching the ball. As usual, some energy is released as heat through friction between the ball and the glove.

        (d)   Assuming that all the kinetic energy is transferred via recoil of the catcher's arm, attach the catcher's mit to a frictionless mechanical arm held a constant distance above the ground. Measure the distance the arm+mit travels and the elapsed time of travel; calculate velocity (distance/time). Knowing the mass of the arm+mit, calculate the kintic energy ($1/2\,mv^2$) transferred to the arm+mit. This experiment neglects other pathways by which the kinetic energy is transferred. It would be difficult to make enough different careful measurements to completely confirm our answer to (c).

5.17   *Analyze.* Given: heat capacity of water = 1 Btu/lb - °F   Find: J/Btu

Plan. heat capacity of water = 4.184 J/g-°C; $\dfrac{J}{g-°C} \rightarrow \dfrac{J}{lb-°F} \rightarrow \dfrac{J}{Btu}$

This strategy requires changing °F to °C. Since this involves the magnitude of a degree on each scale, rather than a specific temperature, the 32 in the temperature relationship is not needed. 100 °C = 180 °F; 5 °C = 9 °F

Solve. $\dfrac{4.184\,J}{g\,-°C} \times \dfrac{453.6\,g}{lb} \times \dfrac{5\,°C}{9\,°F} \times \dfrac{1\,lb - °F}{1\,Btu} = 1054$ J/Btu

5.18   (a)   *Analyze.* Given: 1 kwh; 1 watt = 1 J/s; 1 watt - s = 1 J. Find: conversion factor for joules and kwh.

Plan. kwh → wh → ws → J

Solve. $1\,kwh \times \dfrac{1000\,w}{1\,kw} \times \dfrac{60\,min}{h} \times \dfrac{60\,s}{min} \times \dfrac{1\,J}{1\,w-s} = 3.6 \times 10^6$ J

1 kwh = 3.6×10^6 J

(b)   *Analyze.* Given: 100 watt bulb. Find: heat in kcal radiated by bulb or person in 24 hr.

Plan. 1 watt = 1 J/s; 1 kcal = 4.184×10^3 J; watt → J/s → J → kcal.   *Solve.*

$100\,watt = \dfrac{100\,J}{1\,s} \times \dfrac{60\,sec}{min} \times \dfrac{60\,min}{hr} \times 24\,hr \times \dfrac{1\,kcal}{4.184 \times 10^3\,J} = 2065 = 2.1 \times 10^3\,kcal$

24 hr has 2 sig figs, but 100 watt is ambiguous. The answer to 1 sig fig would be 2×10^3 kcal.

5.19   (a)   In thermodynamics, the *system* is the well-defined part of the universe whose energy changes are being studied.

(b)   A *closed system* can exchange energy but not mass with its surroundings.

(c)   Any part of the universe not part of the system is called the surroundings.

5.20   (a)   The system is *open*, because it exchanges both mass and energy with the surroundings. Mass exchange occurs when solution flows into and out of the apparatus. The apparatus is not insulated, so energy exchange also occurs. Closed systems exchange energy but not mass, while isolated systems exchange neither.

(b)   If the system is defined as shown, it can be closed by blocking the flow in and out, but leaving the flask full of solution.

5.21   (a)   *Work* is a force applied over a distance.

(b)   The amount of work done is the magnitude of the force times the distance over which it is applied. $w = F \times d$.

5.22   (a)   Heat is the energy transferred from a hotter object to a colder object.

        (b)   In open or closed systems (but not isolated systems), heat is transferred from one object (system) to another until the two objects (systems) are at the same temperature.

5.23   (a)   Gravity; work is done because the force of gravity is opposed and the pencil is lifted a distance above the desk.

        (b)   Mechanical force; work is done because the force of the coiled spring is opposed as the spring is compressed over a distance.

5.24   (a)   Electrostatic attraction; no work is done because the particles are held apart at a constant distance.

        (b)   Magnetic attraction; work is done because the nail is moved a distance in opposition to the force of magnetic attraction.

The First Law of Thermodynamics (section 5.2)

5.25   (a)   In any chemical or physical change, energy can be neither created nor destroyed, but it can be changed in form.

        (b)   The total *internal energy* (E) of a system is the sum of all the kinetic and potential energies of the system components.

        (c)   The internal energy of a closed system (where no mass exchange with surroundings occurs) increases when work is done on the system by the surroundings and/or when heat is transferred to the system from the surroundings (the system is heated).

5.26   (a) $\Delta E = q + w$

        (b)   The quantities q and w are negative when the system loses heat to the surroundings (it cools), or does work on the surroundings.

5.27   *Analyze.* Given: heat and work. Find: magnitude and sign of ΔE.

        Plan. In each case, evaluate q and w in the expression $\Delta E = q + w$. For an exothermic process, q is negative; for an endothermic process, q is positive.   *Solve.*

        (a)   q = 0.763 kJ, w = –840 J = 0.840 kJ. ΔE = 0.763 kJ – 0.840 kJ = –0.077 kJ. The process is endothermic.

        (b)   q is negative because the system releases heat, and w is positive because work is done on the system. ΔE = –66.1 kJ + 44.0 kJ = –22.1 kJ. The process is exothermic.

        (c)   q is positive because the system absorbs heat. No work is done, since w = –PΔV and ΔV = 0 (assuming that only P-V work can be done).
               ΔE = 7.25 kJ + 0 kJ = 7.25 kJ. The process is endothermic.

5.28   In each case, evaluate q and w in the expression $\Delta E = q + w$. For an exothermic process, q is negative; for an endothermic process, q is positive.

        (a)   q is negative and w is positive. ΔE = –0.655 kJ + 0.382 kJ = –0.273 kJ. The process is exothermic.

(b)　　q is positive and w is essentially zero. $\Delta E = 322$ J. The process is endothermic.

(c)　　q is zero (the cylinder is perfectly insulated) and w is positive. $\Delta E = 1.44$ kJ. The process is neither endothermic nor exothermic when $q = 0$.

5.29　　*Analyze.* How do the different physical situations (cases) affect the changes to heat and work of the system upon addition of 100 J of energy?

Plan. Use the definitions of heat and work and the First Law to answer the questions.

Solve. If the piston is allowed to move, case (1), the heated gas will expand and push the piston up, doing work on the surroundings. If the piston is fixed, case (2), most of the electrical energy will be manifested as an increase in heat of the system.

(a)　　Since little or no work is done by the system in case (2), the gas will absorb most of the energy as heat; the case (2) gas will have the higher temperature.

(b)　　In case (2), $w = 0$ and $q = 100$ J. In case (1), a significant amount of energy will be used to do work on the surroundings (–w), but some will be absorbed as heat (+q). (The transfer of electrical energy into work is never completely efficient!)

(c)　　ΔE is greater for case (2), because the entire 100 J increases the internal energy of the system, rather than a part of the energy doing work on the surroundings.

5.30　　$E_{el} = \dfrac{\kappa Q_1 Q_2}{r^2}$ For two oppositely charged particles, the sign of E_{el} is negative; the closer the particles, the greater the magnitude of E_{el}.

(a)　　The potential energy becomes less negative as the particles are separated (r increases).

(b)　　ΔE for the process is positive; the internal energy of the system increases as the oppositely charged particles are separated.

(c)　　Work is done on the system to separate the particles so w is positive. We have no direct knowledge of the change in q, except that it cannot be large and negative, because overall $\Delta E = q + w$ is positive.

5.31　　(a)　　A *state function* is a property of a system that depends only on the physical state (pressure, temperature, etc.) of the system, not on the route used by the system to get to the current state.

(b)　　Internal energy and enthalpy **are** state functions; heat **is not** a state function.

(c)　　Volume **is** a state function. The volume of a system depends only on conditions (pressure, temperature, amount of substance), not the route or method used to establish that volume.

5.32　　(a)　　Independent. Potential energy is a state function.

(b)　　Dependent. Some of the energy released could be employed in performing work, as is done in the body when sugar is metabolized; heat is not a state function.

(c)　　Dependent. The work accomplished depends on whether the gasoline is used in an engine, burned in an open flame, or in some other manner. Work is not a state function.

Enthalpy (sections 5.3 and 5.4)

5.33   (a)   Change in enthalpy (ΔH) is usually easier to measure than change in internal energy (ΔE) because, at constant pressure, $\Delta H = q_p$. The heat flow associated with a process at constant pressure can easily be measured as a change in temperature. Measuring ΔE requires a means to measure both q and w.

         (b)   H describes the enthalpy of a system at a certain set of conditions; the value of H depends only on these conditions. q describes energy transferred as heat, an energy *change* which, in the general case, does depend on how the change occurs. We can equate change in enthalpy, ΔH, with heat, q_p, only for the specific conditions of constant pressure and exclusively P-V work.

         (c)   If ΔH is positive, the enthalpy of the system increases and the process is endothermic.

5.34   (a)   When a process occurs under constant external pressure and only P-V work occurs, the enthalpy change (ΔH) equals the amount of heat transferred. $\Delta H = q_p$.

         (b) $\Delta H = q_p$. If the system releases heat, q and ΔH are negative and the enthalpy of the system decreases.

         (c)   If $\Delta H = 0$, $q_p = 0$ and $\Delta E = w$.

5.35   At constant pressure, $\Delta E = \Delta H - P\Delta V$. In order to calculate ΔE, more information about the conditions of the reaction must be known. For an ideal gas at constant pressure and temperature, $P\Delta V = RT\Delta n$. The values of either P and ΔV or T and Δn must be known to calculate ΔE from ΔH.

5.36   At constant volume ($\Delta V = 0$), $\Delta E = q_v$. According to the definition of enthalpy, $H = E + PV$, so $\Delta H = \Delta E + \Delta(PV)$. For an ideal gas at constant temperature and volume, $\Delta PV = V\Delta P = RT\Delta n$. For this reaction, there are 2 mol of gaseous product and 3 mol of gaseous reactants, so $\Delta n = -1$. Thus $V\Delta P$ or $\Delta(PV)$ is negative. Since $\Delta H = \Delta E + \Delta(PV)$, the negative $\Delta(PV)$ term means that ΔH will be smaller or more negative than ΔE.

5.37   *Analyze/Plan.* q = 824 J = 0.824 kJ (heat is absorbed by the system), w = 0.65 kJ (work is done on the system). *Solve.*

         $\Delta E = q + w = 0.824$ kJ + 0.65 kJ = 1.47 kJ. $\Delta H = q = 0.824$ kJ (at constant pressure).

         Check. The reaction is endothermic.

5.38   The gas is the system. If 0.49 kJ of heat is added, q = +0.49 kJ. Work done by the system decreases the overall energy of the system, so w = –214 J = –0.214 kJ .

         $\Delta E = q + w = 0.49$ kJ - 0.214 kJ = 0.276 kJ. $\Delta H = q = 0.49$ kJ (at constant pressure).

5.39   (a) $C_2H_5OH(l) + 3O_2(g) \rightarrow 3H_2O(g) + 2CO_2(g)$ $\Delta H = -1235$ kJ

(b) *Analyze.* How are reactants and products arranged on an enthalpy diagram?

Plan. The substances (reactants or products, collectively) with higher enthalpy are shown on the upper level, and those with lower enthalpy are shown on the lower level.

Solve. For this reaction, ΔH is negative, so the products have lower enthalpy and are shown on the lower level; reactants are on the upper level.. The arrow points in the direction of reactants to products and is labeled with the value of ΔH.

5.40 (a) $Ca(OH)_2(s) \rightarrow CaO(s) + H_2O(g)$

$\Delta H = 109 \text{ kJ}$

(b)

5.41 *Analyze/Plan.* Consider ΔH for the exothermic reaction as written. *Solve.*

(a) $\Delta H = -284.6 \text{ kJ}/2 \text{ mol } O_3(g) = -142.3 \text{ kJ/mol } O_3(g)$

(b) Since ΔH is negative, the reactants, $2O_3(g)$ has the higher enthalpy.

5.42 *Plan.* Consider the sign of an enthalpy change that would convert one of the substances into the other. *Solve.*

(a) $CO_2(s) \rightarrow CO_2(g)$. This change is sublimation, which is endothermic, $+\Delta H$. $CO_2(g)$ has the higher enthalpy.

(b) $H_2 \rightarrow 2H$. Breaking the H–H bond requires energy, so the process is endothermic, $+\Delta H$. Two moles of H atoms have higher enthalpy.

(c) $H_2O(g) \rightarrow H_2(g) + 1/2 \, O_2(g)$. Decomposing H_2O into its elements requires energy and is endothermic, $+\Delta H$. One mole of $H_2(g)$ and 0.5 mol $O_2(g)$ at 25°C have the higher enthalpy.

(d) $N_2(g)$ at 100° $\rightarrow N_2(g)$ at 300°. An increase in the temperature of the sample requires that heat is added to the system, $+q$ and $+\Delta H$. $N_2(g)$ at 300° has the higher enthalpy.

5.43 *Analyze/Plan.* Follow the strategy in Sample Exercise 5.4. *Solve.*

(a) Exothermic (ΔH is negative)

(b) $3.55 \text{ g Mg} \times \dfrac{1 \text{ mol Mg}}{24.305 \text{ g Mg}} \times \dfrac{-1204 \text{ kJ}}{2 \text{ mol Mg}} = -87.9 \text{ kJ heat transferred}$

Check. The units of kJ are correct for heat. The negative sign indicates heat is evolved.

(c) $-234 \text{ kJ} \times \dfrac{2 \text{ mol MgO}}{-1204 \text{ kJ}} \times \dfrac{40.30 \text{ g MgO}}{1 \text{ mol Mg}} = 15.7 \text{ g MgO produced}$

Check. Units are correct for mass. $(200 \times 2 \times 40/1200) \approx (16000/1200) > 10 \text{ g}$

(d) $2\text{MgO}(s) \rightarrow 2\text{Mg}(s) + \text{O}_2(g)$ $\Delta H = +1204 \text{ kJ}$

This is the reverse of the reaction given above, so the sign of ΔH is reversed.

$40.3 \text{ g MgO} \times \dfrac{1 \text{ mol MgO}}{40.30 \text{ g MgO}} \times \dfrac{1204 \text{ kJ}}{2 \text{ mol MgO}} = +602 \text{ kJ heat absorbed}$

Check. 40.3 g MgO is just 1 mol MgO, so the calculated value is the heat absorbed per mol of MgO, 1204 kJ/2 mol MgO = 602 kJ.

5.44   (a)   The sign of ΔH is positive, so the reaction is endothermic.

(b) $24.0 \text{ g CH}_3\text{OH} \times \dfrac{1 \text{ mol CH}_3\text{OH}}{32.04 \text{ g CH}_3\text{OH}} \times \dfrac{252.8 \text{ kJ}}{2 \text{ mol CH}_3\text{OH}} = 94.7 \text{ kJ heat absorbed}$

(c) $82.1 \text{ kJ} \times \dfrac{2 \text{ mol CH}_4}{252.8 \text{ kJ}} \times \dfrac{16.04 \text{ g CH}_4}{1 \text{ mol CH}_4} = 10.4 \text{ g CH}_4 \text{ produced}$

(d)   The sign of ΔH is reversed for the reverse reaction: $\Delta H = -252.8 \text{ kJ}$

$38.5 \text{ g CH}_4 \times \dfrac{1 \text{ mol CH}_4}{16.04 \text{ g CH}_4} \times \dfrac{-252.8 \text{ kJ}}{2 \text{ mol CH}_4} = -303 \text{ kJ heat released}$

5.45   *Analyze.* Given: balanced thermochemical equation, various quantities of substances and/or enthalpy. *Plan.* Enthalpy is an extensive property; it is "stoichiometric." Use the mole ratios implicit in the balanced thermochemical equation to solve for the desired quantity. Use molar masses to change mass to moles and vice versa where appropriate. *Solve.*

(a) $0.450 \text{ mol AgCl} \times \dfrac{-65.5 \text{ kJ}}{1 \text{ mol AgCl}} = -29.5 \text{ kJ}$

Check. Units are correct; sign indicates heat evolved.

(b) $9.00 \text{ g AgCl} \times \dfrac{1 \text{ mol AgCl}}{143.3 \text{ g AgCl}} \times \dfrac{-65.5 \text{ kJ}}{1 \text{ mol AgCl}} = -4.11 \text{ kJ}$

Check. Units correct; sign indicates heat evolved.

(c) $9.25 \times 10^{-4} \text{ mol AgCl} \times \dfrac{+65.5 \text{ kJ}}{1 \text{ mol AgCl}} = 0.0606 \text{ kJ} = 60.6 \text{ J}$

Check. Units correct; sign of ΔH reversed; sign indicates heat is absorbed during the reverse reaction.

5.46   (a) $1.36 \text{ mol O}_2 \times \dfrac{-89.4 \text{ kJ}}{3 \text{ mol O}_2} = -40.53 = -40.5 \text{ kJ}$

(b) $10.4 \text{ g KCl} \times \dfrac{1 \text{ mol KCl}}{74.55 \text{ g KCl}} \times \dfrac{-89.4 \text{ kJ}}{2 \text{ mol KCl}} = -6.2358 = -6.24 \text{ kJ}$

(c)   Since the sign of ΔH is reversed for the reverse reaction, it seems reasonable that other characteristics would be reversed, as well. If the forward reaction proceeds spontaneously, the reverse reaction is probably not spontaneous. Also, we know from experience that KCl(s) does not spontaneously react with atmospheric $O_2(g)$, even at elevated temperature.

5.47   *Analyze.* Given: balanced thermochemical equation. *Plan.* Follow the guidelines given in Section 5.4 for evaluating thermochemical equations.   *Solve.*

(a)   When a chemical equation is reversed, the sign of ΔH is reversed.

$$CO_2(g) + 2H_2O(l) \rightarrow CH_3OH(l) + 3/2\, O_2(g) \qquad \Delta H = +726.5 \text{ kJ}$$

(b)   Enthalpy is extensive. If the coefficients in the chemical equation are multiplied by 2 to obtain all integer coefficients, the enthalpy change is also multiplied by 2.

$$2CH_3OH(l) + 3O_2(g) \rightarrow 2CO_2(g) + 4H_2O(l) \qquad \Delta H = 2(-726.5) \text{ kJ} = -1453 \text{ kJ}$$

(c)   The exothermic forward reaction is more likely to be thermodynamically favored.

(d)   Decrease.   Vaporization (liquid $\rightarrow$ gas) is endothermic. If the product were $H_2O(g)$, the reaction would be more endothermic and would have a smaller negative ΔH. (Depending on temperature, the enthalpy of vaporization for 2 mol H_2O is about +88 kJ, not large enough to cause the overall reaction to be endothermic.)

5.48   (a) $3C_2H_2(g) \rightarrow C_6H_6(l) \qquad \Delta H = -630 \text{ kJ}$

(b) $C_6H_6(l) \rightarrow 3C_2H_2(g) \qquad \Delta H = +630 \text{ kJ}$
        ΔH for the formation of 3 mol of acetylene is 630 kJ. ΔH for the formation of 1 mol of C_2H_2 is then 630 kJ/3 = 210 kJ.

(c)   The exothermic reverse reaction is more likely to be thermodynamically favored.

(d)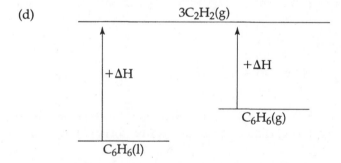

If the reactant is in the higher enthalpy gas phase, the overall ΔH for the reaction has a smaller positive value.

Calorimetry (section 5.5)

The specific heat of water to four significant figures, **4.184 J/g - K,** will be used in many of the following exercises; temperature units of K and °C will be used interchangeably.

5.49   (a)   J/mol-K or J/mol-°C. Heat capacity is the amount of heat in J required to raise the temperature of an object or a certain amount of substance 1 °C or 1 K. Molar heat capacity is the heat capacity of one mole of substance.

(b) $\dfrac{J}{g\cdot{}^\circ C}$ or $\dfrac{J}{g\cdot K}$ Specific heat is a particular kind of heat capacity where the amount of substance is 1 g.

(c) To calculate heat capacity from specific heat, the **mass** of the particular piece of copper pipe must be known.

5.50 *Analyze.* Both objects are heated to 100°C. The two hot objects are placed in the same amount of cold water at the same temperature. Object A raises the water temperature more than object B. *Plan.* Apply the definition of heat capacity to heating the water and heating the objects to determine which object has the greater heat capacity.   *Solve.*

(a) Both beakers of water contain the same mass of water, so they both have the same heat capacity. Object A raises the temperature of its water more than object B, so more heat was transferred from object A than from object B. Since both objects were heated to the same temperature initially, object A must have absorbed more heat to reach the 100° temperature. The greater the heat capacity of an object, the greater the heat required to produce a given rise in temperature. Thus, object A has the greater heat capacity.

(b) Since no information about the masses of the objects is given, we cannot compare or determine the specific heats of the objects.

5.51 *Plan.* Manipulate the definition of specific heat to solve for the desired quantity, paying close attention to units. $C_s = q/(m \times \Delta t)$.   *Solve.*

(a) $\dfrac{4.184\,J}{1\,g\cdot K}$ or $\dfrac{4.184\,J}{1\,g\cdot{}^\circ C}$

(b) $\dfrac{4.184\,J}{1\,g\cdot{}^\circ C} \times \dfrac{18.02\,g\,H_2O}{1\,mol\,H_2O} = \dfrac{75.40\,J}{mol\cdot{}^\circ C}$

(c) $\dfrac{185\,g\,H_2O \times 4.184\,J}{1\,g\cdot{}^\circ C} = 774\,J/{}^\circ C$

(d) $10.00\,kg\,H_2O \times \dfrac{1000\,g}{1\,kg} \times \dfrac{4.184\,J}{1\,g\cdot{}^\circ C} \times \dfrac{1\,kJ}{1000\,J} \times (46.2\,^\circ C - 24.6\,^\circ C) = 904\,kJ$

Check. $(10 \times 4 \times 20) \approx 800$ kJ; the units are correct. Note that the conversion factors for kg → g and J → kJ cancel. An equally correct form of specific heat would be kJ/kg·°C

5.52 (a) In Table 5.2, Hg(l) has the smallest specific heat, so it will require the smallest amount of energy to heat 50.0 g of the substance 10 k.

(b) $50.0\,g\,Hg(l) \times 10\,K \times \dfrac{0.14\,J}{g\cdot K} = 70\,J$

5.53 *Analyze/Plan.* Follow the logic in Sample Exercise 5.5.   *Solve.*

(a) $80.0\,g\,C_8H_{18} \times \dfrac{2.22\,J}{g\cdot K} \times (25.0\,^\circ C - 10.0\,^\circ C) = 2.66 \times 10^3\,J\ (or\ 2.66\,kJ)$

(b)　*Plan.* Calculate the molar heat capacity of octane and compare it with the molar heat capacity of water, 75.40 J/mol-°C, as calculated in Exercise 5.51(b). *Solve.*

$$\frac{2.22\,J}{g\text{-}K}\times\frac{114.2\,g\,C_8H_{18}}{1\,mol\,C_8H_{18}}=\frac{253.58\,J}{mol\text{-}K}=\frac{254\,J}{mol\text{-}K}$$

The molar heat capacity of $C_8H_{18}(l)$, 254 J/mol-K, is greater than that of $H_2O(l)$, so it will require more heat to increase the temperature of octane than to increase the temperature of water.

5.54　(a)　$\text{specific heat}=\dfrac{J}{1\,g\text{-}^\circ C}=\dfrac{322\,J}{100.0\,g\times(50^\circ C-25^\circ C)}=0.1288=\dfrac{0.13\,J}{1\,g\text{-}^\circ C}$

(b)　In general, the greater the heat capacity, the more heat is required to raise the temperature of 1 gram of substance 1°C. The specific heat of gold is 0.13 J/g-°C, while that of iron is 0.45 J/g-°C (Table 5.2). For gold and iron blocks with equal mass, same initial temperature and same amount of heat added, the one with the lower specific heat, gold, will require less heat per °C and have the higher final temperature.

(c)　$\dfrac{0.1288\,J}{1\,g\text{-}^\circ C}\times\dfrac{196.97\,g\,Au}{1\,mol\,Au}=25.37=\dfrac{25\,J}{mol\text{-}^\circ C}$

5.55　*Analyze.* Since the temperature of the water increases, the dissolving process is exothermic and the sign of ΔH is negative. The heat lost by the NaOH(s) dissolving equals the heat gained by the solution.

Plan/Solve. Calculate the heat gained by the solution. The temperature change is 37.8 – 21.6 = 16.2°C. The total mass of solution is (100.0 g H_2O + 6.50 g NaOH) = 106.5 g.

$$106.5\,g\,\text{solution}\times\frac{4.184\,J}{1\,g\text{-}^\circ C}\times16.2^\circ C\times\frac{1\,kJ}{1000\,J}=7.2187=7.22\,kJ$$

This is the amount of heat lost when 6.50 g of NaOH dissolves.

The heat loss per mole NaOH is

$$\frac{-7.2187\,kJ}{6.50\,g\,NaOH}\times\frac{40.00\,g\,NaOH}{1\,mol\,NaOH}=-44.4\,kJ/mol\quad\Delta H=q_p=-44.4\,kJ/mol\,NaOH$$

Check. $(-7/7\times40)\approx-40\,kJ$; the units and sign are correct.

5.56　(a)　Follow the logic in Solution 5.55. The total mass of the solution is (60.0 g H_2O + 4.25 g NH_4NO_3) = 64.25 = 64.3 g. The temperature change of the solution is 22.0 – 16.9 = 5.1°C. The heat lost by the surroundings is

$$64.25\,g\,\text{solution}\times\frac{4.184\,J}{1\,g\text{-}^\circ C}\times5.1^\circ C\times\frac{1\,kJ}{1000\,J}=1.371=1.4\,kJ$$

Thus, 1.4 kJ is absorbed when 4.25 g $NH_4NO_3(s)$ dissolves.

$$\frac{+1.371\,kJ}{4.25\,NH_4NO_3}\times\frac{80.04\,g\,NH_4NO_3}{1\,mol\,NH_4NO_3}=+25.82=+26\,kJ/mol\,NH_4NO_3$$

(b)　This process is endothermic, because the temperature of the surroundings decreases, indicating that heat is absorbed by the system.

5.57   *Analyze/Plan.* Follow the logic in Sample Exercise 5.7.   *Solve.*

$q_{bomb} = -q_{rxn}$; $\Delta T = 30.57°C - 23.44°C = 7.13°C$

$$q_{bomb} = \frac{7.854 \text{ kJ}}{1°C} \times 7.13°C = 56.00 = 56.0 \text{ kJ}$$

At constant volume, $q_v = \Delta E$. ΔE and ΔH are very similar.

$$\Delta H_{rxn} \approx \Delta E_{rxn} = q_{rxn} = -q_{bomb} = \frac{-56.0 \text{ kJ}}{2.200 \text{ g } C_6H_4O_2} = -25.454 = -25.5 \text{ kJ/g } C_6H_4O_2$$

$$\Delta H_{rxn} = \frac{-25.454 \text{ kJ}}{1 \text{ g } C_6H_4O_2} \times \frac{108.1 \text{ g } C_6H_4O_2}{1 \text{ mol } C_6H_4O_2} = -2.75 \times 10^3 \text{ kJ/mol } C_6H_4O_2$$

5.58   (a) $C_6H_5OH(s) + 7O_2(g) \rightarrow 6CO_2(g) + 3H_2O(l)$

        (b) $q_{bomb} = -q_{rxn}$; $\Delta T = 26.37°C - 21.36°C = 5.01°C$

$$q_{bomb} = \frac{11.66 \text{ kJ}}{1°C} \times 5.01°C = 58.417 = 58.4 \text{ kJ}$$

At constant volume, $q_v = \Delta E$. ΔE and ΔH are very similar.

$$\Delta H_{rxn} \approx \Delta E_{rxn} = q_{rxn} = -q_{bomb} = \frac{-58.417 \text{ kJ}}{1.800 \text{ g } C_6H_5OH} = -32.454 = -32.5 \text{ kJ/g } C_6H_5OH$$

$$\Delta H_{rxn} = \frac{-32.454 \text{ kJ}}{1 \text{ g } C_6H_5OH} \times \frac{94.11 \text{ g } C_6H_5OH}{1 \text{ mol } C_6H_5OH} = \frac{-3.054 \times 10^3 \text{ kJ}}{\text{mol } C_6H_5OH}$$

$$= -3.05 \times 10^3 \text{ kJ/mol } C_6H_5OH$$

5.59   *Analyze.* Given: specific heat and mass of glucose, ΔT for calorimeter. Find: heat capacity, C, of calorimeter. *Plan.* All heat from the combustion raises the temperature of the calorimeter. Calculate heat from combustion of glucose, divide by ΔT for calorimeter to get kJ/°C. $\Delta T = 24.72°C - 20.94°C = 3.78°C$ *Solve.*

        (a) $C_{total} = 3.500 \text{ g glucose} \times \dfrac{15.57 \text{ kJ}}{1 \text{ g glucose}} \times \dfrac{1}{3.78°C} = 14.42 = 14.4 \text{ kJ/°C}$

        (b)   Qualitatively, assuming the same exact initial conditions in the calorimeter, twice as much glucose produces twice as much heat, which raises the calorimeter temperature by twice as many °C. Quantitatively,

$$7.000 \text{ g glucose} \times \frac{15.57 \text{ kJ}}{1 \text{ g glucose}} \times \frac{1°C}{14.42 \text{ kJ}} = 7.56°C$$

Check. Units are correct. ΔT is twice as large as in part (a). The result has 3 sig figs, because the heat capacity of the calorimeter is known to 3 sig figs.

5.60   (a) $C = 2.760 \text{ g } C_6H_5COOH \times \dfrac{26.38 \text{ kJ}}{1 \text{ g } C_6H_5COOH} \times \dfrac{1}{8.33°C} = 8.74055 = 8.74 \text{ kJ/°C}$

        (b) $\dfrac{8.74055 \text{ kJ}}{°C} \times 4.95°C \times \dfrac{1}{1.440 \text{ g sample}} = 30.046 = 30.0 \text{ kJ/g sample}$

(c) If water is lost from the calorimeter, there is less water to heat, so the same amount of heat (kJ) from a reaction would cause a larger increase in the calorimeter temperature. The calorimeter constant, kJ/°C, would decrease, because °C is in the denominator of the expression.

Hess's Law (section 5.6)

5.61 Hess's Law is a consequence of the fact that enthalpy is a state function. Since ΔH is independent of path, we can describe a process by any series of steps that add up to the overall process and ΔH for the process is the sum of the ΔH values for the steps.

5.62 (a) *Analyze/Plan.* Arrange the reactions so that in the overall sum, B, appears in both reactants and products and can be canceled. This is a general technique for using Hess's Law. *Solve.*

$$\begin{array}{ll} A \to B & \Delta H = +30 \text{ kJ} \\ \underline{B \to C} & \underline{\Delta H = +60 \text{ kJ}} \\ A \to C & \Delta H = +90 \text{ kJ} \end{array}$$

(b)

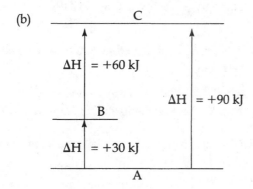

Check. The process of A forming C can be described as A forming B and B forming C.

5.63 *Analyze/Plan.* Follow the logic in Sample Exercise 5.8. Manipulate the equations so that "unwanted" substances can be canceled from reactants and products. Adjust the corresponding sign and magnitude of ΔH. *Solve.*

$$\begin{array}{ll} P_4O_6(s) \to P_4(s) + 3O_2(g) & \Delta H = 1640.1 \text{ kJ} \\ \underline{P_4(s) + 5O_2(g) \to P_4O_{10}(s)} & \underline{\Delta H = -2940.1 \text{ kJ}} \\ P_4O_6(s) + 2O_2(g) \to P_4O_{10}(s) & \Delta H = -1300.0 \text{ kJ} \end{array}$$

Check. We have obtained the desired reaction.

5.64
$$\begin{array}{ll} 2C(s) + O_2(g) + 4H_2(g) \to 2CH_3OH(g) & \Delta H = -402.4 \text{ kJ} \\ \underline{2CO(g) \to O_2(g) + 2C(s)} & \underline{\Delta H = 221.0 \text{ kJ}} \\ 2CO(g) + 4H_2(g) \to 2CH_3OH(g) & \Delta H = -181.4 \text{ kJ} \\ CO(g) + 2H_2(g) \to CH_3OH(g) & \Delta H = (-181.4)/2 = -90.7 \text{ kJ} \end{array}$$

5.65 *Analyze/Plan.* Follow the logic in Sample Exercise 5.9. Manipulate the equations so that "unwanted" substances can be canceled from reactants and products. Adjust the corresponding sign and magnitude of ΔH. *Solve.*

$$C_2H_4(g) \rightarrow 2H_2(g) + 2C(s) \qquad \Delta H = -52.3 \text{ kJ}$$
$$2C(s) + 4F_2(g) \rightarrow 2CF_4(g) \qquad \Delta H = 2(-680 \text{ kJ})$$
$$\underline{2H_2(g) + 2F_2(g) \rightarrow 4HF(g) \qquad \Delta H = 2(-537 \text{ kJ})}$$
$$C_2H_4(g) + 6F_2(g) \rightarrow 2CF_4(g) + 4HF(g) \qquad \Delta H = -2.49 \times 10^3 \text{ kJ}$$

Check. We have obtained the desired reaction.

5.66
$$N_2O(g) \rightarrow N_2(g) + 1/2\,O_2(g) \qquad \Delta H = 1/2\,(-163.2 \text{ kJ})$$
$$NO_2(g) \rightarrow NO(g) + 1/2\,O_2(g) \qquad \Delta H = 1/2(113.1 \text{ kJ})$$
$$\underline{N_2(g) + O_2(g) \rightarrow 2NO(g) \qquad \Delta H = 180.7 \text{ kJ}}$$
$$N_2O(g) + NO_2(g) \rightarrow 3NO(g) \qquad \Delta H = 155.7 \text{ kJ}$$

Enthalpies of Formation (section 5.7)

5.67   (a)   *Standard conditions* for enthalpy changes are usually P = 1 atm and T = 298 K. For the purpose of comparison, standard enthalpy changes, $\Delta H°$, are tabulated for reactions at these conditions.

         (b)   *Enthalpy of formation*, ΔH_f, is the enthalpy change that occurs when a compound is formed from its component elements.

         (c)   *Standard enthalpy of formation*, $\Delta H_f°$, is the enthalpy change that accompanies formation of one mole of a substance from elements in their standard states.

5.68   (a)   Tables of $\Delta H_f°$ are useful because, according to Hess's law, the standard enthalpy of any reaction can be calculated from the standard enthalpies of formation for the reactants and products.

$$\Delta H_{rxn}° = \Sigma\Delta H_f° \text{ (products)} - \Sigma\Delta H_f° \text{ (reactants)}$$

         (b)   The standard enthalpy of formation for any element in its standard state is zero. Elements in their standard states are the reference point for the enthalpy of formation scale.

         (c) $12C(s) + 11H_2(g) + 11/2\,O_2(g) \rightarrow C_{12}H_{22}O_{11}(s)$

5.69   (a) $1/2\,N_2(g) + O_2(g) \rightarrow NO_2(g)$ $\Delta H_f° = 33.84 \text{ kJ}$

         (b) $S(s) + 3/2\,O_2(g) \rightarrow SO_3(g)$ $\Delta H_f° = -395.2 \text{ kJ}$

         (c) $Na(s) + 1/2\,Br_2(l) \rightarrow NaBr(s)$ $\Delta H_f° = -361.4 \text{ kJ}$

         (d) $Pb(s) + N_2(g) + 3O_2(g) \rightarrow Pb(NO_3)_2(s)$ $\Delta H_f° = -451.9 \text{ kJ}$

5.70   (a) $H_2(g) + O_2(g) \rightarrow H_2O_2(g)$ $\Delta H_f° = -136.10 \text{ kJ}$

         (b) $Ca(s) + C(s) + 3/2\,O_2(g) \rightarrow CaCO_3(s)$ $\Delta H_f° = -1207.1 \text{ kJ}$

         (c) $1/4\,P_4(s) + 1/2\,O_2(g) + 3/2\,Cl_2(g) \rightarrow POCl_3(l)$ $\Delta H_f° = -597.0 \text{ kJ}$

         (d) $2C(s) + 3H_2(g) + 1/2\,O_2(g) \rightarrow C_2H_5OH(l)$ $\Delta H_f° = -277.7 \text{ kJ}$

5.71   *Plan.* $\Delta H^{\circ}_{rxn} = \Sigma n \Delta H^{\circ}_f$ (products) $- \Sigma n \Delta H^{\circ}_f$ (reactants). Be careful with coefficients, states, and signs.   *Solve.*

$\Delta H^{\circ}_{rxn} = \Delta H^{\circ}_f \, Al_2O_3(s) + 2\Delta H^{\circ}_f \, Fe(s) - \Delta H^{\circ}_f \, Fe_2O_3(s) - 2\Delta H^{\circ}_f \, Al(s)$

$\Delta H^{\circ}_{rxn} = (-1669.8 \text{ kJ}) + 2(0) - (-822.16 \text{ kJ}) - 2(0) = -847.6 \text{ kJ}$

5.72   Use heats of formation to calculate ΔH° for the combustion of butane.

$C_3H_8(g) + 5O_2(g) \; \rightarrow \; 3CO_2(g) + 4H_2O(l)$

$\Delta H^{\circ}_{rxn} = 3\Delta H^{\circ}_f \, CO_2(g) + 4\Delta H^{\circ}_f \, H_2O(l) - \Delta H^{\circ}_f \, C_3H_8(g) - 5\Delta H^{\circ}_f \, O_2(g)$

$\Delta H^{\circ}_{rxn} = 3(-393.5 \text{ kJ}) + 4(-285.83 \text{ kJ}) - (-103.85 \text{ kJ}) - 5(0) = -2219.97 = -2220.0 \text{ kJ/mol } C_3H_8$

$10.00 \text{ g } C_3H_8 \times \dfrac{1 \, mol \, C_3H_8}{44.096 \text{ g } C_3H_8} \times \dfrac{-2219.97 \text{ kJ}}{1 \, mol \, C_3H_8} = -503.4 \text{ kJ}$

5.73   *Plan.* $\Delta H^{\circ}_{rxn} = \Sigma n \Delta H^{\circ}_f$ (products) $- \Sigma n \Delta H^{\circ}_f$ (reactants). Be careful with coefficients, states and signs.   *Solve.*

(a) $\Delta H^{\circ}_{rxn} = 2\Delta H^{\circ}_f \, SO_3(g) - 2\Delta H^{\circ}_f \, SO_2(g) - \Delta H^{\circ}_f \, O_2(g)$

   $= 2(-395.2 \text{ kJ}) - 2(-296.9 \text{ kJ}) - 0 = -196.6 \text{ kJ}$

(b) $\Delta H^{\circ}_{rxn} = \Delta H^{\circ}_f \, MgO(s) + \Delta H^{\circ}_f \, H_2O(l) - \Delta H^{\circ}_f \, Mg(OH)_2(s)$

   $= -601.8 \text{ kJ} + (-285.83 \text{ kJ}) - (-924.7 \text{ kJ}) = 37.1 \text{ kJ}$

(c) $\Delta H^{\circ}_{rxn} = 4\Delta H^{\circ}_f \, H_2O(g) + \Delta H^{\circ}_f \, N_2(g) - \Delta H^{\circ}_f \, N_2O_4(g) - 4\Delta H^{\circ}_f \, H_2(g)$

   $= 4(-241.82 \text{ kJ}) + 0 - (9.66 \text{ kJ}) - 4(0) = -976.94 \text{ kJ}$

(d) $\Delta H^{\circ}_{rxn} = \Delta H^{\circ}_f \, SiO_2(s) + 4\Delta H^{\circ}_f \, HCl(g) - \Delta H^{\circ}_f \, SiCl_4(l) - 2\Delta H^{\circ}_f \, H_2O(l)$

   $= -910.9 \text{ kJ} + 4(-92.30 \text{ kJ}) - (-640.1 \text{ kJ}) - 2(-285.83 \text{ kJ}) = -68.3 \text{ kJ}$

5.74   (a) $\Delta H^{\circ}_{rxn} = \Delta H^{\circ}_f \, CaCl_2(s) + \Delta H^{\circ}_f \, H_2O(g) - \Delta H^{\circ}_f \, CaO(s) - 2\Delta H^{\circ}_f \, HCl(g)$

   $= -795.8 \text{ kJ} + (-241.82 \text{ kJ}) - (-635.5 \text{ kJ}) - 2(-92.30 \text{ kJ}) = -217.5 \text{ kJ}$

(b) $\Delta H^{\circ}_{rxn} = 2\Delta H^{\circ}_f \, Fe_2O_3(s) - 4\Delta H^{\circ}_f \, FeO(s) - \Delta H^{\circ}_f \, O_2(g)$

   $= 2(-822.16 \text{ kJ}) - 4(-271.9 \text{ kJ}) - (0) = -556.7 \text{ kJ}$

(c) $\Delta H^{\circ}_{rxn} = \Delta H^{\circ}_f \, Cu_2O(s) + \Delta H^{\circ}_f \, NO_2(g) - 2\Delta H^{\circ}_f \, CuO(s) - \Delta H^{\circ}_f \, NO(g)$

   $= -170.7 \text{ kJ} + (33.84 \text{ kJ}) - 2(-156.1 \text{ kJ}) - (90.37 \text{ kJ}) = 85.0 \text{ kJ}$

(d) $\Delta H^{\circ}_{rxn} = 2\Delta H^{\circ}_f \, N_2H_4(g) + 2\Delta H^{\circ}_f \, H_2O(l) - 4\Delta H^{\circ}_f \, NH_3(g) - \Delta H^{\circ}_f \, O_2(g)$

   $= 2(95.40 \text{ kJ}) + 2(-285.83 \text{ kJ}) - 4(-46.19 \text{ kJ}) - (0) = -196.10 \text{ kJ}$

5.75   *Analyze.* Given: combustion reaction, enthalpy of combustion, enthalpies of formation for most reactants and products. Find: enthalpy of formation for acetone.

   Plan. Rearrange the expression for enthalpy of reaction to calculate the desired enthalpy of formation. *Solve.*

$$\Delta H_{rxn}^{\circ} = 3\Delta H_f^{\circ}\,CO_2(g) + 3\Delta H_f^{\circ}\,H_2O(l) - \Delta H_f^{\circ}\,C_3H_6O(l) - 4\Delta H_f^{\circ}\,O_2(g)$$

$$-1790\ kJ = 3(-393.5\ kJ) + 3(-285.83\ kJ) - \Delta H_f^{\circ}\,C_3H_6O(l) - 4(0)$$

$$\Delta H_f^{\circ}\,C_3H_6O(l) = 3(-393.5\ kJ) + 3(-285.83\ kJ) + 1790\ kJ = -248\ kJ$$

5.76 $\Delta H_{rxn}^{\circ} = \Delta H_f^{\circ}\,Ca(OH)_2(s) + \Delta H_f^{\circ}\,C_2H_2(g) - 2\Delta H_f^{\circ}\,H_2O(l) - \Delta H_f^{\circ}\,CaC_2(s)$

$$-127.2\ kJ = -986.2\ kJ + 226.77\ kJ - 2(-285.83\ kJ) - \Delta H_f^{\circ}\,CaC_2(s)$$

$$\Delta H_f^{\circ}\ for\ CaC_2(s) = -60.6\ kJ$$

5.77 (a) $C_8H_{18}(l) + 25/2\,O_2(g) \rightarrow 8CO_2(g) + 9H_2O(g)$ $\Delta H^{\circ} = -5064.9\ kJ$

(b) $8C(s) + 9H_2(g) \rightarrow C_8H_{18}(l)$ $\Delta H_f^{\circ} = ?$

(c)   *Plan.* Follow the logic in Solution 5.75 and 5.76. *Solve.*

$$\Delta H_{rxn}^{\circ} = 8\Delta H_f^{\circ}\,CO_2(g) + 9\Delta H_f^{\circ}\,H_2O(g) - \Delta H_f^{\circ}\,C_8H_{18}(l) - 25/2\,\Delta H_f^{\circ}\,O_2(g)$$

$$-5064.9\ kJ = 8(-393.5\ kJ) + 9(-241.82\ kJ) - \Delta H_f^{\circ}\,C_8H_{18}(l) - 25/2(0)$$

$$\Delta H_f^{\circ}\,C_8H_{18}(l) = 8(-393.5\ kJ) + 9(-241.82\ kJ) + 5064.9\ kJ = -259.5\ kJ$$

5.78 (a) $C_4H_{10}O(l) + 6O_2(g) \rightarrow 4CO_2(g) + 5H_2O(g)$ $\Delta H^{\circ} = -2723.7\ kJ$

(b) $4C(s) + 5H_2(g) + 1/2\,O_2(g) \rightarrow C_4H_{10}O(l)$ $\Delta H_f^{\circ} = ?$

(c) $\Delta H_{rxn}^{\circ} = 4\Delta H_f^{\circ}\,CO_2(g) + 5\Delta H_f^{\circ}\,H_2O(l) - \Delta H_f^{\circ}\,C_4H_{10}O(l) - 6\Delta H_f^{\circ}\,O_2(g)$

$$-2723.7 = 4(-393.5\ kJ) + 5(-285.83\ kJ) - \Delta H_f^{\circ}\,C_4H_{10}O(l) - 6(0)$$

$$\Delta H_f^{\circ}\,C_4H_{10}O(l) = 4(-393.5\ kJ) + 5(-285.83\ kJ) + 2723.7\ kJ = -279.45 = -279.5\ kJ$$

5.79 (a) $C_2H_5OH(l) + 3O_2(g) \rightarrow 2CO_2(g) + 3H_2O(l)$

(b) $\Delta H_{rxn}^{\circ} = 2\Delta H_f^{\circ}\,CO_2(g) + 3\Delta H_f^{\circ}\,H_2O(g) - \Delta H_f^{\circ}\,C_2H_5OH(l) - 3\Delta H_f^{\circ}\,O_2(g)$

$$= 2(-393.5\ kJ) + 3(-241.82\ kJ) - (-277.7\ kJ) - 3(0) = -1234.76 = -1234.8\ kJ$$

(c)   *Plan.* The enthalpy of combustion of ethanol [from part (b)] is –1234.8 kJ/mol. Change mol to mass using molar mass, then mass to volume using density. *Solve.*

$$\frac{-1234.76\ kJ}{mol\ C_2H_5OH} \times \frac{1\ mol\ C_2H_5OH}{46.06844\ g} \times \frac{0.789\ g}{mL} \times \frac{1000\ mL}{L} = -21{,}147 = -2.11 \times 10^4\ kJ/L$$

Check. $(1200/50) \approx 25$; $25 \times 800 \approx 20{,}000$

(d)   *Plan.* The enthalpy of combustion corresponds to any of the molar amounts in the equation as written. Production of –1234.76 kJ also produces 2 mol CO_2. Use this relationship to calculate mass CO_2/kJ.

$$\frac{2\ mol\ CO_2}{-1234.76\ kJ} \times \frac{44.0095\ g\ CO_2}{mol} = 0.071284\ g\ CO_2/kJ\ emitted$$

Check. The negative sign associated with enthalpy indicates that energy is emitted.

5.80 (a) $CH_3OH(l) + 3/2\,O_2(g) \rightarrow CO_2(g) + 2H_2O(g)$

(b) $\Delta H^{\circ}_{rxn} = \Delta H^{\circ}_{f} \, CO_2(g) + 2\Delta H^{\circ}_{f} \, H_2O(g) - \Delta H^{\circ}_{f} \, CH_3OH(l) - 3/2 \, \Delta H^{\circ}_{f} \, O_2(g)$

               $= -393.5 \text{ kJ} + 2(-241.82 \text{ kJ}) - (-238.6 \text{ kJ}) - 3/2(0) = -638.54 = -638.5 \text{ kJ}$

(c) $\dfrac{-638.54 \text{ kJ}}{\text{mol } CH_3OH} \times \dfrac{1 \text{ mol } CH_3OH}{32.04 \text{ g}} \times \dfrac{0.791 \text{ g}}{\text{mL}} \times \dfrac{1000 \text{ mL}}{\text{L}} = 1.58 \times 10^4 \text{ kJ/L produced}$

(d) $\dfrac{1 \text{ mol } CO_2}{-638.54 \text{ kJ}} \times \dfrac{44.0095 \text{ g } CO_2}{\text{mol}} = 0.06892 \text{ g } CO_2/\text{kJ emitted}$

Foods and Fuels (Section 5.8)

5.81   (a)   *Fuel value* is the amount of energy produced when 1 gram of a substance (fuel) is combusted.

         (b)   The fuel value of fats is 9 kcal/g and of carbohydrates is 4 kcal/g. Therefore, 5 g of fat produce 45 kcal, while 9 g of carbohydrates produce 36 kcal; 5 g of fat are a greater energy source.

         (c)   These products of metabolism are expelled as waste via the alimentary tract, $H_2O(l)$ primarily in urine and feces, and $CO_2(g)$ as gas.

5.82   (a)   Fats are appropriate for fuel storage because they are insoluble in water (and body fluids) and have a high fuel value.

         (b)   For convenience, assume 100 g of chips.

$$12 \text{ g protein} \times \frac{17 \text{ kJ}}{1 \text{ g protein}} \times \frac{1 \text{ Cal}}{4.184 \text{ kJ}} = 48.76 = 49 \text{ Cal}$$

$$14 \text{ g fat} \times \frac{38 \text{ kJ}}{1 \text{ g fat}} \times \frac{1 \text{ Cal}}{4.184 \text{ kJ}} = 127.15 = 130 \text{ Cal}$$

$$74 \text{ g carbohydrates} \times \frac{17 \text{ kJ}}{1 \text{ g carbohydrates}} \times \frac{1 \text{ Cal}}{4.184 \text{ kJ}} = 300.67 = 301 \text{ Cal}$$

total Cal = (48.76 + 127.15 + 300.67) = 476.58 = 480 Cal

$$\% \text{ Cal from fat} = \frac{127.15 \text{ Cal fat}}{476.58 \text{ total Cal}} \times 100 = 26.68 = 27\%$$

(Since the conversion from kJ to Cal was common to all three components, we would have determined the same percentage by using kJ.)

         (c) $25 \text{ g fat} \times \dfrac{38 \text{ kJ}}{\text{g fat}} = x \text{ g protein} \times \dfrac{17 \text{ kJ}}{\text{g protein}}; \quad x = 56 \text{ g protein}$

5.83   (a)   *Plan.* Calculate the Cal (kcal) due to each nutritional component of the soup, then sum. *Solve.*

$$2.5 \text{ g fat} \times \frac{38 \text{ kJ}}{1 \text{ g fat}} = 95.0 \text{ or } 0.95 \times 10^2 \text{ kJ}$$

$$14 \text{ g carbohydrates} \times \frac{17 \text{ kJ}}{1 \text{ g carbohydrate}} = 238 \text{ or } 2.4 \times 10^2 \text{ kJ}$$

$$7\,\text{g protein} \times \frac{17\,\text{kJ}}{1\,\text{g protein}} = 119 \text{ or } 1 \times 10^2 \text{ kJ}$$

total energy = 95.0 kJ + 238 kJ + 119 kJ = 452 or 5×10^2 kJ

$$452\,\text{kJ} \times \frac{1\,\text{kcal}}{4.184\,\text{kJ}} \times \frac{1\,\text{Cal}}{1\,\text{kcal}} = 108.03 \text{ or } 1 \times 10^2 \text{ Cal/serving}$$

Check. 100 Cal/serving is a reasonable result; units are correct. The data and the result have 1 sig fig.

(b)   Sodium does not contribute to the calorie content of the food, because it is not metabolized by the body; it enters and leaves as Na^+.

5.84   Calculate the fuel value in a pound of M&M® candies.

$$96\,\text{fat} \times \frac{38\,\text{kJ}}{1\,\text{g fat}} = 3648\,\text{kJ} = 3.6 \times 10^3 \text{kJ}$$

$$320\,\text{g carbohydrate} \times \frac{17\,\text{kJ}}{1\,\text{g carbohydrate}} = 5440\,\text{kJ} = 5.4 \times 10^3 \text{ kJ}$$

$$21\,\text{g protein} \times \frac{17\,\text{kJ}}{1\,\text{g protein}} = 357\,\text{kJ} = 3.6 \times 10^2 \text{ kJ}$$

total fuel value = 3648 kJ + 5440 kJ + 357 kJ = 9445 kJ = 9.4×10^3 kJ/lb

$$\frac{9445\,\text{kJ}}{\text{lb}} \times \frac{1\,\text{lb}}{453.6\,\text{g}} \times \frac{42\,\text{g}}{\text{serving}} = 874.5\,\text{kJ} = 8.7 \times 10^2 \text{kJ/serving}$$

$$\frac{874.5\,\text{kJ}}{\text{serving}} \times \frac{1\,\text{kcal}}{4.184\,\text{kJ}} \times \frac{1\,\text{Cal}}{1\,\text{kcal}} = 209.0\,\text{Cal} = 2.1 \times 10^2 \text{ Cal/serving}$$

Check. 210 Cal is the approximate food value of a candy bar, so the result is reasonable.

5.85   *Plan.* g → mol → kJ → Cal   *Solve.*

$$16.0\,\text{g}\,C_6H_{12}O_6 \times \frac{1\,\text{mol}\,C_6H_{12}O_6}{180.2\,\text{g}\,C_6H_{12}O_6} \times \frac{2812\,\text{kJ}}{\text{mol}\,C_6H_{12}O_6} \times \frac{1\,\text{Cal}}{4.184\,\text{kJ}} = 59.7\,\text{Cal}$$

Check. 60 Cal is a reasonable result for most of the food value in an apple.

5.86 $177\,\text{mL} \times \dfrac{1.0\,\text{g wine}}{1\,\text{mL}} \times \dfrac{0.106\,\text{g ethanol}}{1\,\text{g wine}} \times \dfrac{1\,\text{mol ethanol}}{46.1\,\text{g ethanol}} \times \dfrac{1367\,\text{kJ}}{1\,\text{mol ethanol}} \times \dfrac{1\,\text{Cal}}{4.184\,\text{kJ}}$

$$= 133 = 1.3 \times 10^2 \text{ Cal}$$

Check. A "typical" 6 oz. glass of wine has 150–250 Cal, so this is a reasonable result. Note that alcohol is responsible for most of the food value of wine.

5.87   *Plan.* Use enthalpies of formation to calculate molar heat (enthalpy) of combustion using Hess's Law. Use molar mass to calculate heat of combustion per kg of hydrocarbon. *Solve.*

Propyne: $C_3H_4(g) + 4O_2(g) \rightarrow 3CO_2(g) + 2H_2O(g)$

(a) $\Delta H^\circ_{rxn} = 3(-393.5\,\text{kJ}) + 2(-241.82\,\text{kJ}) - (185.4\,\text{kJ}) - 4(0) = -1849.5$
$$= -1850\,\text{kJ/mol}\,C_3H_4$$

(b) $\dfrac{-1849.5 \text{ kJ}}{1 \text{ mol } C_3H_4} \times \dfrac{1 \text{ mol } C_3H_4}{40.065 \text{ g } C_3H_4} \times \dfrac{1000 \text{ g } C_3H_4}{1 \text{ kg } C_3H_4} = -4.616 \times 10^4 \text{ kJ/kg } C_3H_4$

Propylene: $C_3H_6(g) + 9/2\, O_2(g) \rightarrow 3CO_2(g) + 3H_2O(g)$

(a) $\Delta H^{\circ}_{rxn} = 3(-393.5 \text{ kJ}) + 3(-241.82 \text{ kJ}) - (20.4 \text{ kJ}) - 9/2(0) = -1926.4$

                                                $= -1926 \text{ kJ/mol } C_3H_6$

(b) $\dfrac{-1926.4 \text{ kJ}}{1 \text{ mol } C_3H_6} \times \dfrac{1 \text{ mol } C_3H_6}{42.080 \text{ g } C_3H_6} \times \dfrac{1000 \text{ g } C_3H_6}{1 \text{ kg } C_3H_6} = -4.578 \times 10^4 \text{ kJ/kg } C_3H_6$

Propane: $C_3H_8(g) + 5O_2(g) \rightarrow 3CO_2(g) + 4H_2O(g)$

(a) $\Delta H^{\circ}_{rxn} = 3(-393.5 \text{ kJ}) + 4(-241.82 \text{ kJ}) - (-103.8 \text{ kJ}) - 5(0) = -2044.0$

                                                $= -2044 \text{ kJ/mol } C_3H_8$

(b) $\dfrac{-2044.0 \text{ kJ}}{1 \text{ mol } C_3H_8} \times \dfrac{1 \text{ mol } C_3H_8}{44.096 \text{ g } C_3H_8} \times \dfrac{1000 \text{ g } C_3H_8}{1 \text{ kg } C_3H_8} = -4.635 \times 10^4 \text{ kJ/kg } C_3H_8$

(c)   These three substances yield nearly identical quantities of heat per unit mass, but propane is marginally higher than the other two.

5.88 $\Delta H^{\circ}_{rxn} = \Delta H^{\circ}_f\, CO_2(g) + 2\Delta H^{\circ}_f\, H_2O(g) - \Delta H^{\circ}_f\, CH_4(g) - 2\Delta H^{\circ}_f\, O_2(g)$

            $= -393.5 \text{ kJ} + 2(-241.82 \text{ kJ}) - (-74.8 \text{ kJ}) - 2(0) \text{ kJ} = -802.3 \text{ kJ}$

            $\Delta H^{\circ}_{rxn} = \Delta H^{\circ}_f\, CF_4(g) + 4\Delta H^{\circ}_f\, HF(g) - \Delta H^{\circ}_f\, CH_4(g) - 4\Delta H^{\circ}_f\, F_2(g)$

            $= -679.9 \text{ kJ} + 4(-268.61 \text{ kJ}) - (-74.8 \text{ kJ}) - 4(0) \text{ kJ} = -1679.5 \text{ kJ}$

The second reaction is twice as exothermic as the first. The "fuel values" of hydrocarbons in a fluorine atmosphere are approximately twice those in an oxygen atmosphere. Note that the difference in ΔH° values for the two reactions is in the ΔH°_f for the products, since the ΔH°_f for the reactants is identical.

5.89   *Analyze/Plan.* Given population, Cal/person/day and kJ/mol glucose, calculate kg glucose/yr. Calculate kJ/yr, then kg/yr. 1 billion = 1×10^9. 365 day = 1 yr. 1 Cal = 1 kcal, 4.184 kJ = 1 kcal = 1 Cal. *Solve.*

    $6.8 \times 10^9 \text{ persons} \times \dfrac{1500 \text{ Cal}}{\text{person} - \text{day}} \times \dfrac{365 \text{ day}}{1 \text{ yr}} \times \dfrac{4.184 \text{ kJ}}{1 \text{ Cal}} = 1.5577 \times 10^{16} = 1.6 \times 10^{16} \text{ kJ/yr}$

    $\dfrac{1.5577 \times 10^{16} \text{ kJ}}{\text{yr}} \times \dfrac{1 \text{ mol } C_6H_{12}O_6}{2803 \text{ kJ}} \times \dfrac{180.2 \text{ g } C_6H_{12}O_6}{1 \text{ mol } C_6H_{12}O_6} \times \dfrac{1 \text{ kg}}{1000 \text{ g}} = 1.0 \times 10^{12} \text{ kg } C_6H_{12}O_6 / \text{yr}$

Check. 1×10^{12} kg is 1 *trillion* kg of glucose.

5.90   (a)   Use density to change L to g, molar mass to change g to mol, heat of combustion to change mol to kJ. Ethanol is C_2H_5OH, gasoline is C_8H_{18}. From Exercise 5.79 (c), heat of combustion of ethanol is –1234.8 kJ/mol.

         $1.0 \text{ L } C_2H_5OH \times \dfrac{1000 \text{ mL}}{1 \text{ L}} \times \dfrac{0.79 \text{ g}}{1 \text{ mL}} \times \dfrac{1 \text{ mol } C_2H_5OH}{46.07 \text{ g}} \times \dfrac{1234.8 \text{ kJ}}{1 \text{ mol } C_2H_5OH}$

                                            $= 21,174 = 2.1 \times 10^4 \text{ kJ/L } C_2H_5OH$

$$1.0 \, L \, C_8H_{18} \times \frac{1000 \, mL}{1 \, L} \times \frac{0.70 \, g}{1 \, mL} \times \frac{1 \, mol \, C_8H_{18}}{114.23 \, g \, C_8H_{18}} \times \frac{5400 \, kJ}{1 \, mol \, C_8H_{18}}$$

$$= 33{,}091 = 3.3 \times 10^4 \, kJ/L \, C_8H_{18}$$

(b) If density and heat of combustion of E85 are weighted averages of the values for the pure substances, than energy per liter E85 is also a weighted average of energy per liter for the two substances.

$$kJ/L \, E85 = 0.15(kJ/L \, C_8H_{18}) + 0.85(kJ/L \, C_2H_5OH)$$

$$kJ/L \, E85 = 0.15(33{,}091 \, kJ) + 0.85(21{,}174 \, kJ) = 22{,}962 = 2.3 \times 10^4 \, kJ/L \, E85$$

(c) Whether comparing gal of L, all conversion factors for the two fuels cancel, so we can apply the energy ratio directly to the volume under consideration.

The energy ratio for E85 to gasoline is $(22{,}962/33{,}091) = 0.6939 = 0.69$

$$10 \, gal \, gas \times \frac{kJ \, from \, E85}{0.6939 \, kJ \, from \, gas} = 14.41 = 14 \, gal \, E85$$

(d) If the E85/gasoline energy ratio is 0.69, the the cost ratio must be 0.70 or less in order to "break-even" on price. $0.69(\$3.10) = \$2.14/gal \, E85$

Check. 10 gal gas($3.10/gal) = \$31; 14.4 gal E85($2.14/gal) = \$31

Additional Exercises

5.91   (a)   mi/hr $\rightarrow$ m/s

$$1050 \, \frac{mi}{hr} \times \frac{1.6093 \, km}{1 \, mi} \times \frac{1000 \, m}{1 \, km} \times \frac{1 \, hr}{3600 \, s} = 469.38 = 469.4 \, m/s$$

(b) Find the mass of one N_2 molecule in kg.

$$\frac{28.0134 \, g \, N_2}{1 \, mol} \times \frac{1 \, mol}{6.022 \times 10^{23} \, molecules} \times \frac{1 \, kg}{1000 \, g} = 4.6518 \times 10^{-26}$$

$$= 4.652 \times 10^{-26} \, kg$$

$$E_k = 1/2 \, mv^2 = 1/2 \times 4.6518 \times 10^{-26} \, kg \times (469.38 \, m/s)^2$$

$$= 5.1244 \times 10^{-21} \, \frac{kg \cdot m^2}{s^2} = 5.124 \times 10^{-21} \, J$$

(c) $$\frac{5.1244 \times 10^{-21} \, J}{molecule} \times \frac{6.022 \times 10^{23} \, molecules}{1 \, mol} = 3086 \, J/mol = 3.086 \, kJ/mol$$

5.92   (a) $E_p = mgd = 52.0 \, kg \times 9.81 \, m/s^2 \times 10.8 \, m = 5509.3 \, J = 5.51 \, kJ$

(b) $$E_k = 1/2 \, mv^2; v = (2E_k/m)^{1/2} = \left(\frac{2 \times 5509.3 \, kg \cdot m^2/s^2}{52.0 \, kg} \right)^{1/2} = 14.6 \, m/s$$

(c) Yes, the diver does work on entering (pushing back) the water in the pool.

5.93   Like the combustion of $H_2(g)$ and $O_2(g)$ described in Section 5.4, the reaction that inflates airbags is spontaneous after initiation. Spontaneous reactions are usually exothermic, $-\Delta H$. The airbag reaction occurs at constant atmospheric pressure, $\Delta H = q_p$;

both are likely to be large and negative. When the bag inflates, work is done by the system on the surroundings, so the sign of w is negative.

5.94   Freezing is an exothermic process (the opposite of melting, which is clearly endothermic). When the system, the soft drink, freezes, it releases energy to the surroundings, the can. Some of this energy does the work of splitting the can.

5.95   (a)   It is not surprising that the gas expands when the valve is opened. Gases expand to fill their containers, regardless of other contents. (Nature abhors a vacuum).

    (b)   No work is done when the gas expands, because the evacuated flask is truly empty. There is no surrounding substance to be "pushed back".

    (c) $\Delta E = q + w$. From part (b), no work is done when the gas expands. The flasks are perfectly insulated, so no heat flows. $\Delta E = 0 + 0 = 0$. The answer is a bit surprising, since a definite change occurred that required no work or heat transfer and consequently involved no energy change.

5.96   (a) $q = 0$, $w > 0$ (work done to system), $\Delta E > 0$

    (b)   Since the system (the gas) is losing heat, the sign of q is negative.

    Two interpretations of the final state in (b) are are possible. If the final state in (b) is identical to the final state in (a), $\Delta E(a) = \Delta E(b)$. If the final volumes are identical, case (b) requires either more (non-PV) work or heat input to compress the gas because some heat is lost to the surroundings. (The moral of this story is that the more energy lost by the system as heat, the greater the work on the system required to accomplish the desired change.)

    Alternatively, if w is identical in the two cases and q is negative for case (b), then $\Delta E(b) < \Delta E(a)$. Assuming identical final volumes, the final temperature and pressure in (b) are slightly lower than those values in (a).

5.97 $\Delta E = q + w = +38.95 \text{ kJ} - 2.47 \text{ kJ} = +36.48 \text{ kJ}$

$\Delta H = q_p = +38.95 \text{ kJ}$

5.98   If a function sometimes depends on path, then it is simply not a state function. Enthalpy is a state function, so ΔH for the two pathways leading to the same change of state pictured in Figure 5.10 must be the same. However, q is not the same for the both. Our conclusion must be that $\Delta H \neq q$ for these pathways. The condition for $\Delta H = q_p$ (other than constant pressure) is that the only possible work on or by the system is pressure-volume work. Clearly, the work being done in this scenario is not pressure-volume work, so $\Delta H \neq q$, even though the two changes occur at constant pressure.

5.99   Find the heat capacity of 1.7×10^3 gal H_2O.

$$C_{H_2O} = 1.7 \times 10^3 \text{ gal } H_2O \times \frac{4 \text{ qt}}{1 \text{ gal}} \times \frac{1 \text{ L}}{1.057 \text{ qt}} \times \frac{1 \times 10^3 \text{ cm}^3}{1 \text{ L}} \times \frac{1 \text{ g}}{1 \text{ cm}^3} \times \frac{4.184 \text{ J}}{1 \text{ g} - {}^\circ C}$$

$$= 2.692 \times 10^7 \text{ J}/{}^\circ C = 2.7 \times 10^4 \text{ kJ}/{}^\circ C; \text{ then,}$$

$$\frac{2.692 \times 10^7 \text{ J}}{1 {}^\circ C} \times \frac{1 \text{ g} - {}^\circ C}{0.85 \text{ J}} \times \frac{1 \text{ kg}}{1 \times 10^3 \text{ g}} \times \frac{1 \text{ brick}}{1.8 \text{ kg}} = 1.8 \times 10^4 \text{ or } 18,000 \text{ bricks}$$

Check. $(1.7 \times {\sim}16 \times 10^6)/({\sim}1.6 \times 10^3) \approx 17 \times 10^3$ bricks; the units are correct.

5.100 (a) $q_{Cu} = \dfrac{0.385\,J}{g \cdot K} \times 121.0\,g\,Cu \times (30.1^\circ C - 100.4^\circ C) = -3274.9 = -3.27 \times 10^3\,J$

The negative sign indicates the 3.27×10^3 J are lost by the Cu block.

(b) $q_{H_2O} = \dfrac{4.184\,J}{g \cdot K} \times 150.0\,g\,H_2O \times (30.1^\circ C - 25.1^\circ C) = 3138 = 3.1 \times 10^3\,J$

The positive sign indicates that 3.14×10^3 J are gained by the H_2O.

(c) The difference in the heat lost by the Cu and the heat gained by the water is 3.275 $\times 10^3$ J – 3.138 $\times 10^3$ J = 0.137 $\times 10^3$ J = 1×10^2 J. The temperature change of the calorimeter is 5.0°C. The heat capacity of the calorimeter in J/K is

$0.137 \times 10^3\,J \times \dfrac{1}{5.0^\circ C} = 27.4 = 3 \times 10^1\,J/K.$

Since q_{H_2O} is known to one decimal place, the difference has one decimal place and the result has 1 sig fig.

If the rounded results from (a) and (b) are used,

$C_{calorimeter} = \dfrac{0.2 \times 10^3\,J}{5.0\,^\circ C} = 4 \times 10^1\,J/K.$

(d) $q_{H_2O} = 3.275 \times 10^3\,J = \dfrac{4.184\,J}{g \cdot K} \times 150.0\,g \times (\Delta T)$

$\Delta T = 5.22^\circ C;\ T_f = 25.1^\circ C + 5.22^\circ C = 30.3^\circ C$

5.101 (a) From the mass of benzoic acid that produces a certain temperature change, we can calculate the heat capacity of the calorimeter.

$\dfrac{0.235\,g\ benzoic\ acid}{1.642^\circ C\ change\ observed} \times \dfrac{26.38\,kJ}{1\,g\ benzoic\ acid} = 3.7755 = 3.78\,kJ/^\circ C$

Now we can use this experimentally determined heat capacity with the data for caffeine.

$\dfrac{1.525^\circ C\ rise}{0.265\,g\ caffeine} \times \dfrac{3.7755\,kJ}{1^\circ C} \times \dfrac{194.2\,g\ caffeine}{1\,mol\ caffeine} = 4.22 \times 10^3\,kJ/mol\ caffeine$

(b) The overall uncertainty is approximately equal to the sum of the uncertainties due to each effect. The uncertainty in the mass measurement is 0.001/0.235 or 0.001/0.265, about 1 part in 235 or 1 part in 265. The uncertainty in the temperature measurements is 0.002/1.642 or 0.002/1.525, about 1 part in 820 or 1 part in 760. Thus the uncertainty in heat of combustion from each measurement is

$\dfrac{4220}{235} = 18\,kJ;\quad \dfrac{4220}{265} = 16\,kJ;\quad \dfrac{4220}{820} = 5\,kJ;\quad \dfrac{4220}{760} = 6\,kJ$

The sum of these uncertainties is 45 kJ. In fact, the overall uncertainty is less than this because independent errors in measurement do tend to partially cancel.

5.102 (a) $Mg(s) + 2H_2O(l) \rightarrow Mg(OH)_2(s) + H_2(g)$

$\Delta H_{rxn}^\circ = \Delta H_f^\circ\,Mg(OH)_2(s) + \Delta H_f^\circ\,H_2(g) - 2\Delta H_f^\circ\,H_2O(l) - \Delta H_f^\circ\,Mg(s)$

$= -924.7\,kJ + 0 - 2(-285.83\,kJ) - 0 = -353.04 = -353.0\,kJ$

(b) Use the specific heat of water, 4.184 J/g-°C, to calculate the energy required to heat the water. Use the density of water at 25°C to calculate the mass of H_2O to be heated. (The change in density of H_2O going from 21°C to 79°C does not substantially affect the strategy of the exercise.) Then use the 'heat stoichiometry' in (a) to calculate mass of Mg(s) needed.

$$75 \text{ mL} \times \frac{0.997 \text{ g } H_2O}{\text{mL}} \times \frac{4.184 \text{ J}}{\text{g -°C}} \times 58°C \times \frac{1 \text{ kJ}}{1000 \text{ J}} = 18.146 \text{ kJ} = 18 \text{ kJ required}$$

$$18.146 \text{ kJ} \times \frac{1 \text{ mol Mg}}{353.04 \text{ kJ}} \times \frac{24.305 \text{ g Mg}}{1 \text{ mol Mg}} = 1.249 \text{ g} = 1.2 \text{ g Mg needed}$$

5.103 (a) For comparison, balance the equations so that 1 mole of CH_4 is burned in each.

$$CH_4(g) + O_2(g) \rightarrow C(s) + 2H_2O(l) \qquad \Delta H° = -496.9 \text{ kJ}$$

$$CH_4(g) + 3/2 O_2(g) \rightarrow CO(g) + 2H_2O(l) \qquad \Delta H° = -607.4 \text{ kJ}$$

$$CH_4(g) + 2O_2(g) \rightarrow CO_2(g) + 2H_2O(l) \qquad \Delta H° = -890.4 \text{ kJ}$$

(b) $\Delta H°_{rxn} = \Delta H°_f \, C(s) + 2\Delta H°_f \, H_2O(l) - \Delta H°_f \, CH_4(g) - \Delta H°_f \, O_2(g)$

$= 0 + 2(-285.83 \text{ kJ}) - (-74.8) - 0 = -496.9 \text{ kJ}$

$\Delta H°_{rxn} = \Delta H°_f \, CO(g) + 2\Delta H°_f \, H_2O(l) - \Delta H°_f \, CH_4(g) - 3/2 \Delta H°_f \, O_2(g)$

$= (-110.5 \text{ kJ}) + 2(-285.83 \text{ kJ}) - (-74.8 \text{ kJ}) - 3/2(0) = -607.4 \text{ kJ}$

$\Delta H°_{rxn} = \Delta H°_f \, CO_2(g) + 2\Delta H°_f \, H_2O(l) - \Delta H°_f \, CH_4(g) - 2\Delta H°_f \, O_2(g)$

$= -393.5 \text{ kJ} + 2(-285.83 \text{ kJ}) - (-74.8 \text{ kJ}) - 2(0) = -890.4 \text{ kJ}$

(c) Assuming that $O_2(g)$ is present in excess, the reaction that produces $CO_2(g)$ represents the most negative ΔH per mole of CH_4 burned. More of the potential energy of the reactants is released as heat during the reaction to give products of lower potential energy. The reaction that produces $CO_2(g)$ is the most "downhill" in enthalpy.

5.104 (a)

$$2B(s) + 3/2 O_2(g) \rightarrow B_2O_3(s) \qquad \Delta H° = 1/2(-2509.1 \text{ kJ})$$
$$3H_2(g) + 3/2 O_2(g) \rightarrow 3H_2O(l) \qquad \Delta H° = 3/2(-571.7 \text{ kJ})$$
$$\underline{B_2O_3(s) + 3H_2O(l) \rightarrow B_2H_6(g) + 3O_2(g) \qquad \Delta H° = -(-2147.5 \text{ kJ})}$$
$$2B(s) + 3H_2(g) \rightarrow B_2H_6(g) \qquad \Delta H°_f = +35.4 \text{ kJ}$$

(b) If, like B_2H_6, the combustion of B_5H_9 produces B_2O_3 as the boron-containing product, the heat of combustion of B_5H_9 in addition to data given in part (a) would enable calculation of the heat of formation of B_5H_9.

The combustion reaction is: $B_5H_9(l) + 6O_2(g) \rightarrow 5/2 B_2O_3(s) + 9/2 H_2O(l)$

$$5/4\,[4B(s) + 3O_2(g) \rightarrow 2B_2O_3(s)] \qquad \Delta H° = 5/4(-2509.1\,kJ)$$

$$9/4\,[2H_2(g) + O_2(g) \rightarrow 2H_2O(l)] \qquad \Delta H° = 9/4\,(-571.7\,kJ)$$

$$5/2\,B_2O_3(s) + 9/2\,H_2O(l) \rightarrow B_5H_9(l) + 6O_2(g) \qquad \Delta H° = -\,(\text{heat of combustion})$$

$$5B(s) + 9/2\,H_2(g) \rightarrow B_5H_9(l) \qquad \Delta H_f° \text{ of } B_5H_9(l)$$

$$\Delta H_f° \; B_5H_9(l) = -\,[\text{heat of combustion of } B_5H_9(l)] - 3136.4\,kJ - 1286\,kJ$$

We need to measure the heat of combustion of $B_5H_9(l)$.

5.105   For nitroethane:

$$\frac{1368\,kJ}{1\,mol\,C_2H_5NO_2} \times \frac{1\,mol\,C_2H_5NO_2}{75.072\,g\,C_2H_5NO_2} \times \frac{1.052\,g\,C_2H_5NO_2}{1\,cm^3} = 19.17\,kJ/cm^3$$

For ethanol:

$$\frac{1367\,kJ}{1\,mol\,C_2H_5OH} \times \frac{1\,mol\,C_2H_5OH}{46.069\,g\,C_2H_5OH} \times \frac{0.789\,g\,C_2H_5OH}{1\,cm^3} = 23.4\,kJ/cm^3$$

For methylhydrazine:

$$\frac{1307\,kJ}{1\,mol\,CH_6N_2} \times \frac{1\,mol\,CH_6N_2}{46.072\,g\,CH_6N_2} \times \frac{0.874\,g\,CH_6N_2}{1\,cm^3} = 24.8\,kJ/cm^3$$

Thus, **methylhydrazine** would provide the most energy per unit volume, with ethanol a close second.

5.106   (a) $3C_2H_2(g) \rightarrow C_6H_6(l)$

$$\Delta H_{rxn}° = \Delta H_f° \; C_6H_6(l) - 3\Delta H_f° \; C_2H_2(g) = 49.0\,kJ - 3(226.77\,kJ) = -631.31 = -631.3\,kJ$$

(b)   Since the reaction is exothermic (ΔH is negative), the reactant, 3 moles of $C_2H_2(g)$, has more enthalpy than the product, 1 mole of $C_6H_6(l)$.

(c)   The fuel value of a substance is the amount of heat (kJ) produced when 1 gram of the substance is burned. Calculate the molar heat of combustion (kJ/mol) and use this to find kJ/g of fuel.

$$C_2H_2(g) + 5/2\,O_2(g) \rightarrow 2CO_2(g) + H_2O(l)$$

$$\Delta H_{rxn}° = 2\Delta H_f° \; CO_2(g) + \Delta H_f° \; H_2O(l) - \Delta H_f° \; C_2H_2(g) - 5/2\,\Delta H_f° \; O_2(g)$$

$$= 2(-393.5\,kJ) + (-285.83\,kJ) - 226.77\,kJ - 5/2\,(0) = -1299.6\,kJ/mol\,C_2H_2$$

$$\frac{-1299.6\,kJ}{1\,mol\,C_2H_2} \times \frac{1\,mol\,C_2H_2}{26.036\,g\,C_2H_2} = 49.916 = 50\,kJ/g\,C_2H_2$$

$$C_6H_6(l) + 15/2\,O_2(g) \rightarrow 6CO_2(g) + 3H_2O(l)$$

$$\Delta H_{rxn}° = 6\Delta H_f° \; CO_2(g) + 3\Delta H_f° \; H_2O(l) - \Delta H_f° \; C_6H_6(l) - 15/2\,\Delta H_f° \; O_2(g)$$

$$= 6(-393.5\,kJ) + 3(-285.83\,kJ) - 49.0\,kJ - 15/2\,(0) = -3267.5\,kJ/mol\,C_6H_6$$

$$\frac{-3267.5\,kJ}{1\,mol\,C_6H_6} \times \frac{1\,mol\,C_6H_6}{78.114\,g\,C_6H_6} = 41.830 = 42\,kJ/g\,C_6H_6$$

5.107   The reaction for which we want ΔH is:

$$4NH_3(l) + 3O_2(g) \rightarrow 2N_2(g) + 6H_2O(g)$$

Before we can calculate ΔH for this reaction, we must calculate ΔH_f for $NH_3(l)$.

We know that ΔH_f for $NH_3(g)$ is -46.2 kJ/mol, and that for $NH_3(l) \rightarrow NH_3(g)$, $\Delta H = 23.2$ kJ/mol

Thus, $\Delta H_{vap} = \Delta H_f\ NH_3(g) - \Delta H_f\ NH_3(l)$.

$$23.2\ kJ = -46.2\ kJ - \Delta H_f\ NH_3(l);\ \Delta H_f\ NH_3(l) = -69.4\ kJ/mol$$

Then for the overall reaction, the enthalpy change is:

$$\Delta H_{rxn} = 6\Delta H_f\ H_2O(g) + 2\Delta H_f\ N_2(g) - 4\Delta H_f\ NH_3(l) - 3\Delta H_f\ O_2$$

$$= 6(-241.82\ kJ) + 2(0) - 4(-69.4\ kJ) - 3(0) = -1173.3\ kJ$$

$$\frac{-1173.3\ kJ}{4\ mol\ NH_3} \times \frac{1\ mol\ NH_3}{17.0\ g\ NH_3} = \frac{0.81\ g\ NH_3}{1\ cm^3} \times \frac{1000\ cm^3}{1\ L} = \frac{-1.4 \times 10^4\ kJ}{L\ NH_3}$$

(This result has two significant figures because the density is expressed to two figures.)

$$2CH_3OH(l) + 3O_2(g) \rightarrow 2CO_2(g) + 4H_2O(g)$$

$$\Delta H = 2(-393.5\ kJ) + 4(-241.82\ kJ) - 2(-239\ kJ) - 3(0) = -1276\ kJ$$

$$\frac{-1276\ kJ}{2\ mol\ CH_3OH} \times \frac{1\ mol\ CH_3OH}{32.04\ g\ CH_3OH} \times \frac{0.792\ g\ CH_3OH}{1\ cm^3} \times \frac{1000\ cm^3}{1\ L} = \frac{-1.58 \times 10^4\ kJ}{L\ CH_3OH}$$

In terms of heat obtained per unit volume of fuel, methanol is a slightly better fuel than liquid ammonia.

5.108   **1,3-butadiene**, C_4H_6, MM = 54.092 g/mol

(a) $C_4H_6(g) + 11/2\ O_2(g) \rightarrow 4CO_2(g) + 3H_2O(l)$

$$\Delta H_{rxn}^\circ = 4\Delta H_f^\circ\ CO_2(g) + 3\Delta H_f^\circ\ H_2O(l) - \Delta H_f^\circ\ C_4H_6(g) - 11/2\ \Delta H_f^\circ\ O_2(g)$$

$$= 4(-393.5\ kJ) + 3(-285.83\ kJ) - 111.9\ kJ + 11/2\ (0) = -2543.4\ kJ/mol\ C_4H_6$$

(b) $\dfrac{-2543.4\ kJ}{1\ mol\ C_4H_6} \times \dfrac{1\ mol\ C_4H_6}{54.092\ g} = 47.020 \rightarrow 47\ kJ/g$

(c) $\% H = \dfrac{6(1.008)}{54.092} \times 100 = 11.18\%\ H$

1-butene, C_4H_8, MM = 56.108 g/mol

(a) $C_4H_8(g) + 6O_2(g) \rightarrow 4CO_2(g) + 4H_2O(l)$

$$\Delta H_{rxn}^\circ = 4\Delta H_f^\circ\ CO_2(g) + 4\Delta H_f^\circ\ H_2O(l) - \Delta H_f^\circ\ C_4H_8(g) - 6\Delta H_f^\circ\ O_2(g)$$

$$= 4(-393.5\ kJ) + 4(-285.83\ kJ) - 1.2\ kJ - 6(0) = -2718.5\ kJ/mol\ C_4H_8$$

(b) $\dfrac{-2718.5\ kJ}{1\ mol\ C_4H_8} \times \dfrac{1\ mol\ C_4H_8}{56.108\ g\ C_4H_8} = 48.451 \rightarrow 48\ kJ/g$

(c) $\% \, H = \dfrac{8(1.008)}{56.108} \times 100 = 14.37\% \, H$

n-butane, $C_4H_{10}(g)$, MM = 58.124 g/mol

(a) $C_4H_{10}(g) + 13/2 \, O_2(g) \rightarrow 4CO_2(g) + 5H_2O(l)$

   $\Delta H^{\circ}_{rxn} = 4\Delta H^{\circ}_{f} \, CO_2(g) + 5\Delta H^{\circ}_{f} \, H_2O(l) - \Delta H^{\circ}_{f} \, C_4H_{10}(g) - 13/2 \, \Delta H^{\circ}_{f} \, O_2(g)$

   $= 4(-393.5 \text{ kJ}) + 5(-285.83 \text{ kJ}) - (-124.7 \text{ kJ}) - 13/2(0)$

   $= -2878.5 \text{ kJ/mol } C_4H_{10}$

(b) $\dfrac{-2878.5 \text{ kJ}}{1 \text{ mol } C_4H_{10}} \times \dfrac{1 \text{ mol } C_4H_{10}}{58.124 \text{ g } C_4H_{10}} = 49.523 \rightarrow 50 \text{ kJ/g}$

(c) $\% \, H = \dfrac{10(1.008)}{58.124} \times 100 = 17.34\% \, H$

(d)   It is certainly true that as the mass % H increases, the fuel value (kJ/g) of the hydrocarbon increases, given the same number of C atoms. A graph of the data in parts (b) and (c) (see below) suggests that mass % H and fuel value are directly proportional when the number of C atoms is constant.

5.109 $\Delta E_p = m \, g \, d$. Be careful with units. $1 \text{ J} = 1 \text{ kg} \cdot \text{m}^2/\text{s}^2$

$200 \text{ lb} \times \dfrac{1 \text{ kg}}{2.205 \text{ lb}} \times \dfrac{9.81 \text{ m}}{\text{s}^2} \times \dfrac{45 \text{ ft}}{\text{time}} \times \dfrac{1 \text{ yd}}{3 \text{ ft}} \times \dfrac{1 \text{ m}}{1.0936 \text{ yd}} \times 20 \text{ times}$

$\qquad\qquad = 2.441 \times 10^5 \text{ kg} \cdot \text{m}^2/\text{s}^2 = 2.441 \times 10^5 \text{ J} = 2.4 \times 10^2 \text{ kJ}$

1 Cal = 1 kcal = 4.184 kJ

$2.441 \times 10^2 \text{ kJ} \times \dfrac{1 \text{ Cal}}{4.184 \text{ kJ}} = 58.34 = 58 \text{ Cal}$

No, if all work is used to increase the man's potential energy, 20 rounds of stair-climbing will not compensate for one extra order of 245 Cal fries. In fact, more than 58 Cal of work will be required to climb the stairs, because some energy is required to move limbs and some energy will be lost as heat (see Solution 5.96).

5.110   *Plan.* Use dimensional analysis to calculate the amount of solar energy supplied per m^2 in 1 hr. Use stoichiometry to calculate the amount of plant energy used to produce sucrose per m^2 in 1 hr. Calculate the ratio of energy for sucrose to total solar energy, per m^2 per hr.

Solve. $1\,W = 1\,J/s$, $1\,kW = 1\,kJ/s$

$$\frac{1.0\,kW}{m^2} = \frac{1.0\,kJ/s}{m^2} = \frac{1.0\,kJ}{m^2\text{-}s} \times \frac{60\,s}{1\,min} \times \frac{60\,min}{1\,hr} = \frac{3.6 \times 10^3\,kJ}{m^2\text{-}hr}$$

$$\frac{5645\,kJ}{mol\,sucrose} \times \frac{1\,mol\,sucrose}{342.3\,g\,sucrose} \times \frac{0.20\,g\,sucrose}{m^2\text{-}hr} = 3.298 = 3.3\,kJ/m^2\text{-}hr$$

for sucrose production

$$\frac{3.298\,kJ\,for\,sucrose}{3.6 \times 10^3\,kJ\,total\,solar} \times 100 = 0.092\%\,sunlight\,used\,to\,produce\,sucrose$$

5.111   (a) $6CO_2(g) + 6H_2O(l) \rightarrow C_6H_{12}O_6(s) + 6O_2(g)$, $\Delta H° = 2803\,kJ$

This is the reverse of the combustion of glucose (Section 5.8 and Solution 5.89), so $\Delta H° = -(-2803)\,kJ = +2803\,kJ$.

$$\frac{5.5 \times 10^{16}\,g\,CO_2}{yr} \times \frac{1\,mol\,CO_2}{44.01\,g\,CO_2} \times \frac{2803\,kJ}{6\,mol\,CO_2} = 5.838 \times 10^{17} = 5.8 \times 10^{17}\,kJ$$

     (b) $1\,W = 1\,J/s$; $1\,W\text{-}s = 1\,J$

$$\frac{5.838 \times 10^{17}\,kJ}{yr} \times \frac{1000\,J}{kJ} \times \frac{1\,yr}{365\,d} \times \frac{1\,d}{24\,hr} \times \frac{1\,hr}{60\,min} \times \frac{1\,min}{60\,s} \times \frac{1\,W\text{-}s}{J}$$

$$\times \frac{1\,MW}{1 \times 10^6\,W} = 1.851 \times 10^7\,MW = 1.9 \times 10^7\,MW$$

$$1.9 \times 10^7\,MW \times \frac{1\,plant}{10^3\,MW} = 1.9 \times 10^4 = 19,000\ \text{nuclear power plants}$$

Integrative Exercises

5.112   (a) $CH_4(g) + 2O_2(g) \rightarrow CO_2(g) + 2H_2O(l)$

$$\Delta H° = \Delta H_f°\ CO_2(g) + 2\Delta H_f°\ H_2O(l) - \Delta H_f°\ CH_4(g) - 2\Delta H_f°\ O_2(g)$$

$$= -393.5\,kJ + 2(-285.83\,kJ) - (-74.8\,kJ) - 2(0) = -890.36 = -890.4\,kJ/mol\ CH_4$$

$$\frac{-890.36\,kJ}{mol\,CH_4} \times \frac{1000\,J}{1\,kJ} \times \frac{1\,mol}{6.022 \times 10^{23}\,molecules\,CH_4} = 1.4785 \times 10^{-18}$$

$$= 1.479 \times 10^{-18}\,J/molecule$$

     (b) $1\,eV = 96.485\,kJ/mol$

$$8\,keV \times \frac{1000\,eV}{1\,keV} \times \frac{96.485\,kJ}{eV\text{-}mol} \times \frac{1\,mol}{6.022 \times 10^{23}} \times \frac{1000\,J}{kJ} = 1.282 \times 10^{-15} = 1 \times 10^{-15}\,J/X\text{-ray}$$

The X-ray has approximately 1000 times more energy than is produced by the combustion of 1 molecule of $CH_4(g)$.

5.113   (a),(b) $Ag^+(aq) + Li(s) \rightarrow Ag(s) + Li^+(aq)$

$$\Delta H° = \Delta H_f°\ Li^+(aq) - \Delta H_f°\ Ag^+(aq)$$

$$= -278.5\,kJ - 105.90\,kJ = -384.4\,kJ$$

$$Fe(s) + 2Na^+(aq) \rightarrow Fe^{2+}(aq) + 2Na(s)$$

$$\Delta H^\circ = \Delta H_f^\circ \, Fe^{2+}(aq) - 2\Delta H_f^\circ \, Na^+(aq)$$

$$= -87.86 \text{ kJ} - 2(-240.1 \text{ kJ}) = +392.3 \text{ kJ}$$

$$2K(s) + 2H_2O(l) \rightarrow 2KOH(aq) + H_2(g)$$

$$\Delta H^\circ = 2\Delta H_f^\circ \, KOH(aq) - 2\Delta H_f^\circ \, H_2O(l)$$

$$= 2(-482.4 \text{ kJ}) - 2(-285.83 \text{ kJ}) = -393.1 \text{ kJ}$$

(c) Exothermic reactions are more likely to be favored, so we expect the first and third reactions be favored.

(d) In the activity series of metals, Table 4.5, any metal can be oxidized by the cation of a metal below it on the table.

Ag^+ is below Li, so the first reaction will occur.

Na^+ is above Fe, so the second reaction will not occur.

H^+ (formally in H_2O) is below K, so the third reaction will occur.

These predictions agree with those in part (c).

5.114 (a) $\Delta H^\circ = \Delta H_f^\circ \, NaNO_3(aq) + \Delta H_f^\circ \, H_2O(l) - \Delta H_f^\circ \, HNO_3(aq) - \Delta H_f^\circ \, NaOH(aq)$

$\Delta H^\circ = -446.2 \text{ kJ} - 285.83 \text{ kJ} - (-206.6 \text{ kJ}) - (-469.6 \text{ kJ}) = -55.8 \text{ kJ}$

$\Delta H^\circ = \Delta H_f^\circ \, NaCl(aq) + \Delta H_f^\circ \, H_2O(l) - \Delta H_f^\circ \, HCl(aq) - \Delta H_f^\circ \, NaOH(aq)$

$\Delta H^\circ = -407.1 \text{ kJ} - 285.83 \text{ kJ} - (-167.2 \text{ kJ}) - (-469.6 \text{ kJ}) = -56.1 \text{ kJ}$

$\Delta H^\circ = \Delta H_f^\circ \, NH_3(aq) + \Delta H_f^\circ \, Na^+(aq) + \Delta H_f^\circ \, H_2O(l) - \Delta H_f^\circ \, NH_4^+(aq) - \Delta H_f^\circ \, NaOH(aq)$

$= -80.29 \text{ kJ} - 240.1 \text{ kJ} - 285.83 \text{ kJ} - (-132.5 \text{ kJ}) - (-469.6 \text{ kJ}) = -4.1 \text{ kJ}$

(b) $H^+(aq) + OH^-(aq) \rightarrow H_2O(l)$

(c) The ΔH° values for the first two reactions are nearly identical, -55.8 kJ and -56.1 kJ. The spectator ions by definition do not change during the course of a reaction, so ΔH° is the enthalpy change for the net ionic equation. Since the first two reactions have the same net ionic equation, it is not surprising that they have the same ΔH°.

(d) Strong acids are more likely than weak acids to donate H^+. The neutralizations of the two strong acids are energetically favorable, while the neutralization of $NH_4^+(aq)$ is significangly less favorable. $NH_4^+(aq)$ is probably a weak acid.

5.115 (a) mol Cu = $M \times L$ = 1.00 $M \times$ 0.0500 L = 0.0500 mol

g = mol $\times$ MM = 0.0500 $\times$ 63.546 = 3.1773 = 3.18 g Cu

(b) The precipitate is copper(II) hydroxide, $Cu(OH)_2$.

(c) $CuSO_4(aq) + 2KOH(aq) \rightarrow Cu(OH)_2(s) + K_2SO_4(aq)$, complete

$Cu^{2+}(aq) + 2OH^-(aq) \rightarrow Cu(OH)_2(s)$, net ionic

(d)   The temperature of the calorimeter rises, so the reaction is exothermic and the sign of q is negative.

$$q = -6.2\,°C \times 100\,g \times \frac{4.184\,J}{1\,g\text{-}°C} = -2.6 \times 10^3\,J = -2.6\,kJ$$

The reaction as carried out involves only 0.050 mol of $CuSO_4$ and the stoichiometrically equivalent amount of KOH. On a molar basis,

$$\Delta H = \frac{-2.6\,kJ}{0.050\,mol} = -52\,kJ \quad \text{for the reaction as written in part (c)}$$

5.116   (a) $AgNO_3(aq) + NaCl(aq) \rightarrow NaNO_3(aq) + AgCl(s)$

net ionic equation: $Ag^+(aq) + Cl^-(aq) \rightarrow AgCl(s)$

$\Delta H° = \Delta H_f° \; AgCl(s) - \Delta H_f° \; Ag^+(aq) - \Delta H_f° Cl^-(aq)$

$\Delta H° = -127.0\,kJ - (105.90\,kJ) - (-167.2\,kJ) = -65.7\,kJ$

(b) $\Delta H°$ for the complete molecular equation will be the same as $\Delta H°$ for the net ionic equation. $Na^+(aq)$ and $NO_3^-(aq)$ are spectator ions; they appear on both sides of the chemical equation. Since the overall enthalpy change is the enthalpy of the products minus the enthalpy of the reactants, the contributions of the spectator ions cancel.

(c) $\Delta H° = \Delta H_f° \; NaNO_3(aq) + \Delta H_f° \; AgCl(s) - \Delta H_f° \; AgNO_3(aq) - \Delta H_f° \; NaCl(aq)$

$\Delta H_f° \; AgNO_3(aq) = \Delta H_f° \; NaNO_3(aq) + \Delta H_f° \; AgCl(s) - \Delta H_f° \; NaCl(aq) - \Delta H°$

$\Delta H_f° \; AgNO_3(aq) = -446.2\,kJ + (-127.0\,kJ) - (-407.1\,kJ) - (-65.7\,kJ)$

$\Delta H_f° \; AgNO_3(aq) = -100.4\,kJ/mol$

5.117   (a) $21.83\,g\;CO_2 \times \dfrac{1\,mol\,CO_2}{44.01\,g\,CO_2} \times \dfrac{1\,mol\,C}{1\,mol\,CO_2} \times \dfrac{12.01\,g\,C}{1\,mol\,C} = 5.9572 = 5.957\,g\,C$

$4.47\,g\;H_2O \times \dfrac{1\,mol\,H_2O}{18.02\,g\,H_2O} \times \dfrac{2\,mol\,H}{1\,mol\,H_2O} \times \dfrac{1.008\,g\,H}{mol\,H} = 0.5001 = 0.500\,g\,H$

The sample mass is (5.9572 + 0.5001) = 6.457 g

(b) $5.957\,g\;C \times \dfrac{1\,mol\,C}{12.01\,g\,C} = 0.4960\,mol\,C; \quad 0.4960/0.496 = 1$

$0.500\,g\;H \times \dfrac{1\,mol\,H}{1.008\,g\,H} = 0.496\,mol\,H; \quad 0.496/0.496 = 1$

The empirical formula of the hydrocarbon is CH.

(c)   Calculate "$\Delta H_f°$" for 6.457 g of the sample.

$6.457\,g\;\text{sample} + O_2(g) \rightarrow 21.83\,g\;CO_2(g) + 4.47\,g\;H_2O(g), \;\; \Delta H_{comb}° = -311\,kJ$

$\Delta H_{comb}° = \Delta H_f° \; CO_2(g) + \Delta H_f° \; H_2O(g) - \Delta H_f° \; \text{sample} - \Delta H_f° \; O_2(g)$

$\Delta H_f° \; \text{sample} = \Delta H_f° \; CO_2(g) + \Delta H_f° \; H_2O(g) - \Delta H_{comb}°$

$\Delta H_f° \; CO_2(g) = 21.83\,g\;CO_2 \times \dfrac{1\,mol\,CO_2}{44.01\,g\,CO_2} \times \dfrac{-393.5\,kJ}{mol\,CO_2} = -195.185 = -195.2\,kJ$

$$\Delta H_f^\circ \ H_2O(g) = 4.47 \ g \ H_2O \times \frac{1 \ mol \ H_2O}{18.02 \ g \ H_2O} \times \frac{-241.82 \ kJ}{mol \ H_2O} = -59.985 = -60.0 \ kJ$$

$$\Delta H_f^\circ \ sample = -195.185 \ kJ - 59.985 \ kJ - (-311 \ kJ) = 55.83 = 56 \ kJ$$

$$H_f^\circ = \frac{55.83 \ kJ}{6.457 \ g \ sample} \times \frac{13.02 \ g}{CH \ unit} = 112.6 = 1.1 \times 10^2 \ kJ/CH \ unit$$

(d)   The hydrocarbons in Appendix C with empirical formula CH are C_2H_2 and C_6H_6.

substance	$\Delta H_f^\circ/mol$	$\Delta H_f^\circ/CH$ unit
$C_2H_2(g)$	226.7 kJ	113.4 kJ
$C_6H_6(g)$	82.9 kJ	13.8 kJ
$C_6H_6(l)$	49.0 kJ	8.17 kJ
sample		1.1×10^2 kJ

The calculated value of $\Delta H_f^\circ/CH$ unit for the sample is a good match with acetylene, $C_2H_2(g)$.

5.118   (a) $CH_4(g) \rightarrow C(g) + 4H(g)$ (i) reaction given

$CH_4(g) \rightarrow C(s) + 2H_2(g)$ (ii) reverse of formation

The differences are: the state of C in the products; the chemical form, atoms, or diatomic molecules, of H in the products.

(b)   i. $\Delta H^\circ = \Delta H_f^\circ \ C(g) + 4\Delta H_f^\circ \ H(g) - \Delta H_f^\circ \ CH_4(g)$

$= 718.4 \ kJ + 4(217.94) \ kJ - (-74.8) \ kJ = 1665.0 \ kJ$

ii. $\Delta H^\circ = \Delta H_f^\circ \ CH_4 = -(-74.8) \ kJ = 74.8 \ kJ$

The rather large difference in ΔH° values is due to the enthalpy difference between isolated gaseous C atoms and the orderly, bonded array of C atoms in graphite, C(s), as well as the enthalpy difference between isolated H atoms and H_2 molecules. In other words, it is due to the difference in the enthalpy stored in chemical bonds in C(s) and $H_2(g)$ versus the corresponding isolated atoms.

(c) $CH_4(g) + 4F_2(g) \rightarrow CF_4(g) + 4HF(g)$ $\Delta H^\circ = -1679.5 \ kJ$

The ΔH° value for this reaction was calculated in Solution 5.88.

$$3.45 \ g \ CH_4 \times \frac{1 \ mol \ CH_4}{16.04 \ g \ CH_4} \times 0.21509 = 0.215 \ mol \ CH_4$$

$$1.22 \ g \ F_2 \times \frac{1 \ mol \ F_2}{38.00 \ g \ F_2} = 0.03211 = 0.0321 \ mol \ F_2$$

There are fewer mol F_2 than CH_4, but 4 mol F_2 are required for every 1 mol of CH_4 reacted, so clearly F_2 is the limiting reactant.

$$0.03211 \text{ mol } F_2 \times \frac{-1679.5 \text{ kJ}}{4 \text{ mol } F_2} = -13.48 = -13.5 \text{ kJ heat evolved}$$

5.119   (a)   From Solution 5.17, 1 Btu = 1054 J = 1.054 kJ.

$$5.81 \times 10^{17} \text{ kJ} \times \frac{1 \text{ Btu}}{1.054 \text{ kJ}} \times \frac{1 \text{ Quad}}{1 \times 10^{12} \text{ Btu}} = 5.51 \times 10^5 \text{ Quads}$$

(b)   From Solution 5.112(a), heat of combustion of methane, is –890.4 kJ/mol CH_4.

$$99.5 \text{ Quads} \times \frac{1 \times 10^{12} \text{ Btu}}{1 \text{ Quad}} \times \frac{1.054 \text{ kJ}}{1 \text{ Btu}} \times \frac{1 \text{ mol } CH_4}{890.4 \text{ kJ}} = 1.1778 \times 10^{11} = 1.18 \times 10^{11} \text{ mol } CH_4$$

(c) $$1.1778 \times 10^{11} \text{ mol } CH_4 \times \frac{1 \text{ mol } CO_2}{1 \text{ mol } CH_4} \times \frac{44.01 \text{ g } CO_2}{1 \text{ mol } CO_2} \times \frac{1 \text{ kg}}{1000 \text{ g}} = 5.18 \times 10^9 \text{ kg } CO_2$$

(d)   Exercise 5.111 states that Earth fixes 5.5×10^{16} g or 5.5×10^{13} kg CO_2 via photosynthesis. If only the U.S. produces CO_2, photosynthesis is an adequate means of maintain a stable level of CO_2 in the atmosphere. A more revealing comparison is to estimate the global production of CO_2 from the estimated energy consumption for the year 2015.

$$5.51 \times 10^5 \text{ Quads} \times \frac{5.18 \times 10^9 \text{ kg } CO_2}{99.5 \text{ Quads}} = 2.87 \times 10^{13} \text{ kg } CO_2$$

Earth fixes 5.5×10^{16} g or 5.5×10^{13} kg CO_2 per year. This is twice as much as the CO_2 projected to be produced globally in 2015. Photosynthesis is adequate to maintain a stable level of CO_2 in the short term, but does not provide a large capacity for increased energy consumption and CO_2 production.

6 Electronic Structure of Atoms

Visualizing Concepts

6.1   (a)   Speed is distance traveled per unit time. Measure the distance between the center point and a second reference point, possibly the edge of the container. Using a stop watch, measure the elapsed time between when a wave forms at the center and when it reaches the second reference point. Find the ratio of distance to time.

       (b)   Measure the distance between two wave crests (or troughs or any analogous points on two adjacent waves). Better yet, measure the distance between two crests (or analogous points) that are several waves apart and divide by the number of waves that separate them.

       (c)   Since speed is distance/time, and wavelength is distance, we can calculate frequency by dividing speed by wavelength, $\nu = c/\lambda$.

       (d)   We can measure frequency of the wave by dropping an object such as a cork in the water and counting the number of times per second it moves through a complete cycle of motion.

6.2   Given: 2450 MHz radiation. $Hz = s^{-1}$, unit of frequency. $M = 1 \times 10^6$; 2450×10^6 Hz = 2.45×10^9 Hz = 2.45×10^9 s^{-1}.

       (a)   Find 2.45×10^9 s^{-1} on the frequency axis of Figure 6.4. The wavelength that corresponds to this frequency is approximately $1 \times 10^{-1} = 0.1$ m or 10 cm.

       (b)   No, visible radiation has wavelengths of 4×10^{-7} to 7×10^{-7} m, much shorter than 0.1 m.

       (c)   Energy and wavelength are inversely proportional. Photons of the longer 0.1 m radiation have less energy than visible photons.

       (d)   Radiation of 0.1 m is in the low energy portion of the microwave region. The appliance is probably a microwave oven. (The highest FM radio frequency is 108 MHz, so the device is not an FM radio.)

6.3   Wave (a) corresponds to higher energy radiation. The energy of electromagnetic radiation is directly proportional to frequency and inversely proportional to wavelength. Wave (a) has the shorter wavelength and thus the higher energy.

6.4   (a)   The glowing stove burner is an example of black body radiation, the observational basis for Planck's quantum theory. The wavelengths emitted are related to temperature, with cooler temperatures emitting longer wavelengths and hotter temperatures emitting shorter wavelengths. At the hottest setting, the burner emits orange visible light. At the cooler low setting, the burner emits longer wavelengths out of the visible region, and the burner appears black.

(b) If the burner had a super high setting, the emitted wavelengths would be shorter than those of orange light and the glow color would be more yellowish, progressing to white. (See Figure 6.5.)

6.5 (a) Increase. The rainbow has shorter wavelength blue light on the inside and longer wavelength red light on the outside. (See Figure 6.4.)

(b) Decrease. Wavelength and frequency are inversely related. Wavelength increases so frequency decreases going from the inside to the outside of the rainbow.

(c) The light from the hydrogen discharge tube is not a continuous spectrum, so not all visible wavelengths will be in our "hydrogen discharge rainbow." Starting with the shortest wavelengths, it will be violet followed by blue-violet and blue-green on the inside. Then there will be a gap, and finally a red band. (See the H spectrum in Figure 6.11.)

6.6 (a) $n = 1, n = 4$ (b) $n = 1, n = 2$

(c) Wavelength and energy are inversely proportional; the smaller the energy, the longer the wavelength. In order of increasing wavelength (and decreasing energy): (iii) $n = 2$ to $n = 4$ < (iv) $n = 3$ to $n = 1$ < (ii) $n = 3$ to $n = 2$ < (i) $n = 1$ to $n = 2$

6.7 (a) $\psi^2(x)$ will be positive or zero at all values of x, and have two maxima with larger magnitudes than the maximum in $\psi(x)$.

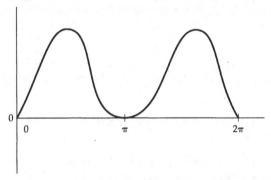

(b) The greatest probability of finding the electron is at the two maxima in $\psi^2(x)$ at $x = \pi/2$ and $3\pi/2$.

(c) There is zero probability of finding the electron at $x = \pi$. This value is called a node.

6.8 (a) 1

(b) p (dumbbell shape, node at the nucleus)

(c) The lobes in the contour representation would extend farther along the y axis. A larger principle quantum number (4p vs. 3p) implies a greater average distance from the nucleus for electrons occupying the orbital.

6.9 (a) In the left-most box, the two electrons cannot have the same spin. The *Pauli exclusion principle* states that no two electrons can have the same set of quantum numbers. Since the first three quantum numbers describe an orbital, the fourth quantum number, m_s, must have different values for two electrons in the same orbital; their "spins" must be opposite.

      (b)   Flip one of the arrows in the left-most box, so that one points up and the other down.

      (c)   Group 6A. The drawing shows three boxes or orbitals at the same energy, so it must represent p orbitals. Since some of these p orbitals are partially filled, they must be the valence orbitals of the element. Elements with four valence electrons in their p orbitals belong to group 6A.

6.10   (a)   Group 7A or 17, the halogens, the column second from the right

      (b)   Group 5A or 15

      (c)   Gallium, atomic number 31, at the intersection of row 4 and group 3A or 13

      (d)   All of the B groups, groups 3-12, in the middle of the major part of the table, not including the two rows of *f*-block elements

The Wave Nature of Light (section 6.1)

6.11   (a)   Meters (m)   (b)   1/seconds (s^{-1})   (c)   meters/second ($m \cdot s^{-1}$ or m/s)

6.12   (a)   Wavelength (λ) and frequency (ν) are inversely proportional; the proportionality constant is the speed of light (c). $\nu = c/\lambda$.

      (b)   Light in the 210–230 nm range is in the ultraviolet region of the spectrum. These wavelengths are slightly shorter than the 400 nm short-wavelength boundary of the visible region.

6.13   (a)   True.

      (b)   False. Ultraviolet light has shorter wavelengths than visible light. [See Solution 6.12(b).]

      (c)   False. X-rays travel at the same speed as microwaves. (X-rays and microwaves are both electromagnetic radiation.)

      (d)   False. Electromagnetic radiation and sound waves travel at different speeds. (Sound is not a form of electromagnetic radiation.)

6.14   (a)   False. The frequency of radiation decreases as the wavelength increases.

      (b)   True.

      (c)   False. Infrared light has lower frequencies than visible light.

      (d)   False. The glow from a fireplace and the energy within a microwave oven are both forms of electromagnetic radiation. (A foghorn blast is a form of sound waves, which are not accompanied by oscillating electric and magnetic fields.)

6.15   *Analyze/Plan.* Use the electromagnetic spectrum in Figure 6.4 to determine the wavelength of each type of radiation; put them in order from shortest to longest wavelength. *Solve.*

      Wavelength of X-rays < ultraviolet < green light < red light < infrared < radio waves

      Check. These types of radiation should read from left to right on Figure 6.4

6.16   Wavelength of (a) gamma rays < (d) yellow (visible) light < (e) red (visible) light < (b) 93.1 MHz FM (radio) waves < (c) 680 kHz or 0.680 MHz AM (radio) waves

6.17   *Analyze/Plan.* These questions involve relationships between wavelength, frequency, and the speed of light. Manipulate the equation $\nu = c/\lambda$ to obtain the desired quantities, paying attention to units.   *Solve.*

(a) $\nu = c/\lambda$; $\dfrac{2.998 \times 10^8 \text{ m}}{\text{s}} \times \dfrac{1}{10 \text{ μm}} \times \dfrac{1 \text{ μm}}{1 \times 10^{-6} \text{ m}} = 3.0 \times 10^{13} \text{ s}^{-1}$

(b) $\lambda = c/\nu$; $\dfrac{2.998 \times 10^8 \text{ m}}{\text{s}} \times \dfrac{1 \text{ s}}{5.50 \times 10^{14}} = 5.45 \times 10^{-7} \text{ m}$ (545 nm)

(c)   The radiation in (b) is in the visible region and is "visible" to humans. The 10 μm (1×10^{-5} m) radiation in (a) is in the infrared region and is not visible.

(d) $50.0 \text{ μs} \times \dfrac{1 \text{ s}}{1 \times 10^6 \text{ μs}} \times \dfrac{2.998 \times 10^8 \text{ m}}{\text{s}} = 1.50 \times 10^4 \text{ m}$

Check. Confirm that powers of 10 make sense and units are correct.

6.18   (a) $\nu = c/\lambda$; $\dfrac{2.998 \times 10^8 \text{ m}}{\text{s}} \times \dfrac{1}{5.0 \times 10^{-5} \text{ m}} = 6.0 \times 10^{12} \text{ s}^{-1}$

(b) $\lambda = c/\nu$; $\dfrac{2.998 \times 10^8 \text{ m}}{\text{s}} \times \dfrac{1 \text{ s}}{2.5 \times 10^8} = 1.2 \text{ m}$

(c)   Neither of the radiations in (a) and (b) can be observed by an X-ray detector. Radiation (a) is infrared and radiation (b) is radio frequency.

(d) $10.5 \text{ fs} \times \dfrac{1 \times 10^{-15} \text{ s}}{1 \text{ fs}} \times \dfrac{2.998 \times 10^8 \text{ m}}{\text{s}} = 3.15 \times 10^{-6} \text{ m} \ (3.15 \text{ μm})$

6.19   *Analyze/Plan.* $\nu = c/\lambda$; change nm → m.

Solve. $\nu = c/\lambda$; $\dfrac{2.998 \times 10^8 \text{ m}}{1 \text{ s}} \times \dfrac{1}{532 \text{ nm}} \times \dfrac{1 \text{ nm}}{1 \times 10^{-9} \text{ m}} = 5.64 \times 10^{14} \text{ s}^{-1}$

The color is green.

Check. $(3000 \times 10^5 / 500 \times 10^{-9}) = 6 \times 10^{14} \text{ s}^{-1}$; units are correct.

6.20   According to Figure 6.4, ultraviolet radiation has both higher frequency and shorter wavelength than infrared radiation. Looking forward to section 6.2, the energy of a photon is directly proportional to frequency ($E = h\nu$), so ultraviolet radiation yields more energy from a photovoltaic device.

Quantized Energy and Photons (section 6.2)

6.21   Quantization means that energy changes can only happen in certain allowed increments. If the human growth quantum is one-foot, growth occurs instantaneously in one-foot increments. That is, a child experiences growth spurts of one-foot; her height changes by one-foot increments.

6.22   Planck's original hypothesis was that energy could only be gained or lost in discrete amounts (quanta) with a certain minimum size. The size of the minimum energy change is related to the frequency of the radiation absorbed or emitted, $\Delta E = h\nu$, and energy changes occur only in multiples of $h\nu$.

Einstein postulated that light itself is quantized, that the minimum energy of a photon (a quantum of light) is directly proportional to its frequency, $E = h\nu$. If a photon that strikes a metal surface has less than the threshold energy, no electron is emitted from the surface. If the photon has energy equal to or greater than the threshold energy, an electron is emitted and any excess energy becomes the kinetic energy of the electron.

6.23 *Analyze/Plan.* These questions deal with the relationships between energy, wavelength, and frequency. Use the relationships $E = h\nu = hc/\lambda$ to calculate the desired quantities. Pay attention to units. *Solve.*

(a) $E = h\nu = 6.626 \times 10^{-34} \text{ J} \cdot \text{s} \times 6.75 \times 10^{12} \text{ s}^{-1} = 4.47 \times 10^{-21} \text{ J}$

(b) $\Delta E = h\nu = \dfrac{hc}{\lambda} = \dfrac{6.626 \times 10^{-34} \text{ J} \cdot \text{s} \times 2.998 \times 10^{8} \text{ m/s}}{322 \text{ nm}} \times \dfrac{1 \text{ nm}}{1 \times 10^{-9} \text{ m}} = 6.17 \times 10^{-19} \text{ J}$

(c) $\lambda = hc/\Delta E = \dfrac{6.626 \times 10^{-34} \text{ J} \cdot \text{s}}{2.87 \times 10^{-18} \text{ J}} \times \dfrac{2.998 \times 10^{8} \text{ m}}{1 \text{ s}} = 6.92 \times 10^{-8} \text{ m} = 69.2 \text{ nm}$

6.24 *Analyze/Plan.* These questions deal with the relationships between energy, wavelength, and frequency. Use the relationships $E = h\nu = hc/\lambda$ to calculate the desired quantities. Pay attention to units. *Solve.*

(a) $\nu = c/\lambda = \dfrac{2.998 \times 10^{8} \text{ m}}{\text{s}} \times \dfrac{1}{650 \text{ nm}} \times \dfrac{1 \text{ nm}}{1 \times 10^{-9} \text{ m}} = 4.6123 \times 10^{14} = 4.61 \times 10^{14} \text{ s}^{-1}$

(b) $\Delta E = h\nu = 6.626 \times 10^{-34} \text{ J} \cdot \text{s} \times 4.6123 \times 10^{14} \text{ s}^{-1} = 3.06 \times 10^{-19} \text{ J}$

(c) The energy gap between the ground and excited states is the energy of a single 650 nm photon emitted when one electron relaxes from the excited to the ground state. $\Delta E = 3.06 \times 10^{-19} \text{ J}$

6.25 *Analyze/Plan.* Use $E = hc/\lambda$; pay close attention to units. *Solve.*

(a) $E = hc/\lambda = 6.626 \times 10^{-34} \text{ J} \cdot \text{s} \times \dfrac{2.998 \times 10^{8} \text{ m}}{1 \text{ s}} \times \dfrac{1}{3.3 \,\mu\text{m}} \times \dfrac{1 \,\mu\text{m}}{1 \times 10^{-6} \text{ m}}$
$$= 6.0 \times 10^{-20} \text{ J}$$

$E = hc/\lambda = 6.626 \times 10^{-34} \text{ J} \cdot \text{s} \times \dfrac{2.998 \times 10^{8} \text{ m}}{1 \text{ s}} \times \dfrac{1}{0.154 \text{ nm}} \times \dfrac{1 \text{ nm}}{1 \times 10^{-9} \text{ m}}$
$$= 1.29 \times 10^{-15} \text{ J}$$

Check. $(6.6 \times 3/3.3) \times (10^{-34} \times 10^{8}/10^{-6}) \approx 6 \times 10^{-20} \text{ J}$

$(6.6 \times 3/0.15) \times (10^{-34} \times 10^{8}/10^{-9}) \approx 120 \times 10^{-17} \approx 1.2 \times 10^{-15} \text{ J}$

The results are reasonable. We expect the longer wavelength 3.3 μm radiation to have the lower energy.

(b) The 3.3 μm photon is in the infrared and the 0.154 nm (1.54×10^{-10} m) photon is in the X-ray region; the X-ray photon has the greater energy.

6.26 $E = h\nu$

$\text{AM}: 6.626 \times 10^{-34} \text{ J} \cdot \text{s} \times \dfrac{1010 \times 10^{3}}{1 \text{ s}} = 6.69 \times 10^{-28} \text{ J}$

FM : 6.626×10^{-34} J-s $\times \dfrac{98.3 \times 10^6}{1 \text{ s}} = 6.51 \times 10^{-26}$ J

The FM photon has about 100 times more energy than the AM photon.

6.27 *Analyze/Plan.* Use $E = hc/\lambda$ to calculate J/photon; Avogadro's number to calculate J/mol; photon/J [the result from part (a)] to calculate photons in 1.00 mJ. Pay attention to units. *Solve.*

(a) $E_{photon} = hc/\lambda = \dfrac{6.626 \times 10^{-34} \text{ J-s}}{325 \times 10^{-9} \text{ m}} \times \dfrac{2.998 \times 10^8 \text{ m}}{\text{s}} = 6.1122 \times 10^{-19}$

$= 6.11 \times 10^{-19}$ J/photon

(b) $\dfrac{6.1122 \times 10^{-19} \text{ J}}{1 \text{ photon}} \times \dfrac{6.022 \times 10^{23} \text{ photons}}{1 \text{ mol}} = 3.68 \times 10^5$ J/mol $= 368$ kJ/mol

(c) $\dfrac{1 \text{ photon}}{6.1122 \times 10^{-19} \text{ J}} \times 1.00 \text{ mJ} \times \dfrac{1 \times 10^{-3} \text{ J}}{1 \text{ mJ}} = 1.64 \times 10^{15}$ photons

Check. Powers of 10 (orders of magnitude) and units are correct.

(d) If the energy of one 325 nm photon breaks exactly one bond, one mol of photons break 1 mol of bonds. The average bond energy in kJ/mol is the energy of 1 mol of photons (from part b) 368 kJ/mol.

6.28 $\dfrac{941 \times 10^3 \text{ J}}{\text{mol N}_2} \times \dfrac{1 \text{ mol}}{6.022 \times 10^{23} \text{ photons}} = 1.563 \times 10^{-18} = 1.56 \times 10^{-18}$ J/photon

$\lambda = hc/E = \dfrac{6.626 \times 10^{-34} \text{ J-s}}{1.563 \times 10^{-18} \text{ J}} \times \dfrac{2.998 \times 10^8 \text{ m}}{1 \text{ s}} = 1.27 \times 10^{-7}$ m $= 127$ nm

According to Figure 6.4, this is ultraviolet radiation.

6.29 *Analyze/Plan.* $E = hc/\lambda$ gives J/photon. Use this result with J/s (given) to calculate photons/s. *Solve.*

(a) The ~1×10^{-6} m radiation is infrared but very near the visible edge.

(b) $E_{photon} = hc/\lambda = \dfrac{6.626 \times 10^{-34} \text{ J-s}}{987 \times 10^{-9} \text{ m}} \times \dfrac{2.998 \times 10^8 \text{ m}}{1 \text{ s}} = 2.0126 \times 10^{-19}$

$= 2.01 \times 10^{-19}$ J/photon

$\dfrac{0.52 \text{ J}}{32 \text{ s}} \times \dfrac{1 \text{ photon}}{2.0126 \times 10^{-19} \text{ J}} = 8.1 \times 10^{16}$ photons/s

Check. $(7 \times 3/1000) \times (10^{-34} \times 10^8/10^{-9}) \approx 21 \times 10^{-20} \approx 2.1 \times 10^{-19}$ J/photon

$(0.5/30/2) \times (1/10^{-19}) = 0.008 \times 10^{19} = 8 \times 10^{16}$ photons/s

Units are correct; powers of 10 are reasonable.

6.30 (a) $3.55 \text{ mm} = 3.55 \times 10^{-3}$ m; the radiation is microwave.

(b) $E_{photon} = hc/\lambda = \dfrac{6.626 \times 10^{-34} \text{ J-s}}{3.55 \times 10^{-3} \text{ m}} \times \dfrac{2.998 \times 10^8 \text{ m}}{1 \text{ s}} = 5.5957 \times 10^{-23}$

$= 5.60 \times 10^{-23}$ J/photon

$$\frac{5.5957 \times 10^{-23} \text{ J}}{1 \text{ photon}} \times \frac{3.2 \times 10^8 \text{ photons}}{1 \text{ s}} \times \frac{60 \text{ s}}{1 \text{ min}} \times \frac{60 \text{ min}}{1 \text{ hr}} = 6.4463 \times 10^{-11}$$

$$= 6.4 \times 10^{-11} \text{ J/hr}$$

6.31   *Analyze/Plan.* Use $E = h\nu$ and $\nu = c/\lambda$. Calculate the desired characteristics of the photons. Assume 1 photon interacts with 1 electron. Compare E_{min} and E_{120} to calculate maximum kinetic energy of the emitted electron.   *Solve.*

(a) $E = h\nu = 6.626 \times 10^{-34} \text{ J} \cdot \text{s} \times 1.09 \times 10^{15} \text{ s}^{-1} = 7.22 \times 10^{-19} \text{ J}$

(b) $\lambda = c/\nu = \dfrac{2.998 \times 10^8 \text{ m}}{1 \text{ s}} \times \dfrac{1 \text{ s}}{1.09 \times 10^{15}} = 2.75 \times 10^{-7} \text{ m} = 275 \text{ nm}$

(c) $E_{120} = hc/\lambda = 6.626 \times 10^{-34} \text{ J} \cdot \text{s} \times \dfrac{2.998 \times 10^8 \text{ m}}{1 \text{ s}} \times \dfrac{1}{120 \text{ nm}} \times \dfrac{1 \text{ nm}}{1 \times 10^{-9} \text{ m}}$

$$= 1.655 \times 10^{-18} = 1.66 \times 10^{-18} \quad \text{J}$$

The excess energy of the 120 nm photon is converted into the kinetic energy of the emitted electron.

$E_k = E_{120} - E_{min} = 16.55 \times 10^{-19} \text{ J} - 7.22 \times 10^{-19} \text{ J} = 9.3 \times 10^{-19} \text{ J/electron}$

Check. E_{120} must be greater than E_{min} in order for the photon to impart kinetic energy to the emitted electron. Our calculations are consistent with this requirement.

6.32   (a) $\nu = E/h = \dfrac{4.41 \times 10^{-19} \text{ J}}{6.626 \times 10^{-34} \text{ J} \cdot \text{s}} = 6.6556 \times 10^{14} = 6.66 \times 10^{14} \text{ s}^{-1}$

(b) $\lambda = hc/E = \dfrac{6.626 \times 10^{-34} \text{ J} \cdot \text{s}}{4.41 \times 10^{-19} \text{ J}} \times \dfrac{2.998 \times 10^8 \text{ m}}{\text{s}} = 4.50 \times 10^{-7} \text{ m} = 450 \text{ nm}$

(c) $E_{405} = hc/\lambda = \dfrac{6.626 \times 10^{-34} \text{ J} \cdot \text{s}}{405 \times 10^{-9} \text{ m}} \times \dfrac{2.998 \times 10^8 \text{ m}}{\text{s}} = 4.9049 \times 10^{-19} = 4.90 \times 10^{-19} \text{ J}$

$E_K = E_{405} - E_{min} = 4.9049 \times 10^{-19} \text{ J} - 4.41 \times 10^{-19} \text{ J} = 0.4949 \times 10^{-19} = 4.9 \times 10^{-20} \text{ J}$

(d)   One electron is emitted per photon. Calculate the number of 405 nm photons in 1.00 μJ. The excess energy in each photon will become the kinetic energy of the electron; it cannot be "pooled" to emit additional electrons.

$$1.00 \text{ μJ} \times \frac{1 \times 10^{-6} \text{ J}}{\text{μJ}} \times \frac{1 \text{ photon}}{4.9049 \times 10^{-19} \text{ J}} \times \frac{1 \text{ e}^-}{1 \text{ photon}} = 2.04 \times 10^{12} \text{ electrons}$$

Bohr's Model; Matter Waves (sections 6.3 and 6.4)

6.33   When applied to atoms, the notion of quantized energies means that only certain energies can be gained or lost, only certain values of ΔE are allowed. The allowed values of ΔE are represented by the lines in the emission spectra of excited atoms.

6.34   (a)   According to Bohr theory, when hydrogen emits radiant energy, electrons are moving from a higher allowed energy state to a lower one. Since only certain energy states are allowed, only certain energy changes can occur. These allowed energy changes correspond ($\lambda = hc/\Delta E$) to the wavelengths of the lines in the emission spectrum of hydrogen.

(b)   When a hydrogen atom changes from the ground state to an excited state, the single electron moves further away from the nucleus, so the atom "expands."

6.35   *Analyze/Plan.* An isolated electron is assigned an energy of zero; the closer the electron comes to the nucleus, the more negative its energy. Thus, as an electron moves closer to the nucleus, the energy of the electron decreases and the excess energy is emitted. Conversely, as an electron moves further from the nucleus, the energy of the electron increases and energy must be absorbed.   *Solve.*

(a)   As the principle quantum number decreases, the electron moves toward the nucleus and energy is emitted.

(b)   An increase in the radius of the orbit means the electron moves away from the nucleus; energy is absorbed.

(c)   An isolated electron is assigned an energy of zero. As the electron moves to the $n = 3$ state closer to the H^+ nucleus, its energy becomes more negative (decreases) and energy is emitted.

6.36   (a)   Absorbed.   (b)   Emitted.   (c)   Absorbed.

6.37   *Analyze/Plan.* Equation 6.5: $E = (-2.18 \times 10^{-18} \text{ J})(1/n^2)$.   *Solve.*

(a) $E_2 = -2.18 \times 10^{-18} \text{ J}/(2)^2 = -5.45 \times 10^{-19} \text{ J}$

       $E_6 = -2.18 \times 10^{-18} \text{ J}/(6)^2 = -6.0556 \times 10^{-20} = -0.606 \times 10^{-19} \text{ J}$

       $\Delta E = E_2 - E_6 = (-5.45 \times 10^{-19} \text{ J}) - (-0.606 \times 10^{-19} \text{ J})$

           $= -4.844 \times 10^{-19} \text{ J} = -4.84 \times 10^{-19} \text{ J}$

       $\lambda = hc/\Delta E = \dfrac{6.626 \times 10^{-34} \text{ J} \cdot \text{s}}{4.844 \times 10^{-19} \text{ J}} \times \dfrac{2.998 \times 10^8 \text{ m}}{\text{s}} = 4.10 \times 10^{-7} \text{ m} = 410 \text{ nm}$

(b)   The visible range is 400–700 nm, so this line is visible; the observed color is violet.

       Check. We expect E_6 to be a more positive (or less negative) than E_2, and it is. ΔE is negative, which indicates emission. The orders of magnitude make sense and units are correct.

6.38   (a) $E_1 = -2.18 \times 10^{-18} \text{ J}/(1)^2 = -2.18 \times 10^{-18} \text{ J}$

       $E_\infty = -2.18 \times 10^{-18} \text{ J}/(\infty)^2 = 0 \text{ J}$

       $\Delta E = E_\infty - E_1 = 0 - (-2.18 \times 10^{-18} \text{ J}) = 2.18 \times 10^{-18} \text{ J} /\text{electron}$

       $\dfrac{2.18 \times 10^{-18} \text{ J}}{\text{electron}} \times \dfrac{6.022 \times 10^{23} \text{ electrons}}{\text{mol}} \times \dfrac{1 \text{ kJ}}{1000 \text{ J}} = 1.31 \times 10^3 \text{ kJ/mol}$

(b)   The result from (a) is $1.31 \times 10^3 \text{ kJ/mol} = 1,310 \text{ kJ/mol}$. Ionization energy calculated from the Bohr model agrees with the experimental result to three significant figures.

6.39   (a)   Only lines with $n_f = 2$ represent ΔE values and wavelengths that lie in the visible portion of the spectrum. Lines with $n_f = 1$ have larger ΔE values and shorter wavelengths that lie in the ultraviolet. Lines with $n_f > 2$ have smaller ΔE values and lie in the lower energy longer wavelength regions of the electromagnetic spectrum.

(b)   *Analyze/Plan.* Use Equation 6.7 to calculate ΔE, then $\lambda = hc/\Delta E$.   *Solve.*

$$n_i = 3, n_f = 2; \quad \Delta E = -2.18 \times 10^{-18} \text{ J}\left[\frac{1}{n_f^2} - \frac{1}{n_i^2}\right] = -2.18 \times 10^{-18} \text{ J }(1/4 - 1/9)$$

$$\lambda = hc/E = \frac{6.626 \times 10^{-34} \text{ J·s} \times 2.998 \times 10^8 \text{ m/s}}{-2.18 \times 10^{-18} \text{ J }(1/4 - 1/9)} = 6.56 \times 10^{-7} \text{ m}$$

This is the red line at 656 nm.

$$n_i = 4, n_f = 2; \quad \lambda = hc/E = \frac{6.626 \times 10^{-34} \text{ J·s} \times 2.998 \times 10^8 \text{ m/s}}{-2.18 \times 10^{-18} \text{ J }(1/4 - 1/16)} = 4.86 \times 10^{-7} \text{ m}$$

This is the blue-green line at 486 nm.

$$n_i = 5, n_f = 2; \quad \lambda = hc/E = \frac{6.626 \times 10^{-34} \text{ J·s} \times 2.998 \times 10^8 \text{ m/s}}{-2.18 \times 10^{-18} \text{ J }(1/4 - 1/25)} = 4.34 \times 10^{-7} \text{ m}$$

This is the blue-violet line at 434 nm.

Check. The calculated wavelengths correspond well to three lines in the H emission spectrum in Figure 6.11, so the results are sensible.

6.40   (a)   Transitions with $n_f = 1$ have larger ΔE values and shorter wavelengths than those with $n_f = 2$. These transitions will lie in the ultraviolet region.

(b) $$n_i = 2, n_f = 1; \quad \lambda = hc/E = \frac{6.626 \times 10^{-34} \text{ J·s} \times 2.998 \times 10^8 \text{ m/s}}{-2.18 \times 10^{-18} \text{ J }(1/1 - 1/4)} = 1.21 \times 10^{-7} \text{ m}$$

$$n_i = 3, n_f = 1; \quad \lambda = hc/E = \frac{6.626 \times 10^{-34} \text{ J·s} \times 2.998 \times 10^8 \text{ m/s}}{-2.18 \times 10^{-18} \text{ J }(1/1 - 1/9)} = 1.03 \times 10^{-7} \text{ m}$$

$$n_i = 4, n_f = 1; \quad \lambda = hc/E = \frac{6.626 \times 10^{-34} \text{ J·s} \times 2.998 \times 10^8 \text{ m/s}}{-2.18 \times 10^{-18} \text{ J }(1/1 - 1/16)} = 0.972 \times 10^{-7} \text{ m}$$

6.41   (a) $93.8 \text{ nm} \times \dfrac{1 \times 10^{-9} \text{ m}}{1 \text{ nm}} = 9.38 \times 10^{-8} \text{ m}$;   this line is in the ultraviolet region.

(b)   *Analyze/Plan.* Only lines with $n_f = 1$ have a large enough ΔE to lie in the ultraviolet region (see Solutions 6.39 and 6.40). Solve Equation 6.7 for n_i, recalling that ΔE is negative for emission.   *Solve.*

$$\frac{-hc}{\lambda} = -2.18 \times 10^{-18} \text{ J}\left[\frac{1}{n_f^2} - \frac{1}{n_i^2}\right]; \quad \frac{hc}{\lambda(2.18 \times 10^{-18} \text{ J})} = \left[1 - \frac{1}{n_i^2}\right]$$

$$-\frac{1}{n_i^2} = \left[\frac{hc}{\lambda(2.18 \times 10^{-18} \text{ J})} - 1\right]; \quad \frac{1}{n_i^2} = \left[1 - \frac{hc}{\lambda(2.18 \times 10^{-18} \text{ J})}\right]$$

$$n_i^2 = \left[1 - \frac{hc}{\lambda(2.18 \times 10^{-18} \text{ J})}\right]^{-1}; \quad n_i = \left[1 - \frac{hc}{\lambda(2.18 \times 10^{-18} \text{ J})}\right]^{-1/2}$$

$$n_i = \left(1 - \frac{6.626 \times 10^{-34} \text{ J-s} \times 2.998 \times 10^8 \text{ m/s}}{9.38 \times 10^{-8} \text{ m} \times 2.18 \times 10^{-18} \text{ J}}\right)^{-1/2} = 6 \text{ (n values must be integers)}$$

$n_i = 6, n_f = 1$

Check. From Solution 6.40, we know that $n_i > 4$ for $\lambda = 93.8$ nm. The calculated result is close to 6, so the answer is reasonable.

6.42   (a) $2626 \text{ nm} \times \dfrac{1 \times 10^{-9} \text{ m}}{1 \text{ nm}} = 2.626 \times 10^{-6} \text{ m}$;   this line is in the infrared.

          (b)   Absorption lines with $n_i = 1$ are in the ultraviolet and with $n_i = 2$ are in the visible. Thus, $n_i \geq 3$, but we do not know the exact value of n_i. Calculate the longest wavelength with $n_i = 3$ ($n_f = 4$). If this is less than 2626 nm, $n_i > 3$.

$$\lambda = hc/E = \frac{6.626 \times 10^{-34} \text{ J-s} \times 2.998 \times 10^8 \text{ m/s}}{-2.18 \times 10^{-18} \text{ J} (1/16 - 1/9)} = 1.875 \times 10^{-6} \text{ m}$$

              This wavelength is shorter than 2.626×10^{-6} m, so $n_i > 3$; try $n_i = 4$ and solve for n_f as in Solution 6.41. Note that ΔE is positive because we are dealing with absorption.

$$n_f = \left(\frac{1}{n_i^2} - \frac{hc}{\lambda(2.18 \times 10^{-18} \text{ J})}\right)^{-1/2} = \left(1/16 - \frac{6.626 \times 10^{-34} \text{ J-s} \times 2.998 \times 10^8 \text{ m/s}}{2.626 \times 10^{-6} \text{ m} \times 2.18 \times 10^{-18} \text{ J}}\right)^{-1/2} = 6$$

$n_f = 6, n_i = 4$

6.43   *Analyze/Plan.* $\lambda = \dfrac{h}{mv}; 1 \text{ J} = \dfrac{1 \text{ kg-m}^2}{s^2};$

        Change mass to kg and velocity to m/s in each case.   *Solve.*

        (a) $\dfrac{50 \text{ km}}{1 \text{ hr}} \times \dfrac{1000 \text{ m}}{1 \text{ km}} \times \dfrac{1 \text{ hr}}{60 \text{ min}} \times \dfrac{1 \text{ min}}{60 \text{ s}} = 13.89 = 14 \text{ m/s}$

$$\lambda = \frac{6.626 \times 10^{-34} \text{ kg-m}^2\text{-s}}{1 \text{ s}^2} \times \frac{1}{85 \text{ kg}} \times \frac{1 \text{ s}}{13.89 \text{ m}} = 5.6 \times 10^{-37} \text{ m}$$

        (b) $10.0 \text{ g} \times \dfrac{1 \text{ kg}}{1000 \text{ g}} = 0.0100 \text{ kg}$

$$\lambda = \frac{6.626 \times 10^{-34} \text{ kg-m}^2\text{-s}}{1 \text{ s}^2} \times \frac{1}{0.0100 \text{ kg}} \times \frac{1 \text{ s}}{250 \text{ m}} = 2.65 \times 10^{-34} \text{ m}$$

        (c)   We need to calculate the mass of a single Li atom in kg.

$$\frac{6.94 \text{ g Li}}{1 \text{ mol Li}} \times \frac{1 \text{ kg}}{1000 \text{ g}} \times \frac{1 \text{ mol}}{6.022 \times 10^{23} \text{ Li atoms}} = 1.152 \times 10^{-26} = 1.15 \times 10^{-26} \text{ kg}$$

$$\lambda = \frac{6.626 \times 10^{-34} \text{ kg-m}^2\text{-s}}{1 \text{ s}^2} \times \frac{1}{1.152 \times 10^{-26} \text{ kg}} \times \frac{1 \text{ s}}{2.5 \times 10^5 \text{ m}} = 2.3 \times 10^{-13} \text{ m}$$

        (d) Calculate the mass of a single O_3 molecule in kg.

$$\frac{48.00 \text{ g O}_3}{1 \text{ mol O}_3} \times \frac{1 \text{ kg}}{1000 \text{ g}} \times \frac{1 \text{ mol}}{6.022 \times 10^{23} \text{ O}_3 \text{ molecules}} = 7.971 \times 10^{-26}$$

$$= 7.97 \times 10^{-26} \text{ kg}$$

$$\lambda = \frac{6.626 \times 10^{-34} \text{ kg-m}^2 \text{-s}}{1 \text{ s}^2} \times \frac{1}{7.971 \times 10^{-26} \text{ kg}} \times \frac{1 \text{ s}}{550 \text{ m}}$$

$$= 1.51 \times 10^{-11} \text{ m (15 pm)}$$

6.44 $\lambda = h/mv$; change mass to kg and velocity to m/s

mass of muon $= 206.8 \times 9.1094 \times 10^{-28} \text{ g} \times \dfrac{1 \text{ kg}}{1000 \text{ g}} = 1.8838 \times 10^{-28} = 1.88 \times 10^{-28}$ kg

$$\lambda = \frac{6.626 \times 10^{-34} \text{ kg-m}^2 \text{-s}}{1 \text{ s}^2} \times \frac{1}{1.8838 \times 10^{-28} \text{ kg}} \times \frac{1 \text{ s}}{8.85 \times 10^3 \text{ m/s}} = 3.97 \times 10^{-10} \text{ m}$$

$$= 3.97 \text{ Å}$$

6.45   *Analyze/Plan.* Use $v = h/m\lambda$; change wavelength to meters and mass of neutron (back inside cover) to kg.   *Solve.*

$$\lambda = 0.955 \text{ Å} \times \frac{1 \times 10^{-10} \text{ m}}{1 \text{ Å}} = 0.955 \times 10^{-10} \text{ m}; \; m = 1.6749 \times 10^{-27} \text{ kg}$$

$$v = \frac{6.626 \times 10^{-34} \text{ kg-m}^2 \text{-s}}{1 \text{ s}^2} \times \frac{1}{1.6749 \times 10^{-27} \text{ kg}} \times \frac{1}{0.955 \times 10^{-10} \text{ m}} = 4.14 \times 10^3 \text{ m/s}$$

Check. $(6.6/1.6/1) \times (10^{-34}/10^{-27}/10^{-10}) \approx 4 \times 10^3 \text{ m/s}$

6.46 $m_e = 9.1094 \times 10^{-31}$ kg (back inside cover of text)

$$\lambda = \frac{6.626 \times 10^{-34} \text{ kg-m}^2 \text{-s}}{1 \text{ s}^2} \times \frac{1}{9.1094 \times 10^{-31} \text{ kg}} \times \frac{1 \text{ s}}{8.95 \times 10^6 \text{ m}} = 8.13 \times 10^{-11} \text{ m}$$

$$8.13 \times 10^{-11} \text{ m} \times \frac{1 \text{ Å}}{1 \times 10^{-10} \text{ m}} = 0.813 \text{ Å}$$

Since atomic radii and interatomic distances are on the order of 1–5 Å (Section 2.3), the wavelength of this electron is comparable to the size of atoms.

6.47   *Analyze/Plan.* Use $\Delta x \geq h/4\pi m \, \Delta v$, paying attention to appropriate units. Note that the uncertainty in speed of the particle (Δv) is important, rather than the speed itself. *Solve.*

(a) $m = 1.50 \text{ mg} \times \dfrac{1 \text{ g}}{1000 \text{ mg}} \times \dfrac{1 \text{ kg}}{1000 \text{ g}} = 1.50 \times 10^{-6} \text{ kg}; \; \Delta v = 0.01 \text{ m/s}$

$$\Delta x \geq = \frac{6.626 \times 10^{-34} \text{ J-s}}{4\pi(1.50 \times 10^{-6} \text{ kg})(0.01 \text{ m/s})} \geq 3.52 \times 10^{-27} = 4 \times 10^{-27} \text{ m}$$

(b) $m = 1.673 \times 10^{-24} \text{ g} = 1.673 \times 10^{-27} \text{ kg}; \; \Delta v = 0.01 \times 10^4 \text{ m/s}$

$$\Delta x \geq = \frac{6.626 \times 10^{-34} \text{ J-s}}{4\pi(1.673 \times 10^{-27} \text{ kg})(0.01 \times 10^4 \text{ m/s})} \geq 3 \times 10^{-10} \text{ m}$$

Check. The more massive particle in (a) has a much smaller uncertainty in position.

6.48 $\Delta x \geq = h/4\pi m \Delta v$; use masses in kg, Δv in m/s.

(a) $$\frac{6.626 \times 10^{-34} \text{ J-s}}{4\pi(9.109 \times 10^{-31} \text{ kg})(0.01 \times 10^5 \text{ m/s})} = 6 \times 10^{-8} \text{ m}$$

(b) $$\frac{6.626 \times 10^{-34} \text{ J-s}}{4\pi(1.675 \times 10^{-27} \text{ kg})(0.01 \times 10^5 \text{ m/s})} = 3 \times 10^{-11} \text{ m}$$

(c)   For particles moving with the same uncertainty in velocity, the more massive neutron has a much smaller uncertainty in position than the lighter electron. In our model of the atom, we know where the massive particles in the nucleus are located, but we cannot know the location of the electrons with any certainty, if we know their speed.

Quantum Mechanics and Atomic Orbitals (sections 6.5 and 6.6)

6.49   (a)   The uncertainty principle states that there is a limit to how precisely we can simultaneously know the position and momentum (related to energy) of an electron. The Bohr model states that electrons move about the nucleus in precisely circular orbits of known radius; each permitted orbit has an allowed energy associated with it. Thus, according to the Bohr model, we can know the exact distance of an electron from the nucleus and its energy. This violates the uncertainty principle.

(b)   De Broglie stated that electrons demonstrate the properties of both particles and waves, that each particle has a wave associated with it. A wave function is the mathematical description of the matter wave of an electron.

(c)   Although we cannot predict the exact location of an electron in an allowed energy state, we can determine the likelihood or probability of finding an electron at a particular position (or within a particular volume). This statistical knowledge of electron location is called the *probability density* or electron density and is a function of ψ^2, the square of the wave function ψ.

6.50   (a)   The Bohr model states with 100% certainty that the electron in hydrogen can be found 0.53 Å from the nucleus. The quantum mechanical model, taking the wave nature of the electron and the uncertainty principle into account, is a statistical model that states the probability of finding the electron in certain regions around the nucleus. While 0.53 Å might be the radius with highest probability, that probability would always be less than 100%.

(b)   The equations of classical physics predict the instantaneous position, direction of motion, and speed of a macroscopic particle; they do not take quantum theory or the wave nature of matter into account. For macroscopic particles, these are not significant, but for microscopic particles like electrons, they are crucial. Schrödinger's equation takes these important theories into account to produce a statistical model of electron location given a specific energy.

(c)   The square of the wave function has the physical significance of an amplitude, or probability. The quantity ψ^2 at a given point in space is the probability of locating the electron within a small volume element around that point at any given instant. The total probability, that is, the sum of ψ^2 over all the space around the nucleus, must equal 1.

6.51   (a)   The possible values of l are (n – 1) to 0. $n = 4$, $l = 3, 2, 1, 0$

        (b)   The possible values of m_l are $-l$ to $+l$. $l = 2$, $m_l = -2, -1, 0, 1, 2$

        (c)   Since the value of m_l is less than or equal to the value of l, $m_l = 2$ must have an l-value greater than or equal to 2. In terms of elements that have been observed, the possibilities are 2, 3 and 4.

6.52   (a)   For $n = 3$, there are three l values (2, 1, 0) and nine m_l values ($l = 2$; $m_l = -2, -1, 0, 1, 2$; $l = 1$, $m_l = -1, 0, 1$; $l = 0$, $m_l = 0$).

        (b)   For $n = 5$, there are five l values (4, 3, 2, 1, 0) and twenty-five m_l values

                ($l = 4$, $m_l = -4$ to $+4$; $l = 3$, $m_l = -3$ to $+3$; $l = 2$, $m_l = -2$ to $+2$; $l = 1$, $m_l = -1$ to $+1$; $l = 0$, $= 0$).

                In general, for each principal quantum number n there are n l-values and n^2 m_l-values. For each shell, there are n kinds of orbitals and n^2 total orbitals.

6.53   (a)   3p: $n = 3$, $l = 1$ (b)   2s: $n = 2$, $l = 0$

        (c)   4f: $n = 4$, $l = 3$ (d)   5d: $n = 5$, $l = 2$

6.54   (a)   2, 1, 1; 2, 1, 0; 2, 1, –1   (b)   5, 2, 2; 5, 2, 1; 5, 2, 0; 5, 2, –1; 5, 2, –2

6.55   Impossible: (a) 1p, only $l = 0$ is possible for $n = 1$; (d) 2d, for $n = 2$, $l = 1$ or 0, but not 2

6.56

n	l	m_l	orbital
2	1	–1	2p (example)
1	0	0	1s
3	–3	2	not allowed (l < n and + only)
3	2	–2	3d
2	0	–1	not allowed ($m_l = -l$ to $+l$)
0	0	0	not allowed (n ≠ 0)
4	2	1	4d
5	3	0	5f

6.57

(a)   (b)   (c)

6.58

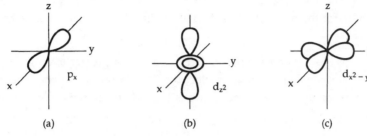

(a)   (b)   (c)

6.59   (a)   The 1s and 2s orbitals of a hydrogen atom have the same overall spherical shape. The 2s orbital has a larger radial extension and one node, while the 1s orbital has continuous electron density. Since the 2s orbital is "larger," there is greater probability of finding an electron further from the nucleus in the 2s orbital.

(b)   A single 2p orbital is directional in that its electron density is concentrated along one of the three Cartesian axes of the atom. The $d_{x^2-y^2}$ orbital has electron density along both the x- and y-axes, while the p_x orbital has density only along the x-axis.

(c)   The average distance of an electron from the nucleus in a 3s orbital is greater than for an electron in a 2s orbital. In general, for the same kind of orbital, the larger the n value, the greater the average distance of an electron from the nucleus of the atom.

(d)   1s < 2p < 3d < 4f < 6s. In the hydrogen atom, orbitals with the same n value are degenerate and energy increases with increasing n value. Thus, the order of increasing energy is given above.

6.60   (a)   In an s orbital, there are $(n-1)$ nodes.

(b)   The $2p_x$ orbital has one node (the yz plane passing through the nucleus of the atom). The 3s orbital has two nodes.

(c)   Probability density, $\psi^2(r)$, is the probability of finding an electron at a single point, r. The radial probability function, P(r), is the probability of finding an electron at any point that is distance r from the nucleus. Figure 6.18 contains plots of P(r) vs. r for 1s, 2s, and 3s orbitals. The most obvious features of these plots are the radii of maximum probability for the three orbitals, and the number and location of nodes for the three orbitals.

By comparing plots for the three orbitals, we see that as n increases, the number of nodes increases and the radius of maximum probability (orbital size) increases.

(d)   2s = 2p < 3s < 4d < 5s. In the hydrogen atom, orbitals with the same n value are degenerate and energy increases with increasing n value.

Many-Electron Atoms and Electron Configurations (sections 6.7 – 6.9)

6.61   (a)   In the hydrogen atom, orbitals with the same principle quantum number, n, have the same energy; they are degenerate.

       (b)   In a many-electron atom, for a given n-value, orbital energy increases with increasing l-value: s < p < d < f.

6.62   (a)   The electron with the greater average distance from the nucleus feels a smaller attraction for the nucleus and is higher in energy. Thus the 3p is higher in energy than 3s.

       (b)   Because it has a larger n value, a 3s electron has a greater average distance from the chlorine nucleus than a 2p electron. The 3s electron experiences a smaller attraction for the nucleus and requires less energy to remove from the chlorine atom.

6.63   (a)   There are two main pieces of experimental evidence for electron "spin": the Stern-Gerlach experiment and line spectra of multi-electron atoms. The Stern-Gerlach experiment shows that a beam of neutral Ag atoms passed through a nonhomogeneous magnetic field is deflected equally in two directions. This shows that atoms with a single unpaired electron interact differently with the magnetic field and suggests that there are two and only two values for an atom's own magnetic field. Examination of the fine details of emission line-spectra of multi-electron atoms reveals that each line is really a close pair of lines. Both observations can be rationalized if electrons have the property of spin.

       (b)   Note that 2 electrons in the same orbital have opposite spin; this is called spin-pairing.

       (c)

6.64   (a)   The Pauli exclusion principle states that no two electrons can have the same four quantum numbers.

       (b)   An alternate statement of the Pauli exclusion principle is that a single orbital can hold a maximum of two electrons. Thus, the Pauli principle limits the maximum number of electrons in a main shell and its subshells, which determines when a new row of the periodic table begins.

6.65   *Analyze/Plan.* Each subshell has an *l*-value associated with it. For a particular *l*-value, permissible m_l-values are $-l$ to $+l$. Each m_l-value represents an orbital, which can hold two electrons.   *Solve.*

      (a) 6   (b) 10   (c) 2   (d) 14

6.66   (a) 4   (b) 14   (c) 2   (d) 2

6.67   (a)   "Valence electrons" are those involved in chemical bonding. They are part (or all) of the outer-shell electrons listed after core electrons in a condensed electron configuration.

      (b)   "Core electrons" are inner shell electrons that have the electron configuration of the nearest noble-gas element.

      (c)   Each box represents an orbital.

      (d)   Each half-arrow in an orbital diagram represents an electron. The direction of the half-arrow represents electron spin.

6.68

Element	(a) C	(b) P	(c) Ne
Electron Configuration	$[He]2s^22p^2$	$[Ne]3s^23p^3$	$[He]2s^22p^6$
Core electrons	2	10	2
Valence electrons	4	5	8
Unpaired electrons	2	3	0

[The concept of "valence electrons" for noble gas elements is problematic, since they are mostly unreactive. We could list the core for neon as [Ne], with no valence or unpaired electrons.]

6.69   *Analyze/Plan.* Follow the logic in Sample Exercise 6.9. *Solve.*

      (a)   Cs: $[Xe]6s^1$ (b)   Ni: $[Ar]4s^23d^8$

      (c)   Se: $[Ar]4s^23d^{10}4p^4$ (d)   Cd: $[Kr]5s^24d^{10}$

      (e)   U: $[Rn]5f^36d^17s^2$. (Note the U and several other *f*-block elements have irregular *d*- and *f*-electron orders.)

      (f)   Pb: $[Xe]6s^24f^{14}5d^{10}6p^2$

6.70   (a)   Mg: $[Ne]3s^2$, 0 unpaired electrons

      (b)   Ge: $[Ar]4s^23d^{10}4p^2$, 2 unpaired electrons

      (c)   Br: $[Ar]4s^23d^{10}4p^5$, 1 unpaired electron

      (d)   V: $[Ar]4s^23d^3$, 3 unpaired electrons

      (e)   Y: $[Kr]5s^24d^1$, 1 unpaired electron

      (f)   Lu: $[Xe]6s^24f^{14}5d^1$, 1 unpaired electron

6.71   (a)   Be, 0 unpaired electrons   (b)   O, 2 unpaired electrons

      (c)   Cr, 6 unpaired electrons   (d)   Te , 2 unpaired electrons

6.72   (a)   7A (halogens), 1 unpaired electron

(b)   4B, 2 unpaired electrons

(c)   3A (row 4 and below), 1 unpaired electron

(d)   the f-block elements Sm and Pu, 6 unpaired electrons

6.73   (a)   The fifth electron would fill the 2p subshell (same n-value as 2s) before the 3s.

(b)   The Ne core has filled 2s and 2p subshells. Either the core is [He] or the outer electron configuration should be $3s^2 3p^3$.

(c)   The 3p subshell would fill before the 3d because it has the lower l-value and the same n-value. (If there were more electrons, 4s would also fill before 3d.)

6.74   Count the total number of electrons to assign the element.

(a)   N: $[He]2s^2 2p^3$ (b)   Se: $[Ar]4s^2 3d^{10} 4p^4$ (c)   Rh: $[Kr]5s^2 4d^7$

Additional Exercises

6.75   (a) $\lambda_A = 1.6 \times 10^{-7}\, m\, /\, 4.5 = 3.56 \times 10^{-8} = 3.6 \times 10^{-8}\, m$

$\lambda_B = 1.6 \times 10^{-7}\, m\, /\, 2 = 8.0 \times 10^{-8}\, m$

(b) $\nu = c/\lambda;\ \nu_A = \dfrac{2.998 \times 10^8\, m}{1\, s} \times \dfrac{1}{3.56 \times 10^{-8}\, m} = 8.4 \times 10^{15}\, s^{-1}$

$\nu_B = \dfrac{2.998 \times 10^8\, m}{1\, s} \times \dfrac{1}{8.0 \times 10^{-8}\, m} = 3.7 \times 10^{15}\, s^{-1}$

(c)   A: ultraviolet, B: ultraviolet

6.76   (a) $\nu = c/\lambda = \dfrac{2.998 \times 10^8\, m}{s} \times \dfrac{1}{589\, nm} \times \dfrac{1\, nm}{1 \times 10^{-9}\, m} = 5.0900 \times 10^{14}$

$= 5.09 \times 10^{14}\, s^{-1}$

(b) $E = h\nu = 6.626 \times 10^{-34}\, J\text{-}s \times 5.0900 \times 10^{14}\, s^{-1} \times \dfrac{6.022 \times 10^{23}\, photons}{mol}$

$\times\, 0.1\, mol = 2.03 \times 10^4\, J = 20.3\, kJ$

(c) $\Delta E = h\nu = \dfrac{hc}{\lambda} = \dfrac{6.626 \times 10^{-34}\, J\text{-}s \times 2.998 \times 10^8\, m/s}{589\, nm} \times \dfrac{1\, nm}{1 \times 10^{-9}\, m}$

$= 3.37 \times 10^{-19}\, J$

(d)   The 589 nm light emission is characteristic of Na^+. If the pickle is soaked in a different salt long enough to remove all Na^+, the 589 nm light would not be observed. Emission at a different wavelength, characteristic of the new salt, would be observed.

6.77   (a)   Elements that emit in the visible: Ba (blue), Ca (violet-blue), K (violet), Na (yellow/orange). (The other wavelengths are in the ultraviolet.)

(b)   Au: shortest wavelength, highest energy

Na: longest wavelength, lowest energy

(c) $\lambda = c/\nu = \dfrac{2.998 \times 10^8 \text{ m/s}}{6.59 \times 10^{14}/\text{s}} \times \dfrac{1 \text{ nm}}{1 \times 10^{-9} \text{ m}} = 455 \text{ nm}, \quad \text{Ba}$

6.78   All electromagnetic radiation travels at the same speed, 2.998×10^8 m/s. Change miles to meters and seconds to some appropriate unit of time.

$$746 \times 10^6 \text{ mi} \times \frac{1.6093 \text{ km}}{1 \text{ mi}} \times \frac{1000 \text{ m}}{1 \text{ km}} \times \frac{1 \text{ s}}{2.998 \times 10^8 \text{ m}} \times \frac{1 \text{ min}}{60 \text{ s}} = 66.7 \text{ min}$$

6.79   (a) $\nu = c/\lambda = \dfrac{2.998 \times 10^8 \text{ m/s}}{320 \text{ nm}} \times \dfrac{1 \text{ nm}}{1 \times 10^{-9} \text{ m}} = 9.37 \times 10^{14} \text{ s}^{-1}$

(b) $E = hc/\lambda = \dfrac{6.626 \times 10^{-34} \text{ J-s} \times 2.998 \times 10^8 \text{ m/s}}{3.20 \times 10^{-7} \text{ m}} \times \dfrac{1 \text{ kJ}}{1000 \text{ J}} \times \dfrac{6.022 \times 10^{23} \text{ photons}}{\text{mole}}$

$= 374 \text{ kJ/mol}$

(c)   UV-B photons have shorter wavelength and higher energy.

(d)   Yes. The higher energy UV-B photons would be more likely to cause sunburn.

6.80 $E = hc/\lambda \rightarrow$ J/photon; total energy = power × time; photons = total energy / J / photon

$$E = \frac{6.626 \times 10^{-34} \text{ J-s} \times 2.998 \times 10^8 \text{ m/s}}{780 \times 10^{-9} \text{ m}} = 2.5468 \times 10^{-19} = 2.55 \times 10^{-19} \text{ J/photon}$$

$$0.10 \text{ mW} = \frac{0.10 \times 10^{-3} \text{ J}}{1 \text{ s}} \times 69 \text{ min} \times \frac{60 \text{ s}}{1 \text{ min}} = 0.4140 = 0.41 \text{ J}$$

$$0.4140 \text{ J} \times \frac{1 \text{ photon}}{2.5468 \times 10^{-19} \text{ J}} = 1.626 \times 10^{18} = 1.6 \times 10^{18} \text{ photons}$$

6.81   (a)   If a plant appears orange, it absorbs the complementary (opposite) color on the color wheel. The plant most strongly absorbs blue light in the range 430-490 nm.

(b) $E = hc/\lambda = \dfrac{6.626 \times 10^{-34} \text{ J-s}}{455 \text{ nm}} \times \dfrac{2.998 \times 10^8 \text{ m}}{1 \text{ s}} \times \dfrac{1 \text{ nm}}{1 \times 10^{-9} \text{ m}} = 4.37 \times 10^{-19} \text{ J}$

6.82 $\dfrac{2.6 \times 10^{-12} \text{ C}}{1 \text{ s}} \times \dfrac{1 \text{ e}^-}{1.602 \times 10^{-19} \text{ C}} \times \dfrac{1 \text{ photon}}{1 \text{ e}^-} = 1.623 \times 10^7 = 1.6 \times 10^7 \text{ photons/s}$

$\dfrac{E}{\text{photon}} = hc/\lambda = \dfrac{6.626 \times 10^{-34} \text{ J-s}}{630 \text{ nm}} \times \dfrac{2.998 \times 10^8 \text{ m}}{1 \text{ s}} \times \dfrac{1 \text{ nm}}{1 \times 10^{-9} \text{ m}} \times \dfrac{1.623 \times 10^7 \text{ photon}}{\text{s}}$

$= 5.1 \times 10^{-12} \text{ J/s}$

6.83　(a)　$v = c/\lambda;$　$\dfrac{2.998 \times 10^8 \text{ m}}{\text{s}} \times \dfrac{1}{680 \text{ nm}} \times \dfrac{1 \text{ nm}}{1 \times 10^{-9} \text{ m}} = 4.4088 \times 10^{14} = 4.41 \times 10^{14} \text{ s}^{-1}$

(b)　Calculate J/photon using $E = hc/\lambda$; change to kJ/mol.

$$E_{photon} = \dfrac{6.626 \times 10^{-34} \text{ J·s}}{680 \times 10^{-9} \text{ m}} \times \dfrac{2.998 \times 10^8 \text{ m}}{\text{s}} = 2.9213 \times 10^{-19} = 2.92 \times 10^{-19} \text{ J/photon}$$

$$\dfrac{2.9213 \times 10^{-19} \text{ J}}{\text{photon}} \times \dfrac{6.022 \times 10^{23} \text{ photons}}{\text{mol}} \times \dfrac{1 \text{ kJ}}{1000 \text{ J}} = 175.92 = 176 \text{ kJ/mol}$$

(c)　Nothing. The incoming (incident) radiation does not transfer sufficient energy to an electron to overcome the attractive forces holding the electron in the metal.

(d)　For frequencies greater than v_o, any "extra" energy not needed to remove the electron from the metal becomes the kinetic energy of the ejected electron. The kinetic energy of the electron is directly proportional to this extra energy.

(e)　Yes. Let E_{total} be the total energy of an incident photon, E_{min} be the minimum energy required to eject an electron, and E_k be the "extra" energy that becomes the kinetic energy of the ejected electron.

$E_{total} = E_{min} + E_k$, $E_k = E_{total} - E_{min} = hv - hv_o$, $E_k = h(v - v_o)$. The slope of the line is the value of h, Planck's constant.

6.84　(a)　"blue" cone, $\lambda_{max} = 450 \text{ nm} = 450 \times 10^{-9} \text{ m}$

$$E = hc/\lambda = \dfrac{6.626 \times 10^{-34} \text{ J·s}}{450 \times 10^{-9} \text{ m}} \times \dfrac{2.998 \times 10^8 \text{ m}}{1 \text{ s}} = 4.41 \times 10^{-19} \text{ J}$$

"green" cone, $\lambda_{max} = 450 \text{ nm} = 450 \times 10^{-9} \text{ m}$

$$E = hc/\lambda = \dfrac{6.626 \times 10^{-34} \text{ J·s}}{545 \times 10^{-9} \text{ m}} \times \dfrac{2.998 \times 10^8 \text{ m}}{1 \text{ s}} = 3.64 \times 10^{-19} \text{ J}$$

"red" cone, $\lambda_{max} = 585 \text{ nm} = 585 \times 10^{-9} \text{ m}$

$$E = hc/\lambda = \dfrac{6.626 \times 10^{-34} \text{ J·s}}{585 \times 10^{-9} \text{ m}} \times \dfrac{2.998 \times 10^8 \text{ m}}{1 \text{ s}} = 3.40 \times 10^{-19} \text{ J}$$

(b)　"blue" scattering efficiency $= \left(\dfrac{1}{450}\right)^4$; "green" scattering efficiency $= \left(\dfrac{1}{545}\right)^4$

$$\text{ratio of "blue" to "green"} = \dfrac{\left(\dfrac{1}{450 \text{ nm}}\right)^4}{\left(\dfrac{1}{545 \text{ nm}}\right)^4} \times \left(\dfrac{545}{450}\right)^4 = 2.15$$

(c)　Mainly, the shorter wavelengths perceived by the "blue" cone are scattered more efficiently, so there is more of the blue light to see. Also, the amplitude of the absorption curve for the "blue" cone is greater than the amplitudes of the other two curves. This indicates that our eyes are more sensitive to blue light than the other wavelengths. (It is also true that the intensities of the different wavelengths reaching Earth are not the same, but this information is not conveyed in the exercise.)

6.85   (a)   Lines with $n_f = 1$ lie in the ultraviolet (see Solution 6.40) and with $n_f = 2$ lie in the visible (see Solution 6.39). Lines with $n_f = 3$ will have smaller ΔE and longer wavelengths and lie in the infrared.

       (b)   Use Equation 6.7 to calculate ΔE, then $\lambda = hc/\Delta E$.

$$n_i = 4, n_f = 3; \Delta E = -2.18 \times 10^{-18} \text{ J} \left[\frac{1}{n_f^2} - \frac{1}{n_i^2} \right] = -2.18 \times 10^{-18} \text{ J } (1/9 - 1/16)$$

$$\lambda = hc/E = \frac{6.626 \times 10^{-34} \text{ J-s} \times 2.998 \times 10^8 \text{ m/s}}{-2.18 \times 10^{-18} (1/9 - 1/16)} = 1.87 \times 10^{-6} \text{ m}$$

$$n_i = 5, n_f = 3; \lambda = hc/E = \frac{6.626 \times 10^{-34} \text{ J-s} \times 2.998 \times 10^8 \text{ m/s}}{-2.18 \times 10^{-18} (1/9 - 1/25)} = 1.28 \times 10^{-6} \text{ m}$$

$$n_i = 6, n_f = 3; \lambda = hc/E = \frac{6.626 \times 10^{-34} \text{ J-s} \times 2.998 \times 10^8 \text{ m/s}}{-2.18 \times 10^{-18} (1/9 - 1/36)} = 1.09 \times 10^{-6} \text{ m}$$

These three wavelengths are all greater than 1 μm or 1×10^{-6} m. They are in the infrared, close to the visible edge (0.7×10^{-6} m).

6.86   (a)   Gaseous atoms of various elements in the sun's atmosphere typically have ground state electron configurations. When these atoms are exposed to radiation from the sun, the electrons change from the ground state to one of several allowed excited states. Atoms absorb the wavelengths of light which correspond to these allowed energy changes. All other wavelengths of solar radiation pass through the atmosphere unchanged. Thus, the dark lines are the wavelengths that correspond to allowed energy changes in atoms of the solar atmosphere. The continuous background is all other wavelengths of solar radiation.

       (b)   The scientist should record the absorption spectrum of pure neon or other elements of interest. The Fraunhofer lines that belong to a particular element will appear at the same wavelength as the lines in the absorption spectrum of that element.

6.87   (a) He^+ is hydrogen-like because it is a one-electron particle. An He atom has two electrons. The Bohr model is based on the interaction of a single electron with the nucleus, but does not accurately account for additional interactions when two or more electrons are present.

       (b)   Divide each energy by the smallest value to find the integer relationship.

         H: $-2.18 \times 10^{-18}/-2.18 \times 10^{-18} = 1$; $Z = 1$

         He^+: $-8.72 \times 10^{-18}/-2.18 \times 10^{-18} = 4$; $Z = 2$

         Li^{2+}: $-1.96 \times 10^{-17}/-2.18 \times 10^{-18} = 9$; $Z = 3$

The ground-state energies are in the ratio of 1:4:9, which is also the ratio Z^2, the square of the nuclear charge for each particle.

The ground state energy for hydrogen-like particles is:

$E = R_H Z^2$. (By definition, n = 1 for the ground state of a one-electron particle.)

(c)   Z = 6 for C^{5+}. $E = -2.18 \times 10^{-18}$ J $(6)^2 = -7.85 \times 10^{-17}$ J

6.88   *Plan.* Change keV to J/electron. Calculate v from kinetic energy. $\lambda = h/mv$.   *Solve.*

$$18.6 \text{ keV} \times \frac{1000 \text{ eV}}{\text{keV}} \times \frac{96.485 \text{ kJ}}{1 \text{ eV} \cdot \text{mol}} \times \frac{1000 \text{ J}}{1 \text{ kJ}} \times \frac{1 \text{ mol}}{6.022 \times 10^{23} \text{ electrons}}$$

$$= 2.980 \times 10^{-15} = 2.98 \times 10^{-15} \text{ J/electron}$$

$$E_k = mv^2/2; \ v^2 = 2E_k/m; \ v = \sqrt{2E_k/m}$$

$$v = \left(\frac{2 \times 2.980 \times 10^{-15} \text{ kg} \cdot \text{m}^2/\text{s}^2}{9.1094 \times 10^{-31} \text{ kg}} \right)^{1/2} = 8.089 \times 10^7 = 8.09 \times 10^7 \text{ m/s}$$

$$\lambda = h/mv = \frac{6.626 \times 10^{-34} \text{ J} \cdot \text{s}}{9.1094 \times 10^{-31} \text{ kg} \times 8.089 \times 10^7 \text{ m/s}} \times \frac{1 \text{ kg} \cdot \text{m}^2/\text{s}^2}{1 \text{ J}} = 8.99 \times 10^{-12} \text{ m} = 8.99 \text{ pm}$$

6.89   Heisenberg postulated that the dual nature of matter places a limitation on how precisely we can know both the position and momentum of an object. This limitation is significant at the subatomic particle level. The *Star Trek* transporter (presumably) disassembles humans into their protons, neutrons and electrons, moves the particles at high speed (possibly the speed of light) to a new location, and reassembles the particles into the human. Heisenberg's uncertainty principle indicates that if we know the momentum (*mv*) of the moving particles, we can't precisely know their position (*x*). If a few of the subatomic particles don't arrive in exactly the correct location, the human would not be reassembled in their original form. So, the "Heisenberg compensator" is necessary to make sure that the transported human arrives at the new location intact.

6.90   (a)   *l*   (b)   *n* and *l*   (c) m_s (d) m_l

6.91   (a)   Probability density, $[\psi(r)]^2$, is the probability of finding an electron at a single point at distance r from the nucleus. The radial probability function, $4\pi r^2$, is the probability of finding an electron at any point on the sphere defined by radius r. $P(r) = 4\pi r^2 [\psi(r)]^2$.

(b)   The term $4\pi r^2$ explains the differences in plots of the two functions. Plots of the probability density, $[\psi(r)^2]$ for s orbitals shown in Figure 6.21 each have their maximum value at r = 0, with (n – 1) smaller maxima at greater values of r. The plots of radial probability, P(r), for the same s orbitals shown in Figure 6.18 have values of zero at r = 0 and the size of the maxima increases. P(r) is the product of $[\psi(r)]^2$ and $4\pi r^2$. At r = 0, the value of $[\psi(r)]^2$ is finite and large, but the value of $4\pi r^2$ is zero, so the value of P(r) is zero. As r increases, the values of $[\psi(r)]^2$ vary as shown in Figure 6.21, but the values of $4\pi r^2$ increase continuously, leading to the increasing size of P(r) maxima as r increases.

(c)

6.92   (a)   The p_z orbital has a nodal plane where z = 0. This is the xy plane.

       (b)   The d_{xy} orbital has four lobes and two nodal planes, the two planes where x = 0 and y = 0. These are the yz and xz planes.

       (c)   The $d_{x^2-y^2}$ has four lobes and two nodal planes, the planes where $x^2 - y^2 = 0$. These are the planes that bisect the x and y axes and contain the z axis.

6.93   (a)   This is the frequency of radiowaves that excite the nuclei from one spin state to the other.

       (b) $\Delta E = h\nu = 6.626 \times 10^{-34} \text{ J-s} \times \dfrac{450 \times 10^6}{\text{s}} = 2.98 \times 10^{-25} \text{ J}$

       (c)   Since $\Delta E = 0$ in the absence of a magnetic field, it is reasonable to assume that the stronger the external field, the greater ΔE. (In fact, ΔE is directly proportional to field strength). Because ΔE is relatively small [see part (b)], the two spin states are almost equally populated, with a very slight excess in the lower energy state. The stronger the magnetic field, the larger ΔE, the greater number of nuclei in the lower energy spin state. With more nuclei in the lower energy state, more are able to absorb the appropriate radio wave photons and reach the higher energy state. This increases the intensity of the NMR signal, which provides more information and more reliable information than a weak absorption signal.

6.94   If m_s had three allowed values instead of two, each orbital would hold three electrons instead of two. Assuming that the same orbitals are available (that there is no change in the n, l, and m_l values), the number of elements in each of the first four rows would be:

1st row: 1 orbital $\times 3 =$ 3 elements

2nd row: 4 orbitals $\times 3 = 12$ elements

3rd row: 4 orbitals $\times 3 = 12$ elements

4th row: 9 orbitals $\times 3 = 27$ elements

The s-block would be 3 columns wide, the p-block 9 columns wide and the d-block 15 columns wide.

6.95   (a)   Si: $[Ne]3s^23p^2$, 2 unpaired electrons

       (b)   Zn: $[Ar]4s^23d^{10}$, 0 unpaired electrons

       (c)   Zr: $[Kr]5s^24d^2$, 2 unpaired electrons

       (d)   Sn: $[Kr]5s^24d^{10}5p^2$, 2 unpaired electrons

       (e)   Ba: $[Xe]6s^2$, 0 unpaired electrons

       (f)   Tl: $[Xe]6s^24f^{14}5d^{10}6p^1$, 1 unpaired electrons

6.96   The core would be the electron configuration of element 118. If no new subshell begins to fill, the condensed electron configuration of element 126 would be similar to those of elements vertically above it on the periodic chart, Pu and Sm. The condensed configuration would be $[118]8s^26f^6$. On the other hand, the 5g subshell could begin to fill after 8s, resulting in the condensed configuration $[118]8s^25g^6$. Exceptions are also possible (likely).

Integrative Exercises

6.97   (a)   We know the wavelength of microwave radiation, the volume of coffee to be heated, and the desired temperature change. Assume the density and heat capacity of coffee are the same as pure water. We need to calculate: (i) the total energy required to heat the coffee and (ii) the energy of a single photon in order to find (iii) the number of photons required.

          (i)   From Chapter 5, the heat capacity of liquid water is 4.184 J/g°C.

             To find the mass of 200 mL of coffee at 23°C, use the density of water given in Appendix B.

$$200 \text{ mL} \times \frac{0.997 \text{ g}}{1 \text{ mL}} = 199.4 = 199 \text{ g coffee}$$

$$\frac{4.184 \text{ J}}{1 \text{ g °C}} \times 199.4 \text{ g} \times (60°C - 23°C) = 3.087 \times 10^4 \text{ J} = 31 \text{ kJ}$$

          (ii) $E = hc/\lambda = 6.626 \times 10^{-34} \text{ J·s} \times \dfrac{2.998 \times 10^8 \text{ m}}{1 \text{ s}} \times \dfrac{1}{0.112 \text{ m}}$

$$= \frac{1.77 \times 10^{-24} \text{ J}}{1 \text{ photon}}$$

          (iii) $3.087 \times 10^4 \text{ J} \times \dfrac{1 \text{ photon}}{1.774 \times 10^{-24} \text{ J}} = 1.7 \times 10^{28}$ photons

       (The answer has 2 sig figs because the temperature change, 37°C, has 2 sig figs.)

      (b)   1 W = 1 J/s. 900 W = 900 J/s. From part (a), 31 kJ are required to heat the coffee.

$$3.087 \times 10^4 \text{ J} \times \frac{1 \text{ s}}{900 \text{ J}} = 34.30 = 34 \text{ s}$$

6.98 $\Delta H^{\circ}_{rxn} = \Delta H^{\circ}_f\, O_2(g) + \Delta H^{\circ}_f\, O(g) - \Delta H^{\circ}_f\, O_3(g)$

$\Delta H^{\circ}_{rxn} = 0 + 247.5\ kJ - 142.3\ kJ = +105.2\ kJ$

$$\frac{105.2\ kJ}{mol\ O_3} \times \frac{1\ mol\ O_3}{6.022 \times 10^{23}\ molecules} \times \frac{1000\ J}{1\ kJ} = \frac{1.747 \times 10^{-19}\ J}{O_3\ molecule}$$

$$\Delta E = hc/\lambda;\ \lambda = \frac{hc}{\Delta E} = \frac{6.626 \times 10^{-34}\ J \cdot s \times 2.998 \times 10^8\ m/s}{1.747 \times 10^{-19}\ J} = 1.137 \times 10^{-6}\ m$$

Radiation with this wavelength is in the infrared portion of the spectrum. (Clearly, processes other than simple photodissociation cause O_3 to absorb ultraviolet radiation.)

6.99   (a)   The electron configuration of Zr is $[Kr]5s^2 4d^2$ and that of Hf is $[Xe]6s^2 4f^{14} 5d^2$. Although Hf has electrons in f orbitals as the rare earth elements do, the 4f subshell in Hf is filled, and the 5d electrons primarily determine the chemical properties of the element. Thus, Hf should be chemically similar to Zr rather than the rare earth elements.

(b) $ZrCl_4(s) + 4Na(l) \rightarrow Zr(s) + 4NaCl(s)$

This is an oxidation-reduction reaction; Na is oxidized and Zr is reduced.

(c) $2ZrO_2(s) + 4Cl_2(g) + 3C(s) \rightarrow 2ZrCl_4(s) + CO_2(g) + 2CO(g)$

$$55.4\ g\ ZrO_2 \times \frac{1\ mol\ ZrO_2}{123.2\ g\ ZrO_2} \times \frac{2\ mol\ ZrCl_4}{2\ mol\ ZrO_2} \times \frac{233.0\ g\ ZrCl_4}{1\ mol\ ZrCl_4} = 105\ g\ ZrCl_4$$

(d)   In ionic compounds of the type MCl_4 and MO_2, the metal ions have a 4+ charge, indicating that the neutral atoms have lost four electrons. Zr, $[Kr]5s^2 4d^2$, loses the four electrons beyond its Kr core configuration. Hf, $[Xe]6s^2 4f^{14} 5d^2$, similarly loses its four 6s and 5d electrons, but not electrons from the "complete" 4f subshell.

6.100   (a)   Each oxide ion, O^{2-}, carries a 2- charge. Each metal oxide is a neutral compound, so the metal ion or ions must adopt a total positive charge equal to the total negative charge of the oxide ions in the compound. The table below lists the electron configuration of the neutral metal atom, the positive charge of each metal ion in the oxide, and the corresponding electron configuration of the metal ion.

i.   K: $[Ar]4s^1$ 1+ $[Ar]$

ii.   Ca: $[Ar]4s^2$ 2+ $[Ar]$

iii.   Sc: $[Ar]4s^2 3d^1$ 3+ $[Ar]$

iv.   Ti: $[Ar]4s^2 3d^2$ 4+ $[Ar]$

v.   V: $[Ar]4s^2 3d^3$ 5+ $[Ar]$

vi.   Cr: $[Ar]4s^1 3d^5$ 6+ $[Ar]$

Each metal atom loses all (valence) electrons beyond the Ar core configuration. In K_2O, Sc_2O_3 and V_2O_5, where the metal ions have odd charges, two metal ions are required to produce a neutral oxide.

(b)   i.   potassium oxide

       ii.   calcium oxide

       iii.   scandium(III) oxide

       iv.   titanium (IV) oxide

       v.   vanadium (V) oxide

       vi.   chromium (VI) oxide

(Roman numerals are required to specify the charges on the transition metal ions, because more than one stable ion may exist.)

(c)   Recall that $\Delta H_f^\circ = 0$ for elements in their standard states. In these reactions, M(s) and $H_2(g)$ are elements in their standard states.

       i. $K_2O(s) + H_2(g) \rightarrow 2K(s) + H_2O(g)$

               $\Delta H^\circ = \Delta H_f^\circ\, H_2O(g) + 2\Delta H_f^\circ\, K(s) - \Delta H\, K_2O(s) - \Delta H_f^\circ\, H_2(g)$

               $\Delta H^\circ = -241.82\ kJ + 2(0) - (-363.2\ kJ) - 0 = 121.4\ kJ$

       ii. $CaO(s) + H_2(g) \rightarrow Ca(s) + H_2O(g)$

               $\Delta H^\circ = \Delta H_f^\circ\, H_2O(g) + \Delta H_f^\circ\, Ca(s) - \Delta H_f^\circ\, CaO(s) - \Delta H_f^\circ\, H_2(g)$

               $\Delta H^\circ = -241.82\ kJ + 0 - (-635.1\ kJ) - 0 = 393.3\ kJ$

       iii. $TiO_2(s) + 2H_2(g) \rightarrow Ti(s) + 2H_2O(g)$

               $\Delta H^\circ = 2\Delta H_f^\circ\, H_2O(g) + \Delta H_f^\circ\, Ti(s) - \Delta H_f^\circ\, TiO_2(s) - 2\Delta H_f^\circ\, H_2(g)$

               $= 2(-241.82) + 0 - (-938.7) - 2(0) = 455.1\ kJ$

       iv. $V_2O_5(s) + 5H_2(g) \rightarrow 2V(s) + 5H_2O(g)$

               $\Delta H^\circ = 5\Delta H_f^\circ\, H_2O(g) + 2\Delta H_f^\circ\, V(s) - \Delta H_f^\circ\, V_2O_5(s) - 5\Delta H_f^\circ\, H_2(g)$

               $= 5(-241.82) + 2(0) - (-1550.6) - 5(0) = 341.5\ kJ$

(d) ΔH_f° becomes more negative moving from left to right across this row of the periodic chart. Since Sc lies between Ca and Ti, the median of the two ΔH_f° values is approximately –785 kJ/mol. However, the trend is clearly not linear. Dividing the ΔH_f° values by the positive charge on the pertinent metal ion produces the values –363, –318, –235, and –310. The value between Ca^{2+} (–318) and Ti^{4+} (–235) is Sc^{3+} (–277). Multiplying (–277) by 3, a value of approximately –830 kJ results. A reasonable range of values for ΔH_f° of $Sc_2O_3(s)$ is then –785 to –830 kJ/mol.

6.101 (a)   Bohr's theory was based on the Rutherford "nuclear" model of the atom. That is, Bohr theory assumed a dense positive charge at the center of the atom and a diffuse negative charge (electrons) surrounding it. Bohr's theory then specified the nature of the diffuse negative charge. The prevailing theory before the nuclear model was Thomson's plum pudding or watermelon model, with discrete electrons scattered about a diffuse positive charge cloud. Bohr's theory could not have been based on the Thomson model of the atom.

(b)   De Broglie's hypothesis is that electrons exhibit both particle and wave properties. Thomson's conclusion that electrons have mass is a particle property, while the nature of cathode rays is a wave property. De Broglie's hypothesis actually rationalizes these two seemingly contradictory observations about the properties of electrons.

6.102   (a) ^{238}U: 92 p, 146 n, 92 e; ^{235}U: 92 p, 143 n, 92 e

In keeping with the definition isotopes, only the number of neutrons is different in the two nuclides. Since the two isotopes have the same number of electrons, they will have the same electron configuration.

(b)   U: [Rn]$7s^2 5f^4$

(c)   From Figure 6.31, the actual electron configuration is [Rn]$7s^2 5f^3 6d^1$. The energies of the 6d and 5f orbitals are very close, and electron configurations of many actinides include 6d electrons.

(d) $^{238}_{92}U \rightarrow ^{234}_{90}Th + ^4_2He$ ^{234}Th has 90 p, 144 n, 90 e. ^{238}U has lost 2 p, 2 n, 2 e.

These are organized into ^4_2He shown in the nuclear reaction above.

(e)   From Figure 6.31, the electron configuration of Th is [Rn]$7s^2 6d^2$. This is not really surprising because there are so many rare earth electron configurations that are exceptions to the expected orbital filling order. However, Th is the only rare earth that has two d valence electrons. Furthermore, the configuration of Th is different than that of Ce, the element above it on the periodic chart, so the electron configuration is at least interesting.

6.103   In each case, radiant energy from the sun in shown as hv.

Energy from the sun irradiates the earth without external intervention. In the absence of an appropriate receiver, the energy is dissipated as heat, as the diagram for the inert black material shows. When sunlight hits a material that can convert the energy to a useable form, such as a leaf or a photovoltaic cell, the sun becomes a sustainable energy source.

7 Periodic Properties of the Elements

Visualizing Concepts

7.1   (a)   The light bulb itself represents the nucleus of the atom. The brighter the bulb, the more nuclear charge the electron "sees." A frosted glass lampshade between the bulb and our eyes reduces the brightness of the bulb. The shade is analogous to core electrons in the atom shielding outer electrons (our eyes) from the full nuclear charge (the bare light bulb).

        (b)   Increasing the wattage of the light bulb mimics moving right along a row of the periodic table. The brighter bulb inside the same shade is analogous to having more protons in the nucleus while the core electron configuration doesn't change.

        (c)   Moving down a family, both the nuclear charge and the core electron configuration change. To simulate the addition of core electrons farther from the nucleus, we would add larger frosted glass shades; to simulate the increase in Z, we would increase the wattage of the bulb. In our analogy, the brightness of the light should decrease, because the increased distance of the observer from the bulb and the additional frosted shades more than compensate for the increase in bulb wattage. This mimics the actual decrease in attraction of a valence electron for the nucleus as we move down a column. (Note that Z_{eff} does increase slightly going down a column, but this property is more than offset by the increased distance of valence electrons from the nucleus.)

7.2   The larger 1.80 Å radius is the so-called *nonbonding* or *van der Waals* radius of a sulfur atom. This is the estimated radius of a sulfur atom involved in a nonbonding (elastic, billiard ball-like) collision with another atom. The smaller 1.02 Å radius is the *bonding* atomic radius of a sulfur atom. A bonding radius is always smaller (shorter) than a nonbonding radius, because bonding is an attractive interaction that brings atoms closer together than they would be in a nonbonding interaction.

7.3   (a)   The bonding atomic radius of A, r_A, is $d_1/2$. The distance d_2 is the sum of the bonding atomic radii of A and X, $r_A + r_X$. Since we know that $r_A = d_1/2$, $d_2 = r_X + d_1/2$, $r_X = d_2 - d_1/2$.

        (b)   The length of the X-X bond is $2r_X$.

$$2r_X = 2(d_2 - d_1/2) = 2d_2 - d_1.$$

7.4

Lines (a) and (b) coincide, but their directions are opposite. Line (a) goes from upper right to lower left, and line (b) from lower left to upper right.

(c) From the diagram, we observe that the trends in bonding atomic radius (size) and ionization energy are opposite each other. As bonding atomic radius increases, ionization energy decreases, and vice versa.

7.5

$$A(g) \rightarrow A^+(g) + e^- \qquad \text{ionization energy of A}$$

$$A(g) + e^- \rightarrow A^-(g) \qquad \text{electron affinity of A}$$

$$A(g) + A(g) \rightarrow A^+(g) + A^-(g) \qquad \text{ionization energy of A + electron affinity of A}$$

The energy change for the reaction is the ionization energy of A plus the electron affinity of A.

This process is endothermic for both nonmetals and metals. Considering data for Cl and Na from Figures 7.9 and 7.11, the endothermic ionization energy term dominates the exothermic electron affinity term, even for Cl which has the most exothermic electron affinity listed.

7.6 (a) $X + 2F_2 \rightarrow XF_4$

(b) If X is a nonmetal, XF_4 is a molecular compound. If X is a metal, XF_4 is ionic. For an ionic compound with this formula, X would have a charge of 4+, and a much smaller bonding atomic radius than F^-. X in the diagram has about the same bonding radius as F, so it is likely to be a nonmetal.

Periodic Table; Effective Nuclear Charge (sections 7.1 and 7.2)

7.7 The number of columns in the various blocks of the periodic chart corresponds to the maximum number of electrons that can occupy the various kinds of atomic orbitals: 2 columns on the left for 2 electrons in s orbitals, 10 columns in the transition metals for 10 electrons in d orbitals, 6 columns on the right for 6 electrons in p orbitals, 14-member rows below for 14 electrons in f orbitals. The order of blocks corresponds to the filling order of atomic orbitals, and the row number corresponds to the principal quantum number of the valence electrons of elements in that row, ns, np, $(n-1)d$, $(n-2)f$.

7.8 Assuming *eka-* means one place below or under, *eka-manganese* on Figure 7.1 is technetium, Tc.

7.9 According to Figure 7.1, the first elements to be discovered, those known since ancient times, were Fe, Cu, Ag, Au, Hg, Sn, Pb, C and S. These elements are present in nature in elemental form; they can be observed directly and their isolation does not require chemical processing. In general, elements are discovered according to their ease of isolation in elemental form. This depends on chemical properties rather than relative abundance.

7.10 (a) Moseley bombarded metal targets with high-energy electrons. These impinging electrons knock out core electrons from metal atoms in the target, creating an electron vacancy or hole. Outer, higher energy electrons in the metal atoms then "drop down" into the lower energy hole. Energy in the form of X-rays is emitted when atomic electrons move from a higher energy to a lower energy state.

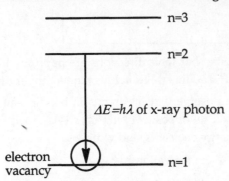

(b) The main determining factor of physical and especially chemical properties is electron configuration. For electrically neutral elements, the number of electrons equals the number of protons, which in turn is the atomic number of an element. Atomic weight is related to mass number, protons plus neutrons. The number of neutrons in its nucleus does influence the mass of an atom, but mass is a minor or non-factor in determining properties.

7.11 (a) *Effective nuclear charge*, Z_{eff}, is a representation of the average electrical field experienced by a single electron. It is the average environment created by the nucleus and the other electrons in the molecule, expressed as a net positive charge at the nucleus. It is approximately the nuclear charge, Z, minus the number of core electrons.

(b) Going from left to right across a period, nuclear charge increases while the number of electrons in the core is constant. This results in an increase in Z_{eff}.

7.12 (a) Electrostatic attraction for the nucleus lowers the energy of an electron, while electron-electron repulsions increase this energy. The concept of effective nuclear charge allows us to model this increase in the energy of an electron as a smaller net attraction to a nucleus with a smaller positive charge, Z_{eff}.

(b) In Be (or any element), the 1s electrons are not shielded by any core electrons, so they experience a much greater Z_{eff} than the 2s electrons.

7.13 (a) *Analyze/Plan.* $Z_{eff} = Z–S$. Find the atomic number, Z, of Na and K. Write their electron configurations and count the number of core electrons. Assume S = number of core electrons.

Solve. Na: Z = 11; [Ne]$3s^1$. In the Ne core there are 10 electrons. $Z_{eff} = 11–10 = 1$. K: Z = 19; [Ar]$4s^1$. In the Ar core there are 18 electrons. $Z_{eff} = 19–18 = 1$.

(b) *Analyze/Plan.* $Z_{eff} = Z–S$. Write the complete electron configuration for each element to show counting for Slater's rules. S = 0.35 (# of electrons with same n) + 0.85 (# of electrons with ($n–1$) + 1 (# of electrons with ($n–2$).

Solve. Na: $1s^2 2s^2 2p^6 3s^1$. $S = 0.35(0) + 0.85(8) + 1(2) = 8.8$. $Z_{eff} = 11 - 8.8 = 2.2$

K: $1s^2 2s^2 2p^6 3s^2 3p^6 4s^1$. $S = 0.35(0) + 0.85(8) + 1(10) = 16.8$. $Z_{eff} = 19 - 16.8 = 2.2$

(c)   For both Na and K, the two values of Z_{eff} are 1.0 and 2.2. The Slater value of 2.2 is closer to the values of 2.51 (Na) and 3.49 (K) obtained from detailed calculations.

(d)   Both approximations, 'core electrons 100% effective' and Slater, yield the same value of Z_{eff} for Na and K. Neither approximation accounts for the gradual increase in Z_{eff} moving down a group.

(e)   Following the trend from detailed calculations, we predict a Z_{eff} value of approximately 4.5 for Rb.

7.14   Follow the method in the preceding question to calculate Z_{eff} values.
(a)   Si: $Z = 14$; [Ne]$3s^2 3p^2$. 10 electrons in the Ne core. $Z_{eff} = 14 - 10 = 4$
Cl: $Z = 17$; [Ne]$3s^2 3p^5$. 10 electrons in the Ne core. $Z_{eff} = 17 - 10 = 7$

(b)   Si: $1s^2 2s^2 2p^6 3s^2 3p^2$. $S = 0.35(3) + 0.85(8) + 1(2) = 9.85$. $Z_{eff} = 14 - 9.85 = 4.15$
Cl: $1s^2 2s^2 2p^6 3s^2 3p^5$. $S = 0.35(6) + 0.85(8) + 1(2) = 10.90$. $Z_{eff} = 17 - 10.90 = 6.10$

(c)   The Slater values of 4.15 (Si) and 6.10 (Cl) are closer to the results of detailed calculations, 4.29 (Si) and 6.12 (Cl).

(d)   The Slater method of approximation more closely approximates the gradual increase in Z_{eff} moving across a row. The 'core 100%-effective' approximation underestimates Z_{eff} for Si but overestimates it for Cl. Slater values are closer to detailed calculations, and a better indication of the change in Z_{eff} moving from Si to Cl.

(e)   Relative to Si, P has one more proton ($Z + 1$) and one more 3p electron ($S + 0.35$), so it is reasonable to predict Z_{eff} +0.65. That is, Z_{eff} for P will be (4.15 + 0.65) = 4.80.

7.15   Krypton has a larger nuclear charge ($Z = 36$) than argon ($Z = 18$). The shielding of electrons in the $n = 3$ shell by the 1s, 2s and 2p core electrons in the two atoms is approximately equal, so the $n = 3$ electrons in Kr experience a greater effective nuclear charge and are thus situated closer to the nucleus.

7.16   Mg < P < K < Ti < Rh. The shielding of electrons in the $n = 3$ shell by 1s, 2s and 2p core electrons in these elements is approximately equal, so the effective nuclear charge increases as Z increases.

Atomic and Ionic Radii (section 7.3)

7.17   (a)   Atomic radii are determined by measuring distances between nuclei (interatomic distances) in various bonding and nonbonding situations.

(b)   Bonding radii are calculated from the internuclear separation of two atoms joined by a chemical bond. Nonbonding radii are calculated from the internuclear separation between two gaseous atoms that collide and move apart, but do not bond.

(c)   For a given element, the nonbonding radius is always larger than the bonding radius. When a chemical bond forms, electron clouds of the two atoms interpenetrate, bringing the two nuclei closer together and resulting in a smaller bonding atomic radius (Figure 7.5).

(d) If a free atom reacts to become part of a covalent molecule, the atom gets smaller; its radius changes from nonbonding to bonding.

7.18 (a) Since the quantum mechanical description of the atom does not specify the exact location of electrons, there is no specific distance from the nucleus where the last electron can be found. Rather, the electron density decreases gradually as the distance from the nucleus increases. There is no quantum mechanical "edge" of an atom.

(b) When nonbonded atoms touch, it is their electron clouds that interact. These interactions are primarily repulsive because of the negative charges of electrons. Thus, the size of the electron clouds determines the nuclear approach distance of nonbonded atoms.

7.19 (a) The atomic (*metallic*) radius of W is the interatomic W-W distance divided by 2, $2.74 \text{ Å}/2 = 1.37 \text{ Å}$.

(b) Under high pressure, we expect atoms in a pure substance to move closer together. That is, the distance between W atoms will decrease.

7.20 The distance between Si atoms in solid silicon is two times the bonding atomic radius from Figure 7.6. The Si–Si distance is $2 \times 1.11 \text{ Å} = 2.22 \text{ Å}$.

The C–C distance in diamond is 1.54 Å (from Section 7.3; from Figure 7.6, $2 \times 0.77 \text{ Å} = 1.54 \text{ Å}$). We expect the Si–Si distance to be greater, because the bonding (valence) electrons in Si are in the n=3 shell, while those in C are in the n=2 shell.

7.21 From bonding atomic radii in Figure 7.6, As–I = 1.19 Å + 1.33 Å = 2.52 Å. This is very close to the experimental value of 2.55 Å in AsI_3.

7.22 Bi–I = 2.81 Å = $r_{Bi} + r_I$. From Figure 7.6, $r_I = 1.33 \text{ Å}$.

r_{Bi} = [Bi–I] – r_I = 2.81 Å – 1.33 Å = 1.48 Å.

7.23 (a) Atomic radii decrease moving from left to right across a row and (b) increase from top to bottom within a group.

(c) O < Si < Ge < I. The order for the first three atoms is unambiguous according to the trends of increasing atomic radius moving down a column and to the left in a row of the table. Moving from Ge to I, radius increases moving down but decreases moving right. It is usually true that a change in row number, which involves a change in principal quantum number of valence electrons, is a larger effect than a horizontal change across a row. This is verified by values for the atomic radii of Ge and I on Figure 7.6.

7.24 (a) The vertical difference in radius is due to a change in principal quantum number of the valence electrons. The horizontal difference in radius is due to the change in electrostatic attraction between an outer electron and a nucleus with one more or one fewer proton. Adding or subtracting a proton has a much smaller radius effect than moving from one principal quantum level to the next.

(b)   Si < Al < Ge < Ga. This order is predicted by the trends in increasing atomic radius moving to the left in a row and down a column of the periodic chart, assuming that changes moving down a column are larger [see part (a)]. That is, the order above assumes that the change from Si to Ge is larger than the change from Si to Al. This order is confirmed by the values in Figure 7.6.

7.25   *Plan.* Locate each element on the periodic charge and use trends in radii to predict their order.   *Solve.*

(a)   Cs > K > Li   (b) Pb > Sn > Si   (c) N > O > F

7.26   (a)   Na < Ca < Ba   (b) As < Sb < Sn

(c)   Be < Si < Al. This order assumes the increase in radius from the second to the third row is greater than the decrease moving right in the third row. Radii in Figure 7.6 confirm this assumption.

7.27   (a)   False. Cations are smaller than their corresponding neutral atoms. Electrostatic repulsions are reduced by removing an electron from a neutral atom, Z_{eff} increases, and the cation is smaller.

(b)   True. [See (a) above.]

(c)   False. I^- is bigger than Cl^-. Going down a column, the n value of the valence electrons increases and they are farther from the nucleus. Valence electrons also experience greater shielding by core electrons. The greater radial extent of the valence electrons outweighs the increase in Z, and the size of particles with like charge increases.

7.28   (a)   As Z stays constant and the number of electrons increases, the electron-electron repulsions increase, the electrons spread apart, and the aion becomes larger. The reverse is true for the cation, which becomes smaller than the neutral atom.

$I^- > I > I^+$

(b)   For cations with the same charge, ionic radii increase going down a column because there is an increase in the principle quantum number and the average distance from the nucleus of the outer electrons.

$Ca^{2+} > Mg^{2+} > Be^{2+}$

(c)   Fe: $[Ar]4s^2 3d^6$; Fe^{2+}: $[Ar]3d^6$; Fe^{3+}: $[Ar]3d^5$. The 4s valence electrons in Fe are on average farther from the nucleus than the 3d electrons, so Fe is larger than Fe^{2+}. Since there are five 3d orbitals, in Fe^{2+} at least one orbital must contain a pair of electrons. Removing one electron to form Fe^{3+} significantly reduces repulsion, increasing the nuclear charge experienced by each of the other d electrons and decreasing the size of the ion. $Fe > Fe^{2+} > Fe^{3+}$

7.29   The size of the red sphere decreases on reaction, so it loses one or more electrons and becomes a cation. Metals lose electrons when reacting with nonmetals, so the red sphere represents a metal. The size of the blue sphere increases on reaction, so it gains one or more electrons and becomes an anion. Nonmetals gain electrons when reacting with metals, so the blue sphere represents a nonmetal.

7.30   The order of radii is $Br^- > Br > F$, so the largest brown sphere is Br^-, the intermediate blue one is Br, and the smallest red one is F.

7.31   (a)   An isoelectronic series is a group of atoms or ions that have the same number of electrons.

(b) Ga^{3+}: Ni; Zr^{4+}: Kr; Mn^{7+}: Ar; I^-: Xe; Pb^{2+}: Hg

7.32   (a) Cl^-, K^+ (b) Mn^{2+}, Fe^{3+} (c) Sn^{2+}, Sb^{3+}

7.33   (a) Cl^-: Ar   (b) Sc^{3+}: Ar

(c) Fe^{2+}: $[Ar]3d^6$. Fe^{2+} has 24 electrons. Neutral Cr has 24 electrons, $[Ar]4s^13d^5$. Because transition metals fill the s subshell first but also lose s electrons first when they form ions, many transition metal ions do not have neutral atoms with the same electron configuration.

(d) Zn^{2+}: $[Ar]3d^{10}$; no neutral atom with same configuration [same reason as (c)].

(e) Sn^{4+}: $[Kr]4d^{10}$; no neutral atom with same electron configuration [same reason as (c)], but Sn^{4+} does have the same configuration as Cd^{2+}.

7.34   (a)   *Analyze/Plan.* Follow the logic in Sample Exercise 7.4.

Solve. Na^+ is smaller. Since F^- and Na^+ are isoelectronic, the ion with the larger nuclear charge, Na^+, has the smaller radius.

(b)   *Analyze/Plan.* The electron configuration of the ions is [Ne] or $[He]2s^22p^6$. The ions have either 10 core electrons or 2 core electrons. Apply Equation 7.1 to both cases and check the result.

Solve. F^-: $Z = 9$. For 10 core electrons, $Z_{eff} = 9 - 10 = -1$. While we might be able to interpret a negative value for Z_{eff}, positive values will be easier to compare; we will assume a He core of 2 electrons.
F^-, $Z = 9$. $Z_{eff} = 9 - 2 = 7$. Na^+: $Z_{eff} = 11 - 2 = 9$

(c)   *Analyze/Plan.* The electron of interest has $n = 2$. There are 7 other $n = 2$ electrons, and two $n = 1$ electrons.
Solve. $S = 0.35(7) + 0.85(2) + 1(0) = 4.15$
F^-: $Z_{eff} = 9 - 4.15 = 4.85$. Na^+: $Z_{eff} = 11 - 4.15 = 6.85$

(d)   For isoelectronic ions (without d electrons), the electron configurations and therefore shielding values (S) are the same. Only the nuclear charge changes. So, as nuclear charge (Z) increases, effective nuclear charge (Z_{eff}) increases and ionic radius decreases.

7.35   (a) K^+ (larger Z) is smaller.

(b) Cl^- and K^+: $[Ne]3s^23p^6$. 10 core electrons
Cl^-, $Z = 17$. $Z_{eff} = 17 - 10 = 7$
K^+, $Z = 19$. $Z_{eff} = 19 - 10 = 9$

(c)   Valence electron, $n = 3$; 7 other $n = 3$ electrons; eight $n = 2$ electrons; two $n = 1$ electrons. $S = 0.35(7) + 0.85(8) + 1(2) = 11.25$
Cl^-: $Z_{eff} = 17 - 11.25 = 5.75$. K^+: $Z_{eff} = 19 - 11.25 = 7.75$

(d)   For isoelectronic ions (without d electrons), the electron configurations and therefore shielding values (S) are the same. Only the nuclear charge changes. So, as nuclear charge (Z) increases, effective nuclear charge (Z_{eff}) increases and ionic radius decreases.

7.36   *Analyze/Plan.* Use relative location on periodic chart and trends in atomic and ionic radii to establish the order.

(a) $Cl < S < K$

(b) $K^+ < Cl^- < S^{2-}$

(c)   Even though K has the largest Z value, the *n*-value of the outer electron is larger than the *n*-value of valence electrons in S and Cl so K atoms are largest. When the 4s electron is removed, K^+ is isoelectronic with Cl^- and S^{2-}. The larger Z value causes the 3p electrons in K^+ to experience the largest effective nuclear charge and K^+ is the smallest ion.

7.37   (a) $Se < Se^{2-} < Te^{2-}$ (b) $Co^{3+} < Fe^{3+} < Fe^{2+}$ (c) $Ti^{4+} < Sc^{3+} < Ca$ (d) $Be^{2+} < Na^+ < Ne$

7.38   Make a table of d(measured), d(ionic radii), d(covalent radii), as well as differences between measured and estimated values. The estimated distances are just the sum of the various ionic radii from Figure 7.7 and covalent radii from Figure 7.6. All distances and differences are given in Å. Use these values to judge accuracy in parts (b) and (c).

(a)

	d(meas)	(a) d(ion)	(b) Δ(ion – meas)	(c) d(cov)	(c) Δ(cov – meas)
Li–F	2.01	2.09	0.08	2.05	0.04
Na–Cl	2.82	2.83	0.01	2.53	–0.29
K–Br	3.30	3.34	0.04	3.10	–0.20
Rb–I	3.67	3.72	0.05	3.44	–0.23

(b)   The agreement between measured distances in specific ionic compounds and predicted distances based on ionic radii is not perfect. Differences for Na–Cl and K–Br are within the 0.04 Å experimental error, while those for Li–F and Rb–I are not. Ionic radii are averages compiled from distances in many ionic compounds containing the ion in question. The sum of these average radii may not give an exact match for the distance in any specific compound, but it will give good distance estimates for many ionic compounds. While ionic radii provide a good estimate of ion-ion distances, the estimates are not the same as experimental values.

(c)   Distance estimates from bonding atomic radii are not as accurate as those from ionic radii, except for Li–F. This indicates that bonding in NaCl, KBr, and RbI is more accurately described as ionic, rather than covalent. The measured bond distance for LiF is midway between the two estimates, indicating that the bonding in LiF could have significant covalent character. The details of these two models will be discussed in Chapter 8.

Ionization Energies; Electron Affinities (sections 7.4 and 7.5)

7.39 $Al(g) \rightarrow Al^+(g) + 1e^-$; $Al^+(g) \rightarrow Al^{2+}(g) + 1e^-$; $Al^{2+}(g) \rightarrow Al^{3+}(g) + 1e^-$

The process for the first ionization energy requires the least amount of energy. When an electron is removed from an atom or ion, electrostatic repulsions are reduced, Z_{eff} increases, and the energy required to remove the next electron increases. This rationale is confirmed by the ionization energies listed in Table 7.2.

7.40   (a) $Pb(g) \rightarrow Pb^+(g) + 1e^-$; $Pb^+(g) \rightarrow Pb^{2+}(g) + 1e^-$

(b) $Zr^{3+}(g) \rightarrow Zr^{4+}(g) + 1e^-$

7.41   (a)   False. Ionization energies are always positive quantities.

(b)   False. F has a greater first ionization energy than O, because Z_{eff} for F is greater than Z_{eff} for O.

(c)   True.

7.42   (a)   The effective nuclear charges of Li and Na are similar, but the outer electron in Li has a smaller *n*-value and is closer to the nucleus than the outer electron in Na. More energy is needed to overcome the greater attraction of the Li electron for the nucleus.

(b)   Sc: [Ar] $4s^2 3d^1$; Ti: [Ar] $4s^2 3d^2$. The fourth ionization of titanium involves removing a 3d valence electron, while the fourth ionization of Sc requires removing a 3p electron from the [Ar] core. The effective nuclear charges experienced by the two 3d electrons in Ti are much more similar than the effective nuclear charges of a 3d valence electron and a 3p core electron in Sc. Thus, the difference between the third and fourth ionization energies of Sc is much larger.

(c)   The electron configuration of Li^+ is $1s^2$ or [He] and that of Be^+ is [He]$2s^1$. Be^+ has one more valence electron to lose while Li^+ has the stable noble gas configuration of He. It requires much more energy to remove a 1s core electron close to the nucleus of Li^+ than a 2s valence electron farther from the nucleus of Be^+.

7.43   (a)   In general, the smaller the atom, the larger its first ionization energy.

(b)   According to Figure 7.9, He has the largest and Cs the smallest first ionization energy of the nonradioactive elements.

7.44   (a)   Moving from F to I in group 7A, first ionization energies decrease and atomic radii increase. The greater the atomic radius, the smaller the electrostatic attraction of an outer electron for the nucleus and the smaller the ionization energy of the element.

(b)   First ionization energies increase slightly going from K to Kr and atomic sizes decrease. As valence electrons are drawn closer to the nucleus (atom size decreases), it requires more energy to completely remove them from the atom (first ionization energy increases). Each trend has a discontinuity at Ga, owing to the increased shielding of the 4p electrons by the filled 3d subshell.

7.45   *Plan.* Use periodic trends in first ionization energy.   *Solve.*

(a) Cl   (b) Ca   (c) K   (d) Ge   (e) Sn

7.46   Greater distance of valence electrons from the nucleus predicts lower first ionization energy in all the pairs of elements below. Z_{eff} decreases moving left along a row, but increases slightly moving down column. These trends are not (solely) predictive of first ionization energy for the pairs of elements in this exercise.

(a)   Ba. Recall that transition metals like Ti lose *ns* electrons first when forming ions. The 6s valence electrons in Ba are farther from the nucleus and have a smaller first ionization energy than the 4s electrons of Ti.

(b)   Ag. Recall that transition elements lose *ns* electrons first when forming ions. The 5s valence electron of Ag is farther from the nucleus and has a lower first ionization energy than the 4s valence electron of Cu.

(c)   Ge. The 4p valence electrons in Ge have a smaller first ionization energy than the 3p valence electrons in Cl. Going from Cl to Ge, the decrease in Z_{eff} moving four places to the left may more than compensate for the small increase moving one place down. If so, the trends in Z_{eff} and distance of valence electrons from the nucleus cooperate to produce the (significantly) lower first ionization energy for Ge.

(d)   Pb. The 6p valence electrons in Pb are farther from the nucleus and have a smaller first ionization energy than the 5p valence electrons in Sb, despite the build-up in nuclear charge (Z) associated with filling the 4f subshell between Sb and Pb.

7.47   *Plan.* Follow the logic of Sample Exercise 7.7.   *Solve.*

(a) Fe^{2+}: $[Ar]3d^6$ (b) Hg^{2+}: $[Xe]4f^{14}5d^{10}$

(c) Mn^{2+}: $[Ar]3d^5$ (d) Pt^{2+}: $[Xe]4f^{14}5d^8$

(e) P^{3-}: $[Ne]3s^23p^6$

7.48   (a) Cr^{3+}: $[Ar]3d^3$

(b) N^{3-}: $[He]2s^22p^6 = [Ne]$, noble-gas configuration

(c) Sc^{3+}: $[Ar]$, noble-gas configuration   (d) Cu^{2+}: $[Ar]3d^9$

(e) Tl^+: $[Xe]6s^24f^{14}5d^{10}$ (f) Au^+: $[Xe]4f^{14}5d^{10}$

7.49   *Plan.* Focus on transition metals, which have d electrons in their outer shell. Use Figure 7.14 to find representative oxidations states for transition metals. Note that, by definition, metals lose electrons to form positive ions.

Solve. Elements in group 10 and beyond have at least 8 d electrons. Of these, the group 10 metals all form 2+ ions with the electron configuration nd^8. Of the elements in groups 11 and 12, only Au adopts a sufficiently high positive charge to form an ion with the configuration nd^8. (Other possibilities not listed on Figure 7.14 exist.)

Ni^{2+}: $[Ar]3d^8$; Pd^{2+}: $[Kr]4d^8$; Pt^{2+}: $[Xe]4f^{14}5d^8$; Au^{3+}: $[Xe]4f^{14}5d^8$

7.50   The 2+ ions of group 8 metals and the 3+ ions of group 9 metals have the electrons configuration nd^6. (Other possibilities not listed on Figure 7.14 exist.)

Fe^{2+}: $[Ar]3d^6$; Ru^{2+}: $[Kr]4d^6$; Os^{2+}: $[Xe]6s^24f^{14}5d^6$

Co^{3+}: $[Ar]3d^6$; Rh^{3+}: $[Kr]4d^6$; Ir^{3+}: $[Xe]6s^24f^{14}5d^6$

7.51   *Analyze/Plan.* Consider the definitions of ionization energy, electron affinity and the electron configuration of Ar. *Solve.*

(a)   Argon is a noble gas, with a very stable core electron configuration. This causes the element to resist chemical change. Positive, endothermic, values for ionization energy and electron affinity mean that energy is required to either remove or add electrons. Valence electrons in Ar experience the largest Z_{eff} of any element in the third row, because the nuclear buildup is not accompanied by an increase in screening. This results in a large, positive ionization energy. When an electron is added to Ar, the n = 3 electrons become core electrons which screen the extra electrons so effectively that Ar^- has a higher energy than an Ar atom and a free electron. This results in a large positive electron affinity.

(b)   The units of electron affinity are kJ/mol.

7.52   No. The process described by electron affinity can be written as: $A + 1e^- \rightarrow A^-$
If ΔE for this process is negative, it means that the energy of A^- is lower than the total energy of A plus the energy of a free electron. If electron affinity is negative, the entity that is lower in energy, or more stable, is the added electron. An electron in an atom or ion is stabilized by its attraction for the atomic nucleus and is lower in energy than a free electron.

7.53   *Analyze/Plan.* Consider the definitions of ionization energy and electron affinity, along with pertinent electron configurations. *Solve.*

Electron affinity : $Br(g)$ $+ 1e^- \rightarrow$ $Br^-(g)$
$[Ar]4s^2 3d^{10} 4p^5$ $[Ar]4s^2 3d^{10} 4p^6$

When a Br atom gains an electron, the Br^- ion adopts the stable electron configuration of Kr. Since the electron is added to the same 4p subshell as other outer electrons, it experiences essentially the same attraction for the nucleus. Thus, the energy of the Br^- ion is lower than the total energy of a Br atom and an isolated electron, and electron affinity is negative.

Electron affinity : $Kr(g)$ $+ 1e^- \rightarrow$ $Kr^-(g)$
$[Ar]4s^2 3d^{10} 4p^6$ $[Ar]4s^2 3d^{10} 4p^6 5s^1$

Energy is required to add an electron to a Kr atom; Kr^- has a higher energy than the isolated Kr atom and free electron. In Kr^- the added electron would have to occupy the higher energy 5s orbital; a 5s electron is farther from the nucleus and effectively shielded by the spherical Kr core and is not stabilized by the nucleus.

7.54   Ionization energy of F^-: $F^-(g) \rightarrow F(g) + 1e^-$

Electron affinity of F: $F(g) + 1e^- \rightarrow F^-(g)$

The two processes are the reverse of each other. The energies are equal in magnitude but opposite in sign. $I_1 (F^-) = -E (F)$

7.55   *Analyze/Plan.* Consider the definitions of ionization energy and electron affinity, along with the appropriate electron configurations. *Solve.*

(a)   Ionization energy of Ne: $Ne(g)$ $\rightarrow$ $Ne^+(g) + 1e^-$
$[He]2s^2 2p^6$ $[He]2s^2 2p^5$

Electron affinity of F: $F(g) + 1e^- \rightarrow F^-(g)$
$[He]2s^2 2p^5$ $[He]2s^2 2p^6$

(b)   The I_1 of Ne is positive, while E_1 of F is negative. All ionization energies are positive.

(c)   One process is apparently the reverse of the other, with one important difference. The Z (and Z_{eff}) for Ne is greater than Z (and Z_{eff}) for F^-. So we expect I_1(Ne) to be somewhat greater in magnitude and opposite in sign to E_1(F). [Repulsion effects approximately cancel; repulsion decrease upon I_1 causes smaller positive value; repulsion increase upon E_1 causes smaller negative value.]

7.56 $Mg^+(g)$ + $1e^-$ $\rightarrow$ $Mg(g)$
[Ne] $3s^1$ [Ne] $3s^2$

This process is the reverse of the first ionization of Mg. The magnitude of the energy change for this process is the same as the magnitude of the first ionization energy of Mg, 738 kJ/mol.

Properties of Metals and Nonmetals (section 7.6)

7.57   The smaller the first ionization energy of an element, the greater the metallic character of that element.

7.58   The first ionization energies are: Ag, 731 kJ/mol; Mn, 717 kJ/mol. According to Figure 7.12, we define metallic character as showing the opposite trend as ionization energy. That is, the smaller the ionization energy, the greater the metallic character. Since Mn has the smaller ionization energy, it should have the greater metallic character. (It is difficult to predict the relative metallic character of these two elements from trends. Ag is one row lower but four columns further right than Mn; these are opposing trend directions.)

7.59   *Analyze/Plan.* Use Figure 7.12, "Metals, metalloids and nonmetals", and Figure 7.14, "Representative oxidation states of the elements", to inform our discussion.

Solve. Agree. An element that commonly forms a cation is a metal. The only exception to this statement shown on Figure 7.14 is antimony, Sb, a metalloid which commonly forms cations. Although Sb is a metalloid, it is far down (in the fifth row) on the chart and likely to have significant metallic character.

7.60   Disagree. According to Figure 7.14, both Sb and Te are metalloids and commonly form ions. Sb forms cations and Te forms anions.

7.61   *Analyze/Plan.* Ionic compounds are formed by combining a metal and a nonmetal; molecular compounds are formed by two or more nonmetals. *Solve.*

Ionic: SnO_2, Al_2O_3, Li_2O, Fe_2O_3; molecular: CO_2, H_2O

Sn, Al, Li and Fe are metals; C and H are nonmetals.

7.62   Follow the logic in Sample Exercise 7.8. Scandium is a metal, so we expect Sc_2O_3 to be ionic. Metal oxides are usually basic and react with acid to form a salt and water. We choose HNO_3(aq) as the acid for our equation.

$Sc_2O_3(s) + 6HNO_3(aq) \rightarrow 2Sc(NO_3)_3(aq) + 3H_2O(l)$.

The net ionic equation is:

$Sc_2O_3(s) + 6H^+(aq) \rightarrow 2Sc^{3+}(aq) + 3H_2O(l)$

7.63 (a) When dissolved in water, an "acidic oxide" produces an acidic (pH < 7) solution. A "basic oxide" dissolved in water produces a basic (pH > 7) solution.

(b) Oxides of nonmetals are acidic. Example: $SO_3(g) + H_2O(l) \rightarrow H_2SO_4(aq)$. Oxides of metals are basic. Example: CaO (quick lime). $CaO(s) + H_2O(l) \rightarrow Ca(OH)_2(aq)$.

7.64 The more nonmetallic the central atom, the more acidic the oxide. In order of increasing acidity: $CaO < Al_2O_3 < SiO_2 < CO_2 < P_2O_5 < SO_3$

7.65 *Analyze/Plan.* Cl_2O_7 is a molecular compound formed by two nonmetallic elements. More specifically, it is a nonmetallic oxide and acidic.   *Solve.*

(a) Dichlorineheptoxide

(b) Elemental chlorine and oxygen are diatomic gases.

$2Cl_2(g) + 7O_2(g) \rightarrow 2Cl_2O_7(l)$

(c) Most nonmetallic oxides we have seen, such as CO_2 and SO_3, are gases. However, oxides with more atoms, such as $P_2O_3(l)$ and $P_2O_5(s)$, exist in other states. A boiling point of 81°C is not totally unexpected for a large molecule like Cl_2O_7.

(d) Cl_2O_7 is an acidic oxide, so it will be more reactive to base, OH^-.

$Cl_2O_7(l) + 2OH^-(aq) \rightarrow 2ClO_4^-(aq) + H_2O(l)$

(e) The oxidation state of Cl in Cl_2O_7 is +7. In this oxidation state, the electron configuration of Cl is $[He]2s^22p^6$ or $[Ne]$.

7.66 (a) $XCl_4(l) + 2H_2O(l) \rightarrow XO_2(s) + 4HCl(g)$

The second product is HCl(g).

(b) If X were a metal, both the oxide and the chloride would be high melting solids. If X were a nonmetal, XO_2 would be a nonmetallic, molecular oxide and probably gaseous, like CO_2, NO_2, and SO_2. Neither of these statements describes the properties of XO_2 and XCl_4, so X is probably a metalloid.

(c) Use the *Handbook of Chemistry* to find formulas and melting points of oxides, and formulas and boiling points of chlorides of selected metalloids.

metalloid	formula of oxide	m.p. of oxide	formula of chloride	b.p. of chloride
boron	B_2O_3	460°C	BCl_3	12°C
silicon	SiO_2	~1700°C	$SiCl_4$	58°C
germanium	GeO	710°C	$GeCl_2$	decomposes
	GeO_2	~1100°C	$GeCl_4$	84°C
arsenic	As_2O_3	315°C	$AsCl_3$	132°C
	As_2O_5	315°C		

Boron, arsenic, and, by analogy, antimony, do not fit the description of X, because the formulas of their oxides and chlorides are wrong. Silicon and germanium, in the same family, have oxides and chlorides with appropriate formulas. Both SiO_2 and GeO_2 melt above 1000°C, but the boiling point of $SiCl_4$ is much closer to that of XCl_4. Element X is silicon.

7.67   (a) $BaO(s) + H_2O(l) \rightarrow Ba(OH)_2(aq)$

(b) $FeO(s) + 2HClO_4(aq) \rightarrow Fe(ClO_4)_2(aq) + H_2O(l)$

(c) $SO_3(g) + H_2O(l) \rightarrow H_2SO_4(aq)$

(d) $CO_2(g) + 2NaOH(aq) \rightarrow Na_2CO_3(aq) + H_2O(l)$

7.68   (a) $K_2O(s) + H_2O(l) \rightarrow 2KOH(aq)$

(b) $P_2O_3(l) + 3H_2O(l) \rightarrow 2H_3PO_3(aq)$

(c) $Cr_2O_3(s) + 6HCl(aq) \rightarrow 2CrCl_3(aq) + 3H_2O(l)$

(d) $SeO_2(s) + 2KOH(aq) \rightarrow K_2SeO_3(aq) + H_2O(l)$

Group Trends in Metals and Nonmetals (sections 7.7 and 7.8)

7.69   Yes, the reactivity of a metal correlates with its first ionization energy. Since metals lose electrons when they form ions, the less energy required for this process, the more reactive the metal. However, we usually observe reactivity of metals in the solid state and ionization energy is a gas phase property, so there are differences between the two properties.

7.70   Rb: $[Kr]5s^1$, r = 2.11 Å   Ag: $[Kr]5s^1 4d^{10}$, r = 1.53 Å

The electron configurations both have a [Kr] core and a single 5s electron; Ag has a completed 4d subshell as well. The smaller radius of Ag indicates that the 5s electron in Ag experiences a much greater effective nuclear charge than the 5s electron in Rb. Ag has a much larger Z (47 vs. 37), and although the 4d electrons in Ag shield the 5s electron somewhat, the increased shielding does not compensate for the large increase in Z. Ag is much less reactive (less likely to lose an electron) because its 5s electron experiences a much larger effective nuclear charge and is more difficult to remove.

7.71   (a)   Ca and Mg are both metals; they tend to lose electrons and form cations when they react. Ca is more reactive because it has a lower ionization energy than Mg. The Ca valence electrons in the 4s orbital are less tightly held because they are farther from the nucleus than the 3s valence electrons of Mg.

(b)   K and Ca are both metals; they tend to lose electrons and form cations when they react. K is more reactive because it has the lower first ionization energy. The 4s valence electron in K is less tightly held because it has the same n value as the valence electrons of Ca and experiences smaller Z and Z_{eff}.

7.72   (a)   All alkali metals except Li form metal peroxides when they react with oxygen; the formation of a peroxide (or a superoxide) eliminates Li. The lilac-purple flame indicates that the metal is potassium (see Figure 7.21).

(b) $K_2O_2(s)$ + $2H_2O(l)$ $\rightarrow$ $H_2O_2(aq)$ + $2\,KOH(aq)$

potassium peroxide   hydrogen peroxide

$KO_2(s)$ + $2H_2O(l)$ $\rightarrow$ $H_2O_2(aq)$ + $2KOH(aq)$ + $O_2(g)$

potassium superoxide   hydrogen peroxide

Both potassium peroxide and potassium superoxide react with water to form hydrogen peroxide. The white solid could be either potassium salt.

7.73   (a) $2K(s) + Cl_2(g) \rightarrow 2KCl(s)$

(b) $SrO(s) + H_2O(l) \rightarrow Sr(OH)_2(aq)$

(c) $4Li(s) + O_2(g) \rightarrow 2Li_2O(s)$

(d) $2Na(s) + S(l) \rightarrow Na_2S(s)$

7.74   (a) $2Cs(s) + 2H_2O(l) \rightarrow 2CsOH(aq) + H_2(g)$

(b) $Sr(s) + 2H_2O(l) \rightarrow Sr(OH)_2(aq) + H_2(g)$

(c) $2Na(s) + O_2(g) \rightarrow Na_2O_2(s)$ (See Equation [7.20].)

(d) $Ca(s) + I_2(s) \rightarrow CaI_2(s)$

7.75   (a)   The reactions of the alkali metals with hydrogen and with a halogen are redox reactions. In both classes of reaction, the alkali metal loses electrons and is oxidized. Both hydrogen and the halogen gain electrons and are reduced. The product is an ionic solid, where either hydride ion, H^-, or a halide ion, X^-, is the anion and the alkali metal is the cation.

(b) $Ca(s) + F_2(g) \rightarrow CaF_2(s)$ $Ca(s) + H_2(g) \rightarrow CaH_2(s)$

Both products are ionic solids containing Ca^{2+} and the corresponding anion in a 1:2 ratio.

7.76   Metallic hydrogen, in the form of an extended solid, will be much more like the other alkali metals, which are also extended solids. "Normal" gaseous hydrogen has a smaller atomic radius and larger first ionization energy than trends would predict for the first member of the alkali metals. Metallic hydrogen would have a larger atomic radius and smaller first ionization energy than "normal" hydrogen. Owing to its smaller first ionization energy, metallic hydrogen will be more reactive than "normal" hydrogen.

7.77

	Br	**Cl**
(a)	$[Ar]4s^24p^5$	$[Ne]3s^23p^5$
(b)	-1	-1
(c)	1140 kJ/mol	1251 kJ/mol
(d)	reacts slowly to form HBr+HOBr	reacts slowly to form HCl+HOCl
(e)	-325 kJ/mol	-349 kJ/mol
(f)	1.14 Å	0.99 Å

The $n = 4$ valence electrons in Br are farther from the nucleus and less tightly held than the $n = 3$ valence electrons in Cl. Therefore, the ionization energy of Cl is greater, the electron affinity is more negative and the atomic radius is smaller.

7.78   *Plan.* Predict the physical and chemical properties of At based on the trends in properties in the halogen (7A) family. *Solve.*

     (a)   F, at the top of the column, is a diatomic gas; I, immediately above At, is a diatomic solid; the melting points of the halogens increase going down the column. At is likely to be a diatomic solid at room temperature.

     (b)   Like the other halogens, we expect it to be a nonmetal. According to Figure 7.12, there are no metalloids in row 6 of the periodic table, and At is a nonmetal. (Looking forward to Chapter 8, the most likely way for At to satisfy the octet rule is for it to gain an electron to form At^-, which makes it a nonmetal.)

     (c)   All halogens form ionic compounds with Na; they have the generic formula NaX. The compound formed by At will have the formula NaAt.

7.79   (a)   The term "inert" was dropped because it no longer described all the group 8A elements.

     (b)   In the 1960s, scientists discovered that Xe would react with substances such as F_2 and PtF_6 that have a strong tendency to remove electrons. Thus, Xe could not be categorized as an "inert" gas.

     (c)   The group is now called the noble gases.

7.80   (a)   Xe has a lower ionization energy than Ne. The valence electrons in Xe are much farther from the nucleus than those of Ne ($n = 5$ vs $n = 2$) and much less tightly held by the nucleus; they are more "willing" to be shared than those in Ne. Also, Xe has empty 5d orbitals that can help to accommodate the bonding pairs of electrons, while Ne has all its valence orbitals filled.

     (b)   In the CRC Handbook of Chemistry and Physics, 79th Edition, Xe – F bond distances in gas phase molecules are listed as: XeF_2, 1.977 Å; XeF_4, 1.94 Å; XeF_6, 1.89 Å. From Figure 7.6, he sum of atomic radii for Xe and F is (1.30 Å + 0.71 Å) = 2.01 Å. Bond lengths in specific compounds are not exactly equal to the sum of estimated atomic radii. Physical state, electronic and steric factors affect bond lengths in specific compounds.

7.81   (a) $2O_3(g) \rightarrow 3O_2(g)$

     (b) $Xe(g) + F_2(g) \rightarrow XeF_2(g)$

           $Xe(g) + 2F_2(g) \rightarrow XeF_4(s)$

           $Xe(g) + 3F_2(g) \rightarrow XeF_6(s)$

     (c) $S(s) + H_2(g) \rightarrow H_2S(g)$

     (d) $2F_2(g) + 2H_2O(l) \rightarrow 4HF(aq) + O_2(g)$

7.82   (a) $Cl_2(g) + H_2O(l) \rightarrow HCl(aq) + HOCl(aq)$

     (b) $Ba(s) + H_2(g) \rightarrow BaH_2(s)$

     (c) $2Li(s) + S(s) \rightarrow Li_2S(s)$

     (d) $Mg(s) + F_2(g) \rightarrow MgF_2(s)$

Additional Exercises

7.83   Up to $Z = 82$, there are three instances where atomic weights are reversed relative to atomic numbers: Ar and K; Co and Ni; Te and I.

   In each case, the most abundant isotope of the element with the larger atomic number (Z) has one more proton, but fewer neutrons than the element with the smaller atomic number. The smaller number of neutrons causes the element with the larger Z to have a smaller than expected atomic weight.

7.84   (a)   2s

   (b)   Slater's rules provide a method for calculating the shielding, S, and Z_{eff} experienced by a particular electron in an atom. Slater assigns a shielding value of 0.35 to electrons with the same n-value, assuming that s and p electrons shield each other to the same extent. However, since s electrons have a finite probability of being very close to the nucleus (Figure 7.3), they shield p electrons more than p electrons shield them. To account for this difference, assign a slightly larger shielding value to s electrons and a slightly samller shielding value to the p electrons. This will produce a slightly greater S and smaller Z_{eff} for p electrons than for s electrons with the same n-value.

7.85   (a)   P: [Ne]$3s^2 3p^3$. $Z_{eff} = Z - S = 15 - 10 = 5$.

   (b)   Four other $n = 3$ electrons, eight $n = 2$ electrons, two $n = 1$ electron. $S = 0.35(4) + 0.85(8) + 1(2) = 10.2$. $Z_{eff} = Z - S = 15 - 10.2 = 4.8$. The approximation in (a) and Slater's rules give very similar values for Z_{eff}.

   (c)   The 3s electrons penetrate the [Ne] core electrons (by analogy to Figure 7.3) and experience less shielding than the 3p electrons. That is, S is greater for 3p electrons, owing to the penetration of the 3s electrons, so Z – S (3p) is less than Z – S (3s).

   (d)   The 3p electrons are the outermost electrons; they experience a smaller Z_{eff} than 3s electrons and thus a smaller attraction for the nucleus, given equal n-values. The first electron lost is a 3p electron. Each 3p orbital holds one electron, so there is no preference as to which 3p electron will be lost.

7.86   If two protons were able to form a bond, they would have to overcome the electrostatic repulsion of like-charged particles. This situation occurs in atomic nuclei, where protons (and neutrons) are so close together that the strong nuclear force overcomes electrostatic repulsion. If two "bare" protons were able to bond, the bond length would be on the order of the size of atomic nuclei, 10^{-15} m.

7.87   Atomic size (bonding atomic radius) is strongly correlated to Z_{eff}, which is determined by Z and S. Moving across the representative elements, electrons added to ns or np valence orbitals do not effectively screen each other. The increase in Z is not accompanied by a similar increase in S; Z_{eff} increases and atomic size decreases. Moving across the transition elements, electrons are added to (n–1)d orbitals and become part of the core electrons, which do significantly screen the ns valence electrons. The increase in Z is accompanied by a larger increase in S for the ns valence electrons; Z_{eff} increases more slowly and atomic size decreases more slowly.

7.88   (a)   The estimated distances in the table below are the sum of the radii of the group 5A elements and H from Figure 7.6.

bonded atoms	estimated distance	measured distance
P – H	1.43	1.419
As – H	1.56	1.519
Sb – H	1.75	1.707

In general, the estimated distances are a bit longer than the measured distances. This probably shows a systematic bias in either the estimated radii or in the method of obtaining the measured values. (Recall that the radii in Figure 7.6 come from measuring many different molecules for each element, not just the bonds listed in this exercise.)

(b)   The principal quantum number of the outer electrons and thus the average distance of these electrons from the nucleus increases from P ($n = 3$) to As ($n = 4$) to Sb ($n = 5$). This causes the systematic increase in M – H distance.

7.89   (a)   The most common oxidation state of the chalcogens is –2, while that of the halogens is –1. Adding one extra electron to a neutral halogen atom fills its valence p orbitals. Adding two extra electrons to a neutral chalcogen atom fills its valence p orbitals.

(b)   The family listed has the larger value of the stated property.

atomic radii, chalcogens

ionic radii of the most common oxidation state, chalcogens

first ionization energy, halogens

second ionization energy, halogens

7.90   Y: $[Kr]5s^24d^1$, Z = 39   Zr: $[Kr]5s^24d^2$, Z = 40

La: $[Xe]6s^25d^1$, Z = 57   Hf: $[Xe]6s^24f^{14}5d^2$, Z = 72

The completed 4f subshell in Hf leads to a much larger change in Z going from Zr to Hf (72 – 40 = 32) than in going from Y to La (57 – 39 = 18). The 4f electrons in Hf do not completely shield the valence electrons, so there is also a larger increase in Z_{eff}. This larger increase in Z_{eff} going from Zr to Hf leads to a smaller increase in atomic radius than in going from Y to La.

7.91   (a) Co^{4+} is smaller.

(b) Co^{4+}, 0.67 Å < Co^{3+}, 0.75 Å < Li^+, 0.90 Å

Values from WebElements©, CN 6, high spin (for comparing equivalent ion environments)

(c)   As Li^+ ions are inserted, smaller Co^{4+} ions are reduced to larger Co^{3+} ions and the lithium colbalt electrode will expand.

(d)   "Sodium colbalt oxide" will probably not work as an electrode material, because Na^+ ions are much larger than Li^+ ions, which are larger than Co^{4+} and Co^{3+} ions. Na^+ ions would be too large to insert into the electrode without disrupting the structure of the material.

(e)   An alternative metal for a sodium version of the electrode would have redox-active ions with larger ionic radii than the Co^{4+} and Co^{3+} ions. Moving left along the fourth row of the periodic table, Fe^{3+}/Fe^{2+} and Mn^{3+}/Mn^{2+} ion couples are possibilities. Both have radii larger than Co^{4+}/Co^{3+} ions. Mn^{3+} is more redox-active than Fe^{3+} and may be a more effective electrode material.

7.92   (a) $2Sr(s) + O_2(g) \rightarrow 2SrO(s)$

(b)   Assume that the corners of the cube are at the centers of the outermost O^{2-} ions, and that the edges each pass through the center of one Sr^{2+} ion. The length of an edge is then $r(O^{2-}) + 2r(Sr^{2+}) + r(O^{2-}) = 2r(O^{2-}) + 2r(Sr^{2+}) = 2(1.32$ Å$) + 2(1.26$ Å$) = 5.16$ Å.

(c)   Density is the ratio of mass to volume.

$$d = \frac{\text{mass SrO in cube}}{\text{vol cube}} = \frac{\text{\# SrO units} \times \text{mass of SrO}}{\text{vol cube}}$$

Calculate the mass of 1 SrO unit in grams and the volume of the cube in cm^3; solve for number of SrO units.

$$\frac{103.62 \text{ g SrO}}{\text{mol}} \times \frac{1 \text{ mol SrO}}{6.022 \times 10^{23} \text{ SrO units}} = 1.7207 \times 10^{-22} = 1.721 \times 10^{-22} \text{ g/SrO unit}$$

$$V = (5.16)^3 \text{ Å}^3 \times \frac{(1 \times 10^{-8})^3 \text{ cm}^3}{\text{Å}^3} = 1.3739 \times 10^{-22} = 1.37 \times 10^{-22} \text{ cm}^3$$

$$d = \frac{\text{\# of SrO units} \times 1.7207 \times 10^{-22} \text{ g/SrO unit}}{1.3739 \times 10^{-22} \text{ cm}^3} = 5.10 \text{ g/cm}^3$$

$$\text{\# of SrO units} = 5.10 \text{ g/cm}^3 \times \frac{1.3739 \times 10^{-22} \text{ cm}^3}{1.7207 \times 10^{-22} \text{ g/SrO unit}} = 4.07 \text{ units}$$

Since the number of formula units must be an integer, there are four SrO formula units in the cube. Using average values for ionic radii to estimate the edge length probably leads to the small discrepancy.

7.93   C: $1s^2 2s^2 2p^2$. I_1 through I_4 represent loss of the 2p and 2s electrons in the outer shell of the atom. The values of I_1–I_4 increase as expected. The nuclear charge is constant, but removing each electron reduces repulsive interactions between the remaining electrons, so effective nuclear charge increases and ionization energy increases. I_5 and I_6 represent loss of the 1s core electrons. These 1s electrons are much closer to the nucleus and experience the full nuclear charge (they are not shielded), so the values of I_5 and I_6 are significantly greater than I_1–I_4. I_6 is larger than I_5 because all repulsive interactions have been eliminated.

7.94   Relative to elements in group 4A, Z_{eff} experienced by an electron added to a group 3A element is smaller, and electron affinity is less negative. Adding an electron to a neutral atom from group 5A requires pairing the electron in an already partially filled p orbital. The resulting electron-electron repulsion offsets some of the electrostatic attraction for the nucleus, and the electron affinity is not as negative as expected.

7.95   (a)   O: [He]$2s^2 2p^4$

O^{2-}: [He]$2s^2 2p^6$ = [Ne]

(b)   O^{3-}: [Ne]$3s^1$ The third electron would be added to the 3s orbital, which is farther from the nucleus and more strongly shielded by the [Ne] core. The overall attraction of this 3s electron for the O nucleus is not large enough for O^{3-} to be a stable particle.

7.96   (a)   P: [Ne] $3s^2 3p^3$; S: [Ne] $3s^2 3p^4$. In P, each 3p orbital contains a single electron, while in S one 3p orbital contains a pair of electrons. Removing an electron from S eliminates the need for electron pairing and reduces electrostatic repulsion, so the overall energy required to remove the electron is smaller than in P, even though Z is greater.

(b)   C: [He] $2s^2 2p^2$; N: [He] $2s^2 2p^3$; O: [He] $2s^2 2p^4$. An electron added to a N atom must be paired in a relatively small 2p orbital, so the additional electron-electron repulsion more than compensates for the increase in Z and the electron affinity is smaller (less exothermic) than that of C. In an O atom, one 2p orbital already contains a pair of electrons, so the additional repulsion from an extra electron is offset by the increase in Z and the electron affinity is greater (more exothermic). Note from Figure 7.11 that the electron affinity of O is only slightly more exothermic than that of C, although the value of Z has increased by 2.

(c)   O$^+$: [He] $2s^2 2p^3$; O^{2+}: [He] $2s^2 2p^2$; F: [He] $2s^2 2p^5$; F$^+$: [He] $2s^2 2p^4$. Both 'core-only' [Z_{eff} (F) = 7; Z_{eff} (O$^+$) = 6] and Slater [Z_{eff} (F) = 5.2; Z_{eff} (O$^+$) = 4.9] predict that F has a greater Z_{eff} than O$^+$. Variation in Z_{eff} does not offer a satisfactory explanation. The decrease in electron-electron repulsion going from F to F$^+$ energetically favors ionization and causes it to be less endothermic than the second ionization of O, where there is no significant decrease in repulsion.

(d)   Mn^{2+}: [Ar]$3d^5$; Mn^{3+}: [Ar] $3d^4$; Cr^{2+}: [Ar] $3d^4$; Cr^{3+}: [Ar] $3d^3$; Fe^{2+}: [Ar] $3d^6$; Fe^{3+}: [Ar] $3d^5$. The third ionization energy of Mn is expected to be larger than that of Cr because of the larger Z value of Mn. The third ionization energy of Fe is less than that of Mn because going from $3d^6$ to $3d^5$ reduces electron repulsions, making the process less endothermic than predicted by nuclear charge arguments.

7.97   (a)   The group 2B metals have complete (*n*–1)d subshells. An additional electron would occupy an *n*p subshell and be substantially shielded by both *n*s and (*n*–1)d electrons. Overall this is not a lower energy state than the neutral atom and a free electron.

(b)   Valence electrons in Group 1B elements experience a relatively large effective nuclear charge due to the buildup in Z with the filling of the (*n*–1)d subshell (and for Au, the 4f subshell.) Thus, the electron affinities are large and negative.

Group 1B elements are exceptions to the usual electron filling order and have the generic electron configuration $ns^1(n-1)d^{10}$. The additional electron would complete the ns subshell and experience repulsion with the other ns electron. Going down the group, size of the ns subshell increases and repulsion effects decrease. That is, effective nuclear charge is greater going down the group because it is less diminished by repulsion, and electron affinities become more negative.

7.98   (a)   For both H and the alkali metals, the added electron will complete an ns subshell (1s for H and ns for the alkali metals) so shielding and repulsion effects will be similar. For the halogens, the electron is added to an np subshell, so the energy change is likely to be quite different.

       (b)   True. Only He has a smaller estimated "bonding" atomic radius, and no known compounds of He exist. The electron configuration of H is $1s^1$. The single 1s electron experiences no repulsion from other electrons and feels the full unshielded nuclear charge. It is held very close to the nucleus. The outer electrons of all other elements that form compounds are shielded by a spherical inner core of electrons and are less strongly attracted to the nucleus, resulting in larger bonding atomic radii.

       (c)   Ionization is the process of removing an electron from an atom. For the alkali metals, the ns electron being removed is effectively shielded by the core electrons, so ionization energies are low. For the halogens, a significant increase in nuclear charge occurs as the np orbitals fill, and this is not offset by an increase in shielding. The relatively large effective nuclear charge experienced by np electrons of the halogens is similar to the unshielded nuclear charge experienced by the H 1s electron. Both H and the halogens have large ionization energies.

       (d)   Ionization energy of hydride: $H^-(g) \rightarrow H(g) + 1e^-$

       (e)   Electron affinity of hydroden: $H(g) + 1e^- \rightarrow H^-(g)$

       The two processes in parts (d) and (e) are the exact reverse of one another. The value for the ionization energy of hydride is equal in magnitude but opposite in sign to the electron affinity of hydrogen.

7.99   Since Xe reacts with F_2, and O_2 has approximately the same ionization energy as Xe, O_2 will probably react with F_2. Possible products would be O_2F_2, analogous to XeF_2, or OF_2.

$$O_2(g) + F_2(g) \rightarrow O_2F_2(g)$$
$$O_2(g) + 2F_2(g) \rightarrow 2OF_2(g)$$

7.100   (a)   C > Si > Ge> Sn > Pb. We know that Pb and Sn are metals, Ge and Si are metalloids and C is a nonmetal. For metals in the same family, such as the alkali metals, the lower the ionization energy, the more metallic and the lower melting. So, we guess that Pb has a lower melting point than Sn. For molecular nonmetals, such as the halogens, melting point usually increases as molecular weight increases. However, Ge, Si and C are not molecular nonmetals. (We will examine the details of bonding in these elements in Chapter 11.) By observation of physical properties, we know all three substances to be very hard solids, considering C in the form of diamond. In fact, diamond is one of the hardest known substances. If melting point is related to hardness, then diamond will be the highest melting. Assume the melting points of the Si and Ge to decrease going down the family.

(b)   From WebElements©, the melting points in °C are:

C, 3500; Si, 1414; Ge, 938.3; Sn, 231.93; Pb, 327.46

We were correct that C is the highest melting, and that Si and Ge decrease going down the family. The melting points of the metals are indeed less than those of C and the metalloids. However, Sn is lowest melting, not Pb. Perhaps this has something to do with the increase in Z and Z_{eff} due to the filling of the f orbitals, which does not impact the properties of the alkali or alkaline earth metals. From Figure 7.9, we see that the ionization energy of Pb is greater than that of Sn, so its higher melting point is not too surprising.

7.101   (a)   The pros are that Zn and Cd are in the same family, have the same electron configuration and thus similar chemical properties. The same can be said for Zn^{2+} and Cd^{2+} ions. Because of their chemical similarity, we expect Cd^{2+} to easily substitute for Zn^{2+} in flexible molecules. The main difference is that Zn^{2+}, with an ionic radius of 0.88 Å, is much smaller than Cd^{2+}, with an ionic radius of 1.09 Å. While Zn^{2+} is beneficial in living systems, Cd^{2+} is toxic. This difference in biological function could be related to the size difference, and is a definite con.

(b) Cu^+ is isoelectronic with Zn^{2+}. That is, the two ions have the same number of electrons and the same electron configurations. The ionic radius of Cu^+ is 0.91 Å, very similar to that of Zn^{2+}. We expect Cu^+ to be a reasonable substitute for Zn^{2+} in terms of chemical properties and size. Electrostatic interactions may vary, because of the difference in charges of the two ions. (All ionic radii are taken from WebElements©.)

7.102   (a)   *Plan.* Use qualitative physical (bulk) properties to narrow the range of choices, then match melting point and density to identify the specific element.   *Solve.*

Hardness varies widely in metals and nonmetals, so this information is not too useful. The relatively high density, appearance, and ductility indicate that the element is probably less metallic than copper. Focus on the block of nine main group elements centered around Sn. Pb is not a possibility because it was used as a comparison standard. The melting point of the five elements closest to Pb are:

Tl, 303.5°C; In, 156.1°C; Sn, 232°C; Sb, 630.5°C; Bi, 271.3°C

The best match is In. To confirm this identification, the density of In is 7.3 g/cm³, also a good match to properties of the unknown element.

(b)   In order to write the correct balanced equation, determine the formula of the oxide product from the mass data, assuming the unknown is In.

5.08 g oxide – 4.20 g In = 0.88 g O
4.20 g In/114.82 g/mol = 0.0366 mol In; 0.0366/0.0366 = 1
0.88 g O/16.00 g/mol = 0.0550 mol O; 0.0550/0.0366 = 1.5

Multiplying by 2 produces an integer ratio of 2 In: 3 O and a formula of In_2O_3. The balanced equation is: $4\,In(s) + 3O_2(g) \rightarrow 2\,In_2O_3(s)$

(c)   According to Figure 7.1, the element In was discovered between 1843–1886. The investigator who first recorded this data in 1822 could have been the first to discover In.

7.103   *Plan.* According to the periodic table on the inside cover of your text, element 116 is in group 6A, so element 117 will be in group 7A, the halogens. Write the electron configuration and use information from Figures 7.6, 7.9, 7.11, 7.14 and Table 7.7 along with periodic trends to estimate values for properties. Remember that element 117 is two rows below iodine, and that the increase in Z and Z_{eff} that accompanies filling of the f orbitals will decrease the size of the changes in ionization energy, electron affinity and atomic size. *Solve.*

Electron configuration:	$[Rn]7s^25f^{14}6d^{10}7p^5$
First ionization energy:	805 kJ/mol
Electron affinity:	–235 kJ/mol
Atomic size:	1.65 Å
Common oxidation state:	–1

7.104   (a)   Si and Ge are in group 4A and have 4 valence electrons. GaAs and GaP have their first element in group 3A with 3 valence electrons and their second element in group 5A with 5 valence electrons. Cd in CdS and CdSe is in group 2B and has 2 valence electrons, while S and Se are in group 6A with 6 valence electrons. In each case, the two elements in the compound semiconductor have an *average* of 4 valence electrons.

(b)   The roman numerals represent the number of valence electrons in the component elements of the compound semiconductor. CdS and CdSe are II-VI materials, while GaAs and GaP are III-V materials.

(c)   Replace Ga with In: InP, InAs, InSb; replace Se with Te: CdTe. It is problematic to replace Cd with Hg, because Hg is toxic. ZnS is ionic and an insulator, so Zn may not be a good substitute for Cd.

Integrative Exercises

7.105   (a) $\nu = c/\lambda; 1\,Hz = 1\,s^{-1}$

$$Ne: \nu = \frac{2.998 \times 10^8 \text{ m/s}}{14.610 \text{ Å}} \times \frac{1 \text{ Å}}{1 \times 10^{-10} \text{ m}} = 2.052 \times 10^{17} \text{ s}^{-1} = 2.052 \times 10^{17} \text{ Hz}$$

$$Ca: \nu = \frac{2.998 \times 10^8 \text{ m/s}}{3.358 \times 10^{-10} \text{ m}} = 8.928 \times 10^{17} \text{ Hz}$$

$$Zn: \nu = \frac{2.998 \times 10^8 \text{ m/s}}{1.435 \times 10^{-10} \text{ m}} = 20.89 \times 10^{17} \text{ Hz}$$

Zr : $\nu = \dfrac{2.998 \times 10^8 \text{ m/s}}{0.786 \times 10^{-10} \text{ m}} = 38.14 \times 10^{17} = 38.1 \times 10^{17}$ Hz

Sn : $\nu = \dfrac{2.998 \times 10^8 \text{ m/s}}{0.491 \times 10^{-10} \text{ m}} = 61.06 \times 10^{17} = 61.1 \times 10^{17}$ Hz

(b)

Element	Z	ν	$\nu^{1/2}$
Ne	10	2.052×10^{17}	4.530×10^8
Ca	20	8.928×10^{17}	9.449×10^8
Zn	30	20.89×10^{17}	14.45×10^8
Zr	40	38.14×10^{17}	19.5×10^8
Sn	50	61.06×10^{17}	24.7×10^8

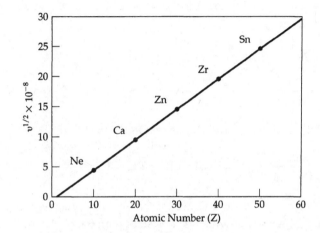

(c)   The plot in part (b) indicates that there is a linear relationship between atomic number and the square root of the frequency of the X-rays emitted by an element. Thus, elements with each integer atomic number should exist. This relationship allowed Moseley to predict the existence of elements that filled "holes" or gaps in the periodic table.

(d)   For Fe, Z = 26. From the graph, $\nu^{1/2} = 12.5 \times 10^8$, $\nu = 1.56 \times 10^{18}$ Hz.

$\lambda = c/\nu = \dfrac{2.998 \times 10^8 \text{ m/s}}{1.56 \times 10^{18} \text{ s}^{-1}} \times \dfrac{1 \text{ Å}}{1 \times 10^{-10} \text{ m}} = 1.92 \text{ Å}$

(e) $\lambda = 0.980 \text{ Å} = 0.980 \times 10^{-10}$ m

$\nu = c/\lambda = \dfrac{2.998 \times 10^8 \text{ m/s}}{0.980 \times 10^{-10} \text{ m}} = 30.6 \times 10^{17}$ Hz; $\nu^{1/2} = 17.5 \times 10^8$

From the graph, $\nu^{1/2} = 17.5 \times 10^8$, Z = 36. The element is krypton, Kr.

7.106   (a)   Li: [He]$2s^1$. Assume that the [He] core is 100% effective at shielding the 2s valence electron $Z_{eff} = Z - S \approx 3 - 2 = 1+$.

(b) The first ionization energy represents loss of the 2s electron.

ΔE = energy of free electron (n = ∞) – energy of electron in ground state (n = 2)

$\Delta E = I_1 = [-2.18 \times 10^{-18} \, J \, (Z^2/\infty^2)] - [-2/18 \times 10^{-18} \, J \, (Z^2/2^2)]$

$\Delta E = I_1 = 0 + 2.18 \times 10^{-18} \, J \, (Z^2/2^2)$

For Li, which is not a one-electron particle, let $Z = Z_{eff}$.

$\Delta E \approx 2.18 \times 10^{-18} \, J \, (+1^2/4) \approx 5.45 \times 10^{-19} \, J/atom$

(c) Change the result from part (b) to kJ/mol so it can be compared to the value in

Table 7.4. $5.45 \times 10^{-19} \, \dfrac{J}{atom} \times \dfrac{6.022 \times 10^{23} \, atom}{mol} \times \dfrac{1 \, kJ}{1000 \, J} = 328 \, kJ/mol$

The value in Table 7.4 is 520 kJ/mol. This means that our estimate for Z_{eff} was a lower limit, that the [He] core electrons do not perfectly shield the 2s electron from the nuclear charge.

(d) From Table 7.4, $I_1 = 520 \, kJ/mol$.

$\dfrac{520 \, kJ}{mol} \times \dfrac{1000 \, J}{kJ} \times \dfrac{1 \, mol}{6.022 \times 10^{23} \, atoms} = 8.6350 \times 10^{-19} \, J/atom$

Use the relationship for I_1 and Z_{eff} developed in part (b).

$Z_{eff}^2 = \dfrac{4(8.6350 \times 10^{-19} \, J)}{2.18 \times 10^{-18} \, J} = 1.5844 = 1.58; \; Z_{eff} = 1.26$

This value, $Z_{eff} = 1.26$, based on the experimental ionization energy, is greater than our estimate from part (a), which is consistent with the explanation in part (c).

7.107 (a) $E = hc/\lambda$; 1 nm = 1 × 10⁻⁹ m; 58.4 nm = 58.4 × 10⁻⁹ m;

1 eV = 96.485 kJ/mol, 1 eV - mol = 96.485 kJ

$E = \dfrac{6.626 \times 10^{-34} \, J\text{-}s \times 2.998 \times 10^8 \, m/s}{58.4 \times 10^{-9} \, m} = 3.4015 \times 10^{-18} = 3.40 \times 10^{-18} \, J/photon$

$\dfrac{3.4015 \times 10^{-18} \, J}{photon} \times \dfrac{1 \, kJ}{1000 \, J} \times \dfrac{6.022 \times 10^{23} \, photons}{mol} \times \dfrac{1 \, eV\text{-}mol}{96.485 \, kJ} = 21.230 = 21.2 \, eV$

(b) $Hg(g) \rightarrow Hg^+(g) + 1e^-$

(c) $I_1 = E_{58.4} - E_K = 21.23 \, eV - 10.75 \, eV = 10.48 = 10.5 \, eV$

$10.48 \, eV \times \dfrac{96.485 \, kJ}{1 \, eV\text{-}mol} = 1.01 \times 10^3 \, kJ/mol$

(d) From Figure 7.9, iodine (I) appears to have the ionization energy closest to that of Hg, approximately 1000 kJ/mol.

7.108   (a)   The X-ray source had an energy of 1253.6 eV. Change eV to J/photon and use the relationship $\lambda = hc/E$ to find wavelength.

$$1253.6 \text{ eV} \times \frac{96.485 \text{ kJ}}{1 \text{ eV} \cdot \text{mol}} \times \frac{1 \text{mol}}{6.0221 \times 10^{23} \text{ photons}} \times \frac{1000 \text{ J}}{1 \text{ kJ}} = 2.0085 \times 10^{-16} \text{ J/photon}$$

$$\lambda = \frac{6.6261 \times 10^{-34} \text{ J} \cdot \text{s} \times 2.9979 \times 10^{8} \text{ m/s}}{2.0085 \times 10^{-16} \text{ J}} = 9.8902 \times 10^{-10} \text{ m} = 0.98902 \text{ nm} = 9.8902 \text{ Å}$$

(b)   Express energies of Hg 4f and O 1s electrons in terms of kJ/mol for comparison with data from Figure 7.9 of the text.

$$\text{Hg 4f}: \quad 105 \text{ eV} \times \frac{96.485 \text{ kJ}}{1 \text{ eV} \cdot \text{mol}} = 10{,}131 = 1.01 \times 10^4 \text{ kJ/mol}$$

$$\text{O 1s}: \quad 531 \text{ eV} \times \frac{96.485 \text{ kJ}}{1 \text{ eV} \cdot \text{mol}} = 51{,}234 = 5.12 \times 10^4 \text{ kJ/mol}$$

By definition, the first ionization energy is the minimum energy required to remove the first electron from an atom. This first electron is the highest energy valence electron in the neutral atom. We expect the energies of valence electrons to be higher than those of core electrons, and first ionization energies to be less than the energy required to remove a lower energy core electron.

For Hg, the first ionization energy is 1007 kJ/mol, while the XPS energy of the 4f electron is 10,100 kJ/mol. The energy required to remove a 4f core electron is 10 times the energy required to remove a 6s valence electron.

For O, the first ionization energy is 1314 kJ/mol, while the XPS energy of a 1s electron is 51,200 kJ/mol. The energy required to remove a 1s core electron is 50 times that required to remove a 2p valence electron.

(c) Hg^{2+}: $[Xe]4f^{14}5d^{10}$; valence electrons are 5d

O^{2-}: $[He]2s^22p^6$ or [Ne]; valence electrons are 2p

(d)   (Recall that Slater's rules are best applied to elements that do not contain d aor f electrons.)
Hg^{2+} 5d valence: n = 5 (5s+5p+5d) has 18 e$^-$; subtract one for the electron under consideration = 17 e$^-$ with the same n value as the one under consideration.
n = 4 (4s+4p+4d+4f) has 32 e$^-$ with (n – 1); n = 3, 2, 1 have (18+8+2) = 28 e$^-$ with (n – 2) or less.

S (5d) = 0.35(17) + 0.85(32) + 1.0(28) = 61.15. Z_{eff} = Z – S = 80 – 61.15 = 18.85

Hg^{2+} 4f: The 4f electrons are not shielded by electrons with n > 4. n = 4 has (32 – 1) = 31 e$^-$; n = 3 has 18 e$^-$ with (n – 1); n = 2, 1 have 10 e$^-$ with (n – 2) or less.

S (4f) = 0.35(31) + 0.85(18) + 1.0(10) = 36.15. Z_{eff} = Z – S = 80 – 36.15 = 43.85

O^{2-} 2p valence: n = 2 has (8 – 1) = 7 e$^-$; n = 1 has 2 e$^-$.

S = 0.35(7) + 0.85(2) = 4.15; Z_{eff} = 8 – 4.15 = 3.85

7.109   (a)
$$Na(g) \rightarrow Na^+(g) + 1e^- \qquad \text{(ionization energy of Na)}$$

$$Cl(g) + 1e^- \rightarrow Cl^-(g) \qquad \text{(electron affinity of Cl)}$$

$$\overline{Na(g) + Cl(g) \rightarrow Na^+(g) + Cl^-(g)}$$

(b) $\Delta H = I_1(Na) + E_1(Cl) = +496 \text{ kJ} - 349 \text{ kJ} = +147 \text{ kJ}$, endothermic

(c)   The reaction $2Na(s) + Cl_2(g) \rightarrow 2NaCl(s)$ involves many more steps than the reaction in part (a). One important difference is the production of NaCl(s) versus NaCl(g). The condensation $NaCl(g) \rightarrow NaCl(s)$ is very exothermic and is the step that causes the reaction of the elements in their standard states to be exothermic, while the gas phase reaction is endothermic.

7.110   (a) Mg_3N_2

(b) $Mg_3N_2(s) + 3H_2O(l) \rightarrow 3MgO(s) + 2NH_3(g)$

The driving force is the production of $NH_3(g)$.

(c)   After the second heating, all the Mg is converted to MgO.

Calculate the initial mass Mg.

$$0.486 \text{ g MgO} \times \frac{24.305 \text{ g Mg}}{40.305 \text{ g MgO}} = 0.293 \text{ g Mg}$$

x = g Mg converted to MgO; y = g Mg converted to Mg_3N_2; $x = 0.293 - y$

$$\text{g MgO} = x\left(\frac{40.305 \text{ g MgO}}{24.305 \text{ g Mg}}\right); \text{g } Mg_3N_2 = y\left(\frac{100.929 \text{ g } Mg_3N_2}{72.915 \text{ g Mg}}\right)$$

$\text{g MgO} + \text{g } Mg_3N_2 = 0.470$

$$(0.293 - y)\left(\frac{40.305}{24.305}\right) + y\left(\frac{100.929}{72.915}\right) = 0.470$$

$$(0.293 - y)(1.6583) + y(1.3842) = 0.470$$

$$-1.6583 y + 1.3842 y = 0.470 - 0.48588$$

$$-0.2741 y = -0.01588 = -0.016$$

$$y = 0.05794 = 0.058 \text{ g Mg in } Mg_3N_2$$

$$\text{g } Mg_3N_2 = 0.05794 \text{ g Mg} \times \frac{100.929 \text{ g } Mg_3N_2}{72.915 \text{ g Mg}} = 0.0802 = 0.080 \text{ g } Mg_3N_2$$

$$\text{mass \% } Mg_3N_2 = \frac{0.0802 \text{ g } Mg_3N_2}{0.470 \text{ g } (MgO + Mg_3N_2)} \times 100 = 17\%$$

(The final mass % has two sig figs because the mass of Mg obtained from solving simultaneous equations has two sig figs.)

(d) $3Mg(s) + 2NH_3(g) \rightarrow Mg_3N_2(s) + 3H_2(g)$

$$6.3 \text{ g Mg} \times \frac{1 \text{ mol Mg}}{24.305 \text{ g Mg}} = 0.2592 = 0.26 \text{ mol Mg}$$

$$2.57 \text{ g NH}_3 \times \frac{1 \text{ mol NH}_3}{17.031 \text{ g NH}_3} = 0.1509 = 0.15 \text{ mol NH}_3$$

$$0.2592 \text{ mol Mg} \times \frac{2 \text{ mol NH}_3}{3 \text{ mol Mg}} = 0.1728 = 0.17 \text{ mol NH}_3$$

0.26 mol Mg requires more than the available NH_3 so NH_3 is the limiting reactant.

$$0.1509 \text{ mol NH}_3 \times \frac{3 \text{ mol H}_2}{2 \text{ mol NH}_3} \times \frac{2.016 \text{ g H}_2}{\text{mol H}_2} = 0.4563 = 0.46 \text{ g H}_2$$

(e) $\Delta H^{\circ}_{rxn} = \Delta H^{\circ}_f \text{ Mg}_3\text{N}_2(s) + 3\Delta H^{\circ}_f \text{ H}_2(g) - 3\Delta H^{\circ}_f \text{ Mg}(s) - 2\Delta H^{\circ}_f \text{ NH}_3(g)$

$= -461.08 \text{ kJ} + 3(0) - 3(0) - 2(-46.19) = -368.70 \text{ kJ}$

7.111   (a) $r_{Bi} = r_{BiBr_3} - r_{Br} = 2.63 \text{ Å} - 1.14 \text{ Å} = 1.49 \text{ Å}$

(b) $Bi_2O_3(s) + 6HBr(aq) \rightarrow 2BiBr_3(aq) + 3H_2O(l)$

(c) Bi_2O_3 is soluble in acid solutions because it act as a base and undergoes acid-base reactions like the one in part (b). It is insoluble in base because it cannot act as an acid. Thus, Bi_2O_3 is a basic oxide, the oxide of a metal. Based on the properties of its oxide, Bi is characterized as a metal.

(d)   Bi: $[Xe]6s^2 4f^{14} 5d^{10} 6p^3$. Bi has five outer electrons in the 6p and 6s subshells. If all five electrons participate in bonding, compounds such as BiF_5 are possible. Also, Bi has a large enough atomic radius (1.49 Å) and low-energy orbitals available to accommodate more than four pairs of bonding electrons.

(e)   The high ionization energy and relatively large negative electron affinity of F, coupled with its small atomic radius, make it the most electron withdrawing of the halogens. BiF_5 forms because F has the greatest tendency to attract electrons from Bi. Also, the small atomic radius of F reduces repulsions between neighboring bonded F atoms. The strong electron withdrawing properties of F are also the reason that only F compounds of Xe are known.

7.112   (a) $4KO_2(s) + 2CO_2(g) \rightarrow 2K_2CO_3(s) + 3O_2(g)$

(b)   K, +1; O, –1/2 (O_2^- is superoxide ion); C, +4; O, –2 $\rightarrow$ K, +1; C, +4; O, –2; O, 0
Oxygen (in the form of superoxide) is oxidized (to O_2) and reduced (to O^{2-}).

(c) $18.0 \text{ g CO}_2 \times \dfrac{1 \text{ mol CO}_2}{44.01 \text{ g CO}_2} \times \dfrac{4 \text{ mol KO}_2}{2 \text{ mol CO}_2} \times \dfrac{71.10 \text{ g KO}_2}{1 \text{ mol KO}_2} = 58.2 \text{ g KO}_2$

$18.0 \text{ g CO}_2 \times \dfrac{1 \text{ mol CO}_2}{44.01 \text{ g CO}_2} \times \dfrac{3 \text{ mol O}_2}{2 \text{ mol CO}_2} \times \dfrac{32.00 \text{ g O}_2}{1 \text{ mol O}_2} = 19.6 \text{ g O}_2$

8 Basic Concepts of Chemical Bonding

Visualizing Concepts

8.1 *Analyze/Plan.* Count the number of electrons in the Lewis symbol. This corresponds to the 'A'-group number of the family.   *Solve.*

(a) Group 4A or 14

(b) Group 2A or 2

(c) Group 5A or 15

(These are the appropriate groups in the s and p blocks, where Lewis symbols are most useful.)

8.2 *Analyze.* Given the size and charge of four different ions, determine their ionic bonding characteristics.

Plan. The magnitude of lattice energy is directly proportional to the charges of the two ions and inversely proportional to their separation. $E_{el} = \kappa Q_1 Q_2 / d$. Apply these concepts to A, B, X and Y.

(a) AY and BX have a 1:1 ratio of cations and anions. In an ionic compound, the total positive and negative charges must be equal. In order to form a 1:1 compound, the magnitude of positive charge on the cation must equal the magnitude of negative charge on the anion. A^{2+} combines with Y^{2-} and B^+ combines with X^- to form 1:1 compounds.

(b) AY has the larger lattice energy. The A–Y and B–X separations are nearly equal. (A is smaller than B, but X is smaller than Y, so the differences in cation and anion radii approximately cancel.) In AY, $Q_1 Q_2 = (2)(2) = 4$, while in BX, $Q_1 Q_2 = (1)(1) = 1$.

(c) BX has the smaller lattice energy. To recap the arguments in part (b), the d values in the two compounds are similar and BX has the smaller $Q_1 Q_2$, so it has the smaller lattice energy.

8.3 *Analyze.* Given a schematic "slab" of NaCl(s), where Cl^- anions are green and Na^+ cations are purple, answer questions regarding the electrostatic interactions between various ions. *Plan.* $E_{el} = \kappa Q_1 Q_2 / d$. Use geometry to estimate or calculate distances when needed. *Solve.*

(a) Purple-green interactions are attractive; these are electrostatic attractions between two oppositely charged ions. The sign of E_{el} for these interactions is negative (–). Purple-purple and green-green interactions are repulsive; these are electrostatic attractions between two ions with the same charge. The sign of E_{el} for these interactions is positive (+).

(b)   The magnitudes of the 1–5 and 3–5 interactions are equal and are larger than the magnitude of the 1–3 interaction. Since 1, 3 and 5 all have the same charge, the magnitude of their interactions depends on the distance between the ions; the shorter the distance the larger the magnitude of the interaction. The distances between any green and any purple ion are the same, d. The distance between 1 and 3 is then $2d$. The 1–5 and 3–5 distances are the hypotenuse of a right isosceles triangle and are equal. This distance is $\sqrt{2}\,d$, which is shorter than the 1–3 distance of $2d$.

(c)   The magnitude of the attractive 1–2 interaction is greater than the magnitude of the repulsive 1–5 interaction. Again, the magnitudes of the charges of the ions are equal, so the ion-ion distances determine the magnitude of the interactions. The 1–2 distance, d, is shorter than the 1–5 distance, $\sqrt{2}\,d$. The magnitude of the attractive 1–2 interaction is greater than the magnitude of the repulsive 1–5 interaction.

(d)   Since the magnitude of the attractive 1–2 interaction is greater than the magnitude of the repulsive 1–3 interaction, the overall sum of interactions in the solid is attractive. For attractive interactions, the sign of E_{el} is negative. This means that the grid (lattice) of ions in the solid has lower energy than a random collection of the same number and kinds of isolated ions; NaCl is a "stable" solid.

8.4   *Analyze/Plan.* Count the valence electrons in the orbital diagram, take ion charge into account, and find the element with this orbital electron count on the periodic table. Write the complete electron configuration for the ion.   *Solve.*

(a)   This ion has six 4d electrons. Transition metals, or d-block elements, have valence electrons in d-orbitals. Transition metal ions first lose electrons from the 5s orbital, then from 4d if required by the charge. This 2+ ion has lost two electrons from 5s, none from 4d. The transition metal with six 4d-electrons is ruthenium, Ru.

(b)   The electron configuration of Ru is $[Kr]5s^2 4d^6$. (The configuration of Ru^{2+} is $[Kr]4d^6$).

8.5   *Analyze/Plan.* This question is a "reverse" Lewis structure. Count the valence electrons shown in the Lewis structure. For each atom, assume zero formal charge and determine the number of valence electrons an unbound atom has. Name the element.   *Solve.*

A: 1 shared e^- pair = 1 valence electron + 3 unshared pairs = 7 valence electrons, F

E: 2 shared pairs = 2 valence electrons + 2 unshared pairs = 6 valence electrons, O

D: 4 shared pairs = 4 valence electrons, C

Q: 3 shared pairs = 3 valence electrons + 1 unshared pair = 5 valence electrons, N

X: 1 shared pair = 1 valence electron, no unshared pairs, H

Z: same as X, H

Check. Count the valence electrons in the Lewis structure. Does the number correspond to the molecular formula CH_2ONF? 12 e^- pair in the Lewis structure. $CH_2ONF = 4 + 2 + 6 + 5 + 7 = 24\ e^-$, 12 e^- pair. The molecular formula we derived matches the Lewis structure.

8.6 (a) HNO$_2$, 18 valence e$^-$, 9 e$^-$ pairs   NO$_2^-$, 18 valence e$^-$, 9 e$^-$ pairs

$$\text{H-}\overset{..}{\underset{..}{\text{O}}}\text{-N=}\overset{..}{\underset{..}{\text{O}}}$$ $$\left[\text{:}\overset{..}{\underset{..}{\text{O}}}\text{-N=}\overset{..}{\underset{..}{\text{O}}}\right]^-$$

(b) The formal charge on N is zero, in both species.

(c) NO$_2^-$ is expected to exhibit resonance; the double bond can be drawn to either oxygen atom. An alternate resonance structure for HNO$_2$ can be drawn, but it has nonzero formal charges on the oxygen atoms. This structure is less likely than the one shown above.

(d) Assuming that the structure shown above is the main contributor to the structure of HNO$_2$, the N=O bond length in HNO$_2$ will be shorter than the N-O lengths in NO$_2^-$. Because there are two equivalent resonance structures for NO$_2^-$, the N-O lengths are approximately an average of N-O single and double bond lengths. These are longer than the full N=O double bond in HNO$_2$.

8.7 *Analyze/Plan.* Since there are no unshared pairs in the molecule, we use single bonds to H to complete the octet of each C atom. For the same pair of bonded atoms, the greater the bond order, the shorter and stronger the bond.   *Solve.*

(a) Moving from left to right along the molecule, the first C needs two H atoms, the second needs one, the third needs none, and the fourth needs one. The complete molecule is:

$$\begin{array}{ccccccc} & \text{H} & & \text{H} & & & \\ & | & 1 & | & 2 & 3 & \\ \text{H} - & \text{C} = & \text{C} - & \text{C} \equiv & \text{C} - \text{H} \end{array}$$

(b) In order of increasing bond length: 3 < 1 < 2

(c) In order of increasing bond enthalpy (strength): 2 < 1 < 3

8.8 *Analyze/Plan.* Given an oxyanion of the type XO$_4^{n-}$, find the identity of X from elements in the third period. Use the generic Lewis structure to determine the identity of X, and to draw the ion-specific Lewis structures. Use the definition of formal charge, [# of valence electrons − # of nonbonding electrons − (# bonding electrons/2)], to draw Lewis structures where X has a formal charge of zero. *Solve.*

(a) According to the generic Lewis structure, each anion has 12 nonbonding and 4 bonding electron pairs, for a total of 32 electrons. Of these 32 electrons, the 4 O atoms contribute (4 × 6) = 24, and the overall negative charges contribute 1, 2 or 3. # X electrons = 32 − 24 − n.

For n = 1−, X has (32 − 24 −1) = 7 valence electrons. X is Cl, and the ion is ClO$_4^-$.

For n = 2−, X has (32 − 24 − 2) = 6 valence electrons. X is S, and the ion is SO$_4^{2-}$.

For n = 3−, X has (32 − 24 − 3) = 5 valence electrons. X is P, and the ion is PO$_4^{3-}$.

Check. The identity of the ions is confirmed in Table 2.5.

(b) In the generic Lewis structure, X has 0 nonbonding electrons and (8/2) = 4 bonding electrons. Differences in formal charge are due to difference in the number of valence electrons on X.

For PO$_4^{3-}$, formal charge of P is (5 − 4) = +1.

For SO$_4^{2-}$, formal charge of S is (6 − 4) = +2.

For ClO$_4^-$, formal charge of Cl is (7 − 4) = +3.

(c)   In order to reduce the formal charge of X to zero, X must have more bonding electrons. This is accomplished by changing the appropriate number of lone pairs on O to multiple bonds between X and O.

$$\left[\begin{array}{c} :O: \\ \| \\ :\ddot{O}-P-\ddot{O}: \\ | \\ :\underset{\cdot\cdot}{O}: \end{array}\right]^{3-} \quad \left[\begin{array}{c} :O: \\ \| \\ :\ddot{O}-S-\ddot{O}: \\ \| \\ :O: \end{array}\right]^{2-} \quad \left[\begin{array}{c} :O: \\ \| \\ \ddot{O}=\overset{\cdot\cdot}{Cl}-\ddot{O}: \\ | \\ :\underset{\cdot\cdot}{O}: \end{array}\right]^{-}$$

Lewis Symbols (section 8.1)

8.9   (a)   Valence electrons are those that take part in chemical bonding, those in the outermost electron shell of the atom. This usually means the electrons beyond the core noble-gas configuration of the atom, although it is sometimes only the outer shell electrons.

(b)   N: $[He]\,2s^2\,2p^3$
       $\underbrace{\qquad\qquad}$ A nitrogen atom has 5 valence electrons.
       Valence electrons

(c) $1s^2 2s^2 2p^6 \quad 3s^2 3p^2$ The atom (Si) has 4 valence electrons.
       $\underbrace{\qquad\quad}_{[Ne]}\underbrace{\qquad}_{valence\ electrons}$

8.10   (a)   Atoms will gain, lose, or share electrons to achieve the nearest noble-gas electron configuration. Except for H and He, this corresponds to eight electrons in the valence shell, thus the term octet rule.

(b)   S: $[Ne]3s^2 3p^4$ A sulfur atom has six valence electrons, so it must gain two electrons to achieve an octet.

(c) $1s^2 2s^2 2p^3 = [He]2s^2 2p^3$ The atom (N) has five valence electrons and must gain three electrons to achieve an octet.

8.11   Si: $1s^2 2s^2 2p^6 3s^2 3p^2$. The 3s and 3p electrons are valence electrons; the 1s, 2s and 2p electrons are nonvalence or core electrons. Valence electrons are involved in chemical bonding, while nonvalence or core electrons are not.

8.12   (a)   Ti: $[Ar]4s^2 3d^2$. Ti has four (4) valence electrons. These valence electrons are available for chemical bonding, while core electons do not participate in chemical bonding.

(b)   Hf: $[Xe]6s^2 4f^{14} 5d^2$

(c)   If Hf and Ti both behave as if they have four (4) valence electrons, the 6s and 5d orbitals in Hf behave as valence orbitals and the 4f behaves as a core orbital. This is reasonable because 4f is complete and 4f electrons are, on average, closer to the nucleus than 5d or 6s electrons.

8.13   (a) $\cdot\overset{\cdot}{Al}\cdot$ (b) $:\overset{\cdot\cdot}{Br}:$ (c) $:\overset{\cdot\cdot}{Ar}:$ (d) $\overset{\cdot}{Sr}$

8.14   (a) $K\cdot$ (b) $\cdot\overset{\cdot}{As}\cdot$ (c) $\left[:Sn\right]^{2+}$ (d) $\left[:\overset{\cdot\cdot}{N}:\right]^{3-}$

Ionic Bonding

8.15 $\mathrm{Mg}\cdot \; + \; :\overset{\cdot\cdot}{\underset{\cdot\cdot}{O}}: \longrightarrow \mathrm{Mg}^{2+} + \left[:\overset{\cdot\cdot}{\underset{\cdot\cdot}{O}}:\right]^{2-}$

8.16 $\mathrm{Ca}\cdot \; + \; \cdot\overset{\cdot\cdot}{\underset{\cdot\cdot}{F}}: \; + \; \cdot\overset{\cdot\cdot}{\underset{\cdot\cdot}{F}}: \longrightarrow \mathrm{Ca}^{2+} \; + \; 2\left[:\overset{\cdot\cdot}{\underset{\cdot\cdot}{F}}:\right]$

8.17   (a) AlF_3 (b) K_2S (c) Y_2O_3 (d) Mg_3N_2

8.18   (a) BaF_2 (b) $CsCl$ (c) Li_3N (d) Al_2O_3

8.19   (a) Sr^{2+}: $[Ar]4s^2 3d^{10}4p^6 = [Kr]$, noble-gas configuration

       (b) Ti^{2+}: $[Ar]3d^2$

       (c) Se^{2-}: $[Ar]4s^2 3d^{10}4p^6 = [Kr]$, noble-gas configuration

       (d) Ni^{2+}: $[Ar]3d^8$

       (e) Br^-: $[Ar]4s^2 3d^{10}4p^6 = [Kr]$, noble-gas configuration

       (f) Mn^{3+}: $[Ar]3d^4$

8.20   (a) Cd^{2+}: $[Kr]4d^{10}$

       (b) P^{3-}: $[Ne]3s^2 3p^6 = [Ar]$, noble-gas configuration

       (c) Zr^{4+}: $[Kr]$, noble-gas configuration

       (d) Ru^{3+}: $[Kr]4d^5$

       (e) As^{3-}: $[Ar]4s^2 3d^{10}4p^6 = [Kr]$, noble-gas configuration

       (f) Ag^+: $[Kr]4d^{10}$

8.21   (a)   *Lattice energy* is the energy required to totally separate one mole of solid ionic compound into its gaseous ions.

       (b)   The magnitude of the lattice energy depends on the magnitudes of the charges of the two ions, their radii, and the arrangement of ions in the lattice. The main factor is the charges, because the radii of ions do not vary over a wide range.

8.22   (a)   NaCl, 788 kJ/mol; KF, 808 kJ/mol

          The two factors that affect lattice energies are ionic charge and radius. The ionic charges, 1+ and 1–, are the same in the two compounds. Since lattice energy is inversely proportional to the ion separation (d), we expect the compound with the smaller lattice energy, NaCl, to have the larger ion separation. That is, the K–F distance should be shorter than the Na–Cl distance.

       (b)   Na–Cl, 1.16 Å + 1.67 Å = 2.83 Å

          K–F, 1.52 Å + 1.19 Å = 2.71 Å

          This estimate of the relative ion separations agrees with the estimate from lattice energies. Ionic radii indicate that the K–F distance is shorter than the Na–Cl distance.

8.23   KF, 808 kJ/mol; CaO, 3414 kJ/mol; ScN, 7547 kJ/mol

The sizes of the ions vary as follows: $Sc^{3+} < Ca^{2+} < K^+$ and $F^- < O^{2-} < N^{3-}$. Therefore, the inter-ionic distances are similar. According to Coulomb's law for compounds with similar ionic separations, the lattice energies should be related as the product of the charges of the ions. The lattice energies above are approximately related as (1)(1): (2)(2): (3)(3) or 1:4:9. Slight variations are due to the small differences in ionic separations.

8.24   (a)   According to Equation 8.4, electrostatic attraction increases with increasing charges of the ions and decreases with increasing radius of the ions. Thus, lattice energy (i) increases as the charges of the ions increase and (ii) decreases as the sizes of the ions increase.

           (b)   KI < LiBr < MgS < GaN. Lattice energy increases as the charges on the ions increase. The ions in KI and LiBr all have 1+ and 1– charges. K^+ is larger than Li^+, and I^- is larger than Br^-. The ion separation is larger in KI, so it has the smaller lattice energy.

8.25   Since the ionic charges are the same in the two compounds, the K–Br and Cs–Cl separations must be approximately equal. Since the radii are related as $Cs^+ > K^+$ and $Br^- > Cl^-$, the difference between Cs^+ and K^+ must be approximately equal to the difference between Br^- and Cl^-. This is somewhat surprising, since K^+ and Cs^+ are two rows apart and Cl^- and Br^- are only one row apart.

8.26   (a)   The ions have 1+ and 1– charges in all three compounds. In NaCl the cationic and anionic radii are smaller than in the other two compounds, so it has the largest lattice energy. In RbBr and CsBr, the anion is the same, but the Cs cation is larger, so CsBr has the smaller lattice energy.

           (b)   In BaO, the magnitude of the charges of both ions is 2; in KF, the magnitudes are 1. Charge considerations alone predict that BaO will have the higher lattice energy. The distance effect is less clear; O^{2-} and F^- are isoelectronic, so F^-, with the larger Z, has a slightly smaller radius. Ba^{2+} is two rows lower on the periodic table than K^+, but it has a greater positive charge, so the radii are probably similar. In any case, the ionic separations in the two compounds are not very different, and the charge effect dominates.

           (c)   In SrO, the ions have 2+ and 2– charges. In $SrCl_2$ the Cl^- anions have 1– charges, so SrO has the larger lattice energy. Also, O^{2-} has a substantially smaller ionic radius than Cl^-, so distance effects also predict that SrO will have the larger lattice energy.

8.27   Equation 8.4 predicts that as the oppositely charged ions approach each other, the energy of interaction will be large and negative. This more than compensates for the energy required to form Ca^{2+} and O^{2-} from the neutral atoms (see Figure 8.5 for the formation of NaCl).

8.28 $Ba(s) \rightarrow Ba(g)$; $Ba(g) \rightarrow Ba^+(g) + 1e^-$; $Ba^+(g) \rightarrow Ba^{2+}(g) + 1e^-$;

$I_2(s) \rightarrow 2I(g)$; $2I(g) + 2e^- \rightarrow 2I^-(g)$, exothermic;

$Ba^{2+}(g) + 2I^-(g) \rightarrow BaI_2(s)$, exothermic

8.29 $RbCl(s) \rightarrow Rb^+(g) + Cl^-(g)$ ΔH (lattice energy) = ?

By analogy to NaCl, Figure 8.5, the lattice energy is

$$\Delta H_{latt} = -\Delta H_f^\circ \, RbCl(s) + \Delta H_f^\circ \, Rb(g) + \Delta H_f^\circ \, Cl(g) + I_1 \, (Rb) + E \, (Cl)$$
$$= -(-430.5 \text{ kJ}) + 85.8 \text{ kJ} + 121.7 \text{ kJ} + 403 \text{ kJ} + (-349 \text{ kJ}) = +692 \text{ kJ/mol}$$

This value is smaller than that for NaCl (+788 kJ/mol) because Rb^+ has a larger ionic radius than Na^+. This means that the value of d in the denominator of Equation 8.4 is larger for RbCl, and the potential energy of the electrostatic attraction is smaller.

8.30 (a) $MgCl_2$, 2326 kJ; $SrCl_2$, 2127 kJ. Since the ionic radius of Ca^{2+} is greater than that of Mg^{2+}, but less than that of Sr^{2+}, the ion separation (d) in $CaCl_2$ will be intermediate as well. We expect the lattice energy of $CaCl_2$ to be in the range 2200-2250 kJ.

(b) By analogy to Figure 8.5:

$$\Delta H_{latt} = -\Delta H_f^\circ \, CaCl_2 + \Delta H_f^\circ \, Ca(g) + 2\Delta H_f^\circ \, Cl(g) + I_1 \, (Ca) + I_2 \, (Ca) + 2E \, (Cl)$$
$$= -(-795.8 \text{ kJ}) + 179.3 \text{ kJ} + 2(121.7 \text{ kJ}) + 590 \text{ kJ} + 1145 \text{ kJ} + 2(-349 \text{ kJ}) = +2256 \text{ kJ}$$

This value is near the range predicted in part (a).

Covalent Bonding, Electronegativity, and Bond Polarity (sections 8.3 and 8.4)

8.31 (a) A *covalent bond* is the bond formed when two atoms share one or more pairs of electrons.

(b) Any simple compound whose component atoms are nonmetals, such as H_2, SO_2, and CCl_4, are molecular and have covalent bonds between atoms.

(c) Covalent because it is a gas even below room temperature.

8.32 K and Ar. K is an active metal with one valence electron. It is most likely to achieve an octet by losing this single electron and to participate in ionic bonding. Ar has a stable octet of valence electrons; it is not likely to form chemical bonds of any type.

8.33 *Analyze/Plan.* Follow the logic in Sample Exercise 8.3.   *Solve.*

Check. Each pair of shared electrons in $SiCl_4$ is shown as a line; each atom is surrounded by an octet of electrons.

8.34

8.35 (a)

(b) A double bond is required because there are not enough electrons to satisfy the octet rule with single bonds and unshared pairs.

(c)   The greater the number of shared electron pairs between two atoms, the shorter the distance between the atoms. If O_2 has a double bond, the O–O distance will be shorter than the O–O single bond distance.

8.36   (a)   The H atoms must be terminal because H can form only one bond.

14 e⁻, 7 e⁻ pairs

H—Ö—Ö—H

(b)   From Solution 8.35, O_2 has a double bond. The O–O bond in H_2O_2 is a single bond, and thus longer than the O–O double bond in O_2.

8.37   (a)   *Electronegativity* is the ability of an atom in a molecule (a bonded atom) to attract electrons to itself.

(b)   The range of electronegativities on the Pauling scale is 0.7–4.0.

(c)   Fluorine, F, is the most electronegative element.

(d)   Cesium, Cs, is the least electronegative element that is not radioactive.

8.38   (a)   The electronegativity of the elements increases going from left to right across a row of the periodic table.

(b)   Electronegativity decreases going down a family of the periodic table.

(c)   Generally, the trends in electronegativity are the same as those in ionization energy and opposite those in electron affinity. That is, the more positive the ionization energy and the more negative the electron affinity (ignoring a few exceptions), the greater the electronegativity of an element.

8.39   *Plan.* Electronegativity increases going up and to the right in the periodic table.
        Solve.

(a)   Mg   (b) S   (c) C   (d) As

Check. The electronegativity values in Figure 8.7 confirm these selections.

8.40   Electronegativity increases going up and to the right in the periodic table.

(a)   O   (b) Al   (c) Cl   (d) F

8.41   The bonds in (a), (c) and (d) are polar because the atoms involved differ in electronegativity. The more electronegative element in each polar bond is:

(a) F   (c) O   (d) I

8.42   The more different the electronegativity values of the two elements, the more polar the bond.

(a)   O–F < C–F < Be–F. This order is clear from the periodic trend.

(b)   S–Br < C–P < O–Cl. Refer to the electronegativity values in Figure 8.7 to confirm the order of bond polarity. The 3 pairs of elements all have the same positional relationship on the periodic table. The more electronegative element is one row above and one column to the left of the less electronegative element. This leads us to conclude that ΔEN is similar for the 3 bonds, which is confirmed by values in Figure 8.7. The most polar bond, O–Cl, involves the most electronegative element, O. Generally, the largest electronegativity differences tend to be between row 2 and row 3 elements. The 2 bonds in this exercise involving elements in row 2 and row 3 do have slightly greater ΔEN than the S–Br bond, between elements in rows 3 and 4.

(c)   C–S < N–O < B–F. You might predict that N–O is least polar since the elements are adjacent on the table. However, the big decrease going from the second row to the third means that the electronegativity of S is not only less than that of O, but essentially the same as that of C. C–S is the least polar.

8.43   (a)   *Analyze/Plan.* Q is the charge at either end of the dipole. $Q = \mu/r$. The values for HBr are $\mu = 0.82$ D and $r = 1.41$ Å. Change Å to m and use the definition of debyes and the charge of an electron to calculate effective charge in units of *e*. *Solve.*

$$Q = \frac{\mu}{r} = \frac{0.82\,D}{1.41\,\text{Å}} \times \frac{1\,\text{Å}}{1 \times 10^{-10}\,m} \times \frac{3.34 \times 10^{-30}\,C\text{-}m}{1\,D} \times \frac{1\,e}{1.60 \times 10^{-19}\,C} = 0.12\,e$$

(b)   From Sample Exercise 8.5, the effective charges on H and Cl in the HCl molecule are +0.178 *e* and –0.178 *e*, respectively. From part (a), the effective charges on H and Br are +0.12 *e* and –0.12 *e*. HBr has a smaller dipole moment and longer bond length than HCl; these properties both contribute to the smaller charge separation in HBr.

8.44   (a)   The more electronegative element, Br, will have a stronger attraction for the shared electrons and adopt a partial negative charge.

(b)   Q is the charge at either end of the dipole.

$$Q = \frac{\mu}{r} = \frac{1.21\,D}{2.49\,\text{Å}} \times \frac{1\,\text{Å}}{1 \times 10^{-10}\,m} \times \frac{3.34 \times 10^{-30}\,C\text{-}m}{1\,D} \times \frac{1\,e}{1.60 \times 10^{-19}\,C} = 0.1014 = 0.101\,e$$

The charges on I and Br are 0.101 *e*.

8.45   *Analyze/Plan.* Generally, compounds formed by a metal and a nonmetal are described as ionic, while compounds formed from two or more nonmetals are covalent. However, substances with metals in a high oxidation state often have properties of molecular compounds. In this exercise we know that one substance in each pair is molecular and one is ionic; we may need to distinguish by comparison. *Solve.*

(a) SiF_4, metalloid and nonmetal, molecular, silicon tetrafluoride.

       LaF_3, metal and nonmetal, ionic, lanthanum(III) fluoride

(b) $FeCl_2$, metal and nonmetal, ionic, iron(II) chloride

       $ReCl_6$, metal in high oxidation state, Re(VI), molecular, rhenium hexachloride

(c) $PbCl_4$, metal and nonmetal, Pb(IV) is relatively high oxidation state, molecular (by contrast with RbCl, which is definitely ionic), lead tetrachloride

       RbCl, metal and nonmetal, ionic, rubidium chloride

8.46   Generally, compounds formed by a metal and a nonmetal are described as ionic, while compounds formed from two or more nonmetals are covalent. However, substances with metals in a high oxidation states often have properties of molecular compounds.

(a) $TiCl_4$, metal and nonmetal, Ti(IV) is a relatively high oxidation state, molecular (by contrast with CaF_2, which is definitely ionic), titanium tetrachloride

        CaF_2, metal and nonmetal, ionic, calcium fluoride

(b) ClF_3, two nonmetals, molecular, chlorine trifluoride

        VF_3, metal and nonmetal, ionic, vanadium(III) fluoride

(c) $SbCl_5$, metalloid and nonmetal, molecular, antimony pentachloride

        AlF_3, metal and nonmetal, ionic, aluminum fluroide

Lewis Structures; Resonance Structures (sections 8.5 and 8.6)

8.47   *Analyze.* Counting the **correct number of valence electrons** is the foundation of every Lewis structure.   *Plan/Solve.*

(a)   Count valence electrons: $4 + (4 \times 1) = 8$ e⁻, 4 e⁻ pairs. Follow the procedure in Sample Exercise 8.6.

$$\begin{array}{c} H \\ | \\ H-Si-H \\ | \\ H \end{array}$$

(b)   Valence electrons: $4 + 6 = 10$ e⁻, 5 e⁻ pairs

$$:C\equiv O:$$

(c)   Valence electrons: $[6 + (2 \times 7)] = 20$ e⁻, 10 e⁻ pairs

$$:\ddot{F}-\ddot{S}-\ddot{F}:$$

    i.   Place the S atom in the middle and connect each F atom with a single bond; this requires 2 e⁻ pairs.

    ii.   Complete the octets of the F atoms with nonbonded pairs of electrons; this requires an additional 6 e⁻ pairs.

    iii.   The remaining 2 e⁻ pairs complete the octet of the central S atom.

(d)   (Draw the structure that obeys the octet rule, for now.) 32 valence e⁻, 16 e⁻ pairs

$$\begin{array}{c} :\ddot{O}: \\ | \\ :\ddot{O}-S-\ddot{O}-H \\ | \\ :O: \\ | \\ H \end{array}$$

(e)   Follow Sample Exercise 8.8. 20 valence e⁻, 10 e⁻ pairs

$$\left[:\ddot{O}-\ddot{C}l-\ddot{O}:\right]^{-}$$

(f)   14 valence e⁻, 7 e⁻ pairs

$$H-\ddot{N}-\ddot{O}-H$$
$$\begin{array}{c} | \\ H \end{array}$$

Check. In each molecule, bonding e⁻ pairs are shown as lines, and each atom is surrounded by an octet of electrons (duet for H).

8.48   (a)   12 valence e⁻, 6 e⁻ pairs

(b)   14 valence e⁻, 7 e⁻ pairs

(c)   50 valence e⁻, 25 e⁻ pairs

(The Lewis structure that obeys the octet rule)

(d)   26 valence e⁻, 13 e⁻ pairs

(e)   26 valence e⁻, 13 e⁻ pairs

(The Lewis structure that obeys they octet rule)

(f)   10 e⁻, 5 e⁻ pairs

8.49   (a)   *Formal charge* is the charge on each atom in a molecule, assuming all atoms have the same electronegativity.

(b)   Formal charges are not actual charges. They are a bookkeeping system that assumes perfect covalency, one extreme for the possible electron distribution in a molecule.

(c)   The other extreme is represented by oxidation numbers, a bookkeeping system which assumes that the more electronegative element holds all electrons in a bond. The true electron distribution is some composite of the two extremes.

8.50   (a)   26 e⁻, 13 e⁻ pairs

The octet rule is satisfied for all atoms in the structure.

(b)   F is more electronegative than P. Assuming F atoms hold all shared electrons, the oxidation number of each F is –1. The oxidation number of P is +3.

(c)   Assuming perfect sharing, the formal charges on all F and P atoms are 0.

(d)   The oxidation number on P is +3; the formal charge is 0. These represent extremes in the possible electron distribution, not the best picture. By virtue of their greater electronegativity, the F atoms carry a partial negative charge, and the P atom a partial positive charge.

8.51   *Analyze/Plan.* Draw the correct Lewis structure: count valence electrons in each atom, total valence electrons and electron pairs in the molecule or ion; connect bonded atoms with a line, place the remaining e⁻ pairs as needed, in nonbonded pairs or multiple bonds, so that each atom is surrounded by an octet (or duet for H). Calculate formal charges: assign electrons to individual atoms [nonbonding e^- + 1/2 (bonding e^-)]; formal charge = valence electrons – assigned electrons. Assign oxidation numbers, assuming that the more electronegative element holds all electrons in a bond.

Solve. Formal charges are shown near the atoms, oxidation numbers (ox. #) are listed below the structures.

(a)   16 e^-, 8 e^- pairs

$$\ddot{\text{O}}{=}\text{C}{=}\ddot{\text{S}}$$
     0   0   0

ox. #: O, –2; C, +4; S, –2

(b)   26 valence e^-, 13 e^- pairs

$$\overset{-1}{:\ddot{\text{O}}:}$$
$$0 \; :\ddot{\text{C}}\text{l}{-}\overset{|}{\underset{+1}{\text{S}}}{-}\ddot{\text{C}}\text{l}: \; 0$$

ox #: S, +4; Cl, –1; O, –2

(c)   26 valence e^-, 13 e^- pairs

$$\left[\begin{array}{c} \overset{-1}{:\ddot{\text{O}}:} \\ | \\ -1 \; :\ddot{\text{O}}{-}\underset{+2}{\text{Br}}{-}\ddot{\text{O}}: \; -1 \end{array} \right]^{1-}$$

ox. #: Br, +5; O, –2

(d)   20 valence e^-, 10 e^- pairs

$$0 \; \text{H}{-}\ddot{\text{O}}{-}\ddot{\text{C}}\text{l}{-}\ddot{\text{O}}: \; -1$$
          0   +1

ox. #: Cl, +3; H, +1; O, –2

Check. Each atom is surrounded by an octet (or duet) and the sum of the formal charges and oxidation numbers is the charge on the particle.

8.52   Formal charges are given near the atoms, oxidation numbers are listed below the structures.

(a)   18 e^-, 9 e^- pairs

$$:\ddot{\text{O}}{-}\ddot{\text{S}}{=}\ddot{\text{O}}$$
   –1   +1   0

ox. #: S, +4; O, –2

(b)   24 e^-, 12 e^- pairs

$$-1 \; :\ddot{\text{O}}{-}\overset{+2}{\underset{|}{\text{S}}}{=}\ddot{\text{O}} \; 0$$
$$\underset{-1}{:\ddot{\text{O}}:}$$

ox. #: S, +6; O, –2

(c)   26 e^-, 13 e^- pairs

$$\left[-1 \; :\ddot{\text{O}}{-}\overset{+1}{\underset{|}{\ddot{\text{S}}}}{-}\ddot{\text{O}}: \; -1 \atop \underset{-1}{:\ddot{\text{O}}:} \right]^{2-}$$

ox. #: S, +4; O, –2

(d) $SO_2 < SO_3 < SO_3^{2-}$

Double bonds are shorter than single bonds. SO_2 has two resonance structures with alternating single and double bonds, for an approximate average "one-and-a-half" bond. SO_3 has three resonance structures with one double and two single bonds, for an approximately, "one-and-a-third" bond. SO_3^{2-} has all single bonds. The order of increasing bond length is the order of decreasing bond type.

SO_2 (1.5) $< SO_3$ (1.3) $< SO_3^{2-}$ (1.0).

8.53   (a)   *Plan.* Count valence electrons, draw all possible correct Lewis structures, taking note of alternate placements for multiple bonds.   *Solve.*

18 e⁻, 9 e⁻ pairs

$$\left[\ddot{\text{O}}=\ddot{\text{N}}-\ddot{\ddot{\text{O}}}\text{:}\right]^{-} \longleftrightarrow \left[\text{:}\ddot{\ddot{\text{O}}}-\ddot{\text{N}}=\ddot{\text{O}}\right]^{-}$$

Check. The octet rule is satisfied.

(b)   *Plan.* Isoelectronic species have the same number of valence electrons and the same electron configuration.   *Solve.*

A single O atom has 6 valence electrons, so the neutral ozone molecule O_3 is isoelectronic with NO_2^-.

$$\ddot{\text{O}}=\ddot{\text{O}}-\ddot{\ddot{\text{O}}}\text{:} \longleftrightarrow \text{:}\ddot{\ddot{\text{O}}}-\ddot{\text{O}}=\ddot{\text{O}}$$

Check. The octet rule is satisfied.

(c)   Since each N–O bond has partial double bond character, the N–O bond length in NO_2^- should be shorter than N–O single bonds but longer than N=O double bonds.

8.54   (a)   18 e⁻, 9 e⁻ pairs

$$\left[\begin{array}{c}\text{:}\ddot{\text{O}}\text{:}\\ | \\ \text{H}-\text{C}=\ddot{\ddot{\text{O}}}\end{array}\right]^{1-} \longleftrightarrow \left[\begin{array}{c}\text{:O:}\\ \| \\ \text{H}-\text{C}-\ddot{\ddot{\text{O}}}\text{:}\end{array}\right]^{1-}$$

(b)   Yes, resonance structures are required to describe the structure.

(c)   The Lewis structure of CO_2 (16 e⁻, 8 e⁻ pairs) is

$$\ddot{\text{O}}=\text{C}=\ddot{\text{O}}$$

In CO_2 the C–O bonds are full double bonds with two shared pairs of electrons. In HCO_2^- the two resonance structures indicate that the C–O bonds have partial, but not full double bond character. The C–O bond lengths in formate will be longer than those in CO_2.

8.55   *Plan/Solve.* The Lewis structures are as follows:

5 e⁻ pairs   8 e⁻ pairs

$$\ddot{\text{O}}=\text{C}=\ddot{\text{O}}$$

$$\text{:C}\equiv\text{O:}$$

12 e⁻ pairs

$$\left[\begin{array}{c}\text{:}\ddot{\text{O}}\text{:}\\ | \\ \text{C}\\ \diagup\;\;\diagdown\\ \text{:}\ddot{\text{O}}\quad\quad\ddot{\text{O}}\text{:}\end{array}\right]^{2-} \left[\begin{array}{c}\text{:}\ddot{\text{O}}\text{:}\\ | \\ \text{C}\\ \diagup\;\;\diagdown\\ \text{:}\ddot{\text{O}}=\quad\quad\ddot{\text{O}}\text{:}\end{array}\right]^{2-} \left[\begin{array}{c}\text{:O:}\\ \| \\ \text{C}\\ \diagup\;\;\diagdown\\ \text{:}\ddot{\text{O}}\quad\quad\ddot{\text{O}}\text{:}\end{array}\right]^{2-}$$

The more pairs of electrons shared by two atoms, the shorter the bond between the atoms. The average number of electron pairs shared by C and O in the three species is 3 for CO, 2 for CO_2, and 1.33 for CO_3^{2-}. This is also the order of increasing bond length: $CO < CO_2 < CO_3^{2-}$.

8.56   The Lewis structures are as follows:

5 e⁻ pairs   9 e⁻ pairs

$[:N\equiv O:]^+$

12 e⁻ pairs

The average number of electron pairs in the N–O bond is 3.0 for NO^+, 1.5 for NO_2^-, and 1.33 for NO_3^-. The more electron pairs shared between two atoms, the shorter the bond. Thus the N–O bond lengths vary in the order $NO^+ < NO_2^- < NO_3^-$.

8.57   (a)   Two equally valid Lewis structures can be drawn for benzene.

                 Each structure consists of alternating single and double C–C bonds; a particular bond is single in one structure and double in the other. The concept of resonance dictates that the true description of bonding is some hybrid or blend of the two Lewis structures. The most obvious blend of these two resonance structures is a molecule with six equivalent C–C bonds, each with some but not total double-bond character. If the molecule has six equivalent C–C bonds, the lengths of these bonds should be equal.

                 (b)   The resonance model described in (a) has six equivalent C–C bonds, each with some double bond character. That is, more than one pair but less than two pairs of electrons is involved in each C–C bond. This model predicts a uniform C–C bond length that is shorter than a single bond but longer than a double bond.

8.58   (a)

                 (b)   The resonance model of this molecule has bonds that are neither single nor double, but somewhere in between. This results in bond lengths that are intermediate between C–C single and C=C double bond lengths.

                 (c)

Exceptions to the Octet Rule (section 8.7)

8.59 (a) The *octet rule* states that atoms will gain, lose, or share electrons until they are surrounded by eight valence electrons.

(b) The octet rule applies to both ionic and covalent compounds, with some exceptions. In ionic compounds, the cation has lost electrons to achieve an octet and the anion has gained electrons to achieve an octet. For example, in $MgCl_2$, Mg loses 2 e$^-$ to become Mg^{2+} with the electron configuration of Ne. Each Cl atom gains one electron to form Cl^- with the electron configuration of Ar. In covalent compounds, such as CCl_4, atoms share electrons in order to surround themselves with an octet.

8.60 Carbon, in group 4A, needs to form four single bonds to achieve an octet, as in CH_4. Nitrogen, in group 5A, needs to form three, as in NH_3. If G = group number and n = the number of single bonds, G + n = 8 is a general relationship for the representative non-metals.

Check: O as in H_2O (G = 6A) + (n = 2 bonds) = 8

8.61 No chlorine oxide will obey the octet rule. Oxygen has six valence electrons, an even number. Any number of oxygen atoms in the molecule will result in an even number of valence electrons from oxygen. Chlorine has seven valence electrons, an odd number. For neutral chlorine oxide molecules, the total number of valence electrons will be an (odd + even) sum, which is always an odd number. A molecule with an odd number of valence electrons cannot obey the octet rule.

8.62 In the third period, atoms have the space and available orbitals to accommodate extra electrons. Since atomic radius increases going down a family, elements in the third period and beyond are less subject to destabilization from additional electron-electron repulsions. Also, the third shell contains d orbitals that are relatively close in energy to 3s and 3p orbitals (the ones that accommodate the octet) and provide an allowed energy state for the extra electrons.

8.63 (a) 26 e$^-$, 13 e$^-$ pairs

$$\left[:\overset{..}{\underset{..}{O}} - \overset{..}{\underset{|}{S}} - \overset{..}{\underset{..}{O}}: \right]^{2-}$$
$$\underset{:\overset{..}{O}:}{}$$

Other resonance structures with one, two, or three double bonds can be drawn. While a structure with three double bonds minimizes formal charges, all structures with double bonds violate the octet rule. The octet rule vs formal charge debate is ongoing.

(b) 6 e$^-$, 3 e$^-$ pairs

$$H - \underset{|}{Al} - H$$
$$H$$

6 electrons around Al; impossible to satisfy octet rule with only 6 valence electrons.

(c)   16 e⁻, 8 e⁻ pairs

$$\left[:N\equiv N-\ddot{N}:\right]^{-} \longleftrightarrow \left[:\ddot{N}-N\equiv N:\right]^{-} \longleftrightarrow \left[:\ddot{N}=N=\ddot{N}:\right]^{-}$$

3 resonance structures; all obey octet rule.

(d)   20 e⁻, 10 e⁻ pairs

$$:\overset{..}{\underset{..}{Cl}}-\overset{\overset{\displaystyle :\overset{..}{Cl}:}{|}}{\underset{\underset{\displaystyle H}{|}}{C}}-H$$

Obeys octet rule.

(e)   40 e⁻, 20 e⁻ pairs

$$:\overset{..}{F}-\overset{\overset{\displaystyle :\overset{..}{F}:}{|}}{\underset{\underset{\displaystyle :\overset{..}{F}:}{|}}{Sb}}\overset{\diagup \overset{..}{F}:}{\diagdown \overset{..}{F}:}$$

Does not obey octet rule; 10 e⁻ around central Sb

8.64   (a)   11 e⁻, 5.5 e⁻ pairs

$$\overset{.}{\underset{.}{N}}=\overset{..}{\underset{.}{O}}$$

Does not obey the octet rule.

(b)   24 e⁻, 12 e⁻ pairs

$$:\overset{..}{\underset{..}{F}}-\overset{\underset{\displaystyle \overset{|}{:\overset{..}{F}:}}{}}{B}-\overset{..}{\underset{..}{F}}:$$

Does not obey the octet rule.

(c)   22 e⁻, 11 e⁻ pairs

$$\left[:\overset{..}{\underset{..}{Cl}}-\overset{..}{\underset{..}{I}}-\overset{..}{\underset{..}{Cl}}:\right]^{1-}$$

Does not obey the octet rule.

(d)   32 e⁻, 16 e⁻ pairs

$$:\overset{..}{\underset{..}{Br}}-\overset{\overset{\displaystyle :\overset{..}{Br}:}{|}}{\underset{\underset{\displaystyle :\overset{..}{Br}:}{|}}{P}}-\overset{..}{\underset{..}{O}}: \qquad :\overset{..}{\underset{..}{Br}}-\overset{\overset{\displaystyle :\overset{..}{Br}:}{|}}{\underset{\underset{\displaystyle :\overset{..}{Br}:}{|}}{P}}=\overset{..}{\underset{.}{O}}$$

The structure on the left obeys the octet rule, while the one on the right minimizes formal charges but does not obey the octet rule.

(e)   36 e⁻, 18 e⁻ pairs

$$:\overset{..}{F}-\overset{\overset{\displaystyle :\overset{..}{F}:}{|}}{\underset{\underset{\displaystyle :\overset{..}{F}:}{|\cdot}}{Xe}}-\overset{..}{F}: \qquad \text{Does not obey the octet rule.}$$

8.65   (a)   16 e⁻, 8 e⁻ pairs

:C̈l—Be—C̈l:

This structure violates the octet rule; Be has only 4 e⁻ around it.

(b)   C̈l=Be=C̈l ⟷ :C̈l—Be≡Cl: ⟷ :Cl≡Be—C̈l:

(c)   The formal charges on each of the atoms in the four resonance structures are:

:C̈l—Be—C̈l: C̈l=Be=C̈l   :C̈l—Be≡Cl: :Cl≡Be—C̈l:
  0   0   0   +1   −2 +1   0   −2   +2   +2   −2   0

Formal charges are minimized on the structure that violates the octet rule; this form is probably dominant.

8.66   (a)   26 e⁻, 13 e⁻ pairs

```
     +3                    +2                    +1                    0
-1 :Ö—Xe—Ö: -1     -1 :Ö—Xe—Ö: -1      0 Ö=Xe=Ö 0        0 Ö=Xe=Ö 0
       |                    ||                    |                    ||
      :O:                  :O:                   :O:                  :O:
       -1                    0                    -1                    0
```

(b)   Yes, the structure with no double bonds obeys the octet rule for all atoms.

(c)   The structure with one double bond has 3 resonance structures (3 possible positions for the double bond), as does the structure with two double and one single bond (3 possible positions for the single bond). The total number of resonance structures is then 8.

(d)   The structure with 3 double bonds minimizes formal charges on all atoms.

8.67   26 e⁻, 13 e⁻ pairs

```
    0  +1  -1  ⎤1-          0   0   0  ⎤1-          0  -1   0  ⎤1-
 H—Ö—S̈—Ö:    ⎥          H—Ö—S̈=Ö     ⎥          H—Ö—S̈=Ö     ⎥
       |        ⎥                |        ⎥                ||        ⎥
      :O:       ⎥               :O:       ⎥               :O:       ⎥
       -1       ⎦                -1       ⎦                0        ⎦
```

Three resonance structures for HSO_3^- are shown above. Because we are dealing with an ion with a 1− charge, the sum of the formal charges of the atoms will be −1. That is, no correct Lewis structure will have all atoms with zero formal charge. The structure with no double bonds obeys the octet rule for all atoms, but does not lead to minimum formal charge. The structures with one and two double bonds both minimize formal charge but do not obey the octet rule. Of these two, the structure with one double bond is preferred because the formal charge is localized on the more electronegative oxygen atom.

8.68   (a)   32 e⁻, 16 e⁻ pairs   (b)

(c)   With no restrictions on the size of the 'expanded' octet around P, there are many structures that neither obey the octet rule nor minimize formal charge. A fairly extreme example is shown below.

Bond Enthalpies (section 8.8)

8.69   *Analyze.* Given: structural formulas. Find: enthalpy of reaction.

Plan. Count the number and kinds of bonds that are broken and formed by the reaction. Use bond enthalpies from Table 8.4 and Equation 8.12 to calculate the overall enthalpy of reaction, ΔH.   *Solve.*

(a) $\Delta H = 2D(O-H) + D(O-O) + 4D(C-H) + D(C=C)$

$-2D(O-H) - 2D(O-C) - 4D(C-H) - D(C-C)$

$\Delta H = D(O-O) + D(C=C) - 2D(O-C) - D(C-C)$

$= 146 + 614 - 2(358) - 348 = -304 \text{ kJ}$

(b) $\Delta H = 5D(C-H) + D(C \equiv N) + D(C=C) - 5D(C-H) - D(C \equiv N) - 2D(C-C)$

$= D(C=C) - 2D(C-C) = 614 - 2(348) = -82 \text{ kJ}$

(c) $\Delta H = 6D(N-Cl) - 3D(Cl-Cl) - D(N \equiv N)$

$= 6(200) - 3(242) - 941 = -467 \text{ kJ}$

8.70   (a) $\Delta H = 3D(C-Br) + D(C-H) + D(Cl-Cl) - 3D(C-Br) - D(C-Cl) - D(H-Cl)$

$= D(C-H) + D(Cl-Cl) - D(C-Cl) - D(H-Cl)$

$\Delta H = 413 + 242 - 328 - 431 = -104 \text{ kJ}$

(b) $\Delta H = 4D(C-H) + 2D(C-S) + 2D(S-H) + D(C-C) + 2D(H-Br)$

$-4D(S-H) - D(C-C) - 2D(C-Br) - 4D(C-H)$

$= 2D(C-S) + 2D(H-Br) - 2D(S-H) - 2D(C-Br)$

$\Delta H = 2(259) + 2(366) - 2(339) - 2(276) = 20 \text{ kJ}$

211

(c) $\Delta H = 4D(N-H) + D(N-N) + D(Cl-Cl) - 4D(N-H) - 2D(N-Cl)$

           $= D(N-N) + D(Cl-Cl) - 2D(N-Cl)$

      $\Delta H = 163 + 242 - 2(200) = 5 \text{ kJ}$

8.71   *Plan.* Draw structural formulas so bonds can be visualized. Then use Table 8.4 and Equation 8.12.   *Solve.*

(a)

     $\Delta H = 8D(C-H) + D(O=O) - 6D(C-H) - 2D(C-O) - 2D(O-H)$

       $= 2D(C-H) + D(O=O) - 2D(C-O) - 2D(O-H)$

       $= 2(413) + (495) - 2(358) - 2(463) = -321 \text{ kJ}$

(b)   H-H   +   Br-Br $\rightarrow$ 2 H-Br

     $\Delta H = D(H-H) + D(Br-Br) - 2D(H-Br)$

       $= (436) + (193) - 2(366) = -103 \text{ kJ}$

(c) $2 \text{ H-O-O-H} \rightarrow 2 \text{ H-O-H} + O = O$

     $\Delta H = 4D(O-H) + 2D(O-O) - 4D(O-H) - D(O=O)$

     $\Delta H = 2D(O-O) - D(O=O) = 2(146) - (495) = -203 \text{ kJ}$

8.72   *Plan.* Draw structural formulas when needed.   *Solve.*

(a)

     $\Delta H = D(C=O) + 2D(C-H) + D(H-Cl) - 3D(C-H) - D(C-O) - D(O-Cl)$

     $\Delta H = D(C=O) + D(H-Cl) - D(C-H) - D(C-O) - D(O-Cl)$

       $= (799) + (431) - (413) - (358) - (203) = 256 \text{ kJ}$

(b) $\text{H-O-O-H} + C \equiv O \rightarrow \text{H-H} + O=C=O$

     $\Delta H = D(O-O) + 2D(O-H) + D(C \equiv O) - D(H-H) - 2D(C=O)$

       $= 146 + 2(463) + 1072 - (436) - 2(799) = 110 \text{ kJ}$

(c)

$$\Delta H = 3D(C=C) + 12D(C-H) - 12D(C-H) - 6D(C-C)$$

$$\Delta H = 3D(C=C) - 6D(C-C)$$

$$\Delta H = 3(614) - 6(348) = -246 \text{ kJ}$$

8.73   *Plan.* Draw structural formulas so bonds can be visualized. Then use Table 8.4 and Equation 8.12.   *Solve.*

(a) $:N\equiv N: + 3\ H{-}H \longrightarrow 2\ H{-}\overset{\cdot\cdot}{N}{-}H$ with H below N

$$\Delta H = D(N \equiv N) + 3D(H{-}H) - 6(N{-}H) = 941 \text{ kJ} + 3(436 \text{ kJ}) - 6(391 \text{ kJ})$$

$$= -97 \text{ kJ}/2 \text{ mol NH}_3; \text{ exothermic}$$

(b)   *Plan.* Use Equation 5.31 to calculate ΔH_{rxn} from ΔH_f° values.

$\Delta H_{rxn}^\circ = \Sigma n\ \Delta H_f^\circ \text{ (products)} - \Sigma n\ \Delta H_f^\circ \text{ (reactants)}.$ $\Delta H_f^\circ \text{ NH}_3(g) = -46.19 \text{ kJ}.$
Solve.

$$\Delta H_{rxn}^\circ = 2\ \Delta H_f^\circ \text{ NH}_3(g) - 3\ \Delta H_f^\circ \text{ H}_2(g) - \Delta H_f^\circ \text{ N}_2(g)$$
$$\Delta H_{rxn}^\circ = 2(-46.19) - 3(0) - 0 = -92.38 \text{ kJ}/2 \text{ mol NH}_3$$

The ΔH calculated from bond enthalpies is slightly more exothermic (more negative) than that obtained using ΔH_f° values.

8.74   (a) $\overset{H}{\underset{H}{>}}C=C\overset{H}{\underset{H}{<}} + H{-}H \longrightarrow H{-}\overset{H\ H}{\underset{H\ H}{C{-}C}}{-}H$

$$\Delta H = 4D(C-H) + D(C=C) + D(H-H) - 6D(C-H) - D(C-C)$$

$$= D(C=C) + D(H-H) - 2D(C-H) - D(C-C)$$

$$\Delta H = 614 + 436 - 2(413) - 348 = -124 \text{ kJ}$$

(b) $\Delta H^\circ = \Delta H_f^\circ \text{ C}_2\text{H}_6(g) - \Delta H_f^\circ \text{ C}_2\text{H}_4(g) - \Delta H_f^\circ \text{ H}_2(g)$

$$= -84.68 - 52.30 - 0 = -136.98 \text{ kJ}$$

The values of ΔH for the reaction differ because the bond enthalpies used in part (a) are average values that can differ from one compound to another. For example, the exact enthalpy of a C–H bond in C_2H_4 is probably not equal to the enthalpy of a C–H bond in C_2H_6. Thus, reaction enthalpies calculated from average bond enthalpies are estimates. On the other hand, standard enthalpies of formation are measured quantities and should lead to accurate reaction enthalpies. The advantage of average bond enthalpies is that they can be used for reactions where no measured enthalpies of formation are available.

8.75   The average Ti–Cl bond enthalpy is just the average of the four values listed. 430 kJ/mol.

8.76   (a)   (i) $C + 2 \, F\text{—}F \longrightarrow F\text{—}\overset{\displaystyle F}{\underset{\displaystyle F}{C}}\text{—}F$

$\Delta H = 2D(F\text{-}F) - 4D(C\text{-}F) = 2(155) - 4(485) = -1630 \text{ kJ}$

(ii) $C\equiv O + 3 \, F\text{—}F \longrightarrow F\text{—}\overset{\displaystyle F}{\underset{\displaystyle F}{C}}\text{—}F + F\text{—}O\text{—}F$

$\Delta H = D(C\equiv O) + 3D(F\text{-}F) - 4D(C\text{-}F) - 2D(O\text{-}F)$

$= 1072 + 3(155) - 4(485) - 2(190) = -783 \text{ kJ}$

(iii) $O\!=\!C\!=\!O + 4 \, (F\text{—}F) \longrightarrow F\text{—}\overset{\displaystyle F}{\underset{\displaystyle F}{C}}\text{—}F + 2 \, F\text{—}O\text{—}F$

$\Delta H = 2D(C\!=\!O) + 4D(F\text{-}F) - 4D(C\text{-}F) - 4D(O\text{-}F)$

$= 2(799) + 4(155) - 4(485) - 4(190) = -482 \text{ kJ}$

Reaction (i) is most exothermic.

(b)   The more oxygen atoms bound to carbon, the less exothermic the reaction in this series.

Additional Exercises

8.77   Six nonradioactive elements in the periodic table have Lewis symbols with single dots. Yes, they are in the same family, assuming H is placed with the alkali metals, as it is on the inside cover of the text. This is because the Lewis symbol represents the number of valence electrons of an element, and all elements in the same family have the same number of valence electrons. By definition of a family, all elements with the same Lewis symbol must be in the same family.

8.78 $E = kQ_1Q_2/d; \quad k = 8.99 \times 10^9 \text{ J-m/C}^2$

(a) $Na^+, Br^-: \; E = \dfrac{-8.99 \times 10^9 \text{ J-m}}{C^2} \times \dfrac{(1 \times 1.60 \times 10^{-19} \text{ C})^2}{(1.16 + 1.82) \times 10^{-10} \text{ m}} = -7.7230 \times 10^{-19}$

$= -7.72 \times 10^{-19} \text{ J}$

The sign of E is negative because one of the interacting ions is an anion; this is an attractive interaction.

On a molar basis: $-7.723 \times 10^{-19} \times 6.022 \times 10^{23} = -4.65 \times 10^5 \text{ J} = -465 \text{ kJ}$

(b) $Rb^+, Br^-: E = \dfrac{-8.99 \times 10^9 \text{ J-m}}{C^2} \times \dfrac{(1 \times 1.60 \times 10^{-19} \text{ C})^2}{(1.66 + 1.82) \times 10^{-10} \text{ m}} = -6.61 \times 10^{-19} \text{ J}$

On a molar basis: $-3.98 \times 10^5 \text{ J} = -398 \text{ kJ}$

(c) $Sr^{2+}, S^{2-}: E = \dfrac{-8.99 \times 10^9 \text{ J-m}}{C^2} \times \dfrac{(2 \times 1.60 \times 10^{-19} \text{ C})^2}{(1.32 + 1.70) \times 10^{-10} \text{ m}} = -3.05 \times 10^{-18} \text{ J}$

On a molar basis: $-1.84 \times 10^6 \text{ J} = -1.84 \times 10^3 \text{ kJ}$

8.79   (a)   Lattice energy is proportional to Q_1Q_2/d. For each of these compounds, Q_1Q_2 is the same. The anion H^- is present in each compound, but the ionic radius of the cation increases going from Be to Ba. Thus, the value of d (the cation-anion separation) increases and the ratio Q_1Q_2/d decreases. This is reflected in the decrease in lattice energy going from BeH_2 to BaH_2.

      (b)   Again, Q_1Q_2 for ZnH_2 is the same as that for the other compounds in the series and the anion is H^-. The lattice energy of ZnH_2, 2870 kJ, is closest to that of MgH_2, 2791 kJ. The ionic radius of Zn^{2+} is similar to that of Mg^{2+}.

8.80   (a)

	Compound	Lattice Energy (kJ)			Compound	Lattice Energy (kJ)	
106 kJ	NaCl	788	56 kJ	104 kJ	LiCl	834	55 kJ
	NaBr	732			**LiBr**	**779**	
	Na I	682			Li I	730	

The difference in lattice energy between LiCl and LiI is 104 kJ. The difference between NaCl and NaI is 106 kJ; the difference between NaCl and NaBr is 56 kJ, or 53% of the difference between NaCl and NaI. Applying this relationship to the Li salts, 0.53(104 kJ) = 55 kJ difference between LiCl and LiBr. The approximate lattice energy of LiBr is (834 – 55) kJ = 779 kJ.

      (b)

	Compound	Lattice Energy (kJ)			Compound	Lattice Energy (kJ)	
106 kJ	NaCl	788	56 kJ	57 kJ	CsCl	657	30 kJ
	NaBr	732			**CsBr**	**627**	
	Na I	682			Cs I	600	

By analogy to the Na salts, the difference between lattice energies of CsCl and CsBr should be approximately 53% of the difference between CsCl and CsI. The lattice energy of CsBr is approximately 627 kJ.

      (c)

	Compound	Lattice Energy (kJ)			Compound	Lattice Energy (kJ)	
578 kJ	MgO	3795	381 kJ	199 kJ	$MgCl_2$	2326	131 kJ
	CaO	3414			$CaCl_2$	2195	
	SrO	3217			$SrCl_2$	2127	

By analogy to the oxides, the difference between the lattice energies of $MgCl_2$ and $CaCl_2$ should be approximately 66% of the difference between $MgCl_2$ and $SrCl_2$. That is, 0.66(199 kJ) = 131 kJ. The lattice energy of $CaCl_2$ is approximately (2326 – 131) kJ = 2195 kJ.

8.81   The charge on M is likely to be 3+. According to Table 8.2, the lattice energy for an ionic compound with the general formula MX and a charge of 2+ on the metal will be in the range of $3\text{-}4 \times 10^3$ kJ/mol. The charge on M must be greater than 2+. ScN, where the charge on Sc is 3+, has a lattice energy of 7547 kJ/mol. It is reasonable to conclude that the charge on M is 3+, and the M–X distance is greater than the Sc–N distance.

8.82 $$E = \frac{-8.99 \times 10^9 \text{ J}\cdot\text{m}}{C^2} \times \frac{4(1.60 \times 10^{-19} \text{ C})^2}{(1.14+1.26) \times 10^{-10} \text{ m}} = -3.836 \times 10^{-18} = -3.84 \times 10^{-18} \text{ J}$$

On a molar basis: $(-3.836 \times 10^{-18} \text{ J})(6.022 \times 10^{23}) = -2.310 \times 10^6 \text{ J} = -2310 \text{ kJ}$

Note that the absolute value of this potential energy is less than the lattice energy of CaO, 3414 kJ/mol. The difference represents the added energy of putting all the $Ca^{2+}O^{2-}$ ion pairs together in a three-dimensional array, similar to the one in Figure 8.3.

8.83   By analogy to the Born-Haber cycle for NaCl(s), Figure 8.4, the enthalpy of formation for NaCl₂(s) is

$\Delta H_f^o NaCl_2(s) = -\Delta H_{latt}NaCl_2 + \Delta H_f^o Na(g) + 2\Delta H_f^o Cl(g) + I_1(Na) + I_2(Na) + 2E(Cl)$

(a) $\Delta H_f^o NaCl_2(s) = -\Delta H_{latt}NaCl_2 + 107.7$ kJ $+ 2(121.7$ kJ$) + 496$ kJ $+ 4562$ kJ

$+ 2(-349$ kJ$)$

$\Delta H_f^o NaCl_2(s) = -\Delta H_{latt}NaCl_2 + 4711$ kJ

The collective energy of the "other" steps in the cycle (vaporization and ionization of Na^{2+}, dissociation of Cl_2 and electron affinity of Cl) is +4711 kJ. In order for the sign of $\Delta H_f^o NaCl_2$ to be negative, the lattice energy would have to be greater than 4711 kJ.

(b) $\Delta H_f^o NaCl_2(s) = -(2326$ kJ$) + 4711$ kJ $= 2385$ kJ

This value is large and positive.

8.84   (a)   A polar molecule has a measurable dipole moment; its centers of positive and negative charge do not coincide. A nonpolar molecule has a zero net dipole moment; its centers of positive and negative charge do coincide.

(b)   Yes. If X and Y have different electronegativities, they have different attractions for the electrons in the molecule. The electron density around the more electronegative atom will be greater, producing a charge separation or dipole in the molecule.

(c) $\mu = Qr$. The dipole moment, μ, is the product of the magnitude of the separated charges, Q, and the distance between them, r.

8.85   (a)   B–O. The most polar bond will be formed by the two elements with the greatest difference in electronegativity. Since electronegativity increases moving right and up on the periodic table, the possibilities are B–O and Te–O. These two bonds are likely to have similar electronegativitiy differences (3 columns apart vs. 3 rows apart). Values from Figure 8.6 confirm the similarity, and show that B–O is slightly more polar.

(b)   Te–I. Both are in the fifth row of the periodic table and have the two largest covalent radii among this group of elements.

(c) TeI_2. Te needs to participate in two covalent bonds to satisfy the octet rule, and each I atom needs to participate in one bond, so by forming a TeI_2 molecule, the octet rule can be satisfied for all three atoms.

$$:\ddot{I}—\ddot{Te}—\ddot{I}:$$

(d) B_2O_3. Although this is probably not a purely ionic compound, it can be understood in terms of gaining and losing electrons to achieve a noble-gas configuration. If each B atom were to lose 3 e^- and each O atom were to gain 2 e^-, charge balance and the octet rule would be satisfied.

P_2O_3. Each P atom needs to share 3 e^- and each O atom 2 e^- to achieve an octet. Although the correct number of electrons seem to be available, a correct Lewis structure is difficult to imagine. In fact, phosphorus (III) oxide exists as P_4O_6 rather than P_2O_3 (Chapter 22).

8.86   (a) $Q = \dfrac{\mu}{r} = \dfrac{1.24\,D}{1.60\,\text{Å}} \times \dfrac{1\,\text{Å}}{1 \times 10^{-10}\,m} \times \dfrac{3.34 \times 10^{-30}\,C\text{-}m}{1\,D} \times \dfrac{1\,e}{1.60 \times 10^{-19}\,C} = 0.1618 = 0.162\,e$

(b)   From Figure 8.7, the electronegativity of Cl is 3.0 and that of O is 3.5. Since O is the more electronegative element, we expect it to have a negative charge in the ClO molecule.

(c)   13 e^-, 6.5 e^- pairs

+1 $\cdot\ddot{\text{Cl}}$——$\ddot{\text{O}}$: -1   0 $\cdot\ddot{\text{Cl}}$=$\ddot{\text{O}}$ 0

Formal charges are minimized for the Lewis structure on the right. This is possible because Cl is a third-row element and can accommodate an expanded octet. The small electronegativity difference and calculated charges both point to a slightly polar covalent molecule. The true bonding situation is a blend of the two extreme Lewis structures, with the right-most structure making the larger contribution.

8.87   Estimate relative attraction for the bonding electron pair by calculating the relative electronegativity of the two atoms. From Figure 8.7, the electronegativity of Br is 2.8 and of Cl is 3.0.

Br has $2.8/(3.0 + 2.8) = 0.48$ of the charge of the bonding e^- pair.

Cl has $3.0/(3.0 + 2.8) = 0.52$ of the charge of the bonding e^- pair.

This amounts to $0.52 \times 2e = 1.04e$ on Cl or $0.04e$ more than a neutral Cl atom. This implies a –0.04 charge on Cl and +0.04 charge on Br.

From Figure 7.7, the covalent radius of Br is 1.14 Å and of Cl is 0.99 Å. The Br–Cl separation is 2.13 Å.

$$\mu = Qr = 0.04e \times \frac{1.60 \times 10^{-19}\,C}{e} \times 2.13\,\text{Å} \times \frac{1 \times 10^{-10}\,m}{\text{Å}} \times \frac{1\,D}{3.34 \times 10^{-30}\,C\text{-}m} = 0.41\,D$$

Clearly, this method is approximate. The estimated dipole moment of 0.41 D is within 28% of the measured value of 0.57 D.

8.88   (a) $2NaAlH_4(s) \rightarrow 2NaH(s) + 2Al(s) + 3H_2(g)$

(b)   Hydrogen is the only nonmetal in $NaAlH_4$, so we expect it to be most electronegative. (The position of H on the periodic table is problematic. Its electronegativity does not fit the typical trend for Gp 1A elements.) For the two metals, Na and Al, electronegativity increases moving up and to the right on the periodic table, so Al is more electronegative. The least electronegative element in the compound is Na.

(c)   Covalent bonds hold polyatomic anions together; elements involved in covalent bonding have smaller electronegativity differences than those that are involved in ionic bonds. Possible covalent bonds in $NaAlH_4$ are Na–H and Al–H. Al and H have a smaller electronegativity difference than Na and H and are more likely to form covalent bonds. The anion has an overall 1– charge, so it can be thought of as four hydride ions and one Al^{3+} ion. The formula is AlH_4^-. For the purpose of counting valence electrons, assume neutral atoms.

$8 \, e^-$, $4 \, e^-$ pairs

$$\left[\begin{array}{c} \text{H} \\ | \\ \text{H}-\text{Al}-\text{H} \\ | \\ \text{H} \end{array} \right]^-$$

8.89 I_3^- has a Lewis structure with an expanded octet of electrons around the central I.

$$:\!\ddot{\text{I}}\!-\!\ddot{\text{I}}\!-\!\ddot{\text{I}}\!:$$

F cannot accommodate an expanded octet because it is too small and has no available d orbitals in its valence shell.

8.90   Formal charge (FC) = # valence e^- – (# nonbonding e^- + 1/2 # bonding e^-)

(a) $18 \, e^-$, $9 \, e^-$ pairs

$$:\!\ddot{\text{O}}\!-\!\ddot{\text{O}}\!=\!\ddot{\text{O}} \longleftrightarrow \ddot{\text{O}}\!=\!\ddot{\text{O}}\!-\!\ddot{\text{O}}\!:$$

FC for the central O = 6 – [2 + 1/2 (6)] = +1

(b) $48 \, e^-$, $24 \, e^-$ pairs

$$\left[\begin{array}{c} \text{F} \quad \text{F} \\ | \, / \\ \text{F}-\text{P}-\text{F} \\ / \, | \\ \text{F} \quad \text{F} \end{array} \right]^-$$ FC for P = 5 – [0 + 1/2 (12)] = –1

The three nonbonded pairs on each F have been omitted.

(c) $17 \, e^-$; $8 \, e^-$ pairs, 1 odd e^-

$$\ddot{\text{O}}\!=\!\dot{\text{N}}\!-\!\ddot{\text{O}}\!: \longleftrightarrow :\!\ddot{\text{O}}\!-\!\dot{\text{N}}\!=\!\ddot{\text{O}}$$

The odd electron is probably on N because it is less electronegative than O. Assuming the odd electron is on N, FC for N = 5 – [1 + 1/2 (6)] = +1. If the odd electron is on O, FC for N = 5 – [2 + 1/2 (6)] = 0.

(d) $28 \, e^-$, $14 \, e^-$ pairs   (e) $32 \, e^-$, $16 \, e^-$ pairs

$$:\!\ddot{\text{C}}\ddot{\text{l}}\!-\!\dot{\text{I}}\!-\!\ddot{\text{C}}\ddot{\text{l}}\!: \\ | \\ :\!\ddot{\text{C}}\ddot{\text{l}}\!:$$ $$\begin{array}{c} :\!\ddot{\text{O}}\!: \\ | \\ :\!\ddot{\text{O}}\!-\!\text{Cl}\!-\!\ddot{\text{O}}\!-\!\text{H} \\ | \\ :\!\ddot{\text{O}}\!: \end{array}$$

FC for I = 7 – [4 + 1/2 (6)] = 0   FC for Cl = 7 – [0 + 1/2 (8)] = +3

8.91   (a)   14e⁻, 7 e⁻ pairs   32 e⁻, 16 e⁻ pairs

$$\left[:\ddot{Cl}-\ddot{O}:\right]^{-}$$

FC on Cl = 7 – [6 + 1/2(2)] = 0

$$\left[\begin{array}{c}:\ddot{O}:\\|\\:\ddot{O}-Cl-\ddot{O}:\\|\\:\ddot{O}:\end{array}\right]^{-}$$

FC on Cl = 7 – [0 + 1/2(8)] = +3

(b)   The oxidation number of Cl is +1 in ClO^- and +7 in ClO_4^-.

(c)   No, it is not uncommon for formal charge and oxidation state to be different. The definition of formal charge assumes that all bonding pairs of electrons are equally shared by the two bonded atoms, that all bonds are purely covalent. The definition of oxidation number assumes that the more electronegative element in the bond gets all of the bonding electrons, that the bonds are purely ionic. These two definitions represent the two extremes of how electron density is distributed between bonded atoms.

In ClO^- and ClO_4^-, Cl is the less electronegative element, so the oxidation numbers have a higher positive value than the formal charges. The true description of the electron density distribution is somewhere between the extremes indicated by formal charge and oxidation number.

(d)   Oxidizing power is the tendency of a substance to be reduced, to gain electrons. Oxidation numbers show the maximum electron deficiency (or excess) of a substance. The higher the oxidation number of the central atom in an oxyanion, the greater its electron deficiency and oxidizing power. Formal charges can also be used to show oxidizing (or reducing) power, but trends are less obvious because the magnitudes are smaller.

8.92   (a)   :N≡N—Ö: ⟷ :N̈—N≡O: ⟷ N̈=N=Ö
                  0   +1   -1   -2   +1   +1   -1   +1   0

In the leftmost structure, the more electronegative O atom has the negative formal charge, so this structure is likely to be most important.

(b)   In general, the more shared pairs of electrons between two atoms, the shorter the bond, and vice versa. That the N–N bond length in N_2O is slightly longer than the typical N≡N indicates that the middle and right resonance structures where the N atoms share less than three electron pairs are contributors to the true structure. That the N–O bond length is slightly shorter than a typical N=O indicates that the middle structure, where N and O share more than two electron pairs, does contribute to the true structure. This physical data indicates that while formal charge can be used to predict which resonance form will be more important to the observed structure, the influence of minor contributors on the true structure cannot be ignored.

8.93   (a) $12 + 3 + 15 = 30$ valence e$^-$, 15 e$^-$ pairs.

Structures with H bound to N and nonbonded electron pairs on C can be drawn, but the structures above minimize formal charges on the atoms.

(b)   The resonance structures indicate that triazine will have six equal C–N bond lengths, intermediate between C–N single and C–N double bond lengths. (See Solutions 8.57 and 8.58.) From Table 8.5, an average C–N length is 1.43 Å, a C=N length is 1.38 Å. The average of these two lengths is 1.405 Å. The C–N bond length in triazine should be in the range 1.40–1.41 Å.

8.94   (a) $24 + 4 + 14 = 42$ valence e$^-$, 21 e$^-$ pairs.   (b)

(c)   In benzene, the six C atoms are equivalent. In ortho-dichlorobenzene, the two C atoms bound to Cl are not equivalent to the four C atoms bound to H. In the two resonance structures above, one has a double bond between the C atoms bound to Cl, and the other has a single bond in this position. The two ortho-dichlorobenzene resonance structures are not equivalent like the resonance structures of benzene.

8.95   An experimentally determined molecular structure will reveal bond lengths and angles of the B–A=B molecule. If resonance structures are important, the two B–A bond lengths will be identical, or nearly so. If the molecule features one single and one double bond, the lengths will be significantly different. (While bond angles often reveal bonding details, in this case bond lengths are telling.)

8.96 $\Delta H = 8D(C-H) - D(C-C) - 6D(C-H) - D(H-H)$

$= 2D(C-H) - D(C-C) - D(H-H)$

$= 2(413) - 348 - 436 = +42$ kJ

$\Delta H = 8D(C-H) + 1/2\ D(O=O) - D(C-C) - 6D(C-H) - 2D(O-H)$

$= 2D(C-H) + 1/2\ D(O=O) - D(C-C) - 2D(O-H)$

$= 2(413) + 1/2\ (495) - 348 - 2(463) = -200$ kJ

The fundamental difference in the two reactions is the formation of 1 mol of H–H bonds versus the formation of 2 mol of O–H bonds. The latter is much more exothermic, so the reaction involving oxygen is more exothermic.

8.97   (a) $\Delta H = 5D(C-H) + D(C-C) + D(C-O) + D(O-H) - 6D(C-H) - 2D(C-O)$

                 $= D(C-C) + D(O-H) - D(C-H) - D(C-O)$

                 $= 348 \text{ kJ} + 463 \text{ kJ} - 413 \text{ kJ} - 358 \text{ kJ}$

        $\Delta H = +40 \text{ kJ}$; ethanol has the lower enthalpy

    (b) $\Delta H = 4D(C-H) + D(C-C) + 2D(C-O) - 4D(C-H) - D(C-C) - D(C=O)$

                 $= 2D(C-O) - D(C=O)$

                 $= 2(358 \text{ kJ}) - 799 \text{ kJ}$

        $\Delta H = -83 \text{ kJ}$; acetaldehyde has the lower enthalpy

    (c) $\Delta H = 8D(C-H) + 4D(C-C) + D(C=C) - 8D(C-H) - 2D(C-C) - 2D(C=C)$

                 $= 2D(C-C) - D(C=C)$

                 $= 2(348 \text{ kJ}) - 614 \text{ kJ}$

        $\Delta H = +82 \text{ kJ}$; cyclopentene has the lower enthalpy

    (d) $\Delta H = 3D(C-H) + D(C-N) + D(C \equiv N) - 3D(C-H) - D(C-C) - D(C \equiv N)$

                 $= D(C-N) - D(C-C)$

                 $= 293 \text{ kJ} - 348 \text{ kJ}$

        $\Delta H = -55 \text{ kJ}$; acetonitrile has the lower enthalpy

8.98   (a)

nitroglycerine

$\Delta H = 20D(C-H) + 8D(C-C) + 12D(C-O) + 24D(O-N) + 12D(N=O)$

                $- [6D(N \equiv N) + 24D(C=O) + 20D(H-O) + D(O=O)]$

$\Delta H = 20(413) + 8(348) + 12(358) + 24(201) + 12(607)$

            $- [6(941) + 24(799) + 20(463) + 495]$

    $= -7129 \text{ kJ}$

$$1.00 \text{ g C}_3\text{H}_5\text{N}_3\text{O}_9 \times \frac{1 \text{ mol C}_3\text{H}_5\text{N}_3\text{O}_9}{227.1 \text{ g C}_3\text{H}_5\text{N}_3\text{O}_9} \times \frac{-7129 \text{ kJ}}{4 \text{ mol C}_3\text{H}_5\text{N}_3\text{O}_9} = 7.85 \text{ kJ/g C}_3\text{H}_5\text{N}_3\text{O}_9$$

    (b) $4C_7H_5N_3O_6(s) \rightarrow 6N_2(g) + 7CO_2(g) + 10H_2O(g) + 21C(s)$

8.99   (a)

$C_3H_6N_6O_6$ $12 + 6 + 30 + 36 = 84 \ e^-$, 42 e^- pairs

42 e^- pairs − 24 shared e^- pairs = 18 unshared (lone) e^- pairs

Use unshared pairs to complete octets on terminal O atoms (15 unshared pairs) and ring N atoms (3 unshared pairs).

(b)   No C=N bonds in the 6-membered ring are possible, because all C octets are complete with 4 bonds to other atoms. N=N are possible, as shown below. There are 8 possibilities involving some combination of N−N and N=N groups [1 with 0 N=N, 3 with 1 N=N, 3 with 2N=N, 1 with 3N=N]. A resonance structure with 1 N=N is shown below.

Each terminal O=N−O group has two possible placements for the N=O. This generates 8 structures with 0 N=N groups (and 3 O = N−O groups), 4 with 1 N=N and 2 O=N−O, 2 with 2 N=N and 1 O=N−O, and 1 with 3 N=N and no O=N−O. This sums to a total of 15 resonance structures (that I can visualize). Can you find others?

(c) $C_3H_6N_6O_6(s) \rightarrow 3CO(g) + 3N_2(g) + 3H_2O(g)$

(d)   The molecule contains N=O, N=N, C−H, C−N, N−O, and N−N bonds. According to Table 8.4, N−N bonds have the smallest bond enthalpy and are weakest.

(e)   Calculate the enthalpy of decomposition for the resonance structure drawn in part (a).

$\Delta H = 3D(N=O) + 3D(N-O) + 3D(N-N) + 6D(N-C) + 6D(C-H)$

      $- 3D(C\equiv O) - 3D(N\equiv N) - 6D(O-H)$

      $= 3(607) + 3(201) + 3(163) + 6(293) + 6(413) - 3(1072) - 3(941) - 6(463)$

      $= -1668 \ kJ/mol \ C_3H_6N_6O_6$

$$5.0 \ g \ C_3H_6N_6O_6 \times \frac{1 \ mol \ C_3H_6N_6O_6}{222.1 \ g \ C_3H_6N_6O_6} \times \frac{-1668 \ kJ}{mol \ C_3H_6N_6O_6} = -37.55 = -38 \ kJ$$

While exchanging N=O and N–O bonds has no effect on the enthalpy calculation, structures with N=N and 2 N–O do have different enthalpy of decomposition. For the resonance structure with 3 N=N and 6 N–O bonds instead of 3 N–N, 3 N–O and 3 N=O, $\Delta H = -2121$ kJ/mol. The actual enthalpy of decomposition is probably somewhere between –1668 and –2121 kJ/mol. The enthalpy change for the decomposition of 5.0 g RDX is then in the range of –38 to –48 kJ.

8.100

When comparing the same pair of bonded atoms (C–N vs. C=N vs. C≡N), the shorter the bond the greater the bond energy, but the two quantities are not necessarily directly proportional. The plot clearly shows that there are no simple length/strength correlations for single bonds alone, double bonds alone, triple bonds alone, or among different pairs of bonded atoms (all C–C bonds vs. all C–N bonds, etc.).

Integrative Exercises

8.101   (a) Ti^{2+} : [Ar]$3d^2$;   Ca : [Ar]$4s^2$. Yes. The two valence electrons in Ti^{2+} and Ca are in different principle quantum levels and different subshells.

(b)   According to the Aufbau Principle, valence electrons will occupy the lowest energy empty orbital. Thus, in Ca the 4s is lower in energy than the 3d, while in Ti^{2+}, the 3d is lower in energy than the 4s.

(c)   No. Since there is only one 4s orbital, the two valence electrons in Ca are paired. There are five degenerate 3d orbitals, so the two valence electrons in Ti^{2+} are unpaired. Ca has no unpaired electrons, Ti^{2+} has two.

8.102   (a) $Sr(s) \rightarrow Sr(g)$ ΔH_f° Sr(g) [ΔH_{sub}° Sr(s)]

$Sr(g) \rightarrow Sr^+(g) + 1\,e^-$ I_1 Sr

$Sr^+(g) \rightarrow Sr^{2+}(g) + 1\,e^-$ I_2 Sr

$Cl_2(g) \rightarrow 2Cl(g)$ $2\,\Delta H_f^\circ$ Cl(g) [D(Cl_2)]

$2Cl(g) + 2\,e^- \rightarrow 2Cl^-(g)$ $2E_1$ Cl

$\underline{SrCl_2(s) \rightarrow Sr(s) + Cl_2(g)}$ $\underline{-\Delta H_f^\circ\ SrCl_2}$

$SrCl_2(s) \rightarrow Sr^{2+}(g) + 2Cl^-(g)$ ΔH_{latt}

223

(b) $\Delta H_f^{\circ}\ SrCl_2(s) = \Delta H_f^{\circ}\ Sr(g) + I_1(Sr) + I_2(Sr) + 2\Delta H_f^{\circ}\ Cl(g) + 2E(Cl) - \Delta H_{latt}\ SrCl_2$

           $\Delta H_f^{\circ}\ SrCl_2(s) = 164.4\ kJ + 549\ kJ + 1064\ kJ + 2(121.7)\ kJ + 2(-349)\ kJ - 2127\ kJ$

                      $= -804\ kJ$

8.103   The pathway to the formation of K_2O can be written:

    $2K(s) \rightarrow 2K(g)$ $2\Delta H_f^{\circ}\ K(g)$

    $2K(g) \rightarrow 2K^+(g) + 2\ e^-$ $2\ I_1(K)$

    $1/2\ O_2(g) \rightarrow O(g)$ $\Delta H_f^{\circ}\ O(g)$

    $O(g) + 1\ e^- \rightarrow O^-(g)$ $E_1(O)$

    $O^-(g) + 1\ e^- \rightarrow O^{2-}(g)$ $E_2(O)$

    $\underline{2K^+(g) + O^{2-}(g) \rightarrow K_2O(s)}$ $\underline{-\Delta H_{latt}\ K_2O(s)}$

    $2K(s) + 1/2\ O_2(g) \rightarrow K_2O(s)$ $\Delta H_f^{\circ}\ K_2O(s)$

    $\Delta H_f^{\circ}\ K_2O(s) = 2\Delta H_f^{\circ}\ K(g) + 2\ I_1(K) + \Delta H_f^{\circ}\ O(g) + E_1(O) + E_2(O) - \Delta H_{latt}\ K_2O(s)$

    $E_2(O) = \Delta H_f^{\circ}\ K_2O(s) + \Delta H_{latt}\ K_2O(s) - 2\Delta H_f^{\circ}\ K(g) - 2\ I_t(K) - \Delta H_f^{\circ}\ O(g) - E_1(O)$

    $E_2(O) = -363.2\ kJ + 2238\ kJ - 2(89.99)\ kJ - 2(419)\ kJ - 247.5\ kJ - (-141)\ kJ$

          $= +750\ kJ$

8.104   To calculate empirical formulas, assume 100 g of sample.

    (a) $\dfrac{76.0\ g\ Ru}{101.07\ g/mol} = 0.752\ mol\ Ru;\ \ 0.752/0.752 = 1\ Ru$

          $\dfrac{24.0\ g\ O}{15.9994\ g/mol} = 1.50\ mol\ O;\ \ 1.50/0.762 = 2\ O$

          The empirical formula of compound 1 is RuO_2.

    (b) $\dfrac{61.2\ g\ Ru}{101.07\ g/mol} = 0.6055\ mol\ Ru;\ \ 0.6055/0.6055 = 1\ Ru$

          $\dfrac{38.8\ g\ O}{15.9994\ g/mol} = 2.425\ mol\ O;\ \ 2.425/0.6055 = 4\ O$

          The empirical formula of compound 2 is RuO_4.

    (c)   Ionic compounds have very high melting points, while the melting points of molecular compounds are lower and variable. Clearly the black powder, m.p. > 1200°C, is ionic and the yellow substance, m.p. = 25°C, is molecular. Substances with metals in high oxidation states are often molecular. RuO_4 contains Ru(VIII), while RuO_2 contains Ru(IV), so RuO_4 is more likely to be molecular. The yellow compound is RuO_4, ruthenium tetroxide. The black compound is RuO_2, ruthenium(IV) oxide.

8.105   (a)   Even though Cl has the greater (more negative) electron affinity, F has a much larger ionization energy, so the electronegativity of F is greater.

          F: k(IE–EA) = k(1681 – (–328)) = k(2009)

          Cl: k(IE–EA) = k(1251 – (–349)) = k(1600)

(b) Electronegativity is the ability of an atom in a molecule to attract electrons to itself. It can be thought of as the ability to hold its own electrons (as measured by ionization energy) and the capacity to attract the electrons of other atoms (as measured by electron affinity). Thus, both properties are relevant to the concept of electronegativity.

(c) EN = k(IE – EA). For F: 4.0 = k(2009), k = 4.0/2009 = 2.0×10^{-3}

(d) Cl: EN = 2.0×10^{-3} (1600) = 3.2

O: EN = 2.0×10^{-3} (1314 – (–141)) = 2.9

These values do not follow the trend on Figure 8.7. The Pauling scale on the figure shows O to be second only to F in electronegativity, more electronegative than Cl. The simple definition EN = k(IE – EA) that employs thermochemical properties of isolated, gas phase atoms does not take into account the complex bonding environment of molecules.

8.106 (a) Assume 100 g.

$$14.52 \text{ g C} \times \frac{1 \text{ mol}}{12.011 \text{ g C}} = 1.209 \text{ mol C}; 1.209 / 1.209 = 1$$

$$1.83 \text{ g H} \times \frac{1 \text{ mol}}{1.008 \text{ g H}} = 1.816 \text{ mol H}; 1.816 / 1.209 = 1.5$$

$$64.30 \text{ g Cl} \times \frac{1 \text{ mol}}{35.453 \text{ g Cl}} = 1.814 \text{ mol Cl}; 1.814 / 1.209 = 1.5$$

$$19.35 \text{ g O} \times \frac{1 \text{ mol}}{15.9994 \text{ g O}} = 1.209 \text{ mol O}; 1.209 / 1.209 = 1.0$$

Multiplying by 2 to obtain an integer ratio, the empirical formula is $C_2H_3Cl_3O_2$.

(b) The empirical formula mass is 2(12.0) + 3(1.0) + 3(35.5) + 2(16) = 165.5. The empirical formula is the molecular formula.

(c) 44 e⁻, 22 e⁻ pairs

8.107 (a) Assume 100 g.

$$62.04 \text{ g Ba} \times \frac{1 \text{ mol}}{137.33 \text{ g Ba}} = 0.4518 \text{ mol Ba}; 0.4518 / 0.4518 = 1.0$$

$$37.96 \text{ g N} \times \frac{1 \text{ mol}}{14.007 \text{ g N}} = 2.710 \text{ mol N}; 2.710 / 0.4518 = 6.0$$

The empirical formula is BaN_6. Ba has an ionic charge of 2+, so there must be two 1– azide ions to balance the charge. The formula of each azide ion is N_3^-.

(b)   16 e⁻, 8 e⁻ pairs

$$\left[:\ddot{N}=N=\ddot{N}:\right]^{-} \longleftrightarrow \left[:N\equiv N-\ddot{\ddot{N}}:\right]^{-} \longleftrightarrow \left[:\ddot{\ddot{N}}-N\equiv N:\right]^{-}$$

$$\quad\;\; -1 \;\; +1 \;\; -1 \qquad\qquad 0 \;\;\; +1 \;\; -2 \qquad\qquad -2 \;\;\; +1 \;\;\; 0$$

(c)   The structure with two double bonds minimizes formal charges and is probably the main contributor.

(d)   The two N–N bond lengths will be equal. The two minor contributors would individually cause unequal N–N distances, but collectively they contribute equally to the lengthening and shortening of each bond. The N–N distance will be approximately 1.24 Å, the average N=N distance.

8.108   (a) C_2H_2: 10 e⁻, 5 e⁻ pair N_2: 10 e⁻, 5 e⁻ pair

$$H-C\equiv C-H \qquad\qquad :N\equiv N:$$

(b)   The enthalpy of formation for N_2 is 0 kJ/mol and for C_2H_2 is 226.77 kJ/mol. N_2 is an extremely stable, unreactive compound. Under appropriate conditions, it can be either oxidized or reduced. C_2H_2 is a reactive gas, used in combination with O_2 for welding and as starting material for organic synthesis.

(c) $2N_2(g) + 5O_2(g) \rightarrow 2N_2O_5(g)$

$2C_2H_2(g) + 5O_2(g) \rightarrow 4CO_2(g) + 2H_2O(g)$

(d) $\Delta H_{rxn}^{\circ}\,(N_2) = 2\Delta H_f^{\circ}\,N_2O_5(g) - 2\Delta H_f^{\circ}\,N_2(g) - 5\Delta H_f^{\circ}\,O_2(g)$

$$= 2(11.30) - 2(0) - 5(0) = 22.60\ \text{kJ}$$

$\Delta H_{ox}^{\circ} = 11.30\ \text{kJ/mol}\ N_2$

$\Delta H_{rxn}^{\circ}\,(C_2H_2) = 4\Delta H_f^{\circ}\,CO_2(g) + 2\Delta H_f^{\circ}\,H_2O(g) - 2\Delta H_f^{\circ}\,C_2H_2(g) - 5\Delta H_f^{\circ}\,O_2(g)$

$$= 4(-393.5\ \text{kJ}) + 2(-241.82\ \text{kJ}) - 2(226.77\ \text{kJ}) - 5(0)$$

$$= -2511.18\ \text{kJ}$$

$\Delta H_{ox}^{\circ}\,(C_2H_2) = -1255.6\ \text{kJ/mol}\ C_2H_2$

The oxidation of C_2H_2 is highly exothermic, which means that the energy state of the combined products is much lower than that of the reactants. The reaction is "downhill" in an energy sense, and occurs readily. The oxidation of N_2 is mildly endothermic (energy of products higher than reactants) and the reaction does not readily occur. This is in agreement with the general reactivities from part (b).

Referring to bond enthalpies in Table 8.4, when the C–H bonds are taken into account, even more energy is required for bond breaking in the oxidation of C_2H_2 than in the oxidation of N_2. The difference seems to be in the enthalpies of formation of the products. $CO_2(g)$ and $H_2O(g)$ have extremely exothermic ΔH_f° values, which cause the oxidation of C_2H_2 to be energetically favorable. $N_2O_5(g)$ has an endothermic ΔH_f° value, which causes the oxidation of N_2 to be energetically unfavorable.

8.109   (a)   Assume 100 g of compound

$$69.6 \text{ g S} \times \frac{1 \text{ mol S}}{32.07 \text{ g}} = 2.17 \text{ mol S}$$

$$30.4 \text{ g N} \times \frac{1 \text{ mol N}}{14.01 \text{ g}} = 2.17 \text{ mol N}$$

S and N are present in a 1:1 mol ratio, so the empirical formula is SN. The empirical formula mass is 46. MM/FW = 184.3/46 = 4 The molecular formula is S_4N_4.

(b)   44 e^-, 22 e^- pairs. Because of its small radius, N is unlikely to have an expanded octet. Begin with alternating S and N atoms in the ring. Try to satisfy the octet rule with single bonds and lone pairs. At least two double bonds somewhere in the ring are required.

These structures carry formal charges on S and N atoms as shown. Other possibilities include:

These structures have zero formal charges on all atoms and are likely to contribute to the true structure. Note that the S atoms that are shown with two double bonds are not necessarily linear, because S has an expanded octet. Other resonance structures with four double bonds are.

In either resonance structure, the two 'extra' electron pairs can be placed on any pair of S atoms in ring, leading to a total of 10 resonance structures. The sulfur atoms alternately carry formal charges of +1 and –1. Without further structural information, it is not possible to eliminate any of the above structures. Clearly, the S_4N_4 molecule stretches the limits of the Lewis model of chemical bonding.

(c)   Each resonance structure has 8 total bonds and more than 8 but less than 16 bonding e^- pairs, so an "average" bond will be intermediate between a S–N single and double bond. We estimate an average S–N single bond length to be 1.77 Å (sum of bonding atomic radii from Figure 7.7). We do not have a direct value for a S–N double bond length. Comparing double and single bond lengths for C–C (1.34 Å, 1.54 Å), N–N (1.24 Å, 1.47 Å) and O–O (1.21 Å, 1.48 Å) bonds from Table 8.5, we see that, on average, a double bond is approximately 0.23 Å shorter than a single bond. Applying this difference to the S–N single bond length, we estimate the S–N double bond length as 1.54 Å. Finally, the intermediate S–N bond length in S_4N_4 should be between these two values, approximately 1.60–165 Å. (The measured bond length is 1.62 Å.)

(d) $S_4N_4 \rightarrow 4S(g) + 4N(g)$

      $\Delta H = 4\Delta H_f^\circ \ S(g) + 4\Delta H_f^\circ \ N(g) - \Delta H_f^\circ \ S_4N_4$

      $\Delta H = 4(222.8 \text{ kJ}) + 4(472.7 \text{ kJ}) - 480 \text{ kJ} = 2302 \text{ kJ}$

This energy, 2302 kJ, represents the dissociation of 8 S–N bonds in the molecule; the average dissociation energy of one S–N bond in S_4N_4 is then 2302 kJ/8 bonds = 287.8 kJ.

8.110   (a)   Yes. In the structure shown in the exercise, each P atom needs 1 unshared pair to complete its octet. This is confirmed by noting that only 6 of the 10 valence e⁻ pairs are bonding pairs.

      (b)   There are six P–P bonds in P_4.

      (c)   20 e⁻, 10 e⁻ pr

             $\overset{\displaystyle ..}{P} = P = P = \overset{\displaystyle ..}{\underset{\displaystyle ..}{P}}$

          In this Lewis structure, the octet rule is satisfied for all atoms. However, it requires P=P, which is uncommon because P has a covalent radius that is too large to accommodate the side-to-side π overlap of parallel p orbitals required for double bond formation.

      (d)   From left to right, the formal charges are on the P atoms in the linear structure are –1, +1, +1, –1. In the tetrahedral structure, all formal charges are zero. Clearly the linear structure does not minimize formal charge and is probably less stable than the tetrahedral structure, owing to the difficulty of P=P bond formation (see above).

8.111   (a) $C_6H_6(g) \rightarrow 6H(g) + 6C(g)$

          $\Delta H^\circ = 6\Delta H_f^\circ \ H(g) + 6\Delta H_f^\circ \ C(g) - \Delta H_f^\circ \ C_6H_6(g)$

          $\Delta H^\circ = 6(217.94) \text{ kJ} + 6(718.4) \text{ kJ} - 82.9 \text{ kJ} = 5535 \text{ kJ}$

      (b) $C_6H_6(g) \rightarrow 6CH(g)$

      (c)

$C_6H_6(g) \rightarrow 6H(g) + 6C(g)$	ΔH°	5535 kJ
$6H(g) + 6C(g) \rightarrow 6CH(g)$	$-6D(C-H)$	$-6(413)$ kJ
$C_6H_6(g) \rightarrow 6CH(g)$		3057 kJ

         3057 kJ is the energy required to break the six C–C bonds in $C_6H_6(g)$. The average bond dissociation energy for one carbon-carbon bond in $C_6H_6(g)$ is

         $\dfrac{3057 \text{ kJ}}{6 \text{ C} - \text{C bonds}} = 509.5 \text{ kJ}.$

(d)   The value of 509.5 kJ is between the average value for a C–C single bond (348 kJ) and a C=C double bond (614 kJ). It is somewhat greater than the average of these two values, indicating that the carbon-carbon bond in benzene is a bit stronger than we might expect.

8.112   (a) $Br_2(l) \rightarrow 2Br(g)$ $\Delta H° = 2\Delta H_f° \, Br(g) = 2(111.8) \, kJ = 223.6 \, kJ$

       (b) $CCl_4(l) \rightarrow C(g) + 4Cl(g)$

$$\Delta H° = \Delta H_f° \, C(g) + 4\Delta H_f° \, Cl(g) - \Delta H_f° \, CCl_4(l)$$

$$= 718.4 \, kJ + 4(121.7) \, kJ - (-139.3) \, kJ = 1344.5$$

$$\frac{1344.5 \, kJ}{4 \, C - Cl \, bonds} = 336.1 \, kJ$$

       (c)

$$H_2O_2(l) \rightarrow 2H(g) + 2O(g)$$
$$\underline{2H(g) + 2O(g) \rightarrow 2OH(g)}$$
$$H_2O_2(l) \rightarrow 2OH(g)$$

$$D(O - O)(l) = 2\Delta H_f° \, H(g) + 2\Delta H_f° \, O(g) - \Delta H_f° \, H_2O_2(l) - 2D(O - H)(g)$$

$$= 2(217.94) \, kJ + 2(247.5) \, kJ - (-187.8) \, kJ - 2(463) \, kJ$$

$$= 193 \, kJ$$

       (d)   The data are listed below.

bond	D gas kJ/mol	D liquid kJ/mol
Br–Br	193	223.6
C–Cl	328	336.1
O–O	146	192.7

Breaking bonds in the liquid requires more energy than breaking bonds in the gas phase. For simple molecules, bond dissociation from the liquid phase can be thought of in two steps:

molecule (l) $\rightarrow$ molecule (g)

molecule (g) $\rightarrow$ atoms (g)

The first step is evaporation or vaporization of the liquid and the second is bond dissociation in the gas phase. Average bond enthalpy in the liquid phase is then the sum of the enthalpy of vaporization for the molecule and the gas phase bond dissociation enthalpies, divided by the number of bonds dissociated. This is greater than the gas phase bond dissociation enthalpy owing to the contribution from the enthalpy of vaporization.

9 Molecular Geometry and Bonding Theories

Visualizing Concepts

9.1   Removing an atom from the equatorial plane of trigonal bipyramid in Figure 9.3 creates a seesaw shape. It might appear that you could also obtain a seesaw by removing two atoms from the square plane of the octahedron. However, one of the B–A–B angles in the seesaw is 120°, so it must be derived from a trigonal bipyramid.

9.2   (a)   120°

        (b)   If the blue balloon expands, the angle between red and green balloons decreases.

        (c)   Nonbonding (lone) electron pairs exert greater repulsive forces than bonding pairs, resulting in compression of adjacent bond angles.

9.3   *Analyze/Plan.*   Visualize the molecular geometry and the electron domain geometries that could produce it. Confirm your choices with Tables 9.2 and 9.3. On Table 9.3, note that octahedral electron domain geometry results in only 3 possible molecular geometries: octahedral, square pyramidal and square planar (not T-shaped, bent or linear). *Solve.*

        (a)   2. Molecular geometry: linear. Possible electron domain geometries: linear, trigonal bipyramidal

        (b)   1. Molecular geometry, T-shaped.   Possible electron domain geometries: trigonal bipyramidal

        (c)   1. Molecular geometry, octahedral. Possible electron domain geometries: octahedral

        (d)   1. Molecular geometry, square-pyramidal. Possible electron domain geometries: octahedral

        (e)   1. Molecular geometry, square planar. Possible electron domain geometries: octahedral

        (f)   1. Molecular geometry, triangular pyramid. Possible electron domain geometries: trigonal bipyramidal. This is an unusual molecular geometry which is not listed in Table 9.3. It could occur if the equatorial substituents on the trigonal bipyramid were extremely bulky, causing the nonbonding electron pair to occupy an axial position.

9.4   (a)   4 e$^-$ domains

        (b)   The molecule has a non-zero dipole moment, because the C–H and C–F bond dipoles do not cancel each other.

        (c)   The dipole moment vector bisects the F–C–F and H–C–H angles, with the negative end of the vector toward the F atoms.

9.5   (a)   The reference point for zero energy on the diagram corresponds to a state where the two Cl atoms are separate and not interacting. This corresponds to an infinite Cl–Cl distance beyond the right extreme of the horizontal axis. The point near the left side of the plot where the curve intersects the x-axis at $E = 0$ has no special meaning.

         (b)   According to the valence-bond model, as atoms approach, their valence atomic orbitals overlap, allowing two electrons of opposite spin to mutually occupy space between the two nuclei. Energy decreases as atom separation decreases because the valence electrons of one atom come close enough to the other atom to be stabilized by both nuclei instead of just one nucleus.

         (c)   The Cl–Cl distance at the energy minimum on the plot is the Cl–Cl bond length.

         (d)   At interatomic separations shorter than the bond distance, the two nuclei begin to repel each other, increasing the overall energy of the system.

         (e)   Energy is shown on the y-axis of the plot. The minimum energy for the two atoms represents the stabilization obtained by bringing two Cl atoms together at the optimum (bond) distance. The y-coordinate of the minimum point on the plot corresponds to the Cl–Cl bond energy, or bond strength.

9.6 SiF_4 32 e⁻, 16 e⁻ pr PF_3 26 e⁻, 13 e⁻ pr SF_2 20 e⁻, 10 e⁻ pr

            ~109°   ~107°   ~105°

In all three molecules, the electron domain geometry is tetrahedral and the approximate bond angle is 109°. But, SiF_4 has 0 nonbonding electron pairs, PF_3 has 1 nonbonding pair, and SF_2 has 2 nonbonding pairs. If nonbonding electron pairs occupy more space than bonding pairs, we expect the bond angles to decrease in the series, perhaps 109°, 107°, 105°.

9.7   The diagram illustrates mixing of a single s and three p atomic orbitals to form sp^3 hybrids.

9.8   (a)   Recall that π bonds require p atomic orbitals, so the maximum hybridization of a C atom involved in a double bond is sp^2 and in a triple bond is sp. There are 6 C atoms in the molecule. Starting on the left, the hybridizations are: sp^2, sp^2, sp^3, sp, sp, sp^3.

         (b)   All single bonds are σ bonds. Double and triple bonds each contain 1 σ bond. This molecule has 8 C–H σ bonds and 5 C–C σ bonds, for a total of 13 σ bonds.

         (c)   Double bonds have 1 π bond and triple bonds have 2 π bonds. This molecule has a total of 3 π bonds.

         (d)   Any central atom with sp^2 hybridization will have bond angles of 120° around it. The two left-most C atoms are sp^2 hybridized, so any angle with one of these C atoms central will be 120°. This amounts to 1 H–C–H, 4 H–C–C and 1 C–C–C angle.

9.9   *Analyze/Plan.* σ molecular orbitals (MOs) are symmetric about the internuclear axis, π MOs are not. Bonding MOs have most of their electron density in the area between the nuclei, antibonding MOs have a node between the nuclei.

      (a)   (i)   Two s atomic orbitals (electron density at each nucleus).

               (ii)   Two p atomic orbitals overlapping end-to-end (node near each nucleus).

               (iii)   Two p atomic orbitals overlapping side-to-side (node near each nucleus).

      (b)   (i)   σ-type (symmetric about the internuclear axis, s orbitals can produce only σ overlap).

               (ii)   σ-type (symmetric about internuclear axis)

               (iii)   π-type (not symmetric about internuclear axis, side-to-side overlap)

      (c)   (i)   antibonding (node between nuclei)

               (ii)   bonding (concentration of electron density between nuclei)

               (iii)   antibonding (node between nuclei)

      (d)   (i)   The nodal plane is between the atom centers, perpendicular to the interatomic axis and equidistant from each atom.

               (ii)   There are two nodal planes; both are perpendicular to the interatomic axis. One is left of the left atom and the second is right of the right atom.

               (iii)   There are two nodal planes; one is between the atom centers, perpendicular to the interatomic axis and equidistant from each atom. The second contains the interatomic axis and is perpendicular to the first.

9.10   (a)   The diagram has five electrons in MOs formed by 2p atomic orbitals. C has two 2p electrons, so X must have three 2p electrons. X is N.

      (b)   The molecule has an unpaired electron, so it is paramagnetic.

      (c)   Atom X is N, which is more electronegative than C. The atomic orbitals of the more electronegative N are slightly lower in energy than those of C. The lower energy π_{2p} bonding molecular orbitals will have a greater contribution from the lower energy N atomic orbitals. (Higher energy π_{2p}^{*} MOs will have a greater contribution from higher energy C atomic orbitals.)

Molecular Shapes; the VSEPR Model (sections 9.1 and 9.2)

9.11   (a)   Yes. The stated shape, linear, defines the bond angle (180°) and the A–B bond length tells the size.

      (b)   No. Atom A could have 0 or 3 nonbonding electron pairs, depending on the total number of electron domains around atom A. Only molecules with 2 or 5 total electron domains about the central atom can possibly result in linear molecular geometry. Refer to Tables 9.2 and 9.3.

9.12   (a)   In a symmetrical tetrahedron, the four bond angles are equal to each other, with values of 109.5°. The H–C–H angles in CH_4 and the O–Cl–O angles in ClO_4^- will have values close to 109.5°.

(b) 'Planar' molecules are flat, so trigonal planar BF_3 is flat. In the trigonal pyramidal NH_3 molecule, the central N atom sits out of the plane of the three H atoms; this molecule is not flat.

9.13 A molecule with tetrahedral molecular geometry has an atom at each vertex of the tetrahedron. A trigonal pyramidal molecule has one vertex of the tetrahedron occupied by a nonbonding electron pair rather than an atom. That is, a trigonal pyramid is a tetrahedron with one vacant vertex.

9.14 (a) three coplanar 120° angles

(b) four 109.5° angles

(c) 90° angles in the equatorial square plane and between axial atoms and those in the square plane, 12 in all; 180° angles between atoms opposite each other, 3 in all

(d) one 180° angle

9.15 (a) An *electron domain* is a region in a molecule where electrons are most likely to be found.

(b) Each balloon in Figure 9.5 occupies a volume of space. The best arrangement is one where each balloon has its "own" space, where they are as far apart as possible and repulsions are minimized. Electron domains are negatively charged regions, so they also adopt an arrangement where repulsions are minimized.

9.16 The negative charge of the electron leads to repulsion between electron domains and causes them to have an effect on molecular structure.

9.17 (a) The number of electron domains in a molecule or ion is the number of bonds (double and triple bonds count as one domain) **plus** the number of nonbonding (lone) electron pairs.

(b) A *bonding electron domain* is a region between two bonded atoms that contains one or more pairs of bonding electrons. A *nonbonding electron domain* is localized on a single atom and contains one pair of nonbonding electrons (a lone pair).

9.18 We expect the nonbonding electron domain in NH_3 to occupy a smaller volume than the one in PH_3. The electronegativity of N, 3.0, is larger than that of P, 2.1. The nonbonding electrons will be more strongly attracted to N than to P, and the volume of the domain will be smaller. This means that the charge density of the nonbonding domain in NH_3 will be greater and it will experience stronger repulsions than the nonbonding domain in PH_3.

9.19 *Analyze/Plan.* Draw the Lewis structure of each molecule and take note of nonbonding (lone) electron pairs about the central atom. *Solve.*

(a) SiH_4, 8 valence e^-, 4 e^- pr, 0 nonbonding pairs, no effect on molecular shape

$$\begin{array}{c} \text{H} \\ | \\ \text{H}-\text{Si}-\text{H} \\ | \\ \text{H} \end{array}$$

(b) PF_3, 26 valence e^-, 13 e^- pr, 1 nonbonding pair on P, influences molecular shape

$$:\overset{\cdot\cdot}{\underset{\cdot\cdot}{F}}—\overset{\cdot\cdot}{P}—\overset{\cdot\cdot}{\underset{\cdot\cdot}{F}}:$$
$$|$$
$$:\overset{\cdot\cdot}{\underset{\cdot\cdot}{F}}:$$

(c)   HBr, 8 valence e^-, 4 e^- pr, 3 nonbonding pairs on Br, no effect on molecular shape because Br is not "central"

$$H—\overset{\cdot\cdot}{\underset{\cdot\cdot}{Br}}:$$

(d)   HCN, 10 valence e^-, 5 e^- pr, 0 nonbonding pairs on C, no effect on molecular shape

$$H—C{\equiv}N:$$

(e) SO_2, 18 valence e^-, 9 e^- pr, 1 nonbonding pair on S, influences molecular shape

$$:\overset{\cdot\cdot}{\underset{\cdot\cdot}{O}}—\overset{\cdot\cdot}{S}{=}\overset{\cdot\cdot}{\underset{\cdot\cdot}{O}} \longleftrightarrow \overset{\cdot\cdot}{\underset{\cdot\cdot}{O}}{=}\overset{\cdot\cdot}{S}—\overset{\cdot\cdot}{\underset{\cdot\cdot}{O}}: \longleftrightarrow \overset{\cdot\cdot}{\underset{\cdot\cdot}{O}}{=}\overset{\cdot\cdot}{S}{=}\overset{\cdot\cdot}{\underset{\cdot\cdot}{O}}$$

9.20   Draw the Lewis structure of each molecule. If it has nonbonding electron pairs on the central atom, decide whether they will cause to bond angles to deviate from ideal values for the particular electron domain geometry.

(a) H_2S, 8 valence e^-, 4 e^- pr, tetrahedral electron domain geometry with 2 nonbonding electron pairs on S will cause the bond angle to deviate from ideal $109.5°$ angles

$$H—\overset{\cdot\cdot}{\underset{\cdot\cdot}{S}}—H$$

(b) BCl_3, 24 valence e^-, 12 e^- pr, trigonal planar electron domain geometry with zero nonbonding pairs on B. We confidently predict $120°$ angles.

$$:\overset{\cdot\cdot}{\underset{\cdot\cdot}{Cl}}—B—\overset{\cdot\cdot}{\underset{\cdot\cdot}{Cl}}:$$
$$|$$
$$:\overset{\cdot\cdot}{\underset{\cdot\cdot}{Cl}}:$$

(c) CH_3I, 14 valence e^-, 7 e^- pr, tetrahedral electron domain geometry with zero nonbonding pairs on C. We confidently predict $109.5°$ angles.

$$\begin{array}{c} H \\ | \\ H—C—\overset{\cdot\cdot}{\underset{\cdot\cdot}{I}}: \\ | \\ H \end{array}$$

(d) CBr_4, 32 valence e^-, 16 e^- pr, tetrahedral electron domain geometry with zero nonbonding pairs on C. We confidently predict $109.5°$ angles.

$$\begin{array}{c} :\overset{\cdot\cdot}{Br}: \\ | \\ :\overset{\cdot\cdot}{\underset{\cdot\cdot}{Br}}—C—\overset{\cdot\cdot}{\underset{\cdot\cdot}{Br}}: \\ | \\ :\overset{\cdot\cdot}{\underset{\cdot\cdot}{Br}}: \end{array}$$

(e) $TeBr_4$, 34 valence e^-, 17 e^- pr, trigonal bipyramidal electron domain geometry with one nonbonding pair on Te. The structure is similar to SF_4 shown in Sample Exercise 9.2. The bond angles will deviate from ideal values, but perhaps not as much as in SF_4. (Structure follows.)

$$: \ddot{Br} :$$

$$: \ddot{Br} - Te - \ddot{Br} :$$

$$: \ddot{Br} :$$

9.21   *Analyze/Plan.* Draw the Lewis structure of each molecule and count the number of nonbonding (lone) electron pairs. Note that the question asks 'in the molecule' rather than just around the central atom. *Solve.*

(a) $(CH_3)_2S$, 20 valence e^-, 10 e^- pr, 2 nonbonding pairs

$$H - \overset{\displaystyle H}{\underset{\displaystyle H}{\overset{|}{\underset{|}{C}}}} - \ddot{S} - \overset{\displaystyle H}{\underset{\displaystyle H}{\overset{|}{\underset{|}{C}}}} - H$$

(b)   HCN, 10 valence e^-, 5 e^- pr, 1 nonbonding pair

$$H - C \equiv N :$$

(c) H_2C_2, 10 valence e^-, 5 e^- pr, 0 nonbonding pairs

$$H - C \equiv C - H$$

(d) CH_3F, 14 valence e^-, 7 e^- pr, 3 nonbonding pairs

$$H - \overset{\displaystyle H}{\underset{\displaystyle H}{\overset{|}{\underset{|}{C}}}} - \ddot{F} :$$

9.22   *Analyze/Plan.* See Table 9.1. *Solve.*

(a)   trigonal planar   (b)   tetrahedral

(c)   trigonal bipyramidal   (d)   octahedral

9.23   The electron-domain geometry indicated by VSEPR describes the arrangement of all bonding and nonbonding electron domains. The molecular geometry describes just the atomic positions. H_2O has the Lewis structure given below; there are four electron domains around oxygen so the electron-domain geometry is tetrahedral, but the molecular geometry of the three atoms is bent.

Lewis structure   electron-domain   molecular geometry
                   geometry

We make this distinction because all electron domains must be considered when describing the atomic arrangement and bond angles in a molecule but the molecular geometry or shape is a description of just the atomic positions.

9.24   If the electron-domain geometry is trigonal bipyramidal, there are five total electron domains around the central atom. An AB_3 molecule has three bonding domains, so there must be two nonbonding domains on A.

9.25   *Analyze/Plan.* See Tables 9.2 and 9.3. Solve.

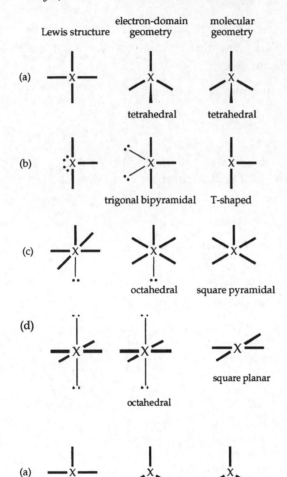

9.26

9.27 *Analyze/Plan.* Follow the logic in Sample Exercise 9.1. *Solve.*

bent (b), linear (l), octahedral (oh), seesaw (ss), square pyramidal (sp),
square planar (spl), tetrahedral (td), trigonal bipyramidal (tbp), trigonal planar (tr),
trigonal pyramidal (tp), T-shaped (T)

	Molecule or ion	Valence electrons	Lewis structure	Electron-domain geometry	Molecular geometry
(a)	HCN	10	:N≡C—H N≡C—H	l	l
(b)	SO₃²⁻	26	*[:Ö—S̈—Ö:]²⁻ [O–S–O]²⁻	td	tp
(c)	SF₄	34	:F̈—S̈—F̈: [F–S–F]	tbp	ss
(d)	PF₆⁻	48	[:F̈—P̈—F̈:]⁻ [F–P–F]⁻	oh	oh
(e)	NH₃Cl⁺	14	[H—N̈—H]⁺ [N]⁺	td	td
(f)	N₃⁻	16	*[:N̈—N≡N:]⁻ [N—N≡N]⁻	l	l

*More than one resonance structure is possible. All equivalent resonance structures predict the same molecular geometry.

9.28 bent (b), linear (l), octahedral (oh), seesaw (ss) square pyramidal (sp), square planar (spl), tetrahedral (td), trigonal bipyramidal (tbp), trigonal planar (tr), trigonal pyramidal (tp), T-shaped (T)

	Molecule or ion	Valence electrons	Lewis structure	Electron-domain Geometry	Molecular geometry
(a)	AsF₃	26	:F̈—As̈—F̈: [As]	td	tp
(b)	CH₃⁺	6	[H—C̈—H]⁺ [C]⁺	tr	tr
(c)	BrF₃	28	:F̈: Br̈—F̈: :F̈: [Br—F]	tbp	T

237

9.28　(Continued). bent (b), linear (l), octahedral (oh), seesaw (ss) square pyramidal (sp), square planar (spl), tetrahedral (td), trigonal bipyramidal (tbp), trigonal planar (tr), trigonal pyramidal (tp), T-shaped (T)

Molecule or ion	Valence electrons	Lewis structure	Electron-domain Geometry	Molecular geometry
(d) ClO_3^-	26		td	tp
(e) XeF_2	22		tbp	l
(f) BrO_2^-	20		td	b

*More than one resonance structure is possible. All equivalent resonance structures predict the same molecular geometry.

9.29　*Analyze/Plan.* Work backwards from molecular geometry, using Tables 9.2 and 9.3. *Solve.*

(a) Electron-domain geometries: i, trigonal planar; ii, tetrahedral; iii, trigonal bipyramidal

(b) nonbonding electron domains: i, 0; ii, 1; iii, 2

(c) N and P. Shape ii has three bonding and one nonbonding electron domains. Li and Al would form ionic compounds with F, so there would be no nonbonding electron domains. Assuming that F always has three nonbonding domains, BF_3 and ClF_3 would have the wrong number of nonbonding domains to produce shape ii.

(d) Cl (also Br and I, since they have seven valence electrons). This T-shaped molecular geometry arises from a trigonal bipyramidal electron-domain geometry with two nonbonding domains (Table 9.3). Assuming each F atom has three nonbonding domains and forms only single bonds with A, A must have seven valence electrons to produce these electron-domain and molecular geometries. It must be in or below the third row of the periodic table, so that it can accommodate more than four electron domains.

9.30　(a) Electron-domain geometries: i, octahedral; ii, tedrahedral; iii, trigonal bipyramidal

(b) nonbonding electron domains: i, 2; ii, 0; iii, 1

(c) S or Se. Shape iii has five electron domains, so A must be in or below the third row of the periodic table. This eliminates Be and C. Assuming each F atom has three nonbonding electron domains and forms only single bonds with A, A must have six valence electrons to produce these electron-domain and molecular geometries.

(d)   Xe. (See Table 9.3) Assuming F behaves typically, A must be in or below the third row and have eight valence electrons. Only Xe fits this description. (Noble gas elements above Xe have not been shown to form molecules of the type AF_4. See Section 7.8.)

9.31   *Analyze/Plan.* Follow the logic in Sample Exercise 9.3.   *Solve.*

(a)   1 – 109°, 2 – 109°   (b)   3 – 109°, 4 – 109°

(c)   5 – 180°   (d)   6 – 120°, 7 – 109°, 8 – 109°

9.32   (a)   1 – 109°, 2 – 120°   (b)   3 – 109°, 4 – 120°

(c)   5 – 109°, 6 – 109°   (d)   7 – 180°, 8 – 109°

9.33   *Analyze/Plan.* Given the formula of each molecule or ion, draw the correct Lewis structure and use principles of VSEPR to answer the question.   *Solve.*

$$F{-}Si{-}F$$ (with F above and below) $$P{-}F$$ (trigonal bipyramidal, F's attached) $$S{-}:$$ (seesaw with F's) $$F{-}As{-}F$$ (with F above, lone pair, F below)

The three nonbonded electron pairs on each F atom have been omitted for clarity.

The two molecules with trigonal bipyramidal electron domain geometry, PF_5 and SF_4, have more than one F–A–F bond angle.

9.34

$$\left[H{-}\ddot{N}{-}H \right]^{-} \qquad H{-}\ddot{N}{-}H \qquad \left[\begin{array}{c} H \\ | \\ H{-}N{-}H \\ | \\ H \end{array} \right]^{+}$$

Each species has four electron domains around the N atom, but the number of nonbonding domains decreases from two to zero, going from NH_2^- to NH_4^+. Since nonbonding domains exert greater repulsive forces on adjacent domains, the bond angles expand as the number of nonbonding domains decreases.

9.35   *Analyze.* Given: molecular formulas. Find: explain features of molecular geometries.

Plan. Draw the correct Lewis structures for the molecules and use VSEPR to predict and explain observed molecular geometry.   *Solve.*

(a) BrF_4^- 36 e^-, 18 e^- pr BF_4^- 32 e^-, 16 e^- pr

$$\left[\begin{array}{c} :\ddot{F}: \\ | \\ :\ddot{F}{-}\ddot{Br}{-}\ddot{F}: \\ | \\ :\ddot{F}: \end{array} \right]^{-} \qquad\qquad \left[\begin{array}{c} :\ddot{F}: \\ | \\ :\ddot{F}{-}B{-}\ddot{F}: \\ | \\ :\ddot{F}: \end{array} \right]^{-}$$

6 e^- pairs around Br   4 e^- pairs around B,
octahedral e^- domain geometry   tetrahedral e^- domain geometry
square planar molecular geometry   tetrahedral molecular geometry

The fundamental feature that determines molecular geometry is the number of electron domains around the central atom, and the number of these that are bonding domains. Although BrF_4^- and BF_4^- are both of the form AX_4^-, the central atoms and thus the number of valence electrons in the two ions are different. This leads to different numbers of e^- domains about the two central atoms. Even though both ions have four bonding electron domains, the six total domains around Br require octahedral domain geometry and square planar molecular geometry, while the four total domains about B lead to tetrahedral domain and molecular geometry.

(b) H_2X, 8 e^-, 4 e^- pr

All molecules in the series have tetrahedral electron domain geometry and bent molecular structure. To a first approximation, the H–X–H angles will be 109°. Any variation will be due to differences in repulsion among the nonbonding and bonding electron domains. The less electronegative the central atom, the larger the nonbonding electron domain, the greater the effect of repulsive forces on adjacent bonding domains. The less electronegative the central atom, the larger the deviation from ideal tetrahedral angles. The angles will vary as $H_2O > H_2S > H_2Se$.

9.36   (a) ClO_2^- 20 e^-, 10 e^- pr

$$\left[\ddot{\underset{..}{O}} - \ddot{\underset{..}{Cl}} - \ddot{\underset{..}{O}} \right]^-$$

4 e^- domains around Cl, tetrahedral e^- domain geometry,
bent molecular geometry bond angle $\lesssim 109.5°$

NO_2^- 18 e^-, 9 e^- pr

$$\left[\ddot{\underset{..}{O}} = \ddot{N} - \ddot{\underset{..}{O}} \right]^- \longleftrightarrow \left[\ddot{\underset{..}{O}} - \ddot{N} = \ddot{\underset{..}{O}} \right]^-$$

3 e^- domains about N (both resonance structures), trigonal planar e^- domain geometry bent molecular geometry bond angle $\lesssim 120°$

Both molecular geometries are described as "bent" because both molecules have two nonlinear bonding electron domains. The bond angles (the angle between the two bonding domains) in the two ions are different because the total number of electron domains, and thus the electron domain geometries are different.

(b) XeF_2 22 e^-, 11 e^- pr

$$:\!\ddot{F}\!-\!\ddot{\underset{..}{Xe}}\!-\!\ddot{F}\!:$$

5 e^- domains around Xe, trigonal bipyramidal e^- domain geometry,
linear molecular geometry

The question here really is: why do the three nonbonding domains all occupy the equatorial plane of the trigonal bipyramid? In a tbp, there are several different kinds of repulsions, bonding domain-bonding domain (bd-bd), bonding domain-nonbonding domain (bd-nd), and nonbonding domain-nonbonding domain (nd-nd). Each of these can have 90°, 120°, or 180° geometry. Since nonbonding domains occupy more space, 90° nd-nd repulsions are most significant and least desirable. The various electron domains arrange themselves to minimize these 90° nd-nd interactions. The arrangement shown above has no 90° nd-nd repulsions. An arrangement with one or two nonbonding domains in axial positions would lead to at least two 90° nd-nd repulsions, a less stable situation. (To convince yourself, tabulate the number and kinds of repulsions for each possible tbp arrangement of 2bd's and 3nd's.)

Shapes and Polarity of Polyatomic Molecules (section 9.3)

9.37   A bond dipole is the asymmetric charge distribution between two bonded atoms with unequal electronegativities. A molecular dipole moment is the three-dimensional sum of all the bond dipoles in a molecule. (A molecular dipole moment is a measurable physical property; a bond dipole is not measurable, unless the molecule is diatomic.)

9.38   For a polar A–X bond in an AX_3 molecule, as the X–A–X bond angle increases from 100° to 120°, the molecular dipole moment decreases. In a symmetrical AX_3 molecule with 120° bond angles, bond dipoles cancel and the molecule is nonpolar. As the bond angle decreases, the resultant of the three bond dipoles becomes larger, and the dipole moment increases.

9.39   *Analyze/plan.* Follow the logic in Sample Exercise 9.4. *Solve.*

     (a) SCl_2, 20 e⁻, 10 e⁻ pr

          :C̤l̤—S̤—C̤l̤:

          tetrahedral e⁻ domain geometry
          bent molecular geometry

          S and Cl have different electronegativities; the S–Cl bonds are polar. The bond dipoles are not opposite each other, so the molecule is polar. The dipole moment vector bisects the Cl–S–Cl bond angle. (A more difficult question is which end of the dipole moment vector is negative. The resultant of the two bond dipoles has its negative end toward the Cl atoms. However, the partial negative charge due to the lone pairs on S points opposite to the negative end of the resultant. A reasonable guess is that the negative end of the dipole moment vector is in the direction of the lone pairs.)

     (b) $BeCl_2$, 16 e⁻, 8 e⁻ pr

          :C̤l̤—Be—C̤l̤:

          linear electron domain and molecular geometry

          (Resonance structures with Be=Cl can be drawn, but electronegativity arguments predict that most electron density will reside on Cl and that the structure above is the main resonance contributor.) Be and Cl have very different electro-negativities, so the Be–Cl bonds are polar. The individual bond dipoles are equal and opposite, so the net molecular dipole moment is zero.

9.40   (a)   If PH_3 is polar, it must have a measurable dipole moment. This means that the three P–H bond dipoles do not cancel. If PH_3 were planar, the P–H bond dipoles would cancel, and the molecule would be nonpolar. The measurable dipole moment of PH_3 is experimental evidence that the molecule cannot be planar.

     (b) O_3, 18 e^-, 9 e^- pr; $:\ddot{O}=\ddot{O}-\ddot{\underset{..}{O}}: \longleftrightarrow :\ddot{\underset{..}{O}}-\ddot{O}=\ddot{O}:$

trigonal planar e^- domain geometry
bent molecular geometry

Since all atoms are the same, the individual bond dipoles are zero. However, the central O atom has a lone pair of electrons which cause an unequal electron (and charge) distribution in the molecule. This lone pair is the source of the dipole moment in O_3.

9.41   (a)   In Exercise 9.29, molecules ii and iii will have nonzero dipole moments. Molecule i has zero nonbonding electron pairs on A, and the 3 A–F dipoles are oriented so that the sum of their vectors is zero (the bond dipoles cancel). Molecules ii and iii have nonbonding electron pairs on A and their bond dipoles do not cancel. A nonbonding electron pair (or pairs) on a central atom almost guarantees at least a small molecular dipole moment, because no bond dipole exactly cancels a nonbonding pair. (Exceptions are molecular geometries with nonbonding electron domains 180° apart.)

     (b) AF_4 molecules will have a zero dipole moment if the 4 A–F bond dipoles are arranged (symmetrically) so that they cancel, and any nonbonding pairs are arranged so that they cancel. Therefore, in Exercise 9.30, molecules i and ii have zero dipole moments and are nonpolar.

9.42   (a)   For a molecule with polar bonds to be nonpolar, the polar bonds must be (symmetrically) arranged so that the bond dipoles cancel. And, any nonbonding pairs about the central atom must be arranged so that they cancel. In most cases, nonbonding e^- domains will be absent from the central atom.

     (b) AB_2: linear e^- domain geometry (edg), linear molecular geometry (mg), trigonal bipyramidal edg, linear mg

           AB_3: trigonal planar edg, trigonal planar mg

           AB_4: tetrahedral edg, tetrahedral mg; octahedral edg, square planar mg

9.43   *Analyze/Plan.* Given molecular formulas, draw correct Lewis structures, determine molecular structure and polarity. *Solve.*

     (a)   Polar, $\Delta EN > 0$

         I–F

     (b)   Nonpolar, the molecule is linear and the bond dipoles cancel.

         $S=C=S$

(c)   Nonpolar, in a symmetrical trigonal planar structure, the bond dipoles cancel.

O
||
S
O   O

(d)   Polar, although the bond dipoles are essentially zero, there is an unequal charge distribution due to the nonbonded electron pair on P.

P̈
Cl   Cl
Cl

(e)   Nonpolar, symmetrical octahedron

F
F   F
S
F   F
F

(f)   Polar, square pyramidal molecular geometry, bond dipoles do not cancel.

F   F
I
F   F
F

9.44   (a)   Nonpolar, in a symmetrical tetrahedral structure (Figure 9.1) the bond dipoles cancel.

Cl
C
Cl   Cl
Cl

(b)   Polar, there is an unequal charge distribution due to the nonbonded electron pair on N.

N̈
H   H
H

(c)   Polar, there is an unequal charge distribution due to the nonbonded electron pair on S.

F
F
S̈
F
F

(d)   Nonpolar, the bond dipoles and the nonbonded electron pairs cancel.

F   F
Xe
F   F

(e)   Polar, the C–H and C–Br bond dipoles are not equal and do not cancel.

Br
C
H   H
H

(f)   Nonpolar, in a symmetrical trigonal planar structure, the bond dipoles cancel.

9.45   *Analyze/Plan.* Given molecular formulas, draw correct Lewis structures, analyze molecular structure and determine polarity.   *Solve.*

(a) $C_2H_2Cl_2$, each isomer has 24 e⁻, 12 e⁻ pr. Lewis structures:

Molecular geometries:

(b)   All three isomers are planar. The molecules on the left and right are polar because the C–Cl bond dipoles do not point in opposite directions. In the middle isomer, the C–Cl bonds and dipoles are pointing in opposite directions (as are the C–H bonds), the molecule is nonpolar and has a measured dipole moment of zero.

(c) C_2H_3Cl (lone pairs on Cl omitted for clarity)

There are four possible placements for Cl:

By rotating each of these structures in various directions, it becomes clear that the four structures are equivalent; C_2H_3Cl has only one isomer. Because C_2H_3Cl has only one C–Cl bond, the bond dipoles do not cancel, and the molecule has a dipole moment.

9.46   Each C–Cl bond is polar. The question is whether the vector sum of the C–Cl bond dipoles in each molecule will be nonzero. In the *ortho* and *meta* isomers, the C–Cl vectors are at 60° and 120° angles, respectively, and their resultant dipole moments are nonzero. In the *para* isomer, the C–Cl vectors are opposite, at an angle of 180°, with a resultant dipole moment of zero. The *ortho* and *meta* isomers are polar, the *para* isomer is nonpolar.

Orbital Overlap; Hybrid Orbitals (sections 9.4 and 9.5)

9.47   (a)   *Orbital overlap* occurs when a valence atomic orbital on one atom shares the same region of space with a valence atomic orbital on an adjacent atom.

(b)   A chemical bond is a concentration of electron density between the nuclei of two atoms. This concentration can take place because orbitals on the two atoms overlap.

9.48   (a)

          2s   2s

      (b)

          $2p_z$ $2p_z$

      (c)

          $2p_z$ 2s

9.49   (a)   4 valence e^-, 2 e^- pairs

H−Mg−H

2 bonding e^- domains, linear e^- domain and molecular geometry

      (b)   The linear electron domain geometry in MgH_2 requires sp hybridization.

      (c)   H $\left(\cdots\right)$ Mg

9.50   By analogy to the H_2 molecule shown in Figure 9.14, as the distance between the atoms decreases, the overlap between their bonding orbitals increases. According to Figure 7.6, the bonding atomic radius for the halogens is in the order F < Cl < Br < I. The order of bond lengths in the molecules is I–F < I–Cl < I–Br < I–I. If the extent of orbital overlap increases as the distance between atoms decreases, I–F has the greatest overlap and I_2 the least. The order for extent of orbital overlap is I–I < I–Br < I–Cl < I–F.

9.51   *Analyze/Plan.* For entries where the molecule is listed, follow the logic in Sample Exercises 9.4 and 9.5. For entries where no molecule is listed, decide electron domain geometry from hybridization (or vice-versa). If the molecule is nonpolar, the terminal atoms will be identical. If the molecule is polar, the terminal atoms will be different, or the central atom will have one or more lone pairs, or both. *Solve.*

Molecule	Molecular Structures	Electron Domain Geometry	Hybrdization of CentralAtom	Dipole Moment Yes or No
CO_2	O=C=O	linear	sp	no
NH_3	H—N—H (with lone pair and H below)	tetrahedral	sp^3	yes

CH_4	(structure)	tetrahedral	sp^3	no
BH_3	(structure)	trigonal planar	sp^2	no
SF_4	(structure)	trigonal bipyramidal	not applicable	yes
SF_6	(structure)	octahedral	not applicable	no
H_2CO	(structure)	trigonal planar	sp^2	yes
PF_5	(structure)	trigonal bipyramidal	not applicable	no
XeF_2	(structure)	trigonal bipyramidal	not applicable	no

9.52   In order for atomic orbitals to mix or hybridize, they must have the same principal quantum number. In each principal quantum level, there are a maximum of three p orbitals. Any hybrid orbital can have contribution from a maximum of three p orbitals. Hybrid orbitals designated sp^4 or sp^5 would require contribution from four or five p orbitals, which is not possible.

9.53   (a)   B: $[He]2s^2 2p^1$

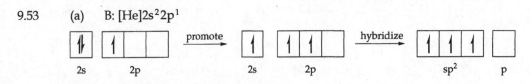

     (b)   The hybrid orbitals are called sp^2.

(c)

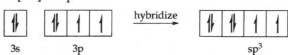

(d)   A single 2p orbital is unhybridized. It lies perpendicular to the trigonal plane of the sp^2 hybrid orbitals.

9.54   (a)   S: [Ne]3s^{2}3p^4

| ⇅ | | ⇅ | ↑ | ↑ | hybridize | ⇅ | ⇅ | ↑ | ↑ |

     3s   3p   sp^3

(b)   The hybrid orbitals are called sp^3.

(c)

(d)   The hybrid orbitals formed in (a) would not be appropriate for SF$_4$. There are five electron domains in SF$_4$, four bonding and one nonbonding. A set of four sp^3 hybrid orbitals could not accommodate all the electron pairs around S.

9.55   *Analyze/Plan.* Given the molecular (or ionic) formula, draw the correct Lewis structure and determine the electron domain geometry, which determines hybridization. *Solve.*

(a)   24 e$^-$, 12 e$^-$ pairs

     :Cl̈—B—C̈l:
          |
        :Cl̈:

     3 e$^-$ pairs around B, trigonal planar e$^-$ domain geometry, sp^2 hybridization

(b)   32 e$^-$, 16 e$^-$ pairs

             :C̈l: ⁻
              |
     :C̈l—Al—C̈l:
              |
             :C̈l:

     4 e$^-$ domains around Al, tetrahedral e$^-$ domain geometry, sp^3 hybridization

(c)   16 e$^-$, 8 e$^-$ pairs

     S̈=C=S̈

     2 e$^-$ domains around C, linear e$^-$ domain geometry, sp hybridization

(d)   8 e$^-$, 4 e$^-$ pairs

        H
        |
   H—Ge—H
        |
        H

     4 e$^-$ pairs around Ge, tetrahedral e$^-$ domain geometry, sp^3 hybridization

9.56　(a)　32 e⁻, 16 e⁻ pairs

$$
\begin{array}{c}
:\ddot{C}l: \\
| \\
:\ddot{C}l-Si-\ddot{C}l: \\
| \\
:\ddot{C}l:
\end{array}
$$

4 e⁻ pairs around Si, tetrahedral e⁻ domain geometry, sp^3 hybridization

(b)　10 e⁻, 5 e⁻ pairs

H—C≡N:

2 e⁻ domains around C, linear e⁻ domain geometry, sp hybridization

(c)　24 e⁻, 12 e⁻ pairs

$$
\begin{array}{c}
:\ddot{O}-S-\ddot{O}: \\
\| \\
:\ddot{O}:
\end{array}
$$

(other resonance structures are possible)

3 e⁻ domains around S, trigonal planar e⁻ domain geometry, sp^2 hybridization

(d)　20 e⁻, 10 e⁻ pairs

:Cl—Te—Cl:

4 e⁻ domains around Te, tetrahedral e⁻ domain geometry, sp^3 hybridization

9.57　(a)　No hybrid orbitals discussed in this chapter have angles of 90°; p atomic orbitals are perpendicular to each other.

(b)　Angles of 109.5° are characteristic of sp^3 hybrid orbitals.

(c)　Angles of 120° can be formed by sp^2 hybrids.

9.58　(a)　The three moieties, BH_4^-, CH_4, and NH_4^+, each have 8 valence e⁻, 4 e⁻ pairs, 4 bonding e⁻ domains, tetrahedral e⁻ domain and molecular geometry and sp^3 hybridization at the central atom.

(b)　The electronegativity of the central atoms decreases in the series N > C > B. The question is: where does the electronegativity of H lie in this series? By examination of electronegativity values in Figure 8.7, H is slightly less electronegative than C, and almost the same as B. The magnitude of the bond dipole decreases in the series N–H > C–H > B–H. The negative end of the dipole is toward N, C, and H, respectively.

(c)　AlH_4^-, SiH_4, and PH_4^+. By the same arguments used in part (a), we expect these three moieties to have the same tetrahedral e⁻ domain and molecular geometry and sp^3 hybridization at the central atom as the species in part (a).

Multiple Bonds (section 9.6)

9.59   (a)   (b)

        (c)   A σ bond is generally stronger than a π bond, because there is more extensive orbital overlap.

        (d)   Two *s* orbitals cannot form a π bond. A π bond has no electron density along the internuclear axis. Overlap of *s* orbitals results in electron density along the internuclear axis. (Another way to say this is that *s* orbitals have the wrong symmetry to form a π bond.)

9.60   (a)   Two unhybridized p orbitals remain, and the atom can form two pi bonds.

        (b)   It would be much easier to twist or rotate around a single sigma bond. Sigma bonds are formed by end-to-end overlap of orbitals and the bonding electron density is symmetric about the internuclear axis. Rotating (twisting) around a sigma bond can be done without disrupting either the orbital overlap or bonding electron density, without breaking the bond.

               The π part of a double bond is formed by side-to-side overlap of p atomic orbitals perpendicular to the internuclear axis. This π overlap locks the atoms into position and makes twisting difficult. Also, only a small twist (rotation) destroys overlap of the *p* orbitals and breaks the π bond.

9.61   *Analyze/Plan.* Draw the correct Lewis structures, count electron domains and decide hybridization. Molecules with π bonds that require all bonded atoms to be in the same plane are planar. For bond-type counting, single bonds are σ bonds, double bonds consist of one σ and one π bond, triple bonds consist of one σ and two π bonds. *Solve.*

        (a)

$$H-\underset{\underset{H}{|}}{\overset{\overset{H}{|}}{C}}-\underset{\underset{H}{|}}{\overset{\overset{H}{|}}{C}}-H \qquad \underset{H}{\overset{H}{\diagdown}}C=C\underset{H}{\overset{H}{\diagup}} \qquad H-C\equiv C-H$$

        (b) sp^3 sp^2 sp

        (c)   nonplanar   planar   planar

        (d) $7\,\sigma, 0\,\pi$ $5\,\sigma, 1\,\pi$ $3\,\sigma, 2\,\pi$

        (e)   Since Si has the same valence electron configuration as C, the structures of the Si analogs would be the same as the C-based molecules. The hybridization at Si is then the same as the hybridization at C. This argument assumes that the Si analogs exist.

               Silicon, which lies in the row below C, has a larger bonding atomic radius and larger atomic orbitals than C. In the analogous compounds, Si–Si distances will be greater than C–C distances. This means that the close approach of Si atoms required to form strong, stable π bonds in Si_2H_4 and Si_2H_2 is not possible and these Si analogs do not readily form.

9.62   (a)   H—N̈—N̈—H   :N≡N:
                      | |
                      H   H

   (b)   The N atoms in N_2H_4 are sp^3 hybridized; there are no unhybridized p orbitals available for π bonding. In N_2, the N atoms are sp hybridized, with two unhybridized p orbitals on each N atom available to form the two π bonds in the N≡N triple bond.

   (c)   The N–N triple bond in N_2 is significantly stronger than the N–N single bond in N_2H_4, because it consists of one σ and two π bonds, rather than a 'plain' sigma bond.   Generally, bond strength increases as the extent of orbital overlap increases. The additional overlap from the two π bonds adds to the strength of the N–N bond in N_2.

9.63   *Analyze/Plan.* Single bonds are σ bonds, double bonds consist of 1 σ and 1 π bond. Each bond is formed by a pair of valence electrons.   *Solve.*

   (a) C_3H_6 has 3(4) + 6(1) = 18 valence electrons

   (b)   8 pairs or 16 total valence electrons form σ bonds

   (c)   1 pair or 2 total valence electrons form π bonds

   (d)   no valence electrons are nonbonding

   (e)   The left and central C atoms are sp^2 hybridized; the right C atom is sp^3 hybridized.

9.64   (a)   The C with a double bond to O has three electron domains and is sp^2 hybridized; the other three C atoms are sp^3 hybridized.

   (b) $C_4H_8O_2$ has 4(4) + 8(1) + 2(6) = 36 valence electrons.

   (c)   13 pairs or 26 total valence electrons form σ bonds

   (d)   1 pair or 2 total valence electrons form π bonds

   (e)   4 pairs or 8 total valence electrons are nonbonding

9.65   *Analyze/Plan.* Given the correct Lewis structure, analyze the electron domain geometry at each central atom. This determines the hybridization and bond angles at that atom. *Solve.*

   (a)   ~109° bond angles about the left most C, sp^3; ~120° bond angles about the right-hand C, sp^2

   (b)   The doubly bonded O can be viewed as sp^2, the other as sp^3; the nitrogen is sp^3 with approximately 109° bond angles.

   (c)   9 σ bonds, 1 π bond

9.66   (a)   1, 120°; 2, 120°; 3, 109°

   (b)   1, sp^2; 2, sp^2; 3, sp^3

   (c)   21 σ bonds

250

9.67   (a)   In a localized π bond, the electron density is concentrated strictly between the two atoms forming the bond. In a delocalized π bond, parallel p orbitals on more than two adjacent atoms overlap and the electron density is spread over all the atoms that contribute p orbitals to the network. There are still two regions of overlap, above and below the σ framework of the molecule.

      (b)   The existence of more than one resonance form is a good indication that a molecule will have delocalized π bonding.

      (c)

The existence of more than one resonance form for NO_2 indicates that the π bond is delocalized. From an orbital perspective, the electron-domain geometry around N is trigonal planar, so the hybridization at N is sp^2. This leaves a p orbital on N and one on each O atom perpendicular to the trigonal plane of the molecule, in the correct orientation for delocalized π overlap. Physically, the two N–O bond lengths are equal, indicating that the two N–O bonds are equivalent, rather than one longer single bond and one shorter double bond.

9.68   (a) $24 \, e^-$, $12 \, e^-$ pairs   (b)

3 electron domains around S, trigonal planar electron-domain geometry, sp^2 hybrid orbitals

      (c)   The multiple resonance structures indicate delocalized π bonding. All four atoms lie in the trigonal plane of the sp^2 hybrid orbitals. On each atom there is a p atomic orbital perpendicular to this plane in the correct orientation for π overlap. The resulting delocalized π electron cloud is Y-shaped (the shape of the molecule) and has electron density above and below the plane of the molecule.

9.69   *Analyze/Plan.* Count valence e^- and e^- pairs in each molecule. Complete the Lewis structure by placing nonbonding electron pairs. Analyze the electron domain geometry at each central atom; visualize and describe the molecular structure. *Solve.*

      (a) $26 \, e^-$, $13 \, e^-$ pairs

The molecule is linear. Each C atom has 2 bonding e^- domains, linear geometry and sp hybridization. This requires that all atoms not only lie in the same plane, but in a line.

      (b) $34 \, e^-$, $17 \, e^-$ pairs

The two central C atoms each have 3 bonding e⁻ domains, trigonal planar geometry and sp² hybridization. Each O–C–O group is planar, while the terminal H atoms can rotate out of these planes. In principle, there is free rotation about the C–C σ bond, but delocalization of the π electrons is possible if the two planes are coincident. It is possible to put all 8 atoms in the same plane.

(c)   12 e⁻, 6 e⁻ pairs

The molecule is planar. Each N atom has 3 bonding e⁻ domains, trigonal planar geometry and sp² hybridization. Since the N atoms share a π bond, the planes must be coincident and all 4 atoms are required to lie in this plane.

9.70   (a)   24 e⁻, 12 e⁻ pairs

The designated C atom has 3 bonding e⁻ domains and sp² hybridization.

(b)   8 e⁻, 4 e⁻ pairs

The P atom has 4 bonding e⁻ domains and sp³ hybridization

(c)   24 e⁻, 12 e⁻ pairs

The Al atom has 3 bonding e⁻ domains and sp² hybridization

(d)   16 e⁻, 8 e⁻ pairs

The designated C atom has 3 bonding e⁻ domains and sp² hybridization.

Molecular Orbitals and Second Row Diatomic Molecules
(sections 9.7 and 9.8)

9.71   (a)   Hybrid orbitals are mixtures (linear combinations) of atomic orbitals from a single atom; the hybrid orbitals remain localized on that atom. Molecular orbitals are combinations of atomic orbitals from two or more atoms. They are associated with the entire molecule, not a single atom.

       (b)   Each MO, like each AO or hybrid, can hold a maximum of two electrons.

       (c)   Antibonding MOs can have electrons in them.

9.72   (a)   An MO, since the AOs come from two different atoms.

       (b)   A hybrid orbital, since the AOs are on the same atom.

       (c)   Yes. The Pauli principle, that no two electrons can have the same four quantum numbers, means that an orbital can hold at most two electrons. (Since n, l, and m_1 are the same for a particular orbital and m_s has only two possible values, an orbital can hold at most two electrons). This is true for atomic and molecular orbitals.

9.73   (a)

       (b)   There is one electron in H_2^+.

       (c)

       (d)   Bond order = 1/2 (1-0) = 1/2

       (e)   Fall apart. The stability of H_2^+ is due to the lower energy state of the σ bonding molecular orbital relative to the energy of a H 1s atomic orbital. If the single electron in H_2^+ is excited to the σ^*_{1s} orbital, its energy is higher than the energy of an H 1s atomic orbital and H_2^+ will decompose into a hydrogen atom and a hydrogen ion.

$$H_2^+ \xrightarrow{h\nu} H + H^+.$$

9.74   (a)

(b) $\boxed{\uparrow}$ σ^*_{1s}

$\boxed{\uparrow\downarrow}$ σ_{1s}

(c)   Bond order = 1/2 (2-1) = ½

(d)   If one electron moves from σ_{1s} to σ^*_{1s}, the bond order becomes –1/2. There is a net increase in energy relative to isolated H atoms, so the ion will decompose.

$$H_2^- \xrightarrow{\text{hv}} H + H^-.$$

9.75

(a)   One. With three mutually perpendicular p orbitals on each atom, only one set can be oriented for end-to-end, sigma overlap.

(b)   Two. The 2 *p* orbitals on each atom not involved in σ bonding can be aligned for side-to-side π overlap.

(c)   Three, 1 σ* and 2 π*. There are a total of 6 p orbitals on the two atoms. When combining AOs to form MOs, total number of orbitals is conserved. If 3 of the 6 MOs are bonding MOs, as described in (a) and (b), then the remaining 3 MOs must be antibonding. They will have the same symmetry as the bonding MOs, 1 σ* and 2 π*.

9.76   (a)   Zero

(b)   The two π_{2p} molecular orbitals are degenerate; they have the same energy, but they have different spatial orientations 90° apart.

(c)   In the bonding MO the electrons are stabilized by both nuclei. In an antibonding MO, the electrons are directed away from the nuclei, so the π_{2p} bonding MO is lower in energy than the π^*_{2p} antibonding MO.

254

9.77   (a)   When comparing the same two bonded atoms, the greater the bond order, the shorter the bond length and the greater the bond energy. That is, bond order and bond energy are directly related, while bond order and bond length are inversely related. When comparing different bonded nuclei, there are no simple relationships (see Solution 8.100).

(b) $Be_2, 4 e^-$ $Be_2^+, 3 e^-$

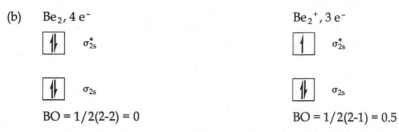

BO = 1/2(2-2) = 0   BO = 1/2(2-1) = 0.5

Be_2 has a bond order of zero and is not energetically favored over isolated Be atoms; it is not expected to exist. Be_2^+ has a bond order of 0.5 and is slightly lower in energy than isolated Be atoms. It will probably exist under special experimental conditions, but be unstable.

9.78   (a) O_2^{2-} has a bond order of 1.0, while O_2^- has a bond order of 1.5. For the same bonded atoms, the greater the bond order the shorter the bond, so O_2^- has the shorter bond.

(b)   The two possible orbital energy level diagrams are:

☐	σ_{2p}^*	☐	σ_{2p}^*
☐☐	π_{2p}^*	☐☐	π_{2p}^*
☐☐	π_{2p}	☐	σ_{2p}
⇅	σ_{2p}	↑↑	π_{2p}
⇅	σ_{2s}^*	⇅	σ_{2s}^*
⇅	σ_{2s}	⇅	σ_{2s}

The magnetic properties of a molecule reveal whether it has unpaired electrons. If the σ_{2p} MOs are lower in energy, B_2 has no unpaired electrons. If the π_{2p} MOs are lower in energy than the σ_{2p} MO, there are two unpaired electrons. The magnetic properties of B_2 must indicate that it has unpaired electrons.

(c)   According to Figure 9.43, the two highest-energy electrons of O_2 are in antibonding π_{2p}^* MOs and O_2 has a bond order of 2.0 Removing these two electrons to form O_2^{2+} produces an ion with bond order 3.0. O_2^{2+} has a stronger O–O bond than O_2, because O_2^{2+} has a greater bond order.

9.79   (a), (b) Substances with no unpaired electrons are weakly repelled by a magnetic field. This property is called *diamagnetism*.

(c) O_2^{2-}, Be_2^{2+} [see Figure 9.43 and Solution 9.77(b)]

9.80   (a)   Substances with unpaired electrons are attracted into a magnetic field. This property is called *paramagnetism*.

       (b)   Weigh the substance normally and in a magnetic field, as shown in Figure 9.44. Paramagnetic substances appear to have a larger mass when weighed in a magnetic field.

       (c)   See Figures 9.35 and 9.43. O_2^+, one unpaired electron; N_2^{2-}, two unpaired electrons; Li_2^+, one unpaired electron

9.81

    (a) B_2^+ (b) Li_2^+ (c) N_2^+ (d) Ne_2^{2+}

       increase   increase   increase   decrease

       Addition of an electron increases bond order if it occupies a bonding MO and decreases stability if it occupies an antibonding MO.

9.82   Determine the number of "valence" (non-core) electrons in each molecule or ion. Use the homonuclear diatomic MO diagram from Figure 9.43 (shown below) to calculate bond order and magnetic properties of each species. The electronegativity difference between heteroatomics increases the energy difference between the 2s AO on one atom and the 2p AO on the other, rendering the "no interaction" MO diagram in Figure 9.43 appropriate.

       (a) CO^+:   9 e⁻, B.O. = (7 – 2) / 2 = 2.5, paramagnetic

       (b) NO^-: 12 e⁻, B.O. = (8 – 4) / 2 = 2.0, paramagnetic

       (c) OF^+: 12 e⁻, B.O. = (8 – 4) / 2 = 2.0, paramagnetic

       (d) NeF^+: 14 e⁻, B.O. = (8 – 6) / 2 = 1.0, diamagnetic

9.83   *Analyze/Plan.* Determine the number of "valence" (non-core) electrons in each molecule or ion. Use the homonuclear diatomic MO diagram from Figure 9.43 (shown below) to calculate bond order and magnetic properties of each species. The electronegativity difference between heteroatomics increases the energy difference between the 2s AO on one atom and the 2p AO on the other, rendering the "no interaction" MO diagram in Figure 9.43 appropriate. *Solve.*

CN: 9 e⁻, B.O. = (7 – 2) / 2 = 2.5

CN⁺:   8 e⁻, B.O. = (6 – 2) / 2 = 2.0

CN⁻:   10 e⁻, B.O. = (8 – 2) / 2 = 3.0

(a)   CN⁻ has the highest bond order and therefore the strongest C–N bond.

(b)   CN and CN⁺. CN has an odd number of valence electrons, so it must have an unpaired electron. The electron configuration for CN is shown in the diagram. Removing one electron from the π_{2p} MOs to form CN⁺ produces an ion with two unpaired electrons. Adding one electron to the π_{2p} MOs of CN to form CN⁻ produces an ion with all electrons paired.

9.84   (a)   The bond order of NO is [1/2 (8 – 3)] = 2.5. The electron that is lost is in an antibonding molecular orbital, so the bond order in NO⁺ is 3.0. The increase in bond order is the driving force for the formation of NO⁺.

(b)   To form NO⁻, an electron is added to an antibonding orbital, and the new bond order is [1/2 (8 – 4)] = 2. The order of increasing bond order and bond strength is: NO⁻ < NO < NO⁺. NO⁻ and NO are paramagnetic with two and one unpaired electrons, respectively. NO⁺ is diamagnetic.

(c)   NO⁺ is isoelectronic with N_2, and NO⁻ is isoelectronic with O_2.

9.85   (a)   3s, $3p_x$, $3p_y$, $3p_z$ (b) π_{3p}

(c)   Two. Note that there are two degenerate π_{3p} bonding molecular orbitals; each holds two electrons. A total of 4 electrons can be designated as π_{3p}, but no single molecular orbital can hold more than two electrons.

(d)   If the MO diagram for P_2 is similar to that of N_2, P_2 will have no unpaired electrons and be diamagnetic.

9.86   (a)   I: 5s, $5p_x$, $5p_y$, $5p_z$; Br: 4s, $4p_x$, $4p_y$, $4p_z$

(b)   By analogy to F_2, the BO of IBr will be 1.

(c)   I and Br have valence atomic orbitals with different principal quantum numbers. This means that the radial extensions (sizes) of the valence atomic orbital that contribute to the MO are different. The n = 5 valence AOs on I are larger than the n = 4 valence AOs on Br.

(d) σ_{np}^{*}

(e)   None

Additional Exercises

9.87   (a)   The physical basis of VSEPR is the electrostatic repulsion of like-charged particles, in this case groups or domains of electrons. That is, owing to electrostatic repulsion, electron domains will arrange themselves to be as far apart as possible.

(b)   The σ-bond electrons are localized in the region along the internuclear axes. The positions of the atoms and geometry of the molecule are thus closely tied to the locations of these electron pairs. Because the π-bond electrons are distributed above and below the plane that contains the σ bonds, these electron pairs do not, in effect, influence the geometry of the molecule. Thus, all σ- and π-bond electrons localized between two atoms are located in the same electron domain.

9.88   The Pauli exclusion principle is the fundamental basis for assigning pairs of electrons with their spins paired to electron domains. The Pauli principle states that no two electrons can have the same four quantum numbers. This means that the maximum occupancy of an orbital, be it atomic, hybrid, molecular, or whatever, is two electrons. And, if two electrons occupy the same orbital, their spins must be paired.

9.89

| e⁻ domain geometry td | tbp | octahedral (oh) |
| molecular shape td | seesaw (ss) | square planar (s) |

Although there are four bonding electron domains in each molecule, the number of nonbonding domains is different in each case. The bond angles and thus the molecular shape are influenced by the total number of electron domains.

9.90   (a)   40 e⁻, 20 e⁻ pairs

5 e⁻ domains
trigonal bipyramidal electron domain geometry

(b)   The greater the electronegativity of the terminal atom, the larger the negative charge centered on the atom, the smaller the effective size of the P–X bonding electron domain. A P–F bond will produce a smaller (and shorter) electron domain than a P–Cl bond.

(c)   The molecular geometry (shape) is also trigonal bipyramidal, because all five electron domains are bonding domains. Because we predicted the P–F electron domain to be smaller, the larger P–Cl bonding domain will occupy the equatorial plane of the molecule, minimizing the number of 90° P–Cl to P–F repulsions. This is the same argument that places a "larger" nonbonding domain in the equatorial position of a molecule like SF_4.

(d)   The molecular geometry is distorted from a perfect trigonal bipyramid because not all electron domains are alike. The 90° P–Cl to P–F repulsions will be greater than the 90° P–F to P–F repulsions, so the F(axial)–P–Cl angles will be greater than 90°. The equatorial F–P–F angles may distort slightly to "make room" for the axial F atoms that are "pushed away" from the equatorial Cl atom.

9.91   For any triangle, the law of cosines gives the length of side c as $c^2 = a^2 + b^2 - 2ab \cos\theta$.

Let the edge length of the cube (uy = vy = vz) = X

The length of the face diagonal (uv) is

$(uv)^2 = (uy)^2 + (vy)^2 - 2(uy)(vy) \cos 90$

$(uv)^2 = X^2 + X^2 - 2(X)(X) \cos 90$

$(uv)^2 = 2X^2; uv = \sqrt{2}X$

The length of the body diagonal (uz) is

$(uz)^2 = (vz^2) + (uv)^2 - 2(vz)(uv) \cos 90$

$(uz)^2 = X^2 + (\sqrt{2}X)^2 - 2(X)(\sqrt{2}X) \cos 90$

$(uz)^2 = 3X^2; uz = \sqrt{3}X$

For calculating the characteristic tetrahedral angle, the appropriate triangle has vertices u, v, and w. Theta, θ, is the angle formed by sides wu and wv and the hypotenuse is side uv.

$wu = wv = uz/2 = \sqrt{3}/2X; uv = \sqrt{2}X$

$(\sqrt{2}X)^2 = (\sqrt{3}/2X)^2 + (\sqrt{3}/2X)^2 - 2(\sqrt{3}/2X)(\sqrt{3}/2) \cos\theta$

$2X^2 = 3/4 X^2 + 3/4 X^2 - 3/2 X^2 \cos\theta$

$2X^2 = 3/2 X^2 - 3/2 X^2 \cos\theta$

$1/2 X^2 = -3/2 X^2 \cos\theta$

$\cos\theta = -(1/2 X^2) / (3/2 X^2) = -1/3 = -0.3333$

    $\theta = 109.47°$

9.92   (a) CO_2, 16 valence e^- (b) $(CN)_2$, 18 valence e^-

$\ddot{O}\!=\!C\!=\!\ddot{O}$ $:N\!\equiv\!C\!-\!C\!\equiv\!N:$

2σ   2π   3σ, 4π

(c) H_2CO, 12 valence e^- (d)   HCOOH, 18 valence e^-

3σ, 1π   4σ, 1π

9.93   (a)

$3(4) + 3(6) + 6(1) = 36\ e^-, 18\ e^-$ pr

(b)   There are 11 σ and 1 π bonds.

(c)   The C=O on the right-hand C atom is shortest. For the same bonded atoms, in this case C and O, the greater the bond order, the shorter the bond.

(d, e)   The right-most C has three e^- domains, so the hybridization is sp^2; bond angles about this C atom are approximately 120°. The middle and left-hand C atoms both have four e^- domains, are sp^3 hybridized, and have bond angles of approximately 109°.

9.94

$μ = 1.03D$ $μ = 0$

BF_3 is a trigonal planar molecule with the central B atom symmetrically surrounded by the three F atoms (Figure 9.12). The individual B–F bond dipoles cancel, and the molecule has a net dipole moment of zero. PF_3 has tetrahedral electron-domain geometry with one of the positions in the tetrahedron occupied by a nonbonding electron pair. The individual P–F bond dipoles do not cancel and the presence of a nonbonding electron pair ensures an asymmetrical electron distribution; the molecule is polar.

9.95   (a)   Square pyramidal

(b)   Yes, there is one nonbonding electron domain on A. If there were only five bonding domains, the shape would be trigonal bipyramidal. With five bonding and one nonbonding electron domains, the molecule has octahedral domain geometry.

(c)   Yes. If the B atoms are halogens, each will have three nonbonding electron pairs; there are five bonding pairs, and A has one nonbonded pair, for a total of $[5(3) + 5 + 1] = 21\ e^-$ pairs and 42 electrons in the Lewis structure. If the five halogens contribute 35 e^-, A must contribute seven valence electrons. A is also a halogen.

9.96 (a) The compound on the right has a dipole moment. In the square planar trans structure on the left, all equivalent bond dipoles can be oriented opposite each other, for a net dipole moment of zero.

(b)

The cis orientation of the Cl atoms in cisplatin means that when they leave, the Pt can bind two adjacent N sites on DNA. This "chelate" orientation (see Chapter 24) tightly binds cisplatin to DNA. Transplatin can bind only one DNA N atom at a time. Thus, to avoid bumping by transplatin NH_3 groups and DNA, the plane of transplatin must rotate away from the DNA backbone. This is a much looser bonding situation than for cisplatin.

9.97

H

x

52.25°

0.925 D

O

1.85 D

104.5°

H

(a) The bond dipoles in H_2O lie along the O–H bonds with the positive end at H and the negative end at O. The dipole moment vector of the H_2O molecule is the resultant (vector sum) of the two bond dipoles. This vector bisects the H–O–H angle and has a magnitude of 1.85 D with the negative end pointing toward O.

(b) Since the dipole moment vector bisects the H–O–H bond angle, the angle between one H–O bond and the dipole moment vector is 1/2 the H–O–H bond angle, 52.25°. Dropping a perpendicular line from H to the dipole moment vector creates the right triangle pictured. If x = the magnitude of the O–H bond dipole, x cos (52.25) = 0.925 D. x = 1.51 D.

(c) The X–H bond dipoles (Table 8.3) and the electronegativity values of X (Figure 8.7) are

	Electronegativity	Bond dipole
F	4.0	1.82
O	3.5	1.51
Cl	3.0	1.08

Since the electronegativity of O is midway between the values for F and Cl, the O–H bond dipole should be approximately midway between the bond dipoles of HF and HCl. The value of the O–H bond dipole calculated in part (b) is consistent with this prediction.

9.98   (a) XeF_6 50 e⁻, 25 e⁻ pairs

       (b)   There are seven electron domains around Xe, and the maximum number of e⁻ domains in Table 9.3 is six.

       (c)   Tie seven balloons together and see what arrangement they adopt (seriously! see Figure 9.5). Alternatively, go to the chemical literature where VSEPR was first proposed and see if there is a preferred orientation for seven e⁻ domains.

       (d)   One of the seven e⁻ domains is a nonbonded domain. The question is whether it occupies an axial or equatorial position. The equatorial plane of a pentagonal bipyramid has F–Xe–F angles of 72°. Placing the nonbonded domain in the equatorial plane would create severe repulsions between it and the adjacent bonded domains. Thus, the nonbonded domain will reside in the axial position. The molecular structure is a pentagonal pyramid.

9.99

       (a)   The molecule is not planar. The CH_2 planes at each end are twisted 90° from one another.

       (b)   Allene has no dipole moment.

       (c)   The bonding in allene would not be described as delocalized. The π electron clouds of the two adjacent C=C are mutually perpendicular. The mechanism for delocalization of π electrons is mutual overlap of parallel p atomic orbitals on adjacent atoms. If adjacent π electron clouds are mutually perpendicular, there is no overlap and no delocalization of π electrons.

9.100   (a)   16 e⁻, 8 e⁻ pairs

(b)   The observed bond length of 1.16 Å is intermediate between the values for N=N, 1.24 Å, and N ≡ N, 1.10 Å. This is consistent with the resonance structures, which indicate contribution from formally double and triple bonds to the true bonding picture in N_3^-.

(c)   In each resonance structure, the central N has two electron domains, so it must be sp hybridized. It is difficult to predict the hybridization of terminal atoms in molecules where there are resonance structures because there are a different number of electron domains around the terminal atoms in each structure. Since the "true" electronic arrangement is a combination of all resonance structures, we will assume that the terminal N–N bonds have some triple bond character and that the terminal N atoms are sp hybridized. (There is no experimental measure of hybridization at terminal atoms, since there are no bond angles to observe.)

(d)   In each resonance structure, N–N σ bonds are formed by sp hybrids and π bonds are formed by unhybridized p orbitals. Nonbonding e⁻ pairs can reside in sp hybrids or p atomic orbitals.

(e)   Recall that electrons in 2s orbitals are on the average closer to the nucleus than electrons in 2p orbitals. Since sp hybrids have greater s orbital character, it is reasonable to expect the radial extension of sp orbitals to be smaller than that of sp^2 or sp^3 orbitals and σ bonds formed by sp orbitals to be slightly shorter than those formed by other hybrid orbitals, assuming the same bonded atoms.

There are no solitary σ bonds in N_3^-. That is, the two σ bonds in N_3^- are each accompanied by at least one π bond between the bonding pair of atoms. Sigma bonds that are part of a double or triple bond must be shorter so that the p orbitals can overlap enough for the π bond to form. Thus, the observation is not applicable to this molecule. (Comparison of C–H bond lengths in C_2H_2, C_2H_4, C_2H_6 and related molecules would confirm or deny the observation.)

9.101   (a) $\ddot{O}=\ddot{O}-\ddot{O}: \quad \longleftrightarrow \quad :\ddot{O}-\ddot{O}=\ddot{O}$

To accommodate the π bonding by all 3 O atoms indicated in the resonance structures above, all O atoms are sp^2 hybridized.

(b)   For the first resonance structure, both sigma bonds are formed by overlap of sp^2 hybrid orbitals, the π bond is formed by overlap of atomic p orbitals, one of the nonbonded pairs on the right terminal O atom is in a p atomic orbital, and the remaining five nonbonded pairs are in sp^2 hybrid orbitals.

(c)   Only unhybridized p atomic orbitals can be used to form a delocalized π system.

(d)   The unhybridized p orbital on each O atom is used to form the delocalized π system, and in both resonance structures one nonbonded electron pair resides in a p atomic orbital. The delocalized π system then contains four electrons, two from the π bond and two from the nonbonded pair in the p orbital.

9.102   (a)   Each C atom is surrounded by three electron domains (two single bonds and one double bond), so bond angles at each C atom will be approximately 120°.

Since there is free rotation around the central C–C single bond, other conformations are possible.

(b) According to Table 8.5, the average C–C length is 1.54 Å, and the average C=C length is 1.34 Å. While the C=C bonds in butadiene appear "normal," the central C–C is significantly shorter than average. Examination of the bonding in butadiene reveals that each C atom is sp^2 hybridized and the π bonds are formed by the remaining unhybridized 2p orbital on each atom. If the central C–C bond is rotated so that all four C atoms are coplanar, the four 2p orbitals are parallel, and some delocalization of the π electrons occurs.

9.103 (a) The diagram shows two s atomic orbitals with opposite phases. Because they are spherically symmetric, the interaction of s orbitals can only produce a σ molecular orbital. Because the two orbitals in the diagram have opposite phases, the interaction excludes electron density from the region between the nuclei. The resulting MO has a node between the two nuclei and is labeled σ_{2s}^*. The principal quantum number designation is arbitrary, because it defines only the size of the pertinent AOs and MOs. Shapes and phases of MOs depend only on these same characteristics of the interacting AOs.

(b) The diagram shows two p atomic orbitals with oppositely phased lobes pointing at each other. End-to-end overlap produces a σ-type MO; opposite phases mean a node between the nuclei and an antibonding MO. The interaction results in a σ_{2p}^* MO.

(c) The diagram shows parallel p atomic orbitals with like-phased lobes aligned. Side-to-side overlap produces a π-type MO; overlap of like-phased lobes concentrates electron density between the nuclei and a bonding MO. The interaction results in a π_{2p} MO.

9.104

σ_{2p}^* ☐

π_{2p}^* [↑|]

σ_{2p} [↑]

π_{2p} [↑↓|↑↓]

σ_{2s}^* [↑↓]

σ_{2s} [↑↓]

(a) N_2 in the first excited state has two unpaired electrons and is paramagnetic.

(b) N_2 in the ground state has a B.O. of 3; in the first excited state (at left) it has a B.O. of 2. Owing to the reduction in bond order, N_2 in the first excited state has a weaker (and longer) N–N bond than N_2 in the ground state.

9.105 We will refer to azo benzene (on the left) as A and hydrazobenzene (on the right) as H.

(a) A: sp^2; H: sp^3

(b)   A: Each N and C atom has one unhybridized p orbital. H: Each C atom has one unhybridized p orbital, but the N atoms have no unhybridized p orbitals.

(c)   A: 120°; H: 109°

(d)   Since all C and N atoms in A have unhybridized p orbitals, all can participate in delocalized π bonding. The delocalized π system extends over the entire molecule, including both benzene rings and the azo "bridge." In H, the N atoms have no unhybridized p orbitals, so they cannot participate in delocalized π bonding. Each of the benzene rings in H is delocalized, but the network cannot span the N atoms in the bridge.

(e)   This is consistent with the answer to (d). In order for the unhybridized p orbitals in A to overlap, they must be parallel. This requires a planar σ bond framework where all atoms in the molecule are coplanar.

(f)   For a molecule to be useful in a solar energy conversion device, it must absorb visible light. This requires a HOMO-LUMO energy gap in the visible region. For organic molecules, the size of the gap is related to the number of conjugated π bonds; the more conjugated π bonds, the smaller the gap and the more likely the molecule is to be colored. Azobenzene has seven conjugated π bonds (π network delocalized over the entire molecule) and appears red-orange. Hydrazobenzene has only three conjugated π bonds (π network on benzene rings only) and appears white. Thus, the smaller HOMO-LUMO energy gap in A causes it to be both intensely colored and a more useful molecule for solar energy conversion.

9.106   (a)   H: $1s^1$; F: $[He]2s^2 2p^5$

             When molecular orbitals are formed from atomic orbitals, the total number of orbitals is conserved. Since H and F have a total of five valence AOs ($H_{1s} + F_{2s} + 3F_{2p}$), the MO diagram for HF has five MOs.

      (b)   H and F have a total of eight valence electrons. Since each MO can hold a maximum of two electrons, four of the five MOs would be occupied.

      (c)

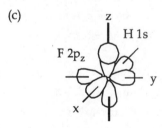

             If H and F lie on the z axis, then the $2p_z$ orbital of F will overlap with the 1s orbital of H.

      (d)   Since F is more electronegative than H, the valence orbitals on F are at lower energy than those on H.

The HF MO diagram has 6 nonbonding, 2 bonding and 0 antibonding electrons. The BO = [2 – 0]/2 = 1. (Nonbonding electrons do not "count" toward bond order.)

(e)   H⎯F̈:

In the Lewis structure for HF, the nonbonding electrons are on the (more electronegative) F atom, as they are in the MO diagram.

9.107   (a)   CO, 10 e⁻, 5 e⁻ pair

:C≡O:

(b)   The bond order for CO, as predicted by the MO diagram in Figure 9.46, is 1/2[8 – 2] = 3.0. A bond order of 3.0 agrees with the triple bond in the Lewis structure.

(c)   Applying the MO diagram in Figure 9.46 to the CO molecule, the highest energy electrons would occupy the π_{2p} MOs. That is, π_{2p} would be the HOMO, highest occupied molecular orbital. If the true HOMO of CO is a σ-type MO, the order of the π_{2p} and σ_{2p} orbitals must be reversed. Figure 9.42 shows how the interaction of the 2s orbitals on one atom and the 2p orbitals on the other atom can affect the relative energies of the resulting MOs. This 2s–2p interaction in CO is significant enough so that the σ_{2p} MO is higher in energy than the π_{2p} MOs, and the σ_{2p} is the HOMO. This is the same energy order of MOs shown for large 2s–2p interaction in homonuclear diatomic molecules in Figure 9.43.

(d)   We expect the atomic orbitals of the more electronegative element to have lower energy than those of the less electronegative element. When atoms of the two elements combine, the lower energy atomic orbitals make a greater contribution to the bonding MOs and the higher energy atomic orbitals make a larger contribution to the antibonding orbitals. Thus, the π_{2p} bonding MOs will have a greater contribution from the more electronegative O atom.

9.108   (a)   The carbon-carbon bond order in ethylene is two. This means that there are two more bonding e⁻ pairs (4 bonding e⁻) than antibonding e⁻ pairs. If one e⁻ is promoted form a bonding to an antibonding MO, there is one fewer bonding e⁻ and one more antibonding e⁻; there is now an excess of two bonding e⁻ or one bonding e⁻ pair. The electron transition reduces the carbon-carbon bond order from two to one.

(b)   A bond order of one corresponds to a single bond, which is a σ bond; there is free rotation about a σ bond. Absorption of a photon of appropriate wavelength breaks the π bond in ethylene but leaves the σ bond intact; it reduces the bond order from two to one. There is facile rotation about the remaining carbon-carbon σ bond.

Integrative Exercises

9.109   (a)   Assume 100 g of compound

$$2.1 \text{ g H} \times \frac{1 \text{ mol H}}{1.008 \text{ g H}} = 2.1 \text{ mol H}; 2.1/2.1 = 1$$

$$29.8 \text{ g N} \times \frac{1 \text{ mol N}}{14.01 \text{ g N}} = 2.13 \text{ mol N}; 2.13/2.1 \approx 1$$

$$68.1 \text{ g O} \times \frac{1 \text{ mol O}}{16.00 \text{ g O}} = 4.26 \text{ mol O}; 4.26/2.1 \approx 2$$

The empirical formula is HNO_2; formula weight = 47. Since the approximate molar mass is 50, the molecular formula is HNO_2.

(b)   Assume N is central, since it is unusual for O to be central, and part (d) indicates as much. HNO_2: 18 valence e⁻

$$\ddot{O}=\ddot{N}-\ddot{O}-H \longleftrightarrow :\ddot{O}-\ddot{N}=\ddot{O}-H$$
$$ -1 \quad 0 \quad +1$$

The second resonance form is a minor contributor due to unfavorable formal charges.

(c)   The electron domain geometry around N is trigonal planar with an O–N–O angle of approximately 120°. If the resonance structure on the right makes a significant contribution to the molecular structure, all four atoms would lie in a plane. If only the left structure contributes, the H could rotate in and out of the molecular plane. The relative contributions of the two resonance structures could be determined by measuring the O–N–O and N–O–H bond angles.

(d)   3 VSEPR e⁻ domains around N, sp² hybridization

(e)   3 σ, 1 π for both structures (or for H bound to N).

9.110   (a) $2SF_4(g) + O_2(g) \rightarrow 2OSF_4(g)$

(b)   40 e⁻, 20 e⁻ pairs

$$
\begin{array}{c}
:\!O\!: \\
\| \\
:\!F\!-\!S\!-\!F\!: \\
:\!F\!: \quad :\!F\!:
\end{array}
$$

There must be a double bond drawn between O and S in order for their formal charges to be zero.

(c)   ΔH = 8D(S–F) + D(O=O) – 8D(S–F) – 2D(S=O)

ΔH = D(O=O) – 2D(S=O) = 495 – 2(523) = –551 kJ, exothermic

(d)   trigonal bipyramidal electron-domain geometry

(e)   Because F is more electronegative than O, S–F bonding domains are smaller than the S=O domain. The structure that minimizes S=O repulsions is more likely (see Solution 9.90). That is, the structure with fewer 90° F– S=O angles and more 120° F– S=O angles is favored. The structure on the right, with O in the equatorial position is more likely. Note that a double bond involving an atom with an expanded octet of electrons, such as the S=O in this molecule, does not have the same geometric implications as a double bond to a first row element.

9.111   (a) PX_3, 26 valence e⁻, 13⁻ pairs

        4 electron domains around P, tetrahedral e⁻ domain geometry,
        If all bonding and nonbonding electron domains are the same size, perfect tetrahedral angles are 109.5°. If all bonding electron domains are the same size but the nonbonding domain is larger, bond angles are somewhat less than 109°.

        (b)   As electronegativity increases (I < Br < Cl < F), the X–P–X angles decreases

        (c)   The greater the electronegativity of X, the larger the magnitude of negative charge centered on X. The more negative charge centered on X, the smaller the P–X bonding domains, the greater the effect of the nonbonding domain and the smaller the bond angle. Also, as the electronegativity of X decreases and the bonding domain size increases, the effect of the large nonbonding domain decreases.

        (d) $PBrCl_4$, 40 valence electrons, 20 e⁻ pairs. The molecule will have trigonal bipyramidal electron-domain geometry (similar to PCl_5 in Table 9.3.) Based on the argument in part (c), the P–Br bond will have greater repulsions with P–Cl bonds than P–Cl bonds have with each other. Therefore, the Br will occupy an equatorial position in the trigonal bipyramid, so that the more unfavorable P–Br to P–Cl repulsions can be situated at larger angles in the equatorial plane.

9.112   (a)   Three electron domains around each central C atom, sp^2 hybridization

        (b)   A 180° rotation around the C=C double bond is required to convert the trans isomer into the cis isomer. A 90° rotation around the bond eliminates all overlap of the p orbitals that form the π bond and it is broken.

(c)   **average bond enthalpy**

C=C   614 kJ/mol

C–C   348 kJ/mol

The difference in these values, 266 kJ/mol, is the average bond enthalpy of a C–C π bond. This is the amount of energy required to break 1 mol of C–C π bonds. The energy per molecule is

$$266 \text{ kJ/mol} \times \frac{1000 \text{ J}}{1 \text{ kJ}} \times \frac{1 \text{ mol}}{6.022 \times 10^{23} \text{ molecules}} = 4.417 \times 10^{-19}$$

$$= 4.42 \times 10^{-19} \text{ J/molecule}$$

(d) $\lambda = hc/E = \dfrac{6.626 \times 10^{-34} \text{ J-s} \times 2.998 \times 10^8 \text{ m/s}}{4.417 \times 10^{-19} \text{ J}} = 4.50 \times 10^{-7} \text{ m} = 450 \text{ nm}$

(e)   Yes, 450 nm light is in the visible portion of the spectrum. A cis-trans isomerization in the retinal portion of the large molecule rhodopsin is the first step in a sequence of molecular transformations in the eye that leads to vision. The sequence of events enables the eye to detect visible photons, in other words, to see.

9.113   (a)   C≡C   839 kJ/mol   (1 σ, 2 π)

C=C   614 kJ/mol   (1 σ, 1 π)

C–C   348 kJ/mol   (1 σ)

The contribution from 1 π bond would be (614–348) 266 kJ/mol. From a second π bond, (839 – 614), 225 kJ/mol. An average π bond contribution would be (266 + 225)/2 = 246 kJ/mol.

This is $\dfrac{246 \text{ kJ/π bond}}{348 \text{ kJ/σ bond}} \times 100 = 71\%$ of the average enthalpy of a σ bond.

(b)   N≡N   941 kJ/mol

N=N   418 kJ/mol

N–N   163 kJ/mol

first π = (418 – 163) = 255 kJ/mol

second π = (941 – 418) = 523 kJ/mol

average π bond enthalpy = (255 + 523)/2 = 389 kJ/mol

This is $\dfrac{389 \text{ kJ/π bond}}{163 \text{ kJ/σ bond}} \times 100 = 240\%$ of the average enthalpy of a σ bond.

N–N σ bonds are weaker than C–C σ bonds, while N–N π bonds are stronger than C–C π bonds. The relative energies of C–C σ and π bonds are similar, while N–N π bonds are much stronger than N–N σ bonds.

(c) N_2H_4, 14 valence e⁻, 7 e⁻ pairs

$$H-\overset{\cdot\cdot}{N}-\overset{\cdot\cdot}{N}-H$$
$$\;\;\;\;\;\;|\;\;\;\;\;|$$
$$\;\;\;\;\;\;H\;\;\;H$$

4 electron domains around N, sp³ hybridization

N_2H_2, 12 valence e⁻, 6 e⁻ pairs

$$H-\overset{\cdot\cdot}{N}=\overset{\cdot\cdot}{N}-H$$

3 electron domains around N, sp² hybridization

N_2, 10 valence e⁻, 5 e⁻ pairs

$$:N\equiv N:$$

2 electron domains around N, sp hybridization

(d)   In the three types of N–N bonds, each N atom has a nonbonding or lone pair of electrons. The lone pair to bond pair repulsions are minimized going from 109° to 120° to 180° bond angles, making the π bonds stronger relative to the σ bond. In the three types of C–C bonds, no lone-pair to bond-pair repulsions exist, and the σ and π bonds have more similar energies.

9.114

(g) ⟶ 6C(g) + 6H(g)

$$\Delta H = 6D(C–H) + 3D(C–C) + 3D(C=C) – 0$$
$$= 6(413 \text{ kJ}) + 3(348 \text{ kJ}) + 3(614 \text{ kJ})$$
$$= 5364 \text{ kJ}$$

(The products are isolated atoms; there is no bond making.)

According to Hess' law:

$$\Delta H° = 6\Delta H_f° \, C(g) + 6\Delta H_f° \, H(g) – \Delta H_f° \, C_6H_6(g)$$
$$= 6(718.4 \text{ kJ}) + 6(217.94 \text{ kJ}) – (82.9 \text{ kJ})$$
$$= 5535 \text{ kJ}$$

The difference in the two results, 171 kJ/mol C_6H_6 is due to the resonance stabilization in benzene. That is, because the π electrons are delocalized, the molecule has a lower overall energy than that predicted for the presence of 3 localized C–C and C=C bonds. Thus, the amount of energy actually required to decompose 1 mole of $C_6H_6(g)$, represented by the Hess' law calculation, is greater than the sum of the localized bond enthalpies (not taking resonance into account) from the first calculation above.

9.115   (a) $3d_{z^2}$

(b)   Ignoring the donut of the d_{z^2} orbital

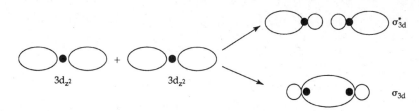

(c) A node is generated in σ_{3d}^{*} because antibonding MOs are formed when AO lobes with opposite phases interact. Electron density is excluded from the internuclear region and a node is formed in the MO.

(d) Sc: $[Ar]4s^2 3d^1$ Omitting the core electrons, there are six e^- in the energy level diagram.

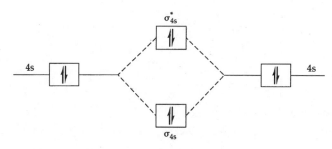

(e) The bond order in Sc_2 is $1/2\,(4-2) = 1.0$.

9.116 (a) The molecular and empirical formulas of the four molecules are:

benzene: molecular, C_6H_6; empirical, CH

napthalene: molecular, $C_{10}H_8$; empirical, C_5H_4

anthracene: molecular, $C_{14}H_{10}$; empirical, C_7H_5

tetracene: molecular, $C_{18}H_{12}$, empirical, C_3H_2

(b) Yes.   Since the compounds all have different empirical formulas, combustion analysis could in principle be used to distinguish them. In practice, the mass % of C in the four compounds is not very different, so the data would have to be precise to at least 3 decimal places and 4 would be better.

(c) $C_{10}H_8(s) + 12O_2(g) \rightarrow 10CO_2(g) + 4H_2O(g)$

(d) $\Delta H_{comb} = 5D(C=C) + 6D(C-C) + 8D(C-H) + 12D(O=O) - 20D(C=O) - 8D(O-H)$

$= 5(614) + 6(348) + 8(413) + 12(495) - 20(799) - 8(463)$

$= -5282$ kJ/mol $C_{10}H_8$

(e)   Yes. For example, the resonance structures of naphthalene are:

(f)   Colored compounds absorb visible light and appear the color of the visible light that they reflect. Colorless compounds typically absorb shorter wavelength, higher energy light. The energy of light absorbed corresponds to the energy gap between the HOMO and LUMO of the molecule. That tetracene absorbs longer wavelength, lower energy visible light indicates that it has the smallest HOMO-LUMO energy gap of the four molecules. Tetracene also has the most conjugated double bonds of the four molecules. We might conclude that the more conjugated double bonds in an organic molecule, the smaller the HOMO-LUMO energy gap. More information about the absorption spectra of anthracene, naphthalene and benzene is needed to confirm this conclusion.

9.117   (a) – (e)

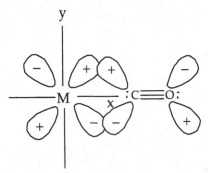

(c)   The two lobes of a p AO have opposite phases. These are shown on the diagram as + and –. An antibonding MO is formed when p AOs with opposite phases interact.

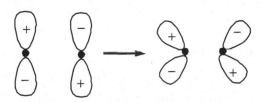

(d)   Note that the d_{xy} AO has lobes that lie between, not on, the x and y axes.

(e)   A π bond forms by overlap of orbitals on M and C. There is electron density above and below, but not along, the M–C axis.

(f)   According to Exercise 9.107, the HOMO of CO is a σ-type MO. So the appropriate MO diagram is shown on the left side of Figure 9.43. A lone CO molecule has 10 valence electrons, the HOMO is σ_{2p} and the bond order is 3.0. The LUMO is π_{2p}^*.

When M and CO interact as shown in the π_{2p}^* diagram, d-π back bonding causes the π_{2p}^* to become partially occupied. Electron density in the π_{2p}^* decreases electron density in the bonding molecular orbitals and decreases the BO of the bound CO. The strength of the C–O bond in a metal–CO complex decreases relative to the strength of the C–O bond in an isolated CO molecule.

9.118   (a)   22 valence e⁻, 11 e⁻ pairs

(The structure on the right does not minimize formal charges and will make a minor contribution to the true structure.)

(b)   Both resonance structures predict the same bond angles. All H–C–N angles are 109°.

(c)   The two extreme Lewis structures predict different bond lengths. As the true bonding model is some blend of the extreme Lewis structures, the true bond lengths are a blend of the extreme values. Our bond length estimates take into account that the structure minimizing formal charge makes a larger contribution to the true structure.

According to Exercise 9.97, the O–H bond length in water is 0.96 Å. According to Figure 7.6, the covalent radius of C is 0.04 Å greater than that of O, so we expect the C–H bond length to be approximately 0.04 Å greater than the O–H distance, about 1.00 Å.

Bond	Length (Å) $N=C=O$	Length (Å) $N\equiv C-O$	Length (Å) estimated
C–H	1.00	1.00	1.00
C–N	1.43	1.43	1.43
N–C	1.38	1.16	1.33
C–O	1.23	1.43	1.28

(d)   The molecule will have a dipole moment. The N–C and C–O bond dipoles are opposite each other, but they are not equal. And, there are nonbonding electron pairs which are not directly opposite each other (in either structure) and will not cancel. There will be a resulting dipole.

10 Gases

Visualizing Concepts

10.1   It would be much easier to drink from a straw on Mars. When a straw is placed in a glass of liquid, the liquid level in the straw equals the liquid level in the glass. The atmosphere exerts equal pressure inside and outside the straw. When we drink through a straw, we withdraw air, thereby reducing the pressure on the liquid inside. If only 0.007 atm is exerted on the liquid in the glass, a very small reduction in pressure inside the straw will cause the liquid to rise.

Another approach is to consider the gravitational force on Mars. Since the pull of gravity causes atmospheric pressure, the gravity on Mars must be much smaller than that on Earth. With a very small Martian gravity holding liquid in a glass, it would be very easy to raise the liquid through a straw.

10.2   (a) $V_1/T_1 = V_2/T_2$ (Charles' Law)   (b) $P_1V_1 = P_2V_2$ (Boyle's Law)

$V_1/300\ K = V_2/500\ K$ $1\ atm \times V_1 = 2\ atm \times V_2$

$V_2 = 5/3\ V_1$ $V_2 = 1/2\ V_1$

300 K, V_1 500 K, V_2 1 atm, V_1 2 atm, V_2

(c) $V_1/T_1 = V_2/T_2$ (Charles' Law)

$V_1/300\ K = V_2/200\ K$

$V_2 = 2/3\ V_1$

300 K, V_1 200 K, V_2

10.3   At constant temperature and volume, pressure depends on total number of particles (Charles' Law). In order to reduce the pressure by a factor of 2, the number of particles must be reduced by a factor of 2. At the lower pressure, the container would have half as many particles as at the higher pressure.

10.4   (a)   At constant pressure and temperature, the container volume is directly proportional to the number of particles present (Avogadro's Law). As the reaction proceeds, 3 gas molecules are converted to 2 gas molecules, so the container volume decreases. If the reaction goes to completion, the final volume would be 2/3 of the initial volume.

               (b)   At constant volume and temperature, pressure is directly proportional to the number of particles . Since the number of molecules decreases as the reaction proceeds, the pressure also decreases. At completion, the final pressure would be 2/3 the initial pressure.

10.5 $PV = nRT$ (ideal gas equation). In the ideal gas equation, R is a constant. Given constant V and n (fixed amount of ideal gas), P and T are directly proportional. If P is doubled, T is also doubled. That is, if P is doubled, T increases by a factor of two.

10.6   Over time, the gases will mix perfectly. Each bulb will contain 4 blue and 3 red atoms. The "blue" gas has the greater partial pressure after mixing, because it has the greater number of particles (at the same T and V as the "red" gas.)

10.7   (a)   Partial pressure depends on the number of particles of each gas present. Red has the fewest particles, then yellow, then blue. $P_{red} < P_{yellow} < P_{blue}$

               (b) $P_{gas} = \chi_{gas} P_t$. Calculate the mole fraction, χ_{gas} = [mol gas / total moles] or [particles gas / total particles]. This is true because Avogadro's number is a counting number, and mole ratios are also particle ratios.

                     χ_{red} = 2 red atoms / 10 total atoms = 0.2; P_{red} = 0.2(1.40 atm) = 0.28 atm

                     χ_{yellow} = 3 yellow atoms / 10 total atoms = 0.3; P_{yellow} = 0.3(1.40 atm) = 0.42 atm

                     χ_{blue} = 5 blue atoms / 10 total atoms = 0.5; P_{blue} = 0.5(1.40 atm) = 0.70 atm

                     Check. (0.28 atm + 0.42 atm + 0.70 atm) = 1.40 atm. The sum of the calculated partial pressures equals the given total pressure.

10.8

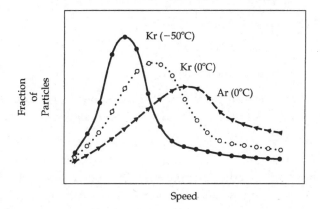

10.9   (a)   At constant temperature, the root mean square (rms) speed (as well as the average speed) of a collection of gas particles is inversely related to molar mass; the lighter the particle, the faster it moves. Therefore, curve B represents He and curve A represents O_2. Curve B has the higher rms speed and He is the lighter gas. Curve A has the lower rms speed and O_2 is the heavier gas.

         (b)   For the same gas, average kinetic energy ($1/2\, mu_{rms}^2$), and therefore root mean square speed (u_{rms}) is directly related to Kelvin temperature. Curve A is the lower temperature and curve B is the higher temperature.

         (c)

                 ——— Most probable speed
                 - - - - rms speed

10.10   (a)   Total pressure is directly related to total number of particles (or total mol particles). P(ii) < P(i) = P(iii)

         (b)   Partial pressure of He is directly related to number of He atoms (yellow) or mol He atoms. P_{He}(iii) < P_{He}(ii) < P_{He}(i)

         (c)   Density is total mass of gas per unit volume. We can use the atomic or molar masses of He (4) and N_2 (28), as relative masses of the particles.

                         mass(i) = 5(4) + 2(28) = 76

                         mass(ii) = 3(4) + 1(28) = 40

                         mass(iii) = 2(4) + 5(28) = 148

                 Since the container volumes are equal, d(ii) < d(i) < d(iii).

         (d)   At the same temperature, all gases have the same averageg kinetic energy. The average kinetic energies of the particles in the three containers are equal.

10.11   The NH_4Cl(s) ring will form at location A. The process described in this exercise is diffusion, rather than simple effusion. According to section 10.8, Graham's law approximates (but does not exactly describe) the diffusion rates of two gases under identical conditions. According to Graham's law, the ratio of rates is inversely related to the ratio of molar masses of the two gases. That is, the lighter gas moves faster than the heavier gas. When introduced into the tube, NH_3, MM = 17, moves faster and therefore farther than HCl, MM = 36. If NH_3 moves farther than HCl, the two gases meet and form $NH_4Cl(s)$ nearer the end where HCl was introduced; this is in the vicinity of location A.

10.12 CCl_4, Cl_2 and H_2O would deviate most, while He, Ne and H_2 would deviate least. At high pressure, gas molecules have relatively little free space in which to move. Both intermolecular attractive forces and the nonzero volume of molecules are important. At low temperature, molecules have less kinetic energy, are less able to overcome attractive forces, and deviations due to intermolecular attractive forces dominate (see Figure 10.23). In Table 10.3, values of *a* show corrections for intermolecular attraction. The gases CCl_4, Cl_2 and H_2O have the largest values of *a*, while He, Ne and H_2 have the smallest. The magnitude of *a* increases as the size and complexity of the molecule increases. CCl_4 and Cl_2 are relatively large gases; H_2O is polar and has hydrogen bonding. He, Ne and H_2 are small, monatomic or nonpolar diatomic. The magnitude of *a* is predictable from molecular structure.

Gas Characteristics; Pressure (sections 10.1 and 10.2)

10.13 In the gas phase, molecules are far apart and in constant motion. In the liquid phase, molecules maintain contact with each other while they move.

(a) A gas is much less dense than a liquid because most of the volume of a gas is empty space.

(b) A gas is much more compressible because of the distance between molecules.

(c) Gaseous molecules are so far apart that there is no barrier to mixing, regardless of the identity of the molecule. All mixtures of gases are homogeneous. Liquid molecules are touching. In order to mix, they must displace one another. Similar molecules displace each other and form homogeneous mixtures. Very dissimilar molecules form heterogeneous mixtures.

(d) Gas molecules are far apart and constantly moving, so a gas expands to the shape and volume of its container. In a liquid sample, molecules are moving but in close contact with each other; there is very little empty space in a liquid. A liquid takes the shape of its container because the molecules are mobile, but maintains its own volume because the molecules are touching.

10.14 (a) Because gas molecules are far apart and in constant motion, the gas expands to fill the container. Attractive forces hold liquid molecules together and the volume of the liquid does not change.

(b) H_2O and CCl_4 molecules are too dissimilar to displace each other and mix in the liquid state. All mixtures of gases are homogeneous. (See Solution 10.13 (c)).

(c) Because gas molecules are far apart, the mass present in 1 mL of a gas is very small. The mass of a gas present in 1 L is on the same order of magnitude as the mass of a liquid present in 1 mL.

10.15 *Analyze.* Given: mass, area. Find: pressure. *Plan.* $P = F/A = m \times a/A$; use this relationship, paying attention to units. *Solve.*

(a) $1\,Pa = \dfrac{1\,N}{m^2} = \dfrac{1\,kg\text{-}m}{s^2} \times \dfrac{1}{m^2} = \dfrac{1\,kg}{m\text{-}s^2}$ Change mass to kg and area to m^2.

$$P = \frac{m \times a}{A} = \frac{130\,lb}{0.50\,in^2} \times \frac{9.81\,m}{1\,s^2} \times \frac{0.454\,kg}{1\,lb} \times \frac{39.4^2\,in^2}{1\,m^2} = 1.798 \times 10^6\,\frac{kg}{m\text{-}s^2}$$

$$= 1.8 \times 10^6\,Pa = 1.8 \times 10^3\,kPa$$

Check. $[1.30 \times 10 \times 0.5 \times (40)^2 / 0.5] \approx (130 \times 16{,}000) \approx 2.0 \times 10^6\,Pa \approx 2.0 \times 10^3\,kPa.$ The units are correct.

(b)   1 atm = 101.325 kPa

$$1.798 \times 10^3\,kPa \times \frac{1\,atm}{101.325\,kPa} = 1.774 \times 10^1 = 18\,atm$$

(c) $1\,atm = 14.70\,lb/in^2$

$$17.74\,atm \times \frac{14.70\,lb/in^2}{1\,atm} = 260.8 = 2.6 \times 10^2\,lb/in^2$$

10.16 $P = m \times a / A;\ 1\,Pa = 1\,kg/m\text{-}s^2;\ A = 3.0\,cm \times 4.1\,cm \times 4 = 49.2 = 49\,cm^2$

$$\frac{262\,kg}{49.2\,cm^2} \times \frac{9.81\,m}{s^2} \times \frac{(100)^2\,cm^2}{1\,m^2} = 5.224 \times 10^5\,\frac{kg}{m\text{-}s^2} = 5.2 \times 10^5\,Pa$$

10.17   *Analyze.* Given: 760 mm column of Hg, densities of Hg and H_2O. Find: height of a column of H_2O at same pressure.

Plan. We must develop a relationship between pressure, height of a column of liquid, and density of the liquid. Relationships that might prove useful: $P = F/A;\ F = m \times a;$ $m = d \times V(density)(volume);\ V = A \times height$ *Solve.*

$$P = \frac{F}{A} = \frac{m \times a}{A} = \frac{d \times V \times a}{A} = \frac{d \times A \times h \times a}{A} = d \times h \times a$$

(a) $P_{Hg} = P_{H_2O};$ Using the relationship derived above: $(d \times h \times a)_{H_2O} = (d \times h \times a)_{Hg}$

Since a, the acceleration due to gravity, is equal in both liquids,
$(d \times h)_{H_2O} = (d \times h)_{Hg}$

$1.00\,g/mL \times h_{H_2O} = 13.6\,g/mL \times 760\,mm$

$$h_{H_2O} = \frac{13.6\,g/mL \times 760\,mm}{1.00\,g/mL} = 1.034 \times 10^4 = 1.03 \times 10^4\,mm = 10.3\,m$$

(b)   Pressure due to H_2O:

1 atm = 1.034×10^4 mm H_2O (from part (a))

$$39\,ft\,H_2O \times \frac{12\,in}{1\,ft} \times \frac{2.54\,cm}{1\,in} \times \frac{10\,mm}{1\,cm} \times \frac{1\,atm}{1.034 \times 10^4\,mm} = 1.150 = 1.2\,atm$$

$$P_{total} = P_{atm} + P_{H_2O} = 0.97\,atm + 1.150\,atm = 2.120 = 2.1\,atm$$

10.18   Using the relationship derived in Solution 10.17 for two liquids under the influence of gravity, $(d \times h)_{1id} = (d \times h)_{Hg}$. At 749 torr, the height of an Hg barometer is 749 mm.

$$\frac{1.20\,g}{1\,mL} \times h_{1id} = \frac{13.6\,g}{1\,mL} \times 760\,mm;\ h_{1id} = \frac{13.6\,g/mL \times 749\,mm}{1.20\,g/mL} = 8.49 \times 10^3\,mm = 8.49\,m$$

10.19   (a)   The tube can have any cross-sectional area. (The height of the Hg column in a barometer is independent of the cross-sectional area. See the expression for pressure derived in Solution 10.17.)

       (b)   At equilibrium, the force of gravity per unit area acting on the mercury column is not equal to the force of gravity per unit area acting on the atmosphere. (F = ma; the acceleration due to gravity is equal for the two substances, but the mass of Hg for a given cross-sectional area is different than the mass of air for this same area.)

       (c)   The column of mercury is held up by the pressure of the atmosphere applied to the exterior pool of mercury.

       (d)   If you took the mercury barometer with you on a trip from the beach to high mountains, the height of the mercury column would decrease with elevation. (Atmospheric pressure decreases as elevation increases.)

10.20   The mercury would fill the tube completely; there would be no vacuum at the closed end. This is because atmospheric pressure will support a mercury column higher than 70 cm, while our tube is only 50 cm. No mercury flows from the tube into the dish and no vacuum forms at the top of the tube.

10.21   *Analyze/Plan.* Follow the logic in Sample Exercise 10.1.   *Solve.*

       (a) $265 \text{ torr} \times \dfrac{1 \text{ atm}}{760 \text{ torr}} = 0.349 \text{ atm}$

       (b) $265 \text{ torr} \times \dfrac{1 \text{ mm Hg}}{1 \text{ torr}} = 265 \text{ mm Hg}$

       (c) $265 \text{ torr} \times \dfrac{1.01325 \times 10^5 \text{ Pa}}{760 \text{ torr}} = 3.53 \times 10^4 \text{ Pa}$

       (d) $265 \text{ torr} \times \dfrac{1.01325 \times 10^5 \text{ Pa}}{760 \text{ torr}} \times \dfrac{1 \text{ bar}}{1 \times 10^5 \text{ Pa}} = 0.353 \text{ bar}$

       (e) $265 \text{ torr} \times \dfrac{1 \text{ atm}}{760 \text{ torr}} \times \dfrac{14.70 \text{ psi}}{1 \text{ atm}} = 5.13 \text{ psi}$

10.22   (a) $0.912 \text{ atm} \times \dfrac{760 \text{ torr}}{1 \text{ atm}} = 693 \text{ torr}$

       (b) $0.685 \text{ bar} \times \dfrac{1 \times 10^5 \text{ Pa}}{1 \text{ bar}} \times \dfrac{1 \text{ kPa}}{1 \times 10^3 \text{ Pa}} = 68.5 \text{ kPa}$

       (c) $655 \text{ mm Hg} \times \dfrac{1 \text{ atm}}{760 \text{ mm Hg}} = 0.862 \text{ atm}$

       (d) $1.323 \times 10^5 \text{ Pa} \times \dfrac{1 \text{ atm}}{1.01325 \times 10^5 \text{ Pa}} = 1.3057 = 1.306 \text{ atm}$

       (e) $2.50 \text{ atm} \times \dfrac{14.70 \text{ psi}}{1 \text{ atm}} = 36.75 = 36.8 \text{ psi}$

10.23   *Analyze/Plan.* Follow the logic in Sample Exercise 10.1.   *Solve.*

       (a) $30.45 \text{ in Hg} \times \dfrac{25.4 \text{ mm}}{1 \text{ in}} \times \dfrac{1 \text{ torr}}{1 \text{ mm Hg}} = 773.4 \text{ torr}$

       [The result has 4 sig figs because 25.4 mm/in is considered to be an exact number.]

(b) $30.45 \text{ in Hg} = 773.4 \text{ torr}; \ 773.4 \text{ torr} \times \dfrac{1 \text{ atm}}{760 \text{ torr}} = 1.018 \text{ atm}$

(c) The pressure in Chicago is greater than **standard atmospheric pressure**, 760 torr or 1 atm, so it makes sense to classify this weather system as a "high pressure system."

10.24   882 mbar = 0.882 bar

(a) $0.882 \text{ bar} \times \dfrac{1 \times 10^5 \text{ Pa}}{1 \text{ bar}} \times \dfrac{1 \text{ atm}}{101{,}325 \text{ Pa}} = 0.8705 = 0.871 \text{ atm}$

(b) $0.882 \text{ bar} = 0.8705 \text{ atm} \times \dfrac{760 \text{ torr}}{1 \text{ atm}} = 661.55 = 662 \text{ torr}$

(c) $0.882 \text{ bar} = 661.55 \text{ torr} \times \dfrac{1 \text{ mm Hg}}{1 \text{ torr}} \times \dfrac{1 \text{ cm Hg}}{10 \text{ mm Hg}} \times \dfrac{1 \text{ in Hg}}{2.54 \text{ cm Hg}} = 26.045 = 26.0 \text{ in Hg}$

10.25   *Analyze/Plan.* Follow the logic in Sample Exercise 10.2.   *Solve.*

(i) The Hg level is lower in the open end than the closed end, so the gas pressure is less than atmospheric pressure.

$P_{gas} = 0.995 \text{ atm} - \left(52 \text{ cm} \times \dfrac{1 \text{ atm}}{76.0 \text{ cm}} \right) = 0.31 \text{ atm}$

(ii) The Hg level is higher in the open end, so the gas pressure is greater than atmospheric pressure.

$P_{gas} = 0.995 \text{ atm} + \left(67 \text{ cm Hg} \times \dfrac{1 \text{ atm}}{76.0 \text{ cm Hg}} \right) = 1.8766 = 1.88 \text{ atm}$

(iii) This is a closed-end manometer, so $P_{gas} = h$.

$P_{gas} = 10.3 \text{ cm} \times \dfrac{1 \text{ atm}}{76.0 \text{ cm}} = 0.136 \text{ atm}$

10.26   (a) The atmosphere is exerting 15.4 cm = 154 mm Hg (torr) more pressure than the gas.

$P_{gas} = P_{atm} - 15.4 \text{ torr} = \left(0.985 \text{ atm} \times \dfrac{760 \text{ torr}}{1 \text{ atm}} \right) - 15.4 \text{ torr} = 733 \text{ torr}$

(b) The gas is exerting 8.7 mm Hg (torr) more pressure than the atmosphere.

$P_{gas} = P_{atm} + 12.3 \text{ torr} = \left(0.99 \text{ atm} \times \dfrac{760 \text{ torr}}{1 \text{ atm}} \right) + 12.3 \text{ torr} = 764.7 \text{ torr} = 7.6 \times 10^2 \text{ torr}$

(Atmospheric pressure of 0.99 atm determines that the result has 2 sig figs.)

The Gas Laws (section 10.3)

10.27   *Analyze/Plan.* Given certain changes in gas conditions, predict the effect on other conditions. Consider the gas law relationships in section 10.3.   *Solve.*

(a) P and V are inversely proportional at constant T. If the volume decreases by a factor of 4, the pressure increases by a factor of 4.

(b) P and T are directly proportional at constant V. If T decreases by a factor of 2, P also decreases by a factor of 2.

(c)   P and n are directly proportional at constant V and T. If n decreases by a factor of 4, P also decreases by a factor of 4.

10.28   *Analyze.* Given: initial P, V, T. Find: final values of P, V, T for certain changes of condition. *Plan.* Select the appropriate gas law relationships from Section 10.3; solve for final conditions, paying attention to units.   *Solve.*

(a) $P_1V_1 = P_2V_2$; the proportionality holds true for any pressure or volume units.

P_1 = 752 torr, V_1 = 5.12 L, P_2 = 1.88 atm

$$V_2 = \frac{P_1V_1}{P_2} = \frac{752\ torr \times 5.12\ L}{1.88\ atm} \times \frac{1\ atm}{760\ torr} = 2.69\ L$$

Check. As pressure increases, volume should decrease; our result agrees with this.

(b) $V_1/T_1 = V_2/T_2$; T must be in Kelvins for the relationship to be true.

V_1 = 5.12 L, T_1 = 21°C = 294 K, T_2 = 175°C = 448 K

$$V_2 = \frac{V_1T_2}{T_1} = \frac{5.12\ L \times 448\ K}{294\ K} = 7.80\ L$$

Check. As temperature increases, volume should increase; our result is consistent with this.

10.29   (a)   Avogadro's hypothesis states that equal volumes of gases at the same temperature and pressure contain equal numbers of molecules. Since molecules react in the ratios of small whole numbers, it follows that the volumes of reacting gases (at the same temperature and pressure) are in the ratios of small whole numbers.

(b)   Since the two gases are at the same temperature and pressure, the ratio of the numbers of atoms is the same as the ratio of volumes. There are 1.5 times as many Xe atoms as Ne atoms.

(c)   Yes. By definition, one mole of an ideal gas (or any other substance) contains Avogadro's number of particles. At a given temperature and pressure, equal numbers of particles occupy the same volume, so one mole of an ideal gas will always occupy the same volume at the given temperature and pressure.

10.30   According to Avogadro's hypothesis, the mole ratios in the chemical equation will be volume ratios for the gases if they are at the same temperature and pressure.

$$N_2(g) + 3H_2(g) \rightarrow 2NH_3(g)$$

The volumes of H_2 and N_2 are in a stoichiometric $\dfrac{3.6\ L}{1.2\ L}$ or $\dfrac{3\ vol\ H_2}{1\ vol\ N_2}$ ratio, so either can be used to determine the volume of $NH_3(g)$ produced.

$$1.2\ L\ N_2 \times \frac{2\ mol\ NH_3}{1\ mol\ N_2} = 2.4\ L\ NH_3(g)\ produced.$$

The Ideal-Gas Equation (section 10.4)

(In *Solutions to Exercises*, the symbol for molar mass is MM.)

10.31   (a)   An ideal gas exhibits pressure, volume, and temperature relationships which are described by the equation PV = nRT. (An ideal gas obeys the ideal-gas equation.)

(b) V = constant/P;   Boyle's Law

       V = constant $\times T$;   Charles Law

       V = constant $\times n$;   Avogadro's Law

       Collecting all the equalities, $V = \dfrac{\text{constant} \times T \times n}{P}$

       If we call the constant R, and multiply both sides by P,

       $PV = RTn$ or $PV = nRT$

(c) $PV = nRT$; P in atmospheres, V in liters, n in moles, T in kelvins

(d) $R = \dfrac{0.08206\ \text{L-atm}}{\text{mol-K}} \times \dfrac{1.01325 \times 10^5\ \text{Pa}}{1\ \text{atm}} \times \dfrac{1\ \text{bar}}{1 \times 10^5\ \text{Pa}} = \dfrac{0.08315\ \text{L-bar}}{\text{mol-K}}$

10.32   (a)   STP stands for standard temperature, 0°C (or 273 K), and standard pressure, 1 atm.

         (b) $V = \dfrac{nRT}{P}$; $V = 1\ \text{mol} \times \dfrac{0.08206\ \text{L-atm}}{\text{mol-K}} \times \dfrac{273\ \text{K}}{1\ \text{atm}}$

            $V = 22.4$ L for 1 mole of gas at STP

         (c)   25°C + 273 = 298 K

            $V = \dfrac{nRT}{P}$; $V = 1\ \text{mol} \times \dfrac{0.08206\ \text{L-atm}}{\text{mol-K}} \times \dfrac{298\ \text{K}}{1\ \text{atm}}$

            $V = 24.5$ L for 1 mol of gas at 1 atm and 25°C

10.33   *Analyze/Plan.* $PV = nRT$. At constant volume and temperature, P is directly proportional to n.

       Solve. For samples with equal masses of gas, the gas with MM = 30 will have twice as many moles of particles and twice the pressure. Thus, flask A contains the gas with MM = 30 and flask B contains the gas with MM = 60.

10.34   n = g/MM; PV = nRT = gRT/MM; MM = gRT/PV.

       2-L flask: MM = 4.8 RT/2.0(X) = 2.4 RT/X

       3-L flask: MM = 0.36 RT/3.0 (0.1 X) = 1.2 RT/X

       The molar masses of the two gases are not equal. The gas in the 2-L flask has a molar mass that is twice as large as the gas in the 3-L flask.

10.35   *Analyze/Plan.* Follow the strategy for calculations involving many variables given in section 10.4.   *Solve.*

       $T = \dfrac{PV}{nR} = 2.00\ \text{atm} \times \dfrac{1.00\ \text{L}}{0.500\ \text{mol}} \times \dfrac{\text{mol-K}}{0.08206\ \text{L-atm}} = 48.7\ \text{K}$

       K = 27°C + 273 = 300 K

       $n = \dfrac{PV}{RT} = 0.300\ \text{atm} \times \dfrac{0.250\ \text{L}}{300\ \text{K}} \times \dfrac{\text{mol-K}}{0.08206\text{-atm}} = 3.05 \times 10^{-3}\ \text{mol}$

       $650\ \text{torr} \times \dfrac{1\ \text{atm}}{760\ \text{torr}} = 0.85526 = 0.855\ \text{atm}$

       $V = \dfrac{nRT}{P} = 0.333\ \text{mol} \times \dfrac{350\ \text{K}}{0.85526\ \text{atm}} \times \dfrac{0.08206\ \text{L-atm}}{\text{mol-K}} = 11.2\ \text{L}$

585 mL = 0.585 L

$$P = \frac{nRT}{V} = 0.250 \text{ mol} \times \frac{295 \text{ K}}{0.585 \text{ L}} \times \frac{0.08206 \text{ L - atm}}{\text{mol - K}} = 10.3 \text{ atm}$$

P	V	N	T
2.00 atm	1.00 L	0.500 mol	**48.7 K**
0.300 atm	0.250 L	**3.05×10^{-3} mol**	27°C
650 torr	**11.2 L**	0.333 mol	350 K
10.3 atm	585 mL	0.250 mol	295 K

10.36   *Analyze/Plan.* Follow the strategy for calculations involving many variables given in section 10.4.   *Solve.*

(a)   n = 1.50 mol, P = 1.25 atm, T = –6°C = 267 K

$$V = \frac{nRT}{P} = 1.50 \text{ mol} \times \frac{0.08206 \text{ L - atm}}{\text{mol - K}} \times \frac{267 \text{ K}}{1.25 \text{ atm}} = 26.3 \text{ L}$$

(b)   n = 3.33×10^{-3} mol, V = 478 mL = 0.478 L

$$P = 750 \text{ torr} \times \frac{1 \text{ atm}}{760 \text{ torr}} = 0.9868 = 0.987 \text{ atm}$$

$$T = \frac{PV}{nR} = 0.9868 \text{ atm} \times \frac{0.478 \text{ L}}{3.33 \times 10^{-3} \text{ mol}} \times \frac{1 \text{ mol - K}}{0.08206 \text{ L - atm}} = 1726 = 1.73 \times 10^3 \text{ K}$$

(c)   n = 0.00245 mol, V = 413 mL = 0.413 L, T = 138°C = 411 K

$$P = \frac{nRT}{V}; = 0.00245 \text{ mol} \times \frac{0.08206 \text{ L - atm}}{\text{mol - K}} \times \frac{411 \text{ K}}{0.413 \text{ L}} = 0.200 \text{ atm}$$

(d)   V = 126.5 L, T = 54°C = 327 K,

$$P = 11.25 \text{ kPa} \times \frac{1 \text{ atm}}{101.325 \text{ kPa}} = 0.11103 = 0.1110 \text{ atm}$$

$$n = \frac{PV}{RT} = 0.11103 \text{ atm} \times \frac{\text{mol - K}}{0.08206 \text{ L - atm}} \times \frac{126.5 \text{ L}}{327 \text{ K}} = 0.523 \text{ mol}$$

10.37   *Analyze/Plan.* Follow the strategy for calculations involving many variables.   *Solve.*

n = g/MM; PV = nRT; PV = gRT/MM; g = MM×PV/RT

P = 1.0 atm, T = 23°C = 296 K, V = 1.75×10^5 ft^3. Change ft^3 to L, then calculate grams (or kg).

$$1.75 \times 10^5 \text{ ft}^3 \times \frac{(12)^3 \text{ in}^3}{\text{ft}^3} \times \frac{(2.54)^3 \text{ cm}^3}{\text{in}^3} \times \frac{1 \text{ L}}{1 \times 10^3 \text{ cm}^3} = 4.9554 \times 10^6 = 4.96 \times 10^6 \text{ L}$$

$$g = \frac{4.003 \text{ g He}}{1 \text{ mol He}} \times \frac{\text{mol - K}}{0.08206 \text{ L - atm}} \times \frac{1.0 \text{ atm} \times 4.955 \times 10^6 \text{ L}}{296 \text{ K}} = 8.2 \times 10^5 \text{ g} = 820 \text{ kg He}$$

10.38   Find the volume of the tube in cm^3; 1 cm^3 = 1 mL.

r = d/2 = 2.5 cm/2 = 1.25 = 1.3 cm; h = 5.5 m = 5.5×10^2 cm

$V = \pi r^2 h = 3.14159 \times (1.25 \text{ cm})^2 \times (5.5 \times 10^2 \text{ cm}) = 2.700 \times 10^3 \text{ cm}^3 = 2.7 \text{ L}$

$PV = \dfrac{g}{MM}RT; \quad g = \dfrac{MM \times PV}{RT}; \quad P = 1.78 \text{ torr} \times \dfrac{1 \text{ atm}}{760 \text{ torr}} = 2.342 \times 10^{-3} = 2.34 \times 10^{-3} \text{ atm}$

$g = \dfrac{20.18 \text{ g Ne}}{1 \text{ mol Ne}} \times \dfrac{\text{mol-K}}{0.08206 \text{ L-atm}} \times \dfrac{2.342 \times 10^{-3} \text{ atm} \times 2.700 \text{ L}}{308 \text{ K}} = 5.049 \times 10^{-3} = 5.0 \times 10^{-3} \text{ g Ne}$

10.39 *Analyze/Plan.* Follow the strategy for calculations involving many variables. *Solve.*

(a) $V = 2.25 \text{ L}; T = 273 + 37°C = 310 \text{ K}; P = 735 \text{ torr} \times \dfrac{1 \text{ atm}}{760 \text{ torr}} = 0.96710 = 0.967 \text{ atm}$

$PV = nRT, \ n = PV/RT, \ \text{number of molecules (\#)} = n \times 6.022 \times 10^{23}$

$\# = \dfrac{0.9671 \text{ atm} \times 2.25 \text{ L}}{310 \text{ K}} \times \dfrac{\text{mol-K}}{0.08206 \text{ L-atm}} \times \dfrac{6.022 \times 10^{23} \text{ molecules}}{\text{mol}}$

$$= 5.15 \times 10^{22} \text{ molecules}$$

(b) $V = 5.0 \times 10^3 \text{ L}; \ T = 273 + 0°C = 273 \text{ K}; P = 1.00 \text{ atm}; \ MM = 28.98 \text{ g/mol}$

$PV = \dfrac{g}{MM}RT; \quad g = \dfrac{MM \times PV}{RT}$

$g = \dfrac{28.98 \text{ g air}}{1 \text{ mol air}} \times \dfrac{\text{mol-K}}{0.08206 \text{ L-atm}} \times \dfrac{1.00 \text{ atm} \times 5.0 \times 10^3 \text{ L}}{273 \text{ K}}$

$$= 6{,}468 \text{ g} = 6.5 \times 10^3 \text{ g air} = 6.5 \text{ kg air}$$

10.40 (a) $P_{O_3} = 3.0 \times 10^{-3} \text{ atm}; T = 250 \text{ K}; V = 1 \text{ L (exact)}$

$\text{\# of } O_3 \text{ molecules} = \dfrac{PV}{RT} \times 6.022 \times 10^{23}$

$\# = \dfrac{3.0 \times 10^{-3} \text{ atm} \times 1 \text{ L}}{250 \text{ K}} \times \dfrac{\text{mol-K}}{0.08206 \text{ L-atm}} \times \dfrac{6.022 \times 10^{23} \text{ molecules}}{\text{mol}}$

$$= 8.8 \times 10^{19} \ O_3 \text{ molecules}$$

(b) $\text{\# of } CO_2 \text{ molecules} = \dfrac{PV}{RT} \times 6.022 \times 10^{23} \times 0.0004$

$\# = \dfrac{1.0 \text{ atm} \times 2.0 \text{ L}}{300 \text{ K}} \times \dfrac{\text{mol-K}}{0.08206 \text{ L-atm}} \times \dfrac{6.022 \times 10^{23} \text{ molecules}}{\text{mol}} \times 0.0004$

$$= 1.957 \times 10^{19} = 2 \times 10^{19} \ CO_2 \text{ molecules}$$

10.41 *Analyze/Plan.* Follow the strategy for calculations involving many variables. *Solve.*

(a) $P = \dfrac{nRT}{V}; n = 0.29 \text{ kg } O_2 \times \dfrac{1000 \text{ g}}{1 \text{ kg}} \times \dfrac{1 \text{ mol } O_2}{32.00 \text{ g } O_2} = 9.0625 = 9.1 \text{ mol}; V = 2.3 \text{ L};$

$T = 273 + 9°C = 282 \text{ K}$

$P = \dfrac{9.0625 \text{ mol}}{2.3 \text{ L}} \times \dfrac{0.08206 \text{ L-atm}}{\text{mol-K}} \times 282 \text{ K} = 91 \text{ atm}$

(b) $V = \dfrac{nRT}{P}; = \dfrac{9.0625 \text{ mol}}{0.95 \text{ atm}} \times \dfrac{0.08206 \text{ L-atm}}{\text{mol-K}} \times 299 \text{ K} = 2.3 \times 10^2 \text{ L}$

10.42 (a) $V = 0.250 \text{ L}, T = 23°C = 296 \text{ K}, n = 2.30 \text{ g } C_3H_8 \times \dfrac{1 \text{ mol } C_3H_8}{44.1 \text{ g } C_3H_8} = 0.052154$

$$= 0.0522 \text{ mol}$$

$$P = \frac{nRT}{V} = 0.052154 \, mol \times \frac{0.08206 \, L\text{-}atm}{mol\text{-}K} \times \frac{296 \, K}{0.250 \, L} = 5.07 \, atm$$

(b)   STP = 1.00 atm, 273 K

$$V = \frac{nRT}{P} = 0.052154 \, mol \times \frac{0.08206 \, L\text{-}atm}{mol\text{-}K} \times \frac{273 \, K}{1.00 \, atm} = 1.1684 = 1.17 \, L$$

(c)   °C = 5/9 (°F − 32°); K = °C + 273.15 = 5/9 (130°F − 32°) + 273.15 = 327.59 = 328 K

$$P = \frac{nRT}{V} = 0.052154 \, mol \times \frac{0.08206 \, L\text{-}atm}{mol\text{-}K} \times \frac{327.59 \, K}{0.250 \, L} = 5.608 = 5.61 \, atm$$

10.43   *Analyze/Plan.* Follow the strategy for calculations involving many variables.   *Solve.*

$$V = 8.70 \, L, \, T = 24°C = 297 \, K, \, P = 895 \, torr \times \frac{1 \, atm}{760 \, torr} = 1.1776 = 1.18 \, atm$$

(a) $g = \dfrac{MM \times PV}{RT}; \, g = \dfrac{70.91 g \, Cl_2}{1 \, mol \, Cl_2} \times \dfrac{mol\text{-}K}{0.08206 \, L\text{-}atm} \times \dfrac{1.1776 \, atm}{297 \, K} \times 8.70 \, L$

$$= 29.8 g \, Cl_2$$

(b) $V_2 = \dfrac{P_1 V_1 T_2}{T_1 P_2} = \dfrac{895 \, torr \times 8.70 \, L \times 273 \, K}{297 \, K \times 760 \, torr} = 9.42 \, L$

(c) $T_2 = \dfrac{P_2 V_2 T_1}{P_1 V_1} = \dfrac{876 \, torr \times 15.00 \, L \times 297 \, K}{895 \, torr \times 8.70 \, L} = 501 \, K$ *527 K = 54°C*

(d) $P_2 = \dfrac{P_1 V_1 T_2}{V_2 T_1} = \dfrac{895 \, torr \times 8.70 \, L \times 331 \, K}{5.00 \, L \times 297 \, K} = 1.73 \times 10^3 \, torr = 2.28 \, atm$

10.44 $T = 23°C = 296 \, K, \, P = 16,500 \, kPa \times \dfrac{1 \, atm}{101.325 \, kPa} = 162.84 = 163 \, atm$

$$V = 55.0 \, gal \times \frac{3.7854 \, L}{1 \, gal} = 208.20 = 208 \, L$$

(a) $g = \dfrac{MM \times PV}{RT}; \, g = \dfrac{32.0 g \, O_2}{1 \, mol \, O_2} \times \dfrac{mol\text{-}K}{0.08206 \, L\text{-}atm} \times \dfrac{162.84 \, atm}{296 \, K} \times 208.20 \, L$

$$= 4.4665 \times 10^4 \, g \, O_2 = 44.7 \, kg \, O_2$$

(b) $V_2 = \dfrac{P_1 V_1 T_2}{T_1 P_2} = \dfrac{16,500 \, kPa \times 208.20 \, L \times 273 \, K}{296 \, K \times 101.325 \, kPa} = 3.13 \times 10^4 \, L$

(c) $T_2 = \dfrac{P_2 T_1}{P_1} = \dfrac{150.0 \, atm \times 296 \, K}{16,500 \, kPa} \times \dfrac{101.325 \, kPa}{1 \, atm} = 272.7 = 273 \, K$

(d) $P_2 = \dfrac{P_1 V_1 T_2}{V_2 T_1} = \dfrac{16,500 \, kPa \times 208.20 \, L \times 297 \, K}{55.0 \, L \times 296 \, K} = 62,671 = 6.27 \times 10^4 \, kPa$

10.45   *Analyze.* Given: mass of cockroach, rate of O_2 consumption, temperature, percent O_2 in air, volume of air. Find: mol O_2 consumed per hour; mol O_2 in 1 quart of air; mol O_2 consumed in 48 hr.

(a)   *Plan/Solve.* V of O_2 consumed = rate of consumption × mass × time. n = PV/RT.

$$5.2 g \times 1 hr \times \frac{0.8 \, mL \, O_2}{1 g\text{-}hr} = 4.16 = 4 \, mL \, O_2 \, consumed$$

(b) $n = \dfrac{PV}{RT} = 1 \, atm \times \dfrac{mol\text{-}K}{0.08206 \, L\text{-}atm} \times \dfrac{0.00416 \, L}{297 \, K} = 1.71 \times 10^{-4} = 2 \times 10^{-4} \, mol \, O_2$

(c)   *Plan/Solve.* qt air $\rightarrow$ L air $\rightarrow$ L O_2 available. mol O_2 available = PV/RT. mol O_2/hr (from part (a)) $\rightarrow$ total mol O_2 consumed. Compare O_2 available and O_2 consumed.

$$1\,\text{qt air} \times \frac{0.946\,\text{L}}{1\,\text{qt}} \times 0.21\,O_2 \text{ in air} = 0.199\,\text{L}\,O_2 \text{ available}$$

$$n = 1\,\text{atm} \times \frac{\text{mol-K}}{0.08206\,\text{L-atm}} \times \frac{0.199\,\text{L}}{297\,\text{K}} = 8.17 \times 10^{-3} = 8 \times 10^{-3}\,\text{mol}\,O_2 \text{ available}$$

$$\text{roach uses} \frac{1.71 \times 10^{-4}\,\text{mol}}{1\,\text{hr}} \times 48\,\text{hr} = 8.21 \times 10^{-3} = 8 \times 10^{-3}\,\text{mol}\,O_2 \text{ consumed}$$

Not only does the roach use 20% of the available O_2, it needs all the O_2 in the jar.

10.46   Change mass to kg; 1 hr = 60 min; pay attention to units.

(a) $185\,\text{lb} \times \dfrac{1\,\text{kg}}{2.2046\,\text{lb}} \times \dfrac{47.5\,\text{mL}\,O_2}{\text{kg-min}} \times 60\,\text{min} = 2.39 \times 10^5\,\text{mL}$

(b) $165\,\text{lb} \times \dfrac{1\,\text{kg}}{2.2046\,\text{lb}} \times \dfrac{65.0\,\text{mL}\,O_2}{\text{kg-min}} \times 60\,\text{min} = 2.92 \times 10^5\,\text{mL}$

10.47   (a)   *Analyze.* Given: 119 tons Hg, 1 atm, 298 K. Find: vol Hg(g). *Plan.* Change tons to grams; use V = gRT/MM×P to calculate volume.   *Solve.*

$$119\,\text{tons} \times \frac{2000\,\text{lb}}{1\,\text{ton}} \times \frac{453.59\,\text{g}}{1\,\text{lb}} = 1.07954 \times 10^8 = 1.08 \times 10^8\,\text{g Hg}$$

$$V = \frac{1.07954 \times 10^8\,\text{g Hg} \times 1\,\text{mol Hg}}{200.59\,\text{g Hg}} \times \frac{0.08206\,\text{L-atm}}{\text{mol-K}} \times \frac{298\,\text{K}}{1\,\text{atm}}$$
$$= 1.3161 \times 10^7 = 1.32 \times 10^7\,\text{L}$$

(b)   *Analyze.* Given: total vol atmospheric gases (air) = $51 \times 10^{12}\,\text{m}^3$; 245 ppb Hg(g) by volume. Find: mol Hg(g) in atmospheres. *Plan.* Change m^3 to L; use definition of ppb to get L Hg(g); use n = PV/RT to calculate mol Hg. Assume STP.   *Solve.*

$$51 \times 10^{12}\,\text{m}^3 \times \frac{10^3\,\text{dm}^3}{1\,\text{m}^3} \times \frac{1\,\text{L}}{1\,\text{dm}^3} = 5.1 \times 10^{16}\,\text{L air}$$

$$5.1 \times 10^{16}\,\text{L air} \times \frac{245\,\text{L Hg(g)}}{1 \times 10^9\,\text{L air}} = 1.2495 \times 10^{10} = 1.2 \times 10^{10}\,\text{L Hg(g)}$$

$$n = \frac{1\,\text{atm} \times 1.2495 \times 10^{10}\,\text{L Hg(g)}}{273\,\text{K}} \times \frac{\text{mol-K}}{0.08206\,\text{L-atm}} = 5.5775 \times 10^8 = 5.6 \times 10^8\,\text{mol Hg(g)}$$

Check. Note that calculating amount of Hg from volume Hg(g) depends on the the assumed temperature of the atmosphere.

10.48   mass = $1800 \times 10^{-9}\,\text{g} = 1.8 \times 10^{-6}\,\text{g}$; V = $1\,\text{m}^3 = 1 \times 10^3\,\text{L}$; T = $273 + 10°\text{C} = 283\,\text{K}$

(a) $P = \dfrac{g\,RT}{MM \times V}$; $P = \dfrac{1.8 \times 10^{-6}\,\text{g Hg} \times 1\,\text{mol Hg}}{200.6\,\text{g Hg}} \times \dfrac{0.08206\,\text{L-atm}}{\text{mol-K}} \times \dfrac{283\,\text{K}}{1 \times 10^3\,\text{L}}$
$$= 2.1 \times 10^{-10}\,\text{atm}$$

(b) $\dfrac{1.8 \times 10^{-6}\,\text{g Hg}}{1\,\text{m}^3} \times \dfrac{1\,\text{mol Hg}}{200.6\,\text{g Hg}} \times \dfrac{6.022 \times 10^{23}\,\text{Hg atoms}}{1\,\text{mol Hg}} = 5.4 \times 10^{15}\,\text{Hg atoms/m}^3$

(c) $1600\,\text{km}^3 \times \dfrac{1000^3\,\text{m}^3}{1\,\text{km}^3} \times \dfrac{1.8 \times 10^{-6}\,\text{g Hg}}{1\,\text{m}^3} = 2.9 \times 10^6\,\text{g Hg/day}$

Further Applications of the Ideal-Gas Equation (section 10.5)

10.49 $Cl_2(g)$ is the most dense at 1.00 atm and 298 K. Gas density is directly proportional to molar mass and pressure, and inversely proportional to temperature (Equation [10.10]). For gas samples at the same conditions, molar mass determines density. Of the three gases listed, Cl_2 has the largest molar mass.

10.50 $CO_2 < SO_2 < HBr$. For gases at the same conditions, density is directly proportional to molar mass. The order of increasing molar mass is the order of increasing density. CO_2, 44 g/mol $< SO_2$, 64 g/mol $< HBr$, 81 g/mol.

10.51   (c) Because the helium atoms are of lower mass than the average air molecule, the helium gas is less dense than air. The balloon thus weighs less than the air displaced by its volume.

10.52   (b) Xe atoms have a higher mass than N_2 molecules. Because both gases at STP have the same number of molecules per unit volume, the Xe gas must be denser.

10.53   *Analyze/Plan.* Conditions (P, V, T) and amounts of gases are given. Rearrange the relationship $PV \times MM = gRT$ to obtain the desired of quantity, paying attention (as always!) to units.   *Solve.*

(a) $d = \dfrac{MM \times P}{RT}$;   MM = 46.0 g/mol; P = 0.970 atm, T = 35°C = 308 K

$d = \dfrac{46.0\,\text{g NO}_2}{1\,\text{mol}} \times \dfrac{\text{mol-K}}{0.08206\,\text{L-atm}} \times \dfrac{0.970\,\text{atm}}{308\,\text{K}} = 1.77\,\text{g/L}$

(b) $MM = \dfrac{gRT}{PV} = \dfrac{2.50\,\text{g}}{0.875\,\text{L}} \times \dfrac{0.08206\,\text{L-atm}}{\text{mol-K}} \times \dfrac{308\,\text{K}}{685\,\text{torr}} \times \dfrac{760\,\text{torr}}{1\,\text{atm}} = 80.1\,\text{g/mol}$

10.54   (a) $d = \dfrac{MM \times P}{RT}$;   MM = 146.1 g/mol, T = 21°C = 294 K, P = 707 torr

$d = \dfrac{146.1\,\text{g}}{1\,\text{mol}} \times \dfrac{\text{mol-K}}{0.08206\,\text{L-atm}} \times \dfrac{707\,\text{torr}}{294\,\text{K}} \times \dfrac{1\,\text{atm}}{760\,\text{torr}} = 5.63\,\text{g/L}$

(b) $MM = \dfrac{dRT}{P} = \dfrac{7.135\,\text{g}}{1\,\text{L}} \times \dfrac{0.08206\,\text{L-atm}}{\text{mol-K}} \times \dfrac{285\,\text{K}}{743\,\text{torr}} \times \dfrac{760\,\text{torr}}{1\,\text{atm}} = 171\,\text{g/mol}$

10.55   *Analyze/Plan.* Given: mass, conditions (P, V, T) of unknown gas. Find: molar mass. MM = gRT/PV. *Solve.*

$MM = \dfrac{gRT}{PV} = \dfrac{1.012\,\text{g}}{0.354\,\text{L}} \times \dfrac{0.08206\,\text{L-atm}}{\text{mol-K}} \times \dfrac{372\,\text{K}}{742\,\text{torr}} \times \dfrac{760\,\text{torr}}{1\,\text{atm}} = 89.4\,\text{g/mol}$

10.56 $MM = \dfrac{gRT}{PV} = \dfrac{0.846\,\text{g}}{0.354\,\text{L}} \times \dfrac{0.08206\,\text{L-atm}}{\text{mol-K}} \times \dfrac{373\,\text{K}}{752\,\text{torr}} \times \dfrac{760\,\text{torr}}{1\,\text{atm}} = 73.9\,\text{g/mol}$

10.57   *Analyze/Plan.* Follow the logic in Sample Exercise 10.9.   *Solve.*

$$\text{mol } O_2 = \frac{PV}{RT} = 3.5 \times 10^{-6} \text{ torr} \times \frac{1 \text{ atm}}{760 \text{ torr}} \times \frac{\text{mol - K}}{0.08206 \text{ L - atm}} \times \frac{0.452 \text{ L}}{300 \text{ K}} = 8.456 \times 10^{-11}$$

$$= 8.5 \times 10^{-11} \text{ mol } O_2$$

$$8.456 \times 10^{-11} \text{ mol } O_2 \times \frac{2 \text{ mol Mg}}{1 \text{ mol } O_2} \times \frac{24.3 \text{ g Mg}}{1 \text{ mol Mg}} = 4.1 \times 10^{-9} \text{ g Mg (4.1 ng Mg)}$$

10.58 $n_{H_2} = \dfrac{P_{H_2}V}{RT}$; $P = 825 \text{ torr} \times \dfrac{1 \text{ atm}}{760 \text{ torr}} = 1.0855 = 1.09 \text{ atm}$; $T = 273 + 21°C = 294 \text{ K}$

$$n_{H_2} = 1.0855 \text{ atm} \times \frac{\text{mol - K}}{0.08206 \text{ L - atm}} \times \frac{145 \text{ L}}{294 \text{ K}} = 6.5242 = 6.52 \text{ mol } H_2$$

$$6.5242 \text{ mol } H_2 \times \frac{1 \text{ mol CaH}_2}{2 \text{ mol } H_2} \times \frac{42.10 \text{ g CaH}_2}{1 \text{ mol CaH}_2} = 137.34 = 137 \text{ g CaH}_2$$

10.59   (a)   *Analyze/Plan.* g glucose → mol glucose → mol CO_2 → V CO_2 *Solve.*

$$24.5 \text{ g} \times \frac{1 \text{ mol glucose}}{180.1 \text{ g}} \times \frac{6 \text{ mol } CO_2}{1 \text{ mol glucose}} = 0.8162 = 0.816 \text{ mol } CO_2$$

$$V = \frac{nRT}{P} = 0.8162 \text{ mol} \times \frac{0.08206 \text{ L - atm}}{\text{mol - K}} \times \frac{310 \text{ K}}{0.970 \text{ atm}} = 21.4 \text{ L } CO_2$$

   (b)   *Analyze/Plan.* g glucose → mol glucose → mol O_2 → V O_2 *Solve.*

$$50.0 \text{ g} \times \frac{1 \text{ mol glucose}}{180.1 \text{ g}} \times \frac{6 \text{ mol } O_2}{1 \text{ mol glucose}} = 1.6657 = 1.67 \text{ mol } O_2$$

$$V = \frac{nRT}{P} = 1.6657 \text{ mol} \times \frac{0.08206 \text{ L - atm}}{\text{mol - K}} \times \frac{298 \text{ K}}{1 \text{ atm}} = 40.7 \text{ L } O_2$$

10.60   Follow the logic in Sample Exercise 10.9. The $H_2(g)$ will be used in a balloon, which operates at atmospheric pressure. Since atmospheric pressure is not explicitly given, assume 1 atm (infinite sig figs).

$$n = \frac{PV}{RT} = 1 \text{ atm} \times \frac{3.1150 \times 10^4 \text{ L}}{295 \text{ K}} \times \frac{\text{mol - K}}{0.08206 \text{ L - atm}} = 1.28678 \times 10^3 = 1.29 \times 10^3 \text{ mol } H_2$$

From the balanced equation, 1 mol of Fe produces 1 mol of H_2, so 1.29×10^3 mol Fe are required.

$$1.28678 \times 10^3 \text{ mol Fe} \times \frac{55.845 \text{ g Fe}}{\text{mol Fe}} \times \frac{1 \text{ kg}}{1000 \text{ g}} = 71.86 = 71.9 \text{ kg Fe}$$

10.61   *Analyze/Plan.* The gas sample is a mixture of $H_2(g)$ and $H_2O(g)$. Find the partial pressure of $H_2(g)$ and then the moles of $H_2(g)$ and Zn(s). *Solve.*

$$P_t = 738 \text{ torr} = P_{H_2} + P_{H_2O}$$

From Appendix B, the vapor pressure of H_2O at 24°C = 22.38 torr

$$P_{H_2} = (738 \text{ torr} - 22.38 \text{ torr}) \times \frac{1 \text{ atm}}{760 \text{ torr}} = 0.9416 = 0.942 \text{ atm}$$

$$n_{H_2} = \frac{P_{H_2}V}{RT} = 0.9416 \text{ atm} \times \frac{\text{mol - K}}{0.08206 \text{ L - atm}} \times \frac{0.159 \text{ L}}{297 \text{ K}} = 0.006143 = 0.00614 \text{ mol } H_2$$

$$0.006143 \text{ mol } H_2 \times \frac{1 \text{ mol Zn}}{1 \text{ mol } H_2} \times \frac{65.39 \text{ g Zn}}{1 \text{ mol Zn}} = 0.402 \text{ g Zn}$$

10.62   The gas sample is a mixture of $C_2H_2(g)$ and $H_2O(g)$. Find the partial pressure of C_2H_2, then moles CaC_2 and C_2H_2.

$P_t = 753 \text{ torr} = P_{C_2H_2} + P_{H_2O}.$ P_{H_2O} at $23\,°C = 21.07$ torr

$P_{C_2H_2} = (753 \text{ torr} - 21.07 \text{ torr}) \times \dfrac{1\,\text{atm}}{760\,\text{torr}} = 0.96307 = 0.963$ atm

$1.524 \text{ g } CaC_2 \times \dfrac{1\,\text{mol } CaC_2}{64.10\,\text{g}} \times \dfrac{1\,\text{mol } C_2H_2}{1\,\text{mol } CaC_2} = 0.023775 = 0.02378$ mol C_2H_2

$V = 0.023775 \text{ mol} \times \dfrac{0.08206\,\text{L - atm}}{\text{mol - K}} \times \dfrac{296\,\text{K}}{0.96307\,\text{atm}} = 0.600 \text{ L } C_2H_2$

Partial Pressures (section 10.6)

10.63   (a)   When the stopcock is opened, the volume occupied by $N_2(g)$ increases from 2.0 L to 5.0 L. At constant T, $P_1V_1 = P_2V_2$. $1.0 \text{ atm} \times 2.0 \text{ L} = P_2 \times 5.0 \text{ L}; P_2 = 0.40$ atm

         (b)   When the gases mix, the volume of $O_2(g)$ increases from 3.0 L to 5.0 L. At constant T, $P_1V_1 = P_2V_2$. $2.0 \text{ atm} \times 3.0 \text{ L} = P_2 \times 5.0 \text{ L}; P_2 = 1.2$ atm

         (c) $P_t = P_{N_2} + P_{O_2} = 0.40 \text{ atm} + 1.2 \text{ atm} = 1.6$ atm

10.64   (a)   The partial pressure of gas A is **not affected** by the addition of gas C. The partial pressure of A depends only on moles of A, volume of container, and conditions; none of these factors changes when gas C is added.

         (b)   The total pressure in the vessel **increases** when gas C is added, because the total number of moles of gas increases.

         (c)   The mole fraction of gas B **decreases** when gas C is added. The moles of gas B stay the same, but the total moles increase, so the mole fraction of B (nB/nt) decreases.

10.65   *Analyze.* Given: amount, V, T of three gases. Find: P of each gas, total P.

       Plan. $P = nRT/V$; $P_t = P_1 + P_2 + P_3 + \cdots$ *Solve.*

         (a) $P_{He} = \dfrac{nRT}{V} = 0.765 \text{ mol} \times \dfrac{0.08206\,\text{L - atm}}{\text{mol - K}} \times \dfrac{298\,\text{K}}{10.00\,\text{L}} = 1.871 = 1.87$ atm

               $P_{Ne} = \dfrac{nRT}{V} = 0.330 \text{ mol} \times \dfrac{0.08206\,\text{L - atm}}{\text{mol - K}} \times \dfrac{298\,\text{K}}{10.00\,\text{L}} = 0.8070 = 0.807$ atm

               $P_{Ar} = \dfrac{nRT}{V} = 0.110 \text{ mol} \times \dfrac{0.08206\,\text{L - atm}}{\text{mol - K}} \times \dfrac{298\,\text{K}}{10.00\,\text{L}} = 0.2690 = 0.269$ atm

         (b) $P_t = 1.871 \text{ atm} + 0.8070 \text{ atm} + 0.2690 \text{ atm} = 2.9470 = 2.95$ atm

10.66   Given mass, V and T of O_2 and He, find the partial pressure of each gas. Sum to find the total pressure in the tank.

       $V = 10.0 \text{ L}$; $T = 19°C$; $19 + 273 = 292$ K

       $n_{O_2} = 51.2 \text{ g } O_2 \times \dfrac{1\,\text{mol } O_2}{31.999\,\text{g } O_2} = 1.600 = 1.60 \text{ mol } O_2$

$$n_{He} = 32.6 \, g \, He \times \frac{1 \, mol \, He}{4.0026 \, g \, He} = 8.1447 = 8.14 \, mol \, He$$

$$P_{O_2} = 1.600 \, mol \times \frac{0.08206 \, L\text{-}atm}{mol\text{-}K} \times \frac{292 \, K}{10.0 \, L} = 3.8338 = 3.84 \, atm$$

$$P_{He} = 8.1447 \, mol \times \frac{0.08206 \, L\text{-}atm}{mol\text{-}K} \times \frac{292 \, K}{10.0 \, L} = 19.5159 = 19.5 \, atm$$

$$P_t = 3.8338 + 19.5159 = 23.3497 = 23.3 \, atm$$

10.67　*Analyze.* Given 390 ppm CO_2 in the atmosphere; 390 L CO_2 in 10^6 total L air. Find: mole fraction CO_2 in the atmosphere. *Plan.* Avogadro's law deals with the relationship between volume and moles of a gas.

Solve. Avogadro's law states that volume of a gas at constant temperature and pressure is directly proportional to moles of the gas. Using volume fraction to express concentration assumes that the 390 L CO_2 and 10^6 total L air are at the same temperature and pressure. That is, 390 L is the volume that the number of moles of CO_2 present in 10^6 L air would occupy at atmospheric temperature and pressure. The mole fraction of CO_2 in the atmosphere is then just the volume fraction from the concentration by volume.

$$\chi_{CO_2} = \frac{390 \, L \, CO_2}{10^6 \, L \, air} = 0.00039$$

10.68　$\chi_{Xe} = 4/100 = 0.04$; $\chi_{Ne} = \chi_{He} = (1 - 0.04)/2 = 0.48$

$$V_t = 0.900 \, mm \times 0.300 \, mm \times 10.0 \, mm \times \frac{1 \, cm^3}{10^3 \, mm^3} \times \frac{1 \, L}{1000 \, cm^3} = 2.70 \times 10^{-6} \, L$$

$$P_t = 500 \, torr \times \frac{1 \, atm}{760 \, torr} = 0.657895 = 0.658 \, atm$$

$$n_t = \frac{PV}{RT} = 0.657895 \, atm \times \frac{mol\text{-}K}{0.08206 \, L\text{-}atm} \times \frac{2.70 \times 10^{-6} \, L}{298 \, K} \times \frac{6.022 \times 10^{23} \, atoms}{mol}$$

$$= 4.3743 \times 10^{16} = 4.37 \times 10^{16} \, total \, atoms$$

Xe atoms = $\chi_{Xe} \times$ total atoms = $0.04(4.3743 \times 10^{16}) = 1.75 \times 10^{15} = 2 \times 10^{15}$ Xe atoms

Ne atoms = He atoms = $0.48(4.3743 \times 10^{16}) = 2.10 \times 10^{16} = 2.1 \times 10^{16}$ Ne and He atoms

Assumptions: In order to calculate total moles of gas and total atoms, we assumed a reasonable room temperature. Since '4% Xe' was not defined, we conveniently assumed mole percent. The 1:1 relationship of Ne to He is assumed to be by volume and not by mass.

10.69　*Analyze.* Given: mass CO_2 at V, T; pressure of air at same V, T. Find: partial pressure of CO_2 at these conditions, total pressure of gases at V, T.

Plan. g $CO_2 \rightarrow$ mol $CO_2 \rightarrow P_{CO_2}$ (via P = nRT/V); $P_t = P_{CO_2} + P_{air}$　　　*Solve.*

$$5.50 \, g \, CO_2 \times \frac{1 \, mol \, CO_2}{44.01 \, g \, CO_2} = 0.12497 = 0.125 \, mol \, CO_2; T = 273 + 24°C = 297 \, K$$

$$P_{CO_2} = 0.12497 \text{ mol} \times \frac{297 \text{ K}}{10.0 \text{ L}} \times \frac{0.08206 \text{ L-atm}}{\text{mol-K}} = 0.30458 = 0.305 \text{ atm}$$

$$P_{air} = 705 \text{ torr} \times \frac{1 \text{ atm}}{760 \text{ torr}} = 0.92763 = 0.928 \text{ atm}$$

$$P_t = P_{CO_2} + P_{air} = 0.30458 + 0.92763 = 1.23221 = 1.232 \text{ atm}$$

(Result has 3 decimal places and 4 sig figs.)

10.70   V $C_2H_5OC_2H_5$(l) → mass $C_2H_5OC_2H_5$ → mol $C_2H_5OC_2H_5$ → $P_{C_2H_5OC_2H_5}$ (at V, T)

$$P_t = P_{N_2} + P_{O_2} + P_{C_2H_5OC_2H_5} \; ; \; T = 273.15 + 35.0°C = 308.15 = 308.2 \text{ K}$$

(a) $5.00 \text{ mL } C_2H_5OC_2H_5 \times \dfrac{0.7134 \text{ g } C_2H_5OC_2H_5}{\text{mL}} \times \dfrac{1 \text{ mol } C_2H_5OC_2H_5}{74.12 \text{ g } C_2H_5OC_2H_5}$

$$= 0.048125 = 0.0481 \text{ mol } C_2H_5OC_2H_5$$

$$P = \frac{nRT}{V} = 0.048125 \text{ mol} \times \frac{308.15}{6.00 \text{ L}} \times \frac{0.08206 \text{ L-atm}}{\text{mol-K}} = 0.20282 = 0.203 \text{ atm}$$

(b) $P_t = P_{N_2} + P_{O_2} + P_{C_2H_5OC_2H_5} = 0.751 \text{ atm} + 0.208 \text{ atm} + 0.203 \text{ atm} = 1.162 \text{ atm}$

10.71   *Analyze/Plan.* The partial pressure of each component is equal to the mole fraction of that gas times the total pressure of the mixture. Find the mole fraction of each component and then its partial pressure.   *Solve.*

$n_t = 0.75 \text{ mol } N_2 + 0.30 \text{ mol } O_2 + 0.15 \text{ mol } CO_2 = 1.20 \text{ mol}$

$$\chi_{N_2} = \frac{0.75}{1.20} = 0.625 = 0.63; \; P_{N_2} = 0.625 \times 2.15 \text{ atm} = 1.344 = 1.3 \text{ atm}$$

$$\chi_{O_2} = \frac{0.30}{1.20} = 0.250 = 0.25; \; P_{O_2} = 0.250 \times 2.15 \text{ atm} = 0.5375 = 0.54 \text{ atm}$$

$$\chi_{CO_2} = \frac{0.15}{1.20} = 0.125 = 0.13; \; P_{CO_2} = 0.125 \times 2.15 \text{ atm} = 0.2688 = 0.27 \text{ atm}$$

Check. $P_T = 1.344 + 0.5375 + 0.2688 = 2.1503 = 2.15 \text{ atm}$. The sum of the partial pressures agrees with the stated total pressure.

10.72 $n_{N_2} = 10.25 \text{ g } N_2 \times \dfrac{1 \text{ mol}}{28.02 \text{ g}} = 0.3658 \text{ mol}; \; n_{H_2} = 1.83 \text{ g } H_2 \times \dfrac{1 \text{ mol}}{2.016 \text{ g}} = 0.9077 = 0.908 \text{ mol}$

$$n_{NH_3} = 7.95 \text{ g } NH_3 \times \frac{1 \text{ mol}}{17.03 \text{ g}} = 0.4668 \text{ mol} = 0.467 \text{ mol}$$

$n_t = 0.3658 + 0.9077 + 0.4668 = 1.7403 = 1.740 \text{ mol}$

$$P_{N_2} = \frac{n_{N_2}}{n_t} \times P_t = \frac{0.3658}{1.7403} \times 1.85 \text{ atm} = 0.389 \text{ atm}$$

$$P_{H_2} = \frac{0.9077}{1.7403} \times 1.85 \text{ atm} = 0.965 \text{ atm}; \; P_{NH_3} = \frac{0.4668}{1.7403} \times 1.85 \text{ atm} = 0.496 \text{ atm}$$

10.73   *Analyze/Plan.* Mole fraction = pressure fraction. Find the desired mole fraction of O_2 and change to mole percent.   *Solve.*

$$\chi_{O_2} = \frac{P_{O_2}}{P_t} = \frac{0.21 \text{ atm}}{8.38 \text{ atm}} = 0.025; \text{ mole \% } = 0.025 \times 100 = 2.5\%$$

10.74   (a) $n_{O_2} = 15.08 \text{ g O}_2 \times \dfrac{1 \text{ mol}}{31.999 \text{ g}} = 0.4713 \text{ mol}; \; n_{N_2} = 8.17 \text{ g N}_2 \times \dfrac{1 \text{ mol}}{28.02 \text{ g}} = 0.292 \text{ mol}$

$n_{H_2} = 2.64 \text{ g H}_2 \times \dfrac{1 \text{ mol}}{2.016 \text{ g}} = 1.31 \text{ mol}; \; n_t = 0.4713 + 0.292 + 1.31 = 2.07 \text{ mol}$

$\chi_{O_2} = \dfrac{n_{O_2}}{n_t} = \dfrac{0.4713}{2.07} = 0.228; \; \chi_{N_2} = \dfrac{n_{N_2}}{n_t} = \dfrac{0.292}{2.07} = 0.141$

$\chi_{H_2} = \dfrac{1.31}{2.07} = 0.633$

  (b) $P_{O_2} = n \times \dfrac{RT}{V}; P_{O_2} = 0.4713 \text{ mol} \times \dfrac{0.08206 \text{ L - atm}}{\text{mol - K}} \times \dfrac{288.15 \text{ K}}{15.50 \text{ L}} = 0.7190 \text{ atm}$

$P_{N_2} = 0.292 \text{ mol} \times \dfrac{0.08206 \text{ L - atm}}{\text{mol - K}} \times \dfrac{288.15 \text{ K}}{15.50 \text{ L}} = 0.445 \text{ atm}$

$P_{H_2} = 1.31 \text{ mol} \times \dfrac{0.08206 \text{ L - atm}}{\text{mol - K}} \times \dfrac{288.15 \text{ K}}{15.50 \text{ L}} = 2.00 \text{ atm}$

10.75   *Analyze/Plan.* $N_2(g)$ and $O_2(g)$ undergo changes of conditions and are mixed. Calculate the new pressure of each gas and add them to obtain the total pressure of the mixture.

$P_2 = P_1 V_1 T_2 / V_2 T_1; P_T = P_{N_2} + P_{O_2}.$ *Solve.*

$P_{N_2} = \dfrac{P_1 V_1 T_2}{V_2 T_1} = \dfrac{5.25 \text{ atm} \times 1.00 \text{ L} \times 293 \text{ K}}{12.5 \text{ L} \times 299 \text{ K}} = 0.41157 = 0.412 \text{ atm}$

$P_{O_2} = \dfrac{P_1 V_1 T_2}{V_2 T_1} = \dfrac{5.25 \text{ atm} \times 5.00 \text{ L} \times 293 \text{ K}}{12.5 \text{ L} \times 299 \text{ K}} = 2.05786 = 2.06 \text{ atm}$

$P_t = 0.41157 \text{ atm} + 2.05786 \text{ atm} = 2.46943 = 2.47 \text{ atm}$

10.76   Calculate the pressure of the gas in the second vessel directly from mass and conditions using the ideal-gas equation.

  (a) $P_{SO_2} = \dfrac{gRT}{MV} = \dfrac{3.00 \text{ g SO}_2}{64.07 \text{ g SO}_2/\text{mol}} \times \dfrac{0.08206 \text{ L - atm}}{\text{mol - K}} \times \dfrac{299 \text{ K}}{10.0 \text{ L}} = 0.11489 = 0.115 \text{ atm}$

  (b) $P_{N_2} = \dfrac{gRT}{MV} = \dfrac{2.35 \text{ g N}_2}{28.01 \text{ g N}_2/\text{mol}} \times \dfrac{0.08206 \text{ L - atm}}{\text{mol - K}} \times \dfrac{299 \text{ K}}{10.0 \text{ L}} = 0.20585 = 0.206 \text{ atm}$

  (c) $P_t = P_{SO_2} + P_{N_2} = 0.11489 \text{ atm} + 0.20585 \text{ atm} = 0.321 \text{ atm}$

Kinetic-Molecular Theory of Gases; Effusion and Diffusion
(sections 10.7 and 10.8)

10.77   (a)   Increase in temperature at constant volume, decrease in volume, increase in pressure

  (b)   Decrease in temperature

  (c)   Increase in volume, decrease in pressure

  (d)   Increase in temperature

10.78   (a)   False. The average kinetic energy per molecule in a collection of gas molecules is the same for all gases at the same temperature.

        (b)   True.

        (c)   False. The molecules in a gas sample at a given temperature exhibit a distribution of kinetic energies.

        (d)   True.

        (e)   False. Gas molecules at the same temperature exhibit a distribution of speeds.

10.79   The fact that gases are readily compressible supports the assumption that most of the volume of a gas sample is empty space.

10.80   Newton's model provides no explanation of the effect of a change in temperature on the pressure of a gas at constant volume or on the volume of a gas at constant pressure. On the other hand, the assumption that the average kinetic energy of gas molecules increases with increasing temperature explains Charles' Law, that an increase in temperature requires an increase in volume to maintain constant pressure.

10.81   Average speed is the numerical mean speed, the sum of the speeds of all particles divided by the total number of particles. The root mean square (rms) speed is the speed of a molecule with the same kinetic energy as the average kinetic energy of the sample. For a given gas sample at a fixed temperature, rms speed is larger (greater) than average speed, but the difference between the two is small.

10.82   The gas undergoes a chemical reaction which has fewer gas particles in products than in reactants. Mass is conserved when a chemical reaction occurs, so the mass of (flask + contents) remains constant. Pressure is directly proportional to number of particles, so pressure decreases as the number of gaseous particles decreases. One simple example of such a reaction is the dimerization of NO_2: $2\,NO_2(g) \rightarrow N_2O_4$.

10.83   *Analyze/Plan.* Apply the concepts of the Kinetic-Molecular Theory (KMT) to the situation where a gas is heated at constant volume. Determine how the quantities in (a)-(d) are affected by this change. *Solve.*

        (a)   Average kinetic energy is proportional to temperature (K), so average kinetic energy of the molecules increases.

        (b)   The average kinetic energy of a gas is $1/2\,mu_{rms}^2$. Molecular mass doesn't change as T increases; average kinetic energy increases so rms speed (u) increases. (Also, $u_{rms} = (3RT/MM)^{1/2}$, so u_{rms} is directly related to T.)

        (c)   As T and thus rms molecular speed increase, molecular momentum (mu) increases and the strength of an average impact with the container wall increases.

        (d)   As T and rms molecular speed increase, the molecules collide more frequently with the container walls, and the total number of collisions per second increases.

10.84   (a)   They have the same number of molecules (equal volumes of gases at the same temperature and pressure contain equal numbers of molecules).

        (b) N_2 is more dense because it has the larger molar mass. Since the volumes of the samples and the number of molecules are equal, the gas with the larger molar mass will have the greater density.

(c)   The average kinetic energies are equal (statement 5, section 10.7).

(d) CH_4 will effuse faster. The lighter the gas molecules, the faster they will effuse (Graham's Law).

10.85   (a)   *Plan.* The larger the molar mass, the slower the average speed (at constant temperature).

Solve. In order of increasing speed (and decreasing molar mass):
$HBr < NF_3 < SO_2 < CO < Ne$

(b)   *Plan.* Follow the logic of Sample Exercise 10.14. *Solve.*

$$u_{rms} = \sqrt{\frac{3RT}{MM}} = \left(\frac{3 \times 8.314 \text{ kg-m}^2/\text{s}^2\text{-mol-K} \times 298 \text{ K}}{71.0 \times 10^{-3} \text{ kg/mol}}\right)^{1/2} = 324 \text{ m/s}$$

(c)   *Plan.* Use Equation 10.23 to calculate the most probable speed, u_{mp}. MM of O_3 = 48.0 g/mol; T = 270 K. *Solve.*

$$u_{mp} = \sqrt{\frac{2RT}{MM}} = \left(\frac{2 \times 8.314 \text{ kg-m}^2/\text{s}^2\text{-mol-K} \times 270 \text{ K}}{48.0 \times 10^{-3} \text{ kg/mol}}\right)^{1/2} = 306 \text{ m/s}$$

10.86   (a)   *Plan.* The greater the molecular (and molar) mass, the smaller the rms and average speeds of the molecules. Calculate the molar mass of each gas, and place them in decreasing order of mass and increasing order of rms and average speed. *Solve.*

CO = 28 g/mol; SF_6 = 146 g/mol; H_2S = 34 g/mol; Cl_2 = 71 g/mol;
HBr = 81 g/mol. In order of increasing speed (and decreasing molar mass):

$SF_6 < HBr < Cl_2 < H_2S < CO$

(b)   *Plan.* Follow the logic of Sample Exercise 10.14. *Solve.*

$$CO: u_{rms} = \sqrt{\frac{3RT}{MM}} = \left(\frac{3 \times 8.314 \text{ kg-m}^2/\text{s}^2\text{-mol-K} \times 300 \text{ K}}{28.0 \times 10^{-3} \text{ kg/mol}}\right)^{1/2} = 5.17 \times 10^2 \text{ m/s}$$

$$Cl_2: u_{rms} = \left(\frac{3 \times 8.314 \text{ kg-m}^2/\text{s}^2\text{-mol-K} \times 300 \text{ K}}{70.9 \times 10^{-3} \text{ kg/mol}}\right)^{1/2} = 3.25 \times 10^2 \text{ m/s}$$

As expected, the lighter molecule moves at the greater speed.

(c)   *Plan.* From Equations [10.22] and [10.23], we see that the ratio of most probable speed to rms speed is $(2/3)^{1/2}$. Use this ratio and the results from part (b) to calculate most probable speeds. *Solve.*

CO: $u_{mp} = (2/3)^{1/2}(5.17 \times 10^2 \text{ m/s}) = 422 \text{ m/s}$

Cl_2: $u_{mp} = (2/3)^{1/2}(3.25 \times 10^2 \text{ m/s}) = 265 \text{ m/s}$

The lighter molecule, CO, has the greater most probable speed. Note that the most probable speed is less than the rms speed, as shown on Figure 10.17(b).

10.87   *Effusion* is the escape of gas molecules through a tiny hole. *Diffusion* is the distribution of a gas throughout space or throughout another substance. On a macroscopic scale, effusion is like hundreds of students leaving an auditorium through one small door, while diffusion is analogous to these students making their way around the quad, which may or may not already contain other students.

10.88   Write each proportionality relationship as an equation, then combine them to obtain a formula for mean free path.

The operational symbols and units are: mean free path, λ, meters (m); temperature, T, kelvins (K); pressure, P, atmospheres (atm); diameter of a gas molecule, d, meters (m), constant, R_{mfp}.

$\lambda = \text{constant} \times T$; $\lambda = \text{constant}/P$; $\lambda = \text{constant}/d^2$

Combining : $\lambda = \dfrac{R_{mfp} \times T}{P \times d^2}$

The units of R_{mfp} are chosen and arranged so that they cancel the units of measurement, leaving an appropriate length unit for λ.

With the units defined above, R_{mfp} will have units of $\dfrac{atm - m^3}{K}$.

(Note that $1\ m^3 = 10^3\ dm^3 = 1000$ L. Substituting, R_{mfp} would have units of $\dfrac{atm - L}{K}$, with the factor of 1000 incorporated into the value of R_{mfp}.)

10.89   *Plan.* The heavier the molecule, the slower the rate of effusion. Thus, the order for increasing rate of effusion is in the order of decreasing mass. *Solve.*

rate $^2H^{37}Cl$ < rate $^1H^{37}Cl$ < rate $^2H^{35}Cl$ < rate $^1H^{35}Cl$

10.90 $\dfrac{rate\,^{235}U}{rate\,^{238}U} = \sqrt{\dfrac{238.05}{235.04}} = \sqrt{1.0128} = 1.0064$

There is a slightly greater rate enhancement for $^{235}U(g)$ atoms than $^{235}UF_6(g)$ molecules (1.0043), because ^{235}U is a greater percentage (100%) of the mass of the diffusing particles than in $^{235}UF_6$ molecules. The masses of the isotopes were taken from *The Handbook of Chemistry and Physics.*

10.91   *Analyze.* Given: relative effusion rates of two gases at same temperature. Find: molecular formula of one of the gases. *Plan.* Use Graham's law to calculate the formula weight of arsenic (III) sulfide, and thus the molecular formula. *Solve.*

$\dfrac{rate\ (sulfide)}{rate\ (Ar)} = \left[\dfrac{39.9}{MM\ (sulfide)}\right]^{1/2} = 0.28$

MM (sulfide) = $39.9 / 0.28^2 = 509$ g/mol (two significant figures)

The empirical formula of arsenic(III) sulfide is As_2S_3, which has a formula mass of 246.1. Twice this is 490 g/mol, close to the value estimated from the effusion experiment. Thus, the formula of the gas phase molecule is As_4S_6.

10.92   The time required is proportional to the reciprocal of the effusion rate.

$\dfrac{rate\ (X)}{rate\ (O_2)} = \dfrac{105\ s}{31\ s} = \left[\dfrac{32\,g\ O_2}{MM_x}\right]^{1/2}$; $MM_x = 32\ g\ O_2 \times \left[\dfrac{105}{31}\right]^2 = 370\,g/mol$ (two sig figs)

Nonideal-Gas Behavior (section 10.9)

10.93   (a)   Nonideal gas behavior is observed at very high pressures and/or low temperatures.

       (b)   The real volumes of gas molecules and attractive intermolecular forces between molecules cause gases to behave nonideally.

       (c)   The ratio PV/RT is equal to the number of moles of particles in an ideal-gas sample; this number should be a constant for all pressure, volume, and temperature conditions. If the value of this ratio changes with increasing pressure, the gas sample is not behaving ideally. That is, the gas is not behaving according to the ideal-gas equation.

            Negative deviations indicate fewer "effective" particles in the sample, a result of attractive forces among particles. Positive deviations indicate more "effective" particles, a result of the real volume occupied by the particles.

10.94   Ideal-gas behavior is most likely to occur at high temperature and low pressure, so the atmosphere on Mercury is more likely to obey the ideal-gas law. The higher temperature on Mercury means that the kinetic energies of the molecules will be larger relative to intermolecular attractive forces. Further, the gravitational attractive forces on Mercury are lower because the planet has a much smaller mass. This means that for the same column mass of gas (Figure 10.1), atmospheric pressure on Mercury will be lower.

10.95   *Plan.* The constants a and b are part of the correction terms in the van der Waals equation. The smaller the values of a and b, the smaller the corrections and the more ideal the gas. *Solve.*

            Ar ($a = 1.34$, $b = 0.0322$) will behave more like an ideal gas than CO_2 ($a = 3.59$, $b = 0.0427$) at high pressures.

10.96   The constant a is a measure of the strength of intermolecular attractions among gas molecules; b is a measure of molecular volume. Both increase with increasing molecular mass and structural complexity.

10.97   *Analyze/Plan.* Follow the logic in Sample Exercise 10.16. Use the ideal-gas equation to calculate pressure in (a), the van der Waals equation in (b). $n = 1.00$ mol, $V = 5.00$ L, $T = 25°C = 298$ K; $a = 6.49$ L^2-atm/mol^2, $b = 0.0562$ L/mol.

       (a) $P = \dfrac{nRT}{V} = 1.00 \text{ mol} \times \dfrac{298 \text{ K}}{5.00 \text{ L}} \times \dfrac{0.08206 \text{ L-atm}}{\text{mol-K}} = 4.89 \text{ atm}$

       (b) $P = \dfrac{nRT}{V - nb} - \dfrac{n^2 a}{V^2};$

            $P = \dfrac{(1.00 \text{ mol})(298 \text{ K})(0.08206 \text{ L-atm/mol-K})}{5.00 \text{ L} - (1.00 \text{ mol})(0.0562 \text{ L/mol})} - \dfrac{(1.00 \text{ mol})^2 (6.49 \text{ } L^2 \text{-atm} / mol^2)}{(5.00 \text{ L})^2}$

            $P = 4.9463 \text{ atm} - 0.2596 \text{ atm} = 4.6868 = 4.69 \text{ atm}$

       (c)   From Sample Exercise 10.16, the difference at 22.41 L between the ideal and van der Waals results is $(1.00 - 0.990) = 0.010$ atm. At 5.00 L, the difference is $(4.89 - 4.69) = 0.20$ atm. The effects of both molecular attractions, the a correction, and molecular volume, the b correction, increase with decreasing volume. For the a correction, V^2 appears in the denominator, so the correction increases exponentially as V decreases. For the _b_ correction, _nb_ is a larger portion of the total volume as V decreases. That is, 0.0562 L is 1.1% of 5.0 L, but only 0.25% of 22.41 L. Qualitatively, molecular attractions are more important as the amount of free space decreases and the number of molecular collisions increase. Molecular volume is a larger part of the total volume as the container volume decreases.

10.98   _Analyze._ Conditions and amount of $CCl_4(g)$ are given. _Plan._ Use ideal-gas equation and van der Waals equation to calculate pressure of gas at these conditions.   _Solve._

(a) $P = 1.00 \text{ mol} \times \dfrac{0.08206 \text{ L-atm}}{\text{mol-K}} \times \dfrac{313 \text{ K}}{33.3 \text{ L}} = 0.771 \text{ atm}$

(b) $P = \dfrac{nRT}{V-nb} - \dfrac{an^2}{V^2} = \dfrac{1.00 \times 0.08206 \times 313}{33.3 - (1.00 \times 0.1383)} - \dfrac{20.4(1.00)^2}{(33.3)^2} = 0.756 \text{ atm}$

Check. The van der Waals result indicates that the real pressure will be less than the ideal pressure. That is, intermolecular forces reduce the effective number of particles and the real pressure. This is reasonable for 1 mole of gas at relatively low temperature and pressure.

(c)   According to Table 10.3, CCl_4 has larger _a_ and _b_ values. That is, CCl_4 experiences stronger intermolecular attractions and has a larger molecular volume than Cl_2 does. CCl_4 will deviate more from ideal behavior at these conditions than Cl_2 will.

10.99   _Analyze._ Given the _b_ value of Xe, 0.0510 L/mol, calculate the radius of a Xe atom.

Plan. Use Avogadro's number to chang L/mol to L/atom. Use the volume formula, $V = 4/3 \pi r^3$ and units conversion to obtain the radius in A. $1 \text{ L} = 1 \text{ dm}^3$.   _Solve._

$\dfrac{0.0510 \text{ L}}{1 \text{ mol Xe}} \times \dfrac{1 \text{ mol Xe}}{6.022 \times 10^{23} \text{ Xe atoms}} \times \dfrac{1 \text{ dm}^3}{1 \text{ L}} = 8.4689 \times 10^{-26} = 8.47 \times 10^{-26} \text{ dm}^3$

$V = 4/3 \pi r^3; \quad r^3 = 3V/4\pi; \quad r = (3V/4\pi)^{1/3}$

$r = \left(\dfrac{3 \times 8.4689 \times 10^{-26} \text{ dm}^3}{4 \times 3.14159} \right)^{1/3} = 2.7243 \times 10^{-9} = 2.72 \times 10^{-9} \text{ dm}$

$2.72 \times 10^{-9} \text{ dm} \times \dfrac{1 \text{ m}}{10 \text{ dm}} \times \dfrac{1 \text{ Å}}{1 \times 10^{-10} \text{ m}} = 2.72 \text{ Å}$

The calculated value is the nonbonding radius. From Figure 7.6 in section 7.3, the bonding atomic radius of Xe is 1.30 Å. We expect the nonbonding radius of an atom to be larger than the bonding radius, but our calculated value is more than twice as large.

10.100   From section 7.3, the nonbonding or _van der Waals_ radius is half of the shortest internuclear distance when two nonbonding atoms collide. So, radii calculated from the van der Waals equation are nonbonding radii. According to the kinetic molecular theory, ideal gas particles undergo perfectly elastic, billiard-ball collisions, in keeping with the definition of nonbonding radii.

Also, from the results of Exercise 10.99, the atomic radius calculated from the van der Waals _b_ value is twice as large as the bonding atomic radius from Figure 7.6. Nonbonding radii are larger than bonding radii because no lasting penetration of electron clouds occurs during a nonbonding collision.

Additional Exercises

10.101 $P_1V_1 = P_2V_2; V_2 = P_1V_1/P_2$

$$V_2 = \frac{3.0\,\text{atm} \times 1.0\,\text{mm}^3}{730\,\text{torr}} \times \frac{760\,\text{torr}}{1\,\text{atm}} = 3.1\,\text{mm}^3$$

10.102 $PV = nRT$, $n = PV/RT$. Since RT is constant, n is proportional to PV.

Total available $n = (15.0\,\text{L} \times 1.00 \times 10^2\,\text{atm}) - (15.0\,\text{L} \times 1.00\,\text{atm}) = 1485$

$$= 1.49 \times 10^3 \text{ L-atm}$$

Each balloon holds $2.00\,\text{L} \times 1.00\,\text{atm} = 2.00$ L-atm

$$\frac{1485\,\text{L-atm available}}{2.00\,\text{L-atm/balloon}} = 742.5 = 742 \text{ balloons}$$

(Only 742 balloons can be filled completely, with a bit of He left over.)

10.103 $P = \dfrac{nRT}{V}$; $n = 1.4 \times 10^{-5}$ mol, $V = 0.600$ L, $T = 23°C = 296$ K

$$P = 1.4 \times 10^{-5}\,\text{mol} \times \frac{0.08206\,\text{L-atm}}{\text{mol-K}} \times \frac{296\,\text{K}}{0.600\,\text{L}} = 5.7 \times 10^{-4}\,\text{atm} = 0.43\,\text{mm Hg}$$

10.104   **(a)**   Change mass CO_2 to mol CO_2. $P = 1.00$ atm, $T = 27°C = 300$ K.

$$6 \times 10^6\,\text{tons CO}_2 \times \frac{2000\,\text{lb}}{\text{ton}} \times \frac{453.6\,\text{g}}{\text{lb}} \times \frac{1\,\text{mol CO}_2}{44.01\,\text{g CO}_2} = 1.237 \times 10^{11} = 1 \times 10^{11}\,\text{mol}$$

$$V = \frac{nRT}{P} = 1.237 \times 10^{11}\,\text{mol} \times \frac{300\,\text{K}}{1.00\,\text{atm}} \times \frac{0.08206\,\text{L-atm}}{\text{mol-K}} =$$
$$3.045 \times 10^{12} = 3 \times 10^{12}\,\text{L}$$

(b) $1.237 \times 10^{11}\,\text{mol CO}_2 \times \dfrac{44.01\,\text{g CO}_2}{\text{mol CO}_2} \times \dfrac{1\,\text{cm}^3}{1.2\,\text{g}} \times \dfrac{1\,\text{L}}{1000\,\text{cm}^3} = 4.536 \times 10^9 = 5 \times 10^9\,\text{L}$

(c) $n = 1.237 \times 10^{11}$ mol, $P = 90$ atm, $T = 36°C = 309$ K

$$V = \frac{nRT}{P} = 1.237 \times 10^{11}\,\text{mol} \times \frac{309\,\text{K}}{90\,\text{atm}} \times \frac{0.08206\,\text{L-atm}}{\text{mol-K}} =$$
$$3.485 \times 10^{10} = 3 \times 10^{10}\,\text{L}$$

10.105   **(a)** $n = \dfrac{PV}{RT} = 3.00\,\text{atm} \times \dfrac{\text{mol-K}}{0.08206\,\text{L-atm}} \times \dfrac{110\,\text{L}}{300\,\text{K}} = 13.4\,\text{mol C}_3\text{H}_8\text{(g)}$

(b) $\dfrac{0.590\,\text{g C}_3\text{H}_8\,(\text{l})}{1\,\text{mL}} \times 110 \times 10^3\,\text{mL} \times \dfrac{1\,\text{mol C}_3\text{H}_8}{44.094\,\text{g}} = 1.47 \times 10^3\,\text{mol C}_3\text{H}_8\,\text{(l)}$

(c)   Using C_3H_8 in a 110 L container as an example, the ratio of moles liquid to moles gas that can be stored in a certain volume is $\dfrac{1.47 \times 10^3\,\text{mol liquid}}{13.4\,\text{mol gas}} = 110.$

A container with a fixed volume holds many more moles (molecules) of C_3H_8(l) because in the liquid phase the molecules are touching. In the gas phase, the molecules are far apart (statement 2, section 10.7), and many fewer molecules will fit in the container.

10.106 $\text{Vol of room} = 12\,\text{ft} \times 20\,\text{ft} \times 9\,\text{ft} \times \dfrac{12^3\,\text{in}^3}{1\,\text{ft}^3} \times \dfrac{2.54^3\,\text{cm}^3}{1^3\,\text{in}^3} \times \dfrac{1\,\text{L}}{1000\,\text{cm}^3} = 61,164 = 6 \times 10^4\,\text{L}$

Calculate the **total** moles of gas in the laboratory at the conditions given.

$n_t = \dfrac{PV}{RT} = 1.00\,\text{atm} \times \dfrac{\text{mol-K}}{0.08206\,\text{L-atm}} \times \dfrac{61,164\,\text{L}}{297\,\text{K}} = 2510 = 3 \times 10^3\,\text{mol gas}$

A $Ni(CO)_4$ concentration of 1 part in 10^9 means 1 mol $Ni(CO)_4$ in 1×10^9 total moles of gas.

$\dfrac{x\,\text{mol } Ni(CO)_4}{2.510 \times 10^3\,\text{mol gas}} = \dfrac{1}{1 \times 10^9} = 2.510 \times 10^{-6} = 3 \times 10^{-6}\,\text{mol } Ni(CO)_4$

$2.510 \times 10^{-6}\,\text{mol } Ni(CO)_4 \times \dfrac{170.74\,\text{g } Ni(CO)_4}{1\,\text{mol } Ni(CO)_4} = 4.286 \times 10^{-3} = 4 \times 10^{-3}\,\text{g} = 4\,\text{mg } Ni(CO)_4$

10.107   (a)   mol = g/MM; assume mol Ar = mol X;

$\dfrac{g\,\text{Ar}}{39.948\,\text{g/mol}} = \dfrac{g\,\text{X}}{MM\,\text{X}}; \quad \dfrac{3.224\,\text{g Ar}}{39.948\,\text{g/mol}} = \dfrac{8.102\,\text{g X}}{MM\,\text{X}}$

$MM\,\text{X} = \dfrac{(8.102\,\text{g X})(39.948\,\text{g/mol})}{3.224\,\text{g Ar}} = 100.39 = 100.4\,\text{g/mol}$

       (b)   Assume mol Ar = mol X. For gases, PV = nRT and n = PV/RT. For moles of the two gases to be equal, the implied assumption is that P, V, and T are constant. Since we use the same container for both gas samples, constant V is a good assumption. Constant P and T are not explicitly stated.

We also assume that the gases behave ideally. At ambient conditions, this is a reasonable assumption.

10.108   It is simplest to calculate the partial pressure of each gas as it expands into the total volume, then sum the partial pressures.

$P_2 = P_1 V_1 / V_2; \quad P_{N_2} = 265\,\text{torr}\,(1.0\,\text{L}/2.5\,\text{L}) = 106 = 1.1 \times 10^2\,\text{torr}$

$P_{Ne} = 800\,\text{torr}\,(1.0\,\text{L}/2.5\,\text{L}) = 320 = 3.2 \times 10^2\,\text{torr}; \quad P_{H_2} = 532\,\text{torr}\,(0.5\,\text{L}/2.5\,\text{L})$

$= 106 = 1.1 \times 10^2\,\text{torr}$

$P_t = P_{N_2} + P_{Ne} + P_{H_2} = (106 + 320 + 106)\,\text{torr} = 532 = 5.3 \times 10^2\,\text{torr}$

10.109   (a) $n = \dfrac{PV}{RT} = 0.980\,\text{atm} \times \dfrac{\text{mol-K}}{0.08206\,\text{L-atm}} \times \dfrac{0.524\,\text{L}}{347\,\text{K}} = 0.018034 = 0.0180\,\text{mol air}$

$\text{mol } O_2 = 0.018034\,\text{mol air} \times \dfrac{0.2095\,\text{mol } O_2}{1\,\text{mol air}} = 0.003778 = 0.00378\,\text{mol } O_2$

       (b) $C_8H_{18}(l) + 25/2\,O_2(g) \rightarrow 8CO_2(g) + 9H_2O(g)$

(The H_2O produced in an automobile engine is in the gaseous state.)

$0.003778\,\text{mol } O_2 \times \dfrac{1\,\text{mol } C_8H_{18}}{12.5\,\text{mol } O_2} \times \dfrac{114.2\,\text{g } C_8H_{18}}{1\,\text{mol } C_8H_{18}} = 0.0345\,\text{g } C_8H_{18}$

10.110   (a)   Pressure percent = mol percent. Change pressure/mol percents to mol fraction. Partial pressure of each gas is mol fraction (χ) times total pressure. $P_x = \chi_x P_t$

$$P_{N_2} = 0.748(0.985 \text{ atm}) = 0.737 \text{ atm}; \quad P_{O_2} = 0.153(0.985 \text{ atm}) = 0.151 \text{ atm}$$

$$P_{CO_2} = 0.037(0.985 \text{ atm}) = 0.03645 = 0.036 \text{ atm}$$

$$P_{H_2O} = 0.062(0.985 \text{ atm}) = 0.06107 = 0.061 \text{ atm}$$

(b) $PV = nRT$, $n = PV/RT$; $P = 0.036$ atm, $V = 0.455$ L, $T = 37°C = 310$ K

$$n = 0.03645 \text{ atm} \times \frac{0.455 \text{ L}}{310 \text{ K}} \times \frac{\text{mol - K}}{0.08206 \text{ L - atm}} = 6.520 \times 10^{-4} = 6.5 \times 10^{-4} \text{ mol}$$

(c) $C_6H_{12}O_6 + 6O_2 \rightarrow 6CO_2 + 6H_2O$

$$6.520 \times 10^{-4} \text{ mol } CO_2 \times \frac{1 \text{ mol } C_6H_{12}O_6}{6 \text{ mol } CO_2} \times \frac{180.15 \text{ g } C_6H_{12}O_6}{1 \text{ mol } C_6H_{12}O_6} = 0.01958$$

$$= 0.020 \text{ g } C_6H_{12}O_6$$

10.111   V and T are the same for He and O_2.

$$P_{He}V = n_{He}RT, \quad P_{He} / n_{He} = RT/V; \quad P_{O_2} / n_{O_2} = RT/V$$

$$\frac{P_{He}}{n_{He}} = \frac{P_{O_2}}{n_{O_2}} = n_{O_2} \times \frac{P_{O_2} \times n_{He}}{P_{He}}; \quad n_{He} = 1.42 \text{ g He} \times \frac{1 \text{ mol He}}{4.003 \text{ g He}} = 0.3547 = 0.355 \text{ mol He}$$

$$n_{O_2} = \frac{158 \text{ torr}}{42.5 \text{ torr}} \times 0.355 \text{ mol} = 1.3188 = 1.32 \text{ mol } O_2; \quad 1.3188 \text{ mol } O_2 \times \frac{32.00 \text{ g } O_2}{1 \text{ mol } O_2} = 42.2 \text{ g } O_2$$

10.112 $$MM_{avg} = \frac{dRT}{P} = \frac{1.104 \text{ g}}{1 \text{ L}} \times \frac{0.08206 \text{ L - atm}}{\text{mol - K}} \times \frac{400 \text{ K}}{355 \text{ torr}} \times \frac{760 \text{ torr}}{1 \text{ atm}} = 77.579 = 77.6 \text{ g/mol}$$

χ = mole fraction O_2; $1 - \chi$ = mole fraction Kr

77.579 g = χ(32.00) + (1 – χ)(83.80)

6.22 = 51.80 χ; χ = 0.120; 12.0% O_2

10.113   (a)   The quantity d/P = MM/RT should be a constant at all pressures for an ideal gas. It is not, however, because of nonideal behavior. If we graph d/P vs P, the ratio should approach ideal behavior at low P. At P = 0, d/P = 2.2525. Using this value in the formula MM = d/P × RT, MM = 50.46 g/mol.

(b)   The ratio d/P varies with pressure because of the finite volumes of gas molecules and attractive intermolecular forces.

10.114   Calculate the number of moles of Ar in the vessel:

$n = (339.854 - 337.428)/39.948 = 0.060729 = 0.06073$ mol

The total number of moles of the mixed gas is the same (Avogadro's Law). Thus, the average atomic weight is $(339.076 - 337.428)/0.060729 = 27.137 = 27.14$. Let the mole fraction of Ne be χ. Then,

$\chi\,(20.183) + (1 - \chi)\,(39.948) = 27.137;\ 12.811 = 19.765\,\chi;\ \chi = 0.6482$

Neon is thus 64.82 mole percent of the mixture.

10.115 $u_{rms} = (3RT/MM)^{1/2};\ u_{rms2} = 2\,u_{rms1};\ T_1 = -33° = 240$ K

$u_{rms1} = (3RT_1/MM)^{1/2};\ u_{rms1}^2 = 3(240)R/MM = 720R/MM$

$u_{rms1} = (720R/MM)^{1/2};\ \ u_{rms2} = 2u_{rms1} = (2)(720R/MM)^{1/2}$

$(2)(720R/MM)^{1/2} = (3RT_2/MM)^{1/2}$

$(2)^2(720R/MM) = 3RT_2/MM;\ (2)^2(720) = 3T_2$

$T_2 = (4)(720)/3 = 960$ K $= 687°C$

Increasing the rms speed (u) by a factor of 2 requires heating to 960 K (or 687°C), increasing the temperature by a factor of 4.

10.116   (a)   Assumption 3 states that attractive and repulsive forces between molecules are negligible. All gases in the list are nonpolar. The largest and most structurally complex molecule, SF_6, is most likely to depart from this assumption.

        (b)   The monatomic gas Ne is smallest and least structurally complex, so it will behave most like an ideal gas.

        (c)   Root-mean-square speed is inversely related to molecular mass. The lightest gas, CH_4, has the highest rms speed.

        (d)   The heaviest and most structurally complex is SF_6. Also, S and F have larger atomic radii than C and H; this means that S–F bonds will be longer than C–H bonds and the volume of SF_6 will be greater than that of CH_4. It is reasonable to assume that SF_6 will occupy the greatest molecular volume relative to total volume. A quantitative measure is the b value in Table 10.3, with units of L/mol. Unfortunately, SF_6 does not appear in Table 10.3.

        (e)   Average kinetic energy is only related to absolute (K) temperature. At the same temperature, they all have the same average kinetic molecular energy.

        (f)   Rate of effusion is inversely related to molecular mass. The lighter the molecule, the faster it effuses. Ne and CH_4 have smaller molecular masses and effuse faster than N_2.

        (g)   If SF_6 occupies the greatest molecular volume [see part (d)], we expect it to have the largest van der Waals b parameter.

10.117   (a)   The effect of intermolecular attraction becomes more significant as a gas is compressed to a smaller volume at constant temperature. This compression causes the pressure, and thus the number of intermolecular collisions, to increase. Intermolecular attraction causes some of these collisions to be inelastic, which amplifies the deviation from ideal behavior.

       (b)   The effect of intermolecular attraction becomes less significant as the temperature of a gas is increased at constant volume. When the temperature of a gas is increased at constant volume, the pressure of the gas, the number of intermolecular collisions, and the average kinetic energy of the gas particles increase. This higher average kinetic energy means that a larger fraction of the molecules has sufficient kinetic energy to overcome intermolecular attractions, even though there are more total collisions. This increases the fraction of elastic collisions, and the gas more closely obeys the ideal-gas equation.

10.118   The larger and heavier the particle, in this case a single atom, the more likely it is to deviate from ideal behavior. Other than Rn, Xe is the largest (atomic radius = 1.30 Å), heaviest (molar mass = 131.3 g/mol) and most dense (5.90 g/L) noble gas. Its susceptibility to intermolecular interactions is also demonstrated by its ability to form compounds like XeF_4.

10.119   (a)   At STP, the molar volume $= 1 \text{ mol} \times \dfrac{0.08206 \text{ L - atm}}{\text{mol - K}} \times \dfrac{273 \text{ K}}{1 \text{ atm}} = 22.4 \text{ L}$

       Dividing the value for b, 0.0322 L/mol, by 4, we obtain 0.00805 L. Thus, the volume of the Ar atoms is (0.00805/22.4)100 = 0.0359% of the total volume.

       (b)   At 200 atm pressure (and 0°C, standard temperature) the molar volume is 0.112 L, and the volume of the Ar atoms is 7.19% of the total volume.

10.120   (a) $120.00 \text{ kg } N_2(g) \times \dfrac{1000 \text{ g}}{1 \text{ kg}} \times \dfrac{1 \text{ mol } N_2}{28.0135 \text{ g N}} = 4283.6 \text{ mol } N_2$

       $P = \dfrac{nRT}{V} = 4283.6 \text{ mol} \times \dfrac{0.08206 \text{ L - atm}}{\text{mol - K}} \times \dfrac{553 \text{ K}}{1100.0 \text{ L}} = 176.72 = 177 \text{ atm}$

       (b)   According to Equation [10.26], $P = \dfrac{nRT}{V - nb} - \dfrac{n^2 a}{V^2}$

       $P = \dfrac{(4283.6 \text{ mol})(0.08206 \text{ L - atm/mol - K})(553 \text{ K})}{1100.0 \text{ L} - (4283.6 \text{ mol})(0.0391 \text{ L/mol})} - \dfrac{(4283.6 \text{ mol})^2 (1.39 \text{ L}^2 \text{ - atm/mol}^2)}{(1100.0 \text{ L})^2}$

       $P = \dfrac{194{,}388 \text{ L - atm}}{1100.0 \text{ L} - 167.5 \text{ L}} - 21.1 \text{ atm} = 208.5 \text{ atm} - 21.1 \text{ atm} = 187.4 \text{ atm}$

       (c)   The pressure corrected for the real volume of the N_2 molecules is 208.5 atm, 31.8 atm higher than the ideal pressure of 176.7 atm. The 21.1 atm correction for intermolecular forces reduces the calculated pressure somewhat, but the "real" pressure is still higher than the ideal pressure. The correction for the real volume of molecules dominates. Even though the value of b is small, the number of moles of N_2 is large enough so that the molecular volume correction is larger than the attractive forces correction.

Integrative Exercises

10.121   (a) $MM = \dfrac{gRT}{VP} = \dfrac{1.56\,g}{1.00\,L} \times \dfrac{0.08206\,L\text{-}atm}{mol\text{-}K} \times \dfrac{323\,K}{0.984\,atm} = 42.0\,g/mol$

Assume 100 g cyclopropane

$100\,g \times 0.857\,C = 85.7\,g\,C \times \dfrac{1\,mol\,C}{12.01\,g} = \dfrac{7.136\,mol\,C}{7.136} = 1\,mol\,C$

$100\,g \times 0.143\,H = 14.3\,g\,H \times \dfrac{1\,mol\,H}{1.008\,g} = \dfrac{14.19\,mol\,H}{7.136} = 2\,mol\,H$

The empirical formula of cyclopropane is CH_2 and the empirical formula weight is 12 + 2 = 14 g. The ratio of molar mass to empirical formula weight, 42.0 g/14 g, is 3; therefore, there are three empirical formula units in one cyclopropane molecule. The molecular formula is $3 \times (CH_2) = C_3H_6$.

(b)   Ar is a monoatomic gas. Cyclopropane molecules are larger and more structurally complex, even though the molar masses of Ar and C_3H_6 are similar. If both gases are at the same relatively low temperature, they have approximately the same average kinetic energy, and the same ability to overcome intermolecular attractions. We expect intermolecular attractions to be more significant for the more complex C_3H_6 molecules, and that C_3H_6 will deviate more from ideal behavior at the conditions listed. This conclusion is supported by the *a* values in Table 10.3. The *a* values for CH_4 and CO_2, more complex molecules than Ar atoms, are larger than the value for Ar. If the pressure is high enough for the volume correction in the van der Waals equation to dominate behavior, the larger C_3H_6 molecules definitely deviate more than Ar atoms from ideal behavior.

(c)   Cyclopropane, C_3H_6, MM = 42.0 g/mol; methane, CH_4 MM = 16.0. Rate of effusion through a pinhole is inversely related to molar mass. Cyclopropane would effuse through a pinhole slower than methane, because it has the greater molar mass.

10.122   *Plan.* Write the balanced equation for the combustion of methanol. Since amounts of both reactants are given, determine the limiting reactant. Use mole ratios to calculate mol H_2O produced, based on the amount of limiting reactant. Change moles to g H_2O, then use density to calculate volume of $H_2O(l)$ produced. Assume the condensed $H_2O(l)$ is at 25°C, where density = 0.99707 g/mol. *Solve.*

methanol = $CH_3OH(l)$. $2CH_3OH(l) + 3O_2(g) \rightarrow 2CO_2(g) + 4H_2O(g)$

$25.0\,mL\,CH_3OH \times \dfrac{0.850\,g\,CH_3OH}{mL} \times \dfrac{1\,mol\,CH_3OH}{32.04\,g} = 0.6632 = 0.663\,mol\,CH_3OH$

$mol\,O_2 = n = \dfrac{PV}{RT} = 1.00\,atm \times \dfrac{12.5\,L}{273\,K} \times \dfrac{mol\text{-}K}{0.08206\,L\text{-}atm} = 0.5580 = 0.558\,mol\,O_2$

$0.558\,mol\,O_2 \times \dfrac{2\,mol\,CH_3OH}{3\,mol\,O_2} = 0.372\,mol\,CH_3OH$

0.558 mol O_2 can react with only 0.372 mol CH_3OH, so O_2 is the limiting reactant. Note that a large volume of $O_2(g)$ is required to completely react with a relatively small volume of $CH_3OH(l)$.

$$0.558 \text{ mol } O_2 \times \frac{4 \text{ mol } H_2O}{3 \text{ mol } O_2} \times \frac{18.02 \text{ g } H_2O}{1 \text{ mol } H_2O} \times \frac{1 \text{ mL } H_2O}{0.99707 \text{ g } H_2O} = 13.446 = 13.4 \text{ mL } H_2O$$

10.123   (a)   Get g C from mL CO_2; get g H from mL H_2O. Also calculate mol C and H, to use in part (b). Get g N by subtraction. Calculate % composition.

n = PV/RT. At STP, P = 1 atm, T = 273 K. (STP implies an infinite number of sig figs)

$$n_{CO_2} = 0.08316 \text{ L} \times \frac{1 \text{ atm}}{273 \text{ K}} \times \frac{\text{mol-K}}{0.08206 \text{ L-atm}} = 0.003712 \text{ mol } CO_2$$

$$0.003712 \text{ mol } CO_2 \times \frac{1 \text{ mol C}}{1 \text{ mol } CO_2} \times \frac{12.0107 \text{ g C}}{\text{mol C}} = 0.044585 = 0.04458 \text{ g } CO_2$$

$$n_{H_2O} = 0.07330 \text{ L} \times \frac{1 \text{ atm}}{273 \text{ K}} \times \frac{\text{mol-K}}{0.08206 \text{ L-atm}} = 3.2720 \times 10^{-3}$$

$$= 3.272 \times 10^{-3} \text{ mol } H_2O$$

$$3.2720 \times 10^{-3} \text{ mol } H_2O \times \frac{2 \text{ mol H}}{1 \text{ mol } H_2O} \times \frac{1.00794 \text{ g H}}{\text{mol H}} = 6.5959 \times 10^{-3}$$

$$= 6.596 \times 10^{-3} \text{ g H}$$

$$\text{mass \% X} = \frac{\text{mass X}}{\text{sample mass}} \times 100; \text{ sample mass} = 100.0 \text{ mg} = 0.1000 \text{ g}$$

$$\% C = \frac{0.044585 \text{ g}}{0.1000 \text{ g}} \times 100 = 44.585 = 44.58\% C$$

$$\% H = \frac{6.5959 \times 10^{-3} \text{ g H}}{0.1000 \text{ g}} \times 100 = 6.5959 = 6.596\% H$$

$$\% Cl = \frac{0.01644 \text{ g Cl}}{0.1000 \text{ g}} \times 100 = 16.44\% Cl$$

% N = 100 – 44.58 – 6.596 – 16.44 = 32.38% N

(b)   0.003712 mol C; $2(3.272 \times 10^{-3}) = 6.544 \times 10^{-3}$ mol H

$$0.01644 \text{ g Cl} \times \frac{1 \text{ mol C}}{35.453 \text{ g Cl}} = 4.637 \times 10^{-4} \text{ mol Cl}$$

0.1000 g sample × 0.3238 mass fraction N = 0.03238 g N

$$0.03238 \text{ g N} \times \frac{1 \text{ mol N}}{14.0067 \text{ g N}} = 0.0023118 = 0.002312 \text{ mol N}$$

Divide by the smallest number of mol to find the simplest ratio of moles.

$$\frac{0.003712 \text{ mol C}}{4.637 \times 10^{-4}} = 8.005 \text{ C}$$

$$\frac{6.544 \times 10^{-3} \text{ mol H}}{4.637 \times 10^{-4}} = 14.11 \text{ H}$$

$$\frac{4.637 \times 10^{-4} \text{ mol Cl}}{4.637 \times 10^{-4}} = 1.000 \text{ Cl}$$

$$\frac{0.002312 \text{ mol N}}{4.637 \times 10^{-4}} = 4.985 \text{ N}$$

If we assume 14.11 is "close" to 14 (a reasonable assumption), the empirical formula is $C_8H_{14}N_5Cl$.

(c)   Molar mass of the compound is required in order to determine molecular formula when the empirical formula is known.

10.124   (a)   *Plan.* Use the ideal-gas law to calculate the moles CO_2 that react.

Solve. P(reacted) = P(initial) – P(final), at constant V, T. Since both CaO and BaO react with CO_2 in a 1:1 mole ratio, mol CaO + mol BaO = mol CO_2. Use molar masses to calculate % CaO in sample.

$$P(reacted) = 730\,torr - 150\,torr = 580\,torr;\ 580\,torr \times \frac{1\,atm}{760\,torr} = 0.76316 = 0.763\,atm$$

$$n = \frac{PV}{RT} = 0.76316\,atm \times \frac{1.0\,L}{298\,K} \times \frac{mol\text{-}K}{0.08206\,L\text{-}atm} = 0.03121 = 0.0312\,mol\,CO_2$$

(b)   *Plan.* Use the stoichiometry of the reaction and definition of moles to calculate the mass and Mass % of CaO.

Solve. $CaO(s) + CO_2(s) \rightarrow CaCO_3(s)$. $BaO(s) + CO_2(g) \rightarrow BaCO_3(s)$

mol CO_2 reacted = mol CaO + mol BaO

Let x = g CaO, 4.00 – x = g BaO

$$0.03121 = \frac{x}{56.08} + \frac{4.00 - x}{153.3}$$

$$0.03121(56.08)(153.3) = 153.3x + 56.08(4.00 - x)$$

$$268.3 = (153.3x - 56.08x) + 224.3$$

$$43.98 = 97.22x,\ x = 0.452 = 0.45\,g\,CaO$$

$$\frac{0.452\,g\,CaO}{4.00\,g\,sample} \times 100 = 11.3 = 11\%\,CaO$$

(By strict sig fig rules, the result has 2 sig figs, because 268 – 224 = 44 has 0 decimal places and 2 sig figs.)

10.125   (a) $5.00\,g\,HCl \times \dfrac{1\,mol\,HCl}{36.46\,g\,HCl} = 0.1371 = 0.137\,mol\,HCl$

$5.00\,g\,NH_3 \times \dfrac{1\,mol\,NH_3}{17.03\,g\,NH_3} = 0.2936 = 0.294\,mol\,NH_3$

The gases react in a 1:1 mole ratio, HCl is the limiting reactant and is completely consumed. (0.2936 mol – 0.1371 mol) = 0.1565 = 0.157 mol NH_3 remain in the system. $NH_3(g)$ is the only gas remaining after reaction.

(b) $V_t = 4.00\,L.\quad P = \dfrac{nRT}{V} = 0.1565\,mol \times \dfrac{0.08206\,L\text{-}atm}{mol\text{-}K} \times \dfrac{298\,K}{4.00\,L} = 0.957\,atm$

(c) $0.137\,mol\,HCl \times \dfrac{1\,mol\,NH_4Cl}{1\,mol\,HCl} \times \dfrac{53.49\,g\,NH_4Cl}{1\,mol\,NH_4Cl} = 7.3284 = 7.33\,g\,NH_4Cl$

10.126 $n = \dfrac{PV}{RT} = 1.00 \text{ atm} \times \dfrac{\text{mol} \cdot \text{K}}{0.08206 \text{ L} \cdot \text{atm}} \times \dfrac{2.7 \times 10^{12} \text{ L}}{273 \text{ K}} = 1.205 \times 10^{11} = 1.2 \times 10^{11} \text{ mol CH}_4$

$CH_4(g) + 2O_2(g) \rightarrow CO_2(g) + 2H_2O(l) \quad \Delta H° = -890.4 \text{ kJ}$

(At STP, H_2O is in the liquid state.)

$\Delta H_{rxn}^{\circ} = \Delta H_f^{\circ} CO_2(g) + 2\Delta H_f^{\circ} H_2O(l) - \Delta H_f^{\circ} CH_4(g) - 2\Delta H_f^{\circ} O_2(g)$

$\Delta H_{rxn}^{\circ} = -393.5 \text{ kJ} + 2(-285.83 \text{ kJ}) - (-74.8 \text{ kJ}) - 0 = -890.4 \text{ kJ}$

$\dfrac{-890.4 \text{ kJ}}{1 \text{ mol CH}_4} \times 1.205 \times 10^{11} \text{ mol CH}_4 = -1.073 \times 10^{14} = -1.1 \times 10^{14} \text{ kJ}$

The negative sign indicates heat evolved by the combustion reaction.

10.127   (a)   19 e⁻, 9.5 e⁻ pairs

            :Ö—Cl—Ö:

            Resonance structures can be drawn with the odd electron on O, but electronegativity considerations predict that it will be on Cl for most of the time.

       (b) ClO_2 is very reactive because it is an odd-electron molecule. Adding an electron (reduction) both pairs the odd electron and completes the octet of Cl. Thus, ClO_2 has a strong tendency to gain an electron and be reduced.

       (c) ClO_2^-, 20 e⁻, 10 e⁻ pairs

            [:Ö—Cl—Ö:]

       (d)   4 e⁻ domains around Cl, O–Cl–O bond angle ~107° (<109° owing to repulsion by nonbonding domains)

       (e)   Calculate mol Cl_2 from ideal-gas equation; determine limiting reactant; mass ClO_2 via mol ratios.

$\text{mol Cl}_2 = \dfrac{PV}{RT} = 1.50 \text{ atm} \times \dfrac{2.00 \text{ L}}{294 \text{ K}} \times \dfrac{\text{mol} \cdot \text{K}}{0.08206 \text{ L} \cdot \text{atm}} = 0.1243 = 0.124 \text{ mol Cl}_2$

$15.0 \text{ g NaClO}_2 \times \dfrac{1 \text{ mol NaClO}_2}{90.44 \text{ g}} = 0.1659 = 0.166 \text{ mol NaClO}_2$

2 mol $NaClO_2$ are required for 1 mol Cl_2, so $NaClO_2$ is the limiting reactant. For every 2 mol $NaClO_2$ reacted, 2 mol ClO_2 are produced, so mol ClO_2 = mol $NaClO_2$.

$0.1659 \text{ mol ClO}_2 \times \dfrac{67.45 \text{ g ClO}_2}{\text{mol}} = 11.2 \text{ g ClO}_2$

10.128   (a)   ft³ $CH_4 \rightarrow$ L $CH_4 \rightarrow$ mol $CH_4 \rightarrow$ mol $CH_3OH \rightarrow$ g $CH_3OH \rightarrow$ L CH_3OH

$10.7 \times 10^9 \text{ ft}^3 \text{ CH}_4 \times \dfrac{1 \text{ yd}^3}{3^3 \text{ ft}^3} \times \dfrac{1 \text{ m}^3}{(1.0936)^3 \text{ yd}^3} \times \dfrac{1 \text{ L}}{1 \times 10^{-3} \text{ m}^3} = 3.03001 \times 10^{11}$

$= 3.03 \times 10^{11} \text{ L CH}_4$

$$n = \frac{PV}{RT} = \frac{3.03 \times 10^{11}\,L \times 1.00\,atm}{298\,K} \times \frac{mol\text{-}K}{0.08206\,L\text{-}atm} = 1.2391 \times 10^{10}$$

$$= 1.24 \times 10^{10}\,mol\,CH_4$$

1 mol CH_4 = 1 mol CH_3OH

$$1.2391 \times 10^{10}\,mol\,CH_3OH \times \frac{32.04\,g\,CH_3OH}{mol\,CH_3OH} \times \frac{1\,mL\,CH_3OH}{0.791\,g} \times \frac{1\,L}{1000\,mL}$$

$$= 5.0189 \times 10^8 = 5.02 \times 10^8\,L\,CH_3OH$$

(b) $CH_4(g) + 2O_2(g) \rightarrow CO_2(g) + 2H_2O(l)$ $\Delta H° = -890.4\,kJ$

$$\Delta H° = \Delta H_f°CO_2(g) + 2\Delta H_f°H_2O(l) - \Delta H_f°CH_4(g) - 2\Delta H_f°O_2(g)$$

$$\Delta H° = -393.5\,kJ + 2(-285.83\,kJ) - (-74.8\,kJ) - 0 = -890.4\,kJ$$

$$1.2391 \times 10^{10}\,mol\,CH_4 \times \frac{-890.4\,kJ}{1\,mol\,CH_4} = -1.10 \times 10^{13}\,kJ$$

$$CH_3OH(l) + 3/2\,O_2(g) \rightarrow CO_2(g) + 2H_2O(l) \quad \Delta H° = -726.6\,kJ$$

$$\Delta H° = \Delta H_f°\,CO_2(g) + 2\Delta H_f°\,H_2O(l) - \Delta H_f°\,CH_3OH(l) - 3/2\,\Delta H_f°\,O_2(g)$$

$$= -393.5\,kJ + 2(-285.83\,kJ) - (-238.6\,kJ) - 0 = -726.6\,kJ$$

$$1.2391 \times 10^{10}\,mol\,CH_3OH \times \frac{-726.6\,kJ}{1\,mol\,CH_3OH} = -9.00 \times 10^{12}\,kJ$$

(c)   Assume a volume of 1.00 L of each liquid.

$$1.00\,L\,CH_4(l) \times \frac{466\,g}{1\,L} \times \frac{1\,mol}{16.04\,g} \times \frac{-890.4\,kJ}{mol\,CH_4} = -2.59 \times 10^4\,kJ/L\,CH_4$$

$$1.00\,L\,CH_3OH \times \frac{791\,g}{1\,L} \times \frac{1\,mol}{32.04\,g} \times \frac{-726.6\,kJ}{mol\,CH_3OH} = -1.79 \times 10^4\,kJ/L\,CH_3OH$$

Clearly $CH_4(l)$ has the higher enthalpy of combustion per unit volume.

10.129   After reaction, the flask contains $IF_5(g)$ and whichever reactant is in excess. Determine the limiting reactant, which regulates the moles of IF_5 produced and moles of excess reactant.

$$I_2(s) + 5F_2(g) \rightarrow 2\,IF_5(g)$$

$$10.0\,g\,I_2 \times \frac{1\,mol\,I_2}{253.8\,g\,I_2} \times \frac{5\,mol\,F_2}{1\,mol\,I_2} = 0.1970 = 0.197\,mol\,F_2$$

$$10.0\,g\,F_2 \times \frac{1\,mol\,F_2}{38.00\,g\,F_2} = 0.2632 = 0.263\,mol\,F_2\,available$$

I_2 is the limiting reactant; F_2 is in excess.

0.263 mol F_2 available – 0.197 mol F_2 reacted = 0.066 mol F_2 remain.

$$10.0\,g\,I_2 \times \frac{1\,mol\,I_2}{253.8\,g\,I_2} \times \frac{2\,mol\,IF_5}{1\,mol\,I_2} = 0.0788\,mol\,IF_5\,produced$$

(a) $P_{IF_5} = \dfrac{nRT}{V} = 0.0788\,\text{mol} \times \dfrac{0.08206\,\text{L - atm}}{\text{mol - K}} \times \dfrac{398\,\text{K}}{5.00\,\text{L}} = 0.515\,\text{atm}$

(b) $\chi_{IF_5} = \dfrac{\text{mol IF}_5}{\text{mol IF}_5 + \text{mol F}_2} = \dfrac{0.0788}{0.0788 + 0.066} = 0.544$

(c) 42 valence e⁻, 21 e⁻ pairs

(d) $0.0788\,\text{mol IF}_5 \times \dfrac{221.90\,\text{g IF}_5}{\text{mol IF}_5} = 17.4857 = 17.5\,\text{g IF}_5$ produced

$0.066\,\text{mol F}_2 \times \dfrac{38.00\,\text{g F}_2}{\text{mol F}_2} = 2.508 = 2.5\,\text{g F}_2$ remain

Total mass in flask = 17.5 g IF_5 + 2.5 g F_2 = 20.00 g; mass is conserved.

10.130 (a) $MgCO_3(s) + 2HCl(aq) \rightarrow MgCl_2(aq) + H_2O(l) + CO_2(g)$

$CaCO_3(s) + 2HCl(aq) \rightarrow CaCl_2(aq) + H_2O(l) + CO_2(g)$

(b) $n = \dfrac{PV}{RT} = 743\,\text{torr} \times \dfrac{1\,\text{atm}}{760\,\text{torr}} \times \dfrac{\text{mol - K}}{0.08206\,\text{L - atm}} \times \dfrac{1.72\,\text{L}}{301\,\text{K}}$

$= 0.06808 = 0.0681\,\text{mol CO}_2$

(c) x = g $MgCO_3$, y = g $CaCO_3$, x + y = 6.53 g

mol $MgCO_3$ + mol $CaCO_3$ = mol CO_2 total

$\dfrac{x}{84.32} + \dfrac{y}{100.09} = 0.06808$; y = 6.53 − x

$\dfrac{x}{84.32} + \dfrac{6.53 - x}{100.09} = 0.06808$

100.09x − 84.32x + 84.32(6.53) = 0.06808 (84.32)(100.09)

15.77x + 550.610 = 574.549; x = 1.52 g $MgCO_3$

mass % $MgCO_3$ = $\dfrac{1.52\,\text{g MgCO}_3}{6.53\,\text{g sample}} \times 100 = 23.3\%$

[By strict sig fig rules, the answer has 2 sig figs: 15.77x + 551 (3 digits from 6.53) = 575; 575 − 551 = 24 (no decimal places, 2 sig figs) leads to 1.5 g $MgCO_3$ and 23% $MgCO_3$]

11 Liquids and Intermolecular Forces

Visualizing Concepts

In this chapter we will use the temperature units °C and K interchangeably when designating specific heats and *changes* in temperature.

11.1   The diagram best describes a **liquid**. In the diagram, the particles are close together, mostly touching but there is no regular arrangement or order. This rules out a gaseous sample, where the particles are far apart, and a crystalline solid, which has a regular repeating structure in all three directions.

11.2   (a)   (i)   Hydrogen bonding; H–F interactions qualify for this narrowly defined interaction.

                 (ii)   London dispersion forces, the only intermolecular forces between nonpolar F_2 molecules.

                 (iii)   Ion-dipole forces between Na^+ cation and the negative end of a polar covalent water molecule.

                 (iv)   Dipole-dipole forces between oppositely charged portions of two polar covalent SO_2 molecules.

         (b)   London dispersion forces in (ii) are probably the weakest.

11.3   The viscosity of glycerol will be greater than that of 1-propanol. Viscosity is the resistance of a substance to flow. The stronger the intermolecular forces in a liquid, the greater its viscosity. Hydrogen bonding is the predominant force for both molecules. Glycerol has three times as many O–H groups and many more H-bonding interactions than 1-propanol, so it experiences stronger intermolecular forces and greater viscosity. (Both molecules have the same carbon-chain length, so dispersion forces are similar.)

11.4   When heat is added to a liquid, the temperature of the liquid rises. If enough heat is added to reach the boiling point, any excess heat is used to vaporize the liquid. If heat is still available when all the liquid is converted to gas, the temperature of the gas rises.

Use the specific heat of $CH_4(l)$ to calculate the amount of heat required to raise the temperature of 32.0 g of $CH_4(l)$ from –170 °C to –161.5 °C. If this is less than 42 kJ, use ΔH_{vap} to calculate the energy required to vaporize the liquid, and so on, until exactly 42.0 kJ has been used to increase the temperature and/or change the state of CH_4.

Heat the liquid to its boiling point: $\Delta T = [-161.5\ °C - (-170\ °C)] = 8.5\ °C = 8.5\ K$

$$\frac{3.48\ J}{g\text{-}K} \times 32.0\ g\ CH_4 \times 8.5\ °C\ =\ 946.56\ =\ 9.5 \times 10^2\ J\ =\ 0.95\ kJ$$

309

Heating $CH_4(l)$ to its boiling point requires only 0.95 kJ. We have added 42 kJ, so there is definitely enough heat to vaporize the liquid. ΔH_{vap} for $CH_4(l)$ is 8.20 kJ/mol. The 32.0 g sample is 2.00 mol $CH_4(l)$, so the energy required to vaporize the sample at –161.5 °C is $(2 \times 8.20$ kJ/mol $=)$ 16.4 kJ. The energy used to heat the sample to –161.5 °C and vaporize it at this temperature is (0.947 kJ + 16.4 kJ) = 17.347 = 17.3 kJ. We have (42.0 kJ – 17.347 kJ) = 24.653 = 24.7 kJ left to heat the gas.

$$\Delta T = 24.65 \text{ kJ} \times \frac{g \cdot K}{2.22 \text{ J}} \times \frac{1000 \text{ J}}{kJ} \times \frac{1}{32.0 \text{ g } CH_4} = 346.99 = 347 \text{ °C}$$

The final temperature of the methane gas, $CH_4(g)$, is then (–161.5 °C + 346.99 °C) = 185.49 = 185 °C.

11.5   (a)   385 mm Hg. Find 30 °C on the horizontal axis, and follow a vertical line from this point to its intersection with the red vapor pressure curve. Follow a horizontal line from the intersection to the vertical axis and read the vapor pressure.

(b)   22 °C. Reverse the procedure outlined in part (a). Find 300 torr on the vertical axis, follow it to the curve and down to the value on the horizontal axis.

(c)   47 °C. The normal boiling point of a liquid is the temperature at which its vapor pressure is 1 atm, or 760 mm Hg. A vapor pressure of 1 atm is very near the top of this diagram, at approximately 47 °C.

11.6   The stronger the intermolecular forces, the greater the average kinetic energy required to escape these forces, and the higher the boiling point. Propanol, $CH_3CH_2CH_2OH$, has hydrogen bonding, by virtue of its –OH group, so it has the higher boiling point. Van der Waals forces in the two liquids are similar because molar masses are the same for both molecules.

11.7   (a)   360 K, the normal boiling point; 260 K, normal freezing point. The left-most line is the freezing/melting curve, the right-most line is the condensation/boiling curve. The normal boiling and freezing points are the temperatures of boiling and freezing at 1 atm pressure.

(b)   The material is solid in the left-most green (or pale blue) zone, liquid in the blue zone, and gas in the tan zone. (i) gas (ii) solid (iii) liquid

(c)   The triple point, where all three phases are in equilibrium, is the point where the three lines on the phase diagram meet. For this substance, the triple point is approximately 185 K at 0.45 atm.

11.8   (a)   The substance is in a liquid crystalline state at temperatures T_1 and T_2. At T_1, the molecules are aligned in layers and the long molecular axes are perpendicular to the layer planes; this describes a smectic A phase. At T_2, the long molecular axes are aligned but the ends are not aligned; this describes a nematic phase.

(b) T_3 is the highest temperature. The molecular arrangement in this phase has the least order, so it represents the highest temperature. (The molecules are closely packed, but not aligned in any way; this describes an ordinary liquid phase.)

Molecular Comparisons of Gases, Liquids, and Solids (section 11.1)

11.9   (a)   solid < liquid < gas

(b)   gas < liquid < solid

(c)   Matter in the gaseous state is most easily compressed, because particles are far apart and there is much empty space.

11.10   (a)   In solids, particles are in essentially fixed positions relative to each other, so the average energy of attraction is stronger than average kinetic energy. In liquids, particles are close together but moving relative to each other. The average attractive energy and average kinetic energy are approximately balanced. In gases, particles are far apart and in constant, random motion. Average kinetic energy is much greater than average energy of attraction.

(b)   As the temperature of a substance is increased, the average kinetic energy of the particles increases. In a collection of particles (molecules), the state is determined by the strength of interparticle forces relative to the average kinetic energy of the particles. As the average kinetic energy increases, more particles are able to overcome intermolecular attractive forces and move to a less ordered state, from solid to liquid to gas.

(c)   If a gas is placed under very high pressure, the particles undergo many collisions with the container and with each other. The large number of particle-particle collisions increases the likelihood that intermolecular attractions will cause the molecules to coalesce (liquefy).

11.11   By observation (or a quick WebElements© search), we know that Ar is a gas, CCl_4 is a liquid and Si is a solid at standard conditions. (Si is a substance in which the particles are held together by chemical bonds, like the ones listed in Table 11.2.) The order of increasing boiling point is then   Ar < CCl_4 < Si.

11.12   By observation (or a quick WebElements© search), we know that Ne is a gas, Br_2 is a liquid and Ga is a solid at standard conditions. The order of increasing boiling point is then   Ne < Br_2 < Ga.

11.13   (a)   At standard temperature and pressure, the molar volumes of Cl_2 and NH_3 are nearly the same because they are both gases. In the gas phase, molecules are far apart and most of the volume occupied by the substance is empty space. Differences in molecular characteristics such as weight, shape and dipole moment have little bearing on the molar volume of a gas.

The ideal gas law states that one mole of any gas at STP will occupy a fixed volume. The slight difference in molar volumes of the two gases is predicted by the van der Waals correction, which quantifies deviation from ideal behavior.

(b)   On cooling to 160 K, both compounds condense from the gas phase to the solid state. Condensation, as the word implies, eliminates most of the empty space between molecules, so we expect a significant decrease in the molar volume.

(c) $\dfrac{1\,cm^3}{2.02\,g\,Cl_2} \times \dfrac{70.096\,g\,Cl_2}{1\,mol\,Cl_2} = 35.1\,cm^3/mol\,Cl_2 = 0.0351\ L/mol\,Cl_2$

$$\frac{1\,cm^3}{0.84\,g\,NH_3} \times \frac{17.031\,g\,NH_3}{1\,mol\,NH_3} = 20.3\,cm^3/mol\,NH_3 = 0.0203\,L/mol\,NH_3$$

(d)   Solid state molar volumes are not as similar as those in the gaseous state. In the solid state, most of the empty space is gone, so molecular characteristics do influence molar volumes. Cl_2 is heavier than NH_3 and the Cl–Cl bond distance is almost double the N–H bond distance (Figure 7.6). Intermolecular attractive forces among polar NH_3 molecules bind them more tightly than forces among nonpolar Cl_2 molecules. These factors all contribute to a molar volume for $Cl_2(s)$ that is almost twice that of $NH_3(s)$.

(e)   Like solids, liquids are condensed phases. That is, there is little empty space between molecules in the liquid state. We expect the molar volumes of the liquids to be closer to those in the solid state than those in the gaseous state.

11.14   (a)   The average distance between molecules is greater in the liquid state. Density is the ratio of the mass of a substance to the volume it occupies. For the same substance in different states, mass will be the same. The smaller the density, the greater the volume occupied, and the greater the distance between molecules. The liquid at 130° has the lower density (1.08 g/cm³), so the average distance between molecules is greater.

(b)   As the temperature of a substance increases, the average kinetic energy and speed of the molecules increases. At the melting point the molecules, on average, have enough kinetic energy to break away from the very orderly array that was present in the solid. As the translational motion of the molecules increases, the occupied volume increases and the density decreases. Thus, the solid density, 1.266 g/cm³ at 15°C, is greater than the liquid density, 1.08 g/cm³ at 130°C.

Intermolecular Forces (section 11.2)

11.15   (a)   London dispersion forces

(b)   dipole-dipole and London dispersion forces

(c)   dipole-dipole or in certain cases hydrogen bonding

11.16   Intermolecular forces are based on charge attraction and repulsion. Because substances must be electrically neutral overall, there are opposite charges (full or partial) in every substance. While repulsions occur, net forces are attractive because attractions lower the overall energy of the sample, and matter tends to exist in the lowest possible energy state.

11.17   (a) SO_2 is a polar covalent molecule, so dipole-dipole and London dispersion forces must be overcome to convert the liquid to a gas.

(b) CH_3COOH is a polar covalent molecule that experiences London dispersion, dipole-dipole, and hydrogen-bonding (O–H bonds) forces. All of these forces must be overcome to convert the liquid to a gas.

(c) H_2Se is a polar covalent molecule that experiences London dispersion and dipole-dipole forces, so these must be overcome to change the liquid into a gas. (H–Se bonds do not lead to hydrogen-bonding interactions.)

11.18   (a) CH_3OH experiences hydrogen bonding, but CH_3SH does not.

(b) Both gases are influenced by London dispersion forces. The heavier the gas particles, the stronger the London dispersion forces. The heavier Xe is a liquid at the specified conditions, while the lighter Ar is a gas.

(c) Both gases are influenced by London dispersion forces. The larger, diatomic Cl_2 molecules are more polarizable, experience stronger dispersion forces, and have the higher boiling point.

(d) Acetone and 2-methylpropane are molecules with similar molar masses and London dispersion forces. Acetone also experiences dipole-dipole forces and has the higher boiling point.

11.19 (a) *Polarizability* is the ease with which the charge distribution (electron cloud) in a molecule can be distorted to produce an instantaneous dipole.

(b) Sb is most polarizable because its valence electrons are farthest from the nucleus and least tightly held.

(c) Polarizability increases as molecular size (and thus molecular weight) increases. In order of increasing polarizability: $CH_4 < SiH_4 < SiCl_4 < GeCl_4 < GeBr_4$

(d) The magnitude of London-dispersion forces and thus the boiling points of molecules increase as polarizability increases. The order of increasing boiling points is the order of increasing polarizability: $CH_4 < SiH_4 < SiCl_4 < GeCl_4 < GeBr_4$

11.20 (a) True. A more polarizable molecule can develop a larger transient dipole, increasing the strength of electrostatic attractions and dispersion forces among molecules.

(b) False. The noble gases are all monoatomic. Going down the family, the atomic radius and the size of the electron cloud increase. The larger the electron cloud, the more polarizable the atom, the stronger the London dispersion forces and the higher the boiling point. (In general, strength of forces and boiling point vary in the same direction, not opposite directions.)

(c) False. Generally, dipole-dipole forces are stronger than dispersion forces for molecules of similar size and mass. The size of the molecule and the magnitude of its dipole moment (if there is one) determine the relative magnitudes of dispersion and dipole-dipole forces.

(d) True. For molecules with similar molecular weights and elemental composition, linear molecules have the possibility for greater contact along and around their surfaces than spherical molecules. Their electron clouds are thus more polarizable, and dispersion forces are greater.

11.21 *Analyze/Plan.* For molecules with similar structures, the strength of dispersion forces increases with molecular size (molecular weight and number of electrons in the molecule).

Solve: (a) H_2S (b) CO_2 (c) GeH_4

11.22 For molecules with similar structures, the strength of dispersion forces increases with molecular size (molecular weight and number of electrons in the molecule).

(a) Br_2

(b) $CH_3CH_2CH_2CH_2CH_2SH$

(c) $CH_3CH_2CH_2Cl$. These two molecules have the same molecular formula and molecular weight (C_3H_7Cl, molecular weight = 78.5 amu), so the shapes of the molecules determine which has the stronger dispersion forces. According to Figure 11.6, the cylindrical (not branched) molecule will have stronger dispersion forces.

11.23 Both hydrocarbons experience dispersion forces. Rod-like butane molecules can contact each other over the length of the molecule, while spherical 2-methylpropane molecules can only touch tangentially. The larger contact surface of butane facilitates stronger forces and produces a higher boiling point.

11.24 Both molecules experience hydrogen bonding through their –OH groups and dispersion forces between their hydrocarbon portions. The position of the –OH group in isopropyl alcohol shields it somewhat from approach by other molecules and slightly decreases the extent of hydrogen bonding. Also, isopropyl alcohol is less rod-like (it has a shorter chain) than propyl alcohol, so dispersion forces are weaker. Since hydrogen bonding and dispersion forces are weaker in isopropyl alcohol, it has the lower boiling point.

11.25 (a) A molecule must contain H atoms bound to either N, O or F atoms in order to participate in hydrogen bonding with like molecules.

(b) **CH_3NH_2** and **CH_3OH** have N–H and O–H bonds, respectively; they will form hydrogen bonds with other molecules of the same kind. (CH_3F has C–F and C–H bonds, but no H–F bonds.)

11.26 (a) HF has the higher boiling point because hydrogen bonding is stronger than dipole-dipole forces.

(b) $CHBr_3$ has the higher boiling point because it has the higher molar mass, which leads to greater polarizability and stronger dispersion forces.

(c) ICl has the higher boiling point because it is a polar molecule. For molecules with similar structures and molar masses, dipole-dipole forces are stronger than dispersion forces.

11.27 (a) Replacing a hydroxyl hydrogen with a CH_3 group eliminates hydrogen bonding in that part of the molecule. This reduces the strength of intermolecular forces and leads to a (much) lower boiling point.

(b) $CH_3OCH_2CH_2OCH_3$ is a larger, more polarizable molecule with stronger London-dispersion forces and thus a higher boiling point.

11.28 (a) C_3H_8, dispersion; C_4H_{10}, dispersion. C_4H_{10} has the higher boiling point due to greater molar mass and similar strength of forces.

(b) $CH_3CH_2OCH_2CH_3$, dipole-dipole, and dispersion; $CH_3CH_2CH_2CH_2OH$, hydrogen bonding, dipole-dipole, and dispersion. $CH_3CH_2CH_2CH_2OH$ has the higher boiling point due to the influence of hydrogen bonding.

(c) SO_2, dipole-dipole and dispersion; SO_3, dispersion. This is a tough call; SO_2 has dipole-dipole forces, but SO_3 has a greater molecular weight. The relative strength of dispersion and dipole-dipole forces depends on the mass and shape of the molecules. SO_3 molecules have greater molecular weight and are planar, so alignment is facile and dispersion forces are strong; SO_3 has the higher boiling point (confirmed by CRC *Handbook of Chemistry and Physics*).

(d) Cl_2CO, dipole-dipole and dispersion; H_2CO, dipole-dipole and dispersion. Cl_2CO has the higher boiling point due to greater molecular weight and stronger dispersion forces. (Note that H_2CO does not have hydrogen bonding, because the H atoms are bound to C, not to O.)

11.29

Physical Property	H_2O	H_2S
Normal Boiling Point, °C	100.00	−60.7
Normal Melting Point, °C	0.00	−85.5

(a)   Based on its much higher normal melting and boiling point, H_2O has stronger intermolecular forces. H_2O, with H bound to O, has hydrogen bonding. H_2S, with H bound to S, has dipole-dipole forces. (The electronegativities of H and S, 2.1 and 2.5, respectively, are similar. The H–S bond dipoles in H_2S are not large, but S does have two nonbonded electron pairs. The molecule has medium polarity.)

(b) H_2S is probably a typical compound, where there is less empty space in the more ordered solid and the solid is denser than the liquid. For H_2O, maximizing the number of hydrogen bonds to each molecule in the solid requires more empty space than in the liquid. The solid is less dense than the liquid and ice floats.

(c)   Specific heat is the energy required to raise the temperature of one gram of the substance one degree Celsius. Raising the temperature of a substance increases average kinetic energy and molecular motion. Hydrogen bonding in water is such a strong attractive interaction that the energy required to disrupt it and increase molecular motion is large.

11.30   (a)   In the solid state, NH_3 molecules are arranged so as to form the maximum number of hydrogen bonds. At the melting point, the average kinetic energy of the molecules is large enough so that they are free to move relative to each other. As they move, old hydrogen bonds break and new ones form, but the strict relative order required for maximum hydrogen bonding is no longer present.

(b)   In the liquid state, molecules are moving relative to one another while touching, which makes some hydrogen bonding possible. When molecules achieve enough kinetic energy to vaporize, the distance between them increases beyond the point where hydrogen bonds can form.

11.31 SO_4^{2-} has a greater negative charge than BF_4^{-}, so ion-ion electrostatic attractions are greater in sulfate salts. These strong forces limit the ion mobility required for the formation of an ionic liquid. (This is called an electronic effect.)

11.32   The longer the alkyl side chain of the 1-alkyl-3-methylimidazolium cation, the more irregular the shape of the cation. Particles with irregular shapes are more difficult to pack into solids, so the melting point of the salt decreases as the length of the alkyl group and irregularity increases. (This is called a steric effect.)

Select Properties of Liquids (section 11.3)

11.33   (a)   Surface tension and viscosity are the result of intermolecular attractive forces or cohesive forces among molecules in a liquid sample. As temperature increases, the number of molecules with sufficient kinetic energy to overcome these attractive forces increases, and viscosity and surface tension decrease.

           (b)   Surface tension and viscosity are both directly related to the strength of intermolecular attractive forces. The same attractive forces that cause surface molecules to be difficult to separate cause molecules elsewhere in the sample to resist movement relative to one another. Liquids with high surface tension have intermolecular attractive forces sufficient to produce a high viscosity as well.

11.34   (a)   *Cohesive* forces bind molecules to each other.

                 Adhesive forces bind molecules to surfaces.

           (b)   The cohesive forces are hydrogen bonding among water molecules and also hydrogen bonding among cellulose molecules in the paper towel. Adhesive forces are any attractive forces between water and cellulose (the paper towel), likely also hydrogen bonding. If adhesive forces between cellulose and water weren't significant, paper towels wouldn't absorb water.

           (c)   The shape of a meniscus depends on the strength of the cohesive forces within a liquid relative to the adhesive forces between the walls of the tube and the liquid. Adhesive forces between polar water molecules and silicates in glass (Figure 11.19) are even stronger than cohesive hydrogen-bonding forces among water molecules, so the meniscus is U-shaped (concave-upward).

11.35   (a) $CHBr_3$ has a higher molar mass, is more polarizable, and has stronger dispersion forces, so the surface tension is greater.

           (b)   As temperature increases, the viscosity of the oil decreases because the average kinetic energy of the molecules increases [Solution 11.33(a)].

           (c)   Adhesive forces between polar water and nonpolar car wax are weak, so the large surface tension of water draws the liquid into the shape with the smallest surface area, a sphere.

           (d)   Surface tension due to dispersion forces in oil is not great. Adhesive forces between nonpolar oil and nonpolar car wax are similar to cohesive forces in oil, so the oil drops spread out on the waxed hood.

11.36   (a)   H—N̈—N̈—H   H—Ö—Ö—H   H—Ö—H
                         | |
                         H   H

           (b)   All have bonds (N–H or O–H, respectively) capable of forming hydrogen bonds. Hydrogen bonding is the strongest intermolecular interaction between neutral molecules and leads to very strong cohesive forces in liquids. The stronger the cohesive forces in a liquid, the greater the surface tension.

11.37   (a)   The three molecules have similar structures and all experience hydrogen bonding, dipole-dipole and dispersion forces. The main difference in the series is the increase in the number of carbon atoms in the alkyl chain, with a corresponding increase in chain length, molecular weight, and strength of dispersion forces. The boiling points, surface tension, and viscosities all increase because the strength of dispersion forces increases.

(b)   Ethylene glycol has an –OH group at both ends of the molecule. This greatly increases the possibilities for hydrogen bonding, so the overall intermolecular attractive forces are greater and the viscosity of ethylene glycol is much greater.

(c)   Water has the highest surface tension but lowest viscosity because it is the smallest molecule in the series. Since water molecules are small, they approach each other closely and form many strong hydrogen bonds. There is no hydrocarbon chain to disrupt hydrogen bond formation or to inhibit their attraction to molecules in the interior of the drop. Water molecules at the surface of a drop are missing a few hydrogen bonds and are strongly pulled into the center of the drop, resulting in high surface tension. The absence of an alkyl chain also means the molecules can move around each other easily, resulting in the low viscosity.

11.38   (a)   For molecules with similar shapes, viscosity usually decreases with decreasing molecular weight. Since n-pentane has one fewer carbon atom and a shorter chain than n-hexane, the molecules are slightly more free to move around each other and n-pentane will have the smaller viscosity.

(b)   At 270 K (–3 °C), both neopentane and n-pentane will be liquids. According to Figure 11.6, neopentane is roughly spherical, while n-pentane is cylindrical or rod-shaped. The spherical neopentane has weaker dispersion forces and the molecules are more free to tumble, so it will have the smaller viscosity.

Phase Changes (Section 11.4)

11.39   (a)   melting, endothermic

(b)   evaporation or vaporization, endothermic

(c)   deposition, exothermic

(d)   condensation, exothermic

11.40   (a)   condensation, exothermic

(b)   sublimation, endothermic

(c)   vaporization (evaporation), endothermic

(d)   freezing, exothermic

11.41   The heat energy required to increase the kinetic energy of molecules enough to melt the solid does not produce a large separation of molecules. The specific order is disrupted, but the molecules remain close together. On the other hand, when a liquid is vaporized, the intermolecular forces which maintain close molecular contacts must be overcome. Because molecules are being separated, the energy requirement is higher than for melting.

11.42   (a)   Liquid ethyl chloride at room temperature is far above its boiling point. When the liquid contacts the room temperature surface, heat sufficient to vaporize the liquid is transferred from the surface to the ethyl chloride, and the heat content of the molecules increases. At constant atmospheric pressure, $\Delta H = q$, so the heat content and the enthalpy content of $C_2H_5Cl(g)$ is higher than that of $C_2H_5Cl(l)$. This indicates that the specific heat of the gas is less than that of the liquid, because the heat content of the gas starts at a higher level.

       (b)   Liquid C_2H_5Cl is vaporized (boiled), C_2H_5Cl (g) is warmed to the final temperature, and the solid surface is cooled to the final temperature. The enthalpy of vaporization (ΔH_{vap}) of $C_2H_5Cl(l)$, the specific heat of $C_2H_5Cl(g)$, and the specific heat of the solid surface must be considered.

11.43   *Analyze.* The heat required to vaporize 60 g of H_2O equals the heat lost by the cooled water.

       Plan. Using the enthalpy of vaporization, calculate the heat required to vaporize 60 g of H_2O in this temperature range. Using the specific heat capacity of water, calculate the mass of water than can be cooled 15 °C if this much heat is lost.

       Solve. Evaporation of 60 g of water requires:

$$60\,g\,H_2O \times \frac{2.4\,kJ}{1\,g\,H_2O} = 1.44 \times 10^2\,kJ = 1.4 \times 10^5\,J$$

       Cooling a certain amount of water by 15 °C:

$$1.44 \times 10^5\,J \times \frac{1\,g\cdot K}{4.184\,J} \times \frac{1}{15\,°C} = 2294 = 2.3 \times 10^3\,g\,H_2O$$

       Check. The units are correct. A surprisingly large mass of water (2300 g ≈ 2.3 L) can be cooled by this method.

11.44   Energy released when 200 g of H_2O is cooled from 15 °C to 0 °C:

$$\frac{4.184\,J}{g\cdot K} \times 200\,g\,H_2O \times 15\,°C = 12.55 \times 10^3\,J = 13\,kJ$$

       Energy released when 200 g of H_2O is frozen (there is no change in temperature during a change of state):

$$\frac{334\,J}{g} \times 200\,g\,H_2O = 6.68 \times 10^4\,J = 66.8\,kJ$$

       Total energy released = 12.55 kJ + 66.8 kJ = 79.35 = 79.4 kJ

       Mass of freon that will absorb 79.4 kJ when vaporized:

$$79.35\,kJ \times \frac{1 \times 10^3\,J}{1\,kJ} \times \frac{1\,g\,CCl_2F_2}{289\,J} = 275\,g\,CCl_2F_2$$

11.45   *Analyze/Plan.* Follow the logic in Sample Exercise 11.3. *Solve.* Physical data for ethanol, C_2H_5OH, is: mp = –114°C; ΔH_{fus} = 5.02 kJ/mol; $C_{s(solid)}$ = 0.97 J/g-K; bp = 78°C; ΔH_{vap} = 38.56 kJ/mol; $C_{s(liquid)}$ = 2.3 J/g-K. *Solve.*

       (a)   Heat the liquid from 35 °C to 78 °C, ΔT = 43 °C = 43 K.

$$42.0\,g\,C_2H_5OH \times \frac{2.3\,J}{g\cdot K} \times 43\,K \times \frac{1\,kJ}{1000\,J} = 4.1538 = 4.2\,kJ$$

Vaporize (boil) the liquid at 78 °C, using ΔH_{vap}.

$$42.0 \text{ g } C_2H_5OH \times \frac{1 \text{ mol } C_2H_5OH}{46.07 \text{ g}} \times \frac{38.56 \text{ kJ}}{\text{mol}} = 35.1535 = 35.2 \text{ kJ}$$

Total energy required is 4.1538 kJ + 35.1535 kJ = 39.3073 = 39.3 kJ.

(b)   Heat the solid from –155 °C to –114 °C, $\Delta T = 41$ °C = 41 K.

$$42.0 \text{ g } C_2H_5OH \times \frac{0.97 \text{ J}}{\text{g - K}} \times 41 \text{ K} \times \frac{1 \text{ kJ}}{1000 \text{ J}} = 1.6703 = 1.7 \text{ kJ}$$

Melt the solid at –114 °C, using ΔH_{fus}.

$$42.0 \text{ g } C_2H_5OH \times \frac{1 \text{ mol } C_2H_5OH}{46.07 \text{ g}} \times \frac{5.02 \text{ kJ}}{\text{mol}} = 4.5765 = 4.58 \text{ kJ}$$

Heat the liquid from –114°C to 78°C, $\Delta T = 192$°C = 192 K.

$$42.0 \text{ g } C_2H_5OH \times \frac{2.3 \text{ J}}{\text{g - K}} \times 192 \text{ K} \times \frac{1 \text{ kJ}}{1000 \text{ J}} = 18.5472 = 19 \text{ kJ}$$

From (a), vaporizing (boiling) 42.0 g of C_2H_5OH liquid at 78°C requires 35.1535 kJ = 35.2 kJ.

Total energy required = 1.6703 kJ + 4.5765 kJ + 18.5472 kJ + 35.1535 kJ = 59.9476

= 60 kJ.

Check. The relative energies of the various steps are reasonable; vaporization is the largest. The sum has no decimal places because (19 kJ) has no decimal places.

11.46   Consider the process in steps, using the appropriate thermochemical constant.

Heat the liquid from 10.00°C to 47.6 °C, $\Delta T = 37.6$ °C = 37.6 K, using the specific heat of the liquid.

$$35.0 \text{ g } C_2Cl_3F_3 \times \frac{0.91 \text{ J}}{\text{g - K}} \times 37.6 \text{ K} \times \frac{1 \text{ kJ}}{1000 \text{ J}} = 1.1976 = 1.2 \text{ kJ}$$

Boil the liquid at 47.6 °C (320.6 K), using the enthalpy of vaporization.

$$35.0 \text{ g } C_2Cl_3F_3 \times \frac{1 \text{ mol } C_2Cl_3F_3}{187.4 \text{ g } C_2Cl_3F_3} \times \frac{27.49 \text{ kJ}}{\text{mol}} = 5.1342 = 5.13 \text{ kJ}$$

Heat the gas from 47.6 °C to 105.00 °C, $\Delta T = 57.4$ °C = 57.4 K, using the specific heat of the gas.

$$35.0 \text{ g } C_2Cl_3F_3 \times \frac{0.67 \text{ J}}{\text{g - K}} \times 57.4 \text{ K} \times \frac{1 \text{ kJ}}{1000 \text{ J}} = 1.3460 = 1.3 \text{ kJ}$$

The total energy required is 1.1967 kJ + 5.1342 kJ + 1.3460 kJ = 7.6778 = 7.7 kJ.

11.47   (a)   The critical pressure is the pressure required to cause liquefaction at the critical temperature.

(b)   The critical temperature is the highest temperature at which a gas can be liquefied, regardless of pressure. As the force of attraction between molecules increases, the critical temperature of the compound increases.

(c)   The temperature of $N_2(l)$ is 77 K. All of the gases in Table 11.5 have critical temperatures higher than 77 K, so all of them can be liquefied at this temperature, given sufficient pressure.

11.48   (a) CCl_3F, CCl_2F_2 and $CClF_3$ are polar molecules that experience dipole-dipole and London dispersion forces with like molecules. CF_4 is a nonpolar compound that experiences only dispersion forces.

(b)   According to Solution 11.47(b), the higher the critical temperature, the stronger the intermolecular attractive forces of a substance. Therefore, the strength of intermolecular attraction increases moving from right to left across the series and as molecular weight increases. $CF_4 < CClF_3 < CCl_2F_2 < CCl_3F$.

(c)   The increasing intermolecular attraction with increasing molecular weight indicates that the critical temperature and pressure of CCl_4 will be greater than that of CCl_3F. Looking at the numerical values in the series, an increase of 88 K in critical temperature and 3.1 atm in critical pressure to the corresponding values for CCl_3F seem reasonable.

Physical Property	CCl_3F	CCl_4(predicted)	CCl_4 (CRC)
Critical Temperature (K)	47.1	557	556.6
Critical Pressure (atm)	43.5	46.6	44.6

The predicted values for CCl_4 are in very good agreement with literature values. The key concept is that dispersion, not dipole-dipole, forces dominate the physical properties in the series.

Vapor Pressure (section 11.5)

11.49   (a)   No effect.

(b)   No effect.

(c)   Vapor pressure decreases with increasing intermolecular attractive forces because fewer molecules have sufficient kinetic energy to overcome attractive forces and escape to the vapor phase.

(d)   Vapor pressure increases with increasing temperature because average kinetic energies of molecules increases.

(e)   Vapor pressure decreases with increasing density. Density, the ratio of mass to volume occupied, increases as molecular weight increases. The strength of attractive dispersion forces also increases, so fewer molecules have sufficient kinetic energy to escape to the vapor phase and vapor pressure decreases.

11.50   A normal boiling point of 56 °C places the liquid-vapor curve for acetone between the curves for diethyl ether and ethanol on Figure 11.25. Following a vertical line of increasing vapor pressure at 25 °C, we first cross the ethanol curve, then the (virtual) acetone curve. This means that, at 25 °C, the vapor pressure of acetone is higher than the vapor pressure of ethanol. (The lower boiling point of acetone is a strong indicator that it will have a higher vapor pressure than ethanol at a given temperature.)

11.51   (a)   *Analyze/Plan.* Given the molecular formulae of several substances, determine the kind of intermolecular forces present, and rank the strength of these forces. The weaker the forces, the more volatile the substance.   *Solve.*

$CBr_4 < CHBr_3 < CH_2Br_2 < CH_2Cl_2 < CH_3Cl < CH_4$

The weaker the intermolecular forces, the higher the vapor pressure, the more volatile the compound. The order of increasing volatility is the order of decreasing strength of intermolecular forces. By analogy to attractive forces in HCl (Section 11.2), the trend will be dominated by dispersion forces, even though four of the molecules ($CHBr_3$, CH_2Br_2, CH_2Cl_2 and CH_3Cl) are polar. Thus, the order of increasing volatility is the order of decreasing molar mass and decreasing strength of dispersion forces.

(b) $CH_4 < CH_3Cl < CH_2Cl_2 < CH_2Br_2 < CHBr_3 < CBr_4$

Boiling point increases as the strength of intermolecular forces increases, so the order of boiling points is the order of increasing strength of forces. This is the order of decreasing volatility and the reverse of the order in part (a).

11.52   (a)   False. The heavier (and larger) CBr_4 has stronger dispersion forces, a higher boiling point, lower vapor pressure and is less volatile.

(b)   True.

(c)   False.

(d)   False.

11.53   (a)   The water in the two pans is at the same temperature, the boiling point of water at the atmospheric pressure of the room. During a phase change, the temperature of a system is constant. All energy gained from the surroundings is used to accomplish the transition, in this case to vaporize the liquid water. The pan of water that is boiling vigorously is gaining more energy and the liquid is being vaporized more quickly than in the other pan, but the temperature of the phase change is the same.

(b)   Vapor pressure does not depend on either volume or surface area of the liquid. As long as the containers are at the same temperature, the vapor pressures of water in the two containers are the same.

11.54   (a)   On a humid day, there are more gaseous water molecules in the air and more are recaptured by the surface of the liquid, making evaporation slower.

(b)   At high altitude, atmospheric pressure is lower and water boils at a lower temperature. This lower boiling temperature at high altitude means that cooking an egg takes longer.

11.55   *Analyze/Plan.* Follow the logic in Sample Exercise 11.4. The boiling point is the temperature at which the vapor pressure of a liquid equals atmospheric pressure. *Solve.*

(a)   The boiling point of ethanol at 200 torr is ~48 °C.

(b)   The vapor pressure of ethanol at 60 °C is approximately 340 torr. Thus, at 60 °C ethyl alcohol would boil at an external pressure of 340 torr.

(c)   The boiling point of diethyl ether at 400 torr is ~17 °C.

(d)   40 °C is above the normal boiling point of diethyl ether, so the pressure at which 40 °C is the boiling point is greater than 760 torr. According to Figure 11.25, a boiling point of 40 °C requires an external pressure of 1000 torr. (At these conditions, the vapor pressure of diethyl ether is 1000 torr.)

11.56   (a)

Temperature (°C)

A plot of vapor pressure vs. temperature data for H_2O from Appendix B is shown above. The vapor pressure of water at body temperature, 37 °C, is approximately 50 torr.

(b)   The data point at 760.0 torr, 100 °C is the normal boiling point of H_2O. This is the temperature at which the vapor pressure of H_2O is equal to a pressure of 1 atm or 760 torr.

(c)   At an external (atmospheric) pressure of 633 torr, the boiling point of H_2O is approximately 96 °C.

(d)   At an external pressure of 774 torr, the boiling point of water is approximately 100.5 °C.

(e)   Follow the logic in Sample Exercise 10.14 to calculate rms speeds at the two temperatures. The rms speed is one way to represent the "average" speed of a large collection of particles.

$u = (3RT/MM)^{1/2}$. $MM = 18.0\,g/mol = 18.0 \times 10^{-3}\,kg/mol$

$R = 8.314\,kg\text{-}m^2/s^2\text{-}mol\text{-}K$. At $T = 96°C = 369\,K$,

$$u = \left(\frac{3(8.314\,kg\text{-}m^2/s^2\text{-}mol\text{-}K)\,369\,K}{18.0 \times 10^{-3}\,kg/mol} \right)^{1/2} = 715\,m/s$$

At $T = 100.5\,°C = 373.6\,K$,

$$u = \left(\frac{3(8.314\,kg\text{-}m^2/s^2\text{-}mol\text{-}K)\,373.6\,K}{18.0 \times 10^{-3}\,kg/mol} \right)^{1/2} = 719.50 = 720\,m/s$$

The difference in the two rms speeds is less than 1% of the average of the two values. Given the precision of estimating boiling temperatures from the plot, the two rms speeds are essentially equal.

Phase Diagrams (section 11.6)

11.57   (a)   The *critical point* is the temperature and pressure beyond which the gas and liquid phases are indistinguishable.

       (b)   The gas/liquid line ends at the critical point because at conditions beyond the critical temperature and pressure, there is no distinction between gas and liquid. In experimental terms, a gas cannot be liquefied at temperatures higher than the critical temperature, regardless of pressure.

11.58   (a)   The *triple point* on a phase diagram represents the temperature and pressure at which the gas, liquid, and solid phases are in equilibrium.

       (b)   No. A phase diagram represents a closed system, one where no matter can escape and no substance other than the one under consideration is present; air cannot be present in the system. Even if air is excluded, at 1 atm of external pressure, the triple point of water is inaccessible, regardless of temperature [see Figure 11.28].

11.59   (a)   The water vapor would deposit to form a solid at a pressure of around 4 torr. At higher pressure, perhaps 5 atm or so, the solid would melt to form liquid water. This occurs because the melting point of ice, which is 0 °C at 1 atm, decreases with increasing pressure.

       (b)   In thinking about this exercise, keep in mind that the **total** pressure is being maintained at a constant 0.50 atm. That pressure is composed of water vapor pressure and some other pressure, which could come from an inert gas. At 100 °C and 0.50 atm, water is in the vapor phase. As it cools, the water vapor will condense to the liquid at the temperature where the vapor pressure of liquid water is 0.50 atm. From Appendix B, we see that condensation occurs at approximately 82 °C. Further cooling of the liquid water results in freezing to the solid at approximately 0 °C. The freezing point of water increases with decreasing pressure, so at 0.50 atm, the freezing temperature is very slightly above 0 °C.

11.60   (a)   Solid CO_2 sublimes to form $CO_2(g)$ at a temperature of about –60 °C.

       (b)   Solid CO_2 melts to form $CO_2(l)$ at a temperature of about –55 °C. The $CO_2(l)$ boils when the temperature reaches approximately –45 °C.

11.61   *Analyze/Plan.* Follow the logic in Sample Exercise 11.5, using the phase diagram for neon.   *Solve.*

       (a)   The normal melting point is the temperature where solid becomes liquid at 1 atm pressure. Following a horizontal line at 1 atm to the solid-liquid line, the normal melting point is approximately 24 K.

       (b)   Neon sublimes, changes directly from solid to gas, at pressures less than the triple point pressure, 0.43 atm.

       (c)   Room temperature is 298 K, in the region where neon is a supercritical fluid. Neon cannot be liquefied at any temperature above the critical temperature, 44 K, regardless of pressure.

11.62   (a)   The normal boiling point is the temperature where liquid becomes gas at 1 atm pressure. Moving vertically down from 1 atm on the liquid-gas line to the temperature axis, the normal boiling point is approximately 27 to 28 K, or –246 °C to –245 °C.

         (b)   The much higher critical temperature and pressure of Ar (150.9 K, 48 atm) compared with those of Ne (25 K, 0.43 atm), indicate that Ar experiences much stronger intermolecular forces than Ne.

11.63   *Analyze/Plan.* Follow the logic in Sample Exercise 11.5, using the phase diagram for methane in Figure 11.30.   *Solve.*

         (a)   According to Sample Exercise 11.5, the triple point of methane (CH_4) is approximately (–180 °C, 0.1 atm). The solid-liquid line in the phase diagram is essentially vertical in the pressure range 0.1-100 atm. This means that conditions at the surface of Titan (–178 °C, 1.6 atm) are very close to the solid-liquid line. Methane on the surface of titan is likely to exist in both solid and liquid forms.

         (b)   Methane is a liquid at –178 °C and 1.6 atm. Moving upward through Titan's atmosphere at a constant temperature of –178 °C, pressure decreases. At a pressure slightly greater than 0.1 atm, we expect to see vaporization to gaseous methane. If we begin with solid methane at 1.6 atm and a temperature slightly below –180 °C, we expect sublimation to gaseous methane at a pressure slightly less than 0.1 atm.

11.64   The density of Ga(s), 5.91 g/cm³, is less than the density of Ga(l), 6.1 g/cm³, just above the melting temperature. "Typically" the density of a solid is greater than the density of its liquid. Gallium is then an atypical substance, like water, where the solid state is denser and more compact than the liquid. This results in a backward sloping solid-liquid line on the phase diagram for water, and we also expect to see this unusual feature on the diagram for gallium.

Liquid Crystals (section 11.7)

11.65   In a nematic liquid crystalline phase, molecules are aligned along their long axes, but the molecular ends are not aligned. In an ordinary liquid, molecules have no orderly arrangement; they are randomly oriented. Both an ordinary liquid and a nematic liquid crystal phase are fluids; molecules are free to move relative to one another. In an ordinary liquid, molecules can move in any direction. In a nematic phase, molecules are free to translate in all dimensions. Molecules cannot tumble or rotate out of the molecular plane, or the order of the nematic phase is lost and the sample becomes an ordinary liquid.

11.66   Reinitzer observed that cholesteryl benzoate has a phase that exhibits properties intermediate between those of the solid and liquid phases. This "liquid-crystalline" phase, formed by melting at 145 °C, is viscous and opaque; its viscosity decreases on heating and it becomes clear at 179 °C.

11.67   The presence of polar groups or nonbonded electron pairs leads to relatively strong dipole-dipole interactions between molecules. These are a significant part of the orienting forces necessary for liquid crystal formation.

11.68   (a)   The molecule has one double bond (and one triple bond).

         (b)   The "LCD molecule" is long relative to its thickness. It has one C=C and one C≡N group that promote rigidity and polarizability along the length of the molecule. The C≡N group also provides dipole-dipole interactions that encourage alignment. Unlike the molecules in Figure 11.33, which contain planar phenyl rings, the LCD molecule contains nonaromatic, nonplanar six-membered rings. These rings are subject to substantial London dispersion effects. They probably contribute to specific physical properties such as the liquid crystal temperature range that make this molecule particularly functional in LCD displays.

11.69   Because order is maintained in at least one dimension, the molecules in a liquid-crystalline phase are not totally free to change orientation. This makes the liquid-crystalline phase more resistant to flow, more viscous, than the isotropic liquid.

11.70   A nematic phase is composed of sheets of molecules aligned along their lengths, but with no additional order within the sheet or between sheets. A cholesteric phase also contains this kind of sheet, but with some ordering between sheets. In a cholesteric phase, there is a characteristic angle between molecules in one sheet and those in an adjacent sheet. That is, one sheet of molecules is twisted at some characteristic angle relative to the next, producing a "screw" axis perpendicular to the sheets.

11.71   As the temperature of a substance increases, the average kinetic energy of the molecules increases. More molecules have sufficient kinetic energy to overcome intermolecular attractive forces, so overall ordering of the molecules decreases as temperature increases. Melting provides kinetic energy sufficient to disrupt alignment in one dimension in the solid, producing a smectic phase with ordering in two dimensions. Additional heating of the smectic phase provides kinetic energy sufficient to disrupt alignment in another dimension, producing a nematic phase with one-dimensional order.

11.72   In the nematic phase, molecules are aligned in one dimension, the long dimension of the molecule. In a smectic phase (A or C), molecules are aligned in two dimensions. Not only are the long directions of the molecules aligned, but the ends are also aligned. The molecules are organized into layers; the height of the layer is related to the length of the molecule.

Additional Exercises

11.73   (a)   decrease   (b)   increase   (c)   increase   (d)   increase
         (e)   increase   (f)   increase   (g)   increase

11.74   (a)   Correct.

         (b)   The lower boiling liquid must experience less total intermolecular forces.

         (c)   If both liquids are structurally similar nonpolar molecules, the lower boiling liquid has a lower molecular weight than the higher boiling liquid.

         (d)   Correct.

         (e)   At their boiling points, both liquids have vapor pressures of 760 mm Hg.

11.75 (a) The cis isomer has stronger dipole-dipole forces; the trans isomer is nonpolar. (Since both molecules have the same molecular weight, we can say that the dipole-dipole and dispersion forces of the cis isomer are stronger than the dispersion-only forces of the trans isomer.)

(b) The molecule with the stronger intermolecular interactions will have the higher boiling point. The cis isomer boils at 60.3 °C and the trans isomer boils at 47.5 °C.

11.76 (a) In dibromomethane, CH_2Br_2, the dispersion force contribution will be larger than for CH_2Cl_2, because bromine is more polarizable than the lighter element chlorine. At the same time, the dipole-dipole contribution for CH_2Cl_2 is greater than for CH_2Br_2 because CH_2Cl_2 has a larger dipole moment.

(b) Just the opposite comparisons apply to CH_2F_2, which is less polarizable and has a higher dipole moment than CH_2Cl_2.

11.77 When a halogen atom (Cl or Br) is substituted for H in benzene, the molecule becomes polar. These molecules experience dispersion forces similar to those in benzene plus dipole-dipole forces, so they have higher boiling points than benzene. C_6H_5Br has a higher molar mass and is more polarizable than C_6H_5Cl, so it has the higher boiling point. C_6H_5OH experiences hydrogen bonding, the strongest force between neutral molecules, so it has the highest boiling point.

11.78 The GC base pair, with more hydrogen bonds, is more stable to heating. In order to break up a base pair by heating, sufficient thermal energy must be added to break the existing hydrogen bonds. With 50% more hydrogen bonds, the GC pair is definitely more stable (harder to break apart) than the AT pair.

11.79 The two O–H groups in ethylene glycol are involved in many hydrogen bonding interactions, leading to its high boiling point and viscosity, relative to pentane, which experiences only dispersion forces.

11.80 The more carbon atoms in the hydrocarbon, the longer the chain, the more polarizable the electron cloud, the higher the boiling point. A plot of the number of carbon atoms versus boiling point is shown below. For 8 C atoms, C_8H_{18}, the boiling point is approximately 130°C.

11.81   Ionic liquids are the liquid phase of ionic compounds. Upon melting, the ions are free to move relative to one another. The ion-ion interparticle attractive forces at work in an ionic liquid are extremely strong relative to dispersion, dipole-dipole and even hydrogen bonding forces operating in most molecular solvents. These powerful ion-ion forces must be broken in order for an ion to escape to the vapor phase. In the distribution of particle energies at room temperature, very few ions have sufficient kinetic energy to escape these interactions and move to the vapor phase. With few particles in the vapor phase, the vapor pressures of ionic liquids are extremely low.

11.82   (a)   Sweat, or salt water, on the surface of the body vaporizes to establish its typical vapor pressure at atmospheric pressure. Since the atmosphere is a totally open system, typical vapor pressure is never reached, and the sweat evaporates continuously. Evaporation is an endothermic process. The heat required to vaporized sweat is absorbed from your body, helping to keep it cool.

          (b)   The vacuum pump reduces the pressure of the atmosphere (air + water vapor) above the water. Eventually, atmospheric pressure equals the vapor pressure of water and the water boils. Boiling is an endothermic process, and the temperature drops if the system is not able to absorb heat from the surroundings fast enough. As the temperature of the water decreases, the water freezes. (On a molecular level, the evaporation of water removes the molecules with the highest kinetic energies from the liquid. This decrease in average kinetic energy is what we experience as a temperature decrease.)

11.83   (a)   If the Clausius-Clapeyron equation is obeyed, a graph of ln P vs 1/T(K) should be linear. Here are the data in a form for graphing.

T(K)	1/T	P(torr)	ln P
280.0	3.571×10^{-3}	32.42	3.479
300.0	3.333×10^{-3}	92.47	4.527
320.0	3.125×10^{-3}	225.1	5.417
330.0	3.030×10^{-3}	334.4	5.812
340.0	2.941×10^{-3}	482.9	6.180

According to the graph, the Clausius-Clapeyron equation is obeyed, to a first approximation.

$$\Delta H_{vap} = -\text{slope} \times R; \quad \text{slope} = \frac{3.479 - 6.180}{(3.571 - 2.941) \times 10^{-3}} = -\frac{2.701}{0.630 \times 10^{-3}} = -4.29 \times 10^3$$

$$\Delta H_{vap} = -(-4.29 \times 10^3) \times 8.314 \text{ J/K - mol} = 35.7 \text{ kJ/mol}$$

          (b)   The normal boiling point is the temperature at which the vapor pressure of the liquid equals atmospheric pressure, 760 torr. From the graph,

ln 760 = 6.63, 1/T for this vapor pressure = 2.828×10^{-3}; T = 353.6 K

11.84   (a)   The Clausius-Clapeyron equation is $\ln P = \dfrac{-\Delta H_{vap}}{RT} + C$.

For two vapor pressures, P_1 and P_2, measured at corresponding temperatures T_1 and T_2, the relationship is

$$\ln P_1 - \ln P_2 = \left(\frac{-\Delta H_{vap}}{RT_1} + C \right) - \left(\frac{-\Delta H_{vap}}{RT_2} + C \right)$$

$$\ln P_1 - \ln P_2 = \frac{-\Delta H_{vap}}{R} \left(\frac{1}{T_1} - \frac{1}{T_2} \right) + C - C; \quad \ln \frac{P_1}{P_2} = \frac{-\Delta H_{vap}}{R} \left(\frac{1}{T_1} - \frac{1}{T_2} \right)$$

   (b) $P_1 = 13.95$ torr, $T_1 = 298$ K; $P_2 = 144.78$ torr, $T_2 = 348$ K

$$\ln \frac{13.95}{144.78} = \frac{-\Delta H_{vap}}{8.314 \text{ J/mol-K}} \left(\frac{1}{298} - \frac{1}{348} \right)$$

$$-2.33974 \, (8.314 \text{ J/mol-K}) = -\Delta H_{vap} \, (4.821 \times 10^{-4} / \text{K})$$

$$\Delta H_{vap} = 4.035 \times 10^4 = 4.0 \times 10^4 \text{ J/mol} = 40 \text{ kJ/mol}$$

$[(1/T_1) - (1/T_2)]$ has 2 sig figs and so does the result.

   (c)   The normal boiling point of a liquid is the temperature at which the vapor pressure of the liquid is 760 torr.

$P_1 = 144.78$ torr, $T_1 = 348$ K; $P_2 = 760$ torr, $T_2 = $ b.p. of octane

$$\ln \left(\frac{144.78}{760.0} \right) = \frac{-4.035 \times 10^4 \text{ J/mol}}{8.314 \text{ J/mol-K}} \left(\frac{1}{348 \text{ K}} - \frac{1}{T_2} \right)$$

$$\frac{-1.6581}{-4.8533 \times 10^3} = 2.874 \times 10^{-3} - \frac{1}{T_2}; \quad \frac{1}{T_2} = 2.874 \times 10^{-3} - 3.416 \times 10^{-4}$$

$$\frac{1}{T_2} = 2.532 \times 10^{-3} = 2.53 \times 10^{-3}; \quad T_2 = 395 \text{ K} (122°\text{C})$$

From the plot of boiling point versus number of carbon atoms in Exercise 11.80, we read an approximate boiling point for octane of 130 °C. These two temperatures are close, but do differ by more than 5%. Considering experimental uncertainties in the vapor pressure data, and the empirical nature of the plot, the two values are surprisingly close. The literature boiling point of octane, 126°C, is exactly midway between our two estimates.

   (d) $P_1 = $ vp of octane at −30°C, $T_1 = 243$ K; $P_2 = 144.78$ torr, $T_2 = 348$ K

$$\ln \frac{P_1}{144.78 \text{ torr}} = \frac{-4.035 \times 10^4 \text{ J/mol}}{8.314 \text{ J/mol-K}} \left(\frac{1}{243} - \frac{1}{348} \right)$$

$$\ln \frac{P_1}{144.78 \text{ torr}} = \frac{-4.035 \times 10^4 \text{ J/mol}}{8.314 \text{ J/mol-K}} \times 1.242 \times 10^{-3} = -6.026 = -6.03$$

$$\frac{P_1}{144.78 \text{ torr}} = e^{-6.026}; \quad P_1 = 0.002415(144.78) = 0.3496 = 0.35 \text{ torr}$$

[This result has 2 sig figs because (ln = −6.03) has 2 decimal places. In a ln or log, the places left of the decimal show order of magnitude, and places right of the decimal show sig figs in the real number.] The result, 0.35 torr at −30°C, is reasonable, since we expect vapor pressure to decrease as temperature decreases, and we are approaching the freeezing point of octane, −57°C.

11.85   Physical data for the two compounds from the *Handbook of Chemistry and Physics*:

	MM	dipole moment	boiling point
CH_2Cl_2	85 g/mol	1.60 D	40.0°C
CH_3I	142 g/mol	1.62 D	42.4°C

(a)   The two substances have very similar molecular structures; each is an unsymmetrical tetrahedron with a single central carbon atom and no hydrogen bonding. Since the structures are very similar, the magnitudes of the dipole-dipole forces should be similar. This is verified by their very similar dipole moments. The heavier compound, CH_3I, will have slightly stronger London dispersion forces. Since the nature and magnitude of the intermolecular forces in the two compounds are nearly the same, it is very difficult to predict which will be more volatile [or which will have the higher boiling point as in part (b)].

(b)   Given the structural similarities discussed in part (a), one would expect the boiling points to be very similar, and they are. Based on its larger molar mass (and dipole-dipole forces being essentially equal) one might predict that CH_3I would have a slightly higher boiling point; this is verified by the known boiling points.

(c)   According to Equation 11.1, $\ln P = \dfrac{-\Delta H_{vap}}{RT} + C$

A plot of $\ln P$ vs. $1/T$ for each compound is linear. Since the order of volatility changes with temperature for the two compounds, the two lines must cross at some temperature; the slopes of the two lines, ΔH_{vap} for the two compounds, and the y-intercepts, C, must be different.

(d)
CH₂Cl₂

ln P	T(K)	1/T
2.303	229.9	4.351×10^{-3}
3.689	250.9	3.986×10^{-3}
4.605	266.9	3.747×10^{-3}
5.991	297.3	3.364×10^{-3}

CH₃I

ln P	T(K)	1/T
2.303	227.4	4.398×10^{-3}
3.689	249.0	4.016×10^{-3}
4.605	266.2	3.757×10^{-3}
5.991	298.5	3.350×10^{-3}

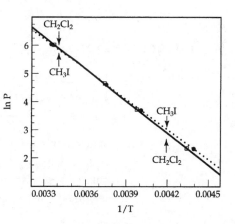

For CH_2Cl_2, $-\Delta H_{vap}/R = $ slope $= \dfrac{(5.991-2.303)}{(3.364 \times 10^{-3} - 4.350 \times 10^{-3})} = \dfrac{-3.688}{0.987 \times 10^{-3}}$

$$= -3.74 \times 10^3 = -\Delta H_{vap}/R$$

$\Delta H_{vap} = 8.314 \,(3.74 \times 10^3) = 3.107 \times 10^4$ J/mol $= 31.1$ kJ/mol

For CH_3I, $-\Delta H_{vap}/R = $ slope $= \dfrac{(5.991-2.303)}{(3.350 \times 10^{-3} - 4.398 \times 10^{-3})} = \dfrac{-3.688}{1.048 \times 10^{-3}} = -3.519 \times 10^3$

$$= -\Delta H_{vap}/R$$

$\Delta H_{vap} = 8.314 \,(3.519 \times 10^3) = 2.926 \times 10^4$ J/mol $= 29.3$ kJ/mol

11.86 In a liquid crystal display (Figure 11.36), the molecules must be oriented to rotate polarized light by 90°. Light is then reflected back through both horizontal and vertical polarizers, producing a bright display. When voltage is applied, the molecules align with the voltage and light cannot pass through the horizontal polarizer, producing a dark spot on the display. At low Antarctic temperatures, the liquid crystalline phase is closer to its freezing point. The molecules have less kinetic energy due to temperature and the applied voltage may not be sufficient to overcome orienting forces among the molecules. If some or all of the molecules do not rotate when the voltage is applied, the display will not function properly.

11.87

Integrative Exercises

11.88 (a) In Table 11.4, viscosity increases as the length of the carbon chain increases. Longer molecular chains become increasingly entangled, increasing resistance to flow.

(b) Whereas viscosity depends on molecular chain length in a critical way, surface tension depends on the strengths of intermolecular interactions between molecules. These dispersion forces do not increase as rapidly with increasing chain length and molecular weight as viscosity does.

(c) The –OH group in n-octyl alcohol gives rise to hydrogen bonding among molecules, which increases molecular entanglement and leads to greater viscosity and higher boiling point.

11.89   (a)   24 valence e⁻, 12 e⁻ pairs

H   :O: H
| ‖ |
H—C—C—C—H
| |
H   H

The geometry around the central C atom is trigonal planar, and around the two terminal C atoms, tetrahedral.

(b)   Polar. The C=O bond is quite polar and the dipoles in the trigonal plane around the central C atom do not cancel.

(c)   Dipole-dipole and London-dispersion forces

(d)   Since the molecular weights of acetone and 1-propanol are similar, the strength of the London-dispersion forces in the two compounds is also similar. The big difference is that 1-propanol has hydrogen bonding, while acetone does not. These relatively strong attractive forces lead to the higher boiling point for 1-propanol.

11.90

It is useful to draw the structural formulas because intermolecular forces are determined by the size and shape (structure) of molecules.

(a)   *Molar mass*: compounds (i) and (ii) have similar rod-like structures; (ii) has a longer rod. The longer chain leads to greater molar mass, stronger London-dispersion forces and higher heat of vaporization.

(b)   *Molecular shape*: compounds (iii) and (v) have the same chemical formula and molar mass but different molecular shapes (they are structural isomers). The more rod-like shape of (v) leads to more contact between molecules, stronger dispersion forces and higher heat of vaporization.

(c)   *Molecular polarity*: rod-like hydrocarbons (i) and (ii) are essentially nonpolar, owing to free rotation about C–C σ bonds, while (iv) is quite polar, owing to the C=O group. (iv) has a smaller molar mass than (ii) but a larger heat of vaporization, which must be due to the presence of dipole-dipole forces in (iv). [Note that (iii) and (iv), with similar shape and molecular polarity, have very similar heats of vaporization.]

(d)   *Hydrogen-bonding interactions*: molecules (v) and (vi) have similar structures, but (vi) has hydrogen bonding and (v) does not. Even though molar mass and thus dispersion forces are larger for (v), (vi) has the higher heat of vaporization. This must be due to hydrogen bonding interactions.

11.91   (a)   In order for butane to be stored as a liquid at temperatures above its boiling point (–5°C), the pressure in the tank must be greater than atmospheric pressure. In terms of the phase diagram of butane, the pressure must be high enough so that, at tank conditions, the butane is "above" the gas-liquid line and in the liquid region of the diagram.

The pressure of a gas is described by the ideal gas law as P = nRT/V; pressure is directly proportional to moles of gas. The more moles of gas present in the tank the greater the pressure, until sufficient pressure is achieved for the gas to liquify. At the point where liquid and gas are in equilibrium and temperature is constant, liquid will vaporize or condense to maintain the equilibrium vapor pressure. That is, as long as some liquid is present, the gas pressure in the tank will be constant.

(b)   If butane gas escapes the tank, butane liquid will vaporize (evaporate) to maintain the equilibrium vapor pressure. Vaporization is an endothermic process, so the butane will absorb heat from the surroundings. The temperature of the tank and the liquid butane will decrease.

(c) $250 \, g \, C_4H_{10} \times \dfrac{1 \, mol \, C_4H_{10}}{58.12 \, g \, C_4H_{10}} \times \dfrac{21.3 \, kJ}{mol} = 91.6 \, kJ$

$V = \dfrac{nRT}{P} = 250 \, g \times \dfrac{1 \, mol}{58.12 \, g} \times \dfrac{0.08206 \, L\text{-}atm}{mol\text{-}K} \times \dfrac{308 \, K}{755 \, torr} \times \dfrac{760 \, torr}{1 \, atm} = 109.44 = 109 \, L$

11.92   *Plan.*

(i)   Using thermochemical data from Appendix B, calculate the energy (enthalpy) required to melt and heat the H_2O.

(ii)   Using Hess's Law, calculate the enthalpy of combustion, ΔH_{comb}, for C_3H_8.

(iii)   Solve the stoichiometry problem.

Solve.

(i)   Heat $H_2O(s)$ from $-20°C$ to $0.0°C$; $5.50 \times 10^3 \, g \, H_2O \times \dfrac{2.092 \, J}{°C} \times 20°C = 2.301 \times 10^2$

Melt $H_2O(s)$; $5.50 \times 10^3 \, g \, H_2O \times \dfrac{6.008 \, kJ}{mol \, H_2O} \times \dfrac{1 \, mol \, H_2O}{18.02 \, g \, H_2O} = 1834 = 1.83 \times 10^3 \, kJ$
$\qquad\qquad\qquad\qquad\qquad\qquad\qquad\qquad\qquad\qquad\qquad\qquad\qquad\qquad\qquad = 2.3 \times 10^2 \, kJ$

Heat $H_2O(l)$ from $0°C$ to $75°C$; $5.50 \times 10^3 \, g \, H_2O \times \dfrac{4.184 \, J}{g\text{-}°C} \times 75°C = 1726 = 1.7 \times 10^3 \, kJ$

Total energy = 230.1 kJ + 1834 kJ + 1726 kJ = 3790 = 3.8×10^3 kJ

(The result is significant to 100 kJ, limited by 1.7×10^3 kJ)

(ii) $C_3H_8(g) + 5O_2(g) \rightarrow 3CO_2(g) + 4H_2O(l)$

Assume that one product is $H_2O(l)$, since this leads to a more negative ΔH_{comb} and fewer grams of $C_3H_8(g)$ required.

$\Delta H_{comb} = 3\Delta H_f° \, CO_2(g) + 4\Delta H_f° \, H_2O(l) - \Delta H_f° \, C_3H_8(g) - 5\Delta H_f° \, O_2(g)$

$\qquad\quad = 3(-393.5 \, kJ) + 4 \, (-285.83 \, kJ) - (-103.85 \, kJ) - 5(0) = -2219.97 = -2220 \, kJ$

(iii) 3.790×10^3 kJ required $\times \dfrac{1\,\text{mol}\,C_3H_8}{2219.97\,\text{kJ}} \times \dfrac{44.096\,g\,C_3H_8}{1\,\text{mol}\,C_3H_8} = 75\,g\,C_3H_8$

     (3.8×10^3 kJ required has 2 sig figs and so does the result)

11.93 $P = \dfrac{nRT}{V} = \dfrac{g}{M}\dfrac{RT}{V}$; $T = 273.15 + 26.0\ ^\circ C = 299.15 = 299.2$ K;   V = 5.00 L

     $g\,C_6H_6(g) = 7.2146 - 5.1493 = 2.0653\,g\,C_6H_6(g)$-

     $P\,(\text{vapor}) = \dfrac{2.0653\,g}{78.11\,g/mol} \times \dfrac{299.15\,K}{5.00\,L} \times \dfrac{0.08206\,L\text{-atm}}{mol\text{-}K} \times \dfrac{760\,torr}{1\,atm} = 98.660 = 98.7$ torr

11.94   *Plan.* Relative humidity and v.p. of H_2O at given $T \rightarrow P_{H_2O} \rightarrow$ ideal-gas law $\rightarrow$

     mol $H_2O(g) \rightarrow H_2O$ molecules. Change $^\circ F \rightarrow {}^\circ C$, volume of room from $ft^3 \rightarrow L$.

     Solve. $^\circ C = 5/9\,(^\circ F - 32)$; $^\circ C = 5/9\,(68\ ^\circ F - 32) = 20\ ^\circ C$;

     r.h. $= (P_{H_2O}$ in air / v.p. of $H_2O) \times 100$

     From Appendix B, v.p. of H_2O at 20 $^\circ C$ = 17.54 torr

     P_{H_2O} in air = r.h. $\times$ v.p. of $H_2O/100 = 58 \times 17.54$ torr$/100 = 10.173 = 10$ torr

     $V = 12\,ft \times 10\,ft \times 8\,ft \times \dfrac{12^3\,in^3}{ft^3} \times \dfrac{2.54^3\,cm^3}{in^3} \times \dfrac{1\,L}{1000\,cm^3} = 2.718 \times 10^4 = 3 \times 10^4$ L

     (The result has 1 sig fig, as does the measurement 8 ft.)

     PV = nRT;   n = PV/RT

     $n = 10.173\,torr \times \dfrac{1\,atm}{760\,torr} \times \dfrac{mol\text{-}K}{0.08206\,L\text{-atm}} \times \dfrac{2.718 \times 10^4\,L}{293\,K} = 15.13 = 2 \times 10^1\,mol\,H_2O$

     $15.13\,\,mol\,H_2O \times \dfrac{6.022 \times 10^{23}\,molecules}{1\,mol} = 9.112 \times 10^{24} = 9 \times 10^{24}\,H_2O$ molecules

12 Solids and Modern Materials

Visualizing Concepts

12.1   When choosing a unit cell, remember that the environment of each lattice point must be identical and that unit cells must *tile* to generate the complete two-dimensional lattice. For a given structure, there are often several ways to draw a unit cell. We will select the unit cell with higher symmetry (more 90° or 120° angles) and smaller area ($a \times b$).

Two-dimensional structure	(i)	(ii)
(a) unit cell		
(b) lattice	Square	Square
(c) cell contents	One black, one white	One black

12.2   (a)   Clearly, the structure is close packed. The question is: cubic or hexagonal? This is a side view of a close packed array, like the one in Figure 12.13. The key is the arrangement of the third row relative to the first. Looking at any three rows of cannon balls, there is a ball in the third row directly above (at the same horizontal position as) one in the first row. This is an ABABAB pattern and the structure is hexagonal close packed.

    (b)   CN = 12, regardless of whether the structure is hexagonal or cubic close packed.

12.3   (a)   There is a Re atom (gray sphere) at each corner of the unit cell: ($8 \times 1/8 = 1$). There is an O atom (red sphere) in the middle of each cell edge: ($12 \times 1/4 = 3$). There are 1 Re and 3 O atoms per unit cell, for an empirical formula of ReO_3.

    (b)   Each cell edge goes through two half Re atoms (at the corners) and one full O atom (centered on the edge). The length of an edge, a, is then

$$a = 2r_{Re} + 2r_O = 2(0.70 \text{ Å}) + 2(1.26 \text{ Å}) = 3.92 \text{ Å}$$

    (c)   The density of a crystalline solid is the mass of the unit cell contents divided by the unit cell volume. There is one ReO_3 unit in each primitive cubic unit cell. The unit cell volume is a^3, $(3.92 \text{ Å})^3$.

$$\frac{1 \, ReO_3 \text{ unit}}{(3.92 \text{ Å})^3} \times \frac{1 \text{ Å}^3}{(10^{-8} \text{ cm})^3} \times \frac{234.205 \text{ g } ReO_3}{6.022 \times 10^{23} \, ReO_3 \text{ units}} = 6.46 \text{ g/cm}^3$$

Check. The units of density are correct.

12.4   (a)   Band A is the valence band.

          (b)   Band B is the conduction band.

          (c)   Band A (the valence band) consists of bonding molecular orbitals (MOs).

          (d)   This is the electronic structure of a p-type doped semiconductor. The electronic structure shows a few empty MOs or "positive" holes in the valence band. This fits the description of a p-type doped semiconductor.

          (e)   The dopant is Ga. Of the three elements listed, only Ga has fewer valance electrons than Ge, the requirement for a p-type dopant.

12.5   The polymer chains in cartoon (a) are linear and have some ordered regions. Those in cartoon (b) are branched, which pushes chains apart, promotes tangling, and prevents the alignment present in (a). We expect linear polymer (a), with ordered regions, to be denser than branched polymer (b).

           The ordered regions of polymer (a) indicate that there are stronger intermolecular forces attracting the chains to each other. Stronger intermolecular forces mean that polymer (a) will have the higher melting point.

12.6   The smaller the nanocrystals, the greater the band gap, E_g, and the shorter the wavelength of emitted light. According to Figure 6.4, the shortest visible wavelengths appear violet or purple and the longest appear red.

          (a)   The 4.0 nm nanocrystals will have the smallest E_g, and emit the longest wavelength. That describes vial 2, the red one.

          (b)   The 2.8 nm nanocrystals will have the largest E_g, and emit the shortest wavelength. That describes vial 1, the green one.

          (c)   The band gap of the 100 nm CdTe crystals is 1.5 eV.

$$\lambda = \frac{hc}{E} = \frac{6.626 \times 10^{-34} \text{ J-s} \times 2.998 \times 10^8 \text{ m}}{\text{s}} \times \frac{1}{1.5 \text{ eV}} \times \frac{1 \text{ eV}}{1.602 \times 10^{-19} \text{ J}} = 8.27 \times 10^{-7} \text{ m}$$

$$\upsilon = \frac{c}{\lambda} = \frac{2.998 \times 10^8 \text{ m/s}}{8.27 \times 10^{-7} \text{ m}} = 3.63 \times 10^{14} \text{ s}^{-1}$$

           The visible portion of the electromagnetic spectrum has wavelengths up to 750 nm (7.50×10^{-7} m). The 100 nm CdTe crystals emit a wavelength longer than this, 827 nm (8.27×10^{-7} m). This light is in the IR portion of the spectrum and is not visible to the human eye.

Classification of Solids (section 12.1)

12.7   In molecular solids, relatively weak intermolecular forces (hydrogen bonding, dipole-dipole, dispersion) bind the molecules in the lattice, so relatively little energy is required to disrupt these forces. In covalent-network solids, covalent bonds join atoms into an extended network. Melting or deforming a covalent-network solid means breaking these covalent bonds, which requires a large amount of energy.

12.8   According to Table 11.2 and Figure 12.1, diamond is a covalent-network solid. Carbon atoms are bound into a three-dimensional network by strong covalent (single) bonds. Silicon, with the same structure, is also a covalent-network solid.

12.9   (a)   hydrogen bonding, dipole-dipole forces, London dispersion forces

         (b)   covalent chemical bonds (mainly)

         (c)   ionic bonds, the electrostatic attraction between anions and cations (mainly)

         (d)   metallic bonds

12.10   (a)   metallic

         (b)   molecular or metallic (physical properties of metals vary widely)

         (c)   covalent-network or ionic

         (d)   covalent-network

12.11   (a)   ionic   (b)   metallic

         (c)   covalent-network   (Based on melting point, it is definitely a network solid. Transition metals in high oxidation states often form bonds with nonmetals that have significant covalent character. It could also be characterized as ionic with some covalent character to the bonds.)

         (d)   molecular   (e)   molecular   (f)   molecular

12.12   (a)   InAs—covalent-network (InAs is a compound semiconductor, with an average of four electrons per atom and somewhat polar covalent bonds.)

         (b)   MgO—ionic crystal (metal and nonmetal)

         (c)   HgS—ionic crystal (metal and nonmetal)

         (d)   In—metallic (metal, Figure 7.12)

         (e)   HBr—molecular (two nonmetals)

12.13   Because of its relatively high melting point and properties as a conducting solution, the solid must be ionic.

12.14   According to Figure 12.1, the solid could be either ionic with low water solubility or network covalent. Due to the extremely high sublimation temperature, it is probably covalent-network.

Structures of Solids (section 12.2)

12.15   *Analyze/Plan.*   Crystalline solids have a regular repeat in all three directions. Amorphous solids have no regular repeating structure. Draw diagrams that reflect these definitions. *Solve.*

a)

crystalline

b)

amorphous

12.16   In amorphous silica (SiO_2) the regular structure of quartz is disrupted; the loose, disordered structure, has many vacant "pockets" throughout. There are fewer SiO_2 groups per volume in the amorphous solid; the packing is less efficient and less dense.

12.17   *Analyze.* Given two two-dimensional structures, draw and describe the unit cells and lattice vectors. *Plan.* When choosing a unit cell, the environment of each lattice point must be identical and the unit cells must *tile* to generate the complete two-dimensional lattice. For a given structure, there are often several ways to draw a unit cell. The radii of A and B are equal. *Solve.*

Two-dimensional structure	(i)	(ii)
(a) unit cell		
(b) γ, a, b	$\gamma = 90°$, $a = b$	$\gamma = 120°$, $a = b$
(c) lattice type	square	hexagonal

12.18

Two-dimensional structure	(i)	(ii)
(a) unit cell		
(b) γ, a, b	$\gamma = 90°$, $a = b$	$\gamma = 90°$, $a \neq b$
(c) lattice type	square	rectangular

12.19   *Plan.* Refer to Figure 12.6 to find geometric characteristics of the seven three dimensional primitive lattices.

(a)   Orthorhombic, $a \neq b \neq c$, $\alpha = \beta = \gamma = 90°$. A rectangular base has unequal side lengths and an angle of 90°. The third lattice vector is perpendicular to the first two and a different length, so all angles are 90° and all vector lengths are unequal.

(b)   Tetragonal, $a = b \neq c$, $\alpha = \beta = \gamma = 90°$. The only difference between the two lattices is that the second has a square (rather than rectangular) base. This means that two of the edge lengths are equal but the third is not, and all angles remain 90°.

12.20   (a)   If the base of the unit cell is an arbitrary parallelogram, $a \neq b$ and the angle between them does not equal 90°. If c is perpendicular to the other two lattice vectors, the angles between c and a, as well as the angles between c and b, are 90°; $a \neq b \neq c$, $\alpha = \beta = 90°$, $\gamma \neq 90°$. The "standard" monoclinic cell is $a \neq b \neq c$, $\alpha = \gamma = 90°$, $\beta \neq 90°$. The unit cell described here is "non-standard", but can be transformed into a "standard" cell by renaming the axes so that the arbitrary angle is between a and c, and a right-handed coordinate system is maintained. The cell described is still monoclinic, by virture of its geometry (actually, by virtue of its symmetry).

(b)   Hexagonal, $a = b \neq c$, $\alpha = \beta = 90°$, $\gamma = 120°$. A two dimensional hexagonal unit cell has $a = b$ and $\gamma = 120°$. If the third lattice vector is perpendicular to the other two, the other two angles are $90°$.

12.21   *Plan.*   Refer to Figure 12.6 to find geometric characteristics of the seven three dimensional primitive lattices.

If no lattice vectors are perpendicular to each other, none of the unit cell angles (α, β, γ) are $90°$. This is characteristic of two of the three dimensional primitive lattices: triclinic and rhombohedral.

12.22   If all three lattice vectors have the same length, $a = b = c$. This is characteristic of two of the three dimensional lattices: cubic and rhombohedral.

12.23   *Analyze.*   Given an element with a body centered cubic lattice, find the minimum number of atoms in a unit cell. *Plan.* Refer to Figures 12.11 and 12.12 to visualize an element (all the same kind of atoms) with a body centered cubic lattice. *Solve.*

A body centered cubic lattice is composed of body centered cubic unit cells. A unit cell contains the minimum number of atoms when it has atoms only at the lattice points. A body centered cubic unit cell like this is shown in Figure 12.12(b). There is one atom totally inside the cell (1×1) and one at each corner ($8 \times 1/8$) for a total of 2 (metal) atoms in the unit cell. (Only metallic elements have body-centered cubic lattices and unit cells.)

12.24   A face centered cubic lattice is composed of face centered cubic unit cells. A unit cell contains the minimum number of atoms when it has atoms only on the lattice points. A face centered cubic unit cell like this is shown in Figure 12.12(c). There is one atom centered on each face ($6 \times 1/2$) and one at each corner ($8 \times 1/8$) for a total of 4 metal atoms in the unit cell.

12.25   *Analyze.*   Given a diagram of the unit cell dimensions and contents of nickel arsenide, determine what kind of lattice this crystal possess, and the empirical formula of the compound. *Plan.* Refer to Figure 12.6 to find geometric characteristics of the seven three dimensional primitive lattices. Decide where atoms of the two elements are located in the unit cell and use Table 12.1 to help determine the empirical formula.

(a) $a = b = 3.57$ Å. $c = 5.10$ Å $\neq a$ or b. $\alpha = \beta = 90°$, $\gamma = 120°$. This unit cell is hexagonal. There are no atoms in the exact middle of the cell or on the face centers, so it is a primitive hexagonal unit cell. Nickel arsenide has a primitive hexagonal unit cell and crystal lattice.

(b)   There are Ni atoms at each corner of the cell ($8 \times 1/8$) and centered on four of the unit cell edges ($4 \times 1/4$) for a total of 2 Ni atoms. There are 2 As atoms totally inside the cell. The unit cell contains 2 Ni and 2 As atoms; the empirical formula is NiAs.

12.26   (a) $a = b = 3.98$ Å. $c = 3.47$ Å $\neq a$ or b. $\alpha = \beta = \gamma = 90°$. This is a tetragonal unit cell and crystal lattice.

         (b)   There is one Sr atom totally inside the cell, Fe atoms at each corner ($8 \times 1/8$), and O atoms centered on eight of the unit cell edges ($8 \times 1/4$). The unit cell contains 1 Sr, 1 Fe and 2 O atoms. The empirical formula is $SrFeO_2$.

Metallic Solids (section 12.3)

12.27   *Analyze/Plan.* Consider trends in atomic mass and volume of the elements listed to explain the variation in density. *Solve.*

        Moving left to right in the period, atomic mass and Z_{eff} increase. The increase in Z_{eff} leads to smaller bonding atomic radii and thus atomic volume. Mass increases, volume decreases, and density increases in the series.

        The variation in densities reflects shorter metal-metal bond distances. These shorter distances suggest that the extent of metal-metal bonding increases in the series. This is consistent with greater occupancy of the bonding band (Section 12.4) as the number of valence electrons increases up to 6. The strength of metal-metal bonds in the series is probably the most important factor influencing the increase in density.

12.28   (b) NiCo alloy and (c) W will have metallic properties. The lattices of these substances are composed of neutral metal atoms. Delocalization of valence electrons produces metallic properties.

        (d) Ge is a metalloid, not a metal. (a) $TiCl_4$ and (e) ScN are ionic compounds; in ionic compounds, electrons are localized on the individual ions, precluding metallic properties.

12.29   *Analyze.* Give diagrams of three structure types, find which is most densely packed and which is least densely packed. *Plan.* Assume that the same element packs in each of the three structures, so that atomic mass and volume are constant. Then we are analyzing the packing efficiency or relative amount of empty space in each structure. *Solve.*

        Structure type A has a face centered cubic unit cell with metal atoms only at the lattice points; this corresponds to a cubic close packed structure. Structure type B has a body centered cubic unit cell with metal atoms at the lattice points; this is also a body centered cubic structure. Structure type C has a hexagonal unit cell with two atoms totally inside the cell. Building up many unit cells into a lattice (Figure 12.14) leads to a hexagonal close packed structure.

        (a)   In both cubic and hexagonal close packed structures, any individual atom has twelve nearest neighbor atoms. Both structures are "closest" packed and have equal amounts of empty space. Structure types A and C have equally dense packing and are more densely packed than structure type B.

        (b)   Structure type B, which is not close packed, has the least dense atom packing.

12.30   (a)   The density of a crystalline solid is (unit cell mass/unit cell volume). Solve for unit cell volume, then use geometry and the properties of a body centered cubic unit cell to calculate the atomic radius of sodium. There are 2 Na atoms in each body centered cubic unit cell (Figure 12.12).

$$V = \frac{\text{unit cell mass}}{\rho} = \frac{2 \text{ Na atoms} \times 22.99 \text{ g Na}}{6.022 \times 10^{23} \text{ Na atoms}} \times \frac{cm^3}{0.97 g} \times \frac{1 \text{Å}^3}{(10^{-8} \text{ cm})^3} = 78.71 = 79 \text{ Å}^3$$

For a cubic unit cell, $V = a^3$. We need the relationship between atomic radius and unit cell edge length for a body centered cubic unit cell. In a body centered cubic metal structure, the atoms touch along the the body diagonal, d_2. Then, $d_2 = 4$ r. From the Pythagorean theorem, $d_2 = \sqrt{3}\,a$. (See Sample Exercise 12.2 for the complete derivation.)

$$a = (V)^{1/3} = (78.71)^{1/3} = 4.2857 = 4.3 \text{ Å.}$$

$$d_2 = 4\,r_{Na}\,;\quad d_2 = \sqrt{3}\,a;\quad r_{Na} = \sqrt{3}\,a/4 = \frac{\sqrt{3} \times 4.2857 \text{ Å}}{4} = 1.8557 = 1.9 \text{ Å}$$

(b)   A cubic close packed metal structure has a face centered cubic unit cell; there are 4 the atoms in each unit cell and atoms touch along the face diagonal, d_1. Then, $d_1 = 4$ r. From the Pythagorean theorem, $d_1 = \sqrt{2}\,a$.

$$d_1 = 4\,r_{Na}\,;\quad d_1 = \sqrt{2}\,a;\quad a = 4\,r_{Na}/\sqrt{2} = \frac{4 \times 1.8557 \text{ Å}}{\sqrt{2}} = 5.2489 = 5.2 \text{ Å} = 5.2 \times 10^{-8} \text{ cm}$$

$$\rho = \frac{4 \text{ Na atoms}}{(5.2489 \times 10^{-8} \text{ cm})^3} \times \frac{22.99 \text{ g Na}}{6.022 \times 10^{23} \text{ Na atoms}} = 1.056 = 1.1 \text{ g/cm}^3$$

Sodium metal with a cubic close packed structure would not float on water.

12.31   *Analyze.* Given the cubic unit cell edge length and arrangement of Ir atoms, calculate the atomic radius and the density of the metal. *Plan.* There is space between the atoms along the unit cell edge, but they touch along the face diagonal. Use the geometry of the right equilateral triangle to calculate the atomic radius. From the definition of density and paying attention to units, calculate the density of Ir(s).   *Solve.*

(a)   The length of the face diagonal of a face-centered cubic unit cell is four times the radius of the atom and $\sqrt{2}$ times the unit cell dimension or edge length, *a* for cubic unit cells.

$$4\,r = \sqrt{2}\,a; r = \sqrt{2}\,a/4 = \frac{\sqrt{2} \times 3.833 \text{ Å}}{4} = 1.3552 = 1.355 \text{ Å}$$

(b)   The density of iridium is the mass of the unit cell contents divided by the unit cell volume. There are 4 Ir atoms in a face-centered cubic unit cell.

$$\rho = \frac{4 \text{ Ir atoms}}{(3.833 \times 10^{-8} \text{ cm})^3} \times \frac{192.22 \text{ g Ir}}{6.022 \times 10^{23} \text{ Ir atoms}} = 22.67 \text{ g/cm}^3$$

Check. The units of density are correct. Note that Ir is quite dense.

12.32   (a)   In a body centered cubic unit cell, there is one atom totally inside the unit cell (1×1) and one atom at each of the eight corners $(8 \times 1/8)$, for a total of 2 Ca atoms in each unit cell.

(b)   Because atoms are only at lattice points in a body centered metal structure, each metal atom has an equivalent environment. That is, atoms at the corner of the cell and the interior atom must have equivalent environments. Consider the Ca atom at the middle of the unit cell. It has eight nearest neighbors, the eight Ca atoms at the corners of the cell. Interior atoms in adjacent unit cells are farther from the reference Ca atom and are not "nearest". (For a corner Ca atom, the eight nearest neighbors are the interior atoms in the eight unit cells that include 1/8 of that corner atom.)

(c)   In a body centered cubic metal structure, the atoms touch along the the body diagonal, d_2. Then, $d_2 = 4$ r. From the Pythagorean theorem, $d_2 = \sqrt{3}\, a$. (See Sample Exercise 12.2 for the complete derivation.)

$$4\, r_{Ca} = \sqrt{3}\, a; \quad a = 4\, r_{Ca} / \sqrt{3} = \frac{4 \times 1.97\,\text{Å}}{\sqrt{3}} = 4.5495 = 4.55\,\text{Å}$$

(d) $$\rho = \frac{2\,\text{Ca atoms}}{(4.5495 \times 10^{-8}\,\text{cm})^3} \times \frac{40.08\,\text{g Ca}}{6.022 \times 10^{23}\,\text{Ca atoms}} = 1.4136 = 1.41\,\text{g/cm}^3$$

12.33   *Analyze.* Given the structure of aluminum metal and the atomic radius of and Al atom, find the number of Al atoms in each unit cell and the coordination number of each Al atom. Calculate (estimate) the length of the unit cell edge and the density of aluminum metal.

Plan. Use Figure 12.14(a) to count the number of Al atoms in one unit cell and visualize the coordination number of each Al atom. There is space between the atoms along the unit cell edge, but they touch along the face diagonal. Use the geometry of the right equilateral triangle and the atomic radius to calculate the unit cell edge length. From the definition of density and paying attention to units, calculate the density of aluminum metal. *Solve.*

(a)   8 corners × 1/8 atom/corner + 6 faces × ½ atom/face = 4 atoms

(b)   Each aluminum atom is in contact with 12 nearest neighbors, 6 in one plane, 3 above that plane, and 3 below. Its coordination number is thus 12.

(c)   The length of the face diagonal of a face-centered cubic unit cell is four times the radius of the metal and $\sqrt{2}$ times the unit cell dimension (usually designated a for cubic cells).

$$4 \times 1.43\,\text{Å} = \sqrt{2} \times a; \quad a = \frac{4 \times 1.43\,\text{Å}}{\sqrt{2}} = 4.0447 = 4.04\,\text{Å} = 4.04 \times 10^{-8}\,\text{cm}$$

(d)   The density of the metal is the mass of the unit cell contents divided by the volume of the unit cell.

$$\text{density} = \frac{4\,\text{Al atoms}}{(4.0447 \times 10^{-8}\,\text{cm})^3} \times \frac{26.98\,\text{g Al}}{6.022 \times 10^{23}\,\text{Al atoms}} = 2.71\,\text{g/cm}^3$$

12.34   *Analyze.* Given the atomic arrangement, length of the cubic unit cell edge and density of the solid, calculate the atomic weight of the element. *Plan.* If we calculate the mass of a single unit cell, and determine the number of atoms in one unit cell, we can calculate the mass of a single atom and of a mole of atoms.   *Solve.*

The volume of the unit cell is $(2.86 \times 10^{-8}\,\text{cm})^3$. The mass of the unit cell is:

$$\frac{7.92\,\text{g}}{\text{cm}^3} \times \frac{(2.86 \times 10^{-8})^3\,\text{cm}^3}{\text{unit cell}} = 1.853 \times 10^{-22}\,\text{g/unit cell}$$

There are two atoms of the element present in the body-centered cubic unit cell. Thus the atomic weight is:

$$\frac{1.853 \times 10^{-22}\,g}{unit\ cell} \times \frac{1\,unit\ cell}{2\,atoms} \times \frac{6.022 \times 10^{23}\,atoms}{1\,mol} = 55.8\,g/mol$$

Check. The result is a reasonable atomic weight and the units are correct. The element could be iron.

12.35   *Analyze/Plan.* Use information in Section 12.3 to define *alloy*, and compare the various types of alloys.   *Solve.*

An *alloy* contains atoms of more than one element and has the properties of a metal. *Solution alloys* are homogeneous mixtures with different kinds of atoms dispersed randomly and uniformly. In *heterogeneous alloys* the components (elements or compounds) are not evenly dispersed and their properties depend not only on composition but methods of preparation. In an *intermetallic compound* the component elements have interacted to form a compound substance, for example, Cu_3As. As with more familiar compounds, these are homogeneous and have definite composition and properties.

12.36   Substitutional and interstitial alloys are both solution alloys. In a *substitutional* alloy, the atoms of the "solute" take positions normally occupied by the "solvent." Substitutional alloys tend to form when solute and solvent atoms are of comparable size and have similar bonding characteristics. In an *interstitial* alloy, the atoms of the "solute" occupy the holes or interstitial positions between "solvent" atoms. Solute atoms are necessarily much smaller than solvent atoms.

12.37   *Analyze/Plan.* Consider the descriptions of various alloy types in Section 12.3. *Solve.*

   (a) $Fe_{0.97}Si_{0.03}$; interstitial alloy. The radii of Fe and Si are substantially different, so Si could fit in "holes" in the Fe lattice. Also, the small amount of Si relative to Fe is characteristic of an interstitial alloy.

   (b) $Fe_{0.60}Ni_{0.40}$, substitutional alloy. The two metals have very similar atomic radii and are present in similar amounts.

   (c) $SmCo_5$, intermetallic compound. The two elements are present in stoichiometric amounts.

12.38   (a) $Cu_{0.66}Zn_{0.34}$, substitutional alloy; similar atomic radii, substantial amounts of both components

   (b) Ag_3Sn, intermetallic compound; set stoichiometric ratio of components

   (c) $Ti_{0.99}O_{0.01}$, interstitial alloy; very different atomic radii, tiny amount of smaller component

12.39   (a)   True

   (b)   False. Interstitial alloys form between elements with very different bonding atomic radii.

   (c)   False. Non-metallic elements are typically found in interstitial alloys.

12.40   (a)   True

   (b)   True

(c)   False. In stainless steel, the chromium atoms replace iron atoms in the structure. (The atomic radii of Fe and Cr are 1.25 Å and 1.27 Å, respectively. Metal atoms with similar radii form substitutional alloys.)

12.41   *Analyze.* Given the color of a gold alloy, find the other element(s) in the alloy and the type of alloy formed. *Plan.* Refer to 'Chemistry Put to Work: ALLOYS OF GOLD'. *Solve.*

(a)   White gold, nickel or palladium, substitutional alloy

(b)   Rose gold, copper, substitutional alloy

(c)   Blue gold, indium, intermetallic compound

(d)   Green gold, silver, substitutional alloy

12.42   Purple gold is $AuAl_2$. The composition is not variable, because it is a compound, not an alloy, which is a mixture. Because of their ordered structures, intermetallic compounds tend to be higher melting and more brittle, but less malleable and ductile than alloys. These properties make them hard to manipulate into shapes and are the reason purple gold is not used to make rings or necklaces.

Metallic Bonding (section 12.4)

12.43   *Analyze/Plan.* Apply the description of the electron-sea model of metallic bonding given in Section 12.4 to the conductivity of metals.   *Solve.*

In the electron-sea model for metallic bonding, valence electrons move about the three-dimensional metallic lattice, while the metal atoms maintain regular lattice positions.

Under the influence of an applied potential the electrons can move throughout the structure, giving rise to high electrical conductivity. The mobility of the electrons facilitates the transfer of kinetic energy and leads to high thermal conductivity.

12.44   (a)   Cr: $[Ar]4s^13d^5$, Z = 24;   Se: $[Ar]4s^23d^{10}4p^4$, Z = 34

Both elements have the [Ar] core configuration and both have six valence electrons. The orbital locations of the six valence electrons are different in the two elements, because Se has more total electrons.

(b)   Different Z and Z_{eff} for the two elements, and the different orbital locations of the valence electrons, are the main factors that lead to the differences in properties. In Cr, the 4s and 3d electrons are the valence electrons. Its Z and Z_{eff} are smaller than those of Se and it is not likely to gain enough electrons to achieve a noble-gas configuration. Thus, Cr loses electrons when it forms ions, acting like a metal. Se is in the same row of the periodic table as Cr, but its 3d subshell is filled, so its valence electrons are in 4s and 4p. Because Se has a larger Z and Z_{eff}, it is more likely to hold its own valence electrons and gain other electrons when it forms ions. That Se needs only two additional electrons to achieve the noble-gas configuration of Kr is also a driving force for it gaining electrons when it forms ions, acting like a nonmetal.

12.45   *Plan.* By analogy to Figure 12.23, the most bonding, lowest energy MOs have the fewest nodes. As energy increases, the number of nodes increases. When constructing an MO diagram from AOs, total number of orbitals is conserved. The MO diagram for a linear chain of six Li atoms will have six MOs, starting with zero nodes and maximum overlap, and ending with five nodes and minimum overlap.   *Solve.*

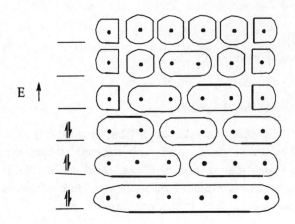

   (a)   Six AOs require six MOs.

   (b)   Zero nodes in lowest energy orbital

   (c)   Five nodes in highest energy orbital

   (d)   Two nodes in the HOMO

   (e)   Three nodes in the LUMO

12.46

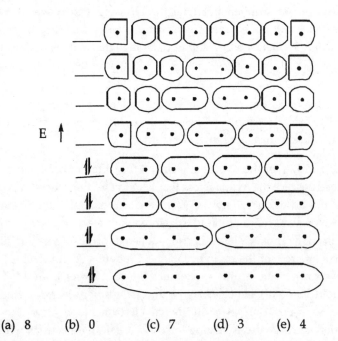

   (a) 8   (b) 0   (c) 7   (d) 3   (e) 4

12.47   *Analyze/Plan.* Consider the definition of ductility, as well as the discussion of metallic bonding in Section 12.4.   *Solve.*

Ductility is the property related to the ease with which a solid can be drawn into a wire. Basically, the softer the solid the more ductile it is. The more rigid the solid, the less ductile it is. For metals, ductility decreases as the strength of metal-metal bonding increases, producing a stiffer lattice less susceptible to distortion.

(a)   Ag is more ductile. Mo, with 6 valence electrons, has a filled bonding band, strong metal-metal interactions, and a rigid lattice. This predicts high hardness and low ductility. Ag, with 12 valence electrons, has filled antibonding as well as bonding bands. Bonding is weaker than in Mo, and Ag is more ductile.

(b)   Zn is more ductile. Si is a covalent-network solid with all valence electrons localized in bonds between Si atoms. Covalent-network substances are high-melting, hard, and not particularly ductile.

12.48   Metals, with few valence electrons, cannot satisfy their "bonding needs" by localized covalent bonds. Metals form structures with several nearest neighbor atoms. (Na and K have body-centered cubic lattices where each atom has eight nearest neighbors.) Bonding electrons are delocalized throughout the lattice. Although bonding electrons are associated with individual atoms, their locations are not restricted. Changes in atomic position due to deformation like cutting (or pounding or shaping) are at least partly accommodated by shifting of the delocalized bonding electrons. In solids with rigid lattices formed by ionic or network covalent bonding, electrons are locked into localized bonds. A small "crack" (shift of atom positions) breaks bonds and leads to total destruction of the lattice and catastrophic failure of the material. Metals, on the other hand, are able to "adjust" to atom dislocation (cuts, cracks, dents, etc.) because of their unique delocalized bonding characteristics.

12.49   Moving across the fifth period from Y to Mo, the melting points of the metals increase. The number of valence electrons also increases, from 3 for Y to 6 for Mo. More valence electrons (up to 6) mean increased occupancy of the bonding molecular orbital band, and increased strength of metallic bonding. Melting requires that atoms are moving relative to each other. Stronger metallic bonding requires more energy to break bonds and mobilize atoms, resulting in higher melting points from Y to Mo.

12.50   In each group, choose the metal that has the number of valence electrons closest to six.

(a)   Re   (b)   Mo   (c)   Ru

Ionic and Molecular Solids (sections 12.5 and 12.6))

12.51   (a)   Sr: Sr atoms occupy the 8 corners of the cube.

8 corners × 1/8 sphere/corner = 1 Sr atom

O: O atoms occupy the centers of the 6 faces of the cube.

6 faces × 1/2 atom/face = 3 O atoms

Ti: There is 1 Ti atom at the body center of the cube.

Formula: $SrTiO_3$

(b)   Twelve. Each Sr atom occupies one corner of 8 unit cells. Sr is coordinated to 3 oxygen positions in each unit cell for a total of 24 oxygen positions. However, each O position is in the center of a cell face, with half-occupancy in each cell. 24 oxygen positions × ½ occupancy = 12 oxygen atoms. Each Ti atom is coordinated to 12 oxygen atoms.

12.52   (a)   Ti: 8 corners × 1/8 sphere/corner + [1 center × 1 sphere/center] = 2 Ti atoms

          O: 4 faces × 1/2 sphere/face + [2 interior × 1 sphere/interior] = 4 O atoms

        Formula: TiO_2

     (b)   From inspection of the unit cell diagram, the Ti at the center of the cell is bound to six (6) O atoms. Each totally interior O atom is bound to three titanium atoms. The coordination number of Ti is 6; the coordination number of O is 3.

12.53   *Analyze/Plan.* Use the structure of NaCl in Figure 12.26(b) to estimate the unit cell edge length based on ionic radii of Na^+ and F^- from Figure 7.7. *Solve.*

     (a)   According to Figure 12.26(b), the length of the unit cell edge in this structure is $2r_{Na^+} + 2r_{F^-}$. $a = 2(1.16 \text{ Å}) + 2(1.19 \text{ Å}) = 4.70 \text{ Å}$

     (b)   The density of NaF is the mass of the unit cell contents divided by the volume of the unit cell. By analogy to the NaCl structure in Figure 12.26(b) and 12.27, there are 8 fluoride ions (green spheres) on the corners of the unit cell, and 6 fluoride ions in the middle of the faces. The number of fluoride ions per unit cell is then 8(1/8) + 6(1/2) = 4. There is 1 sodium ion (purple sphere almost hidden in figure) completely inside the unit cell and 12 sodium ions (purple spheres) along the unit cell edges. The number of sodium ions is then 1 + 12(1/4) = 4. This result satisfies charge balance requirements.

        4 Na^+, 4 F^-, 4 NaF formula units. The mass of 1 NaF formula unit is $41.99 \text{ g}/6.022 \times 10^{23}$ NaF units.

$$d = \frac{4 \text{ NaF units}}{(4.70 \text{ Å})^3} \times \frac{41.99 \text{ g}}{6.022 \times 10^{23} \text{ NaF units}} \times \left(\frac{1 \text{ Å}}{1 \times 10^{-8} \text{ cm}}\right)^3 = 2.69 \text{ g/cm}^3$$

        Check. The value for the density of NaF(s) reported in the *CRC Handbook of Chemistry and Physics*, 74th Ed., is 2.56 g/cm³. The calculated density based on the estimated value of *a* is within 5% of the reported value.

12.54   Calculate the mass of a single unit cell and then use density to find the volume of a single unit cell. The edge length is the cube-root of the volume of a cubic cell. From the previous exercise, there are four PbSe units in a NaCl-type unit cell . The unit cell edge length is designated *a*.

$$8.27 \text{ g/cm}^3 = \frac{4 \text{ PbSe units}}{a^3} \times \frac{286.2 \text{ g}}{6.022 \times 10^{23} \text{ PbSe units}} \times \left(\frac{1 \text{ Å}}{1 \times 10^{-8} \text{ cm}}\right)^3$$

$a^3 = 229.87 \text{ Å}^3$, $a = 6.13 \text{ Å}$

12.55   *Analyze.* Given the atomic arrangement and length of the unit cell side, calculate the density of HgS and HgSe. Qualitatively and quantitatively compare the densities of the two solids. *Plan.* Calculate the mass and volume of a single unit cell and then use them to find density. The unit cell volume is the cube of edge length. *Solve.* The unit cell edge is designated *a*.

(a)   According to Figure 12.26(c) and 12.27, sulfide ions (yellow spheres) occupy the corners and faces of the unit cell (in a face-centered cubic arrangement), for a total of $6(1/2) + 8(1/8) = 4$ S^{2-} ions per unit cell. There are 4 mercury ions (gray spheres) totally in the interior of the cell. This means there are 4 HgS units in a unit cell with the zinc blende structure.

$$\text{density} = \frac{4\,\text{HgS units}}{(5.852\,\text{Å})^3} \times \frac{232.655\,\text{g}}{6.022\times10^{23}\,\text{HgS units}} \times \left(\frac{1\,\text{Å}}{1\times10^{-8}\,\text{cm}}\right)^3 = 7.711\,\text{g/cm}^3$$

(b)   We expect Se^{2-} to have a larger ionic radius than S^{2-}, since Se is below S in the chalcogen family and both ions have the same charge. Thus, HgSe will occupy a larger volume and the unit cell edge will be longer.

(c)   For HgSe, also with the zinc blende structure:

$$\text{density} = \frac{4\,\text{HgSe units}}{(6.085\,\text{Å})^3} \times \frac{279.55\,\text{g HgSe}}{6.022\times10^{23}\,\text{HgSe units}} \times \left(\frac{1\,\text{Å}}{1\times10^{-8}\,\text{cm}}\right)^3 = 8.241\,\text{g/cm}^3$$

Even though HgSe has a larger unit cell volume than HgS, it also has a larger molar mass. The mass of Se is more than twice that of S, while the radius of Se^{2-} is only slightly larger than that of S^{2-} (Figure 7.7). The greater mass of Se accounts for the greater density of HgSe.

12.56   (a)   Each cell edge goes through two half Rb^+ ions (at the corners) and one full I^- ion (centered on the edge). The length of an edge, a, is then

$a = 2r_{Rb} + 2r_I = 2(1.66\,\text{Å}) + 2(2.06\,\text{Å}) = 7.44\,\text{Å}$

(b) $$\text{density} = \frac{4\,\text{RbI units}}{(7.44\,\text{Å})^3} \times \frac{212.37\,\text{g}}{6.022\times10^{23}\,\text{RbI units}} \times \left(\frac{1\,\text{Å}}{1\times10^{-8}\,\text{cm}}\right)^3 = 3.43\,\text{g/cm}^3$$

(c)   In the CsCl-type structure, I^- anions sit at the corners of the cube and an Rb^+ cation sits completely inside the unit cell (at or near the body center). Assume that the anions and cations touch along the body diagonal (bd), so that

bd $= 2r_{Rb} + 2r_I = 2(1.66\,\text{Å}) + 2(2.06\,\text{Å}) = 7.44\,\text{Å}$. (This is the edge length of the NaCl-type structure.)

From Solution 12.32, the relationship between the body diagonal and edge of a cube is: $\text{bd} = \sqrt{3} \times a$; $a = \text{bd}/\sqrt{3}$. $a = 7.44\,\text{Å}/\sqrt{3} = 4.2955 = 4.30\,\text{Å}$

(d)   There is one RbI unit ($8 \times 1/8$ I^- anions and 1 Rb^+ cation) in the CsCl-type unit cell.

$$\text{density} = \frac{1\,\text{RbI unit}}{(4.2955\,\text{Å})^3} \times \frac{212.37\,\text{g}}{6.022\times10^{23}\,\text{RbI units}} \times \left(\frac{1\,\text{Å}}{1\times10^{-8}\,\text{cm}}\right)^3 = 4.45\,\text{g/cm}^3$$

The density of the CsCl-type structure is greater than the density of the NaCl-type structure, owing to the much smaller unit cell volume.

12.57   *Analyze.* Given that CuI, CsI and NaI uniquely adopt one of the structure types pictured in Figure 12.26, match the ionic compound with its structure. Use ionic radii to inform your decision. *Plan.* Note the relative cation/anion ratio in the three structures in Figure 12.26. Match these ratios with those of CuI, CsI and NaI. *Solve.*

(a)   In the CsCl structure, the anion and cation have about the same radius; in the NaCl structure, the anion is somewhat larger than the cation; in the ZnS structure the anion is much larger than the cation.

In the three compounds given, Cs^+ (r = 1.81 Å) and I^- (r = 2.06 Å) have the most similar radii; CsI will adopt the CsCl-type structure. The radii of Na^+ (r = 1.16 Å) and I^- (r = 2.06 Å) are somewhat different; NaI will adopt the NaCl-type structure. The radii of Cu^+ (r = 0.74 Å) and I^- (r = 2.06 Å) are very different; CuI has the ZnS-type structure.

(b)   As cation size decreases, coordination number of the anion decreases. In CsI, I^- has a coordination number of eight; in NaI, I^- has a coordination number of six; in CuI, I^- has a coordination number of four.

12.58   (a)   In CaF_2 the ionic radii are very similar, Ca^{2+} (r = 1.14 Å) and F^- (r = 1.19 Å). In ZnF_2 the cation radius is smaller and the ionic radii are more different, Zn^{2+} (r = 0.88 Å) and F^- (r = 1.19 Å). Cations in both structures in the exercise are shown with equal radii, so direct inspections does not answer the question. We can, however, refer to the trend that, for compounds with the same cation/anion ratio, as cation size decreases, coordination number of the anion decreases. The anion coordination number (CN) for the rutile structure is 3 and for the fluorite structure is 4. The compound with the smaller cation, ZnF_2, will adopt the rutile structure and the compound with the larger cation, CaF_2, will adopt the fluorite structure. (Detailed analysis of coordination numbers follows.)

(b)   Rutile (top) structure, cation (blue) coordination number (CN) = 6, anion (green) CN = 3. [The blue cation in the interior or the cell is coordinated to the six (green) anions associated with the same cell; either of the green interior anions is associated with the triangle of blue cations located inside and at the two nearest corners of the cell.]

Fluorite (bottom) structure, cation (blue) CN = 8, anion (green) CN = 4. [A blue cation at one of the face centers is coordinated to the four nearest green anions inside the cell and to four identical anions in an adjacent cell that also contains the cation. Any of the green interior anions is coordinated to a tetrahedron of blue cations located at one corner and the three nearest face centers.]

12.59   *Analyze.* Given three magnesium compounds in which the coordination number (CN) of Mg^{2+} is six, determine the coordination number of the anion. *Plan.* Use Equation 12.1 with the cation/anion ratio of each compound and the Mg^{2+} coordination number to calculate the anion coordination number in each compound. *Solve.*

(a)   MgS: 1 cation, 1 anion, cation CN = 6

$$\frac{\text{\# of cations per formula unit}}{\text{\# of anions per formula unit}} = \frac{\text{anion coordination number}}{\text{cation coordination number}}$$

$$\text{anion CN} = \frac{\text{cation CN} \times \text{\# of cations per formula unit}}{\text{\# of anions per formula unit}} = \frac{6 \times 1}{1} = 6$$

(b) MgF_2: 1 cation, 2 anions, cation CN = 6

$$\text{anion CN} = \frac{\text{cation CN} \times \text{\# of cations per formula unit}}{\text{\# of anions per formula unit}} = \frac{6 \times 1}{2} = 3$$

(c)   MgO: 1 cation, 1 anion, cation CN = 6, anion CN = 6. The cation/anion ratio and cation CN are the same as in part (a), so the anion CN is the same (6).

12.60 $$\frac{\text{\# of cations per formula unit}}{\text{\# of anions per formula unit}} = \frac{\text{anion coordination number}}{\text{cation coordination number}}$$

$$\text{cation CN} = \frac{\text{anion CN} \times \text{\# of anions per formula unit}}{\text{\# of cations per formula unit}}$$

(a) AlF_3:   1 cation, 3 anions, anion CN = 2; cation CN = (2 × 3)/1 = 6

(b) Al_2O_3: 2 cations, 3 anions, anion CN = 6; cation CN = (6 × 3)/2 = 9

(c)   AlN: 1 cation, 1 anion, anion CN = 4; cation CN = (4 × 1)/1 = 4

12.61   (a)   False. Although both molecular solids and covalent-network solids have covalent bonds, the melting points of molecular solids are much lower because intermolecular forces among their molecules are much weaker than covalent bonds among atoms in a covalent-network solid.

          (b)   True. The statement is true if there are no significant differences in polarity or molar mass of the molecules being compared.

12.62   (a)   False. Melting point is a bulk property, not a molecular property.

          (b)   True. Strengths of intermolecular forces determine properties of the bulk material like melting point.

Covalent-Network Solids (section 12.7)

12.63   (a)   Ionic solids are much more likely to dissolve in water. Polar water molecules can disrupt ionic bonds to surround and separate ions and form a solution, but they cannot break the covalent bonds of a covalent-network solid.

          (b)   Covalent-network solids can become electricity conducting via chemical substitution. Most semiconductors are covalent-network solids, and doping or chemical substitution changes their electrical properties.

12.64   The extended network of localized covalent bonds in a covalent-network solid produces solids that are inflexible, hard and high-melting. The delocalized nature of metallic bonding leads to flexibility, because atoms can move relative to one another without 'breaking' bonds. Metals have a wide range of hardness and melting point, depending on the occupancy of the bands.

          (a)   Ductility, metallic solid

          (b)   Hardness, covalent-network solid and metallic solid, depending on the strength of metallic bonding

          (c)   High melting point, covalent-network solid and metallic solid, depending on the strength of metallic bonding

12.65   *Analyze/Plan.* Follow the logic in Sample Exercise 12.3. *Solve.*

(a)   CdS. Both semiconductors contain Cd; S and Te are in the same family, and S is higher.

(b)   GaN. Ga is in the same family and higher than In; N is in the same family and higher than P.

(c)   GaAs. Both semiconductors contain As; Ga and In are in the same family and Ga is higher.

12.66   (a)   InP. P is in the same family and higher than As.

(b)   AlP. Al and P are horizontally separated, resulting in greater bond polarity, and Al and P are in the row above Ge. Band gap values in Table 12.4 confirm this order.

(c)   AgI. The four elements are in the same row; Ag and I are farther apart than Cd and Te.

12.67   *Analyze.* Given: GaAs. Find: dopant to make n-type semiconductor.

Plan. An n-type semiconductor has extra negative charges. If the dopant replaces a few Ga atoms, it should have more valence electrons than Ga, Group 3A.

Solve. The obvious choice is a Group 4A element, either Ge or Si. Ge would be closer to Ga in bonding atomic radius (Figure 7.6).

12.68   p-type semiconductors have a slight electron deficit. If the dopant replaces As, Group 5A, it should have fewer than five valence electrons. The dopant will be a 4A element, probably Si or Ge. Si would be closer to As in bonding atomic radius.

12.69   (a)   *Analyze.* Given: 1.1 eV. Find: wavelength in meters that corresponds to the energy 1.1 eV. *Plan.* Use dimensional analysis to find wavelength.

Solve. $1 \text{ eV} = 1.602 \times 10^{-19} \text{ J}$ (inside-back cover of text); $\lambda = hc/E$

$$\lambda = 6.626 \times 10^{-34} \text{ J-s} \times \frac{3.00 \times 10^8 \text{ m}}{\text{s}} \times \frac{1}{1.1 \text{ eV}} \times \frac{1 \text{ eV}}{1.602 \times 10^{-19} \text{ J}} = 1.128 \times 10^{-6}$$

$$= 1.1 \times 10^{-6} \text{ m}$$

(b)   Si can absorb energies ≥ 1.1 eV, or wavelengths $\leq 1.1 \times 10^{-6}$ m. The range of wavelengths in the solar spectrum at sea level is 3×10^{-6} to 2×10^{-7} m, or 30×10^{-7} to 2×10^{-7} m, a span of 28×10^{-7} m. Si can absorb 11×10^{-7} to 2×10^{-7} m, a span of 9×10^{-7} m. This represents $\dfrac{9 \times 10^{-7}}{28 \times 10^{-7}} \times 100 = 32\%$ of the wavelengths in the solar spectrum. According to the diagram, these wavelengths represent much more than 32% of the total flux. Silicon does absorb a significant "portion" of the visible light that comes from the sun, whether that "portion" is defined by wavelength range or flux.

12.70   (a)   From Table 12.4, the band gap of CdTe is 1.50 eV (or 145 kJ/mol).

(b) $\lambda = \dfrac{hc}{E} = \dfrac{6.626 \times 10^{-34} \text{ J-s} \times 2.998 \times 10^8 \text{ m}}{s} \times \dfrac{1}{1.50 \text{ eV}} \times \dfrac{1 \text{ eV}}{1.602 \times 10^{-19} \text{ J}}$

$$= 8.267 \times 10^{-7} = 8.27 \times \times 10^{-7} \text{ m}$$

(c)   CdTe can absorb energies ≥ 1.50 eV or wavelengths $\leq 8.27 \times 10^{-7}$ m. The solar spectrum ranges from 30×10^{-7} m to 2×10^{-7} m, a span of 28.27×10^{-7} m. In this range CdTe can absorb from 8.27×10^{-7} m to 2×10^{-7} m, a span of $6.27 \times 10^{-7} = 6 \times 10^{-7}$ m.

$$\dfrac{6.27 \times 10^{-7}}{28 \times 10^{-7}} \times 100 = 22.38 = 22\% \text{ of the solar spectrum}$$

(more than 22% of the total flux)

(d)   CdTe can absorb 22% of the solar spectrum, while Si (see Solution 12.69) can absorb 32%. Whether comparing % of wavelengths or total flux, Si can absorb a larger portion of the solar spectrum than CdTe.

12.71   *Plan/Solve.* Follow the logic in Solution 12.69.

$\lambda = hc/E = 6.626 \times 10^{-34} \text{ J-s} \times \dfrac{3.00 \times 10^8 \text{ m}}{s} \times \dfrac{1}{2.2 \text{ eV}} \times \dfrac{1 \text{ eV}}{1.602 \times 10^{-19} \text{ J}} = 5.640 \times 10^{-7}$

$$= 5.6 \times 10^{-7} \text{ m} = 560 \text{ nm}$$

12.72   The band gap, ΔE of GaAs is 1.43 eV.

$\lambda = \dfrac{hc}{E} = \dfrac{6.626 \times 10^{-34} \text{ J-s} \times 2.998 \times 10^8 \text{ m}}{s} \times \dfrac{1}{1.43 \text{ eV}} \times \dfrac{1 \text{ eV}}{1.602 \times 10^{-19} \text{ J}} = 8.67 \times 10^{-7} \text{ m (867 nm)}$

The visible portion of the electromagnetic spectrum has wavelengths up to 750 nm (7.50×10^{-7} m). GaAs emits longer, 867 nm, light in the IR portion of the spectrum.

12.73   *Analyze/Plan.* From Table 12.4, E_g for GaAs (x = 0) is 1.43 eV and for GaP (x = 1) is 2.26 eV. If E_g varies linearly with x, the band gap for x = 0.5 should be approximately the average of the two extreme values.

Solve. $(1.43 + 2.26)/2 = 1.845 = 1.85$ eV.

$\lambda = hc/E = \dfrac{6.626 \times 10^{-34} \text{ J-s} \times 3.00 \times 10^8 \text{ m}}{s} \times \dfrac{1}{1.845 \text{ eV}} \times \dfrac{1 \text{ eV}}{1.602 \times 10^{-19} \text{ J}}$

$$= 6.72 \times 10^{-7} \text{ m} = 672 \text{ nm}$$

12.74   Reverse the logic in Solution 12.73. Given λ, calculate E_g. Then solve for x assuming the value of E_g is a linear combination of the stoichiometric contributions of GaP and GaAs. That is, $2.26 \text{ x} + 1.43(1 - \text{x}) = E_g$.

$E_g = \dfrac{hc}{\lambda} = \dfrac{6.626 \times 10^{-34} \text{ J-S}}{6.60 \times 10^{-7} \text{ m}} \times \dfrac{2.998 \times 10^8 \text{ m}}{s} \times \dfrac{1 \text{ eV}}{1.602 \times 10^{-19} \text{ J}} = 1.8788 = 1.88 \text{ eV}$

$2.26 \text{ x} + 1.43(1 - \text{x}) = 1.8788$; $2.26 \text{ x} - 1.43 \text{ x} + 1.43 = 1.8788$

$0.83 \text{ x} = 0.4488$; x = 0.5407 = 0.54

Check. From Solution 12.73, an E_g of 1.85 V corresponds to x = 0.5. E_g =1.88 eV should have a very similar composition, and x = 0.54 is very close to x = 0.5. The P/As composition is very sensitive to wavelength, and provides a useful mechanism to precisely tune the wavelength of the diode.

Polymeric Solids (section 12.8)

12.75 Monomers are small molecules with low molecular mass that are joined together to form polymers. They are the repeating units of a polymer. Three (of the many) monomers mentioned in this chapter are

propylene	styrene	isoprene
(propene)	(phenyl ethene)	(2-methyl-1,3-butadiene)

12.76 *n*-decane does not have a sufficiently high chain length or molecular mass to be considered a polymer.

12.77 *Analyze.* Given two types of reactant molecules, we are asked to write a condensation reaction with an ester product. *Plan.* A condensation reaction occurs when two smaller molecules combine to form a larger molecule and a small molecule, often water. Consider the structures of the two reactants and how they could combine to join the larger fragments and split water. *Solve.*

A carboxylic acid contains the $\overset{O}{\underset{\|}{-C}}-OH$ functional group; an alcohol contains the

–OH functional group. These can be arranged to form the $-\overset{O}{\underset{\|}{C}}-O-C$ ester

functional group and H_2O. Condensation reaction to form an ester:

If a dicarboxylic acid (two –COOH groups, usually at opposite ends of the molecule) and a dialcohol (two –OH groups, usually at opposite ends of the molecule) are combined, there is the potential for propagation of the polymer chain at both ends of both monomers. Polyethylene terephthalate (Table 12.5) is an example of a polyester formed from the monomers ethylene glycol and terephthalic acid.

12.78

$$n \; HO-\underset{\underset{O}{\|}}{C}-CH_2-CH_2-\underset{\underset{O}{\|}}{C}\boxed{-O-H \; + \; H}-\underset{\underset{H}{|}}{N}-CH_2-CH_2-NH_2$$

$$\left[-\underset{\underset{O}{\|}}{C}-CH_2-CH_2-\underset{\underset{O}{\|}}{C}-NH-CH_2-CH_2-NH- \right] + 2n \; H_2O$$

12.79   *Analyze/Plan.* Decide whether the given polymer is an addition or condensation polymer. Select the smallest repeat unit and deconstruct it into the monomer(s) with the specific functional group(s) that would form the stated polymer.   *Solve.*

(a)

vinyl chloride (chloroethylene or chloroethene)

(b)

hexanediamine

adipic acid

(c)

ethylene glycol   terephthalic acid

12.80   (a)   By analogy to polyisoprene, Figure 12.42,

$$n \; CH_2{=}CH-\underset{\underset{Cl}{|}}{C}{=}CH_2 \longrightarrow \left[\underset{\underset{H}{|}}{\overset{\overset{H}{|}}{C}}-\underset{\underset{H}{|}}{\overset{\overset{H}{|}}{C}}{=}\underset{\underset{Cl}{|}}{C}-\underset{\underset{H}{|}}{\overset{\overset{H}{|}}{C}} \right]_n$$

(b) $n \; CH_2{=}\underset{\underset{CN}{|}}{CH} \longrightarrow \left[CH_2-\underset{\underset{CN}{|}}{CH} \right]_n$

12.81   *Plan/Solve.* When nylon polymers are made, H_2O is produced as the C–N bonds are formed. Reversing this process (adding H_2O across the C–N bond), we see that the monomers used to produce Nomex™ are:

HOOC   COOH H_2N NH_2

and

12.82

12.83 Most of a polymer backbone is composed of σ bonds. The geometry around individual atoms is tetrahedral with bond angles of 109°, so the polymer is not flat, and there is relatively free rotation around the σ bonds. The flexibility of the molecular chains causes flexibility of the bulk material. Flexibility is enhanced by molecular features that inhibit order, such as branching, and diminished by features that encourage order, such as cross-linking or delocalized π electron density.

Cross-linking is the formation of chemical bonds between polymer chains. It reduces flexibility of the molecular chains and increases the hardness of the material. Cross-linked polymers are less chemically reactive because of the links.

12.84 At the molecular level, the longer, unbranched chains of HDPE fit closer together and have more crystalline (ordered, aligned) regions than the shorter, branched chains of LDPE. Closer packing leads to higher density.

12.85 No. The function of the material (polymer) determines whether high molecular mass and high degree of crystallinity are desirable properties. If the material will be formed into containers or pipes, the rigidity and structural strength associated with high molecular mass are required. If the polymer will be used as a flexible wrapping or as a garment material, high molecular mass and rigidity are undesirable properties.

12.86 (a) An *elastomer* is a polymer material that recovers its shape when released from a distorting force. A typical elastomeric polymer can be stretched to at least twice its original length and return to its original dimensions upon release.

(b) A *thermoplastic material* can be shaped and reshaped by application of heat and/or pressure.

(c) A *thermosetting* plastic can be shaped once, through chemical reaction in the shape-forming process, but cannot easily be reshaped, due to the presence of chemical bonds that cross-link the polymer chains.

Nanomaterials (section 12.9)

12.87 Continuous energy bands of molecular orbitals require a large number of atoms contributing a large number of atomic orbitals to the molecular orbital scheme. If a solid has dimensions 1–10 nm, nanoscale dimensions, there may not be enough contributing atomic orbitals to produce continuous energy bands of molecular orbitals.

12.88 (a) Calculate the wavelength of light that corresponds to 2.4 eV, then look at a visible spectrum such as Figure 6.4 to find the color that corresponds to this wavelength.

$$\lambda = \frac{hc}{E} = \frac{6.626 \times 10^{-34} \text{ J-s} \times 3.00 \times 10^8 \text{ m}}{s} \times \frac{1}{2.4 \text{ eV}} \times \frac{1 \text{ eV}}{1.602 \times 10^{-19} \text{ J}}$$

$$= 5.167 \times 10^{-7} = 5.2 \times 10^{-7} \text{ m (520 nm)}$$

The emitted 520 nm light is green.

(b)   Yes. The wavelength of blue light is shorter than the wavelength of green light. Emitting a shorter wavelength requires a larger band gap. As particle size decreases, band gap increases. Appropriately sized CdS quantum dots, far smaller than a large CdS crystal, would have a band gap greater than 2.4 eV and could emit shorter wavelength blue light.

(c)   No. The wavelength of red light is greater than the wavelength of green light. The large CdS crystal has plenty of AOs contributing to the MO scheme to ensure maximum delocalization. A bigger crystal will not reduce the size of the band gap. The 2.4 eV band gap of the large CdS crystal represents the minimum energy and maximum wavelength of light that can be emitted by this material.

12.89   (a)   False. As particle size decreases, the band gap increases. The smaller the particle, the fewer AOs that contribute to the MO scheme, the more localized the bonding and the larger the band gap.

(b)   False. The wavelength of emitted light corresponds to the energy of the band gap. As particle size decreases, band gap increases and wavelength decreases $(E = hc/\lambda)$.

12.90   True. Blue light has short wavelengths, corresponding to a relatively large band gap. As particle size decreases, band gap increases and wavelength decreases. We could begin with a semiconductor with a smaller band gap and make it a nanoparticle to increase E_g and decrease wavelength. (Nanoparticle size becomes one more way to tune the properties of semiconductors.)

12.91   *Analyze.* Given: Au, 4 atoms per unit cell, 4.08 Å cell edge, volume of sphere = 4/3 π r³. Find: Au atoms in 20 nm diameter sphere.

Plan. Relate the number of Au atoms in the volume of 1 cubic unit cell to the number of Au atoms in a 20 nm diameter sphere. Change units to Å (you could just as well have chosen nm as the common unit), calculate the volumes of the unit cell and sphere, and use a ratio to calculate atoms in the sphere.

Solve. vol of unit cell = (4.08 Å)³ = 67.9173 = 67.9 Å³

20 nm diameter = 10 nm radius; $10 \text{ nm} \times \frac{1 \times 10^{-9} \text{ m}}{1 \text{ nm}} \times \frac{1 \text{ Å}}{1 \times 10^{-10} \text{ m}} = 100 \text{ Å radius}$

(Note that 1 nm = 10 Å.)

vol. of sphere = 4/3 × 3.14159 × (100 Å)³ = 4.18879 × 10⁶ = 4.19 × 10⁶ Å³

$\frac{4 \text{ Au atoms}}{67.9173 \text{ Å}^3} = \frac{x \text{ Au atoms}}{4.18879 \times 10^6 \text{ Å}^3}; x = 2.46699 \times 10^5 = 2.47 \times 10^5 \text{ Au atoms}$

12.92   There are four CdTe formula units in each cubic unit cell. Calculate the number of unit cells contained in a 5 nm cubic crystal. The volume of one unit cell is

$$(6.49)^3 \text{ Å}^3 \times \frac{1 \text{ nm}^3}{10^3 \text{ Å}^3} = 0.2734 = 0.273 \text{ nm}^3$$

The volume of the 5 nm crystal is $5^3 \text{ nm}^3 = 125 = 1 \times 10^2 \text{ nm}^3$

(The dimension 5 nm limits the volume to one sig fig.)

$$\frac{125 \text{ nm}^3/\text{crystal}}{0.2734 \text{ nm}^3/\text{unit cell}} \times \frac{4 \text{ CdTe units}}{\text{unit cell}} = 1829 = 2 \times 10^3 \text{ CdTe units}$$

That is, 2000 (or 1829) Cd atoms and 2000 (or 1829) Te atoms.

Additional Exercises

12.93   According to Figure 12.6, a tetragonal unit cell has a square base, with the third lattice vector perpendicular to the base but with a different length. In other words, $a = b \neq c$, $\alpha = \beta = \gamma = 90°$. To create a face centered tetragonal unit cell, add a lattice point in the center of each face (both square and rectangular faces). Draw a second face centered tetragonal unit cell above or below the first one.

The square base of a new tetragonal unit cell can be drawn by connecting the face centers of the four rectangular faces. Connecting these four face centers with those of the adjacent (old) tetragonal cell creates the new tetragonal unit cell. The lattice point at the center of the old square face becomes the body center of the new unit cell.

12.94   Qualitatively from Figure 12.12, a face-centered cubic structure has a greater portion of its volume occupied by metal atoms and less "empty" space than a body-centered structure. The face-centered structure will have the greater density.

Quantitatively, use the atomic radius of iron, 1.25 Å from Figure 7.6, to estimate the unit cell edge length in each of the structures, then calculate the estimated density of both structures. Recall that a face centered cubic structure has 4 atoms per unit cell, and a body centered structure has 2.

Face centered cubic: $4\,r_{Fe} = \sqrt{2}\,a;\quad a = 4\,r_{Fe}\,/\sqrt{2} = \dfrac{4 \times 1.25\,\text{Å}}{\sqrt{2}} = 3.5355 = 3.54\,\text{Å}$

$$\rho = \frac{4\,\text{Fe atoms}}{(3.5355 \times 10^{-8}\,\text{cm})^3} \times \frac{55.845\,\text{g Fe}}{6.022 \times 10^{23}\,\text{Fe atoms}} = 8.3934 = 8.39\,\text{g/cm}^3$$

Body centered cubic: $4\,r_{Fe} = \sqrt{3}\,a;\quad a = 4\,r_{Fe}\,/\sqrt{3} = \dfrac{4 \times 1.25\,\text{Å}}{\sqrt{3}} = 2.8868 = 2.89\,\text{Å}$

$$\rho = \frac{2\,\text{Fe atoms}}{(2.8868 \times 10^{-8}\,\text{cm})^3} \times \frac{55.845\,\text{g Ca}}{6.022 \times 10^{23}\,\text{Ca atoms}} = 7.7098 = 7.71\,\text{g/cm}^3$$

The face centered cubic structure has the greater density.

12.95   The metallic properties of malleability, ductility, and high electrical and thermal conductivity are results of the delocalization of valence electrons throughout the lattice. Delocalization occurs because metal atom valence orbitals of nearest-neighbor atoms interact to produce nearly continuous molecular orbital energy bands. When C atoms are introduced into the metal lattice, their valence orbitals do not have the same energies as metal orbitals, and the interaction is different. This causes a discontinuity in the band structure and limits delocalization of electrons. The properties of the carbon-infused metal begin to resemble those of a covalent-network lattice with localized electrons (Solution 23.24). The substance is harder and less conductive than the pure metal.

12.96   Density is the mass of the unit cell contents divided by the unit cell volume [(edge length)^3]. Refer to Figure 12.11(c) to determining the number of Ni atoms and Figure 12.17(a) for the number of Ni_3Al units in each unit cell.

Ni: There are 4 Ni atoms in each face-centered cubic unit cell ($8 \times 1/8$ at the corners, $6 \times 1/2$ on the face-centers).

$$\text{density} = \frac{4\,\text{Ni atoms}}{(3.53\,\text{Å})^3} \times \frac{58.6934\,\text{g Ni}}{6.022 \times 10^{23}\,\text{Ni atoms}} \times \left(\frac{\text{Å}}{1 \times 10^{-8}\,\text{cm}}\right)^3 = 8.86\,\text{g/cm}^3$$

Ni_3Al: There is 1 Ni_3Al unit in each cubic unit cell. According to Figure 12.17(a), Ni is at the face-centers ($6 \times 1/2 = 3$ Ni atoms) and Al is at the corners ($8 \times 1/8 = 1$ Al atom); the stoichiometry is correct.

$$\text{density} = \frac{1\,Ni_3Al\,\text{unit}}{(3.56\,\text{Å})^3} \times \frac{203.062\,\text{g } Ni_3Al}{6.022 \times 10^{23}\,\text{Ni atoms}} \times \left(\frac{\text{Å}}{1 \times 10^{-8}\,\text{cm}}\right)^3 = 7.47\,\text{g/cm}^3$$

The density of the Ni_3Al alloy (intermetallic compound) is ~85% of the density of pure Ni. The sizes of the two unit cells are very similar. In Ni_3Al, one out of every four Ni atoms is replaced with an Al atom. The mass of an Al atom is (~27 amu) is about half that of a Ni atom (~59 amu); the mass of the unit cell contents of Ni₃Al is ~7/8 (87.5%) that of Ni, and the densities show the same relationship.

12.97 Ni_3Al: Ni is at the face-centers ($6 \times 1/2 = 3$ Ni atoms) and Al is at the corners ($8 \times 1/8 = 1$ Al atom). The atom ratio in the structure matches the empirical formula.

Nb_3Sn: The top, front and side faces of the unit cell are clearly visible; each has 2 Nb atoms centered on it, as opposed to totally inside the cell. The three opposite faces are not completely visible in the diagram, but must be the same by translational symmetry. Two Nb atoms centered on each of 6 faces (12 × 1/2 = 6 Nb atoms). One Sn atom completely inside the unit cell and one at each corner (1 + 8 × 1/8 = 2 Sn atoms). The atom ratio is 6 Nb : 2 Sn or 3 Nb : 1 Sn; the atom ratio in the structure matches the empirical formula.

$SmCo_5$: One Sm atom at each corner (8 × 1/8 = 1 Sm atom). One Co atom totally inside the unit cell (1 Co atom), two Co atoms centered on the top and bottom faces (4 × 1/2 = 2 Co atoms), four Co atoms centered on 4 side faces (4 × 1/2 = 2 Co atoms), for a total of (1 + 2 + 2 = 5 Co atoms). The ratio is 1 Sm : 5 Co, which matches the empirical formula.

12.98   (a)   CsCl, primitive cubic lattice (Figure 12.26)

        (b)   Au, face-centered cubic lattice (Figure 12.18)

        (c)   NaCl, face-centered cubic lattice (Figure 12.26)

        (d)   Po, primitive cubic lattice, rare for metals (Section 12.3)

        (e)   ZnS, face-centered cubic lattice (Figure 12.26)

12.99   *Analyze/Plan.* Recall the diamond [Figure 12.30(a)] and close-packed metallic structures (Figure 12.14 and others) described in this chapter. Use these structures to draw conclusions about Sn–Sn distance and electrical conductivity in the two allotropes.
Solve.

White tin, with a characteristic metallic structure, is expected to be more metallic in character. The white allotropic form has the properties of a metal, including high electrical conductivity, because the valence electrons are shared with 12 nearest neighbors rather than being localized in four bonds to nearest neighbors as in gray tin. Gray tin, on the other hand, has the diamond structure characteristic of other Group IV semiconductors.

The Sn–Sn distance should be longer in white tin; there are only four valence electrons from each atom, and 12 nearest neighbors. The **average** tin–tin bond order can, therefore, be only about 1/3, whereas in gray tin the bond order is one. Gray tin, with the higher bond order, has a shorter Sn–Sn distance, 2.81 Å. The bond length in white tin, with the lower bond order, is 3.02 Å.

12.100   Electrical conductivity is related to the extent of valence electron delocalization in the material.

In the hexagonal close-packed structure of titanium, each Ti atom has twelve nearest neighbors. The four valence electrons of a Ti atom are delocalized over bonding interactions with twelve neighbors. In the diamond structure of silicon, each Si atom has four nearest neighbors and four valence electrons. These four valence electrons are essentially localized in four covalent (sigma) bonds to the four nearest neighbors. The much more extensive electron delocalization in Ti leads to its significantly greater electrical conductivity.

12.101   (a)   Zinc sulfide, ZnS (Figure 12.26).

        (b)   Covalent. Silicon and carbon are both nonmetals, and their electronegativities are similar.

(c)   In SiC, the C atoms form a face-centered cubic array with Si atoms occupying alternate tetrahedral holes in the lattice. This means that the coordination numbers of both Si and C are 4; each Si is bound to four C atoms in a tetrahedral arrangement, and each C is bound to four Si atoms in a tetrahedral arrangement, producing an extended three-dimensional network. SiC is high-melting because a great deal of chemical energy is stored in the covalent Si–C bonds. Melting requires breaking covalent Si–C bonds, which takes a huge amount of thermal energy. It is hard because the three-dimensional lattice resists any change that would weaken the Si–C bonding network.

12.102   Semiconductors have a filled valence band and an empty conduction bond, separated by a characteristic difference in energy, the band gap, E_g. When a semiconductor is heated, more electrons have sufficient energy to jump the band gap, and conductivity increases. Metals have a partially-filled continuous energy band. Heating a metal increases the average kinetic energy of the metal atoms, usually through increased vibrations within the lattice. The greater vibrational energy of the atoms leads to imperfections in the lattice and discontinuities in the energy band. Thermal vibrations create barriers to electron delocalization and reduce the conductivity of the metal.

12.103

Teflon™ is formed by addition polymerization.

12.104

Hydrogen bonding occurs between —C(=O)—N(H)— amide groups of adjacent chains.

12.105   X-ray *diffraction* is the phenomenon that enables us to measure inter-atomic distances in crystals. Diffraction is most efficient when the wavelength of light is similar to the size of the object (e.g., the slit) doing the diffracting. Inter-atomic distances are on the order of 1-10 Å, and the wavelengths of X-rays are also in this range. Visible light has wavelengths of 400-700 nm, or 4000-7000 Å, too long to be diffracted efficiently by atoms (electrons) in crystals.

12.106 $n\lambda = 2d \sin\theta$; $n = 1$, $\lambda = 1.54$ Å, $\theta = 14.22°$; calculate d.

$$d = \frac{n\lambda}{2\sin\theta} = \frac{1 \times 1.54\,\text{Å}}{2\sin(14.22)} = 3.1346 = 3.13\,\text{Å}$$

12.107   Germanium is in the same family but below Si on the periodic chart. This means that Ge will probably have bonding characteristics and crystal structure similar to those of Si. Since Ge has a larger bonding atomic radius than Si, we expect a larger unit cell and d-spacing for Ge. In Bragg's law, $n\lambda = 2d\sin\theta$, d and $\sin\theta$ are inversely proportional. That is, the larger the d-spacing, the smaller the value of $\sin\theta$ and θ. In a diffraction experiment, we expect a Ge crystal to diffract X-rays at a smaller θ-angle than a Si crystal, assuming the X-rays have the same wavelength.

12.108   (a)   Both diamond (d = 3.5 g/cm^3) and graphite (d = 2.3 g/cm^3) are covalent-network solids with efficient packing arrangements in the solid state; there is relatively little empty space in their respective crystal lattices. Diamond, with bonded C–C distances of 1.54 Å in all directions, is more dense than graphite, with shorter C–C distances within carbon sheets but longer 3.35 Å separations between sheets (Figure 12.30). Buckminsterfullerene has much more empty space, both inside each C_{60} "ball" and between balls, than either diamond or graphite, so its density will be considerably less than 2.3 g/cm^3.

         (b)   In a face-centered cubic unit cell, there are 4 complete C_{60} units.

$$\frac{4\,C_{60}\ \text{units}}{(14.2\,\text{Å})^3} \times \frac{720.66\,\text{g}}{6.022 \times 10^{23}\,C_{60}\ \text{units}} \times \left(\frac{1\,\text{Å}}{1 \times 10^{-8}\,\text{cm}}\right)^3 = 1.67\,\text{g/cm}^3$$

         (1.67 g/cm^3 is the smallest density of the three allotropes: diamond; graphite; and buckminsterfullerene.)

12.109   (a)   n-Type doping will weaken the bonds in a semiconductor. For example, Si, with four valence electrons per atom, has a valence band (made from bonding MOs) which is completely full, and a conduction band (made from antibonding MOs) which is totally empty. Doping a few atoms with more than four valence electrons places a few electrons in the antibonding conduction band, reduces bond order and weakens the bonds in the semiconductor.

         (b)   p-Type doping will also weaken the bonds in a semiconductor. Again consider silicon. Doping a few atoms with less than four valence electrons places fewer electrons in the bonding conduction band, reduces bond order and weakens the bonds in the semiconductor.

Integrative Exercises

12.110   The karat scale is based on mass%, not mol%. In each case, change mol% to mass % Au. Then, karat = mass fraction Au × 24. Determine color using mass% and Figure 12.18.

         (a)   Assume 0.50 mol Ag and 0.50 mol Au.

$$0.50\ \text{mol Ag} \times \frac{107.87\,\text{g Ag}}{\text{mol Ag}} = 53.935 = 54\,\text{g Ag}$$

$$0.50 \, \text{mol Au} \times \frac{196.97 \, \text{g Au}}{\text{mol Au}} = 98.485 = 98 \, \text{g Au}$$

$$\text{mass\% Au} = \frac{98.485 \, \text{g Au}}{(98.485 + 53.935) \, \text{g total}} \times 100 = 64.61 = 65 \, \% \, \text{Au}$$

karat = 0.6461 × 24 = 15.5064 = 16 karat Au

On Figure 12.18, the Au/Ag alloy line is labeled in terms of mass% Ag. For an alloy that is 65% Au and 35% Ag, the color is greenish yellow.

(b)   Assume 0.50 mol Cu and 0.50 mol Au.

$$0.50 \, \text{mol Cu} \times \frac{63.546 \, \text{g Cu}}{\text{mol Cu}} = 31.773 = 32 \, \text{g Cu}$$

$$0.50 \, \text{mol Au} = 98.485 = 98 \, \text{g Au}$$

$$\text{mass\% Au} = \frac{98.485 \, \text{g Au}}{(98.485 + 31.773) \, \text{g total}} \times 100 = 75.61 = 76 \, \% \, \text{Au}$$

karat = 0.7561 × 24 = 18.15 = 18 karat Au

On Figure 12.18, for an alloy that is 76% Au and 24% Cu, the color is reddish gold.

12.111   *Analyze.* Given: mass % of Al, Mg, O; density, unit cell edge length. Find: number of each type of atom. *Plan.* We are not given the type of cubic unit cell, primitive, body centered, face-centered. So we must calculate the number of formula units in the unit cell, using density, cell volume, and formula weight. Begin by determining the empirical formula and formula weight from mass % data. *Solve.* Assume 100 g spinel.

$$37.9 \, \text{g Al} \times \frac{1 \, \text{mol Al}}{26.98 \, \text{g Al}} = 1.405 \, \text{mol Al}; \, 1.405/0.7036 \approx 2$$

$$17.1 \, \text{g Mg} \times \frac{1 \, \text{mol Mg}}{24.305 \, \text{g Mg}} = 0.7036 \, \text{mol Mg}; \, 0.7036/0.7036 = 1$$

$$45.0 \, \text{g O} \times \frac{1 \, \text{mol O}}{16.00 \, \text{g Al}} = 2.813 \, \text{mol O}; \, 2.813/0.7036 \approx 4$$

The empirical formula is Al_2MgO_4; formula weight = 142.3 g/mol

Calculate the number of formula units per unit cell.

8.09 Å = 8.09 × 10⁻¹⁰ m = 8.09 × 10⁻⁸ cm; V = (8.09 × 10⁻⁸)³ cm³

$$\frac{3.57 \, \text{g}}{\text{cm}^3} \times (8.09 \times 10^{-8})^3 \, \text{cm}^3 \times \frac{1 \, \text{mol}}{142.3 \, \text{g}} \times \frac{6.022 \times 10^{23} \, \text{units}}{\text{mol}} = 7.999 = 8$$

There are 8 formula units per unit cell, for a total of 16 Al atoms, 8 Mg atoms, and 32 O atoms.

[The relationship between density (d), unit cell volume (V), number of formula units (Z), formula weight (FW), and Avogadro's number (N) is a useful one. It can be rearranged to calculate any single variable, knowing values for the others. For densities in g/cm³ and unit cell volumes in cm³ the relationship is Z = (N × d × V)/FW.]

12.112   Refer to Section 12.7 and Figure 12.30.

      (a)   In diamond, each C atom is bound to 4 other C atoms. According to VSEPR, the geometry around a central atom with 4 bonding electron pairs is tetrahedral and the C–C–C bond angles are $109°$.

      (b)   In graphite, each C atom is bound to 3 other C atoms in a trigonal planar arrangement. The C–C–C bond angles are $120°$.

12.113   (a)

HDPE

$$\Delta H = D(C=C) - 2D(C-C) = 614 - 2(348) = -82 \text{ kJ/mol } C_2H_4$$

      (b) $(n+1) \text{ HOOC}-(CH_2)_6-\text{COOH} + (n+1) \text{ H}_2N-(CH_2)_6-\text{NH}_2 \longrightarrow$

Nylon 6,6

$$\Delta H = 2D(C-O) + 2D(N-H) - 2D(C-N) - 2D(H-O)$$

$$\Delta H = 2(358) + 2(391) - 2(293) - 2(463) = -14 \text{ kJ/mol}$$

(This is –14 kJ/mol of either reactant.)

      (c) $(n+1) \text{ HOOC}-\bigcirc-\text{COOH} + (n+1) \text{ HO}-CH_2-CH_2-OH \longrightarrow$

PET

$$\Delta H = 2D(C-O) + 2D(O-H) - 2D(C-O) - 2D(O-H) = 0 \text{ kJ}$$

12.114   (a) sp^3 hybrid orbitals at C, $109°$ bond angles around C

      (b)

isotactic

syndiotactic

atactic

Isotactic polypropylene has the highest degree of crystallinity and highest melting point. The regular shape of the polymer backbone allows for close, orderly (almost zipper-like) contact between chains. This maximizes dispersion forces between chains and produces higher order (crystallinity) and melting point. Atactic polypropylene has the least order and the lowest melting point.

(c)   Cotton, with —C— groups and polyester, with —C—O—C groups
                            | ‖
                            OH   O

Both participate in hydrogen bonding interactions with H_2O molecules. These are strong intermolecular forces that hold the "moisture" at the surface of the fabric next to the skin. Polypropylene has no strong interactions with water, and capillary action "wicks" the moisture away from the skin.

12.115   (a)

C—Cl	328 kJ/mol	← lowest
C—C	348 kJ/mol	
C—H	413 kJ/mol	

(b)   C–Cl bonds are weakest, so they are most likely to break upon heating.

(c)   The repeating unit in polyvinyl chloride consists of two C atoms, each in a different environment. Consider the net changes in these two C atoms when the polymer is converted to diamond a high pressure.

Diamond is a covalent-network structure where each C atom is tetrahedrally bound to four other C atoms [Figure 12.30(a)].

Assume that there is no net change to the C–C bonds in the structure, even though they may be broken and reformed. The net change to the 2-C vinyl chloride unit is then breaking three C–H bonds and one C–Cl bond, and making four C–C bonds.

$\Delta H = 3D(C\text{–}H) - D(C\text{–}Cl) - 4D(C\text{–}C) = 3(413) + 328 - 4(348)$

$= 523 \text{ kJ/vinyl choride unit}$

12.116   (a)   Follow the logic outlined in Solution 12.91.

vol. of unit cell $= (5.43 \text{ Å})^3 = 160.1030 = 1.60 \times 10^2 \text{ Å}^3$

$1 \text{ cm}^3 \times \dfrac{(1)^3 \text{ Å}^3}{(1 \times 10^{-8})^3 \text{ cm}^3} = 1 \times 10^{24} \text{ Å}^3 \text{ (volume of material)}$

$\dfrac{4 \text{ Si atoms}}{160.103 \text{ Å}^3} = \dfrac{x \text{ Si atoms}}{1 \times 10^{24} \text{ Å}^3}; x = 2.4984 \times 10^{22} = 2.50 \times 10^{22} \text{ Si atoms}$

(To 1 sig fig, the result is 2×10^{22} Si atoms.)

(b)   1 ppm phosphorus = 1 P atom per 1×10^6 Si atoms

$\dfrac{1 \text{ P atom}}{1 \times 10^6 \text{ Si atoms}} = \dfrac{x \text{ P atoms}}{2.4984 \times 10^{22} \text{ Si Atoms}}; x = 2.4984 \times 10^{22}$

$= 2.50 \times 10^{16} \text{ P atoms}$

$2.4984 \times 10^{16} \text{ P atom} \times \dfrac{1 \text{ mol}}{6.022 \times 10^{23} \text{ atoms}} \times \dfrac{30.97376 \text{ g P}}{\text{mol}} \times \dfrac{1 \text{ mg}}{1 \times 10^{-3} \text{ g}}$

$= 1.29 \times 10^{-3} \text{ mg P } (1.29 \, \mu \text{ g})$

12.117   Avogadro's number is the number of KCl formula units in 74.55 g of KCl.

$74.55 \text{ g KCl} \times \dfrac{1 \text{ cm}^3}{1.984 \text{ g}} \times \dfrac{(1 \times 10^8 \text{ Å})^3}{1 \text{ cm}^3} \times \dfrac{4 \text{ KCl units}}{6.28^3 \text{ Å}^3} = 6.07 \times 10^{23} \text{ KCl formula units}$

12.118   The bonding atomic radius of a Si atom is 1.11 Å (Figure 7.6), so the diameter is 2.22 Å.

$65 \text{ nm} \times \dfrac{1 \times 10^{-9} \text{ m}}{1 \text{ nm}} \times \dfrac{1 \text{ Å}}{1 \times 10^{-10} \text{ m}} \times \dfrac{1 \text{ Si atom}}{2.22 \text{ Å}} = 2.9 \times 10^2 \text{ Si atoms.}$

13 Properties of Solutions

Visualizing Concepts

13.1 <u>(a) < (b) < (c).</u> In Section 13.1, *entropy* is qualitatively defined as randomness or dispersal in space. In container (a) the two kinds of particles are not mixed and the particles are close together, so (a) has the least entropy. In container (b), the particles occupy approximately the same volume as container (a) but the two kinds of particles are homogeneously mixed, so the degree of dispersal and randomness is greater than in (a). In container (c) the two kinds of particles are homogeneously mixed and they occupy a larger volume than in (b), so (c) has the greatest entropy.

13.2 The energy of ion-solvent interaction is greater for Li^+ than Na^+. The smaller size of the Li^+ ion means that ion-dipole interactions with polar water molecules are stronger.

13.3 Lattice energy is the main component of ΔH_{solute}, the enthalpy required to separate solute particles. The greater the lattice energy of the ionic solid, the more endothermic the contribution from $\Delta H_{solute} + \Delta H_{solvent}$ and the more endothermic the overall dissolving process. If ΔH_{soln} is prohibitively endothermic, the substance is not very soluble. The greater the lattice energy of an ionic solid, the less soluble it is in water.

13.4 The blue solid is hydrated $CuSO_4, CuSO_4 \bullet 5H_2O$. The waters of hydration are either associated with Cu^{2+}, SO_4^{2-}, or sit in specific sites in the crystal lattice. When heated in an oven, the water molecules incorporated into the crystal lattice gradually gain kinetic energy and vaporize. The white solid is anhydrous $CuSO_4$, absent the waters of hydration and with a different solid-state structure than the blue hydrate.

13.5 Diagram (b) is the best representation of a saturated solution. There is some undissolved solid with particles that are close together and ordered, in contact with a solution containing mobile, separated solute particles. As much solute has dissolved as can dissolve, leaving some undissolved solid in contact with the saturated solution.

13.6 Solubility increases in the order Ar, 1.50×10^{-3} M < Kr, 2.79×10^{-3} M < Xe, 5×10^{-3} M, the order of increasing polarizability. As the molar mass of the ideal gas increases, atomic size increases and the electron cloud is less tightly held by the nucleus, causing the cloud to be more polarizable. The greater the polarizability, the stronger the dispersion forces between the gas atoms and water, the more likely the gas atom is to stay dissolved rather than escape the solution, the greater the solubility of the gas.

13.7 Vitamin B_6 is likely to be largely water soluble. The three –OH groups and the —Ṅ— can enter into many hydrogen bonding interactions with water. The relatively small molecular size indicates that dispersion forces will not play a large role in intermolecular interactions and the hydrogen bonding will dominate. Vitamin E is likely to be largely fat soluble. The long, rod-like hydrocarbon chain will lead to stronger dispersion forces among vitamin E and the mostly nonpolar fats. Although vitamin E has one –OH and one —Ö— group, the long hydrocarbon chain prevents water from surrounding and separating the vitamin E molecules, reducing its water-solubility.

13.8   According to Figure 13.19, the solubility of CO at 25°C and 1 atm pressure is approximately 0.96 mM. By Henry's Law, $S_g = k P_g$. At the same temperature and pressure, k will be the same, so $S_1/P_1 = S_2/P_2$.

$$\frac{0.96\, mM}{1\, atm} = \frac{2.5\, mM}{x\, atm}; x = \frac{2.5\, mM \times 1\, atm}{0.96\, atm} = 2.6\, atm$$

13.9   (a)   Yes, the *molarity* changes with a change in temperature. Molarity is defined as moles solute per unit volume of solution. If solution volume is different, molarity is different.

          (b)   No, *molality* does not change with change in temperature. Molality is defined as moles solute per kilogram of solvent. Even though the volume of solution has changed due to increased kinetic energy, the mass of solute and solvent have not changed, and the molality stays the same.

13.10   (a)   The blue line represents the solution. According to Raoult's law, the presence of a nonvolatile solute lowers the vapor pressure of a volatile solvent. At any given temperature, the blue line has a lower vapor pressure and represents the solution.

          (b)   The boiling point of a liquid is the temperature at which the vapor pressure of the liquid is equal to atmospheric pressure. Assuming atmospheric pressure of 1.0 atm, the boiling point of the solvent (red line) is approximately 64°C. The boiling point of the solution is approximately 70°C.

13.11   Ideally, 0.50 L. If the volume outside the balloon is very large compared to 0.25 L, solvent will flow across the semipermeable membrane until the molarities of the inner and outer solutions are equal, 0.1 M. This requires an "inner" solution volume twice as large as the initial volume, or 0.50 L. (In reality, osmosis across the balloon membrane is not perfect. The solution concentration inside the balloon will be slightly greater than 0.1 M and the volume of the balloon will be slightly less than 0.50 L.)

13.12   A detergent for solubilizing large hydrophobic proteins (or any other large nonpolar solute, such as greasy dirt) needs a hydrophobic part to interact with the solute, and a hydrophilic part to interact with water. In n-octyl glycoside, the eight-carbon n-octyl chain has strong dispersion interactions with the hydrophobic (nonpolar) protein. The –OH groups on the glycoside (sugar) ring form strong hydrogen bonds with water. This causes the glycoside to dissolve, dragging the hydrophobic protein along with it.

The Solution Process (section 13.1)

13.13   If the magnitude of the enthalpy released due to solute-solvent attractive forces ($-\Delta H_{mix}$) is at least as large as the magnitude of the enthalpy required to separate the solute particles ($+\Delta H_{solute}$), the overall enthalpy of solution (ΔH_{soln}) will be either slightly endothermic (owing to $+\Delta H_{solvent}$) or exothermic. Even if ΔH_{soln} is slightly endothermic, the increase in disorder due to mixing will cause a significant amount of solute to dissolve. If the magnitude of ΔH_{mix} is small relative to the magnitude of ΔH_{solute}, ΔH_{soln} will be large and endothermic (energetically unfavorable) and not much solute will dissolve.

13.14   (a)   For the same solute, NaCl, in different solvents, solute-solute interactions (ΔH_{solute}) are the same. Because water experiences hydrogen bonding while benzene has only dispersion forces, solvent-solvent interactions ($\Delta H_{solvent}$) are greater for water. On the other hand, solute-solvent interactions (ΔH_{mix}) are much weaker between ionic NaCl and nonpolar benzene than between ionic NaCl and polar water. It is the large difference in ΔH_{mix} that causes NaCl to be soluble in water but not in benzene.

     (b)   Ion-dipole forces between cations and water molecules and relatively small lattice energies (ion-ion forces between cations and anions) lead to strongly hydrated cations.

13.15   *Analyze/Plan.* Decide whether the solute and solvent in question are ionic, polar covalent, or nonpolar covalent. Draw Lewis structures as needed. Then state the appropriate type of solute-solvent interaction. *Solve.*

     (a) CCl_4, nonpolar; benzene, nonpolar; dispersion forces

     (b)   methanol, polar with hydrogen bonding; water, polar with hydrogen bonding; hydrogen bonding

     (c)   KBr, ionic; water, polar; ion-dipole forces

     (d)   HCl, polar; CH_3CN, polar; dipole-dipole forces

13.16   From weakest to strongest solvent-solute interactions:

     (b), dispersion forces < (c), hydrogen bonding < (a), ion-dipole

13.17   Very soluble. In order for ΔH_{soln} to be negative (exothermic), ΔH_{mix} must have a greater magnitude than ($\Delta H_{solute} + \Delta H_{solvent}$). The collective attractive interactions formed upon mixing must be greater than the interactions being disrupted in the pure solvent and solute. The entropy of mixing always encourages solubility. In this case, the enthalpy of the system decreases and the entropy increases, so the ionic compound dissolves.

13.18   (a)   This solution process is endothermic. The enthalpy of the solution is greater than the enthalpy of unmixed solute plus solvent.

     (b)   The solution forms because the favorable entropy of mixing outweighs the increase in enthalpy by the solution.

13.19   (a)   Lattice energy is the amount of energy required to completely separate a mole of solid ionic compound into its gaseous ions (Section 8.2). For ionic solutes, this corresponds to ΔH_{solute} (solute-solute interactions) in Equation [13.1].

     (b)   In Equation [13.1], ΔH_{mix} is always exothermic. Formation of attractive interactions, no matter how weak, always lowers the energy of the system, relative to the energy of the isolated particles.

13.20 ΔH_{mix} is much more negative (exothermic) than $\Delta H_{solvent}$ or ΔH_{solute}. Both $\Delta H_{solvent}$ and ΔH_{solute} will be endothermic, because separating solvent molecules or solute ions requires energy. The magnitude of ΔH_{solute} will be larger, because ionic bonds among Li^+ and Cl^- are much stronger than hydrogen bonds among water molecules. Since ΔH_{soln} is exothermic, ΔH_{mix} must be exothermic, and not just more negative than the other two, but more negative than the sum of the other two. This is not surprising, since ΔH_{mix} involves formation of many ion-dipole interactions, strong interparticle forces.

13.21   (a) ΔH_{soln} is determined by the relative magnitudes of the "old" solute-solute (ΔH_{solute}) and solvent-solvent ($\Delta H_{solvent}$) interactions and the new solute-solvent interactions (ΔH_{mix}); $\Delta H_{soln} = \Delta H_{solute} + \Delta H_{solvent} + \Delta H_{mix}$. Since the solute and solvent in this case experience very similar London dispersion forces, the energy required to separate them individually and the energy released when they are mixed are approximately equal. $\Delta H_{solute} + \Delta H_{solvent} \approx -\Delta H_{mix}$. Thus, ΔH_{soln} is nearly zero.

       (b)   Mixing hexane and heptane produces a homogeneous solution from two pure substances, and the randomness of the system increases. Since no strong intermolecular forces prevent the molecules from mixing, they do so spontaneously due to the increase in disorder.

13.22   KBr is quite soluble in water because of the sizeable increase in disorder of the system (ordered KBr lattice → freely moving hydrated ions) associated with the dissolving process. An increase in disorder or randomness in a process tends to make that process spontaneous.

Saturated Solutions; Factors Affecting Solubility (sections 13.1 and 13.2)

13.23   (a)   Supersaturated

       (b)   Add a seed crystal. Supersaturated solutions exist because not enough solute molecules are properly aligned for crystallization to occur. A seed crystal provides a nucleus of already aligned molecules, so that ordering of the dissolved particles is more facile.

13.24   (a) $\dfrac{1.22\ mol\ MnSO_4 \bullet H_2O}{1\ L\ soln} \times \dfrac{169.0\ g\ MnSO_4 \bullet H_2O}{1\ mol} \times 0.100\ L$

$$= 20.6\ g\ MnSO_4 \bullet H_2O/100\ mL$$

The 1.22 *M* solution is unsaturated.

       (b)   Add a known mass, say 5.0 g, of $MnSO_4 \bullet H_2O$, to the unknown solution. If the solid dissolves, the solution is unsaturated. If there is undissolved $MnSO_4 \bullet H_2O$, filter the solution and weigh the solid. If there is less than 5.0 g of solid, some of the added $MnSO_4 \bullet H_2O$, dissolved and the unknown solution is unsaturated. If there is exactly 5.0 g, no additional solid dissolved and the unknown is saturated. If there is more than 5.0 g, excess solute has precipitated and the solution is supersaturated.

13.25 *Analyze/Plan.* On Figure 13.18, find the solubility curve for the appropriate solute. Find the intersection of 40°C and 40 g solute on the graph. If this point is below the solubility curve, more solute can dissolve and the solution is unsaturated. If the intersection is on or above the curve, the solution is saturated. *Solve.*

    (a)   unsaturated   (b)   saturated   (c)   saturated   (d)   unsaturated

13.26   (a)   at 30°C, $\dfrac{10\,g\;KClO_3}{100\,g\;H_2O} \times 250\,g\;H_2O = 25\,g\;KClO_3$

        (b) $\dfrac{66\,g\;Pb(NO_3)_2}{100\,g\;H_2O} \times 250\,g\;H_2O = 165 = 1.7 \times 10^2\;g\;Pb(NO_3)_2$

        (c) $\dfrac{3\,g\;Ce_2(SO_4)_3}{100\,g\;H_2O} \times 250\,g\;H_2O = 7.5 = 8\,g\;Ce_2(SO_4)_3$

13.27 The liquids water and glycerol form homogenous mixtures (solutions), regardless of the relative amounts of the two components. Glycerol has an –OH group on each C atom in the molecule. This structure facilitates strong hydrogen bonding similar to that in water. Like dissolves like and the two liquids are miscible in all proportions.

13.28 Immiscible means that oil and water do not mix homogeneously; they do not dissolve. Many substances are called "oil," but they are typically nonpolar carbon-based molecules with fairly high molecular weights. As such, there are fairly strong dispersion forces among oil molecules. The properties of water are dominated by its strong hydrogen bonding. The dispersion-dipole interactions between water and oil are likely to be weak. Thus, ΔH_{solute} and $\Delta H_{solvent}$ are large and positive, while ΔH_{mix} is small and negative. The net ΔH_{soln} is large and positive, and mixing does not occur.

13.29 *Analyze/Plan.* Evaluate molecules in the four common laboratory solvents for strength of intermolecular interactions with nonpolar solutes. *Solve.* Toluene, $C_6H_5CH_3$, is the best solvent for nonpolar solutes. Without polar groups or nonbonding electron pairs, it forms only dispersion interactions with itself and other molecules. The enthalpy of solution, ΔH_{soln}, is essentially zero (as in Solution 13.21) and solution occurs because of the favorable entropy of mixing.

13.30 We expect alanine to be more soluble in water than hexane. Alanine has a –COOH and a –NH$_2$ group available to form hydrogen bonds with water molecules. While there are some potential dispersion forces between the terminal –CH$_3$ group of alanine and hexane molecules, we expect the hydrogen bonding between alanine and water to be stronger. Stronger intermolecular attractive forces between alanine and water lead to a more negative ΔH_{mix} and more negative (smaller positive) ΔH_{soln} for water than for hexane.

13.31   (a)   Dispersion interactions among nonpolar $CH_3(CH_2)_{16}$ –chains dominate the properties of stearic acid. It is more soluble in nonpolar CCl_4 than polar (hydrogen bonding) water, despite the presence of the –COOH group.

(b)

cyclohexane   dioxane

Dioxane can act as a hydrogen bond acceptor, so it will be more soluble than cyclohexane in water.

13.32 Ibuprofen has a phenyl ring and several –CH₃ groups that form a large nonpolar area covering most of the molecule. This area of the molecule has strong dispersion interactions with like molecules, and does not form strong interactions with polar water. The one isolated carboxyl group of ibuprofen enhances its water solubility.

13.33 *Analyze/Plan.* Hexane is a nonpolar hydrocarbon that experiences dispersion forces with other nonpolar molecules. Solutes that primarily experience dispersion forces will be more soluble in hexane. *Solve.*

(a) CCl_4 is more soluble because dispersion forces among nonpolar CCl_4 molecules are similar to dispersion forces in hexane. Ionic bonds in $CaCl_2$ are unlikely to be broken by weak solute-solvent interactions. For $CaCl_2$, ΔH_{solute} is large, relative to ΔH_{mix}.

(b) Benzene, C_6H_6, is also a nonpolar hydrocarbon and will be more soluble in hexane. Glycerol experiences hydrogen bonding with itself; these solute-solute interactions are less likely to be overcome by weak solute-solvent interactions.

(c) Octanoic acid, $CH_3(CH_2)_6COOH$, will be more soluble than acetic acid CH_3COOH. Both solutes experience hydrogen bonding by –COOH groups, but octanoic acid has a long, rod-like hydrocarbon chain with dispersion forces similar to those in hexane, facilitating solubility in hexane.

13.34 *Analyze/Plan.* Water, H_2O, is a polar solvent that forms hydrogen bonds with other H_2O molecules. The more soluble solute in each case will have intermolecular interactions that are most similar to the hydrogen bonding in H_2O. *Solve.*

(a) Glucose, $C_6H_{12}O_6$, is more soluble because it is capable of hydrogen bonding (Figure 13.12). Nonpolar C_6H_{12} is capable only of dispersion interactions and does not have strong intermolecular interactions with polar (hydrogen bonding) H_2O.

(b) Ionic sodium propionate, CH_3CH_2COONa, is more soluble. Sodium propionate is a crystalline solid, while propionic acid is a liquid. The increase in disorder or entropy when an ionic solid dissolves leads to significant water solubility, despite the strong ion-ion forces (large ΔH_{solute}) present in the solute (see Solution 13.22).

(c) HCl is more soluble because it is a strong electrolyte and completely ionized in water. Ionization leads to ion-dipole solute-solvent interactions, and an increase in disorder. CH_3CH_2Cl is a molecular solute capable of relatively weak dipole-dipole solute-solvent interactions and is much less soluble in water.

13.35   (a)   Carbonated beverages are stored with a partial pressure of $CO_2(g)$ greater than 1 atm above the liquid. A sealed container is required to maintain this CO_2 pressure.

        (b)   Since the solubility of gases increases with decreasing temperature, more $CO_2(g)$ will remain dissolved in the beverage if it is kept cool.

13.36   Pressure has an effect on O_2 solubility in water because, at constant temperature and volume, pressure is directly related to the amount of O_2 available to dissolve. The greater the partial pressure of O_2 above water, the more O_2 molecules are available for dissolution, and the more molecules that strike the surface of the liquid.

Pressure does not affect the amount or physical properties of NaCl, or ionic solids in general, so it has little influence on the dissolving of NaCl in water.

13.37   *Analyze/Plan.* Follow the logic in Sample Exercise 13.3. *Solve.*

$$S_{He} = 3.7 \times 10^{-4} \, M/atm \times 1.5 \, atm = 5.6 \times 10^{-4} \, M$$

$$S_{N_2} = 6.0 \times 10^{-4} \, M/atm \times 1.5 \, atm = 9.0 \times 10^{-4} \, M$$

13.38 $650 \text{ torr} \times \dfrac{1\,atm}{760 \text{ torr}} = 0.855 \, atm; P_{O_2} = \chi_{O_2}(P_t) = 0.21(0.855 \, atm) = 0.1796 = 0.18 \, atm$

$$S_{O_2} = kP_{O_2} = \dfrac{1.38 \times 10^{-3} \, mol}{L\text{-}atm} \times 0.1796 \, atm = 2.5 \times 10^{-4} \, M$$

Concentrations of Solutions (section 13.4)

13.39   *Analyze/Plan.* Follow the logic in Sample Exercise 13.3.   *Solve.*

        (a) $\text{mass \%} = \dfrac{\text{mass solute}}{\text{total mass solution}} \times 100 = \dfrac{10.6 \, g \, Na_2SO_4}{10.6 \, g \, Na_2SO_4 + 483 \, g \, H_2O} \times 100 = 2.15\%$

        (b) $\text{ppm} = \dfrac{\text{mass solute}}{\text{total mass solution}} \times 10^6; \dfrac{2.86 \, g \, Ag}{1 \, ton \, ore} \times \dfrac{1 \, ton}{2000 \, lb} \times \dfrac{1 \, lb}{453.6 \, g} \times 10^6 = 3.15 \, ppm$

13.40   (a) $\text{mass \%} = \dfrac{\text{mass solute}}{\text{total mass solution}} \times 100$

$$\text{mass solute} = 0.035 \, mol \, I_2 \times \dfrac{253.8 \, g \, I_2}{1 \, mol \, I_2} = 8.883 = 8.9 \, g \, I_2$$

$$\text{mass \%} \, I_2 = \dfrac{8.883 \, g \, I_2}{8.883 \, g \, I_2 + 125 \, g \, CCl_4} \times 100 = 6.635 = 6.6\% \, I_2$$

        (b) $\text{ppm} = \dfrac{\text{mass solute}}{\text{total mass solution}} \times 10^6 = \dfrac{0.0079 \, g \, Sr^{2+}}{1 \times 10^3 \, g \, H_2O} \times 10^6 = 7.9 \, ppm \, Sr^{2+}$

13.41   *Analyze/Plan.* Given masses of CH_3OH and H_2O, calculate moles of each component.

        (a)   Mole fraction CH_3OH = (mol CH_3OH)/(total mol)

        (b)   mass % CH_3OH = [(g CH_3OH)/(total mass)] × 100

        (c)   molality CH_3OH = (mol CH_3OH)/(kg H_2O). *Solve.*

(a) $14.6\,g\,CH_3OH \times \dfrac{1\,mol\,CH_3OH}{32.04\,g\,CH_3OH} = 0.4557 = 0.456\,mol\,CH_3OH$

$184\,g\,H_2O \times \dfrac{1\,mol\,H_2O}{18.02\,g\,H_2O} = 10.211 = 10.2\,mol\,H_2O$

$\chi_{CH_3OH} = \dfrac{0.4557}{0.4557 + 10.211} = 0.04272 = 0.0427$

(b) $mass\,\%\,CH_3OH = \dfrac{14.6\,g\,CH_3OH}{14.6\,g\,CH_3OH + 184\,g\,H_2O} \times 100 = 7.35\%\,CH_3OH$

(c) $m = \dfrac{0.4557\,mol\,CH_3OH}{0.184\,kg\,H_2O} = 2.477 = 2.48\,m\,CH_3OH$

13.42   (a) $\dfrac{20.8\,g\,C_6H_5OH}{94.11\,g/mol} = 0.2210 = 0.221\,mol\,C_6H_5OH$

$\dfrac{425\,g\,CH_3CH_2OH}{46.07\,g/mol} = 9.2251 = 9.23\,mol\,CH_3CH_2OH$

$\chi_{C_6H_5OH} = \dfrac{0.2210}{0.2210 + 9.2251} = 0.02340 = 0.0234$

(b) $mass\,\% = \dfrac{20.8\,g\,C_6H_5OH}{20.8\,g\,C_6H_5OH + 425\,g\,CH_3CH_2OH} \times 100 = 4.67\%\,C_6H_5OH$

(c) $m = \dfrac{0.2210\,mol\,C_6H_5OH}{0.425\,kg\,CH_3CH_2OH} = 0.5200 = 0.520\,m\,C_6H_5OH$

13.43   *Analyze/Plan.* Given mass solute and volume solution, calculate mol solute, then molarity = mol solute/L solution. Or, for dilution, $M_c \times L_c = M_d \times L_d$. *Solve.*

(a) $M = \dfrac{mol\,solute}{L\,soln}; \dfrac{0.540\,g\,Mg(NO_3)_2}{0.2500\,L\,soln} \times \dfrac{1\,mol\,Mg(NO_3)_2}{148.3\,g\,Mg(NO_3)_2} = 1.46 \times 10^{-2}\,M\,Mg(NO_3)_2$

(b) $\dfrac{22.4\,g\,LiClO_4 \bullet 3H_2O}{0.125\,L\,soln} \times \dfrac{1\,mol\,LiClO_4 \bullet 3H_2O}{160.4\,g\,LiClO_4 \bullet 3H_2O} = 1.12\,M\,LiClO_4 \bullet 3H_2O$

(c) $M_c \times L_c = M_d \times L_d; 3.50\,M\,HNO_3 \times 0.0250\,L = ?M\,HNO_3 \times 0.250\,L$
      250 mL of 0.350 M HNO_3

13.44   (a) $M = \dfrac{mol\,solute}{L\,soln}; \dfrac{15.0\,g\,Al_2(SO_4)_3}{0.250\,L\,soln} \times \dfrac{1\,mol\,Al_2(SO_4)_3}{342.2\,g\,Al_2(SO_4)_3} = 0.175\,M\,Al_2(SO_4)_3$

(b) $\dfrac{5.25\,g\,Mn(NO_3)_2 \bullet 2H_2O}{0.175\,L\,soln} \times \dfrac{1\,mol\,Mn(NO_3)_2 \bullet 2H_2O}{215.0\,g\,Mn(NO_3)_2 \bullet 2H_2O} = 0.140\,M\,Mn(NO_3)_2$

(c) $M_c \times L_c = M_d \times L_d; 9.00\,M\,H_2SO_4 \times 0.0350\,L = ?M\,H_2SO_4 \times 0.500\,L$
      500 mL of 0.630 M H_2SO_4

13.45   *Analyze/Plan.* Follow the logic in Sample Exercise 13.4.   *Solve.*

(a) $m = \dfrac{mol\,solute}{kg\,solvent}; \dfrac{8.66\,g\,C_6H_6}{23.6\,g\,CCl_4} \times \dfrac{1\,mol\,C_6H_6}{78.11\,g\,C_6H_6} \times \dfrac{1000\,g\,CCl_4}{1\,kg\,CCl_4} = 4.70\,m\,C_6H_6$

(b)   The density of H_2O = 0.997 g/mL = 0.997 kg/L.

$$\frac{4.80 \text{ g NaCl}}{0.350 \text{ L } H_2O} \times \frac{1 \text{ mol NaCl}}{58.44 \text{ g NaCl}} \times \frac{1 \text{ L } H_2O}{0.997 \text{ kg } H_2O} = 0.235 \, m \text{ NaCl}$$

13.46   (a) $16.0 \text{ mol } H_2O \times \dfrac{18.02 \text{ g } H_2O}{1 \text{ mol } H_2O} = 288.3 \text{ g } H_2O = 0.288 \text{ kg } H_2O$

$$m = \frac{1.12 \text{ mol KCl}}{0.2883 \text{ kg } H_2O} = 3.8846 = 3.88 \text{ m KCl}$$

(b) $m = \dfrac{\text{mol solute}}{\text{kg solute}}; \text{mol } S_8 = m \times \text{kg } C_{10}H_8 = 0.12 \, m \times 0.1000 \text{ kg } C_{10}H_8 = 0.012 \text{ mol}$

$$0.012 \text{ mol } S_8 \times \frac{256.5 \text{ g } S_8}{1 \text{ mol } S_8} = 3.078 = 3.1 \text{ g } S_8$$

13.47   *Analyze/Plan.* Assume 1 L of solution. Density gives the total mass of 1 L of solution. The g H_2SO_4/L are also given in the problem. Mass % = (mass solute/total mass solution) × 100. Calculate mass solvent from mass solution and mass solute. Calculate moles solute and solvent and use the appropriate definitions to calculate mole fraction, molality, and molarity.   *Solve.*

(a) $\dfrac{571.6 \text{ g } H_2SO_4}{1 \text{ L soln}} \times \dfrac{1 \text{ L soln}}{1329 \text{ g soln}} = 0.430098 \text{ g } H_2SO_4/\text{g soln}$

mass percent is thus 0.4301 × 100 = 43.01% H_2SO_4

(b)   In a liter of solution there are 1329 − 571.6 = 757.4 = 757 g H_2O.

$$\frac{571.6 \text{ g } H_2SO_4}{98.09 \text{ g/mol}} = 5.827 \text{ mol } H_2SO_4 \, ; \, \frac{757.4 \text{ g } H_2O}{18.02 \text{ g/mol}} = 42.03 = 42.0 \text{ mol } H_2O$$

$$\chi_{H_2SO_4} = \frac{5.827}{42.03 + 5.827} = 0.122$$

(The result has 3 sig figs because (g H_2O) resulting from subtraction is limited to 3 sig figs.)

(c) $\text{molality} = \dfrac{5.827 \text{ mol } H_2SO_4}{0.7574 \text{ kg } H_2O} = 7.693 = 7.69 \, m \, H_2SO_4$

(d) $\text{molarity} = \dfrac{5.827 \text{ mol } H_2SO_4}{1 \text{ L soln}} = 5.827 \, M \, H_2SO_4$

13.48   (a) $\text{mass \%} = \dfrac{\text{mass } C_6H_8O_6}{\text{total mass solution}} \times 100;$

$$\frac{80.5 \text{ g } C_6H_8O_6}{80.5 \text{ g } C_6H_8O_6 + 210 \text{ g } H_2O} \times 100 = 27.71 = 27.7\% \, C_6H_8O_6$$

(b) $\text{mol } C_6H_8O_6 = \dfrac{80.5 \text{ g } C_6H_8O_6}{176.1 \text{ g/mol}} = 0.4571 = 0.457 \text{ mol } C_6H_8O_6$

$$\text{mol } H_2O = \frac{210 \text{ g } H_2O}{18.02 \text{ g/mol}} = 11.654 = 11.7 \text{ mol } H_2O$$

$$\chi_{C_6H_8O_6} = \frac{0.4571 \text{ mol } C_6H_8O_6}{0.4571 \text{ mol } C_6H_8O_6 + 11.654 \text{ mol } H_2O} = 0.0377$$

(c) $m = \dfrac{0.4571 \text{ mol } C_6H_8O_6}{0.210 \text{ kg } H_2O} = 2.18 \, m \, C_6H_8O_6$

(d) $M = \dfrac{\text{mol } C_6H_8O_6}{\text{L solution}}; 290.5 \text{ g soln} \times \dfrac{1 \text{ mL}}{1.22 \text{ g}} \times \dfrac{1 \text{ L}}{1000 \text{ mL}} = 0.2381 = 0.238 \text{ L}$

$$M = \frac{0.4571 \text{ mol } C_6H_8O_6}{0.2381 \text{ L soln}} = 1.92 \, M \, C_6H_8O_6$$

13.49   *Analyze/Plan.* Given: 98.7 mL of $CH_3CN(l)$, 0.786 g/mL; 22.5 mL CH_3OH, 0.791 g/mL. Use the density and volume of each component to calculate mass and then moles of each component. Use the definitions to calculate mole fraction, molality, and molarity. *Solve.*

(a) $\text{mol } CH_3CN = \dfrac{0.786 \text{ g}}{1 \text{ mL}} \times 98.7 \text{ mL} \times \dfrac{1 \text{ mol } CH_3CN}{41.05 \text{ g } CH_3CN} = 1.8898 = 1.89 \text{ mol}$

$$\text{mol } CH_3OH = \frac{0.791 \text{ g}}{1 \text{ mL}} \times 22.5 \text{ mL} \times \frac{1 \text{ mol } CH_3OH}{32.04 \text{ g } CH_3OH} = 0.5555 = 0.556 \text{ mol}$$

$$\chi_{CH_3OH} = \frac{0.5555 \text{ mol } CH_3OH}{1.8898 \text{ mol } CH_3CN + 0.5555 \text{ mol } CH_3OH} = 0.227$$

(b)   Assuming CH_3OH is the solute and CH_3CN is the solvent,

$$98.7 \text{ mL } CH_3CN \times \frac{0.786 \text{ g}}{1 \text{ mL}} \times \frac{1 \text{ kg}}{1000 \text{ g}} = 0.07758 = 0.0776 \text{ kg } CH_3CN$$

$$m_{CH_3OH} = \frac{0.5555 \text{ mol } CH_3OH}{0.07758 \text{ kg } CH_3CN} = 7.1604 = 7.16 \, m \, CH_3OH$$

(c)   The total volume of the solution is 121.2 mL, assuming volumes are additive.

$$M = \frac{0.5555 \text{ mol } CH_3OH}{0.1212 \text{ L solution}} = 4.58 \, M \, CH_3OH$$

13.50   Given: 8.10 g C_4H_4S, 1.065 g/mL; 250.0 mL C_7H_8, 0.867 g/mL

(a) $\text{mol } C_4H_4S = 8.10 \text{ g } C_4H_4S \times \dfrac{1 \text{ mol } C_4H_4S}{84.15 \text{ g } C_4H_4S} = 0.09626 = 0.0963 \text{ mol } C_4H_4S$

$$\text{mol } C_7H_8 = \frac{0.867 \text{ g}}{1 \text{ mL}} \times 250.0 \text{ mL} \times \frac{1 \text{ mol } C_7H_8}{92.14 \text{ g } C_7H_8} = 2.352 = 2.35 \text{ mol}$$

$$\chi_{C_4H_4S} = \frac{0.09626 \text{ mol } C_4H_4S}{0.09626 \text{ mol } C_4H_4S + 2.352 \text{ mol } C_7H_8} = 0.03932 = 0.0393$$

(b) $m_{C_4H_4S} = \dfrac{\text{mol } C_4H_4S}{\text{kg } C_7H_8}; 250.0 \text{ mL} \times \dfrac{0.867 \text{ g}}{1 \text{ mL}} \times \dfrac{1 \text{ kg}}{1000 \text{ g}} = 0.2168 = 0.217 \text{ kg } C_7H_8$

$$m_{C_4H_4S} = \frac{0.09626 \text{ mol } C_4H_4S}{0.2168 \text{ kg } C_7H_8} = 0.444 \ m \ C_4H_4S$$

(c) $8.10 \text{ g } C_4H_4S \times \dfrac{1 \text{ mL}}{1.065 \text{ g}} = 7.606 = 7.61 \text{ mL } C_4H_4S;$

$V_{soln} = 7.61 \text{ mL } C_4H_4S + 250.0 \text{ mL } C_7H_8 = 257.6 \text{ mL}$

$$M_{C_4H_4S} = \frac{0.09626 \text{ mol } C_4H_4S}{0.2576 \text{ L soln}} = 0.374 \ M \ C_4H_4S$$

13.51   *Analyze/Plan.* Given concentration and volume of solution use definitions of the appropriate concentration units to calculate amount of solute; change amount to moles if needed.   *Solve.*

(a) $\text{mol} = M \times L; \dfrac{0.250 \text{ mol } SrBr_2}{1 \text{ L soln}} \times 0.600 \text{ L} = 0.150 \text{ mol } SrBr_2$

(b)   Assume that for dilute aqueous solutions, the mass of the solvent is the mass of solution. Use proportions to get mol KCl.

$$\frac{0.180 \text{ mol KCl}}{1 \text{ kg } H_2O} = \frac{x \text{ mol KCl}}{0.0864 \text{ kg } H_2O}; x = 1.56 \times 10^{-2} \text{ mol KCl}$$

(c)   Use proportions to get mass of glucose, then change to mol glucose.

$$\frac{6.45 \text{ g } C_6H_{12}O_6}{100 \text{ g soln}} = \frac{x \text{ g } C_6H_{12}O_6}{124.0 \text{ g soln}}; x = 8.00 \text{ g } C_6H_{12}O_6$$

$$8.00 \text{ g } C_6H_{12}O_6 \times \frac{1 \text{ mol } C_6H_{12}O_6}{180.2 \text{ g } C_6H_{12}O_6} = 4.44 \times 10^{-2} \text{ mol } C_6H_{12}O_6$$

13.52   (a) $\dfrac{1.50 \text{ mol } HNO_3}{1 \text{ L soln}} \times 0.255 \text{ L} = 0.3825 = 0.383 \text{ mol } HNO_3$

(b)   Assume that for dilute aqueous solutions, the mass of the solvent is the mass of solution.

$$\frac{1.50 \text{ mol NaCl}}{1 \text{ kg } H_2O} = \frac{x \text{ mol}}{50.0 \times 10^{-6} \text{ kg}}; x = 7.50 \times 10^{-5} \text{ mol NaCl}$$

(c) $\dfrac{1.50 \text{ g } C_{12}H_{22}O_{11}}{100 \text{ g soln}} = \dfrac{x \text{ g } C_{12}H_{22}O_{11}}{75.0 \text{ g soln}}; x = 1.125 = 1.13 \text{ g } C_{12}H_{22}O_{11}$

$$1.125 \text{ g } C_{12}H_{22}O_{11} \times \frac{1 \text{ mol } C_{12}H_{22}O_{11}}{342.3 \text{ g } C_{12}H_{22}O_{11}} = 3.287 \times 10^{-3} = 3.29 \times 10^{-3} \text{ mol } C_{12}H_{22}O_{11}$$

13.53   *Analyze/Plan.* When preparing solution, we must know amount of solute and solvent. Use the appropriate concentration definition to calculate amount of solute. If this amount is in moles, use molar mass to get grams; use mass in grams directly. Amount of solvent can be expressed as total volume or mass of solution. Combine mass solute and solvent to produce the required amount (mass or volume) of solution.   *Solve.*

(a) $\text{mol} = M \times L; \dfrac{1.50 \times 10^{-2} \text{ mol KBr}}{1 \text{ L soln}} \times 0.75 \text{ L} \times \dfrac{119.0 \text{ g KBr}}{1 \text{ mol KBr}} = 1.3 \text{ g KBr}$

Weigh out 1.3 g KBr, dissolve in water, dilute with stirring to 0.75 L (750 mL).

(b)   Mass of solution is required, but density is not specified. Use molality to calculate mass fraction, and then the masses of solute and solvent needed for 125 g of solution.

$$\frac{0.180 \text{ mol KBr}}{1000 \text{ g H}_2\text{O}} \times \frac{119.0 \text{ g KBr}}{1 \text{ mol KBr}} = 21.42 = 21.4 \text{ g KBr/kg H}_2\text{O Thus,}$$

$$\text{mass fraction} = \frac{21.42 \text{ g KBr}}{1000 + 21.42} = 0.02097 = 0.0210$$

In 125 g of the 0.180 *m* solution, there are

$$(125 \text{ g soln}) \times \frac{0.02097 \text{ g KBr}}{1 \text{ g soln}} = 2.621 = 2.62 \text{ g KBr}$$

Weigh out 2.62 g KBr, dissolve it in 125 − 2.62 = 122.38 = 122 g H_2O to make exactly 125 g of 0.180 *m* solution.

(c)   Using solution density, calculate the total mass of 1.85 L of solution, and from the mass % of KBr, the mass of KBr required.

$$1.85 \text{ L soln} \times \frac{1000 \text{ mL}}{1 \text{ L}} \times \frac{1.10 \text{ g soln}}{1 \text{ mL}} = 2035 = 2.04 \times 10^3 \text{ g soln}$$

0.120 (2035 g soln) = 244.2 = 244 g KBr

Dissolve 244 g KBr in water, dilute with stirring to 1.85 L.

(d)   Calculate moles KBr needed to precipitate 16.0 g AgBr. $AgNO_3$ is present in excess.

$$16.0 \text{ g AgBr} \times \frac{1 \text{ mol AgBr}}{187.8 \text{ g AgBr}} \times \frac{1 \text{ mol KBr}}{1 \text{ mol AgBr}} = 0.08520 = 0.0852 \text{ mol KBr}$$

$$0.0852 \text{ mol KBr} \times \frac{1 \text{ L soln}}{0.150 \text{ mol KBr}} = 0.568 \text{ L soln}$$

Weigh out 0.0852 mol KBr (10.1 g KBr), dissolve it in a small amount of water, and dilute to 0.568 L.

13.54   (a) $\dfrac{0.110 \text{ mol (NH}_4)_2\text{SO}_4}{1 \text{ L soln}} \times 1.50 \text{ L} \times \dfrac{132.2 \text{ g (NH}_4)_2\text{SO}_4}{1 \text{ mol (NH}_4)_2\text{SO}_4} = 21.81 = 21.8 \text{ g (NH}_4)_2\text{SO}_4$

Weigh 21.8 g $(NH_4)_2SO_4$, dissolve in a small amount of water, continue adding water with thorough mixing up to a total solution volume of 1.50 L.

(b)   Determine the mass fraction of Na_2CO_3 in the solution:

$$\frac{0.65 \text{ mol Na}_2\text{CO}_3}{1000 \text{ g H}_2\text{O}} \times \frac{106.0 \text{ g Na}_2\text{CO}_3}{1 \text{ mol Na}_2\text{CO}_3} = 68.9 \text{ g} = \frac{69 \text{ g Na}_2\text{CO}_3}{1000 \text{ g H}_2\text{O}}$$

$$\text{mass fraction} = \frac{68.9 \text{ g Na}_2\text{CO}_3}{1000 \text{ g H}_2\text{O} + 68.9 \text{ g Na}_2\text{CO}_3} = 0.06446 = 0.064$$

In 225 g of solution, there are 0.06446(225) = 14.503 = 15 g Na_2CO_3.

Weigh out 15 g Na_2CO_3 and dissolve it in 225 − 15 = 210 g H_2O to make exactly 225 g of solution. (210 g H_2O/0.997 g H_2O/mL @ 25° = 211 mL H_2O)

[Carrying 3 sig figs, weigh 14.5 g Na_2CO_3 and dissolve it in 225 − 14.5 = 210.5 g H_2O. This produces a solution that is much closer to 0.65 *m*.]

(c) $1.20 \, L \times \dfrac{1000 \, mL}{1 \, L} \times \dfrac{1.16 \, g}{1 \, mL} = 1392 \, g$ solution; $0.150(1392 \, g \, soln) = 209 \, g \, Pb(NO_3)_2$

Weigh 209 g $Pb(NO_3)$ and add $(1392 - 209) = 1183 \, g \, H_2O$ to make exactly $(1392 = 1.39 \times 10^3) \, g$ or 1.20 L of solution.

$(1183 \, g \, H_2O/0.997 \, g/mL \ @ \ 25°C = 1187 \, mL \, H_2O)$

(d)   Calculate the mol HCl necessary to neutralize 5.5 g $Ba(OH)_2$.

$$Ba(OH)_2(s) + 2HCl(aq) \rightarrow BaCl_2(aq) + 2H_2O(l)$$

$$5.5 \, g \, Ba(OH)_2 + \dfrac{1 \, mol \, Ba(OH)_2}{171 \, g \, Ba(OH)_2} \times \dfrac{2 \, mol \, HCl}{1 \, mol \, Ba(OH)_2} = 0.0643 = 0.064 \, mol \, HCl$$

$$M = \dfrac{mol}{L}; \ L = \dfrac{mol}{M} = \dfrac{0.0643 \, mol \, HCl}{0.50 \, M \, HCl} = 0.1287 = 0.13 \, L = 130 \, mL$$

130 mL of 0.50 *M* HCl are needed.

$$M_c \times L_c = M_d \times L_d; \ 6.0 \, M \times L_c = 0.50 \, M \times 0.1287 \, L; \ L_c = 0.01072 \, L = 11 \, mL$$

Using a pipette, measure exactly 11 mL of 6.0 *M* HCl and dilute with water to a total volume of 130 mL.

13.55   *Analyze/Plan.* Assume a solution volume of 1.00 L. Calculate the mass of 1.00 L of solution and the mass of HNO_3 in 1.00 L of solution. Mass % = (mass solute/mass solution) × 100.   *Solve.*

$$1.00 \, L \times \dfrac{1000 \, mL}{1 \, L} \times \dfrac{1.42 \, g \, soln}{mL \, soln} = 1.42 \times 10^3 \, g \, soln$$

$$16 \, M = \dfrac{16 \, mol \, HNO_3}{1 \, L \, soln} \times \dfrac{63.02 \, g \, HNO_3}{1 \, mol \, HNO_3} = 1008 = 1.0 \times 10^3 \, g \, HNO_3$$

$$mass \% = \dfrac{1008 \, g \, HNO_3}{1.42 \times 10^3 \, g \, soln} \times 100 = 71\% \, HNO_3$$

13.56   *Analyze/Plan.* Assume 1.00 L of solution. Calculate mass of 1 L of solution using density. Calculate mass of NH_3 using mass %, then mol NH_3 in 1.00 L.   *Solve.*

$$1.00 \, L \, soln \times \dfrac{1000 \, mL}{1 \, L} \times \dfrac{0.90 \, g \, soln}{1 \, mL \, soln} = 9.0 \times 10^2 \, g \, soln/L$$

$$\dfrac{900 \, g \, soln}{1.00 \, L \, soln} \times \dfrac{28 \, g \, NH_3}{100 \, g \, soln} \times \dfrac{1 \, mol \, NH_3}{17.03 \, g \, NH_3} = 14.80 = 15 \, mol \, NH_3/L \, soln = 15 \, M \, NH_3$$

13.57   *Analyze.* Given: 80.0% Cu, 20.0% Zn by mass; density = 8750 kg/m^3. Find: (a) *m* of Zn (b) *M* of Zn

(a)   *Plan.* In the brass alloy, Zn is the solute (lesser component) and Cu is the solvent (greater component). *m* = mol Zn/kg Cu. 1 m^3 brass alloy weighs 8750 kg. 80.0% is Cu, 20.0% is Zn. Change g Zn → mol Zn and solve for *m*.   *Solve.*

$$8750 \, kg \, brass \times \dfrac{80 \, g \, Cu}{100 \, g \, brass} = 7.00 \times 10^3 \, kg \, Cu$$

8750 kg brass − 7000 kg Cu = 1750 kg Zn

$$1750 \text{ kg Zn} \times \frac{1000 \text{ g}}{\text{kg}} \times \frac{1 \text{ mol Zn}}{65.39 \text{ g Zn}} = 26{,}762.5 = 2.68 \times 10^4 \text{ mol Zn}$$

$$m = \frac{2.676 \times 10^4 \text{ mol Zn}}{7000 \text{ kg Cu}} = 3.82 \, m \text{ Zn}$$

(b)   *Plan.* M = mol Zn/L brass. Use mol Zn from part (a). Change 1 m$^3 \to$ L brass and calculate M.   *Solve.*

$$1 \text{ m}^3 \times \frac{(10)^3 \text{ dm}^3}{\text{m}^3} \times \frac{1 \text{ L}}{1 \text{ dm}^3} = 1000 \text{ L}$$

$$M = \frac{2.676 \times 10^4 \text{ mol Zn}}{1000 \text{ L brass}} = 26.76 = 26.8 \, M \text{ Zn}$$

13.58   (a) $\dfrac{0.0500 \text{ mol C}_8\text{H}_{10}\text{N}_4\text{O}_2}{1 \text{ kg CHCl}_3} \times \dfrac{194.2 \text{ g C}_8\text{H}_{10}\text{N}_4\text{O}_2}{1 \text{ mol C}_8\text{H}_{10}\text{N}_4\text{O}_2} = 9.7100$

$$= 9.71 \text{ g C}_8\text{H}_{10}\text{N}_4\text{O}_2/\text{kg CHCl}_3$$

$$\frac{9.710 \text{ g C}_8\text{H}_{10}\text{N}_4\text{O}_2}{9.710 \text{ g C}_8\text{H}_{10}\text{N}_4\text{O}_2 + 1000.00 \text{ g CHCl}_3} \times 100 = 0.9617 = 0.962\% \text{ C}_8\text{H}_{10}\text{N}_4\text{O}_2 \text{ by mass}$$

(b) $1000 \text{ g CHCl}_3 \times \dfrac{1 \text{ mol CHCl}_3}{119.4 \text{ CHCl}_3} = 8.375 = 8.38 \text{ mol CHCl}_3$

$$\chi_{\text{C}_8\text{H}_{10}\text{N}_4\text{O}_2} = \frac{0.0500}{0.0500 + 8.375} = 0.00593$$

13.59   *Analyze.* Given: 4.6% CO_2 by volume (in air), 1 atm total pressure. Find: partial pressure and molarity of CO_2 in air.

Plan. 4.6% CO_2 by volume means 4.6 mL of CO_2 could be isolated from 100 mL of air, at the same temperature and pressure. According to Avogadro's Law, equal volumes of gases at the same temperature and pressure contain equal numbers of moles. By inference, the volume ratio of CO_2 to air, 4.6/100 or 0.046, is also the mole ratio.

Solve. $P_{CO_2} = \chi_{CO_2} \times P_t = 0.046 \, (1 \text{ atm}) = 0.046 \text{ atm}$

M = mol CO_2/L air = n/V.   PV = nRT, M = n/V = P/RT

$$M_{CO_2} = \frac{P_{CO_2}}{RT} = \frac{0.046 \text{ atm}}{310 \text{ K}} \times \frac{\text{mol-K}}{0.08206 \text{ L-atm}} = 1.8 \times 10^{-3} \, M$$

13.60   (a)   For gases at the same temperature and pressure, volume % = mol %. The volume and mol % of CO_2 in this breathing air is 4.0%.

(b) $P_{CO_2} = \chi_{CO_2} \times P_t = 0.040 \, (1 \text{ atm}) = 0.040 \text{ atm}$

$$M_{CO_2} = \frac{P_{CO_2}}{RT} = \frac{0.040 \text{ atm}}{310 \text{ K}} \times \frac{\text{mol-K}}{0.08206 \text{ L-atm}} = 1.6 \times 10^{-3} \, M$$

Colligative Properties (section 13.5)

13.61   freezing point depression, $\Delta T_f = K_f(m)$; boiling point elevation, $\Delta T_b = K_b(m)$;

osmotic pressure, $\Pi = M \text{RT}$; vapor pressure lowering, $P_A = \chi_A P_A^\circ$

13.62   (a)   decrease   (b)   decrease

        (c)   increase   (d)   increase

13.63   The vapor pressure over the sucrose solution is higher than the vapor pressure over the glucose solution. Since sucrose has a greater molar mass, 10 g of sucrose contains fewer particles than 10 g of glucose. The solution that contains fewer particles, the sucrose solution, will have the higher vapor pressure.

13.64   (a)   An *ideal solution* is a solution that obeys Raoult's Law.

        (b)   *Analyze/Plan.* Calculate the vapor pressure predicted by Raoult's law and compare it to the experimental vapor pressure. Assume ethylene glycol (eg) is the solute. *Solve.*

$$\chi_{H_2O} = \chi_{eg} = 0.500; \quad P_A = \chi_A P_A{}^\circ = 0.500(149) \text{ torr} = 74.5 \text{ torr}$$

               The experimental vapor pressure (P_A), 67 torr, is less than the value predicted by Raoult's law for an ideal solution. The solution is not ideal.

               Check. An ethylene glycol-water solution has extensive hydrogen bonding, which causes deviation from ideal behavior. We expect the experimental vapor pressure to be less than the ideal value and it is.

13.65   (a)   *Analyze/Plan.* H_2O vapor pressure will be determined by the mole fraction of H_2O in the solution. The vapor pressure of pure H_2O at 338 K (65°C) = 187.5 torr. *Solve.*

$$\frac{22.5 \text{ g } C_{12}H_{22}O_{11}}{342.3 \text{ g/mol}} = 0.06573 = 0.0657 \text{ mol}; \quad \frac{200.0 \text{ g } H_2O}{18.02 \text{ g/mol}} = 11.09878 = 11.10 \text{ mol}$$

$$P_{H_2O} = \chi_{H_2O} \, P_{H_2O}^{\circ} = \frac{11.09878 \text{ mol } H_2O}{11.09878 + 0.06573} \times 187.5 \text{ torr} = 186.4 \text{ torr}$$

        (b)   *Analyze/Plan.* For this problem, it will be convenient to express Raoult's law in terms of the lowering of the vapor pressure of the solvent, ΔP_A.

               $\Delta P_A = P_A{}^\circ - \chi_A P_A{}^\circ = P_A{}^\circ (1 - \chi_A)$. $1 - \chi_A = \chi_B$, the mole fraction of the *solute* particles

               $\Delta P_A = \chi_B P_A{}^\circ$; the vapor pressure of the solvent (A) is lowered according to the mole fraction of solute (B) particles present.   *Solve.*

$$P_{H_2O} \text{ at } 40°C = 55.3 \text{ torr}; \quad \frac{340 \text{ g } H_2O}{18.02 \text{ g/mol}} = 18.868 = 18.9 \text{ mol } H_2O$$

$$\chi_{C_3H_8O_2} = \frac{2.88 \text{ torr}}{55.3 \text{ torr}} = \frac{y \text{ mol } C_3H_8O_2}{y \text{ mol } C_3H_8O_2 + 18.868 \text{ mol } H_2O} = 0.05208 = 0.0521$$

$$0.05208 = \frac{y}{y + 18.868}; 0.05208 \, y + 0.98263 = y; 0.94792 \, y = 0.98263,$$

               $y = 1.0366 = 1.04 \text{ mol } C_3H_8O_2$

               This result has 3 sig figs because (0.340 kg water) has 3 sig figs.

$$1.0366 \text{ mol } C_3H_8O_2 \times \frac{76.09 \text{ g } C_3H_8O_2}{\text{mol } C_3H_8O_2} = 78.88 = 78.9 \text{ g } C_3H_8O_2$$

13 Properties of Solutions — Solutions to Exercises

13.66 **(a)** H_2O vapor pressure will be determined by the mole fraction of H_2O in the solution. The vapor pressure of pure H_2O at 343 K (70°C) = 233.7 torr.

$$\frac{28.5\,g\,C_3H_8O_3}{92.10\,g/mol}=0.3094=0.309\,mol;\quad \frac{125\,g\,H_2O}{18.02\,g/mol}=6.937=6.94\,mol$$

$$P_{H_2O}=\frac{6.937\,mol\,H_2O}{6.937+0.309}\times 233.7\,torr=223.7=224\,torr$$

(b) Calculate χ_B by vapor pressure lowering; $\chi_B=\Delta P_A/P_A^\circ$ (see Solution 13.65(b)). Given moles solvent, calculate moles solute from the definition of mole fraction.

$$\chi_{C_2H_6O_2}=\frac{10.0\,torr}{100\,torr}=0.100$$

$$\frac{1.00\times10^3\,g\,C_2H_5OH}{46.07\,g/mol}=21.71=21.7\,mol\,C_2H_5OH;\,let\,y=mol\,C_2H_6O_2$$

$$\chi_{C_2H_6O_2}=\frac{y\,mol\,C_2H_6O_2}{y\,mol\,C_2H_6O_2+21.71\,mol\,C_2H_5OH}=0.100=\frac{y}{y+21.71}$$

$0.100\,y+2.171=y;\ 0.900\,y=2.171;\ y=2.412=2.41\,mol\,C_2H_6O_2$

$$2.412\,mol\,C_2H_6O_2\times\frac{62.07\,g}{1\,mol}=150\,g\,C_2H_6O_2$$

13.67 *Analyze/Plan.* At 63.5°C, $P_{H_2O}^\circ=175\,torr$, $P_{Eth}^\circ=400\,torr$. Let G = the mass of H_2O and/or C_2H_5OH. *Solve.*

(a)
$$\chi_{Eth}=\frac{\dfrac{G}{46.07\,g\,C_2H_5OH}}{\dfrac{G}{46.07\,g\,C_2H_5OH}+\dfrac{G}{18.02\,g\,H_2O}}$$

Multiplying top and bottom of the right side of the equation by 1/G gives:

$$\chi_{Eth}=\frac{1/46.07}{1/46.07+1/18.02}=\frac{0.02171}{0.02171+0.05549}=0.2812$$

(b) $P_t=P_{Eth}+P_{H_2O};\ P_{Eth}=\chi_{Eth}\times P_{Eth}^\circ;\ P_{H_2O}=\chi_{H_2O}P_{H_2O}^\circ$

$\chi_{Eth}=0.2812,\ P_{Eth}=0.2812\,(400\,torr)=112.48=112\,torr$

$\chi_{H_2O}=1-0.2812=0.7188;\quad P_{H_2O}=0.7188(175\,torr)=125.8=126\,torr$

$P_t=112.5\,torr+125.8\,torr=238.3=238\,torr$

(c) χ_{Eth} in vapor $=\dfrac{P_{Eth}}{P_{total}}=\dfrac{112.5\,torr}{238.3\,torr}=0.4721=0.472$

13.68 **(a)** Since C_6H_6 and C_7H_8 form an ideal solution, we can use Raoult's Law. Since both components are volatile, both contribute to the total vapor pressure of 35 torr.

$$P_t=P_{C_6H_6}+P_{C_7H_8};\ P_{C_6H_6}=\chi_{C_6H_6}P_{C_6H_6}^\circ;\ P_{C_7H_8}=\chi_{C_7H_8}P_{C_7H_8}^\circ$$

$$\chi_{C_7H_8}=1-\chi_{C_6H_6};\ P_T=\chi_{C_6H_6}P_{C_6H_6}^\circ+(1-\chi_{C_6H_6})P_{C_7H_8}^\circ$$

$$35 \text{ torr} = \chi_{C_6H_6}(75 \text{ torr}) + (1 - \chi_{C_6H_6})22 \text{ torr}$$

$$13 \text{ torr} = 53 \text{ torr} (\chi_{C_6H_6}); \quad \chi_{C_6H_6} = \frac{13 \text{ torr}}{53 \text{ torr}} = 0.2453 = 0.25; \quad \chi_{C_7H_8} = 0.7547 = 0.75$$

(b) $P_{C_6H_6} = 0.2453(75 \text{ torr}) = 18.4 \text{ torr}; \quad P_{C_7H_8} = 0.7547(22 \text{ torr}) = 16.6 \text{ torr}$

         In the vapor, $\chi_{C_6H_6} = \dfrac{P_{C_6H_6}}{P_t} = \dfrac{18.4 \text{ torr}}{18.4 \text{ torr} + 16.6 \text{ torr}} = 0.53; \quad \chi_{C_7H_8} = 0.47$

13.69   (a)   Because NaCl is a soluble ionic compound and a strong electrolyte, there are 2 mol dissolved particles for every 1 mol of NaCl solute. $C_6H_{12}O_6$ is a molecular solute, so there is 1 mol of dissolved particles per mol solute. Boiling point elevation is directly related to total moles of dissolved particles; 0.10 m NaCl has more dissolved particles so its boiling point is higher than 0.10 m $C_6H_{12}O_6$.

       (b)   *Analyze/Plan.* $\Delta T = K_b \, m$; K_b for H_2O is 0.51 °C/m (Table 13.3)   *Solve.*

         0.10 m NaCl : $\Delta T = \dfrac{0.51°C}{m} \times 0.20 \, m = 0.102 \,°C; \, T_b = 100.0 + 0.102 = 100.1°C$

         0.10 m $C_6H_{12}O_6$: $\Delta T = \dfrac{0.51°C}{m} \times 0.10 \, m = 0.051 \,°C; \, T_b = 100.0 + 0.051 = 100.1°C$

         Check. Because K_b for H_2O is so small, there is little real difference in the boiling points of the two solutions.

       (c)   In solutions of strong electrolytes like NaCl, electrostatic attractions between ions lead to ion pairing. Ion pairing reduces the effective number of particles in solution, decreasing the **change** in boiling point. The actual boiling point is then lower than the calculated boiling point for a 0.1 M solution.

13.70   *Analyze/Plan.* ΔT_b depends on mol dissolved particles. Assume 100 g of each solution, calculate mol solute and mol dissolved particles. Glucose and sucrose are molecular solutes, but $NaNO_3$ dissociates into 2 mol particles per mol solute. *Solve.*

       10% by mass means 10 g solute in 100 g solution. If we have 10 g of each solute, the one with the smallest molar mass will have the largest mol solute. The molar masses are: glucose, 180.2 g/mol; sucrose, 342.3 g/mol; $NaNO_3$, 85.0 g/mol. $NaNO_3$ has most mol solute, and twice as many dissolved particles, so it will have the highest boiling point. Sucrose has least mol solute and lowest boiling point. Glucose is intermediate.

       In order of increasing boiling point: 10% sucrose < 10% glucose < 10% $NaNO_3$.

13.71   *Analyze/Plan.* Follow the logic in Sample Exercise 13.9. *Solve.*

       The more nonvolatile solute particles, the higher the boiling point of the solution. Since LiBr and $Zn(NO_3)_2$ are electrolytes, the particle concentrations in these solutions are 0.10 m and 0.15 m, respectively (although ion-ion attractive forces may decrease the effective concentrations some-what). Thus, the order of increasing boiling points is:

       0.050 m LiBr < 0.120 m glucose < 0.050 m $Zn(NO_3)_2$

13.72   0.030 *m* phenol > 0.040 *m* glycerin = 0.020 *m* KBr. Phenol is very slightly ionized in water, but not enough to match the number of particles in a 0.040 *m* glycerin solution. The KBr solution is 0.040 *m* in particles, so it has the same freezing point as 0.040 *m* glycerin, which is a nonelectrolyte.

13.73   *Analyze/Plan.* $\Delta T = K(m)$; first, calculate the **molality** of each solution. *Solve.*

(a)   0.22 *m*

(b) $2.45 \text{ mol CHCl}_3 \times \dfrac{119.4 \text{ g CHCl}_3}{\text{mol CHCl}_3} = 292.53 \text{ g} = 0.293 \text{ kg};$

$\dfrac{0.240 \text{ mol C}_{10}\text{H}_8}{0.29253 \text{ kg CHCl}_3} = 0.8204 = 0.820 \; m$

(c) $1.50 \text{ g NaCl} \times \dfrac{1 \text{ mol NaCl}}{58.44 \text{ g NaCl}} \times \dfrac{2 \text{ mol particles}}{1 \text{ mol NaCl}} = 0.05133 = 0.0513 \text{ mol particles}$

$m = \dfrac{0.05133 \text{ mol NaCl}}{0.250 \text{ kg H}_2\text{O}} = 0.20534 = 0.205 \; m$

(d) $2.04 \text{ g KBr} \times \dfrac{1 \text{ mol KBr}}{119.0 \text{ g KBr}} \times \dfrac{2 \text{ mol particles}}{1 \text{ mol KBr}} = 0.03429 = 0.0343 \text{ mol particles}$

$4.82 \text{ g C}_6\text{H}_{12}\text{O}_6 \times \dfrac{1 \text{ mol C}_6\text{H}_{12}\text{O}_6}{180.2 \text{ g C}_6\text{H}_{12}\text{O}_6} = 0.02675 = 0.0268 \text{ mol particles}$

$m = \dfrac{(0.03429 + 0.02675) \text{ mol particles}}{0.188 \text{ kg H}_2\text{O}} = 0.32465 = 0.325 \; m$

Solve. Then, f.p. $= T_f - K_f(m)$; b.p. $= T_b + K_b(m)$; T in °C

	m	**T$_f$**	**-K$_f$(m)**	**f.p.**	**T$_b$**	**+K$_b$(m)**	**b.p.**
(a)	0.22	−114.6	−1.99(0.22) = −0.44	−115.0	78.4	1.22(0.22) = 0.27	78.7
(b)	0.820	−63.5	−4.68(0.820) = −3.84	−67.3	61.2	3.63(0.820) = 2.98	64.2
(c)	0.205	0.0	−1.86(0.205) = −0.381	−0.4	100.0	0.51(0.205) = 0.10	100.1
(d)	0.325	0.0	−1.86(0.325) = −0.605	−0.6	100.0	0.51(0.325) = 0.17	100.2

13.74 $\Delta T = K(m)$; first calculate the **molality** of the solute particles.

(a)   0.25 *m*

(b) $\dfrac{20.0 \text{ g C}_{10}\text{H}_{22}}{0.0500 \text{ kg CHCl}_3} \times \dfrac{1 \text{ mol C}_{10}\text{H}_{22}}{142.3 \text{ g C}_{10}\text{H}_{22}} = 2.811 = 2.81 \; m$

(c) $3.50 \text{ g NaOH} \times \dfrac{1 \text{ mol NaOH}}{40.00 \text{ g NaOH}} \times \dfrac{2 \text{ mol particles}}{1 \text{ mol NaOH}} = 0.1750 = 0.175 \text{ mol particles}$

$m = \dfrac{0.1750 \text{ mol NaCl}}{0.175 \text{ kg H}_2\text{O}} = 1.000 = 1.00 \; m$

(d) $m = \dfrac{0.45 \text{ mol eg} + 2(0.15) \text{ mol KBr}}{0.150 \text{ kg H}_2\text{O}} = \dfrac{0.75 \text{ mol particles}}{0.150 \text{ kg H}_2\text{O}} = 5.0 \; m$

Then, f.p. $= T_f - K_f(m)$; b.p. $= T_b + K_b(m)$; T in °C

	m	T_f	$-K_f(m)$	f.p.	T_b	$+K_b(m)$	b.p.
(a)	0.25	−114.6	−1.99(0.25) = −0.50	−115.1	78.4	1.22(0.25) = 0.31	78.7
(b)	2.81	−63.5	−4.68(2.81) = −13.2	−76.7	61.2	3.63(2.81) = 10.2	71.4
(c)	1.00	0.0	−1.86(1.00) = −1.86	−1.9	100.0	0.51(1.00) = 0.51	100.5
(d)	5.0	0.0	−1.86(5.0) = −9.3	−9.3	100.0	0.51(5.0) = 2.6	102.6

13.75 *Analyze.* Given freezing point of solution and mass of solvent, calculate mass of solute.

Plan. Reverse the logic in Sample Exercise 13.8. Use $\Delta T_f = K_f(m)$ to calculate the required molality, and then apply the definition of molality to calculate moles and grams of $C_2H_6O_2$.

Solve. f.p. of solution = −5.00 °C; f.p. of solvent (H_2O) = 0.0 °C

$\Delta T_f = 5.00\,°C = K_f(m);\ 5.00\,°C = 1.86\,°C/m(m)$

$$m = \frac{5.00\,°C}{1.86\,°C/m} = 2.688 = 2.69\ m\ C_2H_6O_2$$

$$m = \frac{mol\ C_2H_6O_2}{kg\ H_2O} = C_2H_6O_2 = m \times kg\ H_2O$$

$2.688\ m\ C_2H_6O_2 \times 1.00\ kg\ H_2O = 2.688 = 2.69\ mol\ C_2H_6O_2$

$$2.688\ m\ C_2H_6O_2 \times \frac{62.07\ g\ C_2H_6O_2}{1\ mol} = 166.84 = 167\ g\ C_2H_6O_2$$

13.76 Use ΔT_b = find m of aqueous solution, and then use m to calculate ΔT_f and freezing point. $K_b = 0.51$, $K_f = 1.86$.

b.p. = 105.0 °C; $\Delta T_b = 105.0\,°C - 100.0\,°C = 5.0\,°C$

$$\Delta T_b = K_b(m);\ m = \frac{\Delta T_b}{K_b} = \frac{5.0\,°C}{0.51} = 9.804 = 9.8\ m$$

$\Delta T_f = 1.86\,°C/m \times 9.804\ m = 18.24 = 18\ °C;$ freezing point = 0.0 °C − 18.24 °C = −18 °C

13.77 *Analyze/Plan.* $\Pi = M\,RT;\ T = 25\,°C + 273 = 298\ K;\ M = mol\ C_9H_8O_4/L\ soln$ *Solve.*

$$M = \frac{44.2\ mg\ C_9H_8O_4}{0.358\ L} \times \frac{1\ g}{1000\ mg} \times \frac{1\ mol\ C_9H_8O_4}{180.2\ g\ C_9H_8O_4} = 6.851 \times 10^{-4} = 6.85 \times 10^{-4}\ M$$

$$\Pi = \frac{6.851 \times 10^{-4}\ mol}{L} \times \frac{0.08206\ L\text{-}atm}{mol\text{-}K} \times 298\ K = 0.01675 = 0.0168\ atm = 12.7\ torr$$

13.78 $\Pi = MRT;\ T = 20\,°C + 273 = 293\ K$

$$M\ (of\ ions) = \frac{mol\ NaCl \times 2}{L\ soln} = \frac{3.4\ g\ NaCl}{1\ L\ soln} \times \frac{1\ mol\ NaCl}{58.4\ g\ NaCl} \times \frac{2\ mol\ ions}{1\ mol\ NaCl} = 0.116 = 0.12\ M$$

$$\Pi = \frac{0.116\ mol}{L} \times \frac{0.08206\ L\text{-}atm}{mol\text{-}K} \times 293\ K = 2.8\ atm$$

13.79 *Analyze/Plan.* Follow the logic in Sample Exercise 13.11 to calculate the molar mass of adrenaline based on the boiling point data. Use the structure to obtain the molecular formula and molar mass. Compare the two values.   *Solve.*

$$\Delta T_b = K_b \, m; \quad m = \frac{\Delta T_b}{K_b} = \frac{+0.49}{5.02} = 0.0976 = 0.098 \, m \text{ adrenaline}$$

$$m = \frac{\text{mol adrenaline}}{\text{kg CCl}_4} = \frac{\text{g adrenaline}}{\text{MM adrenaline} \times \text{kg CCl}_4}$$

$$\text{MM adrenaline} = \frac{\text{g adrenaline}}{m \times \text{kg CCl}_4} = \frac{0.64 \text{ g adrenaline}}{0.0976 \, m \times 0.0360 \text{ kg CCl}_4} = 1.8 \times 10^2 \text{ g/mol adrenaline}$$

Check. The molecular formula is $C_9H_{13}NO_3$, MM = 183 g/mol. The values agree to 2 sig figs, the precision of the experimental value.

13.80 $\Delta T_f = 5.5 - 4.1 = 1.4; \quad m = \dfrac{\Delta T_f}{K_f} = \dfrac{1.4}{5.12} = 0.273 = 0.27 \, m$

$$\text{MM lauryl alcohol} = \frac{\text{g lauryl alcohol}}{m \times \text{kg C}_6\text{H}_6} = \frac{5.00 \text{ g lauryl alcohol}}{0.273 \times 0.100 \text{ kg C}_6\text{H}_6}$$

$$= 1.8 \times 10^2 \text{ g/mol lauryl alcohol}$$

13.81   *Anayze/Plan.* Follow the logic in Sample Exercise 13.12.   *Solve.*

$$\Pi = MRT; \quad M = \frac{\Pi}{RT}; \quad T = 25 \,^\circ C + 273 = 298 \text{ K}$$

$$M = 0.953 \text{ torr} \times \frac{1 \text{ atm}}{760 \text{ torr}} \times \frac{\text{mol - K}}{0.08206 \text{ L - atm}} \times \frac{1}{298 \text{ K}} = 5.128 \times 10^{-5} = 5.13 \times 10^{-5} \, M$$

$$\text{mol} = M \times L = 5.128 \times 10^{-5} \times 0.210 \text{ L} = 1.077 \times 10^{-5} = 1.08 \times 10^{-5} \text{ mol lysozyme}$$

$$\text{MM} = \frac{g}{\text{mol}} = \frac{0.150 \text{ g}}{1.077 \times 10^{-5} \text{ mol}} = 1.39 \times 10^4 \text{ g/mol lysozyme}$$

13.82 $M = P/RT = \dfrac{0.605 \text{ atm}}{298 \text{ K}} \times \dfrac{\text{mol - K}}{0.08206 \text{ L - atm}} = 0.02474 = 0.0247 \, M$

$$\text{MM} = \frac{g}{M \times L} = \frac{2.35 \text{ g}}{0.02474 \, M \times 0.250 \, L} = 380 \text{ g/mol}$$

13.83   (a)   *Analyze/Plan.* $i = \Pi$ (measured) / Π (calculated for a nonelectrolyte);

           Π (calculated) = M RT. *Solve.*

$$\Pi \text{ (calculated)} = \frac{0.010 \text{ mol}}{L} \times \frac{0.08206 \text{ L - atm}}{\text{mol - K}} \times 298 \text{ K} = 0.2445 = 0.24 \text{ atm}$$

           $i = 0.674 \text{ atm}/0.2445 \text{ atm} = 2.756 = 2.8$

       (b)   The van't Hoff factor is the effective number of particles per mole of solute. The closer the measured i value is to a theoretical integer value, the more ideal the solution. Ion-pairing and other interparticle attractive forces reduce the effective number of particles in solution and reduce the measured value of i. The more concentrated the solution, the greater the ion-pairing and the smaller the measured value of i.

13.84   If these were ideal solutions, they would have equal ion concentrations and equal ΔT_f values. Data in Table 13.4 indicates that the van't Hoff factors (i) for both salts are less than the ideal values. For 0.030 m NaCl, i is between 1.87 and 1.94, about 1.92. For

0.020 m K_2SO_4, i is between 2.32 and 2.70, about 2.62. From Equation 13.15,

ΔT_f (measured) = $i \times \Delta T_f$ (calculated for nonelectrolyte)

NaCl: ΔT_f (measured) = 1.92 × 0.030 m × 1.86 °C/m = 0.11 °C

K_2SO_4: ΔT_f (measured) = 2.62 × 0.020 m × 1.86°C/m = 0.097 °C

0.030 m NaCl would have the larger ΔT_f.

The deviations from ideal behavior are due to ion-pairing in the two electrolyte solutions. K_2SO_4 has more extensive ion-pairing and a larger deviation from ideality because of the higher charge on SO_4^{2-} relative to Cl^-.

Colloids (section 13.6)

13.85   (a)   In the gaseous state, the particles are far apart and intermolecular attractive forces are small. When two gases combine, all terms in Equation [13.1] are essentially zero and the mixture is always homogeneous.

      (b)   The outline of a light beam passing through a colloid is visible, whereas light passing through a true solution is invisible unless collected on a screen. This is the Tyndall effect. To determine whether Faraday's (or anyone's) apparently homogeneous dispersion is a true solution or a colloid, shine a beam of light on it and see if the light is scattered.

13.86   (a)   Suspensions are classified as solutions or colloids according to the size of the dispersed particles. Solute particles have diameters less than 5 nm (50 Å); suspended colloid particles range from 5-1000 nm. Proteins with molecular masses of 30,000 amu or greater are likely to have dimensions in the colloid range. The aqueous suspensions are colloids because of the size of protein molecules. (Large protein molecules remain homogeneously suspended in water because of their many hydrogen bonding interactions with water.)

      (b)   Emulsion. An *emulsifying agent* is one that aids in the formation of an emulsion. It usually has a polar part and a nonpolar part, to facilitate mixing of immiscible liquids with very different molecular polarities.

13.87   (a)   hydrophobic   (b)   hydrophilic   (c)   hydrophobic

      (d)   hydrophobic (but stabilized by adsorbed charges)

13.88   (a)   When the colloid *particle mass* becomes large enough so that gravitational and interparticle attractive forces are greater than the kinetic energies of the particles, settling and aggregation can occur.

      (b)   *Hydrophobic* colloids do not attract a sheath of water molecules around them and thus tend to aggregate from aqueous solution. They can be stabilized as colloids by adsorbing charges on their surfaces. The charged particles interact with solvent water, stabilizing the colloid.

      (c)   *Charges on colloid particles* can stabilize them against aggregation. Particles carrying like charges repel one another and are thus prevented from aggregating and settling out.

13.89   Proteins form hydrophilic colloids because they carry charges on their surface (Figure 13.30). When electrolytes are added to a suspension of proteins, the dissolved ions form ion pairs with the protein surface charges, effectively neutralizing them. The protein's capacity for ion-dipole interactions with water is diminished and the colloid separates into a protein layer and a water layer.

13.90   (a)   The nonpolar hydrophobic tails of soap particles (the hydrocarbon chain of stearate ions) establish attractive intermolecular dispersion forces with the nonpolar oil molecules, while the charged hydrophilic head of the soap particles interacts with H_2O to keep the oil molecules suspended. (This is the mechanism by which laundry detergents remove greasy dirt from clothes.)

   (b)   Electrolytes from the acid neutralize surface charges of the suspended particles in milk, causing the colloid to coagulate.

Additional Exercises

13.91   The outer periphery of the BHT molecule is mostly hydrocarbon-like groups, such as $-CH_3$. The one $-OH$ group is rather buried inside, and probably does little to enhance solubility in water. Thus, BHT is more likely to be soluble in the nonpolar hydrocarbon hexane, C_6H_{14}, than in polar water.

13.92   In this equilibrium system, molecules move from the surface of the solid into solution, while molecules in solution are deposited on the surface of the solid. As molecules leave the surface of the small particles of powder, the reverse process preferentially deposits other molecules on the surface of a single crystal. Eventually, all molecules that were present in the 50 g of powder are deposited on the surface of a 50 g crystal; this can only happen if the dissolution and deposition processes are ongoing.

13.93   Assume that the density of the solution is 1.00 g/mL.

   (a) $4 \, ppm \, O_2 = \dfrac{4 \, mg \, O_2}{1 \, kg \, soln} = \dfrac{4 \times 10^{-3} \, g \, O_2}{1 \, L \, soln} \times \dfrac{1 \, mol \, O_2}{32.0 \, g \, O_2} = 1.25 \times 10^{-4} = 1 \times 10^{-4} \, M$

   (b) $S_{O_2} = kP_{O_2}; \; P_{O_2} = S_{O_2}/k = \dfrac{1.25 \times 10^{-4} \, mol}{L} \times \dfrac{L\text{-}atm}{1.71 \times 10^{-3} \, mol} = 0.0731 = 0.07 \, atm$

   $0.0731 \, atm \times \dfrac{760 \, mm \, Hg}{1 \, atm} = 55.6 = 60 \, mm \, Hg$

13.94   (a) $S_{Rn} = kP_{Rn}; k = S_{Rn}/P_{Rn} = 7.27 \times 10^{-3} \, M/1 \, atm = 7.27 \times 10^{-3} \, mol/L\text{-}atm$

   (b) $P_{Rn} = \chi_{Rn}P_{total}; \; P_{Rn} = 3.5 \times 10^{-6} \, (32 \, atm) = 1.12 \times 10^{-4} = 1.1 \times 10^{-4} \, atm$

   $S_{Rn} = k \, P_{Rn}; S_{Rn} = \dfrac{7.27 \times 10^{-3} \, mol}{L\text{-}atm} \times 1.12 \times 10^{-4} \, atm = 8.1 \times 10^{-7} \, M$

13.95   0.10% by mass means 0.10 g glucose/100 g blood.

   (a) $ppm \, glucose = \dfrac{g \, glucose}{g \, solution} \times 10^6 = \dfrac{0.10 \, g \, glucose}{100 \, g \, blood} \times 10^6 = 1000 \, ppm \, glucose$

   (b) m = mol glucose/kg solvent. Assume that the mixture of nonglucose components is the 'solvent'.

mass solvent = 100 g blood − 0.10 g glucose = 99.9 g solvent = 0.0999 kg solvent

$$\text{mol glucose} = 0.10 \text{ g} \times \frac{1 \text{ mol}}{180.2 \text{ g } C_6H_{12}O_6} = 5.55 \times 10^{-4} = 5.6 \times 10^{-4} \text{ mol glucose}$$

$$m = \frac{5.55 \times 10^{-4} \text{ mol glucose}}{0.0999 \text{ kg solvent}} = 5.6 \times 10^{-3} \, m \text{ glucose}$$

In order to calculate molarity, solution volume must be known. The density of blood is needed to relate mass and volume.

13.96   *Analyze.* Given 13 ppt Au in seawater, find grams of Au in 1.0×10^3 gal seawater. The definition of ppt is (mass solute/mass solution) $\times 10^{12}$.   *Plan.* Assume seawater is a dilute aqueous solution with a density of 1.00 g/mL. Use the definition of ppt to calculate g Au.   *Solve.*

$$\frac{13 \text{ g Au}}{1 \times 10^{12} \text{ g soln}} \times \frac{1.0 \text{ g soln}}{\text{mL soln}} \times \frac{1000 \text{ mL}}{1 \text{ L}} \times \frac{3.7854 \text{ L}}{\text{gal}} \times 1.0 \times 10^3 \text{ gal soln} = 4.9 \times 10^{-5} \text{ g Au}$$

13.97   *Analyze.* The definition of ppb is (mass solute/mass solution) $\times 10^9$.   *Plan.* Use the definition to get g Pb and g solution. Change g Pb to mol Pb, g solution to L solution, calculate molarity. *Solve.*

(a) $9 \text{ ppb} = \dfrac{9 \text{ g Pb}}{1 \times 10^9 \text{ g soln}} \times 10^9$

For dilute aqueous solutions (drinking water) assume that the density of the solution is the density of H_2O.

$$\frac{9 \text{ g Pb}}{1 \times 10^9 \text{ g soln}} \times \frac{1.0 \text{ g soln}}{\text{mL soln}} \times \frac{1000 \text{ mL}}{1 \text{ L}} \times \frac{1 \text{ mol Pb}}{207.2 \text{ g Pb}} = 4.34 \times 10^{-8} \, M = 4 \times 10^{-8} \, M$$

(b)   Change 60 m³ H_2O to cm³ (mL) H_2O to g H_2O (or g soln).

$$60 \text{ m}^3 \times \frac{100^3 \text{ cm}^3}{\text{m}^3} \times \frac{1 \text{ g } H_2O}{\text{cm}^3 \, H_2O} = 6.0 \times 10^7 \text{ g } H_2O \text{ or soln}$$

$$\frac{9 \text{ g Pb}}{1 \times 10^9 \text{ g soln}} \times 6.0 \times 10^7 \text{ g soln} = 0.540 = 0.5 \text{ g Pb}$$

13.98   (a) $\dfrac{1.80 \text{ mol LiBr}}{1 \text{ L soln}} \times \dfrac{86.85 \text{ g LiBr}}{1 \text{ mol LiBr}} = 156.3 = 156 \text{ g LiBr}$

1 L soln = 826 g soln; g CH_3CN = 826 − 156.3 = 669.7 = 670 g CH_3CN

$$m \text{ LiBr} = \frac{1.80 \text{ mol LiBr}}{0.6697 \text{ kg } CH_3CN} = 2.69 \, m$$

(b) $\dfrac{669.7 \text{ g } CH_3CN}{41.05 \text{ g/mol}} = 16.31 = 16.3 \text{ mol } CH_3CN; \quad \chi_{LiBr} = \dfrac{1.80}{1.80 + 16.31} = 0.0994$

(c) $\text{mass \%} = \dfrac{669.7 \text{ g } CH_3CN}{826 \text{ g soln}} \times 100 = 81.1\% \, CH_3CN$

13.99 Mole fraction ethyl alcohol, $\chi_{C_2H_5OH} = \dfrac{P_{C_2H_5OH}}{P^\circ_{C_2H_5OH}} = \dfrac{8\,\text{torr}}{100\,\text{torr}} = 0.08$

$\dfrac{620 \times 10^3\,\text{g}\,C_{24}H_{50}}{338.6\,\text{g/mol}} = 1.83 \times 10^3\,\text{mol}\,C_{24}H_{50}$; let $y = \text{mol}\,C_2H_5OH$

$\chi_{C_2H_5OH} = 0.08 = \dfrac{y}{y + 1.83 \times 10^3}$; $0.92\,y = 146.4$; $y = 1.6 \times 10^2\,\text{mol}\,C_2H_5OH$

(Strictly speaking, y should have 1 sig fig because 0.08 has 1 sig fig, but this severely limits the calculation.)

$1.6 \times 10^2\,\text{mol}\,C_2H_5OH \times \dfrac{46\,\text{g}\,C_2H_5OH}{1\,\text{mol}} = 7.4 \times 10^3\,\text{g}$ or $7.4\,\text{kg}\,C_2H_5OH$

13.100 *Analyze.* Given vapor pressure of both pure water and the aqueous solution and moles H_2O find moles of solute in the solution.

Plan. Use vapor pressure lowering, $P_A = \chi_A P^\circ_A$, to calculate χ_A, mole fraction solvent, and then use the definition of mole fraction to calculate moles solute particles. Because NaCl is a strong electrolyte, there is one mole NaCl for every two moles solute particles. *Solve.*

$\chi_{H_2O} = P_{soln} / P_{H_2O} = 25.7 / 31.8 = 0.80818 = 0.808$

$\chi_{H_2O} = \dfrac{\text{mol}\,H_2O}{\text{mol ions} + \text{mol}\,H_2O}$; $0.80818 = \dfrac{0.115}{(\text{mol ions} + 0.115)}$

$0.80818\,(0.115 + \text{mol ions}) = 0.115$; $0.80818\,(\text{mol ions}) = 0.115 - 0.092940$

mol ions $= 0.02206/0.80818 = 0.02730 = 0.0273$

mol NaCl $=$ mol ions$/2 = 0.02730/2 = 0.01365 = 0.0137$ mol NaCl

13.101 (a) The solvent vapor pressure over each solution is determined by the total particle concentrations present in the solutions. When the particle concentrations are equal, the vapor pressures will be equal and equilibrium established. The particle concentration of the nonelectrolyte is just 0.050 *M*, the ion concentration of the NaCl is 2 × 0.035 *M* = 0.070 *M*. Solvent will diffuse from the less concentrated nonelectrolyte solution. The level of the NaCl solution will rise, and the level of the nonelectrolyte solution will fall.

(b) Let x = volume of solvent transferred

$\dfrac{0.050\,M \times 30.0\,\text{mL}}{(30.0 - x)\,\text{mL}} = \dfrac{0.070\,M \times 30.0\,\text{mL}}{(30.0 + x)\,\text{mL}}$; $1.5(30.0 + x) = 2.1(30.0 - x)$

$45 + 1.5\,x = 63 - 2.1\,x$; $3.6\,x = 18$; $x = 5.0 = 5$ mL transferred

The volume in the nonelectrolyte beaker is (30.0 − 5.0) = 25.0 mL; in the NaCl beaker (30.0 + 5.0) = 35.0 mL.

13.102 In order to answer this question, you will need to find the physical properties (density, freezing point) of ethylene glycol in a source like the *CRC*. Calculate the freezing point of a solution that is 30% ethylene glycol, $C_2H_6O_2$, and 70% water. Since a car owner would typically use volume measurements to make this solution, assume this is a volume percent concentration. Volume percent is a volume ratio that is valid for any volume unit. For convenience, assume 30 mL $C_2H_6O_2$, and 70 mL H_2O. The density of $C_2H_6O_2$ is 1.1088 g/mL. The density of H_2O is 0.997 g/mL at 25°C. Find molality and then ΔT_f for water.

$$30 \text{ mL } C_2H_6O_2 \times \frac{1.1088 \text{ g } C_2H_6O_2}{\text{mL}} = 33.264 = 33 \text{ g } C_2H_6O_2$$

$$\frac{33.264 \text{ g } C_2H_6O_2}{70 \text{ mL } H_2O} \times \frac{1 \text{ mol } C_2H_6O_2}{62.1 \text{ g } C_2H_6O_2} \times \frac{1 \text{ mL } H_2O}{0.997 \text{ g } H_2O} \times \frac{1000 \text{ g}}{\text{kg}} = 7.6752 = 7.7 \text{ m}$$

$$\Delta T_f = 1.86°C/m \ (7.6752 \text{ m}) = 14.27°C$$

$$T_f = 0.0°C - 14.27°C = -14.27 = -14°C$$

In this 30% solution, ethylene glycol is the solute (present in lesser amount) and water is the solvent (present in greater amount). It is the freezing point of water, 0.0°C, that is depressed by the nonvolatile solute ethylene glycol. If pure ethylene glycol is used in the radiator, it freezes at its regular (not depressed) freezing point, –11.5°C. The freezing point of the solution, –14°C, is lower than the freezing point of pure ethylene glycol.

13.103   (a)   0.100 m K_2SO_4 is 0.300 m in particles. H_2O is the solvent.

$$\Delta T_f = K_f m = -1.86(0.300) = -0.558; \ T_f = 0.0 - 0.558 = -0.558°C = -0.6°C$$

(b) ΔT_f (nonelectrolyte) $= -1.86(0.100) = -0.186; \ T_f = 0.0 - 0.186 = -0.186°C = -0.2°C$

T_f (measured) $= i \times T_f$ (nonelectrolyte)

From Table 13.4, i for 0.100 m $K_2SO_4 = 2.32$

T_f (measured) $= 2.32(-0.186°C) = -0.432°C = -0.4°C$

13.104   (a) $K_b = \dfrac{\Delta T_b}{m}; \quad \Delta T_b = 47.46°C - 46.30°C = 1.16°C$

$$m = \frac{\text{mol solute}}{\text{kg } CS_2} = \frac{0.250 \text{ mol}}{400.0 \text{ mL } CS_2} \times \frac{1 \text{ mL } CS_2}{1.261 \text{ g } CS_2} \times \frac{1000 \text{ g}}{1 \text{ kg}} = 0.4956 = 0.496 \text{ m}$$

$$K_b = \frac{1.16°C}{0.4956 \text{ m}} = 2.34°C/m$$

(b) $m = \dfrac{\Delta T_b}{K_b} = \dfrac{(47.08 - 46.30)°C}{2.34°C/m} = 0.333 = 0.33 \text{ m}$

$$m = \frac{\text{mol unknown}}{\text{kg } CS_2}; \quad m \times \text{kg } CS_2 = \frac{\text{g unknown}}{\text{MM unknown}}; \quad MM = \frac{\text{g unknown}}{m \times \text{kg } CS_2}$$

$$50.0 \text{ mL } CS_2 \times \frac{1.261 \text{ g } CS_2}{1 \text{ mL}} \times \frac{1 \text{ kg}}{1000 \text{ g}} = 0.06305 = 0.0631 \text{ kg } CS_2$$

$$MM = \frac{5.39 \text{ g unknown}}{0.333 \text{ m} \times 0.06305 \text{ kg } CS_2} = 257 = 2.6 \times 10^2 \text{ g/mol}$$

13.105 $M = \dfrac{\Pi}{RT} = \dfrac{57.1 \text{ torr}}{298 \text{ K}} \times \dfrac{1 \text{ atm}}{760 \text{ torr}} \times \dfrac{\text{mol-K}}{0.08206 \text{ L-atm}} = 3.072 \times 10^{-3} = 3.07 \times 10^{-3} \text{ M}$

$$\frac{0.036 \text{ g solute}}{100 \text{ g H}_2\text{O}} \times \frac{1000 \text{ g H}_2\text{O}}{1 \text{ kg H}_2\text{O}} = 0.36 \text{ g solute/kg H}_2\text{O}$$

Assuming molarity and molality are the same in this dilute solution, we can then say 0.36 g solute = 3.072×10^{-3} mol; MM = 117 g/mol. Because the salt is completely ionized, the formula weight of the lithium salt is **twice** this calculated value, or **234 g/mol**. The organic portion, $C_nH_{2n+1}O_2^-$, has a formula weight of 234–7 = 227 g. Subtracting 32 for the oxygens, and 1 to make the formula C_nH_{2n}, we have C_nH_{2n}, MM = 194 g/mol. Since each CH_2 unit has a mass of 14, n ≈ 194/14 ≈ 14. The formula for our salt is $LiC_{14}H_{29}O_2$.

Integrative Exercises

13.106 Since these are very dilute solutions, assume that the density of the solution ≈ the density of H_2O ≈ 1.0 g/mL at 25°C. Then, 100 g solution = 100 g H_2O = 0.100 kg H_2O.

(a) CF_4 : $\dfrac{0.0015 \text{ g CF}_4}{0.100 \text{ kg H}_2\text{O}} \times \dfrac{1 \text{ mol CF}_4}{88.00 \text{ g CF}_4} = 1.7 \times 10^{-4} \; m$

$CClF_3$: $\dfrac{0.009 \text{ g CClF}_3}{0.100 \text{ kg H}_2\text{O}} \times \dfrac{1 \text{ mol CClF}_3}{104.46 \text{ g CClF}_3} = 8.6 \times 10^{-4} \; m = 9 \times 10^{-4} \; m$

CCl_2F_2 : $\dfrac{0.028 \text{ g CCl}_2\text{F}_2}{0.100 \text{ kg H}_2\text{O}} \times \dfrac{1 \text{ mol CCl}_2\text{F}_2}{120.9 \text{ g CCl}_2\text{F}_2} = 2.3 \times 10^{-3} \; m$

$CHClF_2$: $\dfrac{0.30 \text{ g CHClF}_2}{0.100 \text{ kg H}_2\text{O}} \times \dfrac{1 \text{ mol CHClF}_2}{86.47 \text{ g CHClF}_2} = 3.5 \times 10^{-2} \; m$

(b) $m = \dfrac{\text{mol solute}}{\text{kg solvent}}$; $M = \dfrac{\text{mol solute}}{\text{L solution}}$

Molality and molarity are numerically similar when kilograms solvent and liters solution are nearly equal. This is true when solutions are dilute, so that the density of the solution is essentially the density of the solvent, and when the density of the solvent is nearly 1 g/mL. That is, for dilute aqueous solutions such as the ones in this problem, $M \approx m$.

(c) Water is a polar solvent; the solubility of solutes increases as their polarity increases. All the fluorocarbons listed have tetrahedral molecular structures. CF_4, a symmetrical tetrahedron, is nonpolar and has the lowest solubility. As more different atoms are bound to the central carbon, the electron density distribution in the molecule becomes less symmetrical and the molecular polarity increases. The most polar fluorocarbon, $CHClF_2$, has the greatest solubility in H_2O. It may act as a weak hydrogen bond acceptor for water.

(d) $S_g = k P_g$. Assume $M = m$ for $CHClF_2$. $P_g = 1$ atm

$$k = \frac{S_g}{P_g} = \frac{M}{P_g}; k = \frac{3.5 \times 10^{-2} \, M}{1.0 \text{ atm}} = 3.5 \times 10^{-2} \text{ mol/L-atm}$$

This value is greater than the Henry's law constant for $N_2(g)$, because $N_2(g)$ is nonpolar and of lower molecular mass than $CHClF_2$. In fact, the Henry's law constant for nonpolar CF_4, 1.7×10^{-4} mol/L-atm is similar to the value for N_2, 6.8×10^{-4} mol L-atm.

13.107 $\dfrac{0.015\,g\,N_2}{1\,L\,blood} \times \dfrac{1\,mol\,N_2}{28.01\,g\,N_2} = 5.355 \times 10^{-4} = 5.4 \times 10^{-4}\,mol\,N_2/L\,blood$

At 100 ft, the partial pressure of N_2 in air is 0.78 (4.0 atm) = 3.12 atm. This is just four times the partial pressure of N_2 at 1.0 atm air pressure. According to Henry's law, $S_g = kP_g$, a 4-fold increase in P_g results n a 4-fold increase in S_g, the solubility of the gas. Thus, the solubility of N_2 at 100 ft is $4(5.355 \times 10^{-4}\,M) = 2.142 \times 10^{-3} = 2.1 \times 10^{-3}\,M$. If the diver suddenly surfaces, the amount of N_2/L blood released is the difference in the solubilities at the two depths: $(2.142 \times 10^{-3}\,mol/L - 5.355 \times 10^{-4}\,mol/L) = 1.607 \times 10^{-3} = 1.6 \times 10^{-3}\,mol\,N_2/L$ blood.

At surface conditions of 1.0 atm external pressure and 37°C = 310 K,

$$V = \frac{nRT}{P} = 1.607 \times 10^{-3}\,mol \times \frac{310\,K}{1.0\,atm} \times \frac{0.08206\,L\text{-}atm}{mol\text{-}K} = 0.041\,L$$

That is, 41 mL of tiny N_2 bubbles are released from each L of blood.

13.108   The stronger the intermolecular forces, the higher the heat (enthalpy) of vaporization.

(a)   None of the substances are capable of hydrogen bonding in the pure liquid, and they have similar molar masses. All intermolecular forces are van der Waals forces, dipole-dipole, and dispersion forces. In decreasing order of strength of forces:

acetone > acetaldehyde > ethylene oxide > cyclopropane

The first three compounds have dipole-dipole and dispersion forces, the last only dispersion forces.

(b)   The order of solubility in hexane should be the reverse of the order above. The least polar substance, cyclopropane, will be most soluble in hexane. Ethanol, CH_3CH_2OH, is capable of hydrogen bonding with the three polar compounds. Thus, acetaldehyde, acetone, and ethylene oxide should be more soluble than cyclopropane, but without further information we cannot distinguish among the polar molecules.

13.109   (a)

(b)   If the lattice energy (U) of the ionic solid (ion-ion forces) is too large relative to the solvation energy of the gaseous ions (ion-dipole forces), ΔH_{soln} will be too large and positive (endothermic) for solution to occur. This is the case for solutes like NaBr. Lattice energy is inversely related to the distance between ions, so salts with large cations like $(CH_3)_4N^+$ have smaller lattice energies than salts with simple cations like Na^+. The smaller lattice energy of $(CH_4)_3NBr$ causes it to be more soluble in nonaqueous polar solvents. Also, the $-CH_3$ groups in the large cation are capable of dispersion interactions with the $-CH_3$ (or other nonpolar groups) of the solvent molecules. This produces a more negative solvation energy for the salts with large cations.

Overall, for salts with larger cations, U is smaller (less positive), the solvation energy of the gaseous ions is more negative, and ΔH_{soln} is less endothermic. These salts are more soluble in polar nonaqueous solvents.

13.110   (a) $Zn(s) + H_2SO_4(aq) \rightarrow ZnSO_4(aq) + H_2(g)$

$$2.050 \text{ g Zn} \times \frac{1 \text{ mol Zn}}{65.39 \text{ g Zn}} = 0.03135 \text{ mol Zn}$$

$$1.00 \text{ } M \text{ } H_2SO_4 \times 0.0150 \text{ L} = 0.0150 \text{ mol } H_2SO_4$$

Since Zn and H_2SO_4 react in a 1:1 mole ratio, H_2SO_4 is the limiting reactant; 0.0150 mol of $H_2(g)$ are produced.

(b) $$P = \frac{nRT}{V} = \frac{0.0150 \text{ mol}}{0.122 \text{ L}} \times \frac{0.08206 \text{ L - atm}}{\text{mol - K}} \times 298 \text{ K} = 3.0066 = 3.01 \text{ atm}$$

(c) $$S_{H_2} = kP_{H_2} = \frac{7.8 \times 10^{-4} \text{ mol}}{\text{L - atm}} \times 3.0066 \text{ atm} = 0.002345 = 2.3 \times 10^{-3} \text{ } M$$

$$\frac{0.002345 \text{ mol } H_2}{\text{L soln}} \times 0.0150 \text{ L} = 3.518 \times 10^{-5} = 3.5 \times 10^{-5} \text{ mol dissolved } H_2$$

$$\frac{3.5 \times 10^{-5} \text{ mol dissolved } H_2}{0.0150 \text{ mol } H_2 \text{ produced}} \times 100 = 0.23\% \text{ dissolved } H_2$$

This is approximately 2.3 parts per thousand; for every 10,000 H_2 molecules, 23 are dissolved. It was reasonable to ignore dissolved $H_2(g)$ in part (b).

13.111   (a) $$\frac{1.3 \times 10^{-3} \text{ mol } CH_4}{\text{L soln}} \times 4.0 \text{ L} = 5.2 \times 10^{-3} \text{ mol } CH_4$$

$$V = \frac{nRT}{P} = \frac{5.2 \times 10^{-3} \text{ mol} \times 298 \text{ K}}{1.0 \text{ atm}} \times \frac{0.08206 \text{ L - atm}}{\text{mol - K}} = 0.13 \text{ L}$$

(b)   All three hydrocarbons are nonpolar; they have zero net dipole moment. In CH_4 and C_2H_6, the C atoms are tetrahedral and all bonds are σ bonds. C_2H_6 has a higher molar mass than CH_4, which leads to stronger dispersion forces and greater water solubility. In C_2H_4, the C atoms are trigonal planar and the π electron cloud is symmetric above and below the plane that contains all the atoms. This planar arrangement facilitates contact between molecules, leading to stronger dispersion forces. The π cloud in C_2H_4 is an area of concentrated electron density that experiences attractive forces with the positive ends of H_2O molecules. These forces increase the solubility of C_2H_4 relative to the other hydrocarbons.

(c) The molecules have similar molar masses. NO is most soluble because it is polar. The triple bond in N_2 is shorter than the double bond in O_2. It is more difficult for H_2O molecules to surround the smaller N_2 molecules, so they are less soluble than O_2 molecules.

(d) H_2S and SO_2 are polar molecules capable of hydrogen bonding with water. Hydrogen bonding is the strongest force between neutral molecules and causes the much greater solubility. H_2S is weakly acidic in water. SO_2 reacts with water to form H_2SO_3, a weak acid. The large solubility of SO_2 is a sure sign that a chemical process has occurred.

(e) N_2 and C_2H_4. N_2 is too small to be easily hydrated, so C_2H_4 is more soluble in H_2O.

NO (31) and C_2H_6 (30). The structures of these two molecules are very different, yet they have similar solubilities. NO is slightly polar, but too small to be easily hydrated. The larger C_2H_6 is nonpolar, but more polarizable (stronger dispersion forces).

NO (31) and O_2 (32). The slightly polar NO is more soluble than the slightly larger (longer O=O bond than $N \equiv O$ bond) but nonpolar O_2.

13.112 The resulting solution is very dilute, so assume ideal behavior. Assume the amount of water consumed in the reaction is negligible. Ignore the solubility of $H_2(g)$ in the solution (see Solution 3.110).

$$1.0\ mm^3 \times \frac{0.535\ g}{cm^3} \times \frac{1^3\ cm^3}{10^3\ mm^3} = 5.35 \times 10^{-4} = 5.4 \times 10^{-4}\ g\ Li$$

$$5.35 \times 10^{-4}\ g\ Li \times \frac{1\ mol\ Li}{6.941\ g\ Li} = 7.708 \times 10^{-5} = 7.7 \times 10^{-5}\ mol\ Li$$

mol Li = mol LiOH; 2 mol ions per mol LiOH

7.708×10^{-5} mol Li = 7.708×10^{-5} mol LiOH = 1.542×10^{-4} mol ions = 1.5×10^{-4} mol ions

$$m = \frac{1.542 \times 10^{-4}\ mol\ ions}{0.500\ L\ H_2O} \times \frac{1\ L}{1000\ mL} \times \frac{1\ mL\ H_2O}{0.997\ g\ H_2O} \times \frac{1000\ g}{1\ kg} = 3.092 \times 10^{-4} = 3.1 \times 10^{-4}\ m$$

$\Delta T_f = K_f\ m = -1.86(3.092 \times 10^{-4}) = -5.8 \times 10^{-4}\ °C; \quad T_f = 0.00000 - 0.00058 = -0.00058\ °C$

The freezing point of the LiOH(aq) solution is essentially zero.

13.113 $\chi_{CHCl_3} = \chi_{C_3H_6O} = 0.500$

(a) For an ideal solution, Raoult's Law is obeyed.

$P_t = P_{CHCl_3} + P_{C_3H_6O}; \quad P_{CHCl_3} = 0.5(300\ torr) = 150\ torr$

$P_{C_3H_6O} = 0.5(360\ torr) = 180\ torr; \quad P_t = 150\ torr + 180\ torr = 330\ torr$

(b)   The real solution has a lower vapor pressure, 250 torr, than an ideal solution of the same composition, 330 torr. Thus, fewer molecules escape to the vapor phase from the liquid. This means that fewer molecules have sufficient kinetic energy to overcome intermolecular attractions. Clearly, even weak hydrogen bonds such as this one are stronger attractive forces than dipole-dipole or dispersion forces. These hydrogen bonds prevent molecules from escaping to the vapor phase and result in a lower than ideal vapor pressure for the solution. There is essentially no hydrogen bonding in the individual liquids.

(c)   According to Coulomb's law, electrostatic attractive forces lead to an overall lowering of the energy of the system. Thus, when the two liquids mix and hydrogen bonds are formed, the energy of the system is decreased and $\Delta H_{soln} < 0$; the solution process is exothermic.

14 Chemical Kinetics

Visualizing Concepts

14.1 *Analyze/Plan.* Given three sets of initial conditions for the same chemical reaction, decide which set will react fastest. Consider the four factors that affect reaction rate.

Solve. All vessels are at the same temperature and no catalyst is present, so these two factors are not pertinent. The initial conditions do differ in physical state and concentration. Vessel 2 has the greatest concentration of reactants A and B, and they are in solution; vessel 2 has the fastest reaction. Vessel 1 has fewer reactants and they are in the solid state. The number of reactant collisions is much less than for mobile reactants in solution. Vessel 3 has reactants in solution, but the concentrations are four times less than in Vessel 2.

14.2 *Analyze/Plan.* Given the plot of [X] vs time, answer questions about reaction speed and rate. Consider the definitions of average reaction rate and instantaneous rate. *Solve.*

(a) X is a product, because its concentration increases with time.

(b) The speed of a reaction is its rate, or how quickly the concentration of a reactant or product changes over time. This graph shows how [X] increases over time. The rate at any particular time, the instantaneous rate, is the slope of the tangent to the curve at that time. Visualizing the tangents at points 0, 1, 2 and 3, we see that the slopes of these lines are decreasing with time. That is, the rate of reaction is decreasing; the reaction is slowing down as time progresses.

(c) The average rate of reaction between any two points on the graph is the slope of the line connecting the two points. Points 1 and 2 are earlier in the reaction when more reactants are available, so the average rate of formation of products is greater. As reactants are used up, the rate of X production decreases, and the average rate between points 2 and 3 is smaller.

14.3 Chemical equation (d), $B \rightarrow 2A$, is consistent with the data. The concentration of A increases with time, and concentration B decreases with time, so B must be a reactant and A must be a product. The ending concentration of A is approximately twice as large as the starting concentration of B, so mole ratio of A:B is 2:1. The reaction is $B \rightarrow 2A$.

14.4 *Analyze/Plan.* Given a plot of increase in [M] over time, answer questions about reaction rate and progress. Consider the definition of reaction rate. *Solve.*

(a) Well, the reaction occurs at a constant rate from t = 0 to t = ~12 min. The plot of [M] vs time from t = 0 to t = 12 is a straight line, so [M] increases at a constant rate and the reaction occurs at a constant rate. The rate is zero after t = 12 min.

(b)   Yes, the reaction is definitely complete at t = 15 min. (It is actually complete near t = 12 min.) [M] does not change after ~12 min. This means that no more M is being produced and the reaction is no longer occurring.

14.5   *Analyze/Plan.* Using the relationship rate = $k[A]^x$, determine the value of x that produces a rate law to match the described situation. *Solve.*

(a)   x = 0. The rate of reaction does not depend on $[A]_0$, so the reaction is zero-order in A.

(b)   x = 2. When $[A]_0$ increases by a factor of 3, rate increases by a factor of $(3)^2 = 9$.

(c)   x = 3. When $[A]_0$ increases by a factor of 2, rate increases by a factor of $(2)^3 = 8$.

14.6   *Analyze.* Given three mixtures and the order of reaction in each reactant, determine which mixture will have the fastest initial rate.

Plan. Write the rate law. Count the number of reactant molecules in each container. The three containers have equal volumes and total numbers of molecules. Use the molecule count as a measure of concentration of NO and O_2. Calculate the initial rate for each container and compare.

Solve. Rate = $k[NO]^2[O_2]$; rate is proportional to $[NO]^2[O_2]$

Container	[NO]	[O_2]	$[NO]^2[O_2] \propto$ rate
(1)	5	4	100
(2)	7	2	98
(3)	3	6	54

The relative rates in containers (1) and (2) are very similar, with (1) having the slightly faster initial rate.

14.7   *Plan.* For a first-order reaction, a plot of ln[A] vs. time is linear, as shown in the diagram. The slope is –k, and the intercept is $[A]_0$. According to the Arrhenius equation [14.19], k increases with increasing temperature. *Solve.*

(a)   Graphs 1 and 2 have the same slope, and thus the same rate constant, k. These experiments are done at the same temperature. The y-intercepts of the two graphs are different; the experiments had different initial concentrations of A.

(b)   Graphs 2 and 3 have the same y-intercept and thus the same starting concentration of A. The slopes of the two graphs are different, so their rate constants are different and they occur at different temperatures. Graph 3, with the smaller slope and k value will occur at the lower temperature.

14.8   *Analyze.* Given concentrations of reactants and products at two times, as represented in the diagram, find $t_{1/2}$ for this first-order reaction.

Plan. For a first order reaction, $t_{1/2} = 0.693/k$; $t_{1/2}$ depends only on k. Use Equation [14.12] to solve for k. *Solve.*

(a)   Since reactants and products are in the same container, use number of particles as a measure of concentration. The red dots are reactant A, and the blue are product B. $[A]_0 = 8$, $[A]_{30} = 2$, t = 30 min.

$$\ln\frac{[A]_t}{[A]_0} = -kt. \quad \ln(2/8) = -k(30 \text{ min}); \quad \frac{-1.3863}{-30 \text{min}} = k;$$

$$k = 0.046210 = 0.0462 \text{ min}^{-1}$$

$$t_{1/2} = 0.693/k = 0.693/0.046210 = 15 \text{ min}$$

By examination, $[A]_0 = 8$, $[A]_{30} = 2$. After 1 half-life, $[A] = 4$; after a second half-life, $[A] = 2$. Thirty minutes represents exactly 2 half-lives, so $t_{1/2} = 15$ min. [This is more straightforward than the calculation, but a less general method.]

 (b) After 4 half-lives, $[A]_t = [A]_0 \times 1/2 \times 1/2 \times 1/2 \times 1/2 = [A]_0/16$. In general, after n half-lives, $[A] = [A]_0/2^n$.

14.9 The reaction profile has a single high point (peak), so the reaction occurs in a single step. This step is necessarily the rate-determining step.

 (1) Total potential energy of the reactants

 (2) E_a, activation energy of the reaction. This is the difference in energy between the potential energy of the activated complex (transition state) and the potential energy of the reactants.

 (3) ΔE, net energy change for the reaction. This is the difference in energy between the products and reactants. (Under appropriate conditions, this could also be ΔH.) For this reaction, the energy of products is lower than the energy of reactants, and the reaction releases energy to the surroundings.

 (4) Total potential energy of the products.

14.10 On a plot of $\ln k$ vs. $1/T$, the slope is $-E_a$ and the y-intercept is $\ln A$, where E_a is activation energy and A is the frequency factor.

 (a) If $E_a(2) > E_a(1)$ and $A_1 = A_2$, the lines will have the same y-intercept, negative slope direction, and the slope of line 2 will be steeper than the slope of line 1.

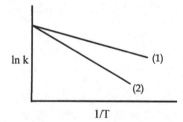

 (b) If $A_2 > A_1$ and $E_a(1) = E_a(2)$, the lines will be parallel with the same negative slopes and different y-intercepts.

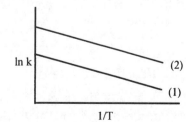

14.11 (a) The red pathway is slower, because it has the greater activation energy, E_a.

   (b) The reaction could occur by both catalyzed and uncatalyzed mechanisms. The initial reactants and final products would be the same, but the transition state and activation energy would be different.

14.12 (a) $NO_2 + F_2 \rightarrow NO_2F + F$

   $NO_2 + F \rightarrow NO_2F$

   (b) $2NO_2 + F_2 \rightarrow 2NO_2F$

   (c) F is the intermediate, because it is produced and then consumed during the reaction.

   (d) rate = $k[NO_2][F_2]$

14.13 This is the profile of a two-step mechanism, $A \rightarrow B$ and $B \rightarrow C$. There is one intermediate, B. Because there are two energy maxima, there are two transition states. The $B \rightarrow C$ step is faster, because its activation energy is smaller. The reaction is exothermic because the energy of the products is lower than the energy of the reactants.

14.14 The most likely transition state shows the relative geometry of both reactants and products. It is reasonable to assume that multiple bonds, with greater total bond energy, remain intact at the expense of single bonds. In the black-and-white diagram below, open circles represent the red balls and closed circles represent the blue.

14.15 (a) $A_2 + AB + AC \rightarrow BA_2 + A + AC$

   $BA_2 + A + AC \rightarrow A_2 + BA_2 + C$

   _____

   net: $AB + AC \rightarrow BA_2 + C$

   (b) A is the intermediate; it is produced and consumed.

   (c) A_2 is the catalyst; it is consumed and reproduced

14.16

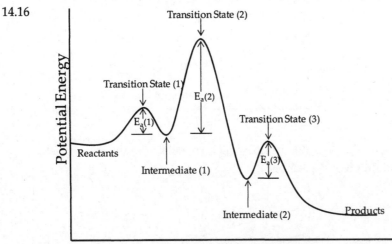

The reaction is exothermic because the energy of products is lower than the energy of reactants. The two intermediates are formed at different rates because $E_a(1) \neq E_a(2)$. In order to have two intermediates, the mechanism must have at least three steps.

Reaction Rates (sections 14.1 and 14.2)

14.17 (a) *Reaction rate* is the change in the amount of products or reactants in a given amount of time; it is the speed of a chemical reaction.

(b) Rates depend on concentration of reactants, physical state (or surface area) of reactants, temperature and presence of catalyst.

(c) No, the rate of disappearance of reactants is not necessarily the same as the rate of appearance of products. The stoichiometry of the reaction (mole ratios of reactants and products) must be known in order to relate rate of disappearance of reactants to rate of appearance of products.

14.18 (a) M/s

(b) The hotter the oven, the faster the cake bakes. Milk sours faster in hot weather than cool weather.

(c) The *average rate* is the rate over a period of time, while the *instantaneous rate* is the rate at a particular time.

14.19 *Analyze/Plan.* Given mol A at a series of times in minutes, calculate mol B produced, molarity of A at each time, change in M of A at each 10 min interval, and ΔM A/s. For this reaction, mol B produced equals mol A consumed. M of A or $[A]$ = mol A/0.100 L. The average rate of disappearance of A for each 10 minute interval is

$$-\frac{\Delta[A]}{s} = -\frac{[A]_1 - [A]_0}{10\ \text{min}} \times \frac{1\ \text{min}}{60\ \text{s}}$$

Solve.

Time (min)	Mol A	(a) Mol B	[A]	Δ[A]	(b) Rate $-(\Delta[A]/s)$
0	0.065	0.000	0.65		
10	0.051	0.014	0.51	−0.14	2.3×10^{-4}
20	0.042	0.023	0.42	−0.09	2×10^{-4}
30	0.036	0.029	0.36	−0.06	1×10^{-4}
40	0.031	0.034	0.31	−0.05	0.8×10^{-4}

(c) $\dfrac{\Delta M_B}{\Delta t} = \dfrac{(0.029 - 0.014)\ \text{mol}/0.100\ \text{L}}{(30 - 10)\ \text{min}} \times \dfrac{1\ \text{min}}{60\ \text{s}} = 1.25 \times 10^{-4} = 1.3 \times 10^{-4}\ M/s$

14.20

Time(s)	Mol A	(a) Mol B	Δ Mol A	(b) Rate $-(\Delta\ \text{mol A/s})$
0	0.100	0.000		
40	0.067	0.033	−0.033	8.3×10^{-4}
80	0.045	0.055	−0.022	5.5×10^{-4}
120	0.030	0.070	−0.015	3.8×10^{-4}
160	0.020	0.080	−0.010	2.5×10^{-4}

(c) The volume of the container must be known to report the rate in units of concentration (mol/L) per time.

14.21   (a)   *Analyze/Plan.* Follow the logic in Sample Exercises 14.1 and 14.2.   *Solve.*

Time (sec)	Time Interval (sec)	Concentration (M)	ΔM	Rate (M/s)
0		0.0165		
2,000	2,000	0.0110	–0.0055	28×10^{-7}
5,000	3,000	0.00591	–0.0051	17×10^{-7}
8,000	3,000	0.00314	–0.00277	9.23×10^{-7}
12,000	4,000	0.00137	–0.00177	4.43×10^{-7}
15,000	3,000	0.00074	–0.00063	2.1×10^{-7}

(b) $\dfrac{\Delta M_B}{\Delta t} = \dfrac{(0.0165 - 0.00074)\ M}{(15,000 - 0)\ s} = 1.0507 \times 10^{-6} = 1.05 \times 10^{-6}\ M/s$

(c)   From the slopes of the lines in the figure at right, the rates are:

at 5000 s,

$12 \times 10^{-7}\ M/s;$

at 8000 s,

$5.8 \times 10^{-7}\ M/s$

14.22   (a)

Time (min)	Time Interval (min)	Concentration (M)	ΔM	Rate (M/s)
0.0		1.85		
54.0	54.0	1.58	–0.27	8.3×10^{-5}
107.0	53.0	1.36	–0.22	6.9×10^{-5}
215.0	108	1.02	–0.34	5.2×10^{-5}
430.0	215	0.580	–0.44	3.4×10^{-5}

(b) $\dfrac{\Delta M_B}{\Delta t} = \dfrac{(1.85 - 0.580)\ M}{(430 - 0)\ min} \times \dfrac{1\ min}{60\ s} = 4.9225 \times 10^{-5} = 4.92 \times 10^{-5}\ M/s$

(c)   From the slopes of the lines in the figure at the right, the rates are: at 75.0 min, $4.2 \times 10^{-3}\,M/\text{min}$, or $7.0 \times 10^{-5}\,M/\text{s}$; at 250 min, $2.1 \times 10^{-3}\,M/\text{min}$ or $3.5 \times 10^{-5}\,M/\text{s}$

14.23   *Analyze/Plan.* Follow the logic in Sample Exercise 14.3.   *Solve.*

(a) $-\Delta[H_2O_2]/\Delta t = \Delta[H_2]/\Delta t = \Delta[O_2]/\Delta t$

(b) $-\Delta[N_2O]/2\Delta t = \Delta[N_2]/2\Delta t = \Delta[O_2]/\Delta t$

       $-\Delta[N_2O]/\Delta t = \Delta[N_2]/\Delta t = 2\Delta[O_2]/\Delta t$

(c) $-\Delta[N_2]/\Delta t = \Delta[NH_3]/2\Delta t;\ -\Delta[H_2]/3\Delta t = \Delta[NH_3]/2\Delta t$

       $-2\Delta[N_2]/\Delta t = \Delta[NH_3]/\Delta t;\ -\Delta[H_2]/\Delta t = 3\Delta[NH_3]/2\Delta t$

(d) $-\Delta[C_2H_5NH_2]/\Delta t = \Delta[C_2H_4]/\Delta t = \Delta[NH_3]/\Delta t$

14.24   (a)   rate $= -\Delta[H_2O]/2\Delta t = \Delta[H_2]/2\Delta t = \Delta[O_2]/\Delta t$

(b)   rate $= -\Delta[SO_2]/2\Delta t = -\Delta[O_2]/\Delta t = \Delta[SO_3]/2\Delta t$

(c)   rate $= -\Delta[NO]/2\Delta t = -\Delta[H_2]/2\Delta t = \Delta[N_2]/\Delta t = \Delta[H_2O]/2\Delta t$

(d)   rate $= -\Delta[N_2]/\Delta t = -\Delta[H_2]/2\Delta t = \Delta[N_2H_4]/\Delta t$

14.25   *Analyze/Plan.* Use Equation [14.4] to relate the rate of disappearance of reactants to the rate of appearance of products. Use this relationship to calculate desired quantities. *Solve.*

(a) $\Delta[H_2O]/2\Delta t = -\Delta[H_2]/2\Delta t = -\Delta[O_2]/\Delta t$

       H_2 is burning, $-\Delta[H_2]/\Delta t = 0.48\ \text{mol/s}$

       O_2 is consumed, $-\Delta[O_2]/\Delta t = -\Delta[H_2]/2\Delta t = 0.48\ \text{mol/s}/2 = 0.24\ \text{mol/s}$

       H_2O is produced, $+\Delta[H_2O]/\Delta t = -\Delta[H_2]/\Delta t = 0.48\ \text{mol/s}$

(b)   The change in total pressure is the sum of the changes of each partial pressure. NO and Cl_2 are disappearing and NOCl is appearing.

       $-\Delta P_{NO}/\Delta t = -56\ \text{torr/min}$

       $-\Delta P_{Cl_2}/\Delta t = \Delta P_{NO}/2\Delta t = -28\ \text{torr/min}$

       $+\Delta P_{NOCl}/\Delta t = -\Delta P_{NO}/\Delta t = +56\ \text{torr/min}$

       $\Delta P_T/\Delta t = -56\ \text{torr/min} - 28\ \text{torr/min} + 56\ \text{torr/min} = -28\ \text{torr/min}$

14.26   (a) $-\Delta[C_2H_4]/\Delta t = \Delta[CO_2]/2\Delta t = \Delta[H_2O]/2\Delta t$

             $-2\Delta[C_2H_4]/\Delta t = \Delta[CO_2]/\Delta t = \Delta[H_2O]/\Delta t$

             C_2H_4 is burning, $-\Delta[C_2H_4]/\Delta t = 0.036 \, M/s$

             CO_2 and H_2O are produced, at twice the rate that C_2H_4 is consumed.

             $\Delta[CO_2]/\Delta t = \Delta[H_2O]/\Delta t = 2(0.036) \, M/s = 0.072 \, M/s$

   (b)   In this reaction, pressure is a measure of concentration.

             $-\Delta[N_2H_4]/\Delta t = -\Delta[H_2]/\Delta t = \Delta[NH_3]/2\Delta t$

             N_2H_4 is consumed, $-\Delta[N_2H_4]/\Delta t = 74 \, torr/hr$

             H_2 is consumed, $-\Delta[H_2]/\Delta t = 74 \, torr/hr$

             NH_3 is produced at twice the rate that N_2H_4 and H_2 are consumed,

             $\Delta[NH_3]/\Delta t = -2\Delta[N_2H_4]/\Delta t = 2(74) \, torr/hr = 148 \, torr/hr$

             $\Delta P_T/\Delta t = (+148 \, torr/hr - 74 \, torr/hr - 74 \, torr/hr) = 0 \, torr/hr$

Rate Laws (section 14.3 and 14.2)

14.27   *Analyze/Plan.* Follow the logic in Sample Exercises 14.4 and 14.5. *Solve.*

   (a)   If [A] is doubled, there will be no change in the rate or the rate constant. The overall rate is unchanged because [A] does not appear in the rate law; the rate constant changes only with a change in temperature.

   (b)   The reaction is zero order in A, second order in B and second order overall.

   (c)   Units of $k = \dfrac{M/s}{M^2} = M^{-1} \, s^{-1}$

14.28   (a)   rate = $k[A][C]^2$

   (b)   rate is proportional to [A], rate doubles

   (c)   rate is not affected by [B], no change

   (d)   rate changes as $[C]^2$, rate increases by a factor of 3^2 or 9

   (e)   rate increases by a factor of $(3)(3)^2 = 27$

   (f)   rate decreases by a factor of $(1/2)(1/2)^2 = 1/8$

14.29   *Analyze/Plan.* Follow the logic in Sample Exercise 14.4.   *Solve.*

   (a)   rate = $k[N_2O_5] = 4.82 \times 10^{-3} \, s^{-1} \, [N_2O_5]$

   (b)   rate = $4.82 \times 10^{-3} \, s^{-1} \, (0.0240 \, M) = 1.16 \times 10^{-4} \, M/s$

   (c)   rate = $4.82 \times 10^{-3} \, s^{-1} \, (0.0480 \, M) = 2.31 \times 10^{-4} \, M/s$

             When the concentration of N_2O_5 doubles, the rate of the reaction doubles.

   (d)   rate = $4.82 \times 10^{-3} \, s^{-1} \, (0.0120 \, M) = 5.78 \times 10^{-5} \, M/s$

             When the concentration of N_2O_5 is halved, the rate of the reaction is halved.

14.30   (a)   rate = $k[H_2][NO]^2$

          (b)   rate = $(6.0 \times 10^4\ M^{-2}\ s^{-1})(0.035\ M)^2(0.015\ M) = 1.1\ M/s$

          (c)   rate = $(6.0 \times 10^4\ M^{-2}\ s^{-1})\ (0.10\ M)^2\ (0.010\ M) = 6.0\ M/s$

          (d)   rate = $(6.0 \times 10^4\ M^{-2}\ s^{-1})\ (0.010\ M)^2\ (0.030\ M) = 0.18\ M/s$

14.31   *Analyze/Plan.* Write the rate law and rearrange to solve for k. Use the given data to calculate k, including units.   *Solve.*

          (a, b) rate = $k[CH_3Br][OH^-]$; $k = \dfrac{\text{rate}}{[CH_3Br][OH^-]}$

              at 298 K, $k = \dfrac{0.0432\ M/s}{(5.0 \times 10^{-3}\ M)(0.050\ M)} = 1.7 \times 10^2\ M^{-1}s^{-1}$

          (c)   Since the rate law is first order in $[OH^-]$, if $[OH^-]$ is tripled, the rate triples.

          (d)   If $[OH^-]$ and $[CH_3Br]$ both triple, the rate increases by a factor of $(3)(3) = 9$.

14.32   (a, b) rate = $k[C_2H_5Br][OH^-]$; $k = \dfrac{\text{rate}}{[C_2H_5Br][OH^-]}$

              at 298 K, $k = \dfrac{1.7 \times 10^{-7}\ M/s}{[0.0477\ M][0.100\ M]} = 3.6 \times 10^{-5}\ M^{-1}s^{-1}$

          (c)   Adding an equal volume of ethyl alcohol reduces both $[C_2H_5Br]$ and $[OH^-]$ by a factor of two. new rate = $(1/2)(1/2) = 1/4$ of old rate

14.33   *Analyze/Plan.* Follow the logic in Sample Exercise 14.6.   *Solve.*

          (a)   From the data given, when $[OCl^-]$ doubles, rate doubles. When $[I^-]$ doubles, rate doubles. The reaction is first order in both $[OCl^-]$ and $[I^-]$. rate = $k[OCl^-][I^-]$

          (b)   Using the first set of data:

              $k = \dfrac{\text{rate}}{[OCl^-][I^-]} = \dfrac{1.36 \times 10^{-4}\ M/s}{(1.5 \times 10^{-3}\ M)(1.5 \times 10^{-3}\ M)} = 60.444 = 60\ M^{-1}\ s^{-1}$

          (c)   rate = $\dfrac{60.444}{M \text{-} s}(2.0 \times 10^{-3}\ M)(5.0 \times 10^{-4}\ M) = 6.0444 \times 10^{-5} = 6.0 \times 10^{-5}\ M/s$

14.34   (a)   From the data given, when $[ClO_2]$ increases by a factor of 3 (experiment 2 to experiment 1), the rate increases by a factor of 9. When $[OH^-]$ increases by a factor of 3 (experiment 2 to experiment 3), the rate increases by a factor of 3. The reaction is second order in $[ClO_2]$ and first order in $[OH^-]$. rate = $k[ClO_2]^2[OH^-]$.

          (b)   Using data from Expt 2:

              $k = \dfrac{\text{rate}}{[ClO_2]^2\ [OH^-]} = \dfrac{0.00276\ M/s}{(0.020\ M)^2\ (0.030\ M)} = 2.3 \times 10^2\ M^{-2}s^{-1}$

          (c)   rate = $2.3 \times 10^2\ M^{-2}\ s^{-1}\ (0.100\ M)^2(0.050\ M) = 0.115 = 0.12\ M/s$

14.35   *Analyze/Plan.* Follow the logic in Sample Exercise 14.6 to deduce the rate law. Rearrange the rate law to solve for k and deduce units. Calculate a k value for each set of concentrations and then average the three values.   *Solve.*

(a) Doubling [NH₃] while holding [BF₃] constant doubles the rate (experiments 1 and 2). Doubling [BF₃] while holding [NH₃] constant doubles the rate (experiments 4 and 5).

Thus, the reaction is first order in both BF_3 and NH_3; rate = k[BF₃][NH₃].

(b) The reaction is second order overall.

(c) From experiment 1: $k = \dfrac{0.2130\ M/s}{(0.250\ M)(0.250\ M)} = 3.41\ M^{-1}\ s^{-1}$

(Any of the five sets of initial concentrations and rates could be used to calculate the rate constant k. The average of these 5 values is $k_{avg} = 3.408 = 3.41\ M^{-1}s^{-1}$)

(d) rate = $3.408\ M^{-1}s^{-1}(0.100\ M)(0.500\ M) = 0.1704 = 0.170\ M/s$

14.36 *Analyze/Plan.* Follow the logic in Sample Exercise 14.6 to deduce the rate law. Rearrange the rate law to solve for k and deduce units. Calculate a k value for each set of concentrations and then average the three values. *Solve.*

(a) Doubling [NO] while holding [O₂] constant increases the rate by a factor of 4 (experiments 1 and 2). Doubling [O₂] while holding [NO] constant doubles the rate (experiments 2 and 3). The reaction is second order in [NO] and first order in [O₂]. rate = k[NO]²[O₂]

(b, c) From experiment 1: $k_1 = \dfrac{1.41 \times 10^{-2}\ M/s}{(0.0126\ M)^2\,(0.0125\ M)} = 7105 = 7.11 \times 10^3\ M^{-2}s^{-1}$

$k_2 = 0.113/(0.0252)^2(0.0250) = 7118 = 7.12 \times 10^3\ M^{-2}\ s^{-1}$

$k_3 = 5.64 \times 10^{-2}/(0.0252)^2(0.125) = 7105 = 7.11 \times 10^3\ M^{-2}\ s^{-1}$

$k_{avg} = (7105 + 7118 + 7105)/3 = 7109 = 7.11 \times 10^3\ M^{-2}\ s^{-1}$

(d) rate = $7.109 \times 10^3\ M^{-2}s^{-1}\ (0.0750\ M)^2(0.0100\ M) = 0.3999 = 0.400\ M/s$

(e) The data are given in terms of the disappearance of NO. Use Equation [14.4] to relate the disappearance of NO to the disappearance of O₂.

$-\Delta[NO]/2\Delta t = -[O_2]/\Delta t$

For the concentrations given in part (d), $\Delta[NO]/\Delta t = 0.400\ M/s$.

$\Delta[O_2]/\Delta t = \Delta[NO]/2\Delta t = 0.400\ M/s/2 = 0.200\ M/s$

14.37 *Analyze/Plan.* Follow the logic in Sample Exercise 4.6 to deduce the rate law. Rearrange the rate law to solve for k and deduce units. Calculate a k value for each set of concentrations and then average the three values. *Solve.*

(a) Increasing [NO] by a factor of 2.5 while holding [Br₂] constant (experiments 1 and 2) increases the rate by a factor 6.25 or (2.5)². Increasing [Br₂] by a factor of 2.5 while holding [NO] constant increases the rate by a factor of 2.5. The rate law for the appearance of NOBr is: rate = $\Delta[NOBr]/\Delta t = k[NO]^2[Br_2]$.

(b) From experiment 1: $k_1 = \dfrac{24\ M/s}{(0.10\ M)^2\,(0.20\ M)} = 1.20 \times 10^4 = 1.2 \times 10^4\ M^{-2}\ s^{-1}$

$k_2 = 150/(0.25)^2(0.20) = 1.20 \times 10^4 = 1.2 \times 10^4 \, M^{-2} \, s^{-1}$

$k_3 = 60/(0.10)^2(0.50) = 1.20 \times 10^4 = 1.2 \times 10^4 \, M^{-2} \, s^{-1}$

$k_4 = 735/(0.35)^2(0.50) = 1.2 \times 10^4 = 1.2 \times 10^4 \, M^{-2} \, s^{-1}$

$k_{avg} = (1.2 \times 10^4 + 1.2 \times 10^4 + 1.2 \times 10^4 + 1.2 \times 10^4)/4 = 1.2 \times 10^4 \, M^{-2} \, s^{-1}$

(c)   Use the reaction stoichiometry and Equation [14.4] to relate the designated rates. $\Delta[NOBr]/2\Delta t = -\Delta[Br_2]/\Delta t$; the rate of disappearance of Br_2 is half the rate of appearance of NOBr.

(d)   Note that the data are given in terms of appearance of NOBr.

$$\frac{-\Delta[Br_2]}{\Delta t} = \frac{k[NO]^2[Br_2]}{2} = \frac{1.2 \times 10^4}{2 \, M^2 \, s} \times (0.075 \, M)^2 \times (0.250 \, M) = 8.4 \, M/s$$

14.38   (a)   Increasing $[S_2O_8^{2-}]$ by a factor of 1.5 while holding $[I^-]$ constant increases the rate by a factor of 1.5 (Experiments 1 and 2). Doubling $[S_2O_8^{2-}]$ and increasing $[I^-]$ by a factor of 1.5 triples the rate ($2 \times 1.5 = 3$, experiments 1 and 3). Thus the reaction is first order in both $[S_2O_8^{2-}]$ and $[I^-]$; rate = k $[S_2O_8^{2-}]$ $[I^-]$.

(b) $k = rate/[S_2O_8^{2-}] \, [I^-]$

$k_1 = 2.6 \times 10^{-6} \, M/s/(0.018 \, M)(0.036 \, M) = 4.01 \times 10^{-3} = 4.0 \times 10^{-3} \, M^{-1}s^{-1}$

$k_2 = 3.9 \times 10^{-6} /(0.027)(0.036) = 4.01 \times 10^{-3} = 4.01 \times 10^{-3} = 4.0 \times 10^{-3} \, M^{-1}s^{-1}$

$k_3 = 7.8 \times 10^{-6} /(0.036)(0.054) = 4.01 \times 10^{-3} = 4.01 \times 10^{-3} = 4.0 \times 10^{-3} \, M^{-1}s^{-1}$

$k_4 = 1.4 \times 10^{-5} /(0.050)(0.072) = 3.89 \times 10^{-3} = 3.9 \times 10^{-3} \, M^{-1}s^{-1}$

$k_{avg} = 3.98 \times 10^{-3} = 4.0 \times 10^{-3} \, M^{-1}s^{-1}$

(c) $-\Delta[S_2O_8^{2-}]/\Delta t = -\Delta[I^-]/3\Delta t$; the rate of disappearance of $S_2O_8^{2-}$ is one-third the rate of disappearance of I^-.

(d)   Note that the data are given in terms of disappearance of $S_2O_8^{2-}$.

$$\frac{-\Delta[I^-]}{\Delta t} = \frac{-3\Delta[S_2O_8^{2-}]}{\Delta t} = 3(3.98 \times 10^{-3} \, M^{-1}s^{-1})(0.025 \, M)(0.050 \, M) = 1.5 \times 10^{-5} \, M/s$$

Change of Concentration with Time (section 14.4)

14.39   (a) $[A]_0$ is the molar concentration of reactant A at time zero, the initial concentration of A. $[A]_t$ is the molar concentration of reactant A at time t. $t_{1/2}$ is the time required to reduce $[A]_0$ by a factor of 2, the time when $[A]_t = [A]_0/2$. k is the rate constant for a particular reaction. k is independent of reactant concentration but varies with reaction temperature.

(b)   A graph of ln[A] vs time yields a straight line for a first-order reaction.

(c)   On graph of ln[A] vs time, the rate constant, k, is the (–slope) of the straight line.

14.40   (a)   A graph of 1/[A] vs time yields a straight line for a second-order reaction.

(b)   On a graph of 1/[A] vs time, the slope of the straight line is the rate constant, k.

(c)   The half-life of a first-order reaction is independent of $[A]_0$, $t_{1/2} = 0.693/k$. Whereas, the half-life of a second-order reaction does depend on $[A]_0$, $t_{1/2} = 1/k[A]_0$.

14.41   For a reaction A → B that is zero-order in A, rate = k. A plot of [A] vs time will be linear, with a slope of –k. (A plot of [B] vs time will also be linear, with a slope of +k.)

14.42

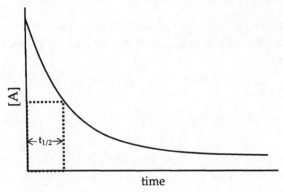

(a)   The graph is not linear. For a reaction first-order in [A], rate changes as [A] changes and the plot of [A] vs time is not linear. If a graph of [A] vs time is linear, the reaction is zero-order in [A]; rate does not depend on [A]. (Or, a plot of **ln[A]** vs t would also be linear.)

(b)   The time at which $[A] = [A]_0/2$ is the half-life, $t_{1/2}$.

14.43   *Analyze/Plan.* The half-life of a first-order reaction depends only on the rate constant, $t_{1/2} = 0.693/k$. Use this relationship to calculate k for a given $t_{1/2}$, and, at a different temperature, $t_{1/2}$ given k. *Solve.*

(a) $t_{1/2} = 2.3 \times 10^5$ s; $t_{1/2} = 0.693/k$, $k = 0.693/t_{1/2}$
        $k = 0.693/2.3 \times 10^5$ s $= 3.0 \times 10^{-6}$ s^{-1}

(b) $k = 2.2 \times 10^{-5}$ s^{-1}. $t_{1/2} = 0.693/2.2 \times 10^{-5}$ s$^{-1} = 3.15 \times 10^4 = 3.2 \times 10^4$ s

14.44   (a)   For a first order reaction, $t_{1/2} = 0.693/k$.

        $t_{1/2} = 0.693/0.271$ s$^{-1} = 2.5572 = 2.56$ s

(b)   For a first order reaction, $\ln[A]_t - \ln[A]_0 = -kt$. $\ln[A]_t = -kt + \ln[A]_0$

        $[A]_0 = 0.050$ *M* I_2, t = 5.12 s, k = 0.271 s^{-1}

        $\ln[I_2] = -0.271$ s^{-1} (5.12 s) $+ \ln(0.050)$

        $\ln[I_2] = -4.3833$, $[I_2] = 0.0125$ *M*

        Check. 5.12 s is 2 half-lives. $[I_2]$ should be reduced by a factor of 4, and it is.

14.45   *Analyze/Plan.* Follow the logic in Sample Exercise 14.7. In this reaction, pressure is a measure of concentration. In (a) we are given k, $[A]_0$, t and asked to find $[A]_t$, using Equation [14.13], the integrated form of the first-order rate law. In (b), $[A_t] = 0.1[A_0]$, find t. *Solve.*

(a) $\ln P_t = -kt + \ln P_0$; $P_0 = 450$ torr; $t = 60$ s

$\ln P_{60} = -4.5 \times 10^{-2}$ s^{-1}(60) + ln(450) = -2.70 + 6.109 = 3.409

$P_{60} = 30.24 = 30$ torr

(b) $P_t = 0.10\ P_0$; $\ln(P_t/P_0) = -kt$

$\ln(0.10\ P_0/P_0) = -kt$, ln(0.10) = -kt; -ln(0.10)/k = t

$t = -(-2.303)/4.5 \times 10^{-2}$ s^{-1} = 51.2 = 51 s

Check. From part (a), the pressure at 60 s is 30 torr, $P_t \sim 0.07\ P_0$. In part (b) we calculate the time where $P_t = 0.10\ P_0$ to be 51 s. This time should be smaller than 60 s, and it is. Data and results in the two parts are consistent.

14.46   (a)   Using Equation [14.13] for a first order reaction: $\ln[A]_t = -kt + \ln[A]_0$

5.0 min = 300 s; $[N_2O_5]_0 = (0.0250$ mol/2.0 L) = 0.0125 = 0.013 M

$\ln[N_2O_5]_{300} = -(6.82 \times 10^{-3}$ s^{-1})(300 s) + ln(0.0125)

$\ln[N_2O_5]_{300} = -2.0460 + (-4.3820) = -6.4280 = -6.43$

$[N_2O_5]_{300} = 1.616 \times 10^{-3} = 1.6 \times 10^{-3}\ M$; mol $N_2O_5 = 1.616 \times 10^{-3}\ M \times 2.0$ L

$$= 3.2 \times 10^{-3} \text{ mol}$$

(b) $[N_2O_5]_t = 0.010$ mol/2.0 L = 0.0050 M; $[N_2O_5]_0 = 0.0125\ M$

ln (0.0050) = $-(6.82 \times 10^{-3}$ s^{-1}) (t) + ln(0.0125)

$t = \dfrac{-[\ln(0.0050) - \ln(0.0125)]}{(6.82 \times 10^{-3} \text{s}^{-1})} = 134.35 = 1.3 \times 10^2 \text{ s} \times \dfrac{1 \text{ min}}{60 \text{ s}} = 2.24 = 2.2$ min

(c) $t_{1/2} = 0.693/k = 0.693/6.82 \times 10^{-3}$ s^{-1} = 101.6 = 102 s or 1.69 min

14.47   *Analyze/Plan.* Given reaction order, various values for t and P_t, find the rate constant for the reaction at this temperature. For a first-order reaction, a graph of lnP vs t is linear with as slope of –k.   *Solve.*

t(s)	$P_{SO_2Cl_2}$	$\ln P_{SO_2Cl_2}$
0	1.000	0
2500	0.947	−0.0545
5000	0.895	−0.111
7500	0.848	−0.165
10000	0.803	−0.219

Graph ln $P_{SO_2Cl_2}$ vs. time. (Pressure is a satisfactory unit for a gas, since the concentration in moles/liter is proportional to P.) The graph is linear with slope -2.19×10^{-5} s^{-1} as shown on the figure. The rate constant k = –slope = 2.19×10^{-5} s^{-1}.

14.48	t(s)	P_{CH_2NC}	$\ln P_{CH_3NC}$
	0	502	6.219
	2000	335	5.814
	5000	180	5.193
	8000	95.5	4.559
	12000	41.7	3.731
	15000	22.4	3.109

A graph of ln P vs t is linear with a slope of $-2.08 \times 10^{-4}\ s^{-1}$. The rate constant, k, = $-$slope = $2.08 \times 10^{-4}\ s^{-1}$. Half-life = $t_{1/2}$ = $0.693/k = 3.33 \times 10^3\ s$.

14.49   *Analyze/Plan.* Given: mol A, t. Change mol to *M* at various times. Make both first- and second-order plots to see which is linear.   *Solve.*

(a)

time(min)	mol A	[A] (M)	ln[A]	1/mol A
0	0.065	0.65	–0.43	1.5
10	0.051	0.51	–0.67	2.0
20	0.042	0.42	–0.87	2.4
30	0.036	0.36	–1.02	2.8
40	0.031	0.31	–1.17	3.2

The plot of 1/[A] vs time is linear, so the reaction is second-order in [A].

(b)   For a second-order reaction, a plot of 1/[A] vs. t is linear with slope k.

k = slope = $(3.2 - 2.0)\ M^{-1}$ / 30 min = $0.040\ M^{-1}\ min^{-1}$

(The best fit to the line yields slope = $0.042\ M^{-1}\ min^{-1}$.)

(c) $t_{1/2} = 1/k[A]_0 = 1/(0.040\ M^{-1}\ min^{-1})(0.65\ M) = 38.46 = 38$ min

(Using the "best-fit" slope, $t_{1/2} = 37$ min.)

14.50   (a)   Make both first- and second-order plots to see which is linear. Moles is a satisfactory concentration unit, since volume is constant.

time(s)	mol A	ln (mol A)	1/mol A
0	0.1000	–2.303	10.00
40	0.067	–2.70	14.9
80	0.045	–3.10	22.2
120	0.030	–3.51	33.3
160	0.020	–3.91	50.0

The plot of ln (mol A) vs time is linear, so the reaction is first-order in A.

(b) $k = -\text{slope} = - [-3.91 - (-2.70)]/120 = 0.010083 = 0.0101 \text{ s}^{-1}$
(The best fit to this line yields the same value for the slope, $0.01006 = 0.0101 \text{ s}^{-1}$)

(c) $t_{1/2} = 0.693/k = 0.693/0.010083 \text{ s}^{-1} = 68.7 \text{ s}$

14.51 *Analyze/Plan.* Follow the logic in Solution 14.49. Make both first and second order plots to see which is linear. *Solve.*

(a)

time(s)	$[NO_2](M)$	$\ln[NO_2]$	$1/[NO_2]$
0.0	0.100	–2.303	10.0
5.0	0.017	–4.08	59
10.0	0.0090	–4.71	110
15.0	0.0062	–5.08	160
20.0	0.0047	–5.36	210

The plot of $1/[NO_2]$ vs time is linear, so the reaction is second order in NO_2.

(b)   The slope of the line is $(210 - 59)\ M^{-1}\ /\ 15.0\ s = 10.07 = 10\ M^{-1}s^{-1} = k$. (The slope of the best-fit line is $10.02 = 10\ M^{-1}s^{-1}$.)

(c)   From the results above, the rate law is: rate $= k[NO_2]^2 = 10\ M^{-1}s^{-1}[NO_2]^2$
Using the rate law, calculate the rate at each of the given initial concentrations.

Rate @ $0.200\ M = 10\ M^{-1}s^{-1}[NO_2]^2 = 10\ M^{-1}s^{-1}[0.200\ M]^2 = 0.400\ M/s$

Rate @ $0.100\ M = 10\ M^{-1}s^{-1}[NO_2]^2 = 10\ M^{-1}s^{-1}[0.100\ M]^2 = 0.100\ M/s$

Rate @ $0.050\ M = 10\ M^{-1}s^{-1}[NO_2]^2 = 10\ M^{-1}s^{-1}[0.050\ M]^2 = 0.025\ M/s$

14.52   (a)   Make both first- and second-order plots to see which is linear.

time(min)	$[C_{12}H_{22}O_{11}](M)$	$\ln[C_{12}H_{22}O_{11}]$	$1/[C_{12}H_{22}O_{11}]$
0	0.316	–1.152	3.16
39	0.274	–1.295	3.65
80	0.238	–1.435	4.20
140	0.190	–1.661	5.26
210	0.146	–1.924	6.85

The plot of $\ln[C_{12}H_{22}O_{11}]$ is linear, so the reaction is first order in $C_{12}H_{22}O_{11}$.

(b) $k = -\text{slope} = -[-1.924 - (-1.295)]\ /\ 171\ \text{min} = 3.68 \times 10^{-3}\ \text{min}^{-1}$

(The slope of the best-fit line is $-3.67 \times 10^{-3}\ \text{min}^{-1}$.)

(c)   For a reaction zero-order in sucrose, the rate does not change as [sucrose] changes. A plot of [sucrose] vs time is linear with negative slope, until all reactant is consumed. $[\text{sucrose}]_t = -kt + [\text{sucrose}]_0$

@39 min, [sucrose] $= -3.68 \times 10^{-3}\ \text{min}^{-1}(39\ \text{min}) + 0.316\ M = 0.17\ M$

@80 min, [sucrose] $= -3.68 \times 10^{-3}\ \text{min}^{-1}(80\ \text{min}) + 0.316\ M = 0.022\ M$

@140 min, [sucrose] $= -3.68 \times 10^{-3}\ \text{min}^{-1}(140\ \text{min}) + 0.316\ M = 0\ M$

@210 min, [sucrose] $= 0\ M$. All sucrose is consumed at $(0.316/3.68 \times 10^{-3}\ \text{min}^{-1})$ $= 85.9\ \text{min}$.

14 Chemical Kinetics

Solutions to Exercises

Temperature and Rate (section 14.5)

14.53 (a) The energy of the collision and the orientation of the molecules when they collide determine whether a reaction will occur.

(b) According to the kinetic-molecular theory (Chapter 10), the higher the temperature, the greater the speed and kinetic energy of the molecules. Therefore, at a higher temperature, there are more total collisions and each collision is more energetic.

(c) Assuming other conditions remain the same, the rate and therefore the rate constant usually increase with an increase in reaction temperature.

14.54 (a) The orientation factor is less important in $H + Cl \rightarrow HCl$, because the reactants are monatomic and spherical (nondirectional); all collision orientations are equally effective.

(b) The kinetic-molecular theory tells us that at some temperature T, there will be a distribution of molecular speeds and kinetic energies, and that the average kinetic energy of the sample is proportional to temperature. That is, as temperature of the sample increases, the average speed and kinetic energy of the molecules increases. At higher temperatures, there will be more molecular collisions (owing to greater speeds) and more energetic collisions (owing to greater kinetic energies). Overall there will be more collisions that have sufficient energy to form an activated complex, and the reaction rate will be greater.

14.55 *Analyze/Plan.* Given the temperature and energy, use Equation [14.18] to calculate the fraction of Ar atoms that have at least this energy. *Solve.*

$$f = e^{-E_a/RT} \quad E_a = 10.0 \text{ kJ/mol} = 1.00 \times 10^4 \text{ J/mol}; \; T = 400 \text{ K} \, (127°C)$$

$$-E_a/RT = -\frac{1.00 \times 10^4 \text{ J/mol}}{400 \text{ K}} \times \frac{\text{mol - K}}{8.314 \text{ J}} = -3.0070 = -3.01$$

$$f = e^{-3.0070} = 4.9 \times 10^{-2}$$

At 400 K, approximately 1 out of 20 molecules has this kinetic energy.

14.56 (a) $f = e^{-E_a/RT} \quad E_a = 160 \text{ kJ/mol} = 1.60 \times 10^5 \text{ J/mol}, \; T = 500 \text{ K}$

$$-E_a/RT = -\frac{1.60 \times 10^5 \text{ J/mol}}{500 \text{ K}} \times \frac{\text{mol - K}}{8.314 \text{ J}} = -38.489 = -38.5$$

$$f = e^{-38.489} = 1.924 \times 10^{-17} = 2 \times 10^{-17}$$

(b) $-E_a/RT = -\dfrac{1.60 \times 10^5 \text{ J/mol}}{520 \text{ K}} \times \dfrac{\text{mol - K}}{8.314 \text{ J}} = -37.009 = -37.0$

$$f = e^{-37.009} = 8.45712 \times 10^{-17} = 8.46 \times 10^{-17}$$

$$\frac{f \text{ at } 520 \text{ K}}{f \text{ at } 500 \text{ K}} = \frac{8.46 \times 10^{-17}}{1.92 \times 10^{-17}} = 4.41$$

An increase of 20 K means that 4.41 times more molecules have this energy.

14.57   *Analyze/Plan.* Use the definitions of activation energy ($E_{max} - E_{react}$) and ΔE ($E_{prod} - E_{react}$) to sketch the graph and calculate E_a for the reverse reaction.   *Solve.*

(a)

$E_a = 7$ kJ

$\Delta E = -66$ kJ

(b) E_a(reverse) = 73 kJ

14.58   *Analyze/Plan.* Use the definitions of activation energy ($E_{max} - E_{react}$) and ΔE ($E_{prod} - E_{react}$) to sketch the graph and calculate E_a for the reverse reaction. *Solve.*

(a)

$E_a = 154$ kJ

$\Delta E = 136$ kJ

(b) E_a(reverse) = 18 kJ

14.59   (a)   False. If you compare two reactions with similar collision factors, the one with the larger activation energy will be *slower*.

(b)   False. A reaction that has a small rate constant will have either a small frequency factor (A), a large activation energy (E_a), or both.

(c)   True.

14.60   (a)   False. If you measure the rate constant for a reaction at different temperatures, you can calculate the overall activation energy, E_a, for the reaction.

(b)   False. Exothermic reactions are not necessarily faster than endothermic reactions. (The rate of a reaction is not determined by the overall enthalpy change going from reactants to products.)

(c)   False. If you double the temperature for a reaction, there is no change to the activation energy, E_a.

14.61   Assuming all collision factors (A) to be the same, reaction rate depends only on E_a; it is independent of ΔE. Based on the magnitude of E_a, reaction (b) is fastest and reaction (c) is slowest.

14.62 E_a for the reverse reaction is:

(a) $45 - (-25) = 70$ kJ   (b) $35 - (-10) = 45$ kJ   (c) $55 - 10 = 45$ kJ

Based on the magnitude of E_a, the reverse of reactions (b) and (c) occur at the same rate, which is faster than the reverse of reaction (a).

14.63   *Analyze/Plan.* Given k_1, at T_1, calculate k_2 at T_2. Change T to Kelvins, then use the Equation [14.21] to calculate k_2. *Solve.*

$T_1 = 20°C + 273 = 293$ K; $T_2 = 60°C + 273 = 333$ K; $k_1 = 2.75 \times 10^{-2} s^{-1}$

(a) $\ln\left(\dfrac{k_1}{k_2}\right) = \dfrac{E_a}{R}\left(\dfrac{1}{333} - \dfrac{1}{293}\right) = \dfrac{75.5 \times 10^3 \text{ J/mol}}{8.314 \text{ J/mol}}(-4.1 \times 10^{-4})$

$\ln(k_1/k_2) = -3.7229 = -3.7;$ $k_1/k_2 = 0.0242 = 0.02;$ $k_2 = \dfrac{0.0275 \text{ s}^{-1}}{0.0242} = 1.14 = 1 \text{ s}^{-1}$

(b) $\ln\left(\dfrac{k_1}{k_2}\right) = \dfrac{125 \times 10^3 \text{ J/mol}}{8.314 \text{ J/mol}}\left(\dfrac{1}{333} - \dfrac{1}{293}\right) = -6.1638 = -6.2$

$k_1/k_2 = 2.104 \times 10^{-3} = 2 \times 10^{-3}$; $k_2 = \dfrac{0.0275 \text{ s}^{-1}}{2.104 \times 10^{-3}} = 13.07 = 1 \times 10 \text{ s}^{-1}$

(c)   The method in parts (a) and (b) assumes that the collision model and thus the Arrhenious equation describe the kinetics of the reactions. That is, activation energy is constant over the temperature range under consideration. There is no assumption about temperature dependence of the frequency factor, because it drops out of the difference equation by subtraction.

14.64 $T_1 = 737°C + 273 = 1010$ K, $k_1 = 0.0796 \ M^{-1}s^{-1}$;

$T_2 = 947°C + 273 = 1220$ K, $k_2 = 0.0815 \ M^{-1}s^{-1}$

$\ln\left(\dfrac{k_1}{k_2}\right) = \dfrac{E_a}{R}\left(\dfrac{1}{T_2} - \dfrac{1}{T_1}\right)$

$\ln\left(\dfrac{0.0796}{0.0815}\right) = \dfrac{E_a}{8.314 \text{ J/mol}}\left(\dfrac{1}{1220} - \dfrac{1}{1010}\right)$

$-0.023589 = \dfrac{E_a \ (-1.704 \times 10^{-4})}{8.314 \text{ J/mol}}$

$E_a = \dfrac{8.314 \ (-0.023589) \text{ J/mol}}{(-1.704 \times 10^{-4})} = 1.151 \times 10^3 \text{ J/mol} = 1.15 \text{ kJ/mol}$

14.65   *Analyze/Plan.* Follow the logic in Sample Exercise 14.11.   *Solve.*

k	ln k	T(K)	1/T($\times 10^3$)
0.0521	−2.955	288	3.47
0.101	−2.293	298	3.36
0.184	−1.693	308	3.25
0.332	−1.103	318	3.14

The slope, -5.71×10^3, equals $-E_a/R$. Thus,
$E_a = 5.71 \times 10^3 \times 8.314$ J/mol $= 47.5$ kJ/mol.

14.66

k	ln k	T(K)	1/T($\times 10^3$)
0.028	−3.58	600	1.67
0.22	−1.51	650	1.54
1.3	0.26	700	1.43
6.0	1.79	750	1.33
23	3.14	800	1.25

Using the relationship $\ln k = \ln A - E_a/RT$, the slope, $-15.94 \times 10^3 = -16 \times 10^3$, is $-E_a/R$.
$E_a = 15.94 \times 10^3 \times 8.314$ J/mol $= 1.3 \times 10^2$ kJ/mol. To calculate A, we will use the rate data at 700 K. From the equation given above, $0.262 = \ln A - 15.94 \times 10^3/700$;
$\ln A = 0.262 + 22.771$. $A = 1.0 \times 10^{10}$.

14.67   *Analyze/Plan.* Given E_a, find the ratio of rates for a reaction at two temperatures. Assuming initial concentrations are the same at the two temperatures, the ratio of rates will be the ratio of rate constants, k_1/k_2. Use Equation [14.21] to calculate this ratio.   *Solve.*

$T_1 = 50°C + 273 = 323$ K; $T_2 = 0°C + 273 = 273$ K

$$\ln\left(\frac{k_1}{k_2}\right) = \frac{E_a}{R}\left[\frac{1}{T_2} - \frac{1}{T_1}\right] = \frac{65.7 \text{ kJ/mol}}{8.314 \text{ J/mol}} \times \frac{1000 \text{ J}}{1 \text{ kJ}}\left[\frac{1}{273} - \frac{1}{323}\right]$$

$\ln(k_1/k_2) = 7.902 \times 10^3 (5.670 \times 10^{-4}) = 4.481 = 4.5$; $k_1/k_2 = 88.3 = 9 \times 10^1$

The reaction will occur 90 times faster at 50°C, assuming equal initial concentrations and Arrhenius kinetics.

14.68   (a) $T_1 = 77°F$; $°C = 5/9 (°F - 32) = 5/9 (77 - 32) = 25°C = 298$ K

              $T_2 = 59°F$; $°C = 5/9 (59-32) = 15°C = 288$ K; $k_1/k_2 = 6$

$$\ln\left(\frac{k_1}{k_2}\right) = \frac{E_a}{R}\left[\frac{1}{T_2} - \frac{1}{T_1}\right]; \quad \ln(6) = \frac{E_a}{8.314 \text{ J/mol}}\left[\frac{1}{288} - \frac{1}{298}\right]$$

$$E_a = \frac{\ln(6)(8.314 \text{ J/mol})}{1.165 \times 10^{-4}} = 1.28 \times 10^5 \text{ J} = 1.3 \times 10^2 \text{ kJ/mol}$$

$T_1 = 77°F = 25°C = 298 \text{ K}; T_2 = 41°F = 5°C = 278 \text{ K}, k_1/k_2 = 40$

$$\ln(40) = \frac{E_a}{8.314 \text{ J/mol}}\left[\frac{1}{278} - \frac{1}{296}\right]; \quad E_a = \frac{\ln(40)(8.314 \text{ J/mol})}{2.414 \times 10^{-4}}$$

$E_a = 1.27 \times 10^5 \text{ J} = 1.3 \times 10^2 \text{ kJ/mol}$

The values are amazingly consistent, considering the precision of the data.

(b)   For a first order reaction, $t_{1/2} = 0.693/k$, $k = 0.693/t_{1/2}$

k_1 at 298 K $= 0.693/2.7 \text{ yr} = 0.257 = 0.26 \text{ yr}^{-1}$

$T_1 = 298 \text{ K}, T_2 = 273 - 15°C = 258 \text{ K}$

$$\ln\left(\frac{0.257}{k_2}\right) = \frac{1.27 \times 10^5 \text{ J}}{8.314 \text{ J/mol}}\left[\frac{1}{258} - \frac{1}{298}\right] = 7.9497$$

$0.257/k_2 = e^{7.9497} = 2.835 \times 10^3$; $k_2 = 0.257/2.835 \times 10^3 = 9.066 \times 10^{-5} = 9.1 \times 10^{-5} \text{ yr}^{-1}$

$t_{1/2} = 0.693/k = 0.693/9.066 \times 10^{-5} = 7.64 \times 10^3 \text{ yr} = 7.6 \times 10^3 \text{ yr}$

Reaction Mechanisms (section 14.6)

14.69   (a)   An *elementary reaction* is a process that occurs in a single event; the order is given by the coefficients in the balanced equation for the reaction.

          (b)   A *unimolecular* elementary reaction involves only one reactant molecule; the activated complex is derived from a single molecule. A *bimolecular* elementary reaction involves two reactant molecules in the activated complex and the overall process.

          (c)   A *reaction mechanism* is a series of elementary reactions that describe how an overall reaction occurs and explain the experimentally determined rate law.

14.70   (a)   The *molecularity* of a process indicates the number of molecules that participate as reactants in the process. A unimolecular process has one reactant molecule, a bimolecular process has two reactant molecules and a termolecular process has three reactant molecules.

          (b)   Termolecular processes are rare because it is highly unlikely that three molecules will simultaneously collide with the correct energy and orientation to form an activated complex.

          (c)   An *intermediate* is a substance that is produced and then consumed during a chemical reaction. It does not appear in the balanced equation for the overall reaction.

14.71   A *transition state* is a high energy complex formed when one or more reactants collide and distort in a way that can lead to formation of product(s). An *intermediate* is the product of an early elementary reaction in a multistep reaction mechanism. A transition state occurs at an an energy maximum or peak of a reaction profile such as Figure 14.20. An intermediate exists at an energy minimum or trough of a reaction profile. Every reaction, single- or multi-step, has a transition state. Only multistep reactions have intermediates.

14.72 A *rate-determining step* is the slow step in a reaction mechanism. It limits the overall reaction rate.

14.73 *Analyze/Plan.* Elementary reactions occur as a single step, so the molecularity is determined by the number of reactant molecules; the rate law reflects reactant stoichiometry. *Solve.*

   (a) unimolecular, rate = $k[Cl_2]$

   (b) bimolecular, rate = $k[OCl^-][H_2O]$

   (c) bimolecular, rate = $k[NO][Cl_2]$

14.74 (a) bimolecular, rate = $k[NO]^2$

   (b) unimolecular, rate = $k[C_3H_6]$

   (c) unimolecular, rate = $k[SO_3]$

14.75 *Analyze/Plan.* Use the definitions of the terms 'intermediate' and 'exothermic', along with the characteristics of reaction profiles, to answer the questions. *Solve.*

   This is a three-step mechanism, $A \rightarrow B$, $B \rightarrow C$, and $C \rightarrow D$.

   (a) There are 2 intermediates, B and C.

   (b) There are 3 energy maxima in the reaction profile, so there are 3 transition states.

   (c) Step $C \rightarrow D$ has the lowest activation energy, so it is fastest.

   (d) The energy of D is slightly greater than the energy of A, so the overall reaction is endothermic.

14.76 (a) Two elementary reactions; two energy maxima

   (b) One intermediate; one energy minimum between reactants and products

   (c) The second step is rate-limiting; second energy maximum and E_a is larger.

   (d) Overall reaction is exothermic; energy of products is lower than energy of reactants.

14.77 *Analyze/Plan.* Follow the logic in Sample Exercise 14.14. *Solve.*

   (a) $H_2(g) + ICl(g) \rightarrow HI(g) + HCl(g)$

   $\underline{HI(g) + ICl(g) \rightarrow I_2(g) + HCl(g)}$
   $H_2(g) + 2ICl(g) \rightarrow I_2(g) + 2HCl(g)$

   (b) Intermediates are produced and consumed during reaction. HI is the intermediate.

   (c) The slow step determines the rate law for the overall reaction. If the first step is slow, the observed rate law is: rate = $k[H_2][ICl]$.

14.78 (a) $2H_2O_2(aq) \rightarrow 2H_2O(l) + O_2(g)$

   (b) $IO^-(aq)$ is the intermediate.

   (c) rate = $k[H_2O_2][I^-]$

14.79   *Analyze.* Given data on concentration of a reactant vs time, determine whether the proposed reaction mechanism is consistent with the data. *Plan.* Based on the graph, decide the order of reaction with respect to [NO]. Write the two possible rate laws, depending on which step is rate-determining. Decide if one of the rate laws, and thus the mechanism, is consistent with the rate data. *Solve.*

The graph of 1/[NO] vs time is linear with positive slope, indicating that the reaction is second order in [NO]. The rate law will include $[NO]^2$. We have no information about reaction order with respect to $[Cl_2]$.

If the first step is slow, the observed rate law is the rate law for this step: rate = $k[NO][Cl_2]$. Since the observed rate law is second-order in [NO], the second step must be slow relative to the first step. Follow the logic in Sample Exercise 14.15 for determining the rate law of a mechanism with a fast initial step.

From the rate-determining second step, rate = $k[NOCl_2][NO]$.

Assuming the first step is a fast equilibrium, $k_1 [NO][Cl_2] = k_{-1} [NOCl_2]$.

Solving for $[NOCl_2]$ in terms of $[NO][Cl_2]$, $[NOCl_2] = \dfrac{k_1}{k_{-1}}[NO][Cl_2]$

$$rate = \dfrac{k_2 k_1}{k_{-1}}[NO][Cl_2][NO] = [NO]^2[Cl_2]$$

This rate law is second order in [NO]. It is consistent with the observed data.

[The graph of 1/[NO] vs time is linear with positive slope, indicating that the reaction is second order in [NO]. The rate law obtained by assuming the second step is rate determining is: rate = $[NO]^2[Cl_2]$. The two step mechanism is consistent with the data.]

14.80   (a)   i. $HBr + O_2 \rightarrow HOOBr$

               ii. $HOOBr + HBr \rightarrow 2HOBr$

               iii. $\underline{2HOBr + 2HBr \rightarrow 2H_2O + 2Br_2}$
                       $4HBr + O_2 \rightarrow 2H_2O + 2Br_2$

        (b)   The observed rate law is: rate = $k[HBr][O_2]$, the rate law for the first elementary step. The first step must be rate-determining.

        (c)   HOOBr and HOBr are both intermediates; HOOBr is produced in i and consumed in ii and HOBr is produced in ii and consumed in iii.

        (d)   Since the first step is rate-determining, it is possible that neither of the intermediates accumulates enough to be detected. This does not disprove the mechanism, but indicates that steps ii and iii are very fast, relative to step i.

Catalysis (section 14.7)

14.81   (a)   A catalyst is a substance that changes (usually increases) the speed of a chemical reaction without undergoing a permanent chemical change itself.

(b)   A homogeneous catalyst is in the same phase as the reactants; a heterogeneous catalyst is in a different phase and is usually a solid.

(c)   A catalyst has no effect on the overall enthalpy change for a reaction. A catalyst does affect activation energy, E_a, which is one way that it changes reaction rate. It can also affect the frequency factor, A.

14.82   (a)   The smaller the particle size of a solid catalyst, the greater the surface area. The greater the surface area, the more active sites and the greater the increase in reaction rate.

(b)   Adsorption is the binding of reactants onto the surface of the heterogeneous catalyst. It is usually the first step in the catalyzed reaction.

14.83   *Analyze/Plan.* Use the structure and unit cell edge of Pt, along with the formulas for volume and surface area of a sphere, to calculate the number of Pt atoms in a 2-nm sphere and on the surface of a 2-nm sphere.

(a)   For a Pt sphere with a 2.0 nm diameter, radius = 1.0 nm.

$$V = 4/3\pi r^3 = \frac{4\pi(1.0 \text{ nm})^3}{3} \times \frac{10^3 \text{Å}^3}{1^3 \text{ nm}^3} = 4.188879 \times 10^3 = 4.2 \times 10^3 \text{Å}^3$$

In a face-centered cubic metal structure, there are 4 metal atoms per unit cell. The volume of the unit cell is $(3.924 \text{ Å})^3 = 60.42 \text{ Å}^3$

$$\frac{4 \text{ Pt atoms}}{60.42 \text{ Å}^3} \times 4.1889 \times 10^3 \text{Å}^3 = 277.3 = 2.8 \times 10^2 \text{ Pt atoms in a 2.0 - nm sphere}$$

(b)   Assume that the "footprint" of an atom is its cross-sectional area, the area of a circle with the radius of the atom. The area of this circle is πr^2. The diameter, d, of a Pt atom is 2.8 Å, so r = d/2 = 1.4 Å. The footprint of the Pt atom is then

$$\pi(1.4 \text{ Å})^2 = 6.1575 = 6.2 \text{ Å}^2$$

The surface area of the 2.0-nm sphere is

$$4\pi r^2 = 4\pi(1.0 \text{ nm})^2 \times \frac{10^2 \text{Å}^2}{1^2 \text{ nm}^2} = 12.56637 \times 10^2 = 1.3 \times 10^3 \text{Å}^2$$

$$\frac{1 \text{ Pt atoms}}{6.1575 \text{ Å}^2} \times 1.2566 \times 10^3 \text{Å}^2 = 204.1 = 2.0 \times 10^2 \text{ surface Pt atoms on a 2.0 - nm sphere.}$$

(c) $\dfrac{204 \text{ surface Pt atoms}}{277 \text{ total Pt atoms}} \times 100 = 74\%$ Pt atoms on the surface

(d)   For a 5.0-nm Pt sphere, radius = 2.5 nm

$$V = 4/3\pi r^3 = \frac{4\pi(2.50 \text{ nm})^3}{3} \times \frac{10^3 \text{Å}^3}{1^3 \text{ nm}^3} = 65.4498 \times 10^3 = 6.5 \times 10^4 \text{Å}^3$$

$$\frac{4 \text{ Pt atoms}}{60.42 \text{ Å}^3} \times 65.4498 \times 10^3 \text{Å}^3 = 4,333 = 4.3 \times 10^3 \text{ Pt atoms in a 5.0 - nm sphere}$$

The surface area of the 5.0-nm sphere is

$$4\pi r^2 = 4\pi(2.5 \text{ nm})^2 \times \frac{10^2 \text{Å}^2}{1^2 \text{ nm}^2} = 7853.98 = 7.9 \times 10^3 \text{Å}^2$$

$$\frac{1 \text{ Pt atoms}}{6.1575 \text{ Å}^2} \times 7.854 \times 10^3 \text{ Å}^2 = 1275.5 = 1.3 \times 10^3 \text{ surface Pt atoms on a } 5.0\text{-nm sphere}$$

$$\frac{1276 \text{ surface Pt atoms}}{4333 \text{ total Pt atoms}} \times 100 = 29\% \text{ Pt atoms on the surface}$$

The calculations in parts (b) and (d) overestimate the number of Pt atoms on the surface of the sphere, because they do not account for empty space between atoms. For the purpose of comparison, it is most important that we use the same method for both spheres.

[Alternatively, use one face of a face-entered cubic unit cell as a model for the surface area that Pt atoms will occupy. On a face, there is the cross-section of 1 Pt atoms in the center and ¼ Pt atom at each corner. This amounts to the cross-sections of two Pt atoms in $(3.924 \text{ Å})^2 = 15.398 = 15.4 \text{ Å}^2$

$$\frac{2 \text{ Pt atoms}}{15.40 \text{ Å}^3} \times 1.2566 \times 10^3 \text{ Å}^2 = 163.2 = 1.6 \times 10^2 \text{ surface Pt atoms on a } 2.0\text{-nm sphere.}$$

$$\frac{163 \text{ surface Pt atoms}}{277 \text{ total Pt atoms}} \times 100 = 59\% \text{ Pt atoms on the surface}$$

Similarly, in a 5.0-nm sphere, there are 1.0×10^3 Pt atoms on the surface, 24% of the total Pt atoms.]

(e)   Both surface models predict that the 2.0-nm sphere will be more catalytically active, because it has a much greater percentage of its atoms on the surface, where they can participate in the chemical reaction.

14.84   For an acid-catalyzed reaction in solution, H^+ is a homogeneous catalyst. It is consumed and then regenerated during the reaction. (This assumes that H^+ is present in excess and that H^+ is not a reactant, that the reactants are neither acids nor bases.) The $[H^+]$ is a maximum at $t = 0$ and when the reaction is complete.

Time or Reaction Progress

14.85   (a) $2[NO_2(g) + SO_2(g) \rightarrow NO(g) + SO_3(g)]$
                  $2NO(g) + O_2(g) \rightarrow 2NO_2(g)$

                $2SO_2(g) + O_2(g) \rightarrow 2SO_3(g)$

     (b) $NO_2(g)$ is a catalyst because it is consumed and then reproduced in the reaction sequence. ($NO(g)$ is an intermediate because it is produced and then consumed.)

     (c)   Since NO_2 is in the same state as the other reactants, this is homogeneous catalysis.

14.86   (a) $2[NO(g) + N_2O(g) \rightarrow N_2(g) + NO_2(g)]$

                            $\underline{2NO_2(g) \rightarrow 2NO(g) + O_2(g)}$

                          $2N_2O(g) \rightarrow 2N_2(g) + O_2(g)$

      (b)   An intermediate is produced and then consumed during the course of the reaction. A catalyst is consumed and then reproduced. In other words, the catalyst is present when the reaction sequence begins and after the last step is completed. In this reaction, NO is the catalyst and NO_2 is an intermediate.

      (c)   No. The proposed mechanism cannot be ruled out, based on the behavior of NO_2. NO_2 functions as an intermediate; it is produced and then consumed during the reaction. That there is no measurable build-up of NO_2 indicates the first step is slow relative to the second; as soon as NO_2 is produced by the slow first step, it is consumed by the faster second step.

14.87   (a)   When using a powdered metal catalyst, only a small percentage of the metal atoms are at the surface of the bulk material and catalytically active. Use of chemically stable supports such as alumina and silica makes it possible to obtain very large surface areas per unit mass of the precious metal catalyst. This is so because the metal can be deposited in a very thin, even monomolecular, layer on the surface of the support.

      (b)   The greater the surface area of the catalyst, the more reaction sites, and the greater the rate of the catalyzed reaction.

14.88   (a)   Catalytic converters are heterogeneous catalysts that adsorb gaseous CO and hydrocarbons and speed up their oxidation to $CO_2(g)$ and $H_2O(g)$. They also adsorb nitrogen oxides, NO_x, and speed up their reduction to $N_2(g)$ and $O_2(g)$. If a catalytic converter is working effectively, the exhaust gas should have very small amounts of the undesirable gases CO, $(NO)_x$ and hydrocarbons.

      (b)   The high temperatures could increase the rate of the desired catalytic reactions given in part (a). It could also increase the rate of undesirable reactions such as corrosion, which decrease the lifetime of the catalytic converter.

      (c)   The rate of flow of exhaust gases over the converter will determine the rate of adsorption of CO, $(NO)_x$ and hydrocarbons onto the catalyst and thus the rate of conversion to desired products. Too fast an exhaust flow leads to less than maximum adsorption. A very slow flow leads to back pressure and potential damage to the exhaust system. Clearly the flow rate must be adjusted to balance chemical and mechanical efficiency of the catalytic converter.

14.89   As illustrated in Figure 14.24, the two C–H bonds that exist on each carbon of the ethylene molecule before adsorption are retained in the process in which a D atom is added to each C (assuming we use D_2 rather than H_2). To put two deuteriums on a single carbon, it is necessary that one of the already existing C–H bonds in ethylene be broken while the molecule is adsorbed, so the H atom moves off as an adsorbed atom, and is replaced by a D. This requires a larger activation energy than simply adsorbing C_2H_4 and adding one D atom to each carbon.

14.90   Just as the π electrons in C_2H_4 are attracted to the surface of a hydrogenation catalyst, the nonbonding electron density on S causes compounds of S to be attracted to these same surfaces. Strong interactions could cause the sulfur compounds to be permanently attached to the surface, blocking active sites and reducing adsorption of alkenes for hydrogenation.

14.91   (a)   Living organisms operate efficiently in a very narrow temperature range; heating to increase reaction rate is not an option. Therefore, the role of enzymes as homogeneous catalysts that speed up desirable reactions without heating and undesirable side-effects is crucial for biological systems.

        (b)   *catalase*: $2H_2O_2 \rightarrow 2H_2O + O_2$; *nitrogenase*: $N_2 \rightarrow 2NH_3$ (nitrogen fixation)

        (c)   This model for enzyme kinetics is similar to the mechanism detailed in Sample Exercise 14.15, where step one is a fast equilibrium and step two is slow and rate-determining. This model assumes that the rate of the bound substrate, ES, being chemically transformed into bound product is slow and rate-determining.

14.92   The individual structure of each enzyme molecule leads to a unique coiling and folding pattern. The resulting shape and electronic properties of the active site in each enzyme leads to its substrate specificity.

14.93   Let k and E_a equal the rate constant and activation energy without the enzyme (uncatalyzed). Let k_c and E_{ac} equal the rate constant and activation energy with the enzyme (catalyzed). A is the same for the uncatalyzed and catalyzed reactions. The difference in activation energies is $E_{ac} - E_a$, $k_c = 1.0 \times 10^6$ s^{-1}, k = 0.039 s^{-1}, T = 25°C = 298 K.

        According to Equation [14.20], ln k = E_a/RT + ln A. Subtracting ln k from ln k_c

$$\ln k_c - \ln k = \left[\frac{-E_{ac}}{RT}\right] + \ln A - \left[\frac{-E_a}{RT}\right] - \ln A$$

$$\ln (k_c/k) = \frac{E_a - E_{ac}}{RT}; \quad E_a - E_{ac} = RT \ln (k_c/k)$$

$$E_a - E_{ac} = \frac{8.314 \text{ J}}{\text{mol - K}} \times 298 \text{ K} \times \ln\frac{1.0 \times 10^6}{0.039} = 42,267 \text{ J} = 42.267 \text{ kJ} = 42 \text{ kJ}$$

        Carbonic anyhdrase lowers the activation energy of the reaction by 42 kJ.

14.94   (a) $(NH_2)_2C{=}O(aq) + H_2O(l) \rightarrow CO_2(g) + 2 NH_3(aq)$

        (b)   According to Equation [14.20], ln k = E_a/RT + ln A. Subtracting ln k from ln k_c

$$\ln k_c - \ln k = \left[\frac{-E_{ac}}{RT_c}\right] + \ln A - \left[\frac{-E_a}{RT}\right] - \ln A; \quad \ln k_c - \ln k = \left[\frac{-E_{ac}}{RT_c}\right] - \left[\frac{-E_a}{RT}\right]$$

$$\ln (3.4 \times 10^4) - \ln (4.15 \times 10^{-5}) = \left[\frac{-E_{ac}}{8.314(294)}\right] - \left[\frac{-E_a}{8.314(373)}\right]$$

        20.5239(8.314)(294)(373) = 294 E_a – 373 E_{ac} ; Dividing through by 294:

        20.5239(8.314)(373) = E_a – (1.27)E_{ac} ; 63,647 J = 64 kJ = E_a – (1.27)E_{ac}

        Dividing though by 373: 50,167 J = 50 kJ = (0.788)E_a – E_{ac}

        (E_a – E_{ac}) is somewhere between 50 kJ and 64 kJ. This is a substantial reduction in activation energy for the enzyme-catalyzed reaction.

14.95 *Analyze/Plan.* Let k = the rate constant for the uncatalyzed reaction,

k_c = the rate constant for the catalyzed reaction

According to Equation [14.20], $\ln k = -E_a/RT + \ln A$

Subtracting $\ln k$ from $\ln k_c$,

$$\ln k_c - \ln k = -\left[\frac{55\ kJ/mol}{RT} + \ln A\right] - \left[-\frac{95\ kJ/mol}{RT} + \ln A\right]. \quad Solve.$$

(a) RT = 8.314 J/mol-K × 298 K × 1 kJ/1000 J = 2.478 kJ/mol; ln A is the same for both reactions.

$$\ln(k_c/k) = \frac{95\ kJ/mol - 55\ kJ/mol}{2.478\ kJ/mol}; \quad k_c/k = 1.024 \times 10^7 = 1 \times 10^7$$

The catalyzed reaction is approximately 10,000,000 (ten million) times faster at 25°C.

(b) RT = 8.314 J/mol-K × 398 K × 1 kJ/1000 J = 3.309 kJ/mol

$$\ln(k_c/k) = \frac{40\ kJ/mol}{3.309\ kJ/mol}; \quad k_c/k = 1.778 \times 10^5 = 2 \times 10^5$$

The catalyzed reaction is 200,000 times faster at 125°C.

14.96 Let k and E_a equal the rate constant and activation energy for the uncatalyzed reaction. Let k_c and E_{ac} equal the rate constant and activation energy of the catalyzed reaction. A is the same for the uncatalyzed and catalyzed reactions. $k_c/k = 1 \times 10^5$, T = 37°C = 310 K.

According to Equation [14.20], $\ln k = -E_a/RT + \ln A$. Subtracting $\ln k$ from $\ln k_c$

$$\ln k_c - \ln k = \left[\frac{-E_{ac}}{RT}\right] + \ln A - \left[\frac{-E_a}{RT}\right] - \ln A$$

$$\ln(k_c/k) = \frac{E_a - E_{ac}}{RT}; \quad E_a - E_{ac} = RT \ln(k_c/k)$$

$$E_a - E_{ac} = \frac{8.314\ J}{mol\text{-}K} \times 310\ K \times \ln(1 \times 10^5) = 2.966 \times 10^4\ J = 29.66\ kJ = 3 \times 10^1\ kJ$$

The enzyme must lower the activation energy by 30 kJ in order to achieve a 1×10^5-fold increase in reaction rate.

Additional Exercises

14.97 A balanced chemical equation shows the overall, net change of a chemical reaction. Most reactions occur as a series of (elementary) steps. The rate law contains only those reactants that form the transition state of the rate-determining step. If a reaction occurs in a single step, the rate law can be written directly from the balanced equation for the step.

14.98 $$rate = \frac{-\Delta[H_2S]}{\Delta t} = \frac{\Delta[Cl^-]}{2\Delta t} = k[H_2S][Cl_2]$$

$$\frac{-\Delta[H_2S]}{\Delta t} = (3.5 \times 10^{-2}\ M^{-1}s^{-1})(2.0 \times 10^{-4}\ M)(0.025\ M) = 1.75 \times 10^{-7} = 1.8 \times 10^{-7}\ M/s$$

$$\frac{\Delta[Cl^-]}{\Delta t} = \frac{-2\Delta[H_2S]}{\Delta t} = 2(1.75 \times 10^{-7} \ M/s) = 3.5 \times 10^{-7} \ M/s$$

14.99   (a) $rate = \dfrac{-\Delta[NO]}{2\Delta t} = \dfrac{-\Delta[O_2]}{\Delta t} = \dfrac{9.3 \times 10^{-5} \ M/s}{2} = 4.7 \times 10^{-5} \ M/s$

      (b,c) $rate = k[NO]^2[O_2]; \quad k = rate/[NO]^2[O_2]$

$$k = \frac{4.7 \times 10^{-5} \ M/s}{(0.040 \ M)^2 (0.035 \ M)} = 0.8393 = 0.84 \ M^{-2} \, s^{-1}$$

      (d)   Since the reaction is second order in NO, if the [NO] is increased by a factor of 1.8, the rate would increase by a factor of 1.8^2, or $(3.24) = 3.2$.

14.100   (a)   The rate increases by a factor of nine when $[C_2O_4{}^{2-}]$ triples (compare experiments 1 and 2). The rate doubles when $[HgCl_2]$ doubles (compare experiments 2 and 3). The apparant rate law is: $rate = k[HgCl_2][C_2O_4{}^{2-}]^2$

      (b) $k = \dfrac{rate}{[HgCl_2][C_2O_4^{2-}]^2}$ Using the data for Experiment 1,

$$k = \frac{(3.2 \times 10^{-5} \ M/s)}{[0.164 \ M][0.15 \ M]^2} = 8.672 \times 10^{-3} = 8.7 \times 10^{-3} \ M^{-2} s^{-1}$$

      (c) $rate = (8.672 \times 10^{-3} \ M^{-2} s^{-1})(0.100 \ M)(0.25 \ M)^2 = 5.4 \times 10^{-5} \ M/s$

14.101   The units of rate are M/s. The reaction must be second order overall if the units of the rate constant are $M^{-1} \, s^{-1}$. If $rate = k[NO_2]^x$, then the cumulative units of $[NO_2]^x$ must be M^2, and $x = 2$.

       If $[NO_2]_0 = 0.100 \ M$ and $[NO_2]_t = 0.025 \ M$, use the integrated form of the second order rate equation, $\dfrac{1}{[A]_t} = kt + \dfrac{1}{[A]_0}$, Equation [14.14], to solve for t.

$$\frac{1}{0.025 \ M} = 0.63 \ M^{-1}s^{-1} \ (t) + \frac{1}{0.100 \ M}; \ \frac{(40 - 10) \ M^{-1}}{0.63 \ M^{-1}s^{-1}} = t = 47.62 = 48 \ s.$$

14.102   For a first order reaction, $t_{1/2} = 0.633/k$. For a second order reaction, $t_{1/2} = 1/k[A]_0$. Half-life is constant over the course of the reaction for first order reactions. Although second order half-life does not appear to depend on t, the value of "$[A]_0$" does change over the course of the reaction, and $t_{1/2}$ increases with time. (For a zero reaction, $t_{1/2}$ decreases with time.)

       The rate law for reaction (1) must be first order, because that is the only reaction type that has a constant half-life. Reaction (2), where $t_{1/2}$ increases with time, is second order.

14.103   (a) $[A]_0$ has been halved four times after four half-lives. That is, $[A]_t = (1/2)^4[A]_0 = (1/16) [A]_0$. Monitor [A]; when it reaches 1/16 of the initial concentration, the reaction has proceeded for four half-lives.

(b)   For a reaction this slow, the graph of [A] vs t is very shallow.   If the reaction takes 6 days to complete 4 half-lives, the half-life is 1.5 days or 18 hours.   Data taken for a period of 2 hours, or 0.08 days, covers a very small portion of the curve and appears linear.

14.104   (a) $t_{1/2} = 0.693/k = 0.693/7.0 \times 10^{-4}\,s^{-1} = 990 = 9.9 \times 10^2\,s$

        (b) $k = \dfrac{0.693}{t_{1/2}} = \dfrac{0.693}{56.3\,min} \times \dfrac{1\,min}{60\,s} = 2.05 \times 10^{-4}\,s^{-1}$

14.105   *Analyze.* Given rate constants for the decay of two radioisotopes, determine half-lives, decay rates, and amount remaining after three half-lives. *Plan.* Determine reaction order.   Based on reaction-order, select the appropriate relationships for (a) rate constant and half-life and (c) rate-constant, time and concentration.   In this example, mass is a measure of concentration.

Solve. Decay of radioiosotopes is a first-order process, since only one species is involved and the decay is not initiated by collision.

        (a)   For a first-order process, $t_{1/2} = 0.693/k$.

                ^{241}Am: $t_{1/2} = 0.693/1.6 \times 10^{-3}\,yr^{-1} = 433.1 = 4.3 \times 10^2\,yr$

                ^{125}I: $t_{1/2} = 0.693/0.011\,day^{-1} = 63.00 = 63$ days

        (b)   For a given sample size, half of the ^{241}Am sample decays in 433 years, whereas half of the ^{125}I sample decays in 63 days. ^{125}I decays at a much faster rate.

        (c)   For a first order process, $\ln[A]_t - \ln[A]_0 = -kt$. $\ln[A]_t = -kt + \ln[A]_0$.

                $[A]_0 = 1.0$ mg; $t = 3\,t_{1/2}$.

                ^{241}Am: $t = 3\,t_{1/2} = 3(433.1\,yr) = 1.299 \times 10^3 = 1.3 \times 10^3$ yr

                $\ln[Am]_t = -1.6 \times 10^{-3}\,yr^{-1}\,(1.299 \times 10^3\,yr) - \ln(1.0) = -2.079 - 0 = -2.08$

                $[Am]_t = 0.125 = 0.13$ mg

                or, mass ^{241}Am remaining $= 1.0\,mg/2^3 = 0.125 = 0.13$ mg

                ^{125}I: For the same size starting sample and number of elapsed half-lives, the same mass, 0.13 mg ^{125}I, will remain. (The difference is that the elapsed time of 3 half-lives (for ^{125}I is 3(63) = 189 days = 0.52 yr, vs. 433 yr for ^{241}Am.)

        (d)   Again, for a first order process, $\ln[A]_t - \ln[A]_0 = -kt$. $\ln[A]_t = -kt + \ln[A]_0$.

                $[A]_0 = 1.0$ mg; $t = 4$ days.

$k_{AM} = 1.6 \times 10^{-3} \text{ yr}^{-1} (1 \text{ yr}/365 \text{ days}) = 4.3836 \times 10^{-6} = 4.4 \times 10^{-6} \text{ day}^{-1}$

^{241}Am: $\ln [\text{Am}]_t = -4.4 \times 10^{-6} \text{ day}^{-1} (4 \text{ days}) - \ln (1.0) = -1.7 \times 10^{-5} - 0 = -1.7 \times 10^{-5}$

The amount of ^{241}Am remaining after 4 days is 0.99998 mg, to three significant figures, 1.00 mg.

^{125}I: $\ln [\text{I}]_t = -0.011 \text{ day}^{-1} (4 \text{ days}) - \ln (1.0) = -0.044 - 0 = -0.044$

The amount of ^{125}I remaining after 4 days is 0.957 grams.

14.106   (a) $k = (8.56 \times 10^{-5} M/s)/(0.200 M) = 4.28 \times 10^{-4} \text{ s}^{-1}$

       (b) $\ln [\text{urea}] = -(4.28 \times 10^{-4} \text{s}^{-1} \times 4.00 \times 10^3 \text{ s}) + \ln (0.500)$

            $\ln [\text{urea}] = -1.712 - 0.693 = -2.405 = -2.41; [\text{urea}] = 0.0903 = 0.090 \, M$

       (c) $t_{1/2} = 0.693/k = 0.693/4.28 \times 10^{-4} \text{ s}^{-1} = 1.62 \times 10^3 \text{ s}$

14.107   (a) $A = \varepsilon bc$, Equation [14.5]. $A = 0.605$, $\varepsilon = 5.60 \times 10^3 \text{ cm}^{-1} M^{-1}$, $b = 1.00 \text{ cm}$

            $c = \dfrac{A}{\varepsilon b} = \dfrac{0.605}{(5.60 \times 10^3 \text{ cm}^{-1} M^{-1})(1.00 \text{ cm})} = 1.080 \times 10^{-4} = 1.08 \times 10^{-4} \, M$

       (b)   Calculate $[c]_t$ using Beer's law. We calculated $[c]_0$ in part (a). Use Equation [14.13] to calculate k.

            $A_{30} = \varepsilon bc_{30}; c_{30} = \dfrac{A_{30}}{\varepsilon b} = \dfrac{0.250}{(5.60 \times 10^3 \text{ cm}^{-1} M^{-1})(1.00 \text{ cm})} = 4.464 \times 10^{-5} \, M$

            $\ln[c]_t = -kt + \ln[c]_0; \dfrac{\ln[c]_0 - \ln[c]_t}{t} = k; t = 30 \text{ min} \times \dfrac{60 \text{ s}}{\text{min}} = 1800 \text{ s}$

            $k = \ln(1.080 \times 10^{-4}) - \ln(4.464 \times 10^{-5}) / 1800 \text{ s} = 4.910 \times 10^{-4} = 4.91 \times 10^{-4} \text{ s}^{-1}$

       (c)   For a first order reaction, $t_{1/2} = 0.693/k$.

            $t_{1/2} = 0.693/4.910 \times 10^{-4} \text{ s}^{-1} = 1.411 \times 10^3 = 1.41 \times 10^3 \text{ s} = 23.5 \text{ min}$

       (d) $A_t = 0.100$; calculate c_t using Beer's law, then t from the first order integrated rate equation.

            $c_t = \dfrac{A}{\varepsilon b} = \dfrac{0.100}{(5.60 \times 10^3 \text{ cm}^{-1} M^{-1})(1.00 \text{ cm})} = 1.786 \times 10^{-5} = 1.79 \times 10^{-5} \, M$

            $t = \dfrac{\ln[c]_0 - \ln[c]_t}{k} = \dfrac{\ln(1.080 \times 10^{-4}) - \ln(1.786 \times 10^{-5})}{4.910 \times 10^{-4} \text{ s}^{-1}}$

            $t = 3.666 \times 10^3 = 3.67 \times 10^3 \text{ s} = 61.1 \text{ min}$

14.108   Calculate [dye] at each time, using Beer's law, $A = \varepsilon bc$; calculate ln[dye] and 1/[dye] and plot these quantities vs time in two separate graphs. The straight-line plot indicates the order of reaction with respect to [dye].

            $A_0 = \varepsilon bc_0; c_0 = \dfrac{A_0}{\varepsilon b} = \dfrac{1.254}{(4.7 \times 10^4 \text{ cm}^{-1} M^{-1})(1.00 \text{ cm})} = 2.668 \times 10^{-5} = 2.7 \times 10^{-5} \, M$

Time (min)	A at 608 nm	[dye]	ln [dye]	1/[dye]
0	1.254	2.7×10^{-5}	–10.53	3.7×10^4
30	0.941	2.0×10^{-5}	–10.82	5.0×10^4
60	0.752	1.6×10^{-5}	–11.04	6.3×10^4
90	0.672	1.4×10^{-5}	–11.16	7.0×10^4
120	0.545	1.2×10^{-5}	–11.36	8.6×10^4

Although the graphs are not absolutely definitive, the plot of 1/[dye] vs time appears to be more linear. (The data point at t = 90 min us "out of line" in both plots and is suspect. More precision and accuracy in the experimental data would be helpful.) Assuming the reaction is second order with respect to the dye, the rate law is: rate = k[dye]^2.

k = slope = $(8.6 \times 10^4 - 3.7 \times 10^4)\ M^{-1}/(120{-}0)$min = $4.1 \times 10^2\ M^{-1}\ \text{min}^{-1}$

(The best-fit slope and k value is $3.9 \times 10^2\ M^{-1}\ \text{min}^{-1}$)

14.109

Time (s)	[C$_5$H$_6$] (M)	ln[C$_5$H$_6$]	1/[C$_5$H$_6$]
0	0.0400	–3.219	25.0
50	0.0300	–3.507	33.3
100	0.0240	–3.730	41.7
150	0.0200	–3.912	50.0
200	0.0174	–4.051	57.5

The plot of 1/[C$_5$H$_6$] vs time is linear and the reaction is second order.

The slope of this line is k. k = slope = $(50.0 - 25.0)\ M^{-1}/(150{-}0)$s = $0.167\ M^{-1}\ \text{s}^{-1}$

(The best-fit slope and k value is $0.163\ M^{-1}\ \text{s}^{-1}$.)

14.110 (a) No. The value of A, which is related to frequency and effectiveness of collisions, can be different for each reaction and k is proportional to A.

(b) From Equation [14.20], reactions with different variations of k with respect to temperature have different activation energies, E_a. The fact that k for the two reactions is the same at a certain temperature is coincidental. The reaction with the higher rate at 35°C has the larger activation energy, because it was able to use the increase in energy more effectively.

14.111

ln k	1/T
−24.17	3.33×10^{-3}
−20.72	3.13×10^{-3}
−17.32	2.94×10^{-3}
−15.24	2.82×10^{-3}

The calculated slope is -1.751×10^4. The activation energy E_a, equals $-$ (slope) $\times$ (8.314 J/mol). Thus, $E_a = 1.8 \times 10^4 \, (8.314) = 1.5 \times 10^5$ J/mol $= 1.5 \times 10^2$ kJ/mol. (The best-fit slope is $-1.76 \times 10^4 = -1.8 \times 10^4$ and the value of E_a is 1.5×10^2 kJ/mol.)

14.112 (a)

$$NO(g) + NO(g) \rightarrow N_2O_2(g)$$

$$N_2O_2(g) + H_2(g) \rightarrow N_2O(g) + H_2O(g)$$

$$\overline{2NO(g) + N_2O_2(g) + H_2(g) \rightarrow N_2O_2(g) + N_2O(g) + H_2O(g)}$$

$$2NO(g) + H_2(g) \rightarrow N_2O(g) + H_2O(g)$$

(b) First reaction: $-\Delta[NO]/\Delta t = k[NO][NO] = k[NO]^2$

Second reaction: $-\Delta[H_2]/\Delta t = k[H_2][N_2O_2]$

(c) N_2O_2 is the intermediate: it is produced in the first step and consumed in the second.

(d) Since $[H_2]$ appears in the rate law, the second step must be slow relative to the first.

14.113 (a)

$$Cl(g) + O_3(g) \rightarrow ClO(g) + O_2(g)$$

$$ClO(g) + O(g) \rightarrow Cl(g) + O_2(g)$$

$$\overline{Cl(g) + O_3(g) + ClO(g) + O(g) \rightarrow ClO(g) + O_2(g) + Cl(g) + O_2(g)}$$

$$O_3(g) + O(g) \rightarrow 2O_2(g)$$

(b) $Cl(g)$ is the catalyst. It is consumed in the first step and reproduced in the second.

(c)   ClO(g) is the intermediate. It is produced in the first step and consumed in the second.

14.114   (a)

Reaction Pathway

14.30 = E_a for reaction [14.30]

14.31 = E_a for reaction [14.31]

(b)   The fact that Br_2 builds up during the reaction tells us that the appearance of Br_2 (reaction [14.30]) is faster than the disappearance of Br_2 (reaction [14.31]). This is the reason that E_a of [14.31] in the energy profile above is larger than E_a of [14.30].

14.115   (a)

$$Cl_2(g) \rightleftharpoons 2Cl(g)$$
$$Cl(g) + CHCl_3(g) \rightarrow HCl(g) + CCl_3(g)$$
$$Cl(g) + CCl_3(g) \rightarrow CCl_4(g)$$

$$\overline{Cl_2(g) + 2Cl(g) + CHCl_3(g) + CCl_3(g) \rightarrow 2Cl(g) + HCl(g) + CCl_3(g) + CCl_4(g)}$$
$$Cl_2(g) + CHCl_3(g) \rightarrow HCl(g) + CCl_4(g)$$

(b)   Cl(g), CCl_3(g)

(c)   Reaction 1 - unimolecular, Reaction 2 - bimolecular, Reaction 3 - bimolecular

(d)   Reaction 2, the slow step, is rate determining.

(e)   If Reaction 2 is rate determining, rate = $k_2[CHCl_3][Cl]$. Cl is an intermediate formed in reaction 1, an equilibrium. By definition, the rates of the forward and reverse processes are equal; $k_1 [Cl_2] = k_{-1} [Cl]^2$. Solving for [Cl] in terms of [Cl_2],

$$[Cl]^2 = \frac{k_1}{k_{-1}}[Cl_2]; \quad [Cl] = \left(\frac{k_1}{k_{-1}}[Cl_2]\right)^{1/2}$$

Substituting into the overall rate law

$$rate = k_2 \left(\frac{k_1}{k_{-1}}\right)^{1/2} [CHCl_3][Cl_2]^{1/2} = k[CHCl_3][Cl_2]^{1/2} \text{ (The overall order is 3/2.)}$$

14.116   (a) $(CH_3)_3AuPH_3 \rightarrow C_2H_6 + (CH_3)AuPH_3$

(b) $(CH_3)_3Au$, $(CH_3)Au$ and PH_3 are intermediates.

(c)   Reaction 1 is unimolecular, Reaction 2 is unimolecular, Reaction 3 is bimolecular.

(d)   Reaction 2, the slow one, is rate determining.

(e)   If Reaction 2 is rate determining, rate = $k_2[(CH_3)_3Au]$.

$(CH_3)_3Au$ is an intermediate formed in Reaction 1, an equilibrium. By definition, the rates of the forward and reverse processes in Reaction 1 are equal:

$k_1[(CH_3)_3 AuPH_3] = k_{-1}[(CH_3)_3Au][PH_3]$; solving for $[(CH_3)_3Au]$,

$$[(CH_3)_3 \; Au] = \frac{k_1[(CH_3)_3 \; AuPH_3]}{k_{-1}[PH_3]}$$

Substituting into the rate law

$$\text{rate} = \left(\frac{k_2 \, k_1}{k_{-1}}\right) \frac{[(CH_3)_3 AuPH_3]}{[PH_3]} = \frac{k[(CH_3)_3 AuPH_3]}{[PH_3]}$$

(f)   The rate is inversely proportional to $[PH_3]$, so adding PH_3 to the $(CH_3)_3AuPH_3$ solution would decrease the rate of the reaction.

14.117   *Enzyme*: carbonic anhydrase; *substrate*: carbonic acid (H_2CO_3); *turnover number*: 1×10^7 molecules/s.

14.118   (a)   The rate law for the slow step is rate = $k_2[ES]$, where ES is an intermediate. Use relationships from the fast equilibrium step to substitute for $[ES]$.

rate of the forward reaction = $k_1[E][S]$

rate of the reverse reaction = $k_{-1}[ES]$

For an equilibrium, rate forward = rate reverse, $k_1[E][S] = k_{-1}[ES]$;

$$[ES] = \frac{k_1}{k_{-1}}[E][S]; \quad \text{Rate} = k_2[ES] = \frac{k_2 k_1}{k_{-1}}[E][S] = k[E][S]$$

(b) $E + I \; \rightleftharpoons \; EI$

Integrative Exercises

14.119   *Analyze/Plan.* $2N_2O_5 \rightarrow 4NO_2 + O_2$ rate = $k[N_2O_5] = 1.0 \times 10^{-5} \, s^{-1} \, [N_2O_5]$

Use the integrated rate law for a first-order reaction, Equation [14.13], to calculate $k[N_2O_5]$ at 20.0 hr. Build a stoichiometry table to determine mol O_2 produced in 20.0 hr. Assuming that $O_2(g)$ is insoluble in chloroform, calculate the pressure of O_2 in the 10.0 L container. *Solve.*

$$20.0 \, \text{hr} \times \frac{60 \, \text{min}}{1 \, \text{hr}} \times \frac{60 \, s}{1 \, \text{min}} = 7.20 \times 10^4 \, s; \; [N_2O_5]_0 = 0.600 \, M$$

$\ln[A]_t - \ln[A]_0 = -kt; \quad \ln[N_2O_5]_t = -kt + \ln[N_2O_5]_0$

$\ln[N_2O_5]_t = -1.0 \times 10^{-5} \, s^{-1} \, (7.20 \times 10^4 \, s) + \ln(0.600) = -0.720 - 0.511 = -1.231$

$[N_2O_5]_t = e^{-1.231} = 0.292 \, M$

N_2O_5 was present initially as 1.00 L of 0.600 M solution.

mol $N_2O_5 = M \times L = 0.600$ mol N_2O_5 initial, 0.292 mol N_2O_5 at 20.0 hr

$$2N_2O_5 \quad \rightarrow \quad 4NO_2 \quad + \quad O_2$$

	$2N_2O_5$	$4NO_2$	O_2
t = 0	0.600 mol	0	0
change	–0.308 mol	0.616 mol	0.154 mol
t = 20 hr	0.292 mol	0.616 mol	0.154 mol

[Note that the reaction stoichiometry is applied to the 'change' line.]

$PV = nRT; P = nRT/V; V = 10.0$ L, $T = 45°C = 318$ K, $n = 0.154$ mol

$$P = 0.154 \text{ mol} \times \frac{318 \text{ K}}{10.0 \text{ L}} \times \frac{0.08206 \text{ L - atm}}{\text{mol - K}} = 0.402 \text{ atm}$$

14.120   (a) $\ln k = -E_a/RT + \ln A$; $E_a = 86.8$ kJ/mol $= 8.68 \times 10^4$ J/mol; $T = 35°C + 273 = 308$ K; $A = 2.10 \times 10^{11} M^{-1} s^{-1}$

$$\ln k = \frac{-8.68 \times 10^4 \text{ J/mol}}{308 \text{ K}} \times \frac{\text{mol - K}}{8.314 \text{ J}} + \ln (2.10 \times 10^{11} M^{-1} s^{-1})$$

$\ln k = -33.8968 + 26.0704 = -7.8264;$ $k = 3.99 \times 10^{-4} M^{-1} s^{-1}$

(b) $\dfrac{0.335 \text{ g KOH}}{0.250 \text{ L soln}} \times \dfrac{1 \text{ mol KOH}}{56.1 \text{ g KOH}} = 0.02389 = 0.0239\ M \text{ KOH}$

$$\frac{1.453 \text{ g } C_2H_5I}{0.250 \text{ L soln}} \times \frac{1 \text{ mol } C_2H_5I}{156.0 \text{ g } C_2H_5I} = 0.03726 = 0.0373\ M\ C_2H_5I$$

If equal volumes of the two solutions are mixed, the initial concentrations in the reaction mixture are 0.01194 M KOH and 0.01863 M C_2H_5I. Assuming the reaction is first order in each reactant:

$\text{rate} = k[C_2H_5I][OH^-] = 3.99 \times 10^{-4} M^{-1}s^{-1} (0.01194\ M)(0.01863\ M) = 8.88 \times 10^{-8}\ M/s$

(c)   Since C_2H_5I and OH^- react in a 1 : 1 mole ratio and equal volumes of the solutions are mixed, the reactant with the smaller concentration, KOH, is the limiting reactant.

(d) $T = 50°C + 273 = 323$ K

$$\ln k = \frac{-8.68 \times 10^4 \text{ J/mol}}{323 \text{ K}} \times \frac{\text{mol - K}}{8.314 \text{ J}} + \ln (2.10 \times 10^{11} M^{-1} s^{-1})$$

$\ln k = -32.3227 + 26.0704 = -6.2523;$ $k = 1.93 \times 10^{-3} M^{-1} s^{-1}$

14.121   Obtaining data for an "Arrhenius" plot like this requires running the reaction several times, each at a different temperature. Different rates and rate constants (k) are obtained at each temperature. We expect a straight line, according to the relationship: $\ln k = -E_a/RT + \ln A$. The slope of the graph is $-E_a$ and the y-intercept is the orientation factor, A. The graph in the exercise demonstrates these characteristics, times two! The graph indicates that reaction requires two different activation energies, depending on temperature.

Assuming that reactants and products are the same at all temperatures, the reaction proceeds through different pathways, depending on temperature. This could mean two totally different reaction mechanisms, or a multi-step mechanism where different steps are rate-determining at different temperatures.

14.122   (a) $\ln k = -E_a/RT + \ln A$, Equation [14.20]. $E_a = 6.3$ kJ/mol $= 6.3 \times 10^3$ J/mol

T = 100°C + 273 = 373 K

$$\ln k = \frac{-6.3 \times 10^3 \text{ J/mol}}{8.314 \text{ J/K - mol} \times 373 \text{ K}} + \ln(6.0 \times 10^8 \ M^{-1}s^{-1})$$

$\ln k = -2.032 + 20.212 = 18.181 = 18.2$; $k = 7.87 \times 10^7 = 8 \times 10^7 \ M^{-1}s^{-1}$

(b)   NO, 11 valence e^-, 5.5 e^- pair (Assume the less electronegative N atom will be electron deficient.)

ONF, 18 valence e^-, 9 e^- pr

$$:\ddot{O}\!=\!\ddot{N}\!-\!\ddot{F}: \longleftrightarrow \left(:\ddot{O}\!-\!\ddot{N}\!=\!\ddot{F} \right)$$

$$:\dot{N}\!=\!\ddot{O}:$$

The resonance form on the right is a very minor contributor to the true bonding picture, due to high formal charges and the unlikely double bond involving F.

(c)   ONF has trigonal planar electron domain geometry, which leads to a "bent" structure with a bond angle of approximately 120°.

(d)

$$\left[\begin{array}{c} O\!=\!N \\ \ \ \ \diagdown \\ \ \ \ \ \ F\!-\!F \end{array} \right]$$

(e)   The electron deficient NO molecule is attracted to electron-rich F_2, so the driving force for formation of the transition state is greater than simple random collisions.

14.123   (a) $\Delta H^{\circ}_{rxn} = 2\Delta H^{\circ}_f \ H_2O(g) + 2\Delta H^{\circ}_f \ Br_2(g) - 4\Delta H^{\circ}_f \ HBr(g) - \Delta H^{\circ}_f \ O_2(g)$

$\Delta H^{\circ}_{rxn} = 2(-241.82) + 2(30.71) - 4(-36.23) - (0) = -277.30$ kJ

(b)   Since the rate of the uncatalyzed reaction is very slow at room temperature, the magnitude of the activation energy for the rate-determining first step must be quite large. At room temperature, the reactant molecules have a distribution of kinetic energies (Chapter 10), but very few molecules even at the high end of the distribution have sufficient energy to form an activated complex. E_a for this step must be much greater than 3/2 RT, the average kinetic energy of the sample.

(c)   20 e^-, 10 e^- pr

$$H\!-\!\ddot{O}\!-\!\ddot{O}\!-\!\ddot{B}r:$$

The intermediate resembles hydrogen peroxide, H_2O_2.

14.124   (a)   D(Cl–Cl) = 242 kJ/mol Cl_2

$$\frac{242 \text{ kJ}}{\text{mol } Cl_2} \times \frac{1000 \text{ J}}{\text{kJ}} \times \frac{1 \text{ mol}}{6.022 \times 10^{23} \text{ molecules}} = 4.019 \times 10^{-19} = 4.02 \times 10^{-19} \text{ J}$$

$$\lambda = hc/E = \frac{6.626 \times 10^{-34} \text{ J-s} \times 2.998 \times 10^8 \text{ m/s}}{4.019 \times 10^{-19} \text{ J}} = 4.94 \times 10^{-7} \text{ m}$$

This wavelength, 494 nm, is in the visible portion of the spectrum.

(b)

Reaction Pathway

(c)   Since D(Cl–Cl) is 242 kJ/mol, $CH_4(g) + Cl_2(g)$ should be about 242 kJ below the starting point on the diagram. For the reaction $CH_4(g) + Cl_2(g) \rightarrow CH_3(g) + HCl(g) + Cl(g)$, E_a is 242 + 17 = 259 kJ. (From bond dissociation enthalpies, ΔH for the overall reaction $CH_4(g) + Cl_2(g) \rightarrow CH_3Cl(g) + Cl(g)$ is –104 kJ, so the graph above is simply a sketch of the relative energies of some of the steps in the process.)

(d) CH_3, 7 valence e⁻, odd electron species

(e)   This sequence is called a chain reaction because Cl• radicals are regenerated in Reaction 4, perpetuating the reaction. Absence of Cl• terminates the reaction, so Cl• + Cl• → Cl_2 is a termination step.

14.125 (a)   A generic Lewis structure for a primary amine is shown below. There are four electron domains about nitrogen, so the hybridization is sp^3. The hybrid orbital picture is shown on the right.

(b)   A reactant that is attracted to the lone pair of electrons on nitrogen will produce a tetrahedral intermediate. This can be a moiety with a full, partial or even transient positive charge. Steric hindrance will not be large, because two of the atoms bound to nitrogen are small hydrogens.

14.126   (a)

Molecule	NO	NO$_2$	N$_2$
Valence e$^-$	11	17	10
e$^-$ pairs	5.5	8.5	5
Lewis structure	$:\dot{N}\!=\!\ddot{O}:$	$:\ddot{O}\!-\!\dot{N}\!=\!\ddot{O}$	$:N\!\equiv\!N:$
Bond order	2	1.5	3
Bond energy	607 kJ/mol	404 kJ/mol	941 kJ/mol

(b)   The bond energies in the table above are from Table 8.4 of the text. The NO$_2$ molecule has two resonance forms and the bond order is 1.5. To obtain an approximate bond energy, average the energies for N=O and N—O:

(607 kJ + 201 kJ)/2 = ~404 kJ/bond in NO$_2$

We know that resonance stabilizes a molecule, so the actual bond energy is probably somewhat greater than this value.

Use Avogadro's number to calculate energy in J/bond, then $\lambda = hc/E$ to calculate wavelength and region of the electromagnetic spectrum. These are the maximum wavelengths that would cause complete bond dissociation.

$$\frac{941 \text{ kJ}}{\text{mol N}_2} \times \frac{1000 \text{ J}}{\text{kJ}} \times \frac{1 \text{ mol}}{6.022 \times 10^{23} \text{ molecules}} = 1.5626 \times 10^{-18} = 1.56 \times 10^{-18} \text{ J}$$

$$\lambda = hc/E = \frac{6.626 \times 10^{-34} \text{ J-s} \times 2.998 \times 10^8 \text{ m/s}}{1.5626 \times 10^{-18} \text{ J}} = 1.27 \times 10^{-7} \text{ m}$$

For NO, the energy per bond is 1.01×10^{-18} J and the wavelength is 1.97×10^{-7} m.

For NO$_2$, the energy per bond is 6.71×10^{-19} J and the wavelength is 2.96×10^{-7} m.

The three 'bond dissociation' wavelengths, 127 nm, 197 nm and 296 nm, are all in the ultraviolet region, near but not in the visible range of 400-700 nm. We expect longer wavelength electronic excitations for the three gases to be in the visible and near UV, in the same relative order as the bond dissociation wavelengths.

(c)   The experiment requires a UV-VIS spectrometer and a gas flow cell that can be attached to the exhaust stream. According to Beer's law, as the concentration of absorbing species decreases, so does the absorbance. By monitoring a different wavelength of maximum absorption (longer than 297 nm) for each gas, we can measure the concentration of each gas at some point in time. We would monitor the stream before the catalytic converter to establish starting concentrations, then after the converter to observe changes. If the catalyst is working, we expect the two longer wavelength peaks for NO and NO$_2$ to decrease in size, and the shorter wavelength peak for N$_2$ to increase.

15 Chemical Equilibrium

Visualizing Concepts

15.1 (a) $k_f > k_r$. According to the Arrhenius equation [14.19], $k = Ae^{-E_a/RT}$. As the magnitude of E_a increases, k decreases. On the energy profile, E_a is the difference in energy between the starting point and the energy at the top of the barrier. Clearly this difference is smaller for the forward reaction, so $k_f > k_r$.

(b) From the Equation [15.5], the equilibrium constant = k_f/k_r. Since $k_f > k_r$, the equilibrium constant for the process shown in the energy profile is greater than 1.

15.2 Yes. The first box is pure reactant A. As the reaction proceeds, some A changes to B. In the fourth and fifth boxes, the relative amounts (concentrations) of A and B are constant. Although the reaction is ongoing the rates of A → B and B → A are equal, and the relative amounts of A and B are constant.

15.3 *Analyze.* Given box diagram and reaction type, determine whether K > 1 for the equilibrium mixture depicted in the box.

Plan. Assign species in the box to reactants and products. Write an equilibrium expression in terms of concentrations. Find the relationship between numbers of molecules and concentration. Calculate K.

Solve. Let red = A, blue = X, red and blue pairs = AX. (The colors of A and X are arbitrary.) There are 3A, 2B, and 8AX in the box.

M = mol/L. Since moles is a counting unit for particles, mol ratios and particle ratios are equivalent. We can use numbers of particles in place of moles in the molarity formula. V = 1 L, so in this case, [A] = number of A particles.

$$K = \frac{[AX]}{[A][X]}; \quad [AX] = 8/V = 8; [A] = 3/V = 3; [X] = 2/V = 2. \quad K = \frac{8}{[3][2]} = \frac{8}{6} = 1.33$$

15.4 *Analyze/Plan.* Given that element A = red and element B = blue, evaluate the species in the reactant and product boxes, and write the reaction. Answer the remaining questions based on the balanced equation. *Solve.*

(a) reactants: $4A_2 + 4B$; products: $4A_2B$

balanced equation: $A_2 + B \rightarrow A_2B$

(b) $K_c = \dfrac{[A_2B]}{[A_2][B]}$

(c) $\Delta n = \Sigma n(\text{prod}) - \Sigma n(\text{react}) = 1 - 2 = -1$.

(d) $K_p = K_c(RT)^{\Delta n}$, Equation [15.14].

If you have a balanced equation, calculate Δn. Use Equation [15.14] to calculate K_p from K_c, or vice versa.

15.5   Your friend is not correct. By definition, a reaction at equilibrium has forward and reverse reactions happening simultaneously at the same rate. So, the faster the forward reaction, the faster the reverse reaction. The equilibrium constant for the reaction is the algebraic ratio of the rate constant for the forward reaction and the rate constant for the reverse reaction, k_f/k_r. The magnitude of the equilibrium constant, K, depends on the relative rate constants, not the speed of the reactions.

15.6   The statement is vaguely correct. If $K_c = 1.5 \times 10^6$, the arithmetic *product* of the concentrations of all product molecules is 1.5×10^6 times the *product* of the concentrations of all reactant molecules. (It does not mean that the sum of all product molecules is 1.5×10^6 times the sum of all reactant molecules.)

15.7   *Analyze/Plan.* The reaction with the largest equilibrium constant has the largest ratio of products to reactants. Count product and reactant molecules. Calculate ratios and compare. *Solve.*

$$K = \frac{[C_2H_4X_2]}{[C_2H_4][X_2]}.$$ Use numbers of molecules as an adequate measure of concentration.

(While the volume terms don't cancel, they are the same for all parts. For the purpose of comparison, we can ignore volume.) *Solve.*

(a)   8 $C_2H_4Cl_2$, 2 Cl_2, 2 C_2H_4. $K = \dfrac{8}{(2)(2)} = 2$

(b)   6 $C_2H_4Br_2$, 4 Br_2, 4 C_2H_4. $K = \dfrac{6}{(4)(4)} = 0.375 = 0.4$

(c)   3 $C_2H_4I_2$, 7 I_2, 7 C_2H_4. $K = \dfrac{3}{(7)(7)} = 0.0612 = 0.06$

From the smallest to the largest equilibrium constant, (c) < (b) < (a).

Check. By inspection, there are the fewest product molecules and the most reactant molecules in (c); most product and least reactant in (a).

15.8   *Analyze.* Given box diagrams, reaction type, and value of K_c, determine whether each reaction mixture is at equilibrium.

Plan. Analyze the contents of each box, express them as concentrations (see Solution 5.3). Write the equilibrium expression, calculate Q for each mixture, and compare it to K_c. If Q = K, the mixture is at equilibrium. If Q < K, the reaction shifts right (more product). If Q > K, the reaction shifts left (more reactant).

Solve. $K_c = \dfrac{[AB]^2}{[A_2][B_2]}.$

For this reaction, $\Delta n = 0$, so the volume terms cancel in the equilibrium expression. In this case, the number of each kind of particle can be used as a representation of moles (see Solution 5.3) and molarity.

(a)   Mixture (i): 1A_2, 1B_2, 6AB; $Q = \dfrac{6^2}{(1)(1)} = 36$

Q > K_c, the mixture is not at equilibrium.

Mixture (ii): $3A_2, 2B_2, 3AB$; $Q = \dfrac{3^2}{(3)(2)} = 1.5$

$Q = K_c$, the mixture is at equilibrium.

Mixture (iii): $3A_2, 3B_2, 2AB$; $Q = \dfrac{2^2}{(3)(3)} = 0.44$

$Q < K_c$, the mixture is not at equilibrium.

(b)   Mixture (i) proceeds toward reactants.

Mixture (iii) proceeds toward products.

15.9   For the reaction $A_2(g) + B(g) \rightleftharpoons A(g) + AB(g)$, $\Delta n = 0$ and $K_p = K_c$. We can evaluate the equilibrium expression in terms of concentration. Also since $\Delta n = 0$, the volume terms in the expression cancel and we can use number of particles as a measure of moles and molarity. The mixture contains 2A, 4AB and $2A_2$.

$$K_c = \frac{[A][AB]}{[A_2][B]} = \frac{(2)(4)}{(2)(B)} = 2; B = 2$$

2 B atoms should be added to the diagram.

15.10   *Analyze.* Given the diagram and reaction type, calculate the equilibrium constant K_c.

Plan. Analyze the contents of the cylinder. Express them as concentrations, using number of particles as a measure of moles, and $V = 2$ L. Write the equilibrium expression in terms of concentration and calculate K_c.   *Solve.*

(a)   The mixture contains $2A_2, 2B, 4AB$. $[A_2] = 2/2 = 1$, $[B] = 2/2 = 1$, $[AB] = 4/2 = 2$.

$$K_c = \frac{[AB]^2}{[A_2][B]^2} = \frac{(2)^2}{(1)(1)^2} = 4$$

(b)   A decrease in volume favors the reaction with fewer particles. This reaction has two particles in products and three in reactants, so a decrease in volume favors products. The number of AB (product) molecules will increase.

Note that a change in volume does not change the value of K_c. If V decreases, the number of AB molecules must increase in order to maintain the equilibrium value of K_c.

15.11   If temperature increases, K of an endothermic reaction increases and K of an exothermic reaction decreases. Calculate the value of K for the two temperatures and compare. For this reaction, $\Delta n = 0$ and $K_p = K_c$. We can ignore volume and use number of particles as a measure of moles and molarity. $K_c = [A][AB]/[A_2][B]$

(1)   300 K, $3A, 5AB, 1A_2, 1B$; $K_c = (3)(5)/(1)(1) = 15$

(2)   500 K, $1A, 3AB, 3A_2, 3B$; $K_c = (1)(3)/(3)(3) = 0.33$

K_c decreases as T increases, so the reaction is exothermic.

15.12   (a)   Exothermic. In both reaction mixtures (orange and blue), [AB] decreases as T increases.

(b)   In the reaction, there are fewer moles of gas in products than reactants, so greater pressure favors production of products. At any single temperature, [AB] is greater at P = y than at P = x. Since the concentration of the product, AB, is greater at P = y, P = y is the greater pressure.

Equilibrium; The Equilibrium Constant (sections 15.1 – 15.4)

15.13   *Analyze/Plan.* Given the forward and reverse rate constants, calculate the equilibrium constant using Equation [15.5]. At equilibrium, the rates of the forward and reverse reactions are equal. Write the rate laws for the forward and reverse reactions and use their equality to answer part (b).   *Solve.*

(a) $K_c = \dfrac{k_f}{k_r}$, Equation [15.5]; $K_c = \dfrac{4.7 \times 10^{-3}\ s^{-1}}{5.8 \times 10^{-1}\ s^{-1}} = 8.1 \times 10^{-3}$

For this reaction, $K_p = K_c = 8.1 \times 10^{-3}$

(b) $rate_f = rate_r$; $k_f[A] = k_r[B]$

Since $k_f < k_r$, in order for the two rates to be equal, [A] must be greater than [B] and the partial pressure of A is greater than the partial pressure of B.

15.14   (a) $K_c = \dfrac{[C][D]}{[A][B]}$; if K_c is large, the numerator of the K_c expression is much greater than the denominator and products will predominate at equilibrium.

(b) $K_c = k_f / k_r$; if K_c is large, k_f is larger than k_r and the forward reaction has the greater rate constant.

15.15   *Analyze/Plan.* Follow the logic in Sample Exercises 15.1 and 15.6.   *Solve.*

(a) $K_c = \dfrac{[N_2O][NO_2]}{[NO]^3}$ (b) $K_c = \dfrac{[CS_2][H_2]^4}{[CH_4][H_2S]^2}$

(c) $K_c = \dfrac{[CO]^4}{[Ni(CO)_4]}$ (d) $K_c = \dfrac{[H^+][F^-]}{[HF]}$

(e) $K_c = \dfrac{[Ag^+]^2}{[Zn^{2+}]}$ (f) $K_c = [H^+][OH^-]$

(g) $K_c = [H^+][OH^-]$

homogeneous: (a), (b), (d), (f), (g); heterogeneous: (c), (e)

15.16   (a) $K_c = \dfrac{[O_2]^3}{[O_3]^2}$ (b) $K_c = \dfrac{1}{[Cl_2]^2}$

(c) $K_c = \dfrac{[C_2H_6]^2[O_2]}{[C_2H_4]^2[H_2O]^2}$ (d) $K_c = \dfrac{[CH_4]}{[H_2]^2}$

(e) $K_c = \dfrac{[Cl_2]^2}{[HCl]^4[O_2]}$ (f) $K_c = \dfrac{[CO_2]^{16}[H_2O]^{18}}{[O_2]^{25}}$

(g) $K_c = \dfrac{[CO_2]^{16}}{[O_2]^{25}}$

homogeneous: (a), (c); heterogeneous: (b), (d), (e), (f), (g)

15.17   *Analyze.* Given the value of K_c or K_p, predict the contents of the equilibrium mixture.

Plan. If K_c or $K_p \gg 1$, products dominate; if K_c or $K_p \ll 1$, reactants dominate. *Solve.*

(a)   mostly reactants ($K_c \ll 1$)

(b)   mostly products ($K_p \gg 1$)

15.18   (a)   equilibrium lies to right, favoring products ($K_p \gg 1$)

(b)   equilibrium lies to left, favoring reactants ($K_c \ll 1$)

15.19   No, the equilibrium constant can never be a negative number. The equilibrium constant is a ratio of concentrations of products to concentration of reactants, or of partial pressures of reactants to partial pressures of products. Concentrations and partial pressures are never negative, and neither is K. (Or, K is a ratio of rate constants, which also cannot have negative values.)

15.20   The equilibrium constant can never be zero. By definition, a reaction at equilibrium has forward and reverse reactions occurring at equal (non-zero) rates. The equilibrium constant is a ratio of the rate constants for the forward and reverse reactions, and rate constants are non-zero numbers. The equilibrium constant is also a ratio of concentrations (or partial pressures) of products to concentrations (or partial pressures) of reactants. Both products and reactants must be present in finite amounts. This means that both the numerator and denominator must have nonzero values, and the ratio, K, is always nonzero.

15.21   *Analyze/Plan.* Follow the logic in Sample Exercise 15.2.   *Solve.*

$PCl_3(g) + Cl_2(g) \rightleftharpoons PCl_5(g)$, $K_c = 0.042$. $\Delta n = 1 - 2 = -1$

$K_p = K_c(RT)^{\Delta n} = 0.042(RT)^{-1} = 0.042/RT$

$K_p = \dfrac{0.042}{(0.08206)(500)} = 0.001024 = 1.0 \times 10^{-3}$

15.22 $SO_2(g) + Cl_2(g) \rightleftharpoons SO_2Cl_2(g)$, $K_p = 34.5$. $\Delta n = 1 - 2 = -1$

$K_p = K_c(RT)^{\Delta n}$; $34.5 = K_c(RT)^{-1} = K_c/RT$;

$K_c = 34.5\ RT = 34.5(0.08206)(303) = 857.81 = 858$

15.23   *Analyze.* Given K_c for a chemical reaction, calculate K_c for the reverse reaction.

Plan. Evaluate which species are favored by examining the magnitude of K_c. The equilibrium expressions for the reaction and its reverse are the reciprocals of each other, and the values of K_c are also reciprocal.   *Solve.*

(a)   For the reaction as written, $K_c < 1$, which means that reactants are favored. At this temperature, the equilibrium favors NO and Br_2.

(b) $K_c(\text{forward}) = \dfrac{[NOBr]^2}{[NO]^2[Br_2]} = 1.3 \times 10^{-2}$

$K_c(\text{reverse}) = \dfrac{[NO]^2[Br_2]}{[NOBr]^2} = \dfrac{1}{1.3 \times 10^{-2}} = 76.92 = 77$

(c) $K_{c2}(\text{reverse}) = \dfrac{[NO][Br_2]^{1/2}}{[NOBr]} = (K_c(\text{reverse}))^{1/2} = (76.92)^{1/2} = 8.8$

15.24 $2H_2(g) + S_2(g) \rightleftharpoons 2H_2S(g)$, $K_c = 1.08 \times 10^7$ at 700°C. $\Delta n = 2 - 3 = -1$.

     (a) $K_p = K_c(RT)^{\Delta n} = 700°C + 273 = 973$ K.

$$K_p = 1.08 \times 10^7 \, (RT)^{-1} = \frac{1.08 \times 10^7}{(0.08206)(973)} = 1.35 \times 10^5$$

     (b)   Both K_p and K_c are much greater than one, so the product, H_2S, is favored at equilibrium. The equilibrium mixture contains mostly H_2S.

     (c) $H_2(g) + \frac{1}{2} S_2(g) \rightleftharpoons H_2S(g)$; $K_{c2} = \dfrac{[H_2S]}{[H_2][S_2]^{1/2}}$

$$K_{c2} = (K_c)^{1/2} = (1.08 \times 10^7)^{1/2} = 3.29 \times 10^3$$

$$K_{p2} = (K_p)^{1/2} = (1.35 \times 10^5)^{1/2} = 368$$

15.25   *Analyze.* Given K_p for a reaction, calculate K_p for a related reaction.

     Plan. The algebraic relationship between the K_p values is the same as the algebraic relationship between equilibrium expressions.

     Solve. $K_p = \dfrac{P_{SO_3}}{P_{SO_2} \times P_{O_2}^{1/2}} = 1.85$

     (a) $K_p = \dfrac{P_{SO_2} \times P_{O_2}^{1/2}}{P_{SO_3}} = \dfrac{1}{1.85} = 0.541$

     (b) $K_p = \dfrac{P_{SO_3}^2}{P_{SO_2}^2 \times P_{O_2}} = (1.85)^2 = 3.4225 = 3.42$

     (c) $K_p = K_c(RT)^{\Delta n}$; $\Delta n = 2 - 3 = -1$; $T = 1000$ K

         $K_p = K_c(RT)^{-1} = K_c/RT$; $K_c = K_p(RT)$

         $K_c = 3.4225(0.08206)(1000) = 280.85 = 281$

15.26 $K_p = \dfrac{P_{HCl}^4 \times P_{O_2}}{P_{Cl_2}^2 \times P_{H_2O}^2} = 0.0752$

     (a) $K_p = \dfrac{P_{Cl_2}^2 \times P_{H_2O}^2}{P_{HCl}^4 \times P_{O_2}} = \dfrac{1}{0.0752} = 13.298 = 13.3$

     (b) $K_p = \dfrac{P_{HCl}^2 \times P_{O_2}^{1/2}}{P_{Cl_2} \times P_{H_2O}} = (0.0752)^{1/2} = 0.2742 = 0.274$

     (c) $K_p = K_c(RT)^{\Delta n}$; $\Delta n = 2.5 - 2 = 0.5$; $T = 480°C + 273 = 753$ K

         $K_p = K_c(RT)^{1/2}$, $K_c = K_p/(RT)^{1/2} = 0.2742/[0.08206 \times 753]^{1/2} = 0.03488 = 0.0349$

15.27   *Analyze/Plan.* Follow the logic in Sample Exercise 15.5.   *Solve.*

$$CoO(s) + H_2(g) \rightleftharpoons Co(s) + H_2O(g) \qquad\qquad K_1 = 67$$

$$Co(s) + CO_2(g) \rightleftharpoons CoO(s) + CO(g) \qquad\qquad K_2 = 1/490$$

$$CoO(s) + H_2(g) + Co(s) + CO_2(g) \rightleftharpoons Co(s) + H_2O(g) + CoO(s) + CO(g)$$

$$H_2(g) + CO_2(g) \rightleftharpoons H_2O(g) + CO(g)$$

$$K_c = K_1 \times K_2 = 67 \times \frac{1}{490} = 0.1367 = 0.14$$

15.28
$$2NO(g) + Br_2(g) \rightleftharpoons 2NOBr(g) \qquad K_1 = 2.0$$

$$N_2(g) + O_2(g) \rightleftharpoons 2NO(g) \qquad K_2 = \frac{1}{2.1 \times 10^{30}}$$

$$\overline{2NO(g) + Br_2(g) + N_2(g) + O_2(g) \rightleftharpoons 2NOBr(g) + 2NO(g)}$$

$$N_2(g) + O_2(g) + Br_2(g) \rightleftharpoons 2NOBr(g)$$

$$K_c = K_1 \times K_2 = 2.0 \times \frac{1}{2.1 \times 10^{30}} = 9.524 \times 10^{-31} = 9.5 \times 10^{-31}$$

15.29   Pure solids and liquids are normally excluded from equilibrium-constant expressions because their concentrations are constant. Molar concentration is the ratio of moles of substance to volume occupied by substance. For a pure solid or liquid, if moles increase, volume occupied increases (and vice versa), so the concentration remains the same.

An alternate explanation involves the use of activities to express amounts of the various reactants and products in an equilibrium mixture. By definition, the activitiy of a pure solid or liquid is one, and it need not appear in the equilibrium-constant expression.

15.30   Concentration of solvent is normally excluded from liquid-phase equilibrium-constant expressions because solvents do not usually participate in the chemical reaction and their concentrations do not change. This constant is incorporated into the value of the equilibrium constant.

15.31   *Analyze/Plan.* Follow the logic in Sample Exercise 15.6.   *Solve.*

(a) $K_p = P_{O_2}$

(b) $K_c = [Hg(solv)]^4[O_2(solv)]$

15.32   (a) $K_p = 1/P_{SO_2}$

(b) $K_c = \dfrac{[Na_2SO_3]}{[Na_2O][SO_2]}$

Calculating Equilibrium Constants (section 15.5)

15.33   *Analyze/Plan.* Calculate molarity of reactants and products. Follow the logic in Sample Exercise 15.8 using concentrations rather than pressures.   *Solve.*

$$[CH_3OH] = \frac{0.0406 \text{ mol}}{2.00 \text{ L}} = 0.0203 \text{ M}$$

$$[CO] = \frac{0.170 \text{ mol CO}}{2.00 \text{ L}} = 0.0850 \text{ M}; \quad [H_2] = \frac{0.302 \text{ mol H}_2}{2.00 \text{ L}} = 0.151 \text{ M}$$

$$K_c = \frac{[CH_3OH]}{[CO][H_2]^2} = \frac{0.0203}{(0.0850)(0.151)^2} = 10.4743 = 10.5$$

15.34 $K_c = \dfrac{[H_2][I_2]}{[HI]^2} = \dfrac{(4.79 \times 10^{-4})(4.79 \times 10^{-4})}{(3.53 \times 10^{-3})^2} = 0.018413 = 0.0184$

15.35   *Analyze/Plan.* Follow the logic in Sample Exercise 15.8.   *Solve.*

(a) $2NO(g) + Cl_2(g) \rightleftharpoons 2NOCl(g)$

$K_p = \dfrac{P_{NOCl}^2}{P_{NO}^2 \times P_{Cl_2}} = \dfrac{(0.28)^2}{(0.095)^2(0.171)} = 50.80 = 51$

(b) $K_p = K_c(RT)^{\Delta n}$; $\Delta n = 2 - 3 = -1$; $K_p = K_c(RT)^{-1} = K_c/(RT)$

$K_c = K_p(RT) = 50.80(0.08206 \times 500) = 2.1 \times 10^3$

15.36   (a) $K_p = \dfrac{P_{PCl_5}}{P_{PCl_3} \times P_{Cl_2}} = \dfrac{1.30 \text{ atm}}{0.124 \text{ atm} \times 0.157 \text{ atm}} = 66.8$

(b)   Since $K_p > 1$, products (the numerator of the K_p expression) are favored over reactants (the denominator of the K_p expression).

(c) $K_p = K_c(RT)^{\Delta n}$; $\Delta n = 1 - 2 = -1$; $K_p = K_c(RT)^{-1} = K_c/(RT)$

$K_c = K_p(RT) = 66.8(0.08206 \times 450) = 2.5 \times 10^3$

15.37   *Analyze/Plan.* Follow the logic in Sample Exercise 15.9. Since the container volume is 1.0 L, mol = *M*.   *Solve.*

(a)   First calculate the change in [NO], $0.062 - 0.10 = -0.038 = -0.04$ *M*. From the stoichiometry of the reaction, calculate the changes in the other pressures. Finally, calculate the equilibrium pressures.

	$2NO(g)$	+	$2H_2(g)$	$\rightleftharpoons$	$N_2(g)$	+	$2H_2O(g)$
initial	0.10 *M*		0.050 *M*		0 *M*		0.10 *M*
change	−0.038 *M*		−0.038 *M*		+0.019 *M*		+0.038 *M*
equil.	0.062 *M*		0.012 *M*		0.019 *M*		0.138 *M*

Strictly speaking, the change in [NO] has two decimal places and thus one sig fig. This limits equilibrium pressures to one sig fig for all but H_2O, and K_c to one sig fig. We compute the extra figures and then round.

(b) $K_c = \dfrac{[N_2][H_2O]^2}{[NO]^2[H_2]^2} = \dfrac{(0.019)(0.138)^2}{(0.062)^2(0.012)^2} = \dfrac{(0.02)(0.14)^2}{(0.06)^2(0.01)^2} = 653.7 = 7 \times 10^2$

15.38   (a)   Calculate the initial concentrations of $H_2(g)$ and $Br_2(g)$ and the equilibrium concentration of $H_2(g)$. *M* = mol/L.

$[H_2]_{init} = 1.374 \text{ g } H_2 \times \dfrac{1 \text{ mol } H_2}{2.0159 \text{ g } H_2} \times \dfrac{1}{2.00 \text{ L}} = 0.34079 = 0.341 \text{ M}$

$[Br_2] = 70.31 \text{ g } Br_2 \times \dfrac{1 \text{ mol } Br_2}{159.81 \text{ g } Br_2} \times \dfrac{1}{2.00 \text{ L}} = 0.21998 = 0.220 \text{ M}$

$[H_2]_{equil} = 0.566 \text{ g } H_2 \times \dfrac{1 \text{ mol } H_2}{2.0159 \text{ g } H_2} \times \dfrac{1}{2.00 \text{ L}} = 0.14038 = 0.140 \text{ M}$

	$H_2(g)$	$+$	$Br_2(g)$	$\rightleftharpoons$	$2HBr(g)$
initial	0.34079 M		0.21998 M		0
change	–0.20041 M		–0.20041 M		+2(0.20041) M
equil.	0.14038 M		0.01957 M		0.40082 M

The change in H_2 is (0.34079 – 0.14038 = 0.20041 = 0.200). The changes in [Br_2] and [HBr] are set by stoichiometry, resulting in the equilibrium concentrations shown in the table.

(b) $K_c = \dfrac{[HBr]^2}{[H_2][Br_2]} = \dfrac{(0.40082)^2}{(0.14038)(0.01957)} = \dfrac{(0.401)^2}{(0.140)(0.020)} = 58.48 = 58$

The equilibrium concentration of Br_2 has 3 decimal places and 2 sig figs, so the value of K_c has 2 sig figs.

15.39   *Analyze/Plan.* Follow the logic in Sample Exercise 15.9, using partial pressures, rather than concentrations.   *Solve.*

(a) $P = nRT/V; P_{CO_2} = 0.2000 \text{ mol} \times \dfrac{500 \text{ K}}{2.000 \text{L}} \times \dfrac{0.08206 \text{ L-atm}}{\text{mol-K}} = 4.1030 = 4.10 \text{ atm}$

$P_{H_2} = 0.1000 \text{ mol} \times \dfrac{500 \text{ K}}{2.000 \text{L}} \times \dfrac{0.08206 \text{ L-atm}}{\text{mol-K}} = 2.0515 = 2.05 \text{ atm}$

$P_{H_2O} = 0.1600 \times \dfrac{500 \text{ K}}{2.000 \text{L}} \times \dfrac{0.08206 \text{ L-atm}}{\text{mol-K}} = 3.2824 = 3.28 \text{ atm}$

(b) The change in P_{H_2O} is 3.51 – 3.28 = 0.2276 = 0.23 atm. From the reaction stoichiometry, calculate the change in the other pressures and the equilibrium pressures.

	$CO_2(g)$	$+$	$H_2(g)$	$\rightleftharpoons$	$CO(g)$	$+$	$H_2O(g)$
initial	4.10 atm		2.05 atm		0 atm		3.28 atm
change	–0.23 atm		–0.23 atm		+0.23		+0.23 atm
equil	3.87 atm		1.82 atm		0.23 atm		3.51 atm

(c) $K_p = \dfrac{P_{CO} \times P_{H_2O}}{P_{CO_2} \times P_{H_2}} = \dfrac{(0.23)(3.51)}{(3.87)(1.82)} = 0.1146 = 0.11$

Without intermediate rounding, equilibrium pressures are $P_{H_2O} = 3.51$, $P_{CO} = 0.2276$, $P_{H_2} = 1.8239$, $P_{CO_2} = 3.8754$ and $K_p = 0.1130 = 0.11$, in good agreement with the value above.

(d) $K_p = K_c(RT)^{\Delta n}$; $\Delta n = 2 - 2 = 0$; $K_p = K_c(RT)^0$; $K_c = K_p = 0.11$

15.40   (a)

	$N_2O_4(g)$	$\rightleftharpoons$	$2NO_2(g)$
initial	1.500 atm		1.000 atm
change	+0.244 atm		–0.488 atm
equil	1.744 atm		0.512 atm

The change in P_{NO_2} is $(1.000 - 0.512) = -0.488$ atm, so the change in $P_{N_2O_4}$ is $+(0.488/2) = +0.244$ atm.

(b) $K_p = \dfrac{P_{NO_2}^2}{P_{N_2O_4}} = \dfrac{(0.512)^2}{(1.744)} = 0.1503 = 0.150$

(c) $K_p = K_c(RT)^{\Delta n}$; $\Delta n = 2 - 1 = 1$; $K_p = K_c(RT)^1 = K_c\,(RT)$

      $K_c = K_p/(RT) = 0.1503/(0.08206 \times 298) = 6.15 \times 10^{-3}$

15.41   *Analyze/Plan.* Follow the logic in Sample Exercise 15.9. $mM = 10^{-3}\,M$

	X(aq)	+	Y(aq)	⇌	XY(aq)
initial	1.0 mM		1.0 mM		0
change	−0.80 mM		−0.80 mM		+0.80 mM
equil.	0.20 mM		0.20 mM		0.80 mM

$$K_c = \frac{[XY]}{[X][Y]} = \frac{(0.80\times10^{-3})}{(0.20\times10^{-3})(0.20\times10^{-3})} = 2.0\times10^4$$

15.42   The initial concentrations of drug candidate and protein are the same in the two experiments, and the two reactions have the same stoichiometry. At equilibrium, the concentration of B-protein complex is greater than the concentration of A-protein complex, so drug B is the better choice for further research. Calculation of equilibrium constants for the two reactions confirms this conclusion.

	A(aq)	+	protein(aq)	⇌	A-protein(aq)
initial	2.00×10^{-6} mM		1.50×10^{-6} mM		0
change	-1.00×10^{-6} mM		-1.00×10^{-6} mM		$+1.00 \times 10^{-6}$ mM
equil.	1.00×10^{-6} mM		0.50×10^{-6} mM		1.00×10^{-6} mM

$$K_c = \frac{[A-protein]}{[A][protein]} = \frac{(1.00\times10^{-6})}{(1.00\times10^{-6})(0.50\times10^{-6})} = 2.0\times10^6$$

	B(aq)	+	protein(aq)	⇌	B-protein(aq)
initial	2.00×10^{-6} mM		1.50×10^{-6} mM		0
change	-1.40×10^{-6} mM		-1.40×10^{-6} mM		$+1.40 \times 10^{-6}$ mM
equil.	0.60×10^{-6} mM		0.10×10^{-6} mM		1.40×10^{-6} mM

$$K_c = \frac{[B-protein]}{[B][protein]} = \frac{(1.40\times10^{-6})}{(0.60\times10^{-6})(0.10\times10^{-6})} = 2.3\times10^7$$

Applications of Equilibrium Constants (section 15.6)

15.43   (a)   A reaction quotient is the result of the law of mass action for a general set of concentrations, whereas the equilibrium constant requires equilibrium concentrations.

      (b)   In the direction of more products, to the right.

(c)   If $Q_c = K_c$, the system is at equilibrium; the concentrations used to calculate Q must be equilibrium concentrations.

15.44   (a)   If the value of Q_c equals the value of K_c, the system is at equilibrium.

        (b)   In the direction of less products (more reactants), to the left.

        (c) $Q_c = 0$ if the concentration of any product is zero.

15.45   *Analyze/Plan.* Follow the logic in Sample Exercise 15.10. We are given molarities, so we calculate Q directly and decide on the direction to equilibrium.   *Solve.*

$$K_c = \frac{[CO][Cl_2]}{[COCl_2]} = 2.19 \times 10^{-10} \text{ at } 100°C$$

(a) $$Q = \frac{(3.3 \times 10^{-6})(6.62 \times 10^{-6})}{(2.00 \times 10^{-3})} = 1.1 \times 10^{-8}; Q > K$$

        The reaction will proceed left to attain equilibrium.

(b) $$Q = \frac{(1.1 \times 10^{-7})(2.25 \times 10^{-6})}{(4.50 \times 10^{-2})} = 5.5 \times 10^{-12}; Q < K$$

        The reaction will proceed right to attain equilibrium.

(c) $$Q = \frac{(1.48 \times 10^{-6})^2}{(0.0100)} = 2.19 \times 10^{-10}; Q = K$$

        The reaction is at equilibrium.

15.46   Calculate the reaction quotient in each case, compare with

$$K_p = \frac{P_{NH_3}^2}{P_{N_2} \times P_{H_2}^3} = 4.51 \times 10^{-5}$$

(a) $$Q = \frac{(98)^2}{(45)(55)^3} = 1.3 \times 10^{-3}$$

        Since $Q > K_p$, the reaction will shift toward reactants to achieve equilibrium.

(b) $$Q = \frac{(57)^2}{(143)(0)^3} = \infty$$

        Since $Q > K_p$, reaction must shift shift toward reactants to achieve equilibrium. There must be **some** H_2 present to achieve equilibrium. In this example, the only source of H_2 is the decomposition of NH_3.

(c) $$Q = \frac{(13)^2}{(27)(82)^3} = 1.1 \times 10^{-5};$$ Q is only slightly less than K_p, so the reaction will

        shift slightly toward products to achieve equilibrium.

15.47   *Analyze/Plan.* Follow the logic in Sample Exercise 15.11. We are given concentrations, so write the K_c expression and solve for $[Cl_2]$. Change molarity to partial pressure using the ideal gas equation and the definition of molarity.   *Solve.*

$$K_c = \frac{[SO_2][Cl_2]}{[SO_2Cl_2]}; \quad [Cl_2] = \frac{K_c[SO_2Cl_2]}{[SO_2]} = \frac{(0.078)(0.108)}{0.052} = 0.16200 = 0.16 \, M$$

$$PV = nRT, \quad P = \frac{n}{V}RT; \quad \frac{n}{V} = M; \quad P = M \, RT; \quad T = 100°C + 273 = 373 \, K$$

$$P_{Cl_2} = \frac{0.16200 \, mol}{L} \times \frac{0.08206 \, L\text{-}atm}{mol\text{-}K} \times 373 \, K = 4.959 = 5.0 \, atm$$

Check. $K_c = \dfrac{(0.052)(0.162)}{(0.108)} = 0.078$. Our values are self-consistent.

15.48 $K_p = \dfrac{P_{SO_3}^2}{P_{SO_2}^2 \times P_{O_2}}; \quad P_{SO_3} = \left(K_p \times P_{SO_2}^2 \times P_{O_2}\right)^{1/2} = [(0.345)(0.135)^2(0.455)]^{1/2} = 0.0535 \, atm$

15.49 *Analyze/Plan.* Follow the logic in Sample Exercise 15.11. In each case, change given masses to molarities solve for the equilibrium molarity of the desired component, and calculate mass of that substance present at equilibrium. *Solve.*

(a) $K_c = \dfrac{[Br]^2}{[Br_2]} = 1.04 \times 10^{-3}$

$$[Br_2] = \frac{0.245 \, g \, Br_2}{0.200 \, L} \times \frac{1 \, mol \, Br_2}{159.8 \, g \, Br_2} = 0.007666 = 0.00767 \, M$$

$$[Br] = (K_c[Br_2])^{1/2} = [(1.04 \times 10^{-3})(0.007666)]^{1/2} = 0.002824 = 0.00282 \, M$$

$$\frac{0.002824 \, mol \, Br}{L} \times 0.200 \, L \times \frac{79.90 \, g \, Br}{mol} = 0.0451 \, g \, Br(g)$$

Check. $K_c = (0.002824)^2 / (0.007666) = 1.04 \times 10^{-3}$

(b) $K_c = \dfrac{[HI]^2}{[H_2][I_2]} = 55.3; \quad [HI] = (K_c[H_2][I_2])^{1/2}$

$$[H_2] = \frac{0.056 \, g \, H_2}{2.00 \, L} \times \frac{1 \, mol \, H_2}{2.016 \, g \, H_2} = 0.01389 = 0.014 \, M$$

$$[I_2] = \frac{4.36 \, g \, I_2}{2.00 \, L} \times \frac{1 \, mol \, I_2}{253.8 \, g I_2} = 0.008589 = 0.00859 \, M$$

$$[HI] = [(55.3)(0.01389)(0.008589)]^{1/2} = 0.08122 = 0.081 \, M$$

$$0.08122 \, M \, HI \times 2.00 \, L \times \frac{127.9 \, g \, HI}{mol \, HI} = 20.78 = 21 \, g \, HI$$

Check. $K_c = \dfrac{(0.08122)^2}{(0.01389)(0.008589)} = 55.3$

15.50 (a) $K_c = \dfrac{[I]^2}{[I_2]} = 3.1 \times 10^{-5}$

$$[I] = \frac{2.67 \times 10^{-2} \, g \, I}{10.0 \, L} \times \frac{1 \, mol \, I}{126.9 \, g \, I} = 2.1040 \times 10^{-5} = 2.10 \times 10^{-5} M$$

$$[I_2] = \frac{[I]^2}{K_c} = \frac{(2.104 \times 10^{-5})^2}{3.1 \times 10^{-5}} = 1.428 \times 10^{-5} = 1.43 \times 10^{-5} M$$

$$\frac{1.428 \times 10^{-5} \text{ mol } I_2}{L} \times 10.0 \text{ L} \times \frac{253.8 \text{ g } I_2}{\text{mol } I_2} = M = 0.0362 \text{ g } I_2$$

Check. $K_c = \dfrac{(2.104 \times 10^{-5})^2}{1.428 \times 10^{-5}} = 3.1 \times 10^{-5}$

(b) $PV = nRT; P = \dfrac{gRT}{MM\,V}$

$$P_{SO_3} = \frac{1.17 \text{ g } SO_3}{80.06 \text{ g/mol}} \times \frac{0.08206 \text{ L-atm}}{\text{K-mol}} \times \frac{700 \text{ K}}{2.00 \text{ L}} = 0.4197 = 0.420 \text{ atm}$$

$$P_{O_2} = \frac{0.105 \text{ g } O_2}{32.00 \text{ g/mol}} \times \frac{0.08206 \text{ L-atm}}{\text{K-mol}} \times \frac{700 \text{ K}}{2.00 \text{ L}} = 0.09424 = 0.0942 \text{ atm}$$

$$K_p = 3.0 \times 10^4 = \frac{P_{SO_3}^2}{P_{SO_2}^2 \times P_{O_2}}; P_{SO_2} = \left[P_{SO_3}^2 / (K_p)(P_{O_2})\right]^{1/2}$$

$$P_{SO_2} = [(0.4197)^2 / (3.0 \times 10^4)(0.09424)]^{1/2} = 7.894 \times 10^{-3} = 7.9 \times 10^{-3} \text{ atm}$$

$$g\,SO_2 = \frac{MM\,PV}{RT} = \frac{64.06 \text{ g } SO_2}{\text{mol } SO_2} \times \frac{\text{K-mol}}{0.08206 \text{ L-atm}} \times \frac{7.894 \times 10^{-3} \text{ atm} \times 2.00 \text{ L}}{700 \text{ K}}$$

$$= 0.01761 = 0.018 \text{ g } SO_2$$

Check. $K_p = [(0.4197)^2 / (7.894 \times 10^{-3})^2 (0.09424] = 3.0 \times 10^4$

15.51   *Analyze/Plan.* Follow the logic in Sample Exercise 15.12. Since molarity of NO is given directly, we can construct the equilibrium table straight away.   *Solve.*

	2NO(g)	⇌	N₂(g)	+	O₂(g)	$K_c = \dfrac{[N_2][O_2]}{[NO]^2} = 2.4 \times 10^3$
initial	0.175 M		0		0	
change	–2x		+x		+x	
equil.	0.175 – 2x		+x		+x	

$$2.4 \times 10^3 = \frac{x^2}{(0.175 - 2x)^2}; (2.4 \times 10^3)^{1/2} = \frac{x}{0.175 - 2x}$$

$x = (2.4 \times 10^3)^{1/2}(0.175 - 2x); x = 8.573 - 97.98x; 98.98x = 8.573, x = 0.08662 = 0.087 M$

$[N_2] = [O_2] = 0.087 M; [NO] = 0.175 - 2(0.08662) = 0.00177 = 0.002 M$

Check. $K_c = (0.08662)^2 / (0.00177)^2 = 2.4 \times 10^3$

15.52 $[Br_2] = 0.25\ mol/3.0\ L = 0.08333 = 0.083\ M;$ $[Cl_2] = 0.55\ mol/3.0\ L = 0.1833 = 0.18\ M$

$$Br_2(g) \ + \ Cl_2(g) \ \rightleftharpoons \ 2BrCl(g) \qquad K_c = \frac{[BrCl]^2}{[Br_2][Cl_2]} = 7.0$$

initial	0.083 M	0.18 M	0
change	–x	–x	+2x
equil.	(0.083 – x)	(0.18 – x)	+2x

$$7.0 = \frac{(2x)^2}{(0.08333-x)(0.1833-x)}; \ \ 4x^2 = 7.0(0.0153 - 0.2666x + x^2); \ \ 0 = 0.1069 - 1.8662x + 3x^2$$

$$x = \frac{1.8662 \pm \sqrt{(-1.8662)^2 - 4(3)(0.1069)}}{2(3)} = 0.06387 = 0.064\ M$$

(The 0.56 M quadratic solution is not chemically meaningful.)

$[BrCl] = 2x = 0.1277 = 0.13\ M;$ $[Br_2] = 0.08333 - 0.06387 = 0.01946 = 0.019\ M$

$[Cl_2] = 0.1833 - 0.06387 = 0.1195 = 0.12\ M$

Check. $K_c = (0.1277)^2 / (0.01946)(0.1195) = 7.0125 = 7.0$

15.53   *Analyze/Plan.* Write the K_p expression, substitute the stated pressure relationship, and solve for P_{Br_2}.   *Solve.*

$$K_p = \frac{P_{NO}^2 \times P_{Br_2}}{P_{NOBr}^2}$$

When $P_{NOBr} = P_{NO}$, these terms cancel and $P_{Br_2} = K_p = 0.416$ atm. This is true for all cases where $P_{NOBr} = P_{NO}$.

15.54 $K_c = [NH_3][H_2S] = 1.2 \times 10^{-4}$. Because of the stoichiometry, equilibrium concentrations of H_2S and NH_3 will be equal; call this quantity y. Then, $y^2 = 1.2 \times 10^{-4}$, $y = 0.010954 = 0.011\ M$.

15.55   (a) $CaSO_4(s) \rightleftharpoons Ca^{2+}(aq) + SO_4{}^{2-}(aq)$ $K_c = [Ca^{2+}][SO_4{}^{2-}] = 2.4 \times 10^{-5}$

       At equilibrium, $[Ca^{2+}] = [SO_4{}^{2-}] = x$

       $K_c = 2.4 \times 10^{-5} = x^2;\ x = 4.9 \times 10^{-3}\ M\ Ca^{2+}$ and $SO_4{}^{2-}$

   (b)   A saturated solution of $CaSO_4(aq)$ is $4.9 \times 10^{-3}\ M$.

       1.4 L of this solution contain:

$$\frac{4.9 \times 10^{-3}\ mol}{L} \times 1.4\ L \times \frac{136.14\ g\ CaSO_4}{mol} = 0.9337 = 0.94\ g\ CaSO_4$$

       A bit more than 1.0 g $CaSO_4$ is needed in order to have some undissolved $CaSO_4(s)$ in equilibrium with 1.4 L of saturated solution.

15.56   (a)   *Analyze/Plan.* If only $PH_3BCl_3(s)$ is present initially, the equation requires that the equilibrium concentrations of $PH_3(g)$ and $BCl_3(g)$ are equal. Write the K_c expression and solve for $x = [PH_3] = [BCl_3]$.   *Solve.*

       $K_c = [PH_3][BCl_3];\ 1.87 \times 10^{-3} = x^2;\ x = 0.043243 = 0.0432\ M\ PH_3$ and BCl_3

(b) Since the mole ratios are 1:1:1, mol $PH_3BCl_3(s)$ required = mol PH_3 or BCl_3 produced.

$$\frac{0.043243 \text{ mol } PH_3}{L} \times 0.250 \text{ L} = 0.01081 = 0.0108 \text{ mol } PH_3 = 0.0108 \text{ mol } PH_3BCl_3$$

$$0.01081 \text{ mol } PH_3BCl_3 \times \frac{151.2 \text{ g } PH_3BCl_3}{1 \text{ mol } PH_3BCl_3} = 1.6346 = 1.63 \text{ g } PH_3BCl_3$$

In fact, some $PH_3BCl_3(s)$ must remain for the system to be in equilibrium, so a bit more than 1.63 g PH_3BCl_3 is needed.

15.57 *Analyze/Plan.* Follow the approach in Solution 15.51. Calculate [IBr] from mol IBr and construct the equilibrium table.

Solve. [IBr] = 0.500 mol / 2.00 L = 0.250 *M*

Since no I_2 or Br_2 was present initially, the amounts present at equilibrium are produced by the reverse reaction and stoichiometrically equal. Let these amounts equal x. The amount of HBr that reacts is then 2x. Substitute the equilibrium molarities (in terms of x) into the equilibrium expression and solve for x.

	I_2 +	Br_2 ⇌	2IBr	$K_c = \dfrac{[IBr]^2}{[I_2][Br_2]} = 280$
initial	0 *M*	0 *M*	0.250 *M*	
change	+x *M*	+x *M*	–2x *M*	
equil.	x *M*	x *M*	(0.250 – 2x) *M*	

$K_c = 280 = \dfrac{(0.250 - 2x)^2}{x^2}$; taking the square root of both sides

$16.733 = \dfrac{0.250 - 2x}{x}$; $16.733x + 2x = 0.250$; $18.733x = 0.250$

x = 0.013345 = 0.0133 *M*; $[I_2] = [Br_2] = 0.0133$ *M*

[IBr] = 0.250 – 2(0.013345) = 0.2233 = 0.223 *M*

Check. $\dfrac{(0.2233)^2}{(0.013345)^2} = 280.$ Our values are self-consistent.

15.58 $CaCrO_4(s) \rightleftharpoons Ca^{2+}(aq) + CrO_4{}^{2-}(aq)$ $K_c = [Ca^{2+}][CrO_4{}^{2-}] = 7.1 \times 10^{-4}$

At equilibrium, $[Ca^{2+}] = [CrO_4{}^{2-}] = x$

$K_c = 7.1 \times 10^{-4} = x^2$, x = 0.0266 = 0.027 *M* Ca^{2+} and $CrO_4{}^{2-}$

15.59 *Analyze/Plan.* Follow the logic in sample Exercise 15.12, using torr in place of *M*. For this reaction, $\Delta n = 0$, and $K_p = K_c$, so we use the more convenient measure of concentration.

	$CH_4(g)$ +	$I_2(g)$ ⇌	$CH_3I(g)$ +	HI(g)
initial	105.1 torr	7.96 torr	0 torr	0 torr
change	–x torr	–x torr	+x torr	+x torr
equil	105.1–x torr	7.96–x torr	+x torr	+x torr

$$K_p = 2.26 \times 10^{-4} = \frac{x^2}{(105.1 - x)(7.96 - x)}; \, x^2 = 2.26 \times 10^{-4}(836.6 - 113.1x + x^2)$$

$$0.999774\,x^2 + 0.02555\,x - 0.18907 = 0; \quad x = \frac{-0.02555 \pm \sqrt{(0.02555)^2 - 4(0.999774)(-0.18907)}}{2(0.999774)}$$

(The negative solution is not chemically meaningful.)

$x = 0.422$ torr; at equilibirum : $P_{CH_3I} = P_{HI} = 0.422$ torr; $P_{CH_4} = 104.7$ torr; $P_{I_2} = 7.54$ torr

15.60

	CH$_3$COOH(solv) +	CH$_3$CH$_2$OH(solv)	$\rightleftharpoons$ CH$_3$COOCH$_2$CH$_3$(g) +	H$_2$O(solv)
initial	0.275 M	3.85 M	0 M	0 M
change	–x M	–x M	+x M	+x M
equil	0.275–x M	3.85–x M	+x M	+x M

$$K_c = 6.68 = \frac{x^2}{(0.275 - x)(3.85 - x)}; \, x^2 = 6.68(1.059 - 4.125\,x + x^2)$$

$$0 = 5.68\,x^2 - 27.56\,x + 7.072; \quad x = \frac{27.56 \pm \sqrt{(-27.56)^2 - 4(5.68)(7.072)}}{2(5.68)} = 0.27185 = 0.272\,M$$

(The 4.58 M quadratic solution is not chemically meaningful.)

$$\frac{0.27185 \text{ mol ethyl acetate}}{L} \times 15.0\,L \times \frac{88.10 \text{ g ethyl acetate}}{mol} = 359.25 = 359 \text{ g ethyl acetate}$$

LeChâtelier's Principle (section 15.7)

15.61 *Analyze/Plan.* Follow the logic in Sample Exercise 15.13.   *Solve.*

(a) Shift equilibrium to the right; more SO$_3$(g) is formed, the amount of SO$_2$(g) decreases.

(b) Heating an exothermic reaction decreases the value of K. More SO$_2$ and O$_2$ will form, the amount of SO$_3$ will decrease. This is fundamentally different than shifting the relative amounts of reactants and products to maintain K; here, the equilibrium position itself changes.

(c) Since, $\Delta n = -1$, a change in volume will affect the equilibrium position and favor the side with more moles of gas. The amounts of SO$_2$ and O$_2$ increase and the amount of SO$_3$ decreases; equilibrium shifts to the left.

(d) No effect. Speeds up the forward and reverse reactions equally.

(e) No effect. Does not appear in the equilibrium expression.

(f) Shift equilibrium to the right; amounts of SO$_2$ and O$_2$ decrease.

15.62 4NH$_3$(g) + 5O$_2$(g) $\rightleftharpoons$ 4NO(g) + 6 H$_2$O(g)

(a) increase [NH$_3$], increase yield NO

(b) increase [H$_2$O], decrease yield NO

(c) decrease [O_2], decrease yield NO

(d) decrease container volume, decrease yield NO (fewer moles gas in reactants)

(e) add catalyst, no change

(f) increase temperature, decrease yield NO (reaction is exothermic)

15.63 *Analyze/Plan.* Given certain changes to a reaction system, determine the effect on K_p, if any. Only changes in temperature cause changes to the value of K_p.   *Solve.*

(a) no effect   (b) no effect   (c) no effect

(d) increase equilibrium constant   (e) no effect

15.64 (a) The reaction must be endothermic ($+\Delta H$) if heating increases the fraction of products.

(b) There must be more moles of gas in the products if increasing the volume of the vessel increases the fraction of products.

15.65 *Analyze/Plan.* Use Hess's Law, $\Delta H^\circ = \Sigma \Delta H_f^\circ$ products $- \Sigma \Delta H_f^\circ$ reactants, to calculate ΔH°. According to the sign of ΔH°, describe the effect of temperature on the value of K. According to the value of Δn, describe the effect of changes to container volume.

Solve.

(a) $\Delta H^\circ = \Delta H_f^\circ NO_2(g) + \Delta H_f^\circ N_2O(g) - 3\Delta H_f^\circ NO(g)$

$\Delta H^\circ = 33.84$ kJ $+ 81.6$ kJ $- 3(90.37$ kJ$) = -155.7$ kJ

(b) The reaction is exothermic because it has a negative value of ΔH°. The equilibrium constant will decrease with increasing temperature.

(c) Δn does not equal zero, so a change in volume at constant temperature will affect the fraction of products in the equilibrium mixture. An increase in container volume would favor reactants, while a decrease in volume would favor products.

15.66 (a) $\Delta H^\circ = \Delta H_f^\circ CH_3OH(g) - \Delta H_f^\circ CO(g) - 2\Delta H_f^\circ H_2(g)$

$= -201.2$ kJ $- (-110.5$ kJ$) - 0$ kJ

$= -90.7$ kJ

(b) The reaction is exothermic; an increase in temperature would decrease the value of K and decrease the yield. A low temperature is needed to maximize yield.

(c) Increasing total pressure would increase the partial pressure of each gas, shifting the equilibrium toward products. The extent of conversion to CH_3OH increases as the total pressure increases.

15.67 For this reaction, there are more moles of product gas than moles of reactant gas. An increase in total pressure increases the partial pressure of each gas, shifting the equilibrium towards reactants. An increase in pressure favors formation of ozone.

15.68 Increasing levels of atmospheric CO_2 provide an alternate CO_2 source to microorganisms. They need to process fewer environmental pollutants in order to maintain their biomass. Increasing levels of atmospheric CO_2 decrease the effectiveness of microorganism bioremediation.

Additional Exercises

15.69   (a)   Since both the forward and reverse processes are elementary steps, we can write the rate laws directly from the chemical equation.

$$rate_f = k_f\,[CO][Cl_2] = rate_r = k_r\,[COCl][Cl]$$

$$\frac{k_f}{k_r} = \frac{[COCl][Cl]}{[CO][Cl_2]} = K$$

$$K_c = \frac{k_f}{k_r} = \frac{1.4\times10^{-28}\,M^{-1}\,s^{-1}}{9.3\times10^{10}\,M^{-1}\,s^{-1}} = 1.5\times10^{-39}$$

For a homogeneous equilibrium in the gas phase, we usually write K in terms of partial pressures. In this exercise, concentrations are more convenient because the rate constants are expressed in terms of molarity. For this reaction, the value of K is the same regardless of how it is expressed, because there is no change in the moles of gas in going from reactants to products.

  (b)   Since the K is quite small, reactants are much more plentiful than products at equilibrium.

  (c)   In order to determine whether the reaction is exothermic or endothermic, We need to know whether an increase in temperature increases or decreases the value of the equilibrium constant, K.

15.70 $2A(g) \rightleftharpoons B(g)$, $K_c = 1$

$$\frac{[B]}{[A]^2} = 1, \quad [B] = [A]^2 \text{ and } [A] = [B]^{1/2}$$

15.71 $CH_4(g) + H_2O(g) \rightarrow CO(g) + 3H_2(g)$

$$K_p = \frac{P_{CO}\times P_{H_2}^3}{P_{CH_4}\times P_{H_2O}}; \quad P = \frac{g\,RT}{MM\,V}; \quad T = 1000\ K$$

$$P_{CO} = \frac{8.62\ g}{28.01\ g/mol} \times \frac{0.08206\ L\text{-}atm}{mol\text{-}K} \times \frac{1000\ K}{5.00\ L} = 5.0507 = 5.05\ atm$$

$$P_{H_2} = \frac{2.60\ g}{2.016\ g/mol} \times \frac{0.08206\ L\text{-}atm}{mol\text{-}K} \times \frac{1000\ K}{5.00\ L} = 21.1663 = 21.2\ atm$$

$$P_{CH_4} = \frac{43.0\ g}{16.04\ g/mol} \times \frac{0.08206\ L\text{-}atm}{mol\text{-}K} \times \frac{1000\ K}{5.00\ L} = 43.9973 = 44.0\ atm$$

$$P_{H_2O} = \frac{48.4\ g}{18.02\ g/mol} \times \frac{0.08206\ L\text{-}atm}{mol\text{-}K} \times \frac{1000\ K}{5.00\ L} = 44.0811 = 44.1\ atm$$

$$K_p = \frac{(5.0507)(21.1663)^3}{(43.9973)(44.0811)} = 24.6949 = 24.7$$

$$K_p = K_c(RT)^{\Delta n}, \quad K_c = K_p/(RT)^{\Delta n}; \quad \Delta n = 4 - 2 = 2$$

$$K_c = (24.6949)/[(0.08206)(1000)]^2 = 3.6673\times10^{-3} = 3.67\times10^{-3}$$

15.72 $[SO_2Cl_2] = \dfrac{2.00 \text{ mol}}{2.00 \text{ L}} = 1.00 \ M$

The change in $[SO_2Cl_2] = 0.56(1.00 \ M) = 0.56 \ M$

	$SO_2Cl_2(g)$	$\rightleftharpoons$	$SO_2(g)$	$+$	$Cl_2(g)$	$K_c = \dfrac{[SO_2][Cl_2]}{[SO_2Cl_2]}$
initial	1.00 M		0		0	
change	$-0.56 \ M$		$+0.56 \ M$		$+0.56 \ M$	
equil.	0.44 M		$+0.56 \ M$		$+0.56 \ M$	

(a) $K_c = \dfrac{(0.56)^2}{0.44} = 0.7127 = 0.71$

(b) $K_p = K_c(RT)^{\Delta n}$; $\Delta n = 2 - 1 = 1$; $K_p = (0.7127)(0.08206)(303) = 17.7214 = 18$

(c) $[SO_2Cl_2] = \dfrac{2.00 \text{ mol}}{15.00 \text{ L}} = 0.13333 = 0.133 \ M$; $\Delta M = 0.56(0.133) = 0.07466 = 0.075 \ M$

The equilibrium concentrations are: $[SO_2Cl_2] = (0.13333 - 0.07466) \ M = 0.05867 = 0.059 \ M$; $[SO_2] = 0.07466 = 0.075 \ M$; $[Cl_2] = 0.07466 = 0.075 \ M$.

$K_c = \dfrac{(0.07466)^2}{0.05867} = 0.09501 = 0.095$; $K_p = (0.09501)(0.08206)(303) = 2.362 = 2.4$

15.73   (a) $H_2(g) + S(s) \rightleftharpoons H_2S(g)$ $K_c = [H_2S]/[H_2]$

(b)   Calculate the molarities of H_2S and H_2.

$[H_2S] = \dfrac{0.46 \text{ g}}{34.1 \text{ g/mol}} \times \dfrac{1}{1.0 \text{ L}} = 0.01349 = 0.013 \ M$

$[H_2] = \dfrac{0.40 \text{ g}}{2.02 \text{ g/mol}} \times \dfrac{1}{1.0 \text{ L}} = 0.1980 = 0.20 \ M$

$K_c = 0.01349/0.1980 = 0.06812 = 0.068$

(c)   Since S is a pure solid, its concentration doesn't change during the reaction, so [S] does not appear in the equilibrium expression.

15.74   (a) $K_p = \dfrac{P_{Br_2} \times P_{NO}^2}{P_{NOBr}^2}$; $P = \dfrac{gRT}{MM \times V}$; $T = 100°C + 273 = 373 \ K$

$P_{Br_2} = \dfrac{4.19 \text{ g}}{159.8 \text{ g/mol}} \times \dfrac{0.08206 \text{ L-atm}}{\text{mol-K}} \times \dfrac{373}{5.00 \text{ L}} = 0.16051 = 0.161 \text{ atm}$

$P_{NO} = \dfrac{3.08 \text{ g}}{30.01 \text{ g/mol}} \times \dfrac{0.08206 \text{ L-atm}}{\text{mol-K}} \times \dfrac{373}{5.00 \text{ L}} = 0.62828 = 0.628 \text{ atm}$

$P_{NOBr} = \dfrac{3.22 \text{ g NOBr}}{109.9 \text{ g/mol}} \times \dfrac{0.08206 \text{ L-atm}}{\text{mol-K}} \times \dfrac{373}{5.00 \text{ L}} = 0.17936 = 0.179 \text{ atm}$

$K_p = \dfrac{(0.16051)(0.62828)^2}{(0.17936)^2} = 1.9695 = 1.97$ $K_p = K_c(RT)^{\Delta n}$, $\Delta n = 3 - 2 = 1$

$K_c = K_p/RT = 1.9695/(0.08206)(373) = 0.064345 = 0.0643$

(b) $P_t = P_{Br_2} + P_{NO} + P_{NOBr} = 0.16051 + 0.62828 + 0.17936 = 0.96815 = 0.968$ atm

(c)   All NO and Br_2 present at equilibrium came from the decomposition of the original NOBr. The mass of original NOBr is the sum of the masses of all compounds at equilibrium.

Original g NOBr = 4.19 gBr_2 + 3.08 g NO + 3.22 g NOBr = 10.49 g

15.75   (a)

	A(g)	⇌	2B(g)
initial	0.75 atm		0
change	−0.39 atm		+0.78 atm
equil.	0.36 atm		0.78 atm

$P_t = P_A + P_B = 0.36$ atm + 0.78 atm = 1.14 atm

(b) $K_p = \dfrac{(P_B)^2}{P_A} = \dfrac{(0.78)^2}{0.36} = 1.690 = 1.7$

(c)   Increasing the volume of the flask favors the reaction with more moles of gas. Doing the reaction in a larger flask maximizes the yield of B.

15.76   (a) $K_p = \dfrac{P_{NH_3}^2}{P_{N_2} \times P_{H_2}^3} = 4.34 \times 10^{-3}; \; T = 300°C + 273 = 573\,K$

$P_{NH_3} = \dfrac{gRT}{MM \times V} = \dfrac{1.05\,g}{17.03\,g/mol} \times \dfrac{0.08206\,L\text{-}atm}{mol\text{-}K} \times \dfrac{573\,K}{1.00\,L} = 2.899 = 2.90$ atm

	N_2(g) +	$3H_2$(g)	⇌	$2NH_3$(g)
initial	0 atm	0 atm		?
change	x	3x		−2x
equil.	x atm	3x atm		2.899 atm

(Remember, only the change line reflects the stoichiometry of the reaction.)

$K_p = \dfrac{(2.899)^2}{(x)(3x)^3} = 4.34 \times 10^{-3}; \; 27\,x^4 = \dfrac{(2.899)^2}{4.34 \times 10^{-3}}; \; x^4 = 71.725$

$x = 2.910 = 2.91$ atm $= P_{N_2}; \; P_{H_2} = 3x = 8.730 = 8.73$ atm

$g_{N_2} = \dfrac{MM \times PV}{RT} = \dfrac{28.02\,g\,N_2}{mol\,N_2} \times \dfrac{mol\text{-}K}{0.08206\,L\text{-}atm} \times \dfrac{2.910\,atm \times 1.00\,L}{573\,K} = 1.73\,g\,N_2$

$g_{H_2} = \dfrac{2.016\,g\,H_2}{mol\,H_2} \times \dfrac{mol\text{-}K}{0.08206\,L\text{-}atm} \times \dfrac{8.730\,atm \times 1.00\,L}{573\,K} = 0.374\,g\,H_2$

(b)   The initial $P_{NH_3} = 2.899$ atm + 2(2.910 atm) = 8.719 = 8.72 atm

$g_{NH_3} = \dfrac{17.03\,g\,NH_3}{mol\,NH_3} \times \dfrac{mol\text{-}K}{0.08206\,L\text{-}atm} \times \dfrac{8.719\,atm \times 1.00\,L}{573\,K} = 3.16\,g\,NH_3$

(c) $P_t = P_{N_2} + P_{H_2} + P_{NH_3} = 2.910$ atm + 8.730 atm + 2.899 atm = 14.54 atm

15.77

	2IBr	$\rightleftharpoons$	I_2	+	Br_2
initial	0.025 atm		0		0
change	$-2x$		x		x
equil.	$(0.025 - 2x)$ atm		x		x

$$K_p = 8.5 \times 10^{-3} = \frac{P_{I_2} \times P_{Br_2}}{P_{IBr}^2} = \frac{x^2}{(0.025 - 2x)^2}; \quad \text{Taking the square root of both sides}$$

$$\frac{x}{0.025 - 2x} = (8.5 \times 10^{-3})^{1/2} = 0.0922; \ x = 0.0922(0.025 - 2x)$$

$x + 0.184x = 0.002305; \ 1.184x = 0.002305; \ x = 0.001947 = 1.9 \times 10^{-3}$

At equilibrium, $P_{I_2} = P_{Br_2} = x = 1.9 \times 10^{-3}$ atm

P_{IBr} at equilibrium $= 0.025 - 2(1.947 \times 10^{-3}) = 0.02111 = 0.021$ atm

Check. $K_p = (0.001947)^2/(0.02111)^2 = 8.5 \times 10^{-3}$; the calculated concentrations are self-consistent.

15.78   **(a)** $K_p = 0.052; \ K_p = K_c(RT)^{\Delta n}; \ \Delta n = 2 - 0 = 2; \ K_c = K_p/(RT)^2$

           $K_c = 0.052/[0.08206)(333)]^2 = 6.964 \times 10^{-5} = 7.0 \times 10^{-5}$

   (b) PH_3BCl_3 is a solid and its concentration is taken as a constant, C.

$$[BCl_3] = \frac{0.0500 \text{ g } BCl_3}{1.500 \text{ L}} \times \frac{\text{mol } BCl_3}{117.17 \text{ g } BCl_3} = 2.8449 \times 10^{-4} = 2.84 \times 10^{-4} M \ BCl_3$$

	PH_3BCl_3	$\rightleftharpoons$	PH_3	+	BCl_3
initial	C		0 M		$2.84 \times 10^{-4} M$
change			$+x \ M$		$+x \ M$
equil.	C		$+x \ M$		$(2.84 \times 10^{-4} + x) \ M$

$K_c = [PH_3][BCl_3]; \ 6.964 \times 10^{-5} = x(2.84 \times 10^{-4} + x); \ x^2 + 2.84 \times 10^{-4} \ x - 6.964 \times 10^{-5} = 0$

$$x = \frac{-2.84 \times 10^{-4} \pm [(2.84 \times 10^{-4})^2 - 4(1)(-6.964 \times 10^{-5})]^{1/2}}{2(1)} = 0.008204 = 8.2 \times 10^{-3} M \ PH_3$$

Check. $K_c = (8.2 \times 10^{-3})(2.84 \times 10^{-4} + 8.2 \times 10^{-3}) = 7.0 \times 10^{-5}$.

15.79 $K_p = P_{NH_3} \times P_{H_2S}; \ P_t = 0.614$ atm

If the equilibrium amounts of NH_3 and H_2S are due solely to the decomposition of $NH_4HS(s)$, the equilibrium pressures of the two gases are equal, and each is 1/2 of the total pressure.

$P_{NH_3} = P_{H_2S} = 0.614 \text{ atm}/2 = 0.307$ atm

$K_p = (0.307)^2 = 0.0943$

15.80   Initial $P_{SO_3} = \dfrac{gRT}{MM\ V} = \dfrac{0.831\ g}{80.07\ g/mol} \times \dfrac{0.08206\ L\text{-}atm}{mol\text{-}K} \times \dfrac{1100\ K}{1.00\ L} = 0.9368 = 0.937\ atm$

	$2SO_3$	$\rightleftharpoons$	$2SO_2$	+	O_2
initial	0.9368 atm		0		0
change	−2x		+2x		+x
equil.	0.9368−2x		2x		x
[equil.]	0.2104 atm		0.7264 atm		0.3632 atm

$P_t = (0.9368-2x) + 2x + x;\ 0.9368 + x = 1.300\ atm;\ x = 1.300 - 0.9368 = 0.3632 = 0.363\ atm$

$K_p = \dfrac{P_{SO_2}^2 \times P_{O_2}}{P_{SO_3}^2} = \dfrac{(0.7264)^2\ (0.3632)}{(0.2104)^2} = 4.3292 = 4.33$

$K_p = K_c(RT)^{\Delta n};\ \Delta n = 3 - 2 = 1;\ K_p = K_c(RT)$

$K_c = K_p/RT = 4.3292/[(0.08206)(1100)] = 0.04796 = 0.0480$

15.81   In general, the reaction quotient is of the form $Q = \dfrac{P_{NOCl}^2}{P_{NO}^2 \times P_{Cl_2}}$.

(a) $Q = \dfrac{(0.11)^2}{(0.15)^2\ (0.31)} = 1.7$

$Q > K_p$. The mixture is not at equilibrium. It will shift to the left and produce more reactants as it moves toward equilibrium.

(b) $Q = \dfrac{(0.050)^2}{(0.12)^2\ (0.10)} = 1.7$

$Q > K_p$. The mixture is not at equilibrium. It will shift to the left and produce more reactants as it moves toward equilibrium.

(c) $Q = \dfrac{(5.10 \times 10^{-3})^2}{(0.15)^2\ (0.20)} = 5.8 \times 10^{-3}$

$Q < K_p$. The mixture is not at equilibrium. It will shift to the right and produce more products as it moves toward equilibrium.

15.82 $K_c = [CO_2] = 0.0108;\ [CO_2] = \dfrac{g\ CO_2}{44.01\ g/mol} \times \dfrac{1}{10.0\ L}$

In each case, calculate $[CO_2]$ and determine the position of the equilibrium.

(a) $[CO_2] = \dfrac{4.25\ g}{44.01\ g/mol} \times \dfrac{1}{10.0\ L} = 9.657 \times 10^{-3} = 9.66 \times 10^{-3}\ M$

$Q = 9.66 \times 10^{-3} < K_c$. The reaction proceeds to the right to achieve equilibrium and the amount of $CaCO_3(s)$ decreases.

(b) $[CO_2] = \dfrac{5.66\ g\ CO_2}{44.01\ g/mol} \times \dfrac{1}{10.0\ L} = 0.0129\ M$

$Q = 0.0129 > K_c$. The reaction proceeds to the left to achieve equilibrium and the amount of $CaCO_3(s)$ increases.

(c)   6.48 g CO_2 means $[CO_2] > 0.0129$ M; $Q > 0.0129 > K_c$, the amount of $CaCO_3$ increases.

15.83 $CO_2(g)$ + $H_2(g)$ $\rightleftharpoons$ $CO(g)$ + $H_2O(g)$

initial   1.50 mol   1.50 mol   0   0

change $-x$ $-x$ $+x$ $+x$

equil. $(1.50-x)$mol $(1.50-x)$mol x x

Since $\Delta n = 0$, the volume terms cancel and we can use moles in place of molarity in the K expression.

$$K_c = 0.802 = \frac{[CO][H_2O]}{[CO_2][H_2O]} = \frac{x^2}{(1.50-x)^2}$$

Take the square root of both sides.

$(0.802)^{1/2} = x/(1.50-x)$; $0.8955(1.50-x) = x$

$1.3433 = 1.8955x$, $x = 0.7087 = 0.709$ mol

$[CO] = [H_2O] = 0.7087$ mol$/3.00$ L $= 0.236$ M

$[CO_2] = [H_2] = (1.50 - 0.709)mol/3.00$ L $= 0.264$ M

15.84   (a) $[CO_2] = \dfrac{25.0 \text{ g } CO_2}{44.01 \text{ g/mol}} \times \dfrac{1}{3.00 \text{ L}} = 0.18935 = 0.189$ M

                    $C(s)$ + $CO_2(g)$ $\rightleftharpoons$ $2CO(g)$

initial   excess   0.189   0

change $-x$ $-x$ $+2x$

equil. $0.189-x$ $+2x$

$K_c = 1.9 = \dfrac{[CO]^2}{[CO_2]} = \dfrac{(2x)^2}{0.189-x}$; $4x^2 = 1.9(0.189 - x)$; $4x^2 + 1.9x - 0.36 = 0$.

Solve the quadratic for x.

$$x = \frac{-1.9 \pm \sqrt{(1.9)^2 - 4(4)(-0.36)}}{2(4)} = 0.14505 = 0.15 \text{ } M$$

$[CO] = 2x = 2(0.14505) = 0.2901 = 0.29$ M

$$\frac{0.2901 \text{ mol CO}}{L} \times 3.00 \text{ L} \times \frac{28.01 \text{ g CO}}{\text{mol}} = 24.38 = 24 \text{ g CO}$$

(b)   The amount of C(s) consumed is related to x. Change M to mol to g C.

$$\frac{0.14505 \text{ mol}}{L} \times 3.00 \text{ L} \times 12.01 \text{ g} = 5.226 = 5.2 \text{ g C consumed}$$

(c)   A smaller vessel at the same temperature increases the total pressure of the mixture. The equilibrium shifts to form fewer total moles of gas, which favors reactants. The yield of CO product will be smaller in a smaller vessel.

(d)   The two K_c values are 0.133 at 298 K and 1.9 at 1000 K. The reaction is endothermic, because K is larger at higher temperature.

15.85 $K_p = \dfrac{P_{CO_2}}{P_{CO}} = 6.0 \times 10^2$

If P_{CO} is 150 torr, P_{CO_2} can never exceed 760 – 150 = 610 torr. Then Q = 610/150 = 4.1. Since this is far less than K, the reaction will shift in the direction of more product. Reduction will therefore occur.

15.86   The anecdote tells us that increasing the volume of the reaction container, the furnace, had no effect on the amount of unreacted CO(g), the amount of CO(g) expelled. This is true for reactions that have the same number of moles of gaseous products and reactants, as this one does. It also means that $K_p = K_c$.

15.87   (a)

$$CCl_4(g) \rightleftharpoons C(s) + 2Cl_2(g)$$

	CCl_4	
initial	2.00 atm	0 atm
change	–x atm	+2x atm
equil.	(2.00–x) atm	2x atm

$$K_p = 0.76 = \dfrac{P_{Cl_2}^2}{P_{CCl_4}} = \dfrac{(2x)^2}{(2.00-x)}$$

$1.52 - 0.76x = 4x^2; \quad 4x^2 + 0.76x - 1.52 = 0$

Using the quadratic formula, a = 4, b = 0.76, c = –1.52

$$x = \dfrac{-0.76 \pm \sqrt{(0.76)^2 - 4(4)(-1.52)}}{2(4)} = \dfrac{-0.76 + 4.99}{8} = 0.5287 = 0.53 \text{ atm}$$

$$\text{Fraction } CCl_4 \text{ reacted} = \dfrac{x \text{ atm}}{2.00 \text{ atm}} = \dfrac{0.5287}{2.00} = 0.264 = 26\%$$

(b) $P_{Cl_2} = 2x = 2(0.5287) = 1.06 \text{ atm}$

$P_{CCl_4} = 2.00 - x = 2.00 - 0.5287 = 1.47 \text{ atm}$

15.88   (a) $Q = \dfrac{P_{PCl_5}}{P_{PCl_3} \times P_{Cl_2}} = \dfrac{(0.20)}{(0.50)(0.50)} = 0.80$

0.80 (Q) > 0.0870 (K), the reaction proceeds to the left.

(b)

$$PCl_3(g) + Cl_2(g) \rightleftharpoons PCl_5(g)$$

	PCl_3	Cl_2	PCl_5
initial	0.50 atm	0.50 atm	0.20 atm
change	+x atm	+x atm	–x atm
equil.	(0.50 + x) atm	(0.50 + x) atm	(0.20 - x) atm

(Since the reaction proceeds to the left, P_{PCl_5} must decrease and P_{PCl_3} and P_{Cl_2} must increase.)

$$K_p = 0.0870 = \frac{(0.20-x)}{(0.50+x)(0.50+x)}; \quad 0.0870 = \frac{(0.20-x)}{(0.250+1.00\,x+x^2)}$$

$$0.0870(0.250 + 1.00x + x^2) = 0.20 - x; \quad -0.17825 + 1.0870x + 0.0870\,x^2 = 0$$

$$x = \frac{-1.0870 \pm \sqrt{(1.0870)^2 - 4(0.0870)(-0.17825)}}{2(0.0870)} = \frac{-1.0870 + 1.1152}{0.174} = 0.162$$

$$P_{PCl_3} = (0.50 + 0.162)\,atm = 0.662 \qquad P_{Cl_2} = (0.50 + 0.162)\,atm = 0.662\,atm$$

$$P_{PCl_5} = (0.20 - 0.162)\,atm = 0.038\,atm$$

To two decimal places, the pressures are 0.66, 0.66 and 0.04 atm, respectively. When substituting into the K_p expression, pressures to three decimal places yield a result much closer to 0.0870.

(c)   Increasing the volume of the container favors the process where more moles of gas are produced, so the reverse reaction is favored and the equilibrium shifts to the left; the mole fraction of Cl_2 increases.

(d)   For an exothermic reaction, increasing the temperature decreases the value of K; more reactants and fewer products are present at equilibrium and the mole fraction of Cl_2 increases.

15.89   *Analyze/Plan.* Calculate the equilibrium pressures of H_2, I_2, and HI, use them to calculate K_p. Set up a new equilibrium table and calculate new equilibrium pressures.   *Solve.*

$$\frac{P}{n} = \frac{RT}{V} = \frac{0.08206\ L\text{-}atm}{mol\text{-}K} \times \frac{731\ K}{5.00} = 11.997\ \frac{atm}{mol}$$

$$P_{H_2} = P_{I_2} = 0.112\ mol \times 11.997\ \frac{atm}{mol} = 1.344 = 1.34\ atm$$

$$P_{HI} = 0.775\ mol \times 11.997\ \frac{atm}{mol} = 9.298 = 9.30\ atm$$

$$H_2(g) + I_2(g) \rightleftharpoons 2HI(g); \quad K_p = \frac{P_{HI}^2}{P_{H_2} \times P_{I_2}} = \frac{(9.298)^2}{(1.344)^2} = 47.861 = 47.9$$

$$P_{HI}\ (added) = 0.200\ mol \times \frac{11.997\ atm}{mol} = 2.3994 = 2.40\ atm$$

	$H_2(g)$	$+$	$I_2(g)$	$\rightleftharpoons$	$2HI(g)$
initial	1.34 atm		1.34 atm		9.30 atm + 2.40 atm
change	+x atm		+x atm		–2x atm
equil.	(1.34+x) atm		(1.34+x) atm		(11.70–2x) atm

$$K_p = 47.86 = \frac{(11.70-2x)^2}{(1.34+x)^2}. \quad \text{Take the square root of both sides:}$$

$$6.918 = \frac{11.70 - 2x}{1.34 + x}; \; 9.270 + 6.918\,x = 11.70 - 2x; \; 8.918\,x = 2.430; \; x = 0.27248 = 0.272$$

$$P_{H_2} = P_{I_2} = 1.34 + 0.272 = 1.612 = 1.61 \text{ atm}; \; P_{HI} = 11.70 - 2(0.272) = 11.156 = 11.16 \text{ atm}$$

Check. $\dfrac{(11.156)^2}{(1.612)^2} = 47.89 = 47.9$

15.90   (a)   Since the volume of the vessel = 1.00 L, mol = M. The reaction will proceed to the left to establish equilibrium.

	A(g) +	2B(g) $\rightleftharpoons$	2C(g)
initial	0 M	0 M	1.00 M
change	+x M	+2x M	−2x M
equil.	x M	2x M	(1.00 − 2x) M

At equilibrium, [C] = (1.00 − 2x) M, [B] = 2x M.

(b)   x must be less than 0.50 M (so that [C], 1.00 −2x, is not less than zero).

(c) $K_c = \dfrac{[C]^2}{[A][B]^2}; \; \dfrac{(1.00 - 2x)^2}{(x)(2x)^2} = 0.25$

$1.00 - 4x + 4x^2 = 0.25(4x)^3; \; x^3 - 4x^2 + 4x - 1 = 0$

(d)

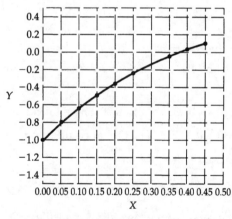

X	Y
0.0	−1.000
0.05	−0.810
0.10	−0.639
0.15	−0.487
0.20	−0.352
0.25	−0.234
0.35	−0.047
0.40	+0.024
0.45	+0.081
~0.383	0.00

(e)   From the plot, x ≈ 0.383 M

[A] = x = 0.383 M; [B] = 2x = 0.766 M

[C] = 1.00 − 2x = 0.234 M

Using the K_c expression as a check:

$K_c = 0.25; \; \dfrac{(0.234)^2}{(0.383)(0.766)^2} = 0.24;$ the estimated values are reasonable.

15.91 $K_p = \dfrac{P_{O_2} \times P_{CO}^2}{P_{CO_2}^2} \approx 1 \times 10^{-13}; P_{O_2} = (0.03)(1 \text{ atm}) = 0.03 \text{ atm}$

$P_{CO} = (0.002)(1 \text{ atm}) = 0.002 \text{ atm}; \quad P_{CO_2} = (0.12)(1 \text{ atm}) = 0.12 \text{ atm}$

$Q = \dfrac{(0.03)(0.002)^2}{(0.12)^2} = 8.3 \times 10^{-6} = 8 \times 10^{-6}$

Since $Q > K_p$, the system will shift to the left to attain equilibrium. Thus a catalyst that promoted the attainment of equilibrium would result in a lower CO content in the exhaust.

15.92   The patent claim is false. A catalyst does not alter the position of equilibrium in a system, only the rate of approach to the equilibrium condition.

Integrative Exercises

15.93   Calculate the initial $[IO_4^-]$, and then construct an equilibrium table to determine $[H_4IO_6^-]$ at equilibrium.

$M_c \times V_c = M_d \times L_d; \quad \dfrac{0.905\ M \times 25.0 \text{ mL}}{500.0 \text{ mL}} = M_d = 0.04525 = 0.0453\ M\ IO_4^-$

$$IO_4^-(aq) \;+\; 2H_2O(l) \;\rightleftharpoons\; H_4IO_6^-(aq)$$

	IO_4^-	$H_4IO_6^-$
initial	0.0453 M	0
change	$-x$	$+x$
equil.	$0.0453 - x$	$+x$

$K_c = 3.5 \times 10^{-2} = \dfrac{[H_4IO_6^-]}{[IO_4^-]} = \dfrac{x}{(0.0453 - x)}$

Because K_c is relatively large and $[IO_4^-]$ is relatively small, we cannot assume x is small relative to 0.0453.

$0.035(0.04525 - x) = x; \; 0.001584 - 0.035x = x; \quad 0.001584 = 1.035x$

$x = 0.001584/1.035 = 0.001530 = 0.0015\ M\ H_4IO_6^-$ at equilibrium

15.94   (a) $AgCl(s) \rightleftharpoons Ag^+(aq) + Cl^-(aq)$

(b) $K_c = [Ag^+][Cl^-]$

(c)   Using thermodynamic data from Appendix C, calculate ΔH for the reaction in part (a).

$\Delta H° = \Delta H_f° \, Ag^+(aq) + \Delta H_f° \, Cl^-(aq) - \Delta H_f° \, AgCl(s)$

$\Delta H° = 105.90 \text{ kJ} - 167.2 \text{ kJ} - (-127.0 \text{ kJ}) = 65.7 \text{ kJ}$

The reaction is endothermic (heat is a reactant), so the solubility of $AgCl(s)$ in $H_2O(l)$ will increase with increasing temperature.

(d)   Calculate the solubility of $AgCl(s)$ in pure water as $[Ag^+]$, in 0.100 M NaCl(aq) as $[Ag^+]$, and in 0.100 M NaCl(aq) as $[AgCl_2]^-$.

In pure water, let $[Ag^+] = [Cl^-] = x$; $K_c = [Ag^+][Cl^-] = x^2 = 1.6 \times 10^{-10}$

$x = (1.6 \times 10^{-10})^{1/2}$; $[Ag^+] = 1.3 \times 10^{-5}\, M\,[Ag^+]$

In 0.100 M NaCl(aq), assuming no formation of $[AgCl_2^-]$,

$[Ag^+] = x$, $[Cl^-] = 0.100 + x$; $K_c = [Ag^+][Cl^-] = x(0.100 + x) = 1.6 \times 10^{-10}$

Assuming x is small relative to 0.100, 0.100 x = 1.6×10^{-10},

$x = 1.6 \times 10^{-9}\, M\,[Ag^+]$

To account for complexation, the formation of soluble $AgCl_2^-$, sum the two reactions and calculate K for the overall process.

$$AgCl(s) \rightleftharpoons Ag^+(aq) + Cl^-(aq) \qquad K_1 = 1.6 \times 10^{-10}$$

$$Ag^+(aq) + 2Cl^-(aq) \rightleftharpoons AgCl_2^-(aq) \qquad K_2 = 1.8 \times 10^5$$

$$AgCl(s) + Ag^+(aq) + 2Cl^-(aq) \rightleftharpoons Ag^+(aq) + Cl^-(aq) + AgCl_2^-(aq) \quad K_c = K_1 \times K_2$$

$$AgCl(s) + Cl^-(aq) \rightleftharpoons AgCl_2^-(aq) \qquad K_c = 2.9 \times 10^{-5}$$

$K_c = [AgCl_2^-]/[Cl^-]$; $[AgCl_2^-] = x$, $[Cl^-] = 0.100 - x$

Assuming x is small relative to 0.100, $2.9 \times 10^{-5} = x/(0.100)$;

$x = 2.9 \times 10^{-6}\, M\,[AgCl_2^-]$

These calculations show that the "solubility" of AgCl, the concentration of any soluble silver species, is actually greatest in pure water, $1.3 \times 10^{-5}\, M\,[Ag^+]$. In 0.100 M NaCl, complexation causes the solubility of silver, $2.9 \times 10^{-6}\, M\,[AgCl_2^-]$, to be greater than that predicted by the common ion effect alone, $1.6 \times 10^{-9}\, M$ $[Ag^+]$, but not as great as its solubility in pure water.

15.95　Consider the energy profile for an exothermic reaction.

The activation energy in the forward direction, E_{af}, equals E_u, and the activation energy in the reverse reaction, E_{ar}, equals $E_u - \Delta H$. (The same is true for an endothermic reaction because the sign of ΔH is the positive and $E_{ar} < E_{af}$). For the reaction in question,

$$K = \frac{k_f}{k_r} = \frac{A_f e^{-E_{af}/RT}}{A_r e^{-E_{ar}/RT}}$$

Since the ln form of the Arrhenius equation is easier to manipulate, we will consider ln K.

$$\ln K = \ln\left(\frac{k_f}{k_r}\right) = \ln k_f - \ln k_r = \frac{-E_{af}}{RT} + \ln A_f - \left[\frac{-E_{ar}}{RT} + \ln A_r\right]$$

Substituting E_u for E_{af} and $(E_u - \Delta H)$ for E_{ar}

$$\ln K = \frac{-E_u}{RT} + \ln A_f - \left[\frac{-(E_u - \Delta H)}{RT} + \ln A_r\right]; \ln K = \frac{-E_u + (E_u - \Delta H)}{RT} + \ln A_f - \ln A_r$$

$$\ln K = \frac{-\Delta H}{RT} + \ln \frac{A_f}{A_r}$$

For the catalyzed reaction, $E_{cat} < E_u$ and $E_{af} = E_{cat}$, $E_{ar} = E_{cat} - \Delta H$. The catalyst does not change the value of ΔH.

$$\ln K_{cat} = \frac{-E_{cat} + (E_{cat} - \Delta H)}{RT} + \ln A_f - \ln A_r$$

$$\ln K_{cat} = \frac{-\Delta H}{RT} + \frac{\ln A_f}{A_r}$$

Thus, assuming A_f and A_r are not changed by the catalyst, $\ln K = \ln K_{cat}$ and $K = K_{cat}$.

15.96　(a)　For the reaction $SO_2(l) \rightarrow SO_2(g)$, $K_p = P_{SO_2}$. From the phase diagram, as T increases P_{SO_2} and K_p increase. For an endothermic reaction, K increases as T increases. The phase diagram tells us that the vaporization of $SO_2(l)$ is an endothermic process.

(b)　Read P_{SO_2} from the liquid-gas line on the phase diagram at 0°C and 100 °C. Note that the pressure axis of the phase diagram is logarithmic with respect to pressure, but linear with respect to logP. In terms of logP, the axis labels would be –1, 0, 1 and 2. The logP values at 0°C and 100 °C are approximately 0.25 and 1.4. The values of P_{SO_2} and K_p are $10^{0.25}$ and $10^{1.4}$, 1.8 and 25, respectively.

(c)　It is not possible to calculate an equilibrium constant between the gas and liquid phases in the supercritical region, because they do not exist separately in this region. That is, the gas and liquid phases are indistinguishable in the supercritical region.

(d)　Gases are most ideal at high temperature and low pressure. The red dot at slightly greater than 240°C is the point where $SO_2(g)$ most closely approaches ideal behavior.

(e)　The point near 15°C is the one at the lowest temperature, but it is also at low pressure. In general, the closer the pressure and temperature conditions are to the point of phase transition, the less ideal the behavior of the gas (because it is nearly a liquid). This describes the point near 115°C and 20 atm, which is at relatively high pressure and near the liquid-gas line.

15.97　Mole % = pressure %. Since the total pressure is 1 atm, mol %/100 = mol fraction = partial pressure. $K_p = P_{CO}^2 / P_{CO_2}$.

Temp (K)	P_{CO_2} (atm)	P_{CO} (atm)	K_P
1123	0.0623	0.9377	14.1
1223	0.0132	0.9868	73.8
1323	0.0037	0.9963	2.7×10^2
1473	0.0006	0.9994	1.7×10^3 (2×10^3)

Because K grows larger with increasing temperature, the reaction must be endothermic in the forward direction.

15.98   (a) $H_2O(l) \rightleftharpoons H_2O(g)$; $K_p = P_{H_2O}$

(b)   At 30°C, the vapor pressure of $H_2O(l)$ is 31.82 torr. $K_P = P_{H_2O} = 31.82$ torr

$K_p = 31.82$ torr $\times$ 1 atm/760 torr $= 0.041868 = 0.04187$ atm

(c)   From part (b), the value of K_p is the vapor pressure of the liquid at that temperature. By definition, vapor pressure = atmospheric pressure = 1 atm at the normal boiling point. $K_p = 1$ atm

15.99   (a)   VSEPR indicates that each O atom has four electron domains about it and thus adopts tetrahedral geometry. One O atom has two covalent bonds to H and two hydrogen bonds to H atoms on the second water molecule. The O atom on the second water molecule has two nonbonding electron pairs. The water dimer is not symmetrical.

(b)   Hydrogen-bonding is the intermolecular interaction involved in water dimer formation.

(c)   Water dimer formation is exothermic, since the value of K decreases as temperature increases.

15.100   The O_2-binding reaction occurs in aqueous solution, so we will write a K_c expression. The amount of $O_2(g)$ will apprear as a pressure. By convention, reactions which involve gaseous and aqueous substances have mixed equilibrium expressions written in terms of both pressures and molar concentrations.

$$K_c = \frac{[Hb\text{-}(O_2)_4]}{P_{O_2}^4 \times [Hb]}$$

The *P50 value* is the partial pressure at which 50% of the hemoglobin is saturated with $O_2(g)$. At this partial pressure, the concentrations of O_2-bound hemoglobin and free hemoglobin are equal, $[Hb - (O_2)_4] = [Hb]$. Substitute the two P50 values into the K_c expression and compare the values for fetal and adult hemoglobin.

at P50, $K_{cF} = \dfrac{1}{P_{O_2}^4} = \dfrac{1}{19^4} = 7.7 \times 10^{-6}$; $K_{cA} = \dfrac{1}{P_{O_2}^4} = \dfrac{1}{26.8^4} = 1.94 \times 10^{-6}$

Comparing the two values, $K_{cF}/K_{cA} = 7.7 \times 10^{-6}/1.94 \times 10^{-6} \approx 4$. The equilibrium constant for O_2-binding by fetal hemoblobin is approximately four times that by adult hemoglobin.

16 Acid-Base Equilibria

Visualizing Concepts

16.1 *Analyze.* From the structures decide which reactant fits the description of a Brønsted-Lowry (B-L) acid, a B-L base, a Lewis acid, and a Lewis base. *Plan.* A B-L acid is an H^+ donor, and a B-L base is an H^+ acceptor. A Lewis acid is an electron pair acceptor and a Lewis base is an electron pair donor. *Solve.*

    (a)   H–X is a B-L acid, because it loses H^+ during reaction. NH_3 is a B-L base, because it gains H^+ during reaction.

    (b)   By virtue of its unshared electron pair, NH_3 is the electron pair donor and Lewis base. HX is the electron pair acceptor and Lewis acid.

16.2 *Plan.* The stronger the acid, the greater the extent of ionization. The stronger the acid, the weaker its conjugate base. In an acid-base reaction, equilibrium will favor the side with the weaker acid and base. *Solve.*

    (a)   HY is stronger than HX. Starting with six HY molecules, four are dissociated; of six HX molecules, only two are dissociated. Because it is dissociated to a greater extent, HY is the stronger acid.

    (b)   If HY is the stronger acid, Y^- is the weaker base and X^- is the stronger base.

    (c)   HX and Y^-, the reactants, are the weaker acid and base. Equilibrium lies to the left, and $K_c < 1$.

16.3 *Plan.* Strong acids are completely ionized. The acid that is least ionized is weakest, and has the smallest K_a value. At equal concentrations, the weakest acid has the smallest $[H^+]$ and highest pH. *Solve.*

    (a)   HY is a strong acid. There are no neutral HY molecules in solution, only H^+ cations and Y^- anions.

    (b)   HX has the smallest K_a value. It has most neutral acid molecules and fewest ions.

    (c)   HX has the fewest H^+ and highest pH.

16.4 *Analyze/Plan.* Consider how K_a and [HA] influence extent of ionization (or percent ionization).

Solve. The greater the extent of ionization, the less valid the approximation that x is small relative to [HA]. The greater the value of K_a, the stronger the acid, the greater the extent of ionization. On the other hand, the smaller the [HA], the greater the percent ionization. The approximation is then most valid for small K_a and large [HA]. Case (a) and (c) have the smaller K_a, with case (c) having the larger initial [HA]. The approximation is most valid for case (c).

16.5   (a)   True. Solution A is the color of methyl orange in acidic solution.

         (b)   False. Methyl orange turns yellow at a pH slightly greater than 4, so solution B could be at any pH greater than 4.

         (c)   True. The basic color of any indicator occurs at higher pH than the acidic color does.

16.6   *Plan.* The definition of percent ionization is $\dfrac{[H^+]}{[HA]_{Initial}} \times 100$. *Solve.*

         (a)   Curve C shows the effect of concentration on percent ionization of a weak acid.

         (b)   For a weak acid, the percent ionization is inversely related to acid concentration; only curve C shows a decrease in percent ionization as acid concentration increases.

16.7   *Analyze/Plan.* Write the formula of each molecule and compare them to the entries in Tables 16.2 and 16.4. Select the molecule that is fits the definition of an acid, and the one that fits the definition of a base. *Solve.*

         (a)   Molecule A is hydroxyl amine, NH_2OH. It is an entry in Table 16.4. Molecule A is an H^+ acceptor because of the nonbonded electron pair on the N atom of the amine ($-NH_2$) group, not because it contains an $-OH$ group. The presence of an $-OH$ group in an organic molecule does not mean that the molecule is a base.

         (b)   Molecule B is formic acid, $HCOOH$. It is similar to CH_3COOH, an entry in Table 16.2. The H atom bonded to O is ionizable and $HCOOH$ is an H^+ donor. In general, organic molecules that contain a carboxyl ($-COOH$) group are acids.

         (c)   Molecule C is methanol, CH_3OH. In organic molecules, the $-OH$ functional group is an alcohol. The H atom bonded to O is not ionizable, and the $-OH$ group does not dissociate in aqueous solution. An alcohol is neither an acid nor a base.

16.8   Diagram C best represents an aqueous solution of NaF; it contains mostly Na^+ and F^-, along with a few HF molecules and OH^- ions. The HF and OH^- are present because F^- is a weak Bronsted base; it accepts H^+ from a water molecule, producing HF and OH^-. The solution is basic because it contains OH^-.

16.9   *Plan.* Evaluate the molecular structures to determine if the acids are binary acids or oxyacids. Consider the trends in acid strength for both classes of acids. *Solve.*

         (a)   If X is the same atom on both molecules, the molecule (b) is more acidic. The carboxylate anion, the conjugate base of this carboxylic acid, is stabilized by resonance, while the conjugate base of (a) is not resonance-stabilized. Stabilization of the conjugate base causes the ionization equilibrium to favor products, and (b) is the stronger acid.

         (b)   Increasing the electronegativity of X increases the strength of both acids. As X becomes more electronegative and attracts more electron density, the O-H bond becomes weaker and more polar. This increases the likelihood of ionization and increases acid strength. An electronegative X group also stabilizes the anionic conjugate bases by delocalizing the negative charge. This causes the ionization equilibrium to favor products, and the values of K_a to increase.

16.10   (a)   *Plan.* Count valence electrons and draw the correct Lewis structures. Consider The definition of Lewis acids and bases.   *Solve.*

$$PCl_4^+ \quad + \quad Cl^- \quad \rightarrow \quad PCl_5$$
$$32\,e^-,\,16\,e^-\,pr \qquad 8\,e^-,\,4\,e^-\,pr \qquad 40\,e^-,\,20\,e^-\,pr$$

PCl_4^+ accepts an electron pair from Cl^-; PCl_4^+ is the Lewis acid and Cl^- is the Lewis base.

   (b)   The hydrated cation is an oxyacid: the ionizable H is attached to O, which is bound to the central cation. As the charge on the cation increases, it attracts more electron density from the O–H bond, which becomes weaker and more polar. The degree of ionization increases and the equilibrium constant (K_a) increases.

Arrhenius and Brønsted-Lowry Acids and Bases (sections 16.1 and 16.2)

16.11   Solutions of HCl and H_2SO_4 taste sour, turn litmus paper red (are acidic), neutralize solutions of bases, react with active metals to form $H_2(g)$ and conduct electricity. The two solutions have these properties in common because both solutes are strong acids. That is, they both ionize completely in H_2O to form $H^+(aq)$ and an anion. (The first ionization step for H_2SO_4 is complete, but the second is not.) The presence of ions enables the solutions to conduct electricity; the presence of $H^+(aq)$ in excess of $1 \times 10^{-7}\,M$ accounts for all the other listed properties.

16.12   When NaOH dissolves in water, it completely dissociates to form $Na^+(aq)$ and $OH^-(aq)$. NH_3 is a Brønsted-Lowry base, an H^+ acceptor. When NH_3 dissolves in water, it participates in the equilibrium $NH_3(aq) + H_2O(l) \rightleftharpoons NH_4^+(aq) + OH^-(aq)$. Thus, the properties of both solutions are dominated by the presence of $OH^-(aq)$. Both solutions taste bitter, turn litmus paper blue (are basic), neutralize solutions of acids, and conduct electricity.

16.13   (a)   According to the Arrhenius definition, an *acid* when dissolved in water increases $[H^+]$. According to the Brønsted-Lowry definition, an *acid* is capable of donating H^+, regardless of physical state. The Arrhenius definition of an acid is confined to an aqueous solution; the Brønsted-Lowry definition applies to any physical state.

   (b) $HCl(g) + NH_3(g) \rightarrow NH_4^+Cl^-(s)$ HCl is the B-L (Brønsted-Lowry) acid; it donates an H^+ to NH_3 to form NH_4^+. NH_3 is the B-L base; it accepts the H^+ from HCl.

16.14   (a)   According to the Arrhenius definition, a *base* when dissolved in water increases $[OH^-]$. According to the Brønsted-Lowry theory, a *base* is an H^+ acceptor regardless of physical state. A Brønsted-Lowry base is not limited to aqueous solution and need not contain OH^- or produce it in aqueous solution.

(b)   Yes, a substance can behave as an Arrhenius base even if it does not contain an OH group. One example is ammonia.

$NH_3(g) + H_2O(l) \rightleftharpoons NH_4^+(aq) + OH^-(aq)$. When NH_3 dissolves in water, it accepts H^+ from H_2O. In doing so, OH^- is produced and $[OH^-]$ in the aqueous solution increases. The OH^- produced was originally part of the H_2O molecule, not part of the NH_3 molecule. Other organic amines behave in a similar manner.

16.15   *Analyze/Plan.* Follow the logic in Sample Exercise 16.1. A conjugate base has one less H^+ than its conjugate acid. A conjugate acid has one more H^+ than its conjugate base. *Solve.*

(a)   (i) IO_3^- (ii) NH_3

(b)   (i) OH^- (ii) H_3PO_4

16.16   A conjugate base has one less H^+ than its conjugate acid. A conjugate acid has one more H^+ than its conjugate base.

(a)   (i) $HCOO^-$ (ii) PO_4^{3-}

(b)   (i) HSO_4^- (ii) $CH_3NH_3^+$

16.17   *Analyze/Plan.* Use the definitions of B-L acids and bases, and conjugate acids and bases to make the designations. Evaluate the changes going from reactant to product to inform your choices.   *Solve.*

	B-L acid	+	**B-L base**	$\rightleftharpoons$	**Conjugate acid**	+	**Conjugate base**
(a)	$NH_4^+(aq)$		$CN^-(aq)$		$HCN(aq)$		$NH_3(aq)$
(b)	$H_2O(l)$		$(CH_3)_3N(aq)$		$(CH_3)_3NH^+(aq)$		$OH^-(aq)$
(c)	$HCOOH(aq)$		$PO_4^{3-}(aq)$		$HPO_4^{2-}(aq)$		$HCOO^-(aq)$

16.18

	B-L acid	+	**B-L base**	$\rightleftharpoons$	**Conjugate acid**	+	**Conjugate base**
(a)	$HBrO(aq)$		$H_2O(l)$		$H_3O^+(aq)$		$BrO^-(aq)$
(b)	$HSO_4^-(aq)$		$HCO_3^-(aq)$		$H_2CO_3(aq)$		$SO_4^{2-}(aq)$
(c)	$H_3O^+(aq)$		$HSO_3^-(aq)$		$H_2SO_3(aq)$		$H_2O(l)$

16.19   *Analyze/Plan.* Follow the logic in Sample Exercise 16.2.   *Solve.*

(a)   Acid: $HC_2O_4^-(aq) + H_2O(l) \rightleftharpoons C_2O_4^{2-}(aq) + H_3O^+(aq)$

                B-L acid   B-L base   conj. base   conj. acid

        Base: $HC_2O_4^-(aq) + H_2O(l) \rightleftharpoons H_2C_2O_4(aq) + OH^-(aq)$

                B-L base   B-L acid   conj. acid   conj. Base

(b) $H_2C_2O_4$ is the conjugate acid of $HC_2O_4^-$.

        $C_2O_4^{2-}$ is the conjugate base of $HC_2O_4^-$.

16.20 (a) $H_2C_6H_7O_5^-(aq) + H_2O(l) \rightleftharpoons H_3C_6H_7O_5(aq) + OH^-(aq)$

(b) $H_2C_6H_7O_5^-(aq) + H_2O(l) \rightleftharpoons HC_6H_7O_5^{2-}(aq) + H_3O^+(aq)$

(c) $H_3C_6H_7O_5$ is the conjugate acid of $H_2C_6H_7O_5^-$

$HC_6H_7O_5^{2-}$ is the conjugate base of $H_2C_6H_7O_5^-$

16.21 *Analyze/Plan.* Based on the chemical formula, decide whether the base is strong, weak or negligible. Is it the conjugate of a strong acid (negligible base), weak acid (weak base) or negligible acid (strong base)? Also check Figure 16.3. To write the formula of the conjugate acid, add a single H and increase the particle charge by one.

(a) CH_3COO^-, weak base; CH_3COOH, weak acid

(b) HCO_3^-, weak base; H_2CO_3, weak acid

(c) O^{2-}, strong base; OH^-, negligible acid

(d) Cl^-, negligible base; HCl, strong acid

(e) NH_3, weak base; NH_4^+, weak acid

16.22 Based on the chemical formula, decide whether the acid is strong, weak, or negligible. Is it one of the known seven strong acids (Section 16.5)? Also check Figure 16.3. Remove a single H and decrease the particle charge by one to write the formula of the conjugate base. *Solve.*

(a) $HCOOH$, weak acid; $HCOO^-$, weak base

(b) H_2, negligible acid; H^-, strong base

(c) CH_4, negligible acid; CH_3^-, strong base

(d) HF, weak acid; F^-, weak base

(e) NH_4^+, weak acid; NH_3, weak base

16.23 *Analyze/Plan.* Given chemical formula, determine strength of acids and bases by checking the known strong acids (Section 16.5). Recall the paradigm "The stronger the acid, the weaker its conjugate base, and vice versa."   *Solve.*

(a) HBr. It is one of the seven strong acids (Section 16.5).

(b) F^-. HCl is a stronger acid than HF, so F^- is the stronger conjugate base.

16.24 (a) $HClO_3$. It is one of the seven strong acids (Section 16.5). Also, in a series of oxyacids with the same central atom (Cl), the acid with more O atoms is stronger (Section 16.10).

(b) HS^-. H_2SO_4 is a stronger acid than H_2S, so HS^- is the stronger conjugate base. In fact, since H_2SO_4 is one of the seven strong acids, HSO_4^- is a negligible base.

16.25 *Analyze/Plan.* Acid-base equilibria favor formation of the weaker acid and base. Compare the relative strengths of the substances acting as acids on opposite sides of the equation. (Bases can also be compared; the conclusion should be the same.)   *Solve.*

Base	+	**Acid**	$\rightleftharpoons$	**Conjugate acid**	+	**Conjugate base**
(a) $O^{2-}(aq)$	+	$H_2O(l)$	$\rightleftharpoons$	$OH^-(aq)$	+	$OH^-(aq)$

H_2O is a stronger acid than OH^-, so the equilibrium lies to the right.

	Base	+	**Acid**	$\rightleftharpoons$	**Conjugate acid**	+	**Conjugate base**
(b)	$HS^-(aq)$	+	$CH_3COOH(aq)$	$\rightleftharpoons$	$H_2S(aq)$	+	$CH_3COO^-(aq)$

CH_3COOH is a stronger acid than H_2S, so the equilibrium lies to the right.

	Base	+	**Acid**	$\rightleftharpoons$	**Conjugate acid**	+	**Conjugate base**
(c)	$NO_2^-(aq)$	+	$H_2O(l)$	$\rightleftharpoons$	$HNO_2(aq)$	+	$OH^-(aq)$

HNO_2 is a stronger acid than H_2O, so the equilibrium lies to the left.

16.26

	Base	+	**Acid**	$\rightleftharpoons$	**Conjugate acid**	+	**Conjugate base**
(a)	$OH^-(aq)$	+	$NH_4^+(aq)$	$\rightleftharpoons$	$H_2O(l)$	+	$NH_3(aq)$

OH^- is a stronger base than NH_3 (Figure 16.3), so the equilibrium lies to the right.

(b)	$CH_3COO^-(aq)$	+	$H_3O^+(aq)$	$\rightleftharpoons$	$CH_3COOH(aq)$	+	$H_2O(l)$

H_3O^+ is a stronger acid than $HC_2H_3O_2$ (Figure 16.3), so the equilibrium lies to the right.

(c)	$F^-(aq)$	+	$HCO_3^-(aq)$	$\rightleftharpoons$	$CO_3^{2-}(aq)$	+	$HF(aq)$

CO_3^{2-} is a stronger base than F^-, so the equilibrium lies to the left.

Autoionization of Water (section 16.3)

16.27 No. In pure water, the only source of H^+ is the autoionization reaction, which produces equal concentrations of H^+ and OH^-. As the temperature of water changes, the value of K_w changes, and the pH at which $[H^+] = [OH^-]$ changes. At 50 °C, if pH = 6.63,

$[H^+] = [OH^-] = 10^{-6.63} = 2.34 \times 10^{-7}$; $K_w = (2.34 \times 10^{-7})(2.34 \times 10^{-7}) = 5.5 \times 10^{-14}$

16.28 (a) $H_2O(l) \rightleftharpoons H^+(aq) + OH^-(aq)$

(b) $K_w = [H^+][OH^-]$. The $[H_2O(l)]$ is omitted because water is a pure liquid. The molarity (mol/L) of pure solids or liquids does not change as equilibrium is established, so it is usually omitted from equilibrium expressions.

(c) If a solution is basic, it contains more OH^- than H^+ ($[OH^-] > [H^+]$).

16.29 *Analyze/Plan.* Follow the logic in Sample Exercise 16.5. In pure water at 25°C, $[H^+] = [OH^-] = 1 \times 10^{-7}$ M. If $[H^+] > 1 \times 10^{-7}$ M, the solution is acidic; if $[H^+] < 1 \times 10^{-7}$ M, the solution is basic. *Solve.*

(a) $[H^+] = \dfrac{K_w}{[OH^-]} = \dfrac{1.0 \times 10^{-14}}{4.5 \times 10^{-4} M} = 2.2 \times 10^{-11} M < 1 \times 10^{-7} M$; basic

(b) $[H^+] = \dfrac{K_w}{[OH^-]} = \dfrac{1.0 \times 10^{-14}}{8.8 \times 10^{-9} M} = 1.1 \times 10^{-6} M > 1 \times 10^{-7} M$; acidic

(c) $[OH^-] = 100[H^+]$; $K_w = [H^+] \times 100[H^+] = 100[H^+]^2$;

$[H^+] = (K_w/100)^{1/2} = 1.0 \times 10^{-8} M < 1 \times 10^{-7} M$; basic

16.30 In pure water at 25°C, $[H^+] = [OH^-] = 1 \times 10^{-7}$ M. If $[OH^-] > 1 \times 10^{-7}$ M, the solution is basic; if $[OH^-] < 1 \times 10^{-7}$ M, the solution is acidic.

(a) $[OH^-] = \dfrac{K_w}{[H^+]} = \dfrac{1.0 \times 10^{-14}}{0.0505 M} = 1.98 \times 10^{-13} M < 1 \times 10^{-7} M$; acidic

(b) $[OH^-] = \dfrac{K_w}{[H^+]} = \dfrac{1.0 \times 10^{-14}}{2.5 \times 10^{-10}\ M} = 4.0 \times 10^{-5}\ M > 1 \times 10^{-7}\ M;\ \text{basic}$

(c) $[H^+] = 1000[OH^-];\ K_w = 1000[OH^-][OH^-] = 1000[OH^-]^2$

$[OH^-] = (K_w/1000)^{1/2} = 3.2 \times 10^{-9}\ M < 1 \times 10^{-7}\ M;\ \text{acidic}$

16.31 *Analyze/Plan.* Follow the logic in Sample Exercise 16.4. Note that the value of the equilibrium constant (in this case, K_w) changes with temperature. *Solve.*

At 0°C, $K_w = 1.2 \times 10^{-15} = [H^+][OH^-]$.

In pure water, $[H^+] = [OH^-];\ 1.2 \times 10^{-15} = [H^+]^2;\ [H^+] = (1.2 \times 10^{-15})^{1/2}$

$[H^+] = [OH^-] = 3.5 \times 10^{-8}\ M$

16.32 $K_w = [D^+][OD^-];$ for pure D_2O, $[D^+] = [OD^-];\ 8.9 \times 10^{-16} = [D^+]^2;$

$[D^+] = [OD^-] = 3.0 \times 10^{-8}\ M$

The pH Scale (section 16.4)

16.33 *Analyze/Plan.* A change of one pH unit (in either direction) is:

$\Delta pH = pH_2 - pH_1 = -(\log[H^+]_2 - \log[H^+]_1) = -\log\dfrac{[H^+]_2}{[H^+]_1} = \pm1.$ The antilog of +1 is 10; the antilog of –1 is 1×10^{-1}. Thus, a ΔpH of one unit represents an increase or decrease in $[H^+]$ by a factor of 10. *Solve.*

(a) $\Delta pH = \pm2.00$ is a change of $10^{2.00};\ [H^+]$ changes by a factor of 100.

(b) $\Delta pH = \pm0.5$ is a change of $10^{0.50};\ [H^+]$ changes by a factor of 3.2.

16.34 $[H^+]_A = 250\,[H^+]_B$ From Solution 16.33, $\Delta pH = -\log\dfrac{[H^+]_B}{[H^+]_A}$

$\Delta pH = -\log\dfrac{[H^+]_B}{250\,[H^+]_B} = -\log\left(\dfrac{1}{250}\right) = 2.40$

The pH of solution A is 2.40 pH units lower than the pH of solution B, because $[H^+]_A$ is 250 times greater than $[H^+]_B$. The greater $[H^+]$, the lower the pH of the solution.

16.35 (a) $K_w = [H^+][OH^-]$. If NaOH is added to water, it dissociates into $Na^+(aq)$ and $OH^-(aq)$. This increases $[OH^-]$ and necessarily decreases $[H^+]$. When $[H^+]$ decreases, pH increases.

(b) $0.0006\ M = 6 \times 10^{-4}\ M$. On Figure 16.5, this is $[H^+] > 1 \times 10^{-4}$ but $< 1 \times 10^{-3}$. The pH is between 3 and 4, closer to 3. We estimate 3.3. If pH < 7, the solution is acidic.

By calculation: $pH = -\log[H^+] = -\log(6 \times 10^{-4}\ M) = 3.2$

(c) pH = 5.2 is between pH 5 and pH 6 on Figure 16.5, closer to pH = 5. At pH = 6, $[H^+] = 1 \times 10^{-6};$ at pH = 5, $[H^+] = 1 \times 10^{-5} = 10 \times 10^{-6}$. A good estimate is $7 \times 10^{-6}\ M\ H^+$.

By calculation: $[H^+] = 10^{-pH} = 10^{-5.2} = 6 \times 10^{-6} M$

At pH = 5, $[OH^-] = 1 \times 10^{-9}$; at pH = 6, $[OH^-] = 1 \times 10^{-8} = 10 \times 10^{-9}$.

Since pH = 5.2 is closer to pH = 5, we estimate $3 \times 10^{-9} M$ OH$^-$.

By calculation: pOH = 14.0 – 5.2 = 8.8

$[OH^-] = 10^{-pOH} = 10^{-8.8} = 2 \times 10^{-9} M$ OH$^-$

16.36　(a)　$K_w = [H^+][OH^-]$. If HNO_3 is added to water, it ionizes to form H^+(aq) and NO_3^- (aq). This increases $[H^+]$ and necessarily decreases $[OH^-]$. When $[H^+]$ increases, pH decreases.

(b)　On Figure 16.5, $1.4 \times 10^{-2} M$ OH$^-$ is between pH = 12 ($1 \times 10^{-2} M$ OH$^-$) and pH 13 ($1 \times 10^{-1} M$ OH$^-$), slightly higher than pH = 12, so we estimate pH = 12.1. If pH > 7, the solution is basic.

(c)　pH = 6.6 is midway between pH 6 and pH 7 on Figure 16.5.

At pH = 7, $[H^+] = 1 \times 10^{-7}$; at pH = 6, $[H^+] = 1 \times 10^{-6} = 10 \times 10^{-7}$.

A reasonable estimate is $5 \times 10^{-7} M$ H$^+$. By calculation:

pH = 6.6, $[H^+] = 10^{-pH} = 10^{-6.6} = 3 \times 10^{-7}$

At pH = 6, $[OH^-] = 1 \times 10^{-8}$; at pH = 7, $[OH^-] = 1 \times 10^{-7} = 10 \times 10^{-8}$.

A reasonable estimate is $5 \times 10^{-8} M$ OH$^-$. By calculation:

pOH = 14.0 – 6.6 = 7.4; $[OH^-] = 10^{-pOH} = 10^{-7.4} = 4 \times 10^{-8} M$ OH$^-$.

16.37　*Analyze/Plan.* At 25°C, $[H^+][OH^-] = 1 \times 10^{-14}$; pH + pOH = 14. Use these relationships to complete the table. If pH < 7, the solution is acidic; if pH > 7, the solution is basic. *Solve.*

$[H^+]$	$[OH^-]$	pH	pOH	acidic or basic
$7.5 \times 10^{-3} M$	$1.3 \times 10^{-12} M$	2.12	11.88	acidic
$2.8 \times 10^{-5} M$	$3.6 \times 10^{-10} M$	4.56	9.44	acidic
$5.6 \times 10^{-9} M$	$1.8 \times 10^{-6} M$	8.25	5.75	basic
$5.0 \times 10^{-9} M$	$2.0 \times 10^{-6} M$	8.30	5.70	basic

Check. pH + pOH = 14; $[H^+][OH^-] = 1 \times 10^{-14}$.

16.38

pH	pOH	$[H^+]$	$[OH^-]$	acidic or basic
5.25	8.75	$5.6 \times 10^{-6} M$	$1.8 \times 10^{-9} M$	acidic
11.98	2.02	$1.1 \times 10^{-12} M$	$9.6 \times 10^{-3} M$	basic
9.36	4.64	$4.4 \times 10^{-10} M$	$2.3 \times 10^{-5} M$	basic
12.93	1.07	$1.2 \times 10^{-13} M$	$8.5 \times 10^{-2} M$	basic

16.39   *Analyze/Plan.* Given pH and a new value of the equilibrium constant K_w, calculate equilibrium concentrations of $H^+(aq)$ and $OH^-(aq)$. The definition of pH remains $pH = -\log[H^+]$.   *Solve.*

pH = 7.40; $[H^+] = 10^{-pH} = 10^{-7.40} = 4.0 \times 10^{-8}\ M$

$K_w = 2.4 \times 10^{-14} = [H^+][OH^-]$; $[OH^-] = 2.4 \times 10^{-14}\ /\ [H^+]$

$[OH^-] = 2.4 \times 10^{-14}\ /\ 4.0 \times 10^{-8} = 6.0 \times 10^{-7}\ M$, pOH $= -\log(6.0 \times 10^{-7}) = 6.22$

Alternately, $pH + pOH = pK_w$. At 37°C, $pH + pOH = -\log(2.4 \times 10^{-14})$

pH + pOH = 13.62; pOH = 13.62 – 7.40 = 6.22

$[OH^-] = 10^{-pOH} = 10^{-6.22} = 6.0 \times 10^{-7}\ M$

16.40   The pH ranges from 5.2–5.6; pOH ranges from (14.0–5.2 =) 8.8 to (14.0–5.6 =) 8.4.

$[H^+] = 10^{-pH}$, $[OH^-] = 10^{-pOH}$

$[H^+] = 10^{-5.2} = 6.31 \times 10^{-6} = 6 \times 10^{-6}\ M$; $[H^+] = 10^{-5.6} = 2.51 \times 10^{-6} = 3 \times 10^{-6}\ M$

The range of $[H^+]$ is $6 \times 10^{-6}\ M$ to $3 \times 10^{-6}\ M$.

$[OH^-] = 10^{-8.8} = 1.58 \times 10^{-9} = 2 \times 10^{-9}\ M$; $[OH^-] = 10^{-8.4} = 3.98 \times 10^{-9} = 4 \times 10^{-9}\ M$.

The range of $[OH^-]$ is $2 \times 10^{-9}\ M$ to $4 \times 10^{-9}\ M$.

(The pH has one decimal place, so concentrations are reported to one sig fig.)

Strong Acids and Bases (section 16.5)

16.41   (a)   A strong acid is completely ionized in aqueous solution; a strong acid is a strong electrolyte.

          (b)   For a strong acid such as HCl, $[H^+]$ = initial acid concentration. $[H^+] = 0.500\ M$

          (c)   HCl, HBr, HI

16.42   (a)   A strong base is completely dissociated in aqueous solution; a strong base is a strong electrolyte.

          (b) $Sr(OH)_2$ is a soluble strong base.

               $Sr(OH)_2(aq) \rightarrow Sr^{2+}(aq) + 2OH^-(aq)$

               $0.035\ M\ Sr(OH)_2(aq) = 0.070\ M\ OH^-$

          (c)   False. Base strength should not be confused with solubility. Base strength describes the tendency of a dissolved molecule (formula unit for ionic compounds such as $Mg(OH)_2$) to dissociate into cations and hydroxide ions. $Mg(OH)_2$ is a strong base because each $Mg(OH)_2$ unit that dissolves also dissociates into $Mg^{2+}(aq)$ and $OH^-(aq)$. $Mg(OH)_2$ is not very soluble, so relatively few $Mg(OH)_2$ units dissolve when the solid compound is added to water.

16.43   *Analyze/Plan.* Follow the logic in Sample Exercise 16.8. Strong acids are completely ionized, so $[H^+]$ = original acid concentration, and $pH = -\log[H^+]$. For the solutions obtained by dilution, use the "dilution" formula, $M_1V_1 = M_2V_2$, to calculate molarity of the acid. *Solve.*

(a) 8.5×10^{-3} M HBr = 8.5×10^{-3} M H^+; pH = $-\log (8.5 \times 10^{-3})$ = 2.07

(b) $\dfrac{1.52 \text{ g HNO}_3}{0.575 \text{ L soln}} \times \dfrac{1 \text{ mol HNO}_3}{63.02 \text{ g HNO}_3} = 0.041947 = 0.0419$ M HNO_3

     $[H^+]$ = 0.0419 M; pH = $-\log (0.041947)$ = 1.377

(c) $M_c \times V_c = M_d \times V_d$; 0.250 M × 0.00500 L = ? M × 0.0500 L

     $M_d = \dfrac{0.250 \ M \ \times \ 0.00500 \text{ L}}{0.0500 \text{ L}} = 0.0250$ M HCl

     $[H^+]$ = 0.0250 M; pH = $-\log (0.0250)$ = 1.602

(d) $[H^+]_{total} = \dfrac{\text{mol } H^+ \text{from HBr} + \text{mol } H^+ \text{from HCl}}{\text{total L solution}}$

     $[H^+]_{total} = \dfrac{(0.100 \ M \text{ HBr} \ \times \ 0.0100 \text{ L}) + (0.200 \ M \ \times \ 0.0200 \text{ L})}{0.0300 \text{ L}}$

     $[H^+]_{total} = \dfrac{1.00 \ \times \ 10^{-3} \text{ mol } H^+ + 4.00 \ \times \ 10^{-3} \text{ mol } H^+}{0.0300 \text{ L}} = 0.1667 = 0.167$ M

     pH = $-\log (0.1667 \ M)$ = 0.778

16.44   For a strong acid, which is completely ionized, $[H^+]$ = the initial acid concentration.

(a)   0.0167 M HNO_3 = 0.0167 M H^+; pH = $-\log (0.0167)$ = 1.777

(b) $\dfrac{0.225 \text{ g HClO}_3}{2.00 \text{ L soln}} \times \dfrac{1 \text{ mol HClO}_3}{84.46 \text{ g HClO}_3} = 1.332 \times 10^{-3} = 1.33 \times 10^{-3}$ M $HClO_3$

     $[H^+]$ = 1.33×10^{-3} M; pH = $-\log (1.332 \times 10^{-3})$ = 2.875

(c) $M_c \times V_c = M_d \times V_d$; 0.500 L = 500 mL

     1.00 M HCl × 15.00 mL HCl = M_d HCl × 500 mL HCl

     M_d HCl = $\dfrac{1.00 \ M \ \times \ 15.00 \text{ mL}}{500 \text{ mL}} = 3.00 \times 10^{-2}$ M HCl = 3.00×10^{-2} M H^+

     pH = $-\log (3.00 \times 10^{-2})$ = 1.523

(d) $[H^+]_{total} = \dfrac{\text{mol } H^+ \text{ from HCl} + \text{mol } H^+ \text{ from HI}}{\text{total L solution}}$; mol = M × L

     $[H^+]_{total} = \dfrac{(0.020 \ M \text{ HCl} \ \times \ 0.0500 \text{ L}) + (0.010 \ M \text{ HI} \ \times \ 0.125 \text{ L})}{0.175 \text{ L}}$

     $[H^+]_{total} = \dfrac{1.0 \ \times \ 10^{-3} \text{ mol } H^+ + 1.25 \ \times \ 10^{-3} \text{ mol } H^+}{0.175 \text{ L}} = 0.01286 = 0.013$ M

     pH = $-\log (0.01286)$ = 1.89

16.45   *Analyze/Plan.* Follow the logic in Sample Exercise 16.9. Strong bases dissociate completely upon dissolving. pOH = $-\log[OH^-]$; pH = 14 – pOH.

(a)   Pay attention to the formula of the base to get $[OH^-]$.   *Solve.*

$[OH^-] = 2[Sr(OH)_2] = 2(1.5 \times 10^{-3} \, M) = 3.0 \times 10^{-3} \, M \, OH^-$ (see Exercise 16.42(b))

$pOH = -\log (3.0 \times 10^{-3}) = 2.52; \, pH = 14 - pOH = 11.48$

(b)   mol/LiOH = g LiOH/molar mass LiOH. $[OH^-]$ = [LiOH].   *Solve.*

$$\frac{2.250 \text{ g LiOH}}{0.2500 \text{ L soln}} \times \frac{1 \text{ mol LiOH}}{23.948 \text{ g LiOH}} = 0.37581 = 0.3758 \, M \text{ LiOH} = [OH^-]$$

$pOH = -\log (0.37581) = 0.4250; \, pH = 14 - pOH = 13.5750$

(c)   Use the dilution formula to get the [NaOH] = $[OH^-]$.   *Solve.*

$M_c \times V_c = M_d \times V_d; \, 0.175 \, M \times 0.00100 \text{ L} = ? \, M \times 2.00 \text{ L}$

$$M_d = \frac{0.175 \, M \times 0.00100 \text{ L}}{2.00 \text{ L}} = 8.75 \times 10^{-5} \, M \text{ NaOH} = [OH^-]$$

$pOH = -\log (8.75 \times 10^{-5}) = 4.058; \, pH = 14 - pOH = 9.942$

(d)   Consider total mol OH^- from KOH and $Ca(OH)_2$, as well as total solution volume. *Solve.*

$$[OH^-]_{total} = \frac{\text{mol } OH^- \text{ from KOH} + \text{mol } OH^- \text{ from } Ca(OH)_2}{\text{total L soln}}$$

$$[OH^-]_{total} = \frac{(0.105 \, M \times 0.00500 \text{ L}) + 2(9.5 \times 10^{-2} \, M \times 0.0150 \text{ L})}{0.0200 \text{ L}}$$

$$[OH^-]_{total} = \frac{0.525 \times 10^{-3} \text{ mol } OH^- + 2.85 \times 10^{-3} \text{ mol } OH^-}{0.0200 \text{ L}} = 0.16875 = 0.17 \, M$$

$pOH = -\log (0.16875) = 0.77; \, pH = 14 - pOH = 13.23$

($9.5 \times 10^{-2} \, M$ has 2 sig figs, so the $[OH^-]$ has 2 sig figs and pH and pOH have 2 decimal places.)

16.46   For a strong base, which is completely dissociated, $[OH^-]$ = the initial base concentration. Then, $pOH = -\log [OH^-]$ and $pH = 14 - pOH$.

(a) $0.182 \, M \text{ KOH} = 0.182 \, M \, OH^-; \, pOH = -\log (0.182) = 0.740; \, pH = 14 - 740 = 13.260$

(b) $\dfrac{3.165 \text{ g KOH}}{0.5000 \text{ L}} \times \dfrac{1 \text{ mol KOH}}{56.106 \text{ g KOH}} = 0.112822 = 0.1128 \, M = [OH^-]$

$pOH = -\log (0.112822) = 0.9476; \, pH = 14 - pOH = 13.0524$

(c) $M_c \times V_c = M_d \times V_d$

$0.0105 \, M \text{ Ca(OH)}_2 \times 10.0 \text{ mL} = M_d \text{ Ca(OH)}_2 \times 500 \text{ mL}$

$$M_d \text{ Ca(OH)}_2 = \frac{0.0105 \, M \text{ Ca(OH)}_2 \times 10.0 \text{ mL}}{500.0 \text{ mL}} = 2.10 \times 10^{-4} \, M \text{ Ca(OH)}_2$$

$\text{Ca(OH)}_2(aq) \rightarrow Ca^{2+}(aq) + 2OH^-(aq)$

$[OH^-] = 2[Ca(OH)_2] = 2(2.10 \times 10^{-4} \, M) = 4.20 \times 10^{-4} \, M$

$pOH = -\log (4.20 \times 10^{-4}) = 3.377; \, pH = 14 - pOH = 10.623$

(d) $[OH^-]_{total} = \dfrac{\text{mol } OH^- \text{ from NaOH} + \text{mol } OH^- \text{ from Ba(OH)}_2}{\text{total L solution}}$

$$\dfrac{(8.2 \times 10^{-3} M \times 0.0400 \text{ L}) + 2(0.015 M \times 0.0200 \text{ L})}{0.0600 \text{ L}}$$

$[OH^-]_{total} = \dfrac{3.28 \times 10^{-4} \text{ mol } OH^- + 6.0 \times 10^{-4} \text{ mol } OH^-}{0.0600 \text{ L}} = 0.01547 = 0.015 M \ OH^-$

pOH = –log (0.01547) = 1.81; pH = 14 – 1.81 = 12.19

16.47 *Analyze/Plan.* pH → pOH → $[OH^-]$ = [NaOH]. *Solve.*

pOH = 14 – pH = 14.00 – 11.50 = 2.50

pOH = 2.50 = –log$[OH^-]$; $[OH^-]$ = $10^{-2.50}$ = $3.2 \times 10^{-3} M$

$[OH^-]$ = [NaOH] = $3.2 \times 10^{-3} M$

16.48 pOH = 14 – pH = 14.00 – 10.05 = 3.95

pOH = 3.95 = –log$[OH^-]$; $[OH^-]$ = $10^{-3.95}$ = $1.122 \times 10^{-4} M$ = $1.1 \times 10^{-4} M$

$[OH^-]$ = 2[Ca(OH)$_2$]; [Ca(OH)$_2$] = $[OH^-]$ / 2 = $1.122 \times 10^{-4} M$ /2 = $5.6 \times 10^{-5} M$

Weak Acids (section 16.6)

16.49 *Analyze/Plan.* Remember that K_a = [products]/[reactants]. If $H_2O(l)$ appears in the equilibrium reaction, it will **not** appear in the K_a expression, because it is a pure liquid. *Solve.*

(a) $HBrO_2(aq) \rightleftharpoons H^+(aq) + BrO_2^-(aq)$; $K_a = \dfrac{[H^+][BrO_2^-]}{[HBrO_2]}$

$HBrO_2(aq) + H_2O(l) \rightleftharpoons H_3O^+(aq) + BrO_2^-(aq)$; $K_a = \dfrac{[H_3O^+][BrO_2^-]}{[HBrO_2]}$

(b) $C_2H_5COOH(aq) \rightleftharpoons H^+(aq) + C_2H_5COO^-(aq)$; $K_a = \dfrac{[H^+][C_2H_5COO^-]}{[C_2H_5COOH]}$

$C_2H_5COOH(aq) + H_2O(l) \rightleftharpoons H_3O^+(aq) + C_2H_5COO^-(aq)$;

$$K_a = \dfrac{[H_3O^+][C_2H_5COO^-]}{[C_2H_5COOH]}$$

16.50 (a) $C_6H_5COOH(aq) \rightleftharpoons H^+(aq) + C_6H_5COO^-(aq)$; $K_a = \dfrac{[H^+][C_6H_5COO^-]}{[HC_6H_5COOH]}$

$C_6H_5COOH(aq) + H_2O(l) \rightleftharpoons H_3O^+(aq) + C_6H_5COO^-(aq)$;

$$K_a = \dfrac{[H_3O^+][C_6H_5COO^-]}{[HC_6H_5COOH]}$$

(b) $HCO_3^-(aq) \rightleftharpoons H^+(aq) + CO_3^{2-}(aq)$; $K_a = \dfrac{[H^+][CO_3^{2-}]}{[HCO_3^-]}$

$HCO_3^-(aq) + H_2O(l) \rightleftharpoons H_3O^+(aq) + CO_3^{2-}(aq)$; $K_a = \dfrac{[H_3O^+][CO_3^{2-}]}{[HCO_3^-]}$

16.51   *Analyze/Plan.* Follow the logic in Sample Exercise 16.10.   *Solve.*

$$CH_3CH(OH)COOH \rightleftharpoons H^+(aq) + CH_3CH(OH)COO^-(aq); K_a = \frac{[H^+][CH_3CH(OH)COO^-]}{[CH_3CH(OH)COOH]}$$

$$[H^+] = [CH_3CH(OH)COO^-] = 10^{-2.44} = 3.63 \times 10^{-3} = 3.6 \times 10^{-3} \, M$$

$$[CH_3CH(OH)COOH] = 0.10 - 3.63 \times 10^{-3} = 0.0964 = 0.096 \, M$$

$$K_a = \frac{(3.63 \times 10^{-3})^2}{(0.0964)} = 1.4 \times 10^{-4}$$

16.52 $$C_6H_5CH_2COOH(aq) \rightleftharpoons H^+(aq) + C_6H_5CH_2COO^-(aq); \quad K_a = \frac{[H^+][C_6H_5CH_2COO^-]}{[C_6H_5CH_2COOH]}$$

$$[H^+] = [C_6H_5CH_2COO^-] = 10^{-2.68} = 2.09 \times 10^{-3} = 2.1 \times 10^{-3} \, M$$

$$[C_6H_5CH_2COOH] = 0.085 - 2.09 \times 10^{-3} = 0.0829 = 0.083 \, M$$

$$K_a = \frac{(2.09 \times 10^{-3})^2}{0.0829} = 5.3 \times 10^{-5}$$

16.53   *Analyze/Plan.* Write the equilibrium reaction and the K_a expression. Use % ionization to get equilibrium concentration of $[H^+]$, and by stoichiometry, $[X^-]$ and $[HX]$. Calculate K_a *Solve.*

$$[H^+] = 0.110 \times [CH_2ClCOOH]_{initial} = 0.0110 \, M$$

	$CH_2ClCOOH(aq)$	$\rightleftharpoons$	$H^+(aq)$	$+$	$CH_2ClCOO^-(aq)$
initial	0.100 M		0		0
equil.	0.089 M		0.0110 M		0.0110 M

$$K_a = \frac{[H^+][CH_2ClCOO^-]}{[CH_2ClCOOH]} = \frac{(0.0110)^2}{0.089} = 1.4 \times 10^{-3}$$

16.54 $$[H^+] = 0.132 \times [BrCH_2COOH]_{initial} = 0.0132 \, M$$

	$BrCH_2COOH(aq)$	$\rightleftharpoons$	$H^+(aq)$	$+$	$BrCH_2COO^-(aq)$
initial	0.100 M		0		0
equil.	0.087		0.0132 M		0.0132 M

$$K_a = \frac{[H^+][BrCH_2COO^-]}{[BrCH_2COOH]} = \frac{(0.0132)^2}{0.087} = 2.0 \times 10^{-3}$$

16.55   *Analyze/Plan.* Write the equilibrium reaction and the K_a expression.

$$[H^+] = 10^{-pH} = [CH_3COO^-]; \quad [CH_3COOH] = x - [H^+].$$

Substitute into the K_a expression and solve for x.   *Solve.*

$$[H^+] = 10^{-pH} = 10^{-2.90} = 1.26 \times 10^{-3} = 1.3 \times 10^{-3} \, M$$

$$K_a = 1.8 \times 10^{-5} = \frac{[H^+][CH_3COO^-]}{[CH_3COOH]} = \frac{(1.26 \times 10^{-3})^2}{(x - 1.26 \times 10^{-3})}$$

$1.8 \times 10^{-5} (x - 1.26 \times 10^{-3}) = (1.26 \times 10^{-3})^2;$

$1.8 \times 10^{-5} x = 1.585 \times 10^{-6} + 2.266 \times 10^{-8} = 1.608 \times 10^{-6};$

$x = 0.08931 = 0.089 \ M \ CH_3COOH$

16.56 $[H^+] = 10^{-pH} = 10^{-3.65} = 2.239 \times 10^{-4} = 2.2 \times 10^{-4} \ M$

$K_a = 6.8 \times 10^{-4} = \dfrac{[H^+][F^-]}{[HF]} = \dfrac{(2.239 \times 10^{-4})^2}{x - 2.239 \times 10^{-4}}$

$6.8 \times 10^{-4}(x - 2.239 \times 10^{-4}) = (2.239 \times 10^{-4})^2;$

$6.8 \times 10^{-4} x = 1.522 \times 10^{-7} + 0.501 \times 10^{-7} = 2.024 \times 10^{-7}$

$x = 2.976 \times 10^{-4} = 3.0 \times 10^{-4} \ M \ HF$

16.57   *Analyze/Plan.* Follow the logic in Sample Exercise 16.12. Write K_a, construct the equilibrium table, solve for $x = [H^+]$, then get equilibrium $[C_6H_5COO^-]$ and $[C_6H_5COOH]$ by substituting $[H^+]$ for x.   *Solve.*

	$C_6H_5COOH(aq)$	$\rightleftharpoons$	$H^+(aq)$	$+$	$C_6H_5COO^-(aq)$
initial	0.050 M		0		0
equil.	(0.050 − x) M		x M		x M

$K_a = \dfrac{[H^+][C_6H_5COO^-]}{[C_6H_5COOH]} = \dfrac{x^2}{(0.050 - x)} \approx \dfrac{x^2}{0.050} = 6.3 \times 10^{-5}$

$x^2 = 0.050 \ (6.3 \times 10^{-5}); \ x = 1.8 \times 10^{-3} \ M = [H^+] = [H_3O^+] = [C_6H_5COO^-]$

$[C_6H_5COOH] = 0.050 - 0.0018 = 0.048 \ M$

Check. $\dfrac{1.8 \times 10^{-3} \ M \ H^+}{0.050 \ M \ C_6H_5COOH} \times 100 = 3.6\%$ ionization; the approximation is valid

16.58

	$HClO_2(aq)$	$\rightleftharpoons$	$H^+(aq)$	$+$	$ClO_2^-(aq)$
initial	0.0125 M		0		0
equil.	(0.0125 − x) M		x M		x M

$K_a = \dfrac{[H^+][ClO_2^-]}{[HClO_2]} = \dfrac{x^2}{(0.0125 - x)} \approx \dfrac{x^2}{0.0125} = 1.1 \times 10^{-2}$

Assuming x is small relative to 0.0125, $x^2 = 0.0125(0.011); \ x = 1.2 \times 10^{-2} \ M$.
Clearly x is not small relative to 0.0125, so we must solve the quadratic formula for $[H^+]$.

$x^2 = 0.011 \ (0.0125 - x); \ x^2 + 0.011x - 1.38 \times 10^{-4} = 0$

$x = \dfrac{-0.011 \pm \sqrt{(0.011)^2 - 4(1)(-1.38 \times 10^{-4})}}{2(1)} = 0.007452 = 0.0075 \ M;$

$[H^+] = [H_3O^+] = [ClO_2^-] = 0.0075 \ M; \ [HClO_2] = 0.0125 - 0.0075 = 0.005045 = 5.0 \times 10^{-3} \ M$

Check. $K_a = \dfrac{(7.5 \times 10^{-3})^2}{5.0 \times 10^{-3}} = 0.011$; our results agree.

16.59   *Analyze/Plan.* Follow the logic in Sample Exercise 16.12.

(a)   *Solve.*

$$C_2H_5COOH(aq) \quad \rightleftharpoons \quad H^+(aq) \quad + \quad C_2H_5COO^-(aq)$$

initial	0.095 M	0	0
equil	(0.095 – x) M	x M	x M

$$K_a = \frac{[H^+][C_2H_5COO^-]}{[C_2H_5COOH]} = \frac{x^2}{(0.095-x)} \approx \frac{x^2}{0.095} = 1.3 \times 10^{-5}$$

$x^2 = 0.095(1.3 \times 10^{-5})$; $x = 1.111 \times 10^{-3} = 1.1 \times 10^{-3}\ M\ H^+$; pH = 2.95

Check. $\dfrac{1.1 \times 10^{-3}\ M\ H^+}{0.095\ M\ C_2H_5COOH} \times 100 = 1.2\%$ ionization; the approximation is valid

(b)   *Solve.*

$$K_a = \frac{[H^+][CrO_4^{2-}]}{[HCrO_4^-]} = \frac{x^2}{(0.100-x)} \approx \frac{x^2}{0.100} = 3.0 \times 10^{-7}$$

$x^2 = 0.100(3.0 \times 10^{-7})$; $x = 1.732 \times 10^{-4} = 1.7 \times 10^{-4}\ M\ H^+$

pH = $-\log(1.732 \times 10^{-4})$ = 3.7614 = 3.76

Check. $\dfrac{1.7 \times 10^{-4}\ M\ H^+}{0.100\ M\ HCrO_4^-} \times 100 = 0.17\%$ ionization; the approximation is valid

(c)   Follow the logic in Sample Exercise 16.15.   pOH = $-\log[OH^-]$. pH = 14 – pOH

Solve.

$$C_5H_5N(aq) + H_2O(l) \quad \rightleftharpoons \quad C_5H_5NH^+(aq) \quad + \quad OH^-(aq)$$

initial	0.120 M	0	0
equil	(0.120 – x) M	x M	x M

$$K_b = \frac{[C_5H_5NH^+][OH^-]}{[C_5H_5N]} = \frac{x^2}{(0.120-x)} \approx \frac{x^2}{0.120} = 1.7 \times 10^{-9}$$

$x^2 = 0.120(1.7 \times 10^{-9})$; $x = 1.428 \times 10^{-5} = 1.4 \times 10^{-5}\ M\ OH^-$; pH = 9.15

Check. $\dfrac{1.4 \times 10^{-5}\ M\ OH^-}{0.120\ M\ C_5H_5N} \times 100 = 0.012\%$ ionization; the approximation is valid

16.60   (a)

$$HOCl(aq) \quad \rightleftharpoons \quad H^+(aq) \quad + \quad OCl^-(aq)$$

initial	0.095 M	0	0
equil	(0.095 – x) M	x M	x M

$$K_a = \frac{[H^+][OCl^-]}{[HOCl]} = \frac{x^2}{(0.095-x)} \approx \frac{x^2}{0.095} = 3.0 \times 10^{-8}$$

$x^2 = 0.095\ (3.0 \times 10^{-8})$; $x = [H^+] = 5.3 \times 10^{-5}\ M$, pH = 4.27

Check. $\dfrac{5.3 \times 10^{-5}\, M\, H^+}{0.095\, M\, HOCl} \times 100 = 0.056\%$ ionization; the approximation is nearly valid.

To 2 sig figs, the quadratic formula gives the same $M\, H^+$.

(b) $\qquad\qquad H_2NNH_2(aq) + H_2O(l) \;\rightleftharpoons\; H_2NNH_3^+(aq) \;+\; OH^-\,(aq)$

initial	0.0085 M	0	0
equil	(0.0085 – x) M	x M	x M

$$K_b = \frac{[H_2NNH_3^+][OH^-]}{[H_2NNH_2]} = \frac{x^2}{(0.0085-x)} \approx \frac{x^2}{0.0085} = 1.3 \times 10^{-6}$$

$x^2 = 0.0085\,(1.3 \times 10^{-6});\; x = [OH^-] = 1.051 \times 10^{-4} = 1.1 \times 10^{-4}\, M$

Clearly $1.1 \times 10^{-4}\, M\, OH^-$ is not small compared to $8.5 \times 10^{-3}\, M\, H_2NNH_2$, and we must solve the quadratic.

$x^2 = 1.3 \times 10^{-6}(0.0085 - x);\;\; x^2 + 1.3 \times 10^{-6}\, x - 1.105 \times 10^{-8} = 0$

$$x = \frac{-1.3\times10^{-6} \pm \sqrt{(1.3\times10^{-6})^2 - 4(1)(-1.105\times10^{-8})}}{2(1)} = 1.0447 \times 10^{-4}$$

$$= 1.0 \times 10^{-4}\, M\, OH^-$$

$pOH = 3.981 = 3.98;\; pH = 14 - pOH = 14 - 3.981 = 10.019 = 10.02$

Check. Although this solution has more than 12% ionization, the difference in $[OH^-]$ between the estimate and the quadratic is not great.

(c) $\qquad\qquad HONH_2(aq) + H_2O(l) \;\rightleftharpoons\; HONH_3^+(aq) \;+\; OH^-\,(aq)$

initial	0.165 M	0	0
equil	(0.165 – x) M	x M	x M

$$K_b = \frac{[HONH_3^+][OH^-]}{[HONH_2]} = \frac{x^2}{(0.165-x)} \approx \frac{x^2}{0.165} = 1.1 \times 10^{-8}$$

$x^2 = 0.165\,(1.1 \times 10^{-8});\; x = [OH^-] = 4.3 \times 10^{-5}\, M,\; pH = 9.63$

Check. $\dfrac{4.3 \times 10^{-5}\, M\, OH^-}{0.165\, M\, HONH_2} \times 100 = 0.026\%$ ionization; the approximation is valid

16.61 *Analyze/Plan.* $K_a = 10^{-pK_a}$. Follow the logic in Sample Exercise 16.13. *Solve.*

Let $[H^+] = [NC_7H_4SO_3^-] = z.\; K_a =$ antilog $(-2.32) = 4.79 \times 10^{-3} = 4.8 \times 10^{-3}$

$\dfrac{z^2}{0.10-z} = 4.79 \times 10^{-3}.$ \quad Since K_a is relatively large, solve the quadratic.

$z^2 + 4.79 \times 10^{-3}\, z - 4.79 \times 10^{-4} = 0$

$$z = \frac{-4.79 \times 10^{-3} \pm \sqrt{(4.79 \times 10^{-3})^2 - 4(1)\,(-4.79 \times 10^{-4})}}{2(1)} = \frac{-4.79 \times 10^{-3} \pm \sqrt{1.937 \times 10^{-3}}}{2}$$

$z = 1.96 \times 10^{-2} = 2.0 \times 10^{-2}\, M\, H^+;\; pH = -\log(1.96 \times 10^{-2}) = 1.71$

16.62   Calculate the initial concentration of $HC_9H_7O_4$.

$$2 \text{ tablets} \times \frac{500 \text{ mg}}{\text{tablet}} \times \frac{1 \text{ g}}{1000 \text{ mg}} \times \frac{1 \text{ mol } HC_9H_7O_4}{180.2 \text{ g } HC_9H_7O_4} = 0.005549 = 0.00555 \text{ mol } HC_9H_7O_4$$

$$\frac{0.005549 \text{ mol } HC_9H_7O_4}{0.250 \text{ L}} = 0.02220 = 0.0222 \text{ M } HC_9H_7O_4$$

	$HC_9H_7O_4 \text{ (aq)}$	$\rightleftharpoons$	$C_9H_7O_4^- +$	$H^+ \text{ (aq)}$
Initial	0.0222 M		0 M	0 M
equil	(0.0222 – x)		x M	x M

$$K_a = 3.3 \times 10^{-4} = \frac{[H^+][C_9H_7O_4^-]}{[HC_9H_7O_4]} = \frac{x^2}{(0.0222 - x)}$$

Assuming x is small compared to 0.0222,

$$x^2 = 0.0222 \, (3.3 \times 10^{-4}); \; x = [H^+] = 2.7 \times 10^{-3} \text{ M}$$

$$\frac{2.7 \times 10^{-3} \text{ M } H^+}{0.0222 \text{ M } HC_9H_7O_4} \times 100 = 12\% \text{ ionization; the approximation is not valid}$$

Using the quadratic formula, $x^2 + 3.3 \times 10^{-4} x - 7.325 \times 10^{-6} = 0$

$$x = \frac{-3.3 \times 10^{-4} \pm \sqrt{(3.3 \times 10^{-4})^2 - 4(1)(-7.325 \times 10^{-6})}}{2(1)} = \frac{-3.3 \times 10^{-4} \pm \sqrt{2.941 \times 10^{-5}}}{2}$$

$$x = 2.547 \times 10^{-3} = 2.5 \times 10^{-3} \text{ M } H^+; \; pH = -\log(2.547 \times 10^{-3}) = 2.594 = 2.59$$

16.63   *Analyze/Plan.* Follow the logic in Sample Exercise 16.13.   *Solve.*

(a)

	$HN_3 \text{(aq)}$	$\rightleftharpoons$	$H^+ \text{(aq)}$	$+$	$N_3^- \text{ (aq)}$
initial	0.400 M		0		0
equil	(0.400 – x) M		x M		x M

$$K_a = \frac{[H^+][N_3^-]}{[HN_3]} = 1.9 \times 10^{-5}; \; \frac{x^2}{(0.400 - x)} \approx \frac{x^2}{0.400} = 1.9 \times 10^{-5}$$

$$x = 0.00276 = 2.8 \times 10^{-3} \text{ M} = [H^+]; \; \% \text{ ionization} = \frac{2.76 \times 10^{-3}}{0.400} \times 100 = 0.69\%$$

(b) $1.9 \times 10^{-5} \approx \dfrac{x^2}{0.100}; x = 0.00138 = 1.4 \times 10^{-3} \text{ M } H^+$

$$\% \text{ ionization} = \frac{1.38 \times 10^{-3} \text{ M } H^+}{0.100 \text{ M } HN_3} \times 100 = 1.4\%$$

(c) $1.9 \times 10^{-5} \approx \dfrac{x^2}{0.0400}; x = 8.72 \times 10^{-4} = 8.7 \times 10^{-4} \text{ M } H^+$

$$\% \text{ ionization} = \frac{8.72 \times 10^{-4} \text{ M } H^+}{0.0400 \text{ M } HN_3} \times 100 = 2.2\%$$

Check. Notice that a tenfold dilution [part (a) versus part (c)] leads to a slightly more than threefold increase in percent ionization.

16.64   (a) $C_2H_5COOH(aq) \rightleftharpoons H^+(aq) + C_2H_5COO^-(aq)$

$$K_a = 1.3 \times 10^{-5} = \frac{[H^+][C_2H_5COO^-]}{[C_2H_5COOH]} = \frac{x^2}{0.250-x}$$

$$x^2 \approx 0.250\,(1.3 \times 10^{-5}); x = 1.803 \times 10^{-3} = 1.8 \times 10^{-3}\,M\,H^+$$

$$\% \text{ ionization} = \frac{1.803 \times 10^{-3}\,M\,H^+}{0.250\,M\,C_2H_5COOH} \times 100 = 0.721\%$$

(b) $\dfrac{x^2}{0.0800} \approx 1.3 \times 10^{-5}; x = 1.020 \times 10^{-3} = 1.0 \times 10^{-3}\,M\,H^+$

$$\% \text{ ionization} = \frac{1.020 \times 10^{-3}\,M\,H^+}{0.0800\,M\,C_2H_5COOH} \times 100 = 1.27\%$$

(c) $\dfrac{x^2}{0.0200} \approx 1.3 \times 10^{-5}; x = 5.099 \times 10^{-4} = 5.1 \times 10^{-4}\,M\,H^+$

$$\% \text{ ionization} = \frac{5.099 \times 10^{-4}\,M\,H^+}{0.0200\,M\,C_2H_5COOH} \times 100 = 2.55\%$$

16.65   *Analyze/Plan.* Let the weak acid be HX. $HX(aq) \rightleftharpoons H^+(aq) + X^-(aq)$. Solve the K_a expression symbolically for $[H^+]$ in terms of $[HX]$. Substitute into the formula for % ionization, $([H^+]/[HX]) \times 100$.   *Solve.*

$$K_a = \frac{[H^+][X^-]}{[HX]}; [H^+] = [X^-] = y; K_a = \frac{y^2}{[HX]-y}; \text{ assume that \% ionization is small}$$

$$K_a = \frac{y^2}{[HX]}; y = K_a^{1/2}\,[HX]^{1/2}$$

$$\% \text{ ionization} = \frac{y}{[HX]} \times 100 = \frac{K_a^{1/2}\,[HX]^{1/2}}{[HX]} \times 100 = \frac{K_a^{1/2}}{[HX]^{1/2}} \times 100$$

That is, percent ionization varies inversely as the square root of concentration HX.

16.66 $HX(aq) \rightleftharpoons H^+(aq) + X^-(aq); K_a = \dfrac{[H^+][X^-]}{[HX]}$

$[H^+] = [X^-]$; assume the % ionization is small; $K_a = \dfrac{[H^+]^2}{[HX]}; [H^+] = K_a^{1/2}\,[HX]^{1/2}$

$pH = -\log K_a^{1/2}\,[HX]^{1/2} = -\log K_a^{1/2} - \log [HX]^{1/2}; \ pH = -1/2 \log K_a - 1/2 \log [HX]$

This is the equation of a straight line, where the intercept is $-1/2 \log K_a$, the slope is $-1/2$, and the independent variable is $\log [HX]$.

16.67   *Analyze/Plan.* Follow the logic in Sample Exercise 16.14. Citric acid is a triprotic acid with three K_a values that do not differ by more than 10^3. We must consider all three steps. Also, $C_6H_5O_7^{3-}$ is only produced in step 3.

Solve. <u>Assumptions</u> are explained as they are used in the solution.

$$H_3C_6H_5O_7(aq) \rightleftharpoons H^+(aq) + H_2C_6H_5O_7^-(aq) \qquad K_{a1} = 7.4 \times 10^{-4}$$

$$H_2C_6H_5O_7^-(aq) \rightleftharpoons H^+(aq) + HC_6H_5O_7^{2-}(aq) \qquad K_{a2} = 1.7 \times 10^{-5}$$

$$HC_6H_5O_7^{2-}(aq) \rightleftharpoons H^+(aq) + C_6H_5O_7^{3-}(aq) \qquad K_{a3} = 4.0 \times 10^{-7}$$

To calculate the pH of a 0.040 M solution, <u>assume</u> initially that only the first ionization is important:

	$H_3C_6H_5O_7(aq)$	$\rightleftharpoons$	$H^+(aq)$	+	$H_2C_6H_5O_7^-(aq)$
initial	0.040 M		0		0
equil.	$(0.040 - x)\ M$		$x\ M$		$x\ M$

$$K_{a_1} = \frac{[H^+][H_2C_6H_5O_7^-]}{[H_3C_6H_5O_7]} = \frac{x^2}{(0.040-x)} = 7.4 \times 10^{-4}$$

$x^2 = (0.040 - x)(7.4 \times 10^{-4})$; $\underline{x^2 \approx (0.040)(7.4 \times 10^{-4})}$; $x = 0.00544 = 5.4 \times 10^{-3}\ M$

Since this value for x is rather large in relation to 0.050, a better approximation for x can be obtained by substituting this first estimate into the expression for x^2, then solving again for x:

$$x^2 = (0.040 - x)\ (7.4 \times 10^{-4}) = (0.040 - 5.44 \times 10^{-3})\ (7.4 \times 10^{-4})$$

$$x^2 = 2.557 \times 10^{-5};\ x = 5.057 \times 10^{-3} = 5.1 \times 10^{-3}\ M$$

(This is the same result obtained from the quadratic formula.)

The correction to the value of x, though not large, is significant. Does the second ionization produce a significant additional concentration of H^+?

	$H_2C_6H_5O_7^-(aq)$	$\rightleftharpoons$	$H^+(aq)$	+	$HC_6H_5O_7^{2-}(aq)$
initial	$5.1 \times 10^{-3}\ M$		$5.1 \times 10^{-3}\ M$		0
equil.	$(5.1 \times 10^{-3} - y)$		$(5.1 \times 10^{-3} + y)$		y

$$K_{a_2} = \frac{[H^+][HC_6H_5O_7^{2-}]}{[H_2C_6H_5O_7^-]} = 1.7 \times 10^{-5};\ \frac{(5.1 \times 10^{-3} + y)(y)}{(5.1 \times 10^{-3} - y)} = 1.7 \times 10^{-5}$$

<u>Assume</u> that y is small relative to 5.1×10^{-3}; that is, that additional ionization of $H_2C_6H_5O_7^-$ is small, then

$$\frac{(5.1 \times 10^{-3})y}{(5.1 \times 10^{-3})} = 1.7 \times 10^{-5}\ M;\ y = 1.7 \times 10^{-5}\ M$$

This value is indeed small compared to $5.1 \times 10^{-3}\ M$; $[H^+]$ and pH are determined by the first ionization step. If we were only interested in pH, we could stop here. However, to calculate $[C_6H_5O_7^{3-}]$, we must consider the third ionization, with adjusted $[H^+] = 5.1 \times 10^{-3} + 1.7 \times 10^{-5} = 5.12 \times 10^{-3}\ M\ (= 5.1 \times 10^{-3})$

	$HC_6H_5O_7^{2-}$	$\rightleftharpoons$	H^+ (aq)	+	$C_6H_5O_7^{3-}$ (aq)
initial	$1.7 \times 10^{-5}\,M$		$5.12 \times 10^{-3}\,M$		0
equil.	$1.7 \times 10^{-5} - z$		$5.12 \times 10^{-3} + z$		z

$$K_{a_3} = \frac{[H^+][C_6H_5O_7^{3-}]}{[HC_6H_5O_7^{2-}]} = \frac{(5.12 \times 10^{-3} + z)(z)}{(1.7 \times 10^{-5} - z)} = 4.0 \times 10^{-7}$$

Assume z is small relative to 5.12×10^{-3}, but not relative to 1.7×10^{-5}.

$(4.0 \times 10^{-7})(1.7 \times 10^{-5} - z) = 5.12 \times 10^{-3}\,z; 6.8 \times 10^{-12} - 4.0 \times 10^{-7}\,z = 5.12 \times 10^{-3}\,z;$

$6.8 \times 10^{-12} = 5.12 \times 10^{-3}\,z + 4.0 \times 10^{-7}\,z = 5.12 \times 10^{-3}\,z; z = 1.33 \times 10^{-9} = 1.3 \times 10^{-9}\,M$

$[C_6H_5O_7^{3-}] = 1.3 \times 10^{-9}\,M; [H^+] = 5.12 \times 10^{-3}\,M + 1.3 \times 10^{-9}\,M = 5.1 \times 10^{-3}\,M$

$pH = -\log(5.12 \times 10^{-3}) = 2.29$

The concentration of citrate ion, $[C_6H_5O_7^{3-}]$, is much less than $[H^+]$. Note that neither the second nor third ionizations contributed significantly to $[H^+]$ and pH.

16.68 $H_2C_4H_4O_6$ (aq) $\rightleftharpoons$ H^+ (aq) + $HC_4H_4O_6^-$ (aq) $K_{a1} = 1.0 \times 10^{-3}$

$HC_4H_4O_6^-$ (aq $\rightleftharpoons$ H^+ (aq) + $C_4H_4O_6^{2-}$ (aq) $K_{a2} = 4.6 \times 10^{-5}$

Begin by calculating the $[H^+]$ from the first ionization. The equilibrium concentrations are $[H^+] = [HC_4H_4O_6^-] = x$, $[H_2C_4H_4O_6] = 0.25 - x$.

$$K_{a1} = \frac{[H^+][HC_4H_4O_6^-]}{[H_2C_4H_4O_6]} = \frac{x^2}{0.25 - x}; x^2 + 1.0 \times 10^{-3}\,x - 2.5 \times 10^{-4} = 0$$

Using the quadratic formula, $x = 1.532 \times 10^{-2} = 0.015\,M\,H^+$ from the first ionization. Next calculate the H^+ contribution from the second ionization.

	$HC_4H_4O_6^-$ (aq)	$\rightleftharpoons$	H^+ (aq)	+	$C_4H_4O_6^{2-}$ (aq)
initial	0.015		0.015		0
equil.	$(0.015 - y)$		$(0.015 + y)$		y

$$K_{a2} = \frac{(0.015 + y)(y)}{(0.015 - y)} = 4.6 \times 10^{-5}; \text{assuming } y \text{ is small compared to } 0.015,$$

$y = 4.6 \times 10^{-5}\,M\,C_4H_4O_6^{2-}$ (aq)

This approximation is reasonable, since 4.6×10^{-5} is only 0.3% of 0.015. $[H^+] = 0.015\,M$ (first ionization) + 4.6×10^{-5} (second ionization). Since 4.6×10^{-5} is 0.3% of 0.015 M, it can be safely ignored when calculating total $[H^+]$. Thus, $pH = -\log(0.01532) = 1.18148 = 1.181$.

Assumptions:

1)   The ionization can be treated as a series of steps (valid by Hess' law).

2)   The extent of ionization in the second step (y) is small relative to that from the first step (valid for this acid and initial concentration). This assumption was used twice, to calculate the value of y from K_{a2} and to calculate total $[H^+]$ and pH.

Weak Bases (section 16.7)

16.69　(a)　$HONH_3^+$

　　　(b)　When hydroxylamine acts as a base, the nitrogen atom accepts a proton.

　　　(c)　14 e⁻, 7 e⁻ pairs

$$H-\overset{..}{\underset{..}{O}}-\overset{\displaystyle H}{\underset{\displaystyle H}{N}}-H \qquad \left[H-\overset{..}{\underset{..}{O}}-\overset{\displaystyle H}{\underset{\displaystyle H}{N}}-H \right]^+ \qquad \left[H-\overset{\displaystyle H}{\underset{..}{O}}-\overset{\displaystyle H}{\underset{\displaystyle H}{N}}-H \right]^+$$

　　　　　　　　　　　　　　　　　　FC on N is +1　　　　　　　　　FC on O is +1

In neutral hydroxylamine, both O and N have zero formal charges. Nitrogen is less electronegative than oxygen, and more likely to share a lone pair of electrons with an incoming (and electron deficient) H^+. The resulting cation with the +1 formal charge on N is more stable than the one with the +1 formal charge on O.

16.70　(a)　*Analyze/Plan.* To determine relative strength, compare the K_b values of the two bases. *Solve.*

$$K_b \text{ for } OCl^- = \frac{K_w}{K_a \text{ for } HClO} = \frac{1.0 \times 10^{-14}}{3.0 \times 10^{-8}} = 3.3 \times 10^{-7}$$

K_b for hydroxylamine is 1.1×10^{-8}. OCl^- is a stronger base than hydroxylamine.

　　　(b)　When OCl^- acts as a base, the O atom is the proton acceptor.

　　　(c)　14 e⁻, 7 e⁻ pairs　　$\left[:\overset{..}{\underset{..}{Cl}}-\overset{..}{\underset{..}{O}}: \right]^-$

In OCl^- the –1 formal charge is on O. H^+ attaches to the atom with the negative formal charge.

16.71　*Analyze/Plan.* Remember that K_b = [products]/[reactants]. If $H_2O(l)$ appears in the equilibrium reaction, it will not appear in the K_b expression, because it is a pure liquid. *Solve.*

　　　(a)　$(CH_3)_2NH(aq) + H_2O(l) \rightleftharpoons (CH_3)_2NH_2^+(aq) + OH^-(aq); K_b = \dfrac{[(CH_3)_2NH_2^+][OH^-]}{[(CH_3)_2NH]}$

　　　(b)　$CO_3^{2-}(aq) + H_2O(l) \rightleftharpoons HCO_3^-(aq) + OH^-(aq); K_b = \dfrac{[HCO_3^-][OH^-]}{[CO_3^{2-}]}$

　　　(c)　$HCOO^-(aq) + H_2O(l) \rightleftharpoons HCOOH(aq) + OH^-(aq); K_b = \dfrac{[HCOOH][OH^-]}{[HCOO^-]}$

16.72　(a)　$C_3H_7NH_2(aq) + H_2O(l) \rightleftharpoons C_3H_7NH_3^+(aq) + OH^-(aq); K_b = \dfrac{[C_3H_7NH_3^+][OH^-]}{[C_3H_7NH_2]}$

　　　(b)　$HPO_4^{2-}(aq) + H_2O(l) \rightleftharpoons H_2PO_4^-(aq) + OH^-(aq); K_b = \dfrac{[H_2PO_4^-][OH^-]}{[HPO_4^{2-}]}$

(c) $C_6H_5CO_2^-(aq) + H_2O(l) \rightleftharpoons C_6H_5CO_2H(aq) + OH^-(aq); \; K_b = \dfrac{[C_6H_5CO_2H][OH^-]}{[C_6H_5CO_2^-]}$

16.73   *Analyze/Plan.* Follow the logic in Sample Exercise 16.15.   *Solve.*

$$C_2H_5NH_2(aq) + H_2O(l) \; \rightleftharpoons \; C_2H_5NH_3^+(aq) \; + \; OH^-(aq)$$

initial	0.075 M		0	0
equil.	(0.075 – x) M		x M	x M

$$K_b = \frac{[C_2H_5NH_3^+][OH^-]}{[C_2H_5NH_2]} = \frac{(x)(x)}{(0.075-x)} = \frac{x^2}{0.075} = 6.4 \times 10^{-4}$$

$x^2 = 0.075 \, (6.4 \times 10^{-4}); \; x = [OH^-] = 6.9 \times 10^{-3} \, M; \; pH = 11.84$

Check. $\dfrac{6.9 \times 10^{-3} \, M \; OH^-}{0.075 \, M \; C_2H_5NH_2} \times 100 = 9.2\%$ ionization; the assumption is not valid

To obtain a more precise result, the K_b expression is rewritten in standard quadratic form and solved via the quadratic formula.

$$\frac{x^2}{0.075-x} = 6.4 \times 10^{-4}; \; x^2 + 6.4 \times 10^{-4} \, x - 4.8 \times 10^{-5} = 0$$

$$x = \frac{-b \pm \sqrt{b^2 - 4ac}}{2a} = \frac{-6.4 \times 10^{-4} \pm \sqrt{(6.4 \times 10^{-4})^2 - 4(1)(-4.8 \times 10^{-5})}}{2}$$

$x = 6.62 \times 10^{-3} = 6.6 \times 10^{-3} \, M \; OH^-; \; pOH = 2.18, \; pH = 14.00 - pOH = 11.82$

Note that the pH values obtained using the two algebraic techniques are very similar.

16.74 $BrO^-(aq) + H_2O(l) \; \rightleftharpoons \; HOBr(aq) \; + \; OH^-(aq)$

initial	0.724 M		0	0
equil.	(0.724 – x) M		x M	x M

$$K_b = \frac{[HOBr][OH^-]}{[BrO^-]} = \frac{x^2}{0.724-x} \approx \frac{x^2}{0.724} = 4.0 \times 10^{-6}$$

$x^2 = 0.724 \, (4.0 \times 10^{-6}); \; x = [OH^-] = 1.70 \times 10^{-3} = 1.7 \times 10^{-3} \, M; \; pH = 11.23$

Check. $\dfrac{1.7 \times 10^{-3} \, M \; OH^-}{0.724 \, M \; BrO^-} \times 100 = 0.24\%$ hydrolysis; the approximation is valid

16.75   *Analyze/Plan.* Given pH and initial concentration of base, calculate all equilibrium concentrations. pH $\rightarrow$ pOH $\rightarrow$ [OH$^-$] at equilibrium. Construct the equilibrium table and calculate other equilibrium concentrations. Substitute into the K_b expression and calculate K_b.   *Solve.*

(a) $[OH^-] = 10^{-pOH}; \; pOH = 14 - pH = 14.00 - 11.33 = 2.67$

       $[OH^-] = 10^{-2.67} = 2.138 \times 10^{-3} = 2.1 \times 10^{-3} \, M$

$$C_{10}H_{15}ON(aq) + H_2O(l) \rightleftharpoons C_{10}H_{15}ONH^+(aq) + OH^-(aq)$$

initial	0.035 M	0	0
equil.	0.033 M	$2.1 \times 10^{-3}\ M$	$2.1 \times 10^{-3}\ M$

(b) $K_b = \dfrac{[C_{10}H_{15}ONH^+][OH^-]}{[C_{10}H_{15}ON]} = \dfrac{(2.138 \times 10^{-3})^2}{(0.03286)} = 1.4 \times 10^{-4}$

16.76 (a) pOH = 14.00 – 9.95 = 4.05; $[OH^-] = 10^{-4.05} = 8.91 \times 10^{-5} = 8.9 \times 10^{-5}\ M$

$$C_{18}H_{21}NO_3(aq) + H_2O(1) \rightleftharpoons C_{18}H_{21}NO_3H^+(aq) + OH^-(aq)$$

initial	0.0050 M	0	0
equil.	$(0.0050 - 8.9 \times 10^{-5})$	$8.9 \times 10^{-5}\ M$	$8.9 \times 10^{-5}\ M$

$K_b = \dfrac{[C_{18}H_{21}NO_3H^+][OH^-]}{[C_{18}H_{21}NO_3]} = \dfrac{(8.91 \times 10^{-5})^2}{(0.0050 - 8.91 \times 10^{-5})} = 1.62 \times 10^{-6} = 1.6 \times 10^{-6}$

(b) $pK_b = -\log(K_b) = -\log(1.62 \times 10^{-6}) = 5.79$

The K_a – K_b Relationship; Acid-Base Properties of Salts
(sections 16.8 and 16.9)

16.77 (a) For a conjugate acid/conjugate base pair such as $C_6H_5OH/C_6H_5O^-$, K_b for the conjugate base is always K_w/K_a for the conjugate acid. K_b for the conjugate base can always be calculated from K_a for the conjugate acid, so a separate list of K_b values is not necessary.

(b) $K_b = K_w/K_a = 1.0 \times 10^{-14} / 1.3 \times 10^{-10} = 7.7 \times 10^{-5}$

(c) K_b for phenolate $(7.7 \times 10^{-5}) > K_b$ for ammonia (1.8×10^{-5}).

Phenolate is a stronger base than NH_3.

16.78 The stronger a base, the weaker its conjugate acid. From the K_a values in Table 16.3, place the conjugate acids of these oxyanions in order of increasing K_a value, increasing acid strength and decreasing conjugate base strength. Use K_{a2} for H_2SO_4, H_2CO_3, and H_2SO_3 and K_{a3} for H_3PO_4.

In order of increasing K_a value and acid strength: $HPO_4^{2-} < HCO_3^- < HSO_3^- < HSO_4^-$

In order of decreasing base strength: $PO_4^{3-} > CO_3^{2-} > SO_3^{2-} > SO_4^{2-}$

16.79 *Analyze/Plan.* Given K_a, determine relative strengths of the acids and their conjugate bases. The greater the magnitude of K_a, the stronger the acid and the weaker the conjugate base. K_b (conjugate base) = K_w/K_a. *Solve.*

(a) Acetic acid is stronger, because it has the larger K_a value.

(b) Hypochlorite ion is the stronger base because the weaker acid, hypochlorous acid, has the stronger conjugate base.

(c) K_b for $CH_3COO^- = K_w/K_a$ for $CH_3COOH = 1.0 \times 10^{-14}/1.8 \times 10^{-5} = 5.6 \times 10^{-10}$

K_b for $ClO^- = K_w/K_a$ for $HClO = 1 \times 10^{-14}/3.0 \times 10^{-8} = 3.3 \times 10^{-7}$

Note that K_b for ClO^- is greater than K_b for CH_3COO^-.

16.80   (a)   Ammonia is the stronger base because it has the larger K_b value.

       (b)   Hydroxylammonium is the stronger acid because the weaker base, hydroxylamine, has the stronger conjugate acid.

       (c) K_a for $NH_4^+ = K_w/K_b$ for $NH_3 = 1.0 \times 10^{-14}/1.8 \times 10^{-5} = 5.6 \times 10^{-10}$

          K_a for $HONH_3^+ = K_w/K_b$ for $HONH_2 = 1.0 \times 10^{-14}/1.1 \times 10^{-8} = 9.1 \times 10^{-7}$

          Note that K_a for $HONH_3^+$ is larger than K_a for NH_4^+.

16.81   *Analyze.* When the solute in an aqueous solution is a salt, evaluate the acid/base properties of the component ions.

       (a)   *Plan.* NaBrO is a soluble salt and thus a strong electrolyte. When it is dissolved in H_2O, it dissociates completely into Na^+ and BrO^-. $[NaBrO] = [Na^+] = [BrO^-] = 0.10\ M$. Na^+ is the conjugate acid of the strong base NaOH and thus does not influence the pH of the solution. BrO^-, on the other hand, is the conjugate base of the weak acid HBrO and **does** influence the pH of the solution. Like any other weak base, it hydrolyzes water to produce $OH^-(aq)$. Solve the equilibrium problem to determine $[OH^-]$.   *Solve.*

	$BrO^-(aq)$	$+\ H_2O(l)$	$\rightleftharpoons$	$HBrO(aq)$	$+$	$OH^-(aq)$
initial	$0.10\ M$			0		0
equil.	$(0.10 - x)\ M$			$x\ M$		$x\ M$

$$K_b \text{ for } BrO^- = \frac{[HBrO][OH^-]}{[BrO^-]} = \frac{K_w}{K_a \text{ for } HBrO} = \frac{1 \times 10^{-14}}{2.5 \times 10^{-9}} = 4.00 \times 10^{-6} = 4.0 \times 10^{-6}$$

$$4.00 \times 10^{-6} = \frac{(x)(x)}{(0.10-x)}; \text{ assume the percent of } BrO^- \text{ that hydrolyzes is small}$$

$x^2 = 0.10\ (4.00 \times 10^{-6}); x = [OH^-] = 6.32 \times 10^{-4} = 6.3 \times 10^{-4}\ M$

$pOH = 3.20; pH = 14 - 3.20 = 10.80$

       (b)   *Plan.* $NaHS(aq) \rightarrow Na^+(aq) + HS^-(aq)$

          HS^- is the conjugate base of H_2S and its hydrolysis reaction will determine the $[OH^-]$ and pH of the solution (see similar explanation for NaBrO in part (a)). We will assume the process $HS^-(aq) \rightleftharpoons H^+(aq) + S^-(aq)$ will not significantly affect the $[OH^-]$ in solution because K_{a2} for H_2S is so small. Solve the equilibrium problem for $[OH^-]$.   *Solve.*

	$HS^-(aq)$	$+\ H_2O(l)$	$\rightleftharpoons$	$H_2S(aq)$	$+\ OH^-(aq)$
initial	$0.080\ M$			0	0
equil.	$(0.080 - x)\ M$			x	x

$$K_b = \frac{[H_2S][OH^-]}{[HS^-]} = \frac{K_w}{K_a \text{ for } H_2S} = \frac{1.0 \times 10^{-14}}{9.5 \times 10^{-8}} = 1.053 \times 10^{-7} = 1.1 \times 10^{-7}$$

$1.053 \times 10^{-7} = \dfrac{x^2}{(0.080 - x)}$; $x^2 = 0.080 (1.053 \times 10^{-7})$; $x = 9.177 \times 10^{-5} = 9.2 \times 10^{-5}$ M OH^-

(Assume x is small compared to 0.080); pOH = 4.04; pH = 14 – 4.04 = 9.96

Check. $\dfrac{9.2 \times 10^{-5}\ M\ OH^-}{0.080\ M\ HS^-} \times 100 = 0.12\%$ hydrolysis; the approximation is valid

(c)   *Plan.* For the two salts present, Na^+ and Ca^{2+} are negligible acids. NO_2^- is the conjugate base of HNO_2 and will determine the pH of the solution. *Solve.*

Calculate total $[NO_2^-]$ present initially.

$[NO_2^-]_{total} = [NO_2^-]$ from $NaNO_2 + [NO_2^-]$ from $Ca(NO_2)_2$

$[NO_2^-]_{total} = 0.10\ M + 2(0.20\ M) = 0.50\ M$

The hydrolysis equilibrium is:

$$NO_2^-(aq) + H_2O(l) \rightleftharpoons HNO_2 + OH^-(aq)$$

initial	0.50 M	0	0
equil.	(0.50 – x) M	x M	x M

$K_b = \dfrac{[HNO_2][OH^-]}{[NO_2^-]} = \dfrac{K_w}{K_a \text{ for } HNO_2} = \dfrac{1.0 \times 10^{-14}}{4.5 \times 10^{-4}} = 2.22 \times 10^{-11} = 2.2 \times 10^{-11}$

$2.2 \times 10^{-11} = \dfrac{x^2}{(0.50 - x)} \approx \dfrac{x^2}{0.50}$; $x^2 = 0.50 (2.22 \times 10^{-11})$

$x = 3.33 \times 10^{-6} = 3.3 \times 10^{-6}\ M\ OH^-$; pOH = 5.48; pH = 14 – 5.48 = 8.52

16.82   (a)   Proceeding as in Solution 16.81(a):

$$F^-(aq) + H_2O(l) \rightleftharpoons HF(aq) + OH^-(aq)$$

initial	0.105 M	0 M	0 M
equil	(0.105 – x) M	x M	x M

$K_b \text{ for } F^- = \dfrac{[HF][OH^-]}{[F^-]} = \dfrac{K_w}{K_a \text{ for } HF} = \dfrac{1.0 \times 10^{-14}}{6.8 \times 10^{-4}} = 1.47 \times 10^{-11} = 1.5 \times 10^{-11}$

$1.5 \times 10^{-11} = \dfrac{(x)(x)}{(0.105 - x)}$; assume the amount of F^- that hydrolyzes is small

$x^2 = 0.105(1.47 \times 10^{-11})$; $x = [OH^-] = 1.243 \times 10^{-6} = 1.2 \times 10^{-6}\ M$

pOH = 5.91; pH = 14 – 5.91 = 8.09

(b) $Na_2S(aq) \rightarrow S^{2-}(aq) + 2Na^+(aq)$

$S^{2-}(aq) + H_2O(l) \rightleftharpoons HS^-(aq) + OH^-(aq)$

As in part (a) above, $[OH^-] = [HS^-] = x$; $[S^{2-}] = 0.035\ M$

$$K_b = \frac{[HS^-][OH^-]}{[S^{2-}]} = \frac{K_w}{K_a \text{ for } HS^-} = \frac{1.0 \times 10^{-14}}{1 \times 10^{-19}} = 1 \times 10^5$$

Since $K_b \gg 1$, the equilibrium above lies far to the right and $[OH^-] = [HS^-] = 0.035\ M$. K_b for $HS^- = 1.05 \times 10^{-7}$; $[OH^-]$ produced by further hydrolysis of HS^- amounts to $6.1 \times 10^{-5}\ M$. The second hydrolysis step does not make a significant contribution to the total $[OH^-]$ and pH.

$[OH^-] = 0.035\ M$; pOH = 1.46, pH = 12.54

(c)   As in Solution 16.81(c), calculate $[CH_3COO^-]$.

$[CH_3COO^-]_t = [CH_3COO^-]$ from $CH_3COONa + [CH_3COO^-]$ from $(CH_3COO)_2Ba$
$[CH_3COO^-]_t = 0.045\ M + 2(0.055\ M) = 0.155\ M$

The hydrolysis equilibrium is $CH_3COO^-\ (aq) + H_2O(l) \rightleftharpoons$
$$CH_3COOH\,(aq) + OH^-(aq)$$

$$K_b = \frac{[CH_3COOH][OH^-]}{[CH_3COO^-]} = \frac{K_w}{K_a \text{ for } CH_3COOH} = \frac{1.0 \times 10^{-14}}{1.8 \times 10^{-5}} = 5.56 \times 10^{-10}$$

$$= 5.6 \times 10^{-10}$$

$[OH^-] = [CH_3COOH] = x$, $[CH_3COO^-] = 0.155 - x$

$$K_b = 5.56 \times 10^{-10} = \frac{x^2}{(0.155 - x)}; \text{ assume } x \text{ is small compared to } 0.155\ M$$

$x^2 = 0.155\,(5.56 \times 10^{-10})$; $x = [OH^-] = 9.280 \times 10^{-6} = 9.3 \times 10^{-6}$

pH $= 14 + \log(9.280 \times 10^{-6}) = 8.97$

16.83   *Analyze/Plan.* Given the formula of a salt, predict whether an aqueous solution will be acidic, basic, or neutral. Evaluate the acid-base properties of both ions and determine the overall effect on solution pH. *Solve.*

(a)   acidic; NH_4^+ is a weak acid, Br^- is negligible.

(b)   acidic; Fe^{3+} is a highly charged metal cation and a Lewis acid; Cl^- is negligible.

(c)   basic; CO_3^{2-} is the conjugate base of HCO_3^-; Na^+ is negligible.

(d)   neutral; both K^+ and ClO_4^- are negligible.

(e)   acidic; $HC_2O_4^-$ is amphoteric, but K_a for the acid dissociation (6.4×10^{-5}) is much greater than K_b for the base hydrolysis $(1.0 \times 10^{-14} / 5.9 \times 10^{-2} = 1.7 \times 10^{-13})$.

16.84   (a)   acidic; Al^{3+} is a highly charged metal cation and a Lewis acid; Cl^- is negligible.

(b)   neutral; both Na^+ and Br^- are negligible.

(c)   basic; ClO^- is the conjugate base of HClO; Na^+ is negligible.

(d)   acidic; $CH_3NH_3^+$ is the conjugate acid of CH_3NH_2; NO_3^- is negligible.

(e)   basic; SO_3^{2-} is the conjugate base of H_2SO_3; Na^+ is negligible.

16.85   *Plan.* Estimate pH using relative base strength and then calculate to confirm prediction. NaCl is a neutral salt, so it is not the unknown. The unknown is a relatively weak base, because a pH of 8.08 is not very basic. Since F^- is a weaker base than OCl^-, the unknown is probably NaF. Calculate K_b for the unknown from the data provided. *Solve.*

$[OH^-] = 10^{-pOH}$; $pOH = 14.00 - pH = 14.00 - 8.08 = 5.92$

$[OH^-] = 10^{-5.92} = 1.202 \times 10^{-6} = 1.2 \times 10^{-6}\ M = [HX]$

$[NaX] = [X^-] = 0.050\ \text{mol salt}/0.500\ \text{L} = 0.10\ M$

$$K_b = \frac{[OH^-][HX]}{[X^-]} = \frac{(1.202 \times 10^{-6})^2}{(0.10 - 1.2 \times 10^{-6})} = \frac{(1.202 \times 10^{-6})^2}{0.10} = 1.4 \times 10^{-11}$$

K_b for $F^- = K_w/K_a$ for $HF = 1.0 \times 10^{-14}/6.8 \times 10^{-4} = 1.5 \times 10^{-11}$

The unknown is NaF.

16.86   *Plan.* Estimate pH of salt solution by evaluating the ions in the salts. Calculate to confirm if necessary. *Solve.*

KBr: salt of strong acid and strong base, neutral solution. The unknown is probably KBr. Check the others to be sure.

NH_4Cl: salt of a weak base and a strong acid, acidic solution

KCN: salt of a strong base and a weak acid, basic solution

K_2CO_3: salt of a strong base and a weak acid (HCO_3^-), basic solution

Only KBr fits the acid-base properties of the unknown.

Acid-Base Character and Chemical Structure (section 16.10)

16.87   (a)   As the electronegativity of the central atom (X) increases, more electron density is withdrawn from the X–O and O–H bonds, respectively. In water, the O–H bond is ionized to a greater extent and the strength of the oxyacid increases.

(b)   As the number of nonprotonated oxygen atoms in the molecule increases, they withdraw electron density from the other bonds in the molecule and the strength of the oxyacid increases.

16.88   (a)   For binary compounds where X atoms are in the same period, the more polar the X–H bond, the stronger the acid and the weaker the base. Oxygen is more electronegative than nitrogen, so the O–H bonds in H_2O are more polar than the N–H bonds in NH_3 and NH_3 is the stronger base. Also, less electronegative N is more likely than O to share its nonbonding electrons with an incoming H^+ and NH_3 is a better H^+ acceptor.

(b)   The C–H bonds in CH_4 are essentially nonpolar and the molecule has no nonbonding electron pairs. CH_4 has no acid or base properties, so NH_3 is a stronger base.

16.89   (a) HNO_3 is a stronger acid than HNO_2 because it has one more nonprotonated oxygen atom, and thus a higher oxidation number on N.

(b)   For binary hydrides, acid strength increases going down a family, so H_2S is a stronger acid than H_2O.

(c) H_2SO_4 is a stronger acid because H^+ is much more tightly held by the anion HSO_4^-.

(d)   For oxyacids, the greater the electronegativity of the central atom, the stronger the acid, so H_2SO_4 is a stronger acid than H_2SeO_4.

(e) CCl_3COOH is stronger because the electronegative Cl atoms withdraw electron density from other parts of the molecule, which weakens the O–H bond and makes H^+ easier to remove. Also, the electronegative Cl delocalizes negative charge on the carboxylate anion. This stabilizes the conjugate base, favoring products in the ionization equilibrium and increasing K_a.

16.90   (a)   For binary hydrides, acid strength increases going across a row, so HCl is a stronger acid than H_2S.

(b)   For oxyacids, the more electronegative the central atom, the stronger the acid, so H_3PO_4 is a stronger acid than H_3AsO_4.

(c) $HBrO_3$ has one more nonprotonated oxygen and a higher oxidation number on Br, so it is a stronger acid than $HBrO_2$.

(d)   The first dissociation of a polyprotic acid is always stronger because H^+ is more tightly held by an anion, so $H_2C_2O_4$ is a stronger acid than $HC_2O_4^-$.

(e)   The conjugate base of benzoic acid, $C_6H_5COO^-$, is stabilized by resonance, while the conjugate base of phenol, $C_6H_5O^-$, is not. C_6H_5COOH has greater tendency to form its conjugate base and is the stronger acid.

16.91   (a) BrO^- (HClO is the stronger acid due to a more electronegative central atom, so BrO^- is the stronger base.)

(b) BrO^- ($HBrO_2$ has more nonprotonated O atoms and is the stronger acid, so BrO^- is the stronger base.)

(c) HPO_4^{2-} (larger negative charge, greater attraction for H^+)

16.92   (a) NO_2^- (HNO_3 is the stronger acid because it has more nonprotonated O atoms, so NO_2^- is the stronger base.)

(b) PO_4^{3-} (K_a for $HAsO_4^{2-}$ is greater than K_a for HPO_4^{2-}, so K_b for PO_4^{3-} is greater and PO_4^{3-} is the stronger base. Note that P is more electronegative than As and H_3PO_4 is a stronger acid than H_3AsO_4, which could lead to the conclusion that AsO_4^{3-} is the stronger base. As in all cases, the measurement of base strength, K_b, supercedes the prediction. Chemistry is an experimental science.

(c) CO_3^{2-} (The more negative the anion, the stronger the attraction for H^+.)

16.93   (a)   True.

(b)   False. In a series of acids that have the same central atom, acid strength increases with the number of nonprotonated oxygen atoms bonded to the central atom.

(c)   False. H_2Te is a stronger acid than H_2S because the H–Te bond is longer, weaker, and more easily dissociated than the H–S bond.

16.94   (a)   True.

(b)   False. For oxyacids with the same structure but different central atom, the acid strength **increases** as the electronegativity of the central atom increases.

(c)   False. HF is a weak acid, weaker than the other hydrogen halides, primarily because the H–F bond energy is exceptionally high.

Lewis Acids and Bases (section 16.11)

16.95   Yes. If a substance is an Arrhenius base, it must also be a Brønsted-Lowry base and a Lewis base. The Arrhenius definition (hydroxide ion) is the most restrictive, the Brønsted-Lowry (H^+ acceptor) more general and the Lewis (electron pair donor) most general. Since a hydroxide ion is both an H^+ acceptor and an electron pair donor, any substance that fits the narrow Arrhenius definition will fit the broader Brønsted-Lowry and Lewis definitions.

16.96   No. If a substance is a Lewis acid, it is not necessarily a Brønsted-Lowry or an Arrhenius acid. The Lewis definition of an acid, an electron pair acceptor, is most general. A Lewis acid does not necessarily fit the more narrow description of a Brønsted-Lowry or Arrhenius acid. An electron pair acceptor isn't necessarily an H^+ donor, nor must it produce H^+ in aqueous solution. An example is Al^{3+}, which is a Lewis acid, but has no ionizable hydrogen.

16.97   *Analyze/Plan.* Identify each reactant as an electron pair donor (Lewis base) or electron pair acceptor (Lewis acid). Remember that a Brønsted-Lowry acid is necessarily a Lewis acid, and a Brønsted-Lowry base is necessarily a Lewis base (Solution 16.95).   *Solve.*

	Lewis Acid	**Lewis Base**
(a)	$Fe(ClO_4)_3$ or Fe^{3+}	H_2O
(b)	H_2O	CN^-
(c)	BF_3	$(CH_3)_3N$
(d)	HIO	NH_2^-

16.98

	Lewis Acid	**Lewis Base**
(a)	HNO_2 (or H^+)	OH^-
(b)	$FeBr_3$ (Fe^{3+})	Br^-
(c)	Zn^{2+}	NH_3
(d)	SO_2	H_2O

16.99   (a) Cu^{2+}, higher cation charge

(b) Fe^{3+}, higher cation charge

(c) Al^{3+}, smaller cation radius, same charge

16.100   (a) $ZnBr_2$, smaller cation radius, same charge

(b) $Cu(NO_3)_2$, higher cation charge

(c) $NiBr_2$, smaller cation radius, same charge

Additional Exercises

16.101 To compare base strength, compare either K_b or pK_b values. The stronger the base, the larger the K_b and the smaller the pK_b. (pK_b is the negative log of K_b; pK_b increases as base strength decreases.)

pK_b for NH_3 = $-\log(1.8 \times 10^{-5})$ = 4.74. pK_b for $(C_2H_5)_3N$ = 2.99

$(C_2H_5)_3N$ is a stronger base than NH_3 by virture of its smaller pK_b.

16.102 (a) Correct.

(b) Incorrect. A Brønsted-Lowry acid must have ionizable hydrogen. Lewis acids are electron pair acceptors, but need not have ionizable hydrogen.

(c) Correct.

(d) Incorrect. K^+ is a negligible Lewis acid because it is the conjugate of strong base KOH. Its relatively large ionic radius and low positive charge render it a poor attractor of electron pairs.

(e) Correct.

16.103 The equilibrium favors the weaker acid and base. That is, the stronger acid will be ionized; the weaker acid will not.

(a) The equilibrium lies to the right. HPO_4^{2-} is a weaker acid than NH_4^+, and NH_3 is a weaker base than PO_4^{3-}. The equilibrium favors products and $K > 1$.

(b) The equilibrium lies to the left. CH_3COOH is a weaker acid than HF, and F^- is a weaker base than CH_3COO^-. The equilibrium favors reactants and $K < 1$.

16.104 $H_3C_6H_5O_7$ + CH_3NH_2 $\rightarrow$ $CH_3NH_3^+$ + $H_2C_6H_5O_7^-$

citric acid   methylamine   odorless salt

$$H_3C_6H_5O_7 \rightleftharpoons H^+ + H_2C_6H_5O_7^- \qquad K_{a_1} = 7.4 \times 10^{-4}$$

$$CH_3NH_2 + H_2O \rightleftharpoons CH_3NH_3^+ + OH^- \qquad K_b = 4.4 \times 10^{-4}$$

$$H^+ + OH^- \rightleftharpoons H_2O \qquad 1/K_w = 1/1.0 \times 10^{-14}$$

$$H_3C_6H_5O_7 + CH_3NH_2 + H_2O + H^+ + OH^- \rightleftharpoons H_2C_6H_5O_7^- + CH_3NH_3^+ + H^+ + OH^- + H_2O$$

$$H_3C_6H_5O_7 + CH_3NH_2 \rightleftharpoons H_2C_6H_5O_7^- + CH_3NH_3^+$$

$$K = \frac{K_{a_1} \times K_b}{K_w} = \frac{(7.4 \times 10^{-4})(4.4 \times 10^{-4})}{1.0 \times 10^{-14}} = 3.256 \times 10^7 = 3.3 \times 10^7$$

16.105 (a) A higher O_2 concentration displaces protons from Hb, producing a more acidic solution, with lower pH in the lungs than in the tissues.

(b) $[H^+]$ = antilog (-7.4) = 4.0×10^{-8} M. At body temperature, 37°C, $K_w = 2.4 \times 10^{-14}$ (see Solution 16.39). At this temperature, a "neutral" solution has $[H^+] = 1.5 \times 10^{-7}$ and pH 6.81. Even though the frame of reference is a bit different at this temperature, blood at pH 7.4 is slightly basic.

(c)   The equilibrium indicates that a high $[H^+]$ shifts the equilibrium toward the proton-bound form HbH^+, which means a lower concentration of HbO_2 in the blood. Thus the ability of hemoglobin to transport oxygen is impeded.

16.106   Upon dissolving, Li_2O dissociates to form Li^+ and O^{2-}. According to Equation 16.22, O^{2-} is completely protonated in aqueous solution.

$Li_2O(s) + H_2O(l) \rightarrow 2Li^+(aq) + 2OH^-(aq)$

Thus, initial $[Li_2O] = [O_2^-]$; $[OH^-] = 2[O^{2-}] = 2[Li_2O]$

$$[Li_2O] = \frac{mol\ Li_2O}{L\ solution} = 2.50\ g\ Li_2O \times \frac{1\,mol\ Li_2O}{29.88\ g\ Li_2O} \times \frac{1}{1.500\ L} = 0.0558 = 0.0558\ M$$

$[OH^-] = 0.11156 = 0.112\ M$; $pOH = 0.9525 = 0.953$; $pH = 14.00 - pOH = 13.0475 = 13.048$

16.107   The solution with the higher pH has the lower $[H^+]$.

(a)   For solutions with equal concentrations, the weaker acid will have a lower $[H^+]$ and higher pH.

(b)   The acid with $K_a = 8 \times 10^{-6}$ is the weaker acid, so it has the higher pH.

(c)   The base with $pK_b = 4.5$ is the stronger base, has greater $[OH^-]$ and smaller $[H^+]$, so higher pH.

16.108   Assume $T = 25°C$. If $[OH^-] = 2.5 \times 10^{-9}\ M$, $pOH = 8.60$ and $pH = 5.40$. This does not make sense (!) because NaOH is a strong base. Usually we assume that $[H^+]$ and $[OH^-]$ from the autoionization of water do not contribute to the overall $[H^+]$ and $[OH^-]$. However, for acid or base solute concentrations less than $1 \times 10^{-6}\ M$, the autoionization of water produces significant $[H^+]$ and $[OH^-]$ and we must consider it when calculating pH.

	$H_2O(l)$	$\rightleftharpoons$	$[H^+]$	$+$	$[OH^-]$
initial	C		0		$2.5 \times 10^{-9}\ M$
equil	C		x		$(x + 2.5 \times 10^{-9})\ M$

$K_w = 1.0 \times 10^{-14} = [H^+][OH^-] = (x)(x + 2.5 \times 10^{-9})$; $x^2 + 2.5 \times 10^{-9}\ x - 1.0 \times 10^{-14} = 0$

From the quadratic formula, $x = \dfrac{-2.5 \times 10^{-9} \pm \sqrt{(2.5 \times 10^{-9})^2 - 4(1)(-1 \times 10^{-14})}}{2(1)}$

$$= 9.876 \times 10^{-8} = 9.9 \times 10^{-8}\ M\ H^+$$

$[H^+] = 9.9 \times 10^{-8}\ M$; $[OH^-] = (9.876 \times 10^{-8} + 2.5 \times 10^{-9}) = 1.013 \times 10^{-7} = 1.0 \times 10^{-7}\ M$

$pH = 7.0054 = 7.01$

Check: $[9.876 \times 10^{-8}][1.013 \times 10^{-7}] = 1.0 \times 10^{-14}$. Now our answer makes sense. The very small concentration of OH^- from the solute raises the solution pH to slightly more than 7.

16.109 $K_a = \dfrac{[H^+][C_5H_{11}COO^-]}{[C_5H_{11}COOH]}$; $[H^+] = [C_5H_{11}COO^-] = 10^{-pH} = 10^{-2.94} = 0.001148$

$$= 1.1 \times 10^{-3} \, M$$

$[C_5H_{11}COOH] = \dfrac{11 \, g \, C_5H_{11}COOH}{L} \times \dfrac{1 \, mol \, C_5H_{11}COOH}{116.16 \, g \, C_5H_{11}COOH} = 0.09470 = 0.095 \, M$

$K_a = \dfrac{[H^+][C_5H_{11}COO^-]}{[C_5H_{11}COOH]} = \dfrac{(0.001148)^2}{(0.09470 - 0.001148)} = 1.4092 \times 10^{-5} = 1.4 \times 10^{-5}$

16.110 (a) $K_b = K_w/K_a$; $pK_b = 14 - pK_a$; $pK_b = 14 - 4.84 = 9.16$

(b) K_a for butyric acid (buCOOH) is $10^{-4.84} = 1.4454 \times 10^{-5} = 1.4 \times 10^{-5}$

$K_a = \dfrac{[H^+][buCOO^-]}{[buCOOH]}$; $[H^+] = [buCOO^-] = x$; $[buCOOH] = 0.050 - x$

$1.4454 \times 10^{-5} = \dfrac{x^2}{0.050 - x}$; assume x is small relative to 0.050

$x^2 = 7.227 \times 10^{-7}$; $x = [H^+] = 8.501 \times 10^{-4} = 8.5 \times 10^{-4} \, M \, H^+$; $pH = 3.07$

(This represents 1.7% ionization, so the approximation is valid.)

(c) K_b for butyrate anion (buCOO⁻) is $10^{-9.16} = 6.918 = 6.918 \times 10^{-10} = 6.9 \times 10^{-10}$

$K_b = \dfrac{[OH^-][buCOOH]}{[buCOO^-]}$; $[OH^-] = [buCOOH] = x$; $[buCOO^-] = 0.050 - x$

$6.918 \times 10^{-10} = \dfrac{x^2}{0.050 - x}$; assume x is small relative to 0.050

$x^2 = 3.459 \times 10^{-11}$; $x = [OH^-] = 5.881 \times 10^{-6} = 5.9 \times 10^{-6} \, M \, OH^-$

$pOH = 5.23$, $pH = 8.77$

16.111 *Analyze/Plan.* Evaluate the acid-base properties of the cation and anion to determine whether a solution of the salt will be acidic, basic, or neutral. *Solve.*

(i) NH_4NO_3: NH_4^+, weak conjugate acid of NH_3; NO_3^-, negligible conjugate base of HNO_3; acidic solution.

(ii) $NaNO_3$: Na^+, negligible conjugate acid of $NaOH$; NO_3^-, negligible conjugate base of HNO_3; neutral solution.

(iii) CH_3COONH_4: NH_4^+, weak conjugate acid of NH_3, $K_a = K_w/1.8 \times 10^{-5} = 5.6 \times 10^{-10}$; CH_3COO^-, weak conjugate base of CH_3COOH, $K_b = K_w/1.8 \times 10^{-5} = 5.6 \times 10^{-10}$; neutral solution ($K_a$ for the cation and K_b for the anion are accidentally equal, producing a neutral solution).

(iv)   NaF: Na^+, negligible conjugate acid of NaOH; F^-, weak conjugate base of HF, $K_b = K_w/6.8 \times 10^{-4} = 1.5 \times 10^{-11}$; basic solution.

(v) CH_3COONa: Na^+, negligible; CH_3COO^-, weak base, $K_b = 5.6 \times 10^{-10}$, basic solution.

In order of increasing acidity and decreasing pH: 0.1 M CH_3COONa > 0.1 M NaF > 0.1 M CH_3COONH_4 = 0.1 M $NaNO_3$ > 0.1 M NH_4Cl; (v) > (iv) > (iii) ~ (ii) > (i)

(iv) and (v) are both bases, and (v) has the greater K_b value and higher pH. (ii) and (iii) are both neutral and (i) is acidic.

16.112   Call each compound in the neutral form Q.

Then, $Q(aq) + H_2O(l) \rightleftharpoons QH^+(aq) + OH^-$. $K_b = [QH^+][OH^-]/[Q]$

The ratio in question is $[QH^+]/[Q]$, which equals $K_b/[OH^-]$ for each compound. At pH = 2.5, pOH = 11.5, $[OH^-] =$ antilog $(-11.5) = 3.16 \times 10^{-12} = 3 \times 10^{-12}$ M. Now calculate $K_b/[OH^-]$ for each compound:

Nicotine $\dfrac{[QH^+]}{[Q]} = 7 \times 10^{-7}/3.16 \times 10^{-12} = 2 \times 10^5$

Caffeine $\dfrac{[QH^+]}{[Q]} = 4 \times 10^{-14}/3.16 \times 10^{-12} = 1 \times 10^{-2}$

Strychnine $\dfrac{[QH^+]}{[Q]} = 1 \times 10^{-6}/3.16 \times 10^{-12} = 3 \times 10^5$

Quinine $\dfrac{[QH^+]}{[Q]} = 1.1 \times 10^{-6}/3.16 \times 10^{-12} = 3.5 \times 10^5$

For all the compounds except caffeine the protonated form has a much higher concentration than the neutral form. However, for caffeine, a very weak base, the neutral form dominates.

16.113   (a)   Consider the formation of the zwitterion as a series of steps (Hess' law).

$$NH_2-CH_2-COOH + H_2O \rightleftharpoons NH_2-CH_2-COO^- + H_3O^+ \qquad K_a$$

$$NH_2-CH_2-COOH + H_2O \rightleftharpoons {}^+NH_3-CH_2-COOH + OH^- \qquad K_b$$

$$H_3O^+ + OH^- \rightleftharpoons 2H_2O \qquad 1/K_w$$

$$NH_2-CH_2-COOH \rightleftharpoons {}^+NH_3-CH_2-COO^- \qquad \dfrac{K_a \times K_b}{K_w}$$

$$K = \dfrac{K_a \times K_b}{K_w} = \dfrac{(4.3 \times 10^{-3})(6.0 \times 10^{-5})}{1.0 \times 10^{-14}} = 2.6 \times 10^7$$

The large value of K indicates that formation of the zwitterion is favorable. The assumption is that the same NH_2-CH_2-COOH molecule is acting like an acid ($-COOH \rightarrow H^+ + -COO^-$) and a base ($-NH_2 + H^+ \rightarrow NH_3^+$), simultaneously. Glycine is both a stronger acid and a stronger base than water, so the H^+ transfer should be intramolecular, as long as there are no other acids or bases in the solution.

(b)   Since glycine exists as the zwitterion in aqueous solution, the pH is determined by the equilibrium below.

$$^+NH_3-CH_2-COO^- + H_2O \rightleftharpoons NH_2-CH_2-COO^- + H_3O^+$$

$$K_a = \frac{[NH_2-CH_2-COO^-][H_3O^+]}{[^+NH_3-CH_2-COO^-]} = \frac{K_w}{K_b} = \frac{1.0 \times 10^{-14}}{6.0 \times 10^{-5}} = 1.67 \times 10^{-10} = 1.7 \times 10^{-10}$$

$$x = [H_3O^+] = [NH_2-CH_2-COO^-]; \; K_a = 1.67 \times 10^{-10} = \frac{(x)(x)}{(0.050-x)} \approx \frac{x^2}{0.050}$$

$$x = [H_3O^+] = 2.89 \times 10^{-6} = 2.9 \times 10^{-6} \, M; \; pH = 5.54$$

(c)   In a strongly acidic solution the $-CO_2^-$ function would be protonated, so glycine would exist as $^+H_3NCH_2COOH$. In strongly basic solution the $-NH_3^+$ group would be deprotonated, so glycine would be in the form $H_2NCH_2CO_2^-$.

16.114   The general Lewis structures for these acids and their conjugate bases are shown below.

where X = H or Cl.

Replacement of H on the acid by the more electronegative chlorine atoms causes the central carbon to become more positively charged, thus withdrawing more electrons from the attached COOH group, in turn causing the O–H bond to be more polar, so that H^+ is more readily ionized.

For the conjugate base (two resonance structures), the electronegative X atoms delocalize negative charge and stabilize these forms relative to the unsubstituted anions. This favors products in the ionization equilibrium and increases the value of K_a.

To calculate pH proceed as usual, except that the full quadratic formula must be used for all but acetic acid.

Acid	pH
acetic	3.37
chloroacetic	2.51
dichloroacetic	2.09
trichloroacetic	2.0

Integrative Exercises

16.115   At 25°C, $[H^+] = [OH^-] = 1.0 \times 10^{-7} \, M$

$$\frac{1.0 \times 10^{-7} \, mol \, H^+}{1 L \, H_2O} \times 0.0010 \, L \times \frac{6.022 \times 10^{23} \, H^+ \, ions}{mol \, H^+} = 6.0 \times 10^{13} \, H^+ \, ions$$

16.116 *Analyze.* Given mass % and density of concentrated HCl, calculate volume of concentrated solution required to produce 10.0 L of HCl with pH = 2.05. *Plan.* Calculate molarity of concentrated solution from density and mass %. Calculate molarity of dilute solution from pH. Use the dilution formula to calculate volume (mL) concentrated solution required. *Solve.*

$$\frac{1.18 \text{ g conc. soln.}}{\text{mL conc. soln.}} \times \frac{36.0 \text{ g HCl}}{100 \text{ g conc. soln.}} \times \frac{1000 \text{ mL}}{1 \text{ L}} \times \frac{1 \text{ mol HCl}}{36.46 \text{ g HCl}} = 11.651 \text{ mol HCl/L}$$

$$= 11.7 \text{ M HCl/L}$$

For the dilute HCl solution, $[H^+] = 10^{-pH} = 10^{-2.05} = 8.913 \times 10^{-3} = 8.9 \times 10^{-3}$ M HCl

$M_c \times L_c = M_d \times M_d; 11.651 \times L_c = 8.913 \times 10^{-3}$ M × 10.0 L;

$$L_c = 7.650 \times 10^{-3}; 7.650 \times 10^{-3} \text{ L} \times \frac{1000 \text{ mL}}{1 \text{ L}} = 7.65 = 7.7 \text{ mL conc. HCl}$$

16.117 $[H^+] = 10^{-pH} = 10^{-2} = 1 \times 10^{-2}$ M H^+; 1×10^{-2} M × 0.400 L = $4.0 \times 10^{-3} = 4 \times 10^{-3}$ mol H^+

$HCl(aq) + HCO_3^-(aq) \rightarrow Cl^-(aq) + H_2O(l) + CO_2(g)$

$$4 \times 10^{-3} \text{ mol } H^+ = 4 \times 10^{-3} \text{ mol } HCO_3^- \times \frac{84.01 \text{ g NaHCO}_3}{1 \text{ mol } HCO_3^-} = 0.336 = 0.3 \text{ g NaHCO}_3$$

16.118 *Analyze.* If pH were directly related to CO_2 concentration, this exercise would be simple. Unfortunately, we must solve the equilibrium problem for the diprotic acid H_2CO_3 to calculate $[H^+]$ and pH. We are given ppm CO_2 in the atmosphere at two different times, and the pH that corresponds to one of these CO_2 levels. We are asked to find pH at the other atmospheric CO_2 level.

Plan. Assume all dissolved CO_2 is present as H_2CO_3 (aq) (Sample Exercise 16.14).

pH → $[H^+]$ → $[H_2CO_3]$. While H_2CO_3 is a diprotic acid, the two K_a values differ by more than 10^3, so we can ignore the second ionization when calculating $[H_2CO_3]$. Change 380 ppm CO_2 to pressure and calculate the Henry's law constant for CO_2. Calculate the dissolved $[CO_2] = [H_2CO_3]$ at 315 ppm, then solve the K_{a1} expression for $[H^+]$ and pH.

(a) *Solve.* $H_2CO_3(aq) \rightleftharpoons H^+(aq) + HCO_3^-(aq)$

$$K_{a1} = 4.3 \times 10^{-7} = \frac{[H^+][HCO_3^-]}{[H_2CO_3]}; [H^+] = 10^{-5.4} = 3.98 \times 10^{-6} = 4 \times 10^{-6} \text{ M}$$

$[H^+] = [HCO_3^-]; [H_2CO_3] = x - 4 \times 10^{-6}$

$$4.3 \times 10^{-7} = \frac{(3.98 \times 10^{-6})^2}{(x - 3.98 \times 10^{-6})}; 4.3 \times 10^{-7} x = 1.585 \times 10^{-11} + 1.711 \times 10^{-12}$$

$x = 1.756 \times 10^{-11}/4.3 \times 10^{-7} = 4.084 \times 10^{-5} = 4 \times 10^{-5}$ M H_2CO_3

380 ppm = 380 mol $CO_2/1 \times 10^6$ mol air = 0.000380 mol % CO_2

Because of the properties of gases, mol % = pressure %. $P_{CO_2} = 0.000380$ atm. According to Equation [13.4], $S_{CO_2} = kP_{CO_2}$;

4.084×10^{-5} mol/L $= k(3.80 \times 10^{-4}$ atm$)$ $k = 0.1075 = 0.1$ mol/L-atm.

Forty years ago, $S_{CO_2} = 0.1075 \dfrac{\text{mol}}{\text{L-atm}} \times 3.15 \times 10^{-4}$ atm $= 3.385 \times 10^{-5}$

$$= 3 \times 10^{-5}\ M$$

Now solve K_{a1} for $[H^+]$ at this $[H_2CO_3]$. $[H^+] = x$

We cannot assume x is small, because $[H_2CO_3]$ is so low.

$4.3 \times 10^{-7} = x^2/(3.385 \times 10^{-5} - x)$; $x^2 + 4.3 \times 10^{-7}x - 1.456 \times 10^{-11} = 0$

$$x = \frac{-4.3 \times 10^{-7} \pm \sqrt{(4.3 \times 10^{-7})^2 - 4(-1.456 \times 10^{-11})}}{2} = \frac{-4.3 \times 10^{-7} + 7.644 \times 10^{-6}}{2}$$

$$= 3.607 \times 10^{-6} = 4 \times 10^{-6}\ M\ H^+$$

$[H^+] = 4 \times 10^{-6}\ M$, pH $= 5.443 = 5.4$

(Note that, to the precision that the pH data is reported, the change in atmospheric CO_2 leads to no change in pH.)

(b)   From part (a), $[H_2CO_3]$ today $= 4.084 \times 10^{-5}\ M$

$$\frac{4.084 \times 10^{-5}\ \text{mol}\ H_2CO_3}{1\ L} \times 20.0\ L = 8.168 \times 10^{-4} = 8 \times 10^{-4}\ \text{mol}\ CO_2$$

$$V = \frac{nRT}{P} = 8.168 \times 10^{-4}\ \text{mol} \times \frac{298\ K}{1.0\ \text{atm}} \times \frac{0.08206\ \text{L-atm}}{\text{mol-K}} = 0.01997 = 0.02\ L = 20\ mL$$

16.119   (a)   24 valence e^-, 12 e^- pairs

The formal charges on all atoms are zero. Structures with multiple bonds lead to nonzero formal charges. There are three electron domains about Al. The electron-domain geometry and molecular structure are trigonal planar.

(b)   The Al atom in $AlCl_3$ has an incomplete octet and is electron deficient. It "needs" to accept another electron pair, to act like a Lewis acid.

(c)

Both the Al and N atoms in the product have tetrahedral geometry.

(d)   The Lewis theory is most appropriate. H^+ and $AlCl_3$ are both electron pair acceptors, Lewis acids.

16.120   *Plan.* Use acid ionization equilibrium to calculate the total moles of particles in solution. Use density to calculate kg solvent. From the molality (m) of the solution, calculate ΔT_b and T_b. *Solve.*

	HSO_4^- (aq)	$\rightleftharpoons$	H^+ (aq)	+	SO_4^{2-} (aq)
Initial	0.10 M		0		0
equil.	0.10 – x M		x M		x M
	0.071 M		0.029 M		0.029 M

$$K_a = 1.2 \times 10^{-2} = \frac{[H^+][SO_4^{2-}]}{[HSO_4^-]} = \frac{x^2}{0.10-x}; \; K_a \text{ is relatively large, so use the quadratic.}$$

$$x^2 + 0.012\,x - 0.0012 = 0; \; x = \frac{-0.012 \pm \sqrt{(0.012)^2 - 4(1)(-0.0012)}}{2}; \; x = 0.029 \; M \; H^+, SO_4^{2-}$$

Total ion concentration = 0.10 M Na$^+$ + 0.071 M HSO$_4^-$ + 0.029 M H$^+$ + 0.029 M SO$_4^{2-}$

$$= 0.229 = 0.23 \; M.$$

Assume 100.0 mL of solution. 1.002 g/mL × 100.0 mL = 100.2 g solution.

$$0.10 \; M \; NaHSO_4 \times 0.1000 \; L = 0.010 \; mol \; NaHSO_4 \times \frac{120.1 \; g \; NaHSO_4}{mol \; NaHSO_4}$$

$$= 1.201 = 1.2 \; g \; NaHSO_4$$

100.2 g soln – 1.201 g NaHSO$_4$ = 99.0 g = 0.099 kg H$_2$O

$$m = \frac{mol \; ions}{kg \; H_2O} = \frac{0.229 \; M \times 0.1000 \; L}{0.0990 \; kg} = 0.231 = 0.23 \; m \; ions$$

$$\Delta T_b = K_b(m) = 0.52°C/m \times (0.23 \; m) = +0.12°C: T_b = 100.0 + 0.12 = 100.1°C$$

16.121   Rx 1: $\Delta H = D(H-F) + 2D(H-O) - 3D(H-O) = D(H-F) - D(H-O)$

            $\Delta H = 567 \; kJ - 463 \; kJ = 104 \; kJ$

      Rx 2: $\Delta H = D(H-Cl) + 2D(H-O) - 3D(H-O) = D(H-Cl) - D(H-O)$

            $\Delta H = 431 \; kJ - 463 \; kJ = -32 \; kJ$

The reaction involving HCl is exothermic, while the reaction involving HF is endothermic, owing to the smaller bond dissociation enthalpy of H–Cl. HCl is a stronger acid than HF, and the enthalpy of ionization for HCl is exothermic, while that of HF is endothermic. This is consistent with the trend in acid strength for binary acids with heavy atoms (X) in the same family. That is, the longer and weaker the H–X bond, the stronger the acid (and the more exothermic the ionization reaction).

16.122   Calculate M of the solution from osmotic pressure, and K_b using the equilibrium expression for the hydrolysis of cocaine. Let Coc = cocaine and CocH$^+$ be the conjugate acid of cocaine.

$$\Pi = M\,RT; \; M = \Pi/RT = \frac{52.7 \; torr}{288 \; K} \times \frac{1 \; atm}{760 \; torr} \times \frac{mol \cdot K}{0.08206 \; L \cdot atm}$$

$$= 0.002934 = 2.93 \times 10^{-3} \; M \; Coc$$

pH = 8.53; pOH = 14 – pH = 5.47; [OH$^-$] = $10^{-5.47}$ = 3.39 × 10^{-6} = 3.4 × 10^{-6} M

$$\begin{array}{cccccc} & Coc(aq) + H_2O(l) & \rightleftharpoons & CocH^+(aq) & + & OH^-(aq) \end{array}$$

initial $2.93 \times 10^{-3}\,M$ 0   0

equil. $(2.93 \times 10^{-3} - 3.4 \times 10^{-6})\,M$ $3.4 \times 10^{-6}\,M$ $3.4 \times 10^{-6}\,M$

$$K_b = \frac{[CocH^+][OH^-]}{[Coc]} = \frac{(3.39 \times 10^{-6})^2}{(2.934 \times 10^{-3} - 3.39 \times 10^{-6})} = 3.9 \times 10^{-9}$$

Note that % hydrolysis is small in this solution, so "x," $3.4 \times 10^{-6}\,M$, is small compared to $2.93 \times 10^{-3}\,M$ and could be ignored in the denominator of the calculation.

16.123   (a)   rate = $k[IO_3^-][SO_3^{2-}][H^+]$

        (b) $\Delta pH = pH_2 - pH_1 = 3.50 - 5.00 = -1.50$

             $\Delta pH = -\log[H^+]_2 - (-\log[H^+]_1); \; -\Delta pH = \log[H^+]_2 - \log[H^+]_1$

             $-\Delta pH = \log[H^+]_2 / [H^+]_1; \; [H^+]_2 / [H^+]_1 = 10^{-\Delta pH}$

             $[H^+]_2/[H^+]_1 = 10^{1.50} = 31.6 = 32$. The rate will increase by a factor of 32 if $[H^+]$ increases by a factor of 32. The reaction goes faster at lower pH.

        (c)   Since H^+ does not appear in the overall reaction, it is either a catalyst or an intermediate. An intermediate is produced and then consumed during a reaction, so its contribution to the rate law can usually be written in terms of concentrations of other reactants (Sample Exercise 14.15). A catalyst is present at the beginning and end of a reaction and can appear in the rate law if it participates in the rate-determining step (Solution 14.84). This reaction is pH dependent because H^+ is a homogeneous catalyst that participates in the rate-determining step.

16.124   (a)   (i) $HCO_3^-(aq) \rightleftharpoons H^+(aq) + CO_3^{2-}(aq)$ $K_1 = K_{a2}$ for $H_2CO_3 = 5.6 \times 10^{-11}$

                   $H^+(aq) + OH^-(aq) \rightleftharpoons H_2O(l)$ $K_2 = 1/K_w = 1 \times 10^{14}$

                ───────────────────────────────────

                   $HCO_3^-(aq) + OH^-(aq) \rightleftharpoons CO_3^{2-}(aq) + H_2O(l)$ $K = K_1 \times K_2 = 5.6 \times 10^3$

           (ii) $NH_4^+(aq) \rightleftharpoons H^+(aq) + NH_3(aq)$ $K_1 = K_a$ for $NH_4^+ = 5.6 \times 10^{-10}$

                   $CO_3^{2-}(aq) + H^+(aq) \rightleftharpoons HCO_3^-(aq)$ $K_2 = 1/K_{a2}$ for $H_2CO_3 = 1.8 \times 10^{10}$

                ───────────────────────────────────

                   $NH_4^+(aq) + CO_3^{2-}(aq) \rightleftharpoons HCO_3^-(aq) + NH_3(aq)$ $K = K_1 \times K_2 = 10$

        (b)   Both (i) and (ii) have K > 1, although K = 10 is not **much** greater than 1. Both could be written with a single arrow. (This is true in general when a strong acid or strong base, $H^+(aq)$ or $OH^-(aq)$, is a reactant.)

17 Additional Aspects of Aqueous Equilibria

Visualizing Concepts

17.1 *Analyze*. Given diagrams showing equilibrium mixtures of HX and X⁻ with different compositions, decide which has the highest pH. HX is a weak acid and X⁻ is its conjugate base. *Plan*. Evaluate the contents of the boxes. Use acid-base equilibrium principles to relate $[H^+]$ to box composition. *Solve*.

Use the following acid ionization equilibrium to describe the mixtures:
$HX(aq) \rightleftharpoons H^+(aq) + X^-(aq)$. Each box has 4 HX molecules, but differing amounts of X⁻ ions. The greater the amount of X⁻ (conjugate base), for the same amount of HX (weak acid), the lower the amount of H^+ and the higher the pH. The middle box, with most X⁻, has least H^+ and highest pH.

17.2 (a) According to Figure 16.7, methyl orange is yellow above pH 4.5 and red (really pink) below pH 3.5. The beaker on the left has a pH greater than 4.5, and the one on the right has pH less than 3.5. (By calculation, pH of left beaker = 4.7, pH of right beaker = 2.9.) The right beaker, with lower pH and greater $[H^+]$, is pure acetic acid. The left beaker contains equal amounts of the weak acid and its conjugate base, acetic acid and acetate ion. Adding the "common-ion" acetate (in the form of sodium acetate) shifts the acid ionization equilibrium to the left, decreases $[H^+]$, and raises pH.

(b) When small amounts of NaOH are added, the left beaker is better able to maintain its pH. For solutions of the same weak acid, pH depends on the **ratio** of conjugate base to conjugate acid. Small additions of base (or acid) have the least effect when this ratio is close to one. The left beaker is a buffer because it contains a weak conjugate acid-conjugate base pair and resists rapid pH change upon addition of small amounts of strong base or acid.

17.3 $[HX] > [X^-]$. Buffers prepared from weak acids (HX) and their conjugate bases (X⁻, usually in the form of a salt) have pH values in a range of approximately 2 pH units, centered around pK_a for the weak acid. If concentration of the weak acid is greater than concentration of the conjugate base, pH < pK_a. If concentration of the conjugate base is greater than concentration of the weak acid, pH > pK_a. This is generally true for buffers containing a weak conjugate acid (CA) and conjugate base (CB) pair.

[CA] > [CB], pH of buffer < pK_a of CA

[CA] < [CB], pH of buffer > pK_a of CA

17.4   *Analyze/Plan.* When strong acid is added to a buffer, it reacts with conjugate base (CB) to produce conjugate acid (CA). [CA] increases and [CB] decreases. The opposite happens when strong base is added to a buffer, [CB] increases and [CA] decreases. Match these situations to the drawings.   *Solve.*

The buffer begins with equal concentrations of HX and X^-.

(a)   After addition of strong acid, [HX] will increase and $[X^-]$ will decrease. Drawing (3) fits this description.

(b)   Adding of strong base causes [HX] to decrease and $[X^-]$ to increase. Drawing (1) matches the description.

(c)   Drawing (2) shows both [HX] and $[X^-]$ to be smaller than the initial concentrations shown on the left. This situation cannot be achieved by adding strong acid or strong base to the original buffer.

17.5   *Analyze/Plan.* Consider the reaction $HA + OH^- \rightarrow A^- + H_2O$. What are the major species present in solution at the listed stages of the titration? Which diagram represents these species?   *Solve.*

(a)   *Before addition of NaOH*, the solution is mostly HA. The only A^- is produced by the ionization equilibrium of HA and is too small to appear in the diagram. This situation is shown in diagram (iii), which contains only HA.

(b)   *After addition of NaOH but before the equivalence point*, some, but not all, HA has been converted to A^-. The solution contains a mixture of HA and A^-; this is shown in diagram (i).

(c)   *At the equivalence point*, all HA has been converted to A^-, with no excess HA or OH^- present. This is shown in diagram (iv).

(d)   *After the equivalence point*, the same amount of A^- is present as at the equivalence point, plus some excess OH^-. This is diagram (ii).

17.6   *Analyze/Plan.* In each case, the first substance is in the buret, and the second is in the flask. If acid is in the flask, the initial pH is low; with base in the flask, the pH starts high. Strong acids have lower pH than weak acids; strong bases have higher pH than weak bases. Polyprotic acids and bases have more than one "jump" in pH.

(a)   Strong base in flask, pH starts high, ends low as acid is added. Only diagram (ii) fits this description.

(b)   Weak acid in flask, pH starts low, but not extremely low. Diagrams (i), (iii), and (iv) all start at low pH and get higher. Diagram (i) has very low initial pH, and likely has strong acid in the flask. Diagram (iv) has two pH jumps, so it has a polyprotic acid in the flask. Diagram (iii) best fits the profile of adding a strong base to a weak acid.

(c)   Strong acid in the flask, pH starts very low, diagram (i).

(d)   Polyprotic acid, more than one pH jump, diagram (iv).

17.7   *Analyze.* Given two titration curves where 0.10 M NaOH is the titrant, decide which represents the more concentrated acid, and which the stronger acid.

Plan. For equal volumes of acid, concentration is related to volume of titrant (0.10 M NaOH) at the equivalence points. To determine K_a, pH = pK_a half-way to the equivalence point.

Solve.

(a)   Both acids have one ionizable hydrogen, because there is one "jump" in each titration curve. For equal volumes of acid, and the same titrant, the more concentrated acid requires a greater volume of titrant to reach equivalence. The equivalence point of the blue curve is at 25 mL NaOH, the red curve at 35 mL NaOH. The red acid is more concentrated.

(b)   According to the Henderson-Hasselbach equation, pH = $pK_a + \log \dfrac{[\text{conj. base}]}{[\text{conj. acid}]}$.

At half-way to the equivalence point, [conj. acid] = [conj. base] and pH = pK_a of the conjugate acid. For the blue curve, half-way is 12.5 mL NaOH. The pH at this volume is approximately 7.0. For the red curve, half-way is 17.5 mL NaOH. The pH at this volume is approximately 4.2. A pK_a of 7 corresponds to K_a of 1×10^{-7}, while pK_a of 4.2 corresponds to K_a of 6×10^{-5}. The red acid has the larger K_a value.

Note that the stronger acid, the one with the larger K_a value, has a larger change in pH (jump) at the equivalence point. Also note that initial acid pH was not a definitive measure of acid strength, because the acids have different starting concentrations. Both K_a values and concentration contribute to solution pH.

17.8   *Analyze/Plan.* The beaker of saturated $Cd(OH)_2(aq)$ contains undissolved $Cd(OH)_2(s)$, $Cd^{2+}(aq)$, and $OH^-(aq)$. Decide how amounts of each of these three components change when HCl(aq) is added. *Solve.*

When HCl(aq) is added, it reacts with $OH^-(aq)$ to form $H_2O(l)$ and $Cl^-(aq)$. (Both have been omitted from the figure.) When $OH^-(aq)$ is removed from solution, more $Cd(OH)_2(s)$ dissolves to replace it; $[Cd^{2+}(aq)]$ increases, $[OH^-(aq)]$ decreases and the amount of undissolved $Cd(OH)_2(s)$ decreases. In the resulting solution, $[Cd^{2+}(aq)]$ is greater than $[OH^-(aq)]$ and there is less undissolved solid on the bottom of the beaker. Beaker A accurately represents the solution after equilibrium is reestablished.

17.9   *Analyze/Plan.* Common anions or cations decrease the solubility of salts. Ions that participate in acid-base or complex ion equilibria increase solubility.   *Solve.*

(a) $CO_2{}^{3-}$ from $BaCO_3$ reacts with H^+ from HNO_3, causing solubility of $BaCO_3$ to increase with increasing HNO_3 concentration. This behavior matches the right diagram.

(b)   Extra $CO_2{}^{3-}$ from Na_2CO_3 decreases the solubility of $BaCO_3$. Solubility of $BaCO_3$ decreases as $[Na_2CO_3]$ increases. This behavior matches the left diagram.

(c) $NaNO_3$ has no common ions, nor does it enter into acid-base or complex ion equilibria with Ba^{2+} or CO_3^{2-}; it does not affect the solubility of $BaCO_3$. This behavior is shown in the center diagram.

17.10   *Analyze/Plan.* Calculate the molarity of the solution assuming all $Ca(OH)_2(s)$ dissolves. Use this concentration along with the K_{sp} expression for $Ca(OH)_2$ to answer the questions.

(a) $$[Ca(OH)_2] = \frac{0.370 \text{ g Ca(OH)}_2}{0.500 \text{ L soln}} \times \frac{1 \text{ mol Ca(OH)}_2}{74.093 \text{ g Ca(OH)}_2} = 0.00998745 = 0.00999 \text{ } M$$

$[Ca^{2+}] = 0.00999 \text{ } M; [OH^-] = 2(0.00998745) = 0.0199749 = 0.0200 \text{ } M;$

$K_{sp} = [Ca^{2+}][OH^-]^2$. Calculate the reaction quotient using the calculated molarities. If it is equal to or greater than K_{sp}, the resulting solution is saturated.

$Q = (0.0098745)(0.0199749)^2 = 3.99 \times 10^{-6}$.

$Q < K_{sp}$ (6.5×10^{-6}) and the solution is not saturated.

(b)   Consider the beakers individually.

(i)   The 50 mL of 1.0 M HCl is more than enough to neutralize 50 mL of 0.0200 M OH^-(aq). No precipitate forms.

(ii)   NaCl does not react with $Ca(OH)_2$ and the two compounds contain no common ions. No precipitate forms.

(iii) $CaCl_2$ does contain a common ion. Calculate Q for the resulting solution to see if $Ca(OH)_2$ precipitates. $[OH^-]$ in the new solution is 0.00999 M, because it is diluted by a factor of 2. $[Ca^{2+}] = (1.0 + 0.00999)/2 = 0.5050 \text{ } M$.

$Q = (0.5050)(0.00999)^2 = 5.04 \times 10^{-5}$.

$Q > K_{sp}$ (6.5×10^{-6}) and $Ca(OH)_2$ precipitates.

(iv)   A common ion with a different concentration; $[Ca^{2+}] = (0.10 + 0.00999)/2 = 0.0550 = 0.055 \text{ } M$. $Q = (0.0550)(0.0999)^2 = 5.49 \times 10^{-6}$. $Q \approx K_{sp}$ (6.5×10^{-6}); the solution is very nearly saturated, but no precipitate forms.

17.11   A metal hydroxide that is soluble at very low and very high pH's, that is, in strong acid or strong base, is called amphoteric.

17.12   According to Figure 17.23, the two precipitating agents are 6 M HCl (first) and H_2S in 0.2 M HCl (second).

Cation A = Ag^+ (precipitates as AgCl)

Cation B = Cu^+ (precipitates as CuS, acid insoluble)

Cation C = Ni^{2+} (remains in acidic solution)

Common-Ion Effect (section 17.1)

17.13   (a)   The extent of ionization of a weak electrolyte is decreased when a strong electrolyte containing an ion in common with the weak electrolyte is added to it.

(b) $NaNO_2$

17.14 (a) For a generic weak base B, $K_b = \dfrac{[HB^+][OH^-]}{[B]}$. If an external source of HB^+ such

as HB^+Cl^- is added to a solution of B(aq), $[HB^+]$ increases, decreasing $[OH^-]$ and increasing [B], effectively suppressing the ionization (hydrolysis) of B.

(b) NH_4Cl

17.15 *Analyze/Plan.* Follow the logic in Sample Exercise 17.1.

(a)

	$C_2H_5COOH(aq)$	$\rightleftharpoons$	$H^+(aq)$	+	$C_2H_5COO^-(aq)$
i	0.085 M				0.060 M
c	$-x$		$+x$		$+x$
e	(0.085 – x) M		$+x$ M		(0.060 + x) M

$$K_a = 1.3 \times 10^{-5} = \frac{[H^+][C_2H_5COO^-]}{[C_2H_5COOH]} = \frac{(x)(0.060+x)}{(0.085-x)}$$

Assume x is small compared to 0.060 and 0.085.

$$1.3 \times 10^{-5} = \frac{0.060\,x}{0.085}; x = 1.8 \times 10^{-5} = [H^+], pH = 4.73$$

Check. Since the extent of ionization of a weak acid or base is suppressed by the presence of a conjugate salt, the 5% rule usually holds true in buffer solutions.

(b)

	$(CH_3)_3N(aq) + H_2O(l)$	$\rightleftharpoons$	$(CH_3)_3NH^+(aq)$	+	$OH^-(aq)$
i	0.075 M		0.10 M		
c	$-x$		$+x$		$+x$
e	(0.075 – x) M		(0.10 + x) M		$+x$ M

$$K_b = 6.4 \times 10^{-5} = \frac{[OH^-][(CH_3)_3NH^+]}{[(CH_3)_3N]} = \frac{(x)(0.10+x)}{(0.075-x)} \approx \frac{0.10\,x}{0.075}$$

$x = 4.8 \times 10^{-5} = [OH^-], pOH = 4.32, pH = 14.00 - 4.32 = 9.68$

Check. In a buffer, if [conj. acid] > [conj. base], pH < pK_a of the conj. acid. If [conj. acid] < [conj. base], pH > pK_a of the conj. acid. In this buffer, pK_a of $(CH_3)_3NH^+$ is 9.81. $[(CH_3)_3NH^+] > [(CH_3)_3N]$ and pH = 9.68, less than 9.81.

(c) mol = $M \times$ L; mol $CH_3COOH = 0.15\,M \times 0.0500$ L $= 7.5 \times 10^{-3}$ mol

mol $CH_3COO^- = 0.20\,M \times 0.0500$ L $= 0.010$ mol

	$CH_3COOH(aq)$	$\rightleftharpoons$	$H^+(aq)$	+	$CH_3COO^-(aq)$
i	7.5×10^{-3} mol		0		0.010 mol
c	$-x$		$+x$		$+x$
e	$(7.5 \times 10^{-3} - x)$ mol		$+x$ mol		(0.010 + x) mol

$[CH_3COOH(aq)] = (7.5 \times 10^{-3} - x)$ mol/0.1000 L;

$[CH_3COO^-(aq)] = (0.010 + x)$ mol/0.1000 L

$$K_a = 1.8 \times 10^{-5} = \frac{[H^+][CH_3COO^-]}{[CH_3COOH]} = \frac{(x)\,(0.010+x)/0.1000\,L}{(0.0075-x)/0.1000\,L} \approx \frac{x(0.010)}{0.0075}$$

$x = 1.35 \times 10^{-5}\,M = 1.4 \times 10^{-5}\,M\,H^+; pH = 4.87$

Check. pK_a for $CH_3COOH = 4.74$. $[CH_3COO^-] > [CH_3COOH]$, pH of buffer = 4.87, greater than 4.74.

17.16   *Analyze/Plan.* Follow the logic in Sample Exercise 17.1.   *Solve.*

(a)   HCOOH is a weak acid, and HCOONa contains the common ion $HCOO^-$, the conjugate base of HCOOH. Solve the common-ion equilibrium problem.

	HCOOH(aq)	⇌	H⁺(aq)	+	HCOO⁻(aq)
i	0.100 M				0.250 M
c	–x		+x		+x
e	(0.100 – x) M		+x M		(0.250 + x) M

$$K_a = 1.8 \times 10^{-4} = \frac{[H^+][HCOO^-]}{[HCOOH]} = \frac{(x)\,(0.250+x)}{(0.100-x)} \approx \frac{0.250\,x}{0.100}$$

$x = 7.20 \times 10^{-5} = 7.2 \times 10^{-5}\,M = [H^+], pH = 4.14$

Check. Since the extent of ionization of a weak acid or base is suppressed by the presence of a conjugate salt, the 5% rule usually holds true in buffer solutions.

(b) C_5H_5N is a weak base, and C_5H_5NHCl contains the common ion $C_5H_5NH^+$, which is the conjugate acid of C_5H_5N. Solve the common ion equilibrium problem.

	C₅H₅N(aq) + H₂O(l)	⇌	C₅H₅NH⁺(aq)	+	OH⁻(aq)
i	0.510 M		0.450 M		
c	–x		+x		+x
e	(0.510 – x) M		(0.450 + x) M		+x M

$$K_b = 1.7 \times 10^{-9} = \frac{[C_5H_5NH^+][OH^-]}{[C_5H_5N]} = \frac{(0.450 + x)\,(x)}{(0.510-x)} \approx \frac{0.450\,x}{0.510}$$

$x = 1.927 \times 10^{-9} = 1.9 \times 10^{-9}\,M = [OH^-], pOH = 8.715, pH = 14.00 - 8.715 = 5.29$

Check. In a buffer, if [conj. acid] > [conj. base], pH < pK_a of the conj. acid. If [conj. acid] < [conj. base], pH > pK_a of the conj. acid. In this buffer, pK_a of $C_5H_5NH^+$ is 5.23. $[C_5H_5NH^+] < [C_5H_5N]$ and pH = 5.29, greater than 5.23.

(c)   mol = $M \times L$; mol HF = 0.050 $M \times 0.055$ L = 2.75 $\times 10^{-3} = 2.8 \times 10^{-3}$ mol;
mol $F^- = 0.10\,M \times 0.125$ L = 0.0125 = 0.013 mol

	HF(aq)	$\rightleftharpoons$	H^+(aq)	+	F^-(aq)
i	2.75×10^{-3} mol		0		0.0125 mol
c	$-x$		$+x$		$+x$
e	$(2.75 \times 10^{-3} - x)$ mol		$+x$		$(0.0125 + x)$ mol

$[HF] = (2.75 \times 10^{-3} + x)/0.180$ L; $[F^-] = (0.0125 + x)/0.180$ L
Note that the volumes will cancel when substituted into the K_a expression.

$$K_a = 6.8 \times 10^{-4} = \frac{[H^+][F^-]}{[HF]} = \frac{x(0.0125+x)/0.180}{(2.75 \times 10^{-3}-x)/0.180} \approx \frac{x(0.0125)}{0.00275}$$

$x = 1.50 \times 10^{-4} = 1.5 \times 10^{-4}$ M H^+; pH = 3.83

Check. pK_a for HF = 3.17. [HF] < [F^-], pH of buffer = 3.83, greater than 3.17.

17.17   *Analyze/Plan.* We are asked to calculate % ionization of (a) a weak acid and (b) a weak acid in a solution containing a common ion, its conjugate base. Calculate % ionization as in Sample Exercise 16.13. In part (b), the concentration of the common ion is 0.085 M, not x, as in part (a).   *Solve.*

$$buCOOH(aq) \rightleftharpoons H^+ (aq) + buCOO^- (aq) \quad K_a = \frac{[H^+][buCOO^-]}{[buCOOH]} = 1.5 \times 10^{-5}$$

equil (a)   0.0075 – x M x M x M
equil (b)   0.0075 – x M x M $0.085 + x$ M

(a) $K_a = 1.5 \times 10^{-5} = \dfrac{x^2}{0.0075-x} \approx \dfrac{x^2}{0.0075}$; $x = [H^+] = 3.354 \times 10^{-4} = 3.4 \times 10^{-4}$ M H^+

$$\% \text{ ionization} = \frac{3.4 \times 10^{-4} \, M \, H^+}{0.0075 \, M \, buCOOH} \times 100 = 4.5\% \text{ ionization}$$

(b) $K_a = 1.5 \times 10^{-5} = \dfrac{(x)(0.085+x)}{0.0075-x} \approx \dfrac{0.085 \, x}{0.0075}$; $x = 1.3 \times 10^{-6}$ M H^+

$$\% \text{ ionization} = \frac{1.3 \times 10^{-6} \, M \, H^+}{0.0075 \, M \, buCOOH} \times 100 = 0.018\% \text{ ionization}$$

Check. Percent ionization is much smaller when the "common ion" is present.

17.18 $CH_3CH(OH)COOH \rightleftharpoons H^+ (aq) + CH_3CH(OH)COO^-$

equil (a)   0.125 – x M x M x M
equil (b)   0.125 – x M x M $0.0075 + x$ M

$$K_a = \frac{[H^+][CH_3CH(OH)COO^-]}{[CH_3CH(OH)COOH]} = 1.4 \times 10^{-4}$$

(a) $K_a = 1.4 \times 10^{-4} = \dfrac{x^2}{0.125-x} \approx \dfrac{x^2}{0.125}$; $x = [H^+] = 4.18 \times 10^{-3}$ M = 4.2×10^{-3} M H^+

$$\% \text{ ionization} = \frac{4.2 \times 10^{-3} \, M \, H^+}{0.125 \, M \, CH_3CH(OH)COOH} \times 100 = 3.4\% \text{ ionization}$$

(b) $K_a = 1.4 \times 10^{-4} = \dfrac{(x)(0.0075+x)}{0.125-x} \approx \dfrac{0.0075\,x}{0.125}; x = 2.3 \times 10^{-3} \, M \, H^+$

% ionization $= \dfrac{2.3 \times 10^{-3} \, M \, H^+}{0.125 \, M \, CH_3CH(OH)COOH} \times 100 = 1.9\%$ ionization

Buffered Solutions (section 17.2)

17.19 CH_3COOH and CH_3COONa are a weak conjugate acid/conjugate base pair which acts as a buffer because unionized CH_3COOH reacts with added base, while CH_3COO^- combines with added acid, leaving $[H^+]$ relatively unchanged. Although HCl and NaCl are a conjugate acid/conjugate base pair, Cl^- is a negligible base. That is, it has no tendency to combine with added acid to form molecular HCl. Any added acid simply increases $[H^+]$ in an HCl/NaCl mixture. In general, the conjugate bases of strong acids are negligible and mixtures of strong acids and their conjugate salts do not act as buffers.

17.20   NaOH is a strong base and will react with CH_3COOH to form CH_3COONa. As long as CH_3COOH is present in excess, the resulting solution will contain both the conjugate acid $CH_3COOH(aq)$ and the conjugate base $CH_3COO^-(aq)$, the requirements for a buffer.

mmol $= M \times$ mL; mmol $CH_3COOH = 1.00 \, M \times 100$ mL $= 10.0$ mmol

mmol NaOH $= 0.100 \, M \times 50$ mL $= 5.0$ mmol

	CH_3COOH (aq)	+	NaOH(aq)	$\rightarrow$	CH_3COONa (aq)	+ $H_2O(l)$
initial	10.0 mmol		5.0 mmol			
after rx	5.0 mmol		0		5.0 mmol	

Mixing these two solutions has created a buffer by partial neutralization of the weak acid CH_3COOH.

17.21   *Analyze/Plan.* Follow the logic in Sample Exercise 17.3. Assume that % ionization is small in these buffers (Solutions 17.17 and 17.18).   *Solve.*

(a) $K_a = \dfrac{[H^+][CH_3CH(OH)COO^-]}{[CH_3CH(OH)COOH]}$; $[H^+] = \dfrac{[K_a][CH_3CH(OH)COOH]}{[CH_3CH(OH)COO^-]}$

$[H^+] = \dfrac{1.4 \times 10^{-4}\,(0.12)}{(0.11)}$; $[H^+] = 1.53 \times 10^{-4} = 1.5 \times 10^{-4}\,M$; pH $= 3.82$

(b)   mol $= M \times$ L; total volume $= 85$ mL $+ 95$ mL $= 180$ mL

$[H^+] = \dfrac{K_a[CH_3CH(OH)COOH]}{[CH_3CH(OH)COO^-]} = \dfrac{1.4 \times 10^{-4}\,(0.13\,M \times 0.085\,L)/0.180\,L}{(0.15\,M \times 0.095\,L)/0.180\,L}$

$[H^+] = \dfrac{1.4 \times 10^{-4}\,(0.13 \times 0.085)}{(0.15 \times 0.095)}$; $[H^+] = 1.086 \times 10^{-4} = 1.1 \times 10^{-4}\,M$; pH $= 3.96$

17.22 Assume that % ionization is small in these buffers (Solutions 17.17 and 17.18).

(a) The conjugate acid in this buffer is HCO_3^-, so use K_{a2} for H_2CO_3, 5.6×10^{-11}

$$K_a = \frac{[H^+][CO_3^{2-}]}{[HCO_3^-]}; [H^+] = \frac{K_a[HCO_3^-]}{[CO_3^{2-}]} = \frac{5.6 \times 10^{-11}(0.105)}{(0.125)}$$

$[H^+] = 4.70 \times 10^{-11} = 4.7 \times 10^{-11} M; pH = 10.33$

(b) mol = $M \times$ L; total volume = 140 mL = 0.140 L

$$[H^+] = \frac{K_a(0.20\,M \times 0.065\,L)/0.140\,L}{(0.15\,M \times 0.075\,L)/0.140\,L} = \frac{5.6 \times 10^{-11}(0.20 \times 0.065)}{(0.15 \times 0.075)}$$

$[H^+] = 6.47 \times 10^{-11} = 6.5 \times 10^{-11} M; pH = 10.19$

17.23 (a) *Analyze/Plan.* Follow the logic in Sample Exercises 17.1 and 17.3. As in Sample Exercise 17.1, start by calculating concentrations of the components. *Solve.*

$$CH_3COOH(aq) \rightleftharpoons H^+(aq) + CH_3COO^-(aq); K_a = 1.8 \times 10^{-5} = \frac{[H^+][CH_3COO^-]}{[CH_3COOH]}$$

$[CH_3COOH] = 0.150\,M$

$$[CH_3COO^-] = \frac{20.0\,g\,CH_3COONa}{0.500\,L\,soln} \times \frac{1\,mol\,CH_3COONa}{82.04\,g\,CH_3COONa} = 0.488\,M$$

$$[H^+] = \frac{K_a[CH_3COOH]}{[CH_3COO^-]} = \frac{1.8 \times 10^{-5}(0.150-x)}{(0.488+x)} \approx \frac{1.8 \times 10^{-5}(0.150)}{(0.488)}$$

$[H^+] = 5.533 \times 10^{-6} = 5.5 \times 10^{-6} M, pH = 5.26$

(b) *Plan.* On the left side of the equation, write all ions present in solution after HCl or NaOH is added to the buffer. Using acid-base properties and relative strengths, decide which ions will combine to form new products. *Solve.*

$$Na^+(aq) + CH_3COO^-(aq) + H^+(aq) + Cl^-(aq) \rightarrow CH_3COOH(aq) + Na^+(aq) + Cl^-(aq)$$

(c) $CH_3COOH(aq) + Na^+(aq) + OH^-(aq) \rightarrow CH_3COO^-(aq) + H_2O(l) + Na^+(aq)$

17.24 NH_4^+/NH_3 is a basic buffer. Either the hydrolysis of NH_3 or the dissociation of NH_4^+ can be used to determine the pH of the buffer. Using the dissociation of NH_4^+ leads directly to $[H^+]$ and facilitates use of the Henderson-Hasselbach relationship.

(a) $NH_4^+(aq) \rightleftharpoons H^+(aq) + NH_3(aq)$

$$K_a = \frac{K_w}{K_b} = \frac{1.0 \times 10^{-14}}{1.8 \times 10^{-5}} = 5.56 \times 10^{-10} = 5.6 \times 10^{-10}$$

$[NH_3] = 1.00\,M\,NH_3$

$$[NH_4^+] = \frac{10.0\,g\,NH_4Cl}{0.250\,L} \times \frac{1\,mol\,NH_4Cl}{53.50\,g\,NH_4Cl} = 0.74766 = 0.748\,M\,NH_4^+$$

$$K_a = \frac{[H^+][NH_3]}{[NH_4^+]}; [H^+] = \frac{K_a[NH_4^+]}{[NH_3]} = \frac{5.56 \times 10^{-10}\,(0.74766 - x)}{(1.00 + x)} \approx \frac{5.56 \times 10^{-10}\,(0.74766)}{(1.00)}$$

$$[H^+] = 4.1537 \times 10^{-10} = 4.15 \times 10^{-10}\,M, \text{ pH} = 9.382$$

(b) $NH_3(aq) + H^+(aq) + NO_3^-(aq) \rightarrow NH_4^+(aq) + NO_3^-(aq)$

(c) $NH_4^+(aq) + Cl^-(aq) + K^+(aq) + OH^-(aq) \rightarrow NH_3(aq) + H_2O(l) + Cl^-(aq) + K^+(aq)$

17.25   *Analyze/Plan.* Follow the logic in Sample Exercise 16.12 and 17.4.   *Solve.*

(a) $K_a = 6.8 \times 10^{-4} = \dfrac{x^2}{1.00 - x} = \dfrac{x^2}{1.00}; \quad x = [H^+] = 0.02608 = 0.026\,M; \quad \text{pH} = 1.58$

There is 2.6% ionization, so the approximation is valid.

(b)   In this problem, $[F^-]$ is the unknown.

pH = 3.00, $[H^+] = 10^{-3.00} = 1.0 \times 10^{-3}$; $[HF] = 1.00 - 0.0010 = 0.999\,M$

$$K_a = 6.8 \times 10^{-4} = \frac{1.0 \times 10^{-3}\,[F^-]}{0.999}; [F^-] = 0.6793 = 0.68\,M$$

$$\frac{0.6793\,\text{mol NaF}}{1\,L} \times \frac{41.990\,\text{g NaF}}{1\,\text{mol NaF}} \times 1.25\,L = 35.654 = 36\,\text{g NaF}$$

17.26   (a) $C_6H_5COOH(aq) \rightleftharpoons H^+(aq) + C_6H_5COO^-(aq)$

$$K_a = 6.3 \times 10^{-5} = \frac{[H^+][C_6H_5COO^-]}{[C_6H_5COOH]}; [C_6H_5COOH] = 0.0200\,M;$$

$$[H^+] = [C_6H_5COO^-] = x$$

$$K_a = 6.3 \times 10^{-5} \approx \frac{x^2}{0.02000}; \quad x = [H^+] = 1.123 \times 10^{-3} = 1.1 \times 10^{-3}\,M; \quad \text{pH} = 2.95$$

Note that C_6H_5COOH is 5.6% ionized. Solving the quadratic for $[H^+]$ yields $(1.0914 \times 10^{-3} =) 1.1 \times 10^{-3}\,M\,H^+$, pH = 2.96; this is not a significant difference.

(b) $[H^+] = \dfrac{K_a[C_6H_5COOH]}{[C_6H_5COO^-]}; \quad [H^+] = 10^{-4.00} = 1.0 \times 10^{-4}\,M$

$[C_6H_5COOH] = 0.0200\,M$; calculate $[C_6H_5COO^-]$. Because the common ion $C_6H_5COO^-$ reduces % ionization, we assume the 5% approximation is valid.

$$[C_6H_5COO^-] = \frac{K_a[C_6H_5COOH]}{[H^+]} = \frac{6.3 \times 10^{-5}\,(0.0200)}{1.0 \times 10^{-4}} = 0.01260 = 0.013\,M$$

$$\frac{0.0126\,\text{mol C}_6H_5COONa}{L} \times 1.50\,L \times \frac{144.11\,\text{g C}_6H_5COONa}{1\,\text{mol C}_6H_5COONa}$$

$$= 2.724 = 2.7\,\text{g C}_6H_5COONa$$

17.27   *Analyze/Plan.* Follow the logic in Sample Exercise 17.3 and 17.5.   *Solve.*

(a) $K_a = \dfrac{[H^+][CH_3COO^-]}{[CH_3COOH]}; [H^+] = \dfrac{K_a[CH_3COOH]}{[CH_3COO^-]}$

$$[H^+] \approx \frac{1.8 \times 10^{-5}\,(0.10)}{(0.13)} = 1.385 \times 10^{-5} = 1.4 \times 10^{-5}\ M;\ pH = 4.86$$

(b) $CH_3COOH(aq)$ + $KOH(aq)$ → $CH_3COO^-(aq) + H_2O(l) + K^+(aq)$

0.10 mol	0.02 mol	0.13 mol
−0.02 mol	−0.02 mol	+0.02 mol
0.08 mol	0 mol	0.15 mol

$$[H^+] = \frac{1.8 \times 10^{-5}\,(0.08\ \text{mol}/1.00\ \text{L})}{(0.15\ \text{mol}/1.00\ \text{L})} = 9.60 \times 10^{-6} = 1 \times 10^{-5}\ M;\ pH = 5.02 = 5.0$$

(c) $CH_3COO^-(aq)$ + $HNO_3(aq)$ → $CH_3COOH(aq) + NO_3^-(aq)$

0.13 mol	0.02 mol	0.10 mol
−0.02 mol	−0.02 mol	+0.02 mol
0.11 mol	0 mol	0.12 mol

$$[H^+] = \frac{1.8 \times 10^{-5}\,(0.12\ \text{mol}/1.00\ \text{L})}{(0.11\ \text{mol}/1.00\ \text{L})} = 1.96 \times 10^{-5} = 2.0 \times 10^{-5}\ M;\ pH = 4.71$$

17.28 (a) $K_a = \dfrac{[H^+][C_2H_5COO^-]}{[C_2H_5COOH]};\ [H^+] = \dfrac{K_a[C_2H_5COOH]}{[C_2H_5COO^-]}$

Since this expression contains a ratio of concentrations, we can ignore total volume and work directly with moles.

$$[H^+] = \frac{1.3 \times 10^{-5}\,(0.15 - x)}{(0.10 + x)} \approx \frac{1.3 \times 10^{-5}\,(0.15)}{0.10} = 1.950 \times 10^{-5} = 2.0 \times 10^{-5}\ M,\ pH = 4.71$$

(b) $C_2H_5COOH(aq)$ + $OH^-(aq)$ → $C_2H_5COO^-(aq) + H_2O(l)$

0.15 mol	0.01 mol	0.10 mol
−0.01 mol	−0.01 mol	+0.01 mol
0.14 mol	0 mol	0.11 mol

$$[H^+] \approx \frac{1.3 \times 10^{-5}\,(0.14)}{(0.11)} = 1.6545 \times 10^{-5} = 1.7 \times 10^{-5}\ M;\ pH = 4.78$$

(c) $C_2H_5COO^-(aq)$ + $HI(aq)$ → $C_2H_5COOH(aq) + I^-(aq)$

0.10 mol	0.01 mol	0.15 mol
−0.01 mol	−0.01 mol	+0.01 mol
0.09 mol	0 mol	0.16 mol

$$[H^+] \approx \frac{1.3 \times 10^{-5}\,(0.16)}{(0.09)} = 2.3111 \times 10^{-5} = 2 \times 10^{-5}\ M;\ pH = 4.6$$

17.29 *Analyze/Plan.* Calculate the [conj. base]/[conj. acid] ratio in the H_2CO_3/HCO_3^- blood buffer. Write the acid dissociation equilibrium and K_a expression. Find K_a for H_2CO_3 in Appendix D. Calculate $[H^+]$ from the pH and solve for the ratio. *Solve.*

$$H_2CO_3(aq) \rightleftharpoons H^+(aq) + HCO_3^-(aq) \quad K_a = \frac{[H^+][HCO_3^-]}{[H_2CO_3]}; \frac{[HCO_3^-]}{[H_2CO_3]} = \frac{K_a}{[H^+]}$$

(a) at pH = 7.4, $[H^+] = 10^{-7.4} = 4.0 \times 10^{-8}$ M; $\dfrac{[HCO_3^-]}{[H_2CO_3]} = \dfrac{4.3 \times 10^{-7}}{4.0 \times 10^{-8}} = 11$

(b) at pH = 7.1, $[H^+] = 7.9 \times 10^{-8}$ M; $\dfrac{[HCO_3^-]}{[H_2CO_3]} = 5.4$

17.30 $\dfrac{6.5 \text{ g NaH}_2\text{PO}_4}{0.355 \text{ L soln}} \times \dfrac{1 \text{ mol NaH}_2\text{PO}_4}{120 \text{ g NaH}_2\text{PO}_4} = 0.153 = 0.15$ M

$\dfrac{8.0 \text{ g Na}_2\text{HPO}_4}{0.355 \text{ L soln}} \times \dfrac{1 \text{ mol Na}_2\text{HPO}_4}{142 \text{ g Na}_2\text{HPO}_4} = 0.159 = 0.16$ M

Use Equation [17.9] to find the pH of the buffer. K_a for $H_2PO_4^-$ is K_{a2} for H_3PO_4, 6.2×10^{-8}

$$pH = -\log(6.2 \times 10^{-8}) + \log\frac{0.159}{0.153} = 7.2076 + 0.0167 = 7.22$$

17.31 *Analyze.* Given six solutions, decide which two should be used to prepare a pH 3.50 buffer. Calculate the volumes of the two 0.10 M solutions needed to make approximately 1 L of buffer.

Plan. A buffer must contain a conjugate acid/conjugate base (CA/CB) pair. By examining the chemical formulas, decide which pairs of solutions could be used to make a buffer. If there is more than one possible pair, calculate pK_a for the acids. A buffer is most effective when its pH is within 1 pH unit of pK_a for the conjugate acid component. Select the pair with pK_a nearest to 3.50. Use Equation [17.9] to calculate the [CB]/[CA] ratio and the volumes of 0.10 *M* solutions needed to prepare 1 L of buffer. *Solve.*

There are three CA/CB pairs:

HCOOH/HCOONa, $pK_a = 3.74$

CH_3COOH/CH_3COONa, $pK_a = 4.74$

H_3PO_4/NaH_2PO_4, $pK_a = 2.12$

The most appropriate solutions are HCOOH/HCOONa, because pK_a for HCOOH is nearest to 3.50.

$$pH = pKa + \log\frac{[CB]}{[CA]}; \quad 3.50 = 3.7447 + \log\frac{[HCOONa]}{[HCOOH]}$$

$$\log\frac{[HCOONa]}{[HCOOH]} = -0.2447; \quad \frac{[HCOONa]}{[HCOOH]} = 0.5692 = 0.57$$

Since we are making a total of 1 L of buffer,

let y = vol HCOONa and (1 – y) = vol HCOOH.

$$0.5692 = \frac{[HCOONa]}{[HCOOH]} = \frac{(0.10\,M \times y)/1L}{[0.10\,M \times (1-y)]/1\,L}; \; 0.5692[0.10(1-y)] = 0.10\,y;$$

$0.05692 = 0.15692\,y;\; y = 0.3627 = 0.36\,L$

360 mL of 0.10 M HCOONa, 640 mL of 0.10 M HCOOH.

Check. The pH of the buffer is less than pK_a for the conjugate acid, indicating that the amount of CA in the buffer is greater than the amount of CB. This agrees with our result.

17.32 The solutes listed contain three possible conjugate acid/conjugate base (CA/CB) pairs. These are:

HCOOH/HCOONa, $pK_a = 3.74$

CH_3COOH/CH_3COONa, $pK_a = 4.74$

HCN/NaCN, $pK_a = 9.31$

For maximum buffer capacity, pK_a should be within 1 pH unit of the buffer. The acetic acid/acetate pair are most appropriate for a buffer with pH 5.00.

$$pH = pK_a + \log\frac{[CB]}{[CA]};\; 5.00 = 4.745 + \log\frac{[CH_3COONa]}{[CH_3COOH]}$$

$$\log\frac{[CH_3COONa]}{[CH_3COOH]} = 0.2553;\; \frac{[CH_3COONa]}{[CH_3COOH]} = 1.800 = 1.8$$

Since we are making a total of 1 L of buffer,
let y = vol CH_3COONa and (1 – y) = vol CH_3COOH.

$$1.800 = \frac{[CH_3COONa]}{[CH_3COOH]} = \frac{(0.10\,M \times y)/1.0\,L}{[0.10\,M \times (1-y)]/1.0\,L} = \frac{0.10\,y}{0.10 - 0.10\,y}$$

$1.800(0.10 - 0.10\,y) = 0.10\,y;\; 0.1800 = 0.2800\,y;\; y = 0.6429 = 0.64\,L$

640 mL of 0.10 M CH_3COONa, 360 mL CH_3COOH

Check. pH (buffer) > pK_a (CA) and the calculated amount of CB in the buffer is greater than the amount of CA.

Acid-Base Titrations (section 17.3)

17.33 (a) Curve B. The initial pH is lower and the equivalence point region is steeper.

(b) pH at the approximate equivalence point of curve A = 8.0

pH at the approximate equivalence point of curve B = 7.0

(c) Volume of base required to reach the equivalence point depends only on moles of acid present; it is independent of acid strength. Since acid B requires 40 mL and acid A requires only 30 mL, more moles of acid B are being titrated. For equal volumes of A and B, the concentration of acid B is greater.

17.34 (a) The quantity of base required to reach the equivalence point is the same in the two titrations, assuming both sample solutions contain equal moles of acid.

(b)   The pH is higher initially in the titration of a weak acid.

(c)   The pH is higher at the equivalence point in the titration of a weak acid.

(d)   The pH in excess base is essentially the same for the two cases.

(e)   In titrating a weak acid, one needs an indicator that changes at a higher pH than for the strong acid titration. The choice is more critical because the change in pH close to the equivalence point is smaller for the weak acid titration.

17.35   (a)   False. The same volume of NaOH(aq) is required to reach the equivalence point of both titrations, because moles of acid to be titrated are the same in both flasks.

(b)   True. CH_3COONa, the salt formed in the titration of CH_3COOH, produces a basic solution, while $NaNO_3$, formed in the titration of HNO_3 produces a neutral solution.

(c)   True. Even though the pH values at the equivalence points of the two titrations are different, phenolphthalein changes color over a wide range of pH values and is appropriate for both titrations.

17.36   (a)   False. The pH at the beginning of the titration of the weaker acid, CH_3COOH, will be higher.

(b)   True. Past the equivalence point, the titration curves are very similar (but not identical.

(c)   False. According to Figures 17.13 and 17.14, methyl red is suitable for the titration of the strong acid HNO_3, but not for the titration of the weak acid CH_3COOH.

17.37   *Analyze.* Given reactants, predict whether pH at the equivalence point of a titration is less than, equal to or greater than 7.

Plan. At the equivalence point of a titration, only product is present in solution; there is no excess of either reactant. Determine the product of each reaction and whether a solution of it is acidic, basic or neutral.   *Solve.*

(a) $NaHCO_3(aq) + NaOH(aq) \rightarrow Na_2CO_3(aq) + H_2O(l)$

At the equivalence point, the major species in solution are Na^+ and CO_3^{2-}. Na^+ is negligible and CO_3^{2-} is the CB of HCO_3^-. The solution is basic, above pH 7.

(b) $NH_3(aq) + HCl(aq) \rightarrow NH_4Cl(aq)$

At the equivalence point, the major species are NH_4^+ and Cl^-. Cl^- is negligible, NH_4^+ is the CA of NH_3. The solution is acidic, below pH 7.

(c) $KOH(aq) + HBr(aq) \rightarrow KBr(aq) + H_2O(l)$

At the equivalence point, the major species are K^+ and Br^-; both are negligible. The solution is at pH 7.

17.38   (a) $HCOOH(aq) + NaOH(aq) \rightarrow HCOONa(aq) + H_2O(l)$

At the equivalence point, the major species are Na^+ and $HCOO^-$. Na^+ is negligible and $HCOO^-$ is the CB of $HCOOH$. The solution is basic, above pH 7.

(b) $Ca(OH)_2(aq) + 2HClO_4(aq) \rightarrow Ca(ClO_4)_2(aq) + 2H_2O(l)$

At the equivalence point, the major species are Ca^{2+} and ClO_4^-; both are negligible. The solution is at pH 7.

(c) $C_5H_5N(aq) + HNO_3(aq) \rightarrow C_5H_5NH^+NO_3^-(aq)$

At the equivalence point, the major species are $C_5H_5NH^+$ and NO_3^-. NO_3^- is negligible and $C_5H_5NH^+$ is the CA of C_5H_5N. The solution is acidic, below pH 7.

17.39   The second color change, from yellow to blue near pH = 8.5, is more suitable for the titration of a weak acid with a strong base. The salt present at the equivalence point of this type of titration produces a slightly basic solution. The second color change of Thymol blue is in the correct pH range to show (indicate) the equivalence point.

17.40   (a)   At the equivalence point, moles HX added = moles B initially present =

0.10 M × 0.0300 L = 0.0030 moles HX added.

(b) $BH^+(aq)$

(c)   Both K_a for BH^+ and concentration BH^+ determine pH at the equivalence point.

(d)   Because the pH at the equivalence point will be less than 7, methyl red would be more appropriate.

17.41   *Analyze/Plan.* We are asked to calculate the volume of 0.0850 M NaOH required to titrate various acid solutions to their equivalence point. At the equivalence point, moles base added equals moles acid initially present. Solve the stoichiometry problem, recalling that mol = M × L. In part (c) calculate molarity of HCl from g/L and proceed as outlined above. *Solve.*

(a) $40.0 \text{ mL HNO}_3 \times \dfrac{0.0900 \text{ mol HNO}_3}{1000 \text{ mL soln}} \times \dfrac{1 \text{ mol NaOH}}{1 \text{ mol HNO}_3} \times \dfrac{1000 \text{ mL soln}}{0.0850 \text{ mol NaOH}}$

$= 42.353 = 42.4 \text{ mL NaOH soln}$

(b) $35.0 \text{ mL CH}_3\text{COOH} \times \dfrac{0.0850 \; M \text{ CH}_3\text{COOH}}{1000 \text{ mL soln}} \times \dfrac{1 \text{ mol NaOH}}{1 \text{ mol CH}_3\text{COOH}} \times \dfrac{1000 \text{ mL soln}}{0.0850 \text{ mol NaOH}}$

$= 35.0 \text{ mL NaOH soln}$

(c) $\dfrac{1.85 \text{ g HCl}}{1 \text{ L soln}} \times \dfrac{1 \text{ mol HCl}}{36.46 \text{ g HCl}} = 0.05074 = 0.0507 \; M \text{ HCl}$

$50.0 \text{ mL HCl} \times \dfrac{0.05074 \text{ mol HCl}}{1000 \text{ mL}} \times \dfrac{1 \text{ mol NaOH}}{1 \text{ mol HCl}} \times \dfrac{1000 \text{ mL soln}}{0.0850 \text{ mol NaOH}}$

$= 29.847 = 29.8 \text{ mL NaOH soln}$

17.42   (a) $45.0 \text{ mL NaOH} \times \dfrac{0.0950 \text{ mol NaOH}}{1000 \text{ mL soln}} \times \dfrac{1 \text{ mol HCl}}{1 \text{ mol NaOH}} \times \dfrac{1000 \text{ mL soln}}{0.105 \text{ mol HCl}}$

$= 40.7 \text{ mL HCl soln}$

(b) $22.5 \text{ mL NH}_3 \times \dfrac{0.118 \text{ mol NH}_3}{1000 \text{ mL soln}} \times \dfrac{1 \text{ mol HCl}}{1 \text{ mol NH}_3} \times \dfrac{1000 \text{ mL soln}}{0.105 \text{ mol HCl}}$

$$= 25.3 \text{ mL HCl soln}$$

(c) $125.0 \text{ mL} \times \dfrac{1.35 \text{ g NaOH}}{1000 \text{ mL}} \times \dfrac{1 \text{ mol NaOH}}{40.00 \text{ g NaOH}} \times \dfrac{1 \text{ mol HCl}}{1 \text{ mol NaOH}} \times \dfrac{1000 \text{ mL soln}}{0.105 \text{ mol HCl}}$

$$= 40.2 \text{ mL HCl soln}$$

17.43 *Analyze/Plan.* Follow the logic in Sample Exercise 17.6 for the titration of a strong acid with a strong base. *Solve.*

moles $H^+ = M_{HBr} \times L_{HBr} = 0.200 \, M \times 0.0200 \text{ L} = 4.00 \times 10^{-3} \text{ mol}$

moles $OH^- = M_{NaOH} \times L_{NaOH} = 0.200 \, M \times L_{NaOH}$

	mL_{HBr}	mL_{NaOH}	Total Volume	Moles H^+	Moles OH^-	Molarity Excess Ion	pH
(a)	20.0	15.0	35.0	4.00×10^{-3}	3.00×10^{-3}	$0.0286(H^+)$	1.544
(b)	20.0	19.9	39.9	4.00×10^{-3}	3.98×10^{-3}	$5 \times 10^{-4}(H^+)$	3.3
(c)	20.0	20.0	40.0	4.00×10^{-3}	4.00×10^{-3}	$1 \times 10^{-7}(H^+)$	7.0
(d)	20.0	20.1	40.1	4.00×10^{-3}	4.02×10^{-3}	$5 \times 10^{-4}(OH^-)$	10.7
(e)	20.0	35.0	55.0	4.00×10^{-3}	7.00×10^{-3}	$0.0545(OH^-)$	12.737

molarity of excess ion = moles ion / total vol in L

(a) $\dfrac{4.00 \times 10^{-3} \text{ mol } H^+ - 3.00 \times 10^{-3} \text{ mol } OH^-}{0.0350 \text{ L}} = 0.0286 \, M \, H^+$

(b) $\dfrac{4.00 \times 10^{-3} \text{ mol } H^+ - 3.98 \times 10^{-3} \text{ mol } OH^-}{0.0339 \text{ L}} = 5.01 \times 10^{-4} = 5 \times 10^{-4} \, M \, H^+$

(c) equivalence point, mol H^+ = mol OH^-

NaBr does not hydrolyze, so $[H^+] = [OH^-] = 1 \times 10^{-7} \, M$

(d) $\dfrac{4.02 \times 10^{-3} \text{ mol } OH^- - 4.00 \times 10^{-3} \text{ mol } H^+}{0.0401 \text{ L}} = 4.99 \times 10^{-4} = 5 \times 10^{-4} \text{ M } OH^-$

(e) $\dfrac{7.00 \times 10^{-3} \text{ mol } OH^- - 4.00 \times 10^{-3} \text{ mol } H^+}{0.0550 \text{ L}} = 0.054545 = 0.0545 \text{ M } OH^-$

17.44 moles $OH^- = M_{KOH} \times L_{KOH} = 0.150 \, M \times 0.0200 \text{ L} = 3.00 \times 10^{-3} \text{ mol}$

moles $H^+ = M_{HClO_4} \times L_{HClO_4} = 0.125 \, M \times L_{HClO_4}$

	mL_{KOH}	mL_{HClO_4}	Total Volume	Moles OH$^-$	Moles H$^+$	Molarity Excess Ion	pH
(a)	20.0	20.0	40.0	3.00×10^{-3}	2.50×10^{-3}	$0.013(OH^-)$	12.10
(b)	20.0	23.0	43.0	3.00×10^{-3}	2.88×10^{-3}	$2.9 \times 10^{-3}(OH^-)$	11.46
(c)	20.0	24.0	44.0	3.00×10^{-3}	3.00×10^{-3}	$1.0 \times 10^{-7}(OH^-)$	7.00
(d)	20.0	25.0	45.0	3.00×10^{-3}	3.13×10^{-3}	$2.8 \times 10^{-3}(H^+)$	2.56
(e)	20.0	30.0	50.0	3.00×10^{-3}	3.75×10^{-3}	$0.015(H^+)$	1.82

$$\text{molarity of excess ion} = \frac{\text{moles ion}}{\text{total vol in L}}$$

(a) $\dfrac{3.00 \times 10^{-3} \text{ mol OH}^- - 2.50 \times 10^{-3} \text{ mol H}^+}{0.0400 \text{ L}} = 0.0125 = 0.013 \; M \text{ OH}^-$

(b) $\dfrac{3.00 \times 10^{-3} \text{ mol OH}^- - 2.875 \times 10^{-3} \text{ mol H}^+}{0.0430 \text{ L}} = 2.91 \times 10^{-3} = 2.9 \times 10^{-3} \; M \text{ OH}^-$

(c) equivalence point, mol H$^+$ = mol OH$^-$

KClO$_4$ does not hydrolyze, so [H$^+$] = [OH$^-$] = $1 \times 10^{-7} \; M$

(d) $\dfrac{3.125 \times 10^{-3} \text{ mol H}^+ - 3.00 \times 10^{-3} \text{ mol OH}^-}{0.0450 \text{ L}} = 2.78 \times 10^{-3} = 2.8 \times 10^{-3} \; M \text{ H}^+$

(e) $\dfrac{3.75 \times 10^{-3} \text{ mol H}^+ - 3.00 \times 10^{-3} \text{ mol OH}^-}{0.0500 \text{ L}} = 0.0150 = 0.015 \; M \text{ H}^+$

17.45 *Analyze/Plan.* Follow the logic in Sample Exercise 17.7 for the titration of a weak acid with a strong base. *Solve.*

(a) At 0 mL, only weak acid, CH$_3$COOH, is present in solution. Using the acid ionization equilibrium

$$CH_3COOH(aq) \; \rightleftharpoons \; H^+(aq) \; + \; CH_3COO^-(aq)$$

Initial	0.150 M	0	0
equil	0.150 – x M	x M	x M

$K_a = \dfrac{[H^+][CH_3COO^-]}{[CH_3COOH]} = 1.8 \times 10^{-5}$ (Appendix D)

$1.8 \times 10^{-5} = \dfrac{x^2}{(0.150 - x)} \approx \dfrac{x^2}{0.150}; x^2 = 2.7 \times 10^{-6}; x = [H^+] = 0.001643$

$= 1.6 \times 10^{-3} \; M; \text{pH} = 2.78$

(b)–(f) Calculate the moles of each component after the acid-base reaction takes place.
Moles CH$_3$COOH originally present = $M \times L$ = 0.150 M × 0.0350 L = 5.25×10^{-3} mol.
Moles NaOH added = $M \times L$ = 0.150 M × y mL.

		NaOH(aq) +	CH$_3$COOH (aq) →	CH$_3$COONa(aq) + H$_2$O(l)
		(0.150 M × 0.0175 L) =		
(b)	before rx	2.625 × 10^{-3} mol	5.25 × 10^{-3} mol	
	after rx	**0**	**2.625 × 10^{-3} mol**	**2.63 × 10^{-3} mol**
		(0.150 M × 0.0345 L) =		
(c)	before rx	5.175 × 10^{-3} mol	5.25 × 10^{-3} mol	
	after rx	**0**	**0.075 × 10^{-3} mol**	**5.18 × 10^{-3} mol**
		(0.150 M × 0.0350 L) =		
(d)	before rx	5.25 × 10^{-3} mol	5.25 × 10^{-3} mol	
	after rx	**0**	**0**	**5.25 × 10^{-3} mol**
		(0.150 M × 0.0355 L) =		
(e)	before rx	5.325 × 10^{-3} mol	5.25 × 10^{-3} mol	
	after rx	**0.075 × 10^{-3} mol**	**0**	**5.25 × 10^{-3} mol**
		(0.150 M × 0.0500 L) =		
(f)	before rx	7.50 × 10^{-3} mol	5.25 × 10^{-3} mol	
	after rx	**2.25 × 10^{-3} mol**	**0**	**5.25 × 10^{-3} mol**

Calculate the molarity of each species (M = mol/L) and solve the appropriate
equilibrium problem in each part.

(b) V_T = 35.0 mL CH$_3$COOH + 17.5 mL NaOH = 52.5 mL = 0.0525 L

$$[CH_3COOH] = \frac{2.625 \times 10^{-3} \text{ mol}}{0.0525} = 0.0500 \text{ M}$$

$$[CH_3COO^-] = \frac{2.625 \times 10^{-3} \text{ mol}}{0.0525} = 0.0500 \text{ M}$$

CH$_3$COOH(aq) $\rightleftharpoons$ H$^+$(aq) + CH$_3$COO$^-$(aq)

equil   0.0500 – x M x M 0.0500 + x M

$$K_a = \frac{[H^+][CH_3COO^-]}{[CH_3COOH]}; [H^+] = \frac{K_a[CH_3COOH]}{[CH_3COO^-]}$$

$$[H^+] = \frac{1.8 \times 10^{-5}(0.0500-x)}{(0.0500+x)} = 1.8 \times 10^{-5} M \, H^+; pH = 4.74$$

(c) $$[CH_3COOH] = \frac{7.5 \times 10^{-5} \text{ mol}}{0.0695 \text{ L}} = 0.001079 = 1.1 \times 10^{-3} M$$

$$[CH_3COO^-] = \frac{5.175 \times 10^{-3} \text{ mol}}{0.0695 \text{ L}} = 0.07446 = 0.074 \ M$$

$$[H^+] = \frac{1.8 \times 10^{-5} (1.079 \times 10^{-3} - x)}{(0.07446 + x)} \approx 2.6 \times 10^{-7} \ M \ H^+; \ pH = 6.58$$

(d)   At the equivalence point, only CH_3COO^- is present.

$$[CH_3COO^-] = \frac{5.25 \times 10^{-3} \text{ mol}}{0.0700 \text{ L}} = 0.0750 \ M$$

The pertinent equilibrium is the base hydrolysis of CH_3COO^-.

	$CH_3COO^-(aq) + H_2O(l)$	$\rightleftharpoons$	$CH_3COOH(aq) +$	$OH^-(aq)$
initial	0.0750 M		0	0
equil	0.0750 – x M		x	x

$$K_b = \frac{K_w}{K_a \text{ for } CH_3COOH} = \frac{1.0 \times 10^{-14}}{1.8 \times 10^{-5}} = 5.56 \times 10^{-10} = 5.6 \times 10^{-10} = \frac{[CH_3COOH][OH^-]}{[CH_3COO^-]}$$

$$5.56 \times 10^{-10} = \frac{x^2}{0.0750 - x}; \ x^2 \approx 5.56 \times 10^{-10} (0.0750); \ x = 6.458 \times 10^{-6}$$

$$= 6.5 \times 10^{-6} \ M \ OH^-$$

$$pOH = -\log(6.458 \times 10^{-6}) = 5.19; \ pH = 14.00 - pOH = 8.81$$

(e)   After the equivalence point, the excess strong base determines the pOH and pH. The $[OH^-]$ from the hydrolysis of CH_3COO^- is small and can be ignored.

$$[OH^-] = \frac{0.075 \times 10^{-3} \text{ mol}}{0.0705 \text{ L}} = 1.064 \times 10^{-3} = 1.1 \times 10^{-3} \ M; \ pOH = 2.97$$

$$pH = 14.00 - 2.97 = 11.03$$

(f) $[OH^-] = \dfrac{2.25 \times 10^{-3} \text{ mol}}{0.0850 \text{ L}} = 0.0265 \ M \ OH^-; \ pOH = 1.577; \ pH = 14.00 - 1.577 = 12.423$

17.46   (a)   Weak base problem: $K_b = 1.8 \times 10^{-5} = \dfrac{[NH_4^+][OH^-]}{[NH_3]}$

At equilibrium, $[OH^-] = x$, $[NH_3] = (0.030 - x)$; $[NH_4^+] = x$

$$1.8 \times 10^{-5} = \frac{x^2}{(0.050 - x)} \approx \frac{x^2}{0.050}; \ x = [OH^-] = 9.487 \times 10^{-4} = 9.5 \times 10^{-4} \ M$$

$$pH = 14.00 - 3.02 = 10.98$$

(b–f)   Calculate mol NH_3 and mol NH_4^+ after the acid-base reaction takes place. 0.050 M NH_3 × 0.0300 L = 1.5×10^{-3} mol NH_3 present initially.

		$NH_3(aq)$	$+$	$HCl(aq)$	$\rightarrow$	$NH_4^+(aq) + Cl^-(aq)$
				$(0.025\ M \times 0.0200\ L) =$		
(b)	before rx	1.5×10^{-3} mol		0.50×10^{-3} mol		0 mol
	after rx	**1.0×10^{-3} mol**		**0 mol**		**5.0×10^{-4} mol**
				$(0.025\ M \times 0.0590\ L) =$		
(c)	before rx	1.5×10^{-3} mol		1.475×10^{-3} mol		0 mol
	after rx	**2.5×10^{-5} mol**		**0 mol**		**1.475×10^{-3} mol**
				$(0.025\ M \times 0.0600\ L) =$		
(d)	before rx	1.5×10^{-3} mol		1.5×10^{-3} mol		0 mol
	after rx	**0 mol**		**0 mol**		**1.5×10^{-3} mol**
				$(0.025\ M \times 0.0610\ L) =$		
(e)	before rx	1.5×10^{-3} mol		1.525×10^{-3} mol		0 mol
	after rx	**0 mol**		**2.5×10^{-5} mol**		**1.5×10^{-3} mol**
				$(0.025\ M \times 0.0650\ L) =$		
(f)	before rx	1.5×10^{-3} mol		1.625×10^{-3} mol		0 mol
	after rx	**0 mol**		**1.25×10^{-4} mol**		**1.5×10^{-3} mol**

(b)   Using the acid dissociation equilibrium for NH_4^+ (so that we calculate $[H^+]$ directly), $NH_4^+(aq) \rightleftharpoons H^+(aq) + NH_3(aq)$

$$K_a = \frac{[H^+][NH_3]}{[NH_4^+]} = \frac{K_w}{K_b \text{ for } NH_3} = \frac{1.0 \times 10^{-14}}{1.8 \times 10^{-5}} = 5.56 \times 10^{-10} = 5.6 \times 10^{-10}$$

$$[NH_3] = \frac{1.0 \times 10^{-3} \text{ mol}}{0.0500 \text{ L}} = 0.020\ M; [NH_4^+] = \frac{5.0 \times 10^{-4} \text{ mol}}{0.0500 \text{ L}} = 0.010\ M$$

$$[H^+] = \frac{5.56 \times 10^{-10}\ [NH_4^+]}{[NH_3]} \approx \frac{5.56 \times 10^{-10}\ (0.010)}{(0.020)} = 2.78 \times 10^{-10}; pH = 9.56$$

(We will assume $[H^+]$ is small compared to $[NH_3]$ and $[NH_4^+]$.)

(c) $[NH_3] = \dfrac{2.5 \times 10^{-5} \text{ mol}}{0.0890 \text{ L}} = 2.8 \times 10^{-4}\ M; [NH_4^+] = \dfrac{1.475 \times 10^{-3} \text{ mol}}{0.0890 \text{ L}} = 0.017\ M$

$$[H^+] = \frac{5.56 \times 10^{-10}\ (0.017)}{(2.8 \times 10^{-4})} = 3.38 \times 10^{-8} = 3.4 \times 10^{-8}\ M; pH = 7.47$$

(d)   At the equivalence point, $[H^+] = [NH_3] = x$

$$[NH_4^+] = \frac{1.5 \times 10^{-3}\ M}{0.0900 \text{ L}} = 0.01667 = 0.017\ M$$

$$5.56 \times 10^{-10} = \frac{x^2}{0.01667}; x = [H^+] = 3.043 \times 10^{-6} = 3.0 \times 10^{-6} \; M; pH = 5.52$$

(e)   Past the equivalence point, $[H^+]$ from the excess HCl determines the pH.

$$[H^+] = \frac{2.5 \times 10^{-5} \; mol}{0.0910 \; L} = 2.747 \times 10^{-4} = 2.7 \times 10^{-4} \; M; pH = 3.56$$

(f)   Past the equivalence point, $[H^+]$ from the excess HCl determines the pH.

$$[H^+] = \frac{1.25 \times 10^{-4} \; mol}{0.0950 \; L} = 1.316 \times 10^{-3} = 1.3 \times 10^{-3} \; M; pH = 2.88$$

17.47   *Analyze/Plan.* Calculate the pH at the equivalence point for the titration of several bases with 0.200 M HBr. The volume of 0.200 M HBr required in all cases equals the volume of base and the final volume = $2V_{base}$. The concentration of the salt produced at the equivalence point is $\dfrac{0.200 \; M \times V_{base}}{2V_{base}} = 0.100 \; M$.

In each case, identify the salt present at the equivalence point, determine its acid-base properties (Section 16.9), and solve the pH problem.   *Solve.*

(a)   NaOH is a strong base; the salt present at the equivalence point, NaBr, does not affect the pH of the solution. 0.100 M NaBr, pH = 7.00

(b) $HONH_2$ is a weak base, so the salt present at the equivalence point is $HONH_3^+Br^-$. This is the salt of a strong acid and a weak base, so it produces an acidic solution.

0.100 M $HONH_3^+Br^-$; $HONH_3^+(aq)$ $\rightleftharpoons$ $H^+(aq)$ + $HONH_2$

                          [equil]   0.100 – x   x   x

$$K_a = \frac{[H^+][HONH_2]}{[HONH_3^+]} = \frac{K_w}{K_b} = \frac{1.0 \times 10^{-14}}{1.1 \times 10^{-8}} = 9.09 \times 10^{-7} = 9.1 \times 10^{-7}$$

Assume x is small with respect to [salt].

$K_a = x^2 / 0.100; x = [H^+] = 3.02 \times 10^{-4} = 3.0 \times 10^{-4} \; M$, pH = 3.52

(c) $C_6H_5NH_2$ is a weak base and $C_6H_5NH_3^+Br^-$ is an acidic salt.

0.100 M $C_6H_5NH_3^+Br^-$.   Proceeding as in (b):

$$K_a = \frac{[H^+][C_6H_5NH_2]}{[C_6H_5NH_3^+]} = \frac{K_w}{K_b} = 2.33 \times 10^{-5} = 2.3 \times 10^{-5}$$

$[H^+]^2 = 0.100(2.33 \times 10^{-5}); [H^+] = 1.52 \times 10^{-3} = 1.5 \times 10^{-3} \; M$, pH = 2.82

17.48   The volume of NaOH solution required in all cases is

$$V_{base} = \frac{V_{acid} \times M_{acid}}{M_{base}} = \frac{(0.100) \; V_{acid}}{(0.080)} = 1.25 \; V_{acid}$$

The total volume at the equivalence point is $V_{base} + V_{acid} = 2.25\ V_{acid}$.

The concentration of the salt at the equivalence point is $\dfrac{M_{acid}\ V_{acid}}{2.25\ V_{acid}} = \dfrac{0.100}{2.25} = 0.0444\ M$

(a) $0.0444\ M$ NaBr, pH = 7.00

(b) $0.0444\ M$ NaClO$_2$; $ClO_2^-(aq) + H_2O(l) \rightleftharpoons HClO_2(aq) + OH^-(aq)$

$$K_b = \frac{[HClO_2][OH^-]}{[ClO_2^-]} = \frac{K_w}{K_a} = \frac{1.0 \times 10^{-14}}{1.1 \times 10^{-2}} = 9.09 \times 10^{-13} = 9.1 \times 10^{-13}$$

$[HClO_2] = [OH^-]$; $[ClO_2^-] \approx 0.0444\ M$

$[OH^-]^2 \approx 0.0444(9.09 \times 10^{-13})$; $[OH^-] = 2.01 \times 10^{-7} = 2.0 \times 10^{-7}\ M$, pOH = 6.70;

$$pH = 7.30$$

Note that HClO$_2$ is a relatively strong acid (large Ka value), so the pH at the equivalence point is not much greater than 7.0. Since [OH$^-$] from the hydrolysis of ClO$_2^-$ is very small, the autoionization equilibrium should be considered for a more accurate value of the equivalence point pH.

Let $[H^+] = x$, $[OH^-] = (2.0 \times 10^{-7}\ M + x)$; $1.0 \times 10^{-14} = (x)(2.0 \times 10^{-7}\ M + x)$

Solving the quadratic equation gives a pH of 7.38.

(c) $C_6H_5COO^-(aq) + H_2O(l) \rightleftharpoons C_6H_5COOH(aq) + OH^-(aq)$

$$K_b = \frac{[C_6H_5COO^-][OH^-]}{[C_6H_5COOH]} = \frac{K_w}{K_a} = \frac{1.0 \times 10^{-14}}{6.3 \times 10^{-5}} = 1.59 \times 10^{-10} = 1.6 \times 10^{-10}$$

$[OH^-]^2 \approx 0.0444(1.59 \times 10^{-8})$; $[OH^-] = 2.655 \times 10^{-6} = 2.7 \times 10^{-6}$, pH = 8.42

Solubility Equilibria and Factors Affecting Solubility
(sections 17.4 and 17.5)

17.49   (a)   The concentration of undissolved solid does not appear in the solubility product expression because it is constant as long as there is solid present. Concentration is a ratio of moles solid to volume of the solid; solids occupy a specific volume not dependent on the solution volume. As the amount (moles) of solid changes, the volume changes proportionally, so that the ratio of moles solid to volume solid is constant.

     (b)   *Analyze/Plan.* Follow the example in Sample Exercise 17.9.   *Solve.*

         $K_{sp} = [Ag^+][I^-]$; $K_{sp} = [Sr^{2+}][SO_4^{2-}]$; $K_{sp} = [Fe^{2+}][OH^-]^2$; $K_{sp} = [Hg_2^{2+}][Br^-]^2$

17.50   (a)   Solubility is the amount (grams, moles) of solute that will dissolve in a certain volume of solution. Solubility-product constant is an equilibrium constant, the product of the molar concentrations of all the dissolved ions in solution.

     (b) $K_{sp} = [Mn^{2+}][CO_3^{2-}]$; $K_{sp} = [Hg^{2+}][OH^-]^2$; $K_{sp} = [Cu^{2+}]^3[PO_4^{3-}]^2$

17.51 *Analyze/Plan.* Follow the logic in Sample Exercise 17.10. *Solve.*

(a) $CaF_2(s) \rightleftharpoons Ca^{2+}(aq) + 2F^-(aq); \quad K_{sp} = [Ca^{2+}][F^-]^2$

The molar solubility is the moles of CaF_2 that dissolve per liter of solution. Each mole of CaF_2 produces **1** mol $Ca^{2+}(aq)$ and **2** mol $F^-(aq)$.

$[Ca^{2+}] = 1.24 \times 10^{-3} M; [F^-] = 2 \times 1.24 \times 10^{-3} M = 2.48 \times 10^{-3} M$

$K_{sp} = (1.24 \times 10^{-3})(2.48 \times 10^{-3})^2 = 7.63 \times 10^{-9}$

(b) $SrF_2(s) \rightleftharpoons Sr^{2+}(aq) + 2F^-(aq); \quad K_{sp} = [Sr^{2+}][F^-]^2$

Transform the gram solubility to molar solubility.

$$\frac{1.1 \times 10^{-2} \text{ g } SrF_2}{0.100 \text{ L}} \times \frac{1 \text{ mol } SrF_2}{125.6 \text{ g } SrF_2} = 8.76 \times 10^{-4} = 8.8 \times 10^{-4} \text{ mol } SrF_2/L$$

$[Sr^{2+}] = 8.76 \times 10^{-4} M; [F^-] = 2(8.76 \times 10^{-4} M)$

$K_{sp} = (8.76 \times 10^{-4})(2(8.76 \times 10^{-4}))^2 = 2.7 \times 10^{-9}$

(c) $Ba(IO_3)_2(s) \rightleftharpoons Ba^{2+}(aq) + 2IO_3^-(aq); \quad K_{sp} = [Ba^{2+}][IO_3^-]^2$

Since 1 mole of dissolved $Ba(IO_3)_2$ produces 1 mole of Ba^{2+}, the molar solubility of $Ba(IO_3)_2 = [Ba^{2+}]$. Let $x = [Ba^{2+}]; [IO_3^-] = 2x$

$K_{sp} = 6.0 \times 10^{-10} = (x)(2x)^2; 4x^3 = 6.0 \times 10^{-10}; x^3 = 1.5 \times 10^{-10}; x = 5.3 \times 10^{-4} M$

The molar solubility of $Ba(IO_3)_2$ is 5.3×10^{-4} mol/L.

17.52 (a) $PbBr_2(s) \rightleftharpoons Pb^{2+}(aq) + 2Br^-(aq)$

$K_{sp} = [Pb^{2+}][Br^-]^2; [Pb^{2+}] = 1.0 \times 10^{-2} M, [Br^-] = 2.0 \times 10^{-2} M$

$K_{sp} = (1.0 \times 10^{-2} M)(2.0 \times 10^{-2} M)^2 = 4.0 \times 10^{-6}$

(b) $AgIO_3(s) \rightleftharpoons Ag^+(aq) + IO_3^-(aq); \quad K_{sp} = [Ag^+][IO_3^-]$

$[Ag^+] = [IO_3^-] = \dfrac{0.0490 \text{ g } AgIO_3}{1.00 \text{ L soln}} \times \dfrac{1 \text{ mol } AgIO_3}{282.8 \text{ g } AgIO_3} = 1.733 \times 10^{-4} = 1.73 \times 10^{-4} M$

$K_{sp} = (1.733 \times 10^{-4} M)(1.733 \times 10^{-4} M) = 3.00 \times 10^{-8}$

(c) $Ca(OH)_2(s) \rightleftharpoons Ca^{2+}(aq) + 2OH^-(aq); \quad K_{sp} = [Ca^{2+}][OH^-]^2$

$[Ca^{2+}] = x, [OH^-] = 2x; K_{sp} = 6.5 \times 10^{-6} = (x)(2x)^2$

$6.5 \times 10^{-6} = 4x^3; x = [Ca^{2+}] = 0.01176 = 0.012 M; [OH^-] = 0.02351 = 0.024 M$

$pH = 14 - pOH = 14 - 1.629 = 12.37$

17.53 *Analyze/Plan.* Given gram solubility of a compound, calculate K_{sp}. Write the dissociation equilibrium and K_{sp} expression. Change gram solubility to molarity of the individual ions, taking the stoichiometry of the compound into account. Calculate K_{sp}. *Solve.*

$$CaC_2O_4(s) \rightleftharpoons Ca^{2+}(aq) + C_2O_4^{2-}(aq); \quad K_{sp} = [Ca^{2+}][C_2O_4^{2-}]$$

$$[Ca^{2+}] = [C_2O_4^{2-}] = \frac{0.0061 \text{ g } CaC_2O_4}{1.00 \text{ L soln}} \times \frac{1 \text{ mol } CaC_2O_4}{128.1 \text{ g } CaC_2O_4} = 4.76 \times 10^{-5} = 4.8 \times 10^{-5} \ M$$

$$K_{sp} = (4.76 \times 10^{-5} \ M)(4.76 \times 10^{-5} \ M) = 2.3 \times 10^{-9}$$

17.54 $PbI_2(s) \rightleftharpoons Pb^{2+}(aq) + 2I^-(aq); \quad K_{sp} = [Pb^{2+}][I^-]^2$

$$[Pb^{2+}] = \frac{0.54 \text{ g } PbI_2}{1.00 \text{ L soln}} \times \frac{1 \text{ mol } PbI_2}{461.0 \text{ g } PbI_2} = 1.17 \times 10^{-3} = 1.2 \times 10^{-3} \ M$$

$$[I^-] = 2[Pb^{2+}]; \ K_{sp} = [Pb^{2+}](2[Pb^{2+}])^2 = 4[Pb^{2+}]^3 = 4(1.17 \times 10^{-3})^3 = 6.4 \times 10^{-9}$$

17.55   *Analyze/Plan.* Follow the logic in Sample Exercises 17.11 and 17.12.   *Solve.*

(a) $AgBr(s) \rightleftharpoons Ag^+(aq) + Br^-(aq); \quad K_{sp} = [Ag^+][Br^-] = 5.0 \times 10^{-13}$

molar solubility $= x = [Ag^+] = [Br^-]; K_{sp} = x^2$

$x = (5.0 \times 10^{-13})^{1/2}; x = 7.1 \times 10^{-7}$ mol AgBr/L

(b)   Molar solubility $= x = [Br^-]; [Ag^+] = 0.030 \ M + x$

$K_{sp} = (0.030 + x)(x) \approx 0.030(x)$

$5.0 \times 10^{-13} = 0.030(x); x = 1.7 \times 10^{-11}$ mol AgBr/L

(c)   Molar solubility $= x = [Ag^+]$

There are two sources of Br^-: $NaBr(0.10 \ M)$ and $AgBr(x \ M)$

$K_{sp} = (x)(0.10 + x);$ Assuming x is small compared to $0.10 \ M$

$5.0 \times 10^{-13} = 0.10 \ (x); x \approx 5.0 \times 10^{-12}$ mol AgBr/L

17.56 $LaF_3(s) \rightleftharpoons La^{3+}(aq) + 3F^-(aq); \quad K_{sp} = [La^{3+}][F^-]^3$

(a)   molar solubility $= x = [La^{3+}]; [F^-] = 3x$

$K_{sp} = 2 \times 10^{-19} = (x)(3x)^3; 2 \times 10^{-19} = 27 \ x^4; x = (7.41 \times 10^{-21})^{1/4}, x = 9.28 \times 10^{-6}$

$$= 9 \times 10^{-6} \ M \ La^{3+}$$

$$\frac{9.28 \times 10^{-6} \text{ mol } LaF_3}{1 \text{ L}} \times \frac{195.9 \text{ g } LaF_3}{1 \text{ mol}} = 1.82 \times 10^{-3} = 2 \times 10^{-3} \text{ g } LaF_3/L$$

(b)   molar solubility $= x = [La^{3+}]$

There are two sources of F^-: $KF(0.010 \ M)$ and $LaF_3 \ (3x \ M)$

$K_{sp} = (x)(0.010 + 3x)^3;$ assume x is small compared to $0.010 \ M.$

$2 \times 10^{-19} = (0.010)^3 \ x; x = 2 \times 10^{-19}/1.0 \times 10^{-6} = 2 \times 10^{-13} \ M \ La^{3+}$

$$\frac{2 \times 10^{-13} \text{ mol } LaF_3}{1 \text{ L}} \times \frac{195.9 \text{ g } LaF_3}{1 \text{ mol}} = 3.92 \times 10^{-11} = 4 \times 10^{-11} \text{ g } LaF_3/L$$

(c)   molar solubility = x, $[F^-] = 3x$, $[La^{3+}] = 0.050\ M + x$

$K_{sp} = (0.050 + x)(3x)^3$; assume x is small compared to 0.050 M.

$2 \times 10^{-19} = (0.050)(27\ x^3) = 1.35\ x^3$; $x = (1.48 \times 10^{-19})^{1/3} = 5.29 \times 10^{-7} = 5 \times 10^{-7}\ M$

$$\frac{5.29 \times 10^{-7}\ \text{mol LaF}_3}{1\ \text{L}} \times \frac{195.9\ \text{g LaF}_3}{1\ \text{mol}} = 1.04 \times 10^{-4} = 1 \times 10^{-4}\ \text{g LaF}_3/\text{L}$$

17.57   *Analyze/Plan.* Given a saturated solution of CaF_2 in contact with undissolved $CaF_2(s)$, consider the effect of adding $CaCl_2(s)$. The two salts have the Ca^{2+} ion in common. *Solve.* As $CaCl_2$ is added, $[Ca^{2+}]$ increases, K_{sp} is exceeded, and additional CaF_2 precipitates until equilibrium is reestablished. At the new equilibrium position:

(a)   The amount of $CaF_2(s)$ on the bottom of the beaker increases because the added Ca^{2+} from $CaCl_2$ decreases the solubility of CaF_2.

(b)   The $[Ca^{2+}]$ in solution increases because of the added $CaCl_2$.

(c)   The $[F^-]$ in solution decreases because $CaF_2(s)$ precipitates upon addition of $CaCl_2$. The product of $[Ca^{2+}]$ and $[F^-]$, the K_{sp}, is the same.

17.58   As KI is added, $[I^-]$ increases, K_{sp} is exceeded, and additional PbI_2 precipitates until equilibrium is reestablished. At the new equilibrium position:

(a)   The amount of $PbI_2(s)$ on the bottom of the beaker increases because the added I^- from KI decreases the solubility of PbI_2.

(b)   The $[Pb^{2+}]$ in solution decreases because $PbI_2(s)$ precipitates upon addition of KI.

(c)   The $[I^-]$ in solution increases because of the added KI. The product of $[Pb^{2+}]$ and $[I^-]$, the K_{sp}, is the same.

17.59   *Analyze/Plan.* We are asked to calculate the solubility of a slightly-soluble hydroxide salt at various pH values. This is a common ion problem; pH tells us not only $[H^+]$ but also $[OH^-]$, which is an ion common to the salt. Use pH to calculate $[OH^-]$, then proceed as in Sample Exercise 17.12. *Solve.*

$Mn(OH)_2(s) \rightleftharpoons Mn^{2+}(aq) + 2OH^-(aq)$; $K_{sp} = 1.6 \times 10^{-13}$

Since $[OH^-]$ is set by the pH of the solution, the solubility of $Mn(OH)_2$ is just $[Mn^{2+}]$.

(a)   pH = 7.0, pOH = 14 – pH = 7.0, $[OH^-] = 10^{-pOH} = 1.0 \times 10^{-7}\ M$

$$K_{sp} = 1.6 \times 10^{-13} = [Mn^{2+}](1.0 \times 10^{-7})^2;\ [Mn^{2+}] = \frac{1.6 \times 10^{-13}}{1.0 \times 10^{-14}} = 16\ M$$

$$\frac{16\ \text{mol Mn(OH)}_2}{1\ \text{L}} \times \frac{88.95\ \text{g Mn(OH)}_2}{1\ \text{mol Mn(OH)}_2} = 1423 = 1.4 \times 10^3\ \text{g Mn(OH)}_2/\text{L}$$

Check. Note that the solubility of $Mn(OH)_2$ in pure water is $3.6 \times 10^{-5}\ M$, and the pH of the resulting solution is 9.0. The relatively low pH of a solution buffered to pH 7.0 actually increases the solubility of $Mn(OH)_2$.

(b) pH = 9.5, pOH = 4.5, $[OH^-]$ = 3.16 × 10^{-5} = 3.2 × 10^{-5} M

$$K_{sp} = 1.6 \times 10^{-13} = [Mn^{2+}](3.16 \times 10^{-5})^2; [Mn^{2+}] = \frac{1.6 \times 10^{-13}}{1.0 \times 10^{-9}} = 1.6 \times 10^{-4} \, M$$

1.6 × 10^{-4} M Mn(OH)$_2$ × 88.95 g/mol = 0.0142 = 0.014 g/L

(c) pH = 11.8, pOH = 2.2, $[OH^-]$ = 6.31 × 10^{-3} = 6.3 × 10^{-3} M

$$K_{sp} = 1.6 \times 10^{-13} = [Mn^{2+}](6.31 \times 10^{-3})^2; [Mn^{2+}] = \frac{1.6 \times 10^{-13}}{3.98 \times 10^{-5}} = 4.0 \times 10^{-9} \, M$$

4.02 × 10^{-9} M Mn(OH)$_2$ × 88.95 g/mol = 3.575 × 10^{-7} = 3.6 × 10^{-7} g/L

17.60 Ni(OH)$_2$(s) $\rightleftharpoons$ Ni^{2+}(aq) + 2OH$^-$(aq); K_{sp} = 6.0 × 10^{-16}

Since the $[OH^-]$ is set by the pH of the solution, the solubility of Ni(OH)$_2$ is just $[Ni^{2+}]$.

(a) pH = 8.0, pOH = 14 – pH = 6.0, $[OH^-]$ = 10^{-pOH} = 1 × 10^{-6} M

$$K_{sp} = 6.0 \times 10^{-16} = [Ni^{2+}](1.0 \times 10^{-6})^2; [Ni^{2+}] = \frac{6.0 \times 10^{-16}}{1.0 \times 10^{-12}} = 6.0 \times 10^{-4} = 6 \times 10^{-4} \, M$$

(b) pH = 10.0, pOH = 4.0, $[OH^-]$ = 1.0 × 10^{-4} = 1 × 10^{-4} M

$$K_{sp} = 6.0 \times 10^{-16} = [Ni^{2+}][1.0 \times 10^{-4}]^2; [Ni^{2+}] = \frac{6.0 \times 10^{-16}}{1.0 \times 10^{-8}} = 6.0 \times 10^{-8} = 6 \times 10^{-8} \, M$$

(c) pH = 12.0, pOH = 2.0, $[OH^-]$ = 1.0 × 10^{-2} = 1 × 10^{-2} M

$$K_{sp} = 6.0 \times 10^{-16} = [Ni^{2+}][1.0 \times 10^{-2}]^2; [Ni^{2+}] = \frac{6.0 \times 10^{-16}}{1.0 \times 10^{-4}} = 6.0 \times 10^{-12} = 6 \times 10^{-12} \, M$$

17.61 *Analyze/Plan.* Follow the logic in Sample Exercise 17.13.   *Solve.*

If the anion of the salt is the conjugate base of a weak acid, it will combine with H$^+$, reducing the concentration of the free anion in solution, thereby causing more salt to dissolve. More soluble in acid: (a) ZnCO$_3$, (b) ZnS, (d) AgCN, (e) Ba$_3$(PO$_4$)$_2$

17.62 If the anion in the slightly soluble salt is the conjugate base of a strong acid, there will be no reaction.

(a) MnS(s) + 2H$^+$(aq) $\rightarrow$ H$_2$S(aq) + Mn^{2+}(aq)

(b) PbF$_2$(s) + 2H$^+$(aq) $\rightarrow$ 2HF(aq) + Pb^{2+}(aq)

(c) AuCl$_3$(s) + H$^+$(aq) $\rightarrow$ no reaction

(d) Hg$_2$C$_2$O$_4$(s) + 2H$^+$(aq) $\rightarrow$ H$_2$C$_2$O$_4$(aq) + Hg$_2$$^{2+}$(aq)

(e) CuBr(s) + H$^+$(aq) $\rightarrow$ no reaction

17.63 *Analyze/Plan.* Follow the logic in Sample Exercise 17.14. *Solve.*

The formation equilibrium is

$$Ni^{2+}(aq) + 6NH_3(aq) \rightleftharpoons Ni(NH_3)_6{}^{2+}(aq) \quad K_f = \frac{[Ni(NH_3)_6^{2+}]}{[Ni^{2+}][NH_3]^6} = 1.2 \times 10^9$$

Assuming that nearly all the Ni^{2+} is in the form $Ni(NH_3)_6{}^{2+}$,

$[Ni(NH_3)_6^{2+}] = 1 \times 10^{-3} M; [Ni^{2+}] = x; [NH_3] = 0.20 M$

$$1.2 \times 10^9 = \frac{(1 \times 10^{-3})}{x(0.20)^6}; x = 1.30 \times 10^{-8} = 1 \times 10^{-8} M = [Ni^{2+}]$$

17.64 $NiC_2O_4(s) \rightleftharpoons Ni^{2+}(aq) + C_2O_4{}^{2-}(aq); \quad K_{sp} = [Ni^{2+}][C_2O_4{}^{2-}] = 4 \times 10^{-10}$

When the salt has just dissolved, $[C_2O_4{}^{2-}]$ will be 0.020 M. Thus $[Ni^{2+}]$ must be less than $4 \times 10^{-10} / 0.020 = 2 \times 10^{-8} M$. To achieve this low $[Ni^{2+}]$ we must complex the Ni^{2+} ion with NH_3: $Ni^{2+}(aq) + 6NH_3(aq) \rightleftharpoons Ni(NH_3)_6{}^{2+}(aq)$. Essentially all Ni(II) is in the form of the complex, so $[Ni(NH_3)_6{}^{2+}] = 0.020$. Find K_f for $Ni(NH_3)_6{}^{2+}$ in Table 17.1.

$$K_f = \frac{[Ni(NH_3)_6^{2+}]}{[Ni^{2+}][NH_3]^6} = \frac{(0.020)}{(2 \times 10^{-8})[NH_3]^6} = 1.2 \times 10^9; [NH_3]^6 = 8.33 \times 10^{-4};$$

$$[NH_3] = 0.307 = 0.3 \ M$$

17.65 *Analyze/Plan.* Calculate the solubility of AgI in pure water according to the method in Sample Exercise 17.11. Obtain K_{eq} for the complexaction reaction, making use of pertinent K_{sp} and K_f values from Appendix D and Table 17.1. Write the dissociation equilibrium for AgI and the formation reaction for $Ag(CN)_2{}^-$. Use algebra to manipulate these equations and their associated equilibrium constants to obtain the desired reaction and its equilibrium constant. Finally, use this K_{eq} value to calculate the solubility of AgI in 0.100 M NaCN solution. *Solve.*

(a) $AgI(s) \rightleftharpoons Ag^+(aq) + I^-(aq); \quad K_{sp} = [Ag^+][I^-] = 8.3 \times 10^{-17}$

molar solubility $= x = [Ag^+] = [I^-]; K_{sp} = x^2$

$x = (8.3 \times 10^{-17})^{1/2}; x = 9.1 \times 10^{-9}$ mol AgI/L

(b) $$AgI(s) \rightleftharpoons Ag^+(aq) + I^-(aq)$$

$$Ag^+(aq) + 2CN^-(aq) \rightleftharpoons Ag(CN)_2{}^-(aq)$$

$$AgI(s) + 2CN^-(aq) \rightleftharpoons Ag(CN)_2{}^-(aq) + I^-(aq)$$

$$K = K_{sp} \times K_f = [Ag^+][I^-] \times \frac{[Ag(CN)_2^-]}{[Ag^+][CN^-]^2} = (8.3 \times 10^{-17})(1 \times 10^{21}) = 8 \times 10^4$$

(c) K is much greater than one for the reaction of AgI(s) with CN^-. This means that the reaction goes to completion. For a AgI(s) in 0.100 M NaCN solution, CN^- is the limiting reactant. Two moles of CN^- react with one mole of AgI, so the solublility of AgI in 0.100 M NaCN is $(0.100/2) = 0.0500 M$.

17.66 According to Table D-3, Ksp for $Ag_2S(s)$ is of the type

$$Ag_2S(s) + H_2O(l) \rightleftharpoons 2Ag^+(aq) + HS^-(aq) + OH^-(aq) \qquad K_{sp}$$

$$HS^-(aq) + H^+(aq) \rightleftharpoons H_2S(aq) \qquad 1/K_{a1}$$

$$2[Ag^+(aq) + 2Cl^-(aq) \rightleftharpoons AgCl_2^-(aq)] \qquad K_f^2$$

___

$$Ag_2S(s) + H_2O(l) + H^+(aq) + 4Cl^-(aq) \rightleftharpoons 2AgCl_2^-(aq) + H_2S(aq)$$

Add $H^+(aq)$ to each side to obtain the overall reacation

$$Ag_2S(s) + 2H^+(aq) + 4Cl^-(aq) \rightleftharpoons 2AgCl_2^-(aq) + H_2S(aq)$$

$$K = \frac{K_{sp} \times K_f^2}{K_{a1}} = \frac{(6 \times 10^{-51})(1.1 \times 10^5)^2}{(9.5 \times 10^{-8})} = 7.64 \times 10^{-34} = 8 \times 10^{-34}$$

Precipitation and Separation of Ions (section 17.6)

17.67 *Analyze/Plan.* Follow the logic in Sample Exercise 17.15. Precipitation conditions: will Q (see Chapter 15) exceed K_{sp} for the compound? *Solve.*

(a) In base, Ca^{2+} can form $Ca(OH)_2(s)$.

$$Ca(OH)_2(s) \rightleftharpoons Ca^{2+}(aq) + 2OH^-(aq); \quad K_{sp} = [Ca^{2+}][OH^-]^2$$

$Q = [Ca^{2+}][OH^-]^2; [Ca^{2+}] = 0.050\,M;$ pOH $= 14 - 8.0 = 6.0;$ $[OH^-] = 1.0 \times 10^{-6}\,M$

$Q = (0.050)(1.0 \times 10^{-6})^2 = 5.0 \times 10^{-14};$ $K_{sp} = 6.5 \times 10^{-6}$ (Appendix D)

$Q < K_{sp}$, no $Ca(OH)_2$ precipitates.

(b) $Ag_2SO_4(s) \rightleftharpoons 2Ag^+(aq) + SO_4^{2-}(aq); \quad K_{sp} = [Ag+]^2[SO_4^{2-}]$

$$[Ag^+] = \frac{0.050\,M \times 100\,mL}{110\,mL} = 4.545 \times 10^{-2} = 4.5 \times 10^{-2}\,M$$

$$[SO_4^{2-}] = \frac{0.050\,M \times 10\,mL}{110\,mL} = 4.545 \times 10^{-3} = 4.5 \times 10^{-3}\,M$$

$Q = (4.545 \times 10^{-2})^2 (4.545 \times 10^{-3}) = 9.4 \times 10^{-6};$ $K_{sp} = 1.5 \times 10^{-5}$

$Q < K_{sp}$, no Ag_2SO_4 precipitates.

17.68 (a) $Co(OH)_2(s) \rightleftharpoons Co^{2+}(aq) + 2OH^-(aq); K_{sp} = [Co^{2+}][OH^-]^2 = 1.3 \times 10^{-15}$

pH $= 8.5;$ pOH $= 14 - 8.5 = 5.5;$ $[OH^-] = 10^{-5.5} = 3.16 \times 10^{-6} = 3 \times 10^{-6}\,M$

$Q = (0.020)(3.16 \times 10^{-6})^2 = 2 \times 10^{-13};$ $Q > K_{sp}$, $Co(OH)_2$ will precipitate

(b) $AgIO_3(s) \rightleftharpoons Ag^+(aq) + IO_3^-(aq); K_{sp} = [Ag+][IO_3^-] = 3.1 \times 10^{-8}$

$$[Ag^+] = \frac{0.010\,M\,Ag^+ \times 0.020\,L}{0.030\,L} = 6.667 \times 10^{-3} = 6.7 \times 10^{-3}\,M$$

$$[IO_3^-] = \frac{0.015 \, M \, IO_3^- \times 0.010 \, L}{0.030 \, L} = 5.000 \times 10^{-3} = 5.0 \times 10^{-3} \, M$$

$$Q = (6.667 \times 10^{-3})(5.00 \times 10^{-3}) = 3.3 \times 10^{-5}; \, Q > K_{sp}, \, AgIO_3 \text{ will precipitate}$$

17.69   *Analyze/Plan.* We are asked to calculate pH necessary to precipitate $Mn(OH)_2(s)$ if the resulting Mn^{2+} concentration is $\leq 1 \, \mu g/L$.

$$Mn(OH)_2(s) \rightleftharpoons Mn^{2+}(aq) + 2OH^-(aq); \, K_{sp} = [Mn^{2+}][OH^-]^2 = 1.6 \times 10^{-13}$$

At equilibrium, $[Mn^{2+}][OH^-]^2 = 1.6 \times 10^{-13}$. Change concentration $Mn^{2+}(aq)$ to mol/L and solve for $[OH^-]$.   *Solve.*

$$\frac{1 \, \mu g \, Mn^{2+}}{1 \, L} \times \frac{1 \times 10^{-6} \, g}{1 \, \mu g} \times \frac{1 \, mol \, Mn^{2+}}{54.94 \, g \, Mn^{2+}} = 1.82 \times 10^{-8} = 2 \times 10^{-8} \, M \, Mn^{2+}$$

$$1.6 \times 10^{-13} = (1.82 \times 10^{-8})[OH^-]^2; \, [OH^-]^2 = 8.79 \times 10^{-6}; \, [OH^-] = 2.96 \times 10^{-3} = 3 \times 10^{-3} \, M$$

$$pOH = 2.53; \, pH = 14 - 2.53 = 11.47 = 11.5$$

17.70 $PbI_2(s) \rightleftharpoons Pb^{2+}(aq) + 2I^-(aq); \, K_{sp} = [Pb^{2+}][I^-]^2 = 8.49 \times 10^{-9}$

(This K_{sp} value is taken from *CRC Handbook of Chemistry and Physics*, 74th Edition.)

$$[Pb^{2+}] = \frac{0.10 \, M \times 0.2 \, mL}{10.2 \, mL} = 1.96 \times 10^{-3} = 2 \times 10^{-3} \, M; \, [I^-] = \left(\frac{8.49 \times 10^{-9}}{1.96 \times 10^{-3} \, M}\right)^{1/2} = 2.08 \times 10^{-3} = 2 \times 10^{-3} \, M$$

$$\frac{2.08 \times 10^{-3} \, mol \, I^-}{1 \, L} \times \frac{126.90 \, g \, I^-}{1 \, mol \, I^-} \times 0.0102 \, L = 2.69 \times 10^{-3} \, g \, I^- = 3 \times 10^{-3} \, g \, I^-$$

17.71   *Analyze/Plan.* We are asked which ion will precipitate first from a solution containing $Pb^{2+}(aq)$ and $Ag^+(aq)$ when $I^-(aq)$ is added. Follow the logic in Sample Exercise 17.16. Calculate $[I^-]$ needed to initiate precipitation of each ion. The cation that requires lower $[I^-]$ will precipitate first.   *Solve.*

$$Ag^+: \, K_{sp} = [Ag^+][I^-]; \, 8.3 \times 10^{-17} = (2.0 \times 10^{-4})[I^-]; \, [I^-] = \frac{8.3 \times 10^{-17}}{2.0 \times 10^{-4}} = 4.2 \times 10^{-13} \, M \, I^-$$

$$Pb^{2+}: \, K_{sp} = [Pb^{2+}][I^-]^2; \, 7.9 \times 10^{-9} = (1.5 \times 10^{-3})[I^-]^2; \, [I^-] = \left(\frac{7.9 \times 10^{-9}}{1.5 \times 10^{-3}}\right)^{1/2} = 2.3 \times 10^{-3} \, M \, I^-$$

AgI will precipitate first, at $[I^-] = 4.2 \times 10^{-13} \, M$.

17.72   (a)   Precipitation will begin when $Q = K_{sp}$.

$BaSO_4: K_{sp} = [Ba^{2+}][SO_4^{2-}] = 1.1 \times 10^{-10}$

$1.1 \times 10^{-10} = (0.010)[SO_4^{2-}]; \, [SO_4^{2-}] = 1.1 \times 10^{-8} \, M$

$SrSO_4: K_{sp} = [Sr^{2+}][SO_4^{2-}] = 3.2 \times 10^{-7}$

$3.2 \times 10^{-7} = (0.010)[SO_4^{2-}]; \, [SO_4^{2-}] = 3.2 \times 10^{-5} \, M$

The $[SO_4^{2-}]$ necessary to begin precipitation is the smaller of the two values, $1.1 \times 10^{-8}\ M\ SO_4^{2-}$.

(b) Ba^{2+} precipitates first, because it requires the smaller $[SO_4^{2-}]$.

(c) Sr^{2+} will begin to precipitate when $[SO_4^{2-}]$ in solution (not bound in $BaSO_4$) reaches $3.2 \times 10^{-5}\ M$.

17.73   *Analyze/Plan.* We are asked which ion will precipitate first when dilute $Ag^+(aq)$ is added to a solution containing $0.20\ M\ CrO_4^{2-}$, $0.10\ M\ CO_3^{2-}$ and $0.10\ M\ Cl^-$. The anions are present at different concentrations and their silver compounds have different stoichiometry, so we cannot directly compare K_{sp} values. Follow the logic in Sample Exercise 17.16. Calculate $[Ag^+]$ needed to initiate precipitation of each ion. The anion that requires lowest $[Ag^+]$ will precipitate first, and so on. *Solve.*

Ag_2CrO_4: $K_{sp} = [Ag^+]^2[CrO_4^{2-}] = 1.2 \times 10^{-12}$

$1.2 \times 10^{-12} = [Ag^+]^2(0.20);\ [Ag^+]^2 = 6.0 \times 10^{-12};\ [Ag^+] = 2.4 \times 10^{-6}\ M$

Ag_2CO_3: $K_{sp} = [Ag^+]^2[CO_3^{2-}] = 8.1 \times 10^{-12}$

$8.1 \times 10^{-12} = [Ag^+]^2(0.10);\ [Ag^+]^2 = 8.1 \times 10^{-11};\ [Ag^+] = 9.0 \times 10^{-6}\ M$

$AgCl$: $K_{sp} = [Ag^+][Cl^-] = 1.8 \times 10^{-10}$

$1.8 \times 10^{-10} = [Ag^+](0.10);\ [Ag^+] = 1.8 \times 10^{-9}$

$AgCl$ requires the smallest $[Ag^+]$ for precipitation and it will precipitate first. The other two will precipitate almost simultaneously.

17.74   It is not appropriate to compare K_{sp} values directly, because the stoichiometries of the the two precipitates are different.

(a)   Precipitation will begin when $Q = K_{sp}$.

$CaSO_4$: $K_{sp} = [Ca^{2+}][SO_4^{2-}] = 2.4 \times 10^{-5}$

$2.4 \times 10^{-5} = (0.20)[SO_4^{2-}];\ [SO_4^{2-}] = 1.2 \times 10^{-4}\ M$

Ag_2SO_4: $K_{sp} = [Ag^+]^2[SO_4^{2-}] = 1.5 \times 10^{-5}$

$1.5 \times 10^{-5} = (0.30)^2[SO_4^{2-}];\ [SO_4^{2-}] = 1.7 \times 10^{-4}\ M$

$CaSO_4$ requires the smaller $[SO_4^{2-}]$ for precipitation and it will precipitate first.

(b)   The $[SO_4^{2-}]$ necessary to begin precipitation is the smaller of the two values, $1.2 \times 10^{-4}\ M\ SO_4^{2-}$.

$$1.2 \times 10^{-4}\ M = \frac{1.0\ M\ SO_4^{2-} \times x\ L}{(0.010 + x\ L)};\ x = (0.010)1.2 \times 10^{-4} = 1.2 \times 10^{-6}\ L.$$

We assume x is small compared to 0.010 L. The required volume is then 1.2×10^{-6} L or 0.0012 mL or 1.2 μL. If one drop is approximately 0.2 mL, precipitation will begin as the first drop of $1.0\ M\ Na_2SO_4$ solution is added.

17 Additional Aspects of Aqueous Equilibria

Qualitative Analysis for Metallic Elements (section 17.7)

17.75 *Analyze/Plan.* Use Figure 17.23 and the description of the five qualitative analysis "groups" in Section 17.7 to analyze the given data. *Solve.*

The first two experiments eliminate Group 1 and 2 ions (Figure 17.23). The fact that no insoluble phosphates form in the filtrate from the third experiment rules out Group 4 ions. The ions which might be in the sample are those of Group 3, that is, Al^{3+}, Fe^{3+}, Cr^{3+}, Zn^{2+}, Ni^{2+}, Mn^{2+}, or Co^{2+}, and those of Group 5, NH_4^+, Na^+ or K^+.

17.76 Initial solubility in water rules out CdS and HgO. Formation of a precipitate on addition of HCl indicates the presence of $Pb(NO_3)_2$ (formation of $PbCl_2$). Formation of a precipitate on addition of H_2S at pH 1 probably indicates $Cd(NO_3)_2$ (formation of CdS). (This test can be misleading because enough Pb^{2+} can remain in solution after filtering $PbCl_2$ to lead to visible precipitation of PbS.) Absence of a precipitate on addition of H_2S at pH 8 indicates that $ZnSO_4$ is not present. The yellow flame test indicates presence of Na^+. In summary, $Pb(NO_3)_2$ and Na_2SO_4 are definitely present, $Cd(NO_3)_2$ is probably present, and CdS, HgO and $ZnSO_4$ are definitely absent.

17.77 *Analyze/Plan.* We are asked to devise a procedure to separate various pairs of ions in aqueous solutions. In each case, refer to Figure 17.23 to find a set of conditions where the solubility of the two ions differs. Construct a procedure to generate these conditions. *Solve.*

(a) Cd^{2+} is in Gp. 2, but Zn^{2+} is not. Make the solution acidic using 0.2 M HCl; saturate with H_2S. CdS will precipitate, ZnS will not.

(b) $Cr(OH)_3$ is amphoteric but $Fe(OH)_3$ is not. Add excess base; $Fe(OH)_3(s)$ precipitates, but Cr^{3+} forms the soluble complex $Cr(OH)_4^-$.

(c) Mg^{2+} is a member of Gp. 4, but K^+ is not. Add $(NH_4)_2HPO_4$ to a basic solution; Mg^{2+} precipitates as $MgNH_4PO_4$, K^+ remains in solution.

(d) Ag^+ is a member of Gp. 1, but Mn^{2+} is not. Add 6 M HCl, precipitate Ag^+ as AgCl(s).

17.78 (a) Make the solution slightly acidic and saturate with H_2S; CdS will precipitate, Na^+ remains in solution.

(b) Make the solution acidic, saturate with H_2S; CuS will precipitate, Mg^{2+} remains in solution.

(c) Add HCl, $PbCl_2$ precipitates. (It is best to carry out the reaction in an ice-water bath to reduce the solubility of $PbCl_2$.)

(d) Add dilute HCl; AgCl precipitates, Hg^{2+} remains in solution.

17.79 (a) Because phosphoric acid is a weak acid, the concentration of free $PO_4^{3-}(aq)$ in an aqueous phosphate solution is low except in strongly basic media. In less basic media, the solubility product of the phosphates of interest is not exceeded.

(b) K_{sp} for those cations in Group 3 is much larger. Thus, to exceed K_{sp}, a higher $[S^{2-}]$ is required. This is achieved by making the solution more basic.

(c)   They should all redissolve in strongly acidic solution, e.g., in 12 M HCl (the chlorides of all Group 3 metals are soluble).

17.80   The addition of $(NH_4)_2HPO_4$ could result in precipitation of salts from metal ions of the other groups. The $(NH_4)_2HPO_4$ will render the solution basic, so metal hydroxides could form as well as insoluble phosphates. It is essential to separate the metal ions of a group from other metal ions before carrying out the specific tests for that group.

Additional Exercises

17.81   *Analyze/Plan.* Follow the approach for deriving the Henderson-Hasselbach (H−H) equation from the K_a expression shown in Section 17.2. Begin with a general K_b expression. *Solve.*

$$B(aq) + H_2O(l) \rightleftharpoons BH^+(aq) + OH^-(aq); \quad K_b = \frac{[BH^+][OH^-]}{[B]}$$

$pOH = -\log[OH^-]$; rearrange K_b to solve for $[OH^-]$.

$$[OH^-] = \frac{K_b[B]}{[BH^+]}; \text{ take the } -\log \text{ of both sides}$$

$-\log[OH^-] = -\log K_b + (-\log[B] - (-\log[BH^+]))$

$pOH = pK_b + \log[BH^+] - \log[B]$

$$pOH = pK_b + \log \frac{[BH^+]}{[B]}$$

17.82   Benzene sulfonic acid = BSOH, sodium benzene sulfonate = BSONa

Use Equation 17.9, pH = pK_a + log [CB]/[CA].

pH = 2.25 + log(0.125 M BSONa/0.150 M BSOH)

pH = 2.25 + log(0.8333) = 2.25 + (−0.0792) = 2.17

17.83   The equilibrium of interest is

$$HC_5H_3O_3(aq) \rightleftharpoons H^+(aq) + C_5H_3O_3^-(aq); K_a = 6.76 \times 10^{-4} = \frac{[H^+][C_5H_3O_3^-]}{[HC_5H_3O_3]}$$

Begin by calculating $[HC_5H_3O_3]$ and $[C_5H_3O_3^-]$ for each case.

(a) $\dfrac{25.0 \text{ g } HC_5H_3O_3}{0.250 \text{ L soln}} \times \dfrac{1 \text{ mol } HC_5H_3O_3}{112.1 \text{ g } HC_5H_3O_3} = 0.8921 = 0.892 \ M \ HC_5H_3O_3$

$\dfrac{30.0 \text{ g } NaC_5H_3O_3}{0.250 \text{ L soln}} \times \dfrac{1 \text{ mol } NaC_5H_3O_3}{134.1 \text{ g } NaC_5H_3O_3} = 0.8949 = 0.895 \ M \ C_5H_3O_3^-$

$[H^+] = \dfrac{K_a[HC_5H_3O_3]}{[C_5H_3O_3^-]} = \dfrac{6.76 \times 10^{-4} (0.8921 - x)}{(0.8949 + x)} \approx \dfrac{6.76 \times 10^{-4}(0.8921)}{(0.8949)}$

$[H^+] = 6.74 \times 10^{-4} \ M$, pH = 3.171

(b)   For dilution, $M_1 V_1 = M_2 V_2$

$$[HC_5H_3O_3] = \frac{0.250\ M \times 30.0\ mL}{125\ mL} = 0.0600\ M$$

$$[C_5H_3O_3^-] = \frac{0.220\ M \times 20.0\ mL}{125\ mL} = 0.0352\ M$$

$$[H^+] \approx \frac{6.76 \times 10^{-4}\ (0.0600)}{0.0352} = 1.15 \times 10^{-3}\ M, pH = 2.938$$

(yes, $[H^+]$ is $< 5\%$ of $0.0352\ M$)

(c) $0.0850\ M \times 0.500\ L = 0.0425\ mol\ HC_5H_3O_3$

$1.65\ M \times 0.0500\ L = 0.0825\ mol\ NaOH$

	$HC_5H_3O_3(aq)$	+	$NaOH(aq)$	$\rightarrow$	$NaC_5H_3O_3(aq) + H_2O(l)$
initial	0.0425 mol		0.0825 mol		
reaction	–0.0425 mol		–0.0425 mol		+0.0425 mol
after	0 mol		0.0400 mol		0.0425 mol

The strong base NaOH dominates the pH; the contribution of $C_5H_3O_3^-$ is negligible. This combination would be "after the equivalence point" of a titration. The total volume is 0.550 L.

$$[OH^-] = \frac{0.0400\ mol}{0.550\ L} = 0.0727\ M; pOH = 1.138, pH = 12.862$$

17.84 $K_a = \dfrac{[H^+][In^-]}{[HIn]}$; at pH = 4.68, $[HIn] = [In^-]$; $[H^+] = K_a$; $pH = pK_a = 4.68$

17.85   (a) $HA(aq) + B(aq) \rightleftharpoons HB^+(aq) + A^-(aq)$ $K_{eq} = \dfrac{[HB^+][A^-]}{[HA][B]}$

(b)   Note that the solution is slightly basic because B is a stronger base than HA is an acid. (Or, equivalently, that A^- is a stronger base than HB^+ is an acid.) Thus, a little of the A^- is used up in reaction: $A^-(aq) + H_2O(l) \rightleftharpoons HA(aq) + OH^-(aq)$. Since pH is not very far from neutral, it is reasonable to assume that the reaction in part (a) has gone far to the right, and that $[A^-] \approx [HB^+]$ and $[HA] \approx [B]$. Then

$$K_a = \frac{[A^-][H^+]}{[HA]} = 8.0 \times 10^{-5}; \text{ when } pH = 9.2, [H^+] = 6.31 \times 10^{-10} = 6 \times 10^{-10}\ M$$

$$\frac{[A^-]}{[HA]} = 8.0 \times 10^{-5}/6.31 \times 10^{-10} = 1.268 \times 10^5 = 1 \times 10^5$$

From the assumptions above, $\dfrac{[A^-]}{[HA]} = \dfrac{[HB^+]}{[B]}$, so $K_{eq} \approx \dfrac{[A^-]^2}{[HA]^2} = 1.608 \times 10^{10} = 2 \times 10^{10}$

(c) K_b for the reaction $B(aq) + H_2O(l) \rightleftharpoons BH^+(aq) + OH^-(aq)$ can be calculated by noting that the equilibrium constant for the reaction in part (a) can be written as $K = K_a (HA) \times K_b (B) / K_w$. (You should prove this to yourself.) Then,

$$K_b\,(B) = \frac{K \times K_w}{K_a\,(HA)} = \frac{(1.608 \times 10^{10})(1.0 \times 10^{-14})}{8.0 \times 10^{-5}} = 2.010 = 2$$

$K_b\,(B)$ is larger than $K_a\,(HA)$, as it must be if the solution is basic.

17.86   (a) $K_a = \dfrac{[H^+][HCOO^-]}{[HCOOH]}; [H^+] = \dfrac{K_a[HCOOH]}{[HCOO^-]}$

Buffer A : $[HCOOH] = [HCOO^-] = \dfrac{1.00\ mol}{1.00\ L} = 1.00\ M$

$[H^+] = \dfrac{1.8 \times 10^{-4}\,(1.00\ M)}{(1.00\ M)} = 1.8 \times 10^{-4}\ M, pH = 3.74$

Buffer B : $[HCOOH] = [HCOO^-] = \dfrac{0.010\ mol}{1.00\ L} = 0.010\ M$

$[H^+] = \dfrac{1.8 \times 10^{-4}\,(0.010\ M)}{(0.010\ M)} = 1.8 \times 10^{-4}\ M, pH = 3.74$

The pH of a buffer is determined by the identity of the conjugate acid/conjugate base pair (that is, the relevant K_a value) and the ratio of concentrations of the conjugate acid and conjugate base. The absolute concentrations of the components is not relevant. The pH values of the two buffers are equal because they both contain HCOOH and HCOONa and the [HCOOH] / [$HCOO^-$] *ratio* is the same in both solutions.

   (b)   Buffer capacity is determined by the absolute amount of conjugate acid and conjugate base available to absorb strong acid (H^+) or strong base (OH^-) that is added to the buffer. Buffer A has the greater capacity because it contains the greater absolute concentrations of HCOOH and $HCOO^-$.

   (c)   Buffer A:

	HCOO$^-$	+	HCl	→	HCOOH	+	Cl$^-$
	1.00 mol		0.001 mol		1.00 mol		
	0.999 mol		0		1.001 mol		

$[H^+] = \dfrac{1.8 \times 10^{-4}\,(1.001)}{(0.999)} = 1.8 \times 10^{-4}\ M, pH = 3.74$

(In a buffer calculation, volumes cancel and we can substitute moles directly into the K_a expression.)

Buffer B:

	HCOO$^-$	+	HCl	→	HCOOH	+	Cl$^-$
	0.010 mol		0.001 mol		0.010 mol		
	0.009 mol		0		0.011 mol		

$$[H^+] = \frac{1.8 \times 10^{-4} \, (0.011)}{(0.009)} = 2.2 \times 10^{-4} \, M, \, pH = 3.66$$

(d)   Buffer A: $1.00 \, M \, HCl \times 0.010 \, L = 0.010 \, mol \, H^+$ added

         mol HCOOH $= 1.00 + 0.010 = 1.01$ mol

         mol $HCOO^-$ $= 1.00 - 0.010 = 0.99$ mol

$$[H^+] = \frac{1.8 \times 10^{-4} \, (1.01)}{(0.99)} = 1.8 \times 10^{-4} \, M, \, pH = 3.74$$

     Buffer B: mol HCOOH $= 0.010 + 0.010 = 0.020$ mol $= 0.020 \, M$

        mol $HCOO^-$ $= 0.010 - 0.010 = 0.000$ mol

The solution is no longer a buffer; the only source of $HCOO^-$ is the dissociation of HCOOH.

$$K_a = \frac{[H^+][COO^-]}{[HCOOH]} = \frac{x^2}{(0.020 - x) \, M}$$

The extent of ionization is greater than 5%; from the quadratic formula, $x = [H^+] = 1.8 \times 10^{-3}$, pH $= 2.74$.

(e)   Adding 10 mL of $1.00 \, M$ HCl to buffer B exceeded its capacity, while the pH of buffer A was unaffected. This is quantitative confirmation that buffer A has a significantly greater capacity than buffer B. In fact, 1.0 L of 1.0 M HCl would be required to exceed the capacity of buffer A. Buffer A, with 100 times more HCOOH and $HCOO^-$ has 100 times the capacity of buffer B.

17.87 $\dfrac{0.15 \, mol \, CH_3COOH}{1 \, L \, soln} \times 0.750 \, L = 0.1125 = 0.11 \, mol \, CH_3COOH$

$0.1125 \, mol \, CH_3COOH \times \dfrac{60.05 \, g \, CH_3COOH}{1 \, mol \, CH_3COOH} \times \dfrac{1 \, g \, gl \, acetic \, acid}{0.99 \, g \, CH_3COOH} \times \dfrac{1.00 \, mL \, gl \, acetic \, acid}{1.05 \, g \, gl \, acetic \, acid}$

$$= 6.5 \, mL \, glacial \, acetic \, acid$$

At pH 4.50, $[H^+] = 10^{-4.50} = 3.16 \times 10^{-5} = 3.2 \times 10^{-5} \, M$; this is small compared to $0.15 \, M \, CH_3COOH$.

$$K_a = \frac{(3.16 \times 10^{-5})[CH_3COO^-]}{0.15} = 1.8 \times 10^{-5}; \, [CH_3COO^-] = 0.0854 = 0.085 \, M$$

$$\frac{0.0854 \, mol \, CH_3COONa}{1 \, L \, soln} \times 0.750 \, L \times \frac{82.03 \, g \, CH_3COONa}{1 \, mol \, CH_3COONa} = 5.253 = 5.25 \, g \, CH_3COONa$$

17.88   (a)   For a monoprotic acid (one H^+ per mole of acid), at the equivalence point moles OH^- added = moles H^+ originally present

      $M_B \times V_B = g \, acid/molar \, mass$

$$MM = \frac{g\ acid}{M_B \times V_B} = \frac{0.2140\ g}{0.0950\ M \times 0.0274\ L} = 82.21 = 82.2\ g/mol$$

(b)   initial mol HA $= \dfrac{0.2140\ g}{82.21\ g/mol} = 2.603 \times 10^{-3} = 2.60 \times 10^{-3}$ mol HA

mol OH^- added to pH $6.50 = 0.0950\ M \times 0.0150\ L = 1.425 \times 10^{-3}$

$$= 1.43 \times 10^{-3}\ mol\ OH^-$$

	HA(aq)	+	NaOH(aq)	→	NaA(aq) + H₂O
before rx	2.603×10^{-3} mol		1.425×10^{-3} mol		0
change	-1.425×10^{-3} mol		-1.425×10^{-3} mol		$+1.425 \times 10^{-3}$ mol
after rx	1.178×10^{-3} mol		0		1.425×10^{-3} mol

$$[HA] = \frac{1.178 \times 10^{-3}\ mol}{0.0400\ L} = 0.02945 = 0.0295\ M$$

$$[A^-] = \frac{1.425 \times 10^{-3}\ mol}{0.0400\ L} = 0.03563 = 0.0356\ M; [H^+] = 10^{-6.50} = 3.162 \times 10^{-7}$$

$$= 3.2 \times 10^{-7}\ M$$

The mixture after reaction (a buffer) can be described by the acid dissociation equilibrium.

	HA(aq)	⇌	H⁺(aq)	+	A⁻(aq)
initial	0.0295 M		0		0.0356 M
equil	$(0.0295 - 3.2 \times 10^{-7}\ M)$		$3.2 \times 10^{-7}\ M$		$(0.0356 + 3.2 \times 10^{-7})\ M$

$$K_a = \frac{[H^+][A^-]}{[HA]} \approx \frac{(3.162 \times 10^{-7})(0.03563)}{(0.02945)} = 3.8 \times 10^{-7}$$

(Although we have carried 3 figures through the calculation to avoid rounding errors, the data dictate an answer with 2 significant figures.)

17.89   (a)   For a monoprotic acid (one H^+ per mole of acid), at the equivalence point moles OH^- added = moles H^+ originally present

$M_B \times V_B$ = g acid/molar mass

$$MM = \frac{g\ acid}{M_B \times V_B} = \frac{0.1687\ g}{0.1150\ M \times 0.0155\ L} = 94.642 = 94.6\ g/mol$$

(b)   initial mol HA $= \dfrac{0.1687\ g}{94.642\ g/mol} = 1.783 \times 10^{-3} = 1.78 \times 10^{-3}$ mol HA

mol OH^- added to pH $2.85 = 0.1150\ M \times 0.00725\ L = 8.338 \times 10^{-4}$

$$= 8.34 \times 10^{-4}\ mol\ OH^-$$

	HA(aq)	+	NaOH(aq)	→	NaA(aq) + H₂O
before rx	1.783×10^{-3} mol		0.834×10^{-3} mol		0
change	-0.834×10^{-3} mol		-0.834×10^{-3} mol		0.834×10^{-3} mol
after rx	0.949×10^{-3} mol		0		0.834×10^{-3} mol

$$[\text{HA}] = \frac{9.49 \times 10^{-4} \text{ mol}}{0.0325 \text{ L}} = 0.02919 = 0.0292 \; M$$

$$[\text{A}^-] = \frac{8.34 \times 10^{-4} \text{ mol}}{0.0325 \text{ L}} = 0.02565 = 0.0257 \; M$$

$$[\text{H}^+] = 10^{-2.85} = 1.413 \times 10^{-3} = 1.4 \times 10^{-3}$$

The mixture after reaction (a buffer) can be described by the acid dissociation equilibrium.

	HA(aq)	⇌	H⁺(aq)	+	A⁻(aq)
initial	0.0292 M		0		0.0257 M
equil	$(0.0292 - 1.4 \times 10^{-3} \; M)$		$1.4 \times 10^{-3} \; M$		$(0.0257 + 1.4 \times 10^{-3}) \; M$

$$K_a = \frac{[\text{H}^+][\text{A}^-]}{[\text{HA}]} \approx \frac{(1.413 \times 10^{-3})(0.02707)}{(0.02778)} = 1.4 \times 10^{-3}$$

(Although we have carried extra figures through the calculation to avoid rounding errors, the data dictate an answer with 2 significant figures.)

17.90 At the equivalence point of a titration, moles strong base added equals moles weak acid initially present. $M_B \times V_B$ = mol base added = mol acid initial

At the half-way point, the volume of base is one-half of the volume required to reach the equivalence point, and the moles base delivered equals one-half of the mol acid initially present. This means that one-half of the weak acid HA is converted to the conjugate base A⁻. If exactly half of the acid reacts, mol HA = mol A⁻ and [HA] = [A⁻] at the half-way point.

From Equation [17.9], $\text{pH} = \text{pK}_a + \log \dfrac{[\text{conj. base}]}{[\text{conj. acid}]} = \text{pK}_a + \log \dfrac{[\text{A}^-]}{[\text{HA}^-]}$.

If [A⁻]/[HA] = 1, log(1) = 0 and pH = pK$_a$ of the weak acid being titrated.

17.91 The reaction involved is HA(aq) + OH⁻(aq) ⇌ A⁻(aq) + H₂O(l). We thus have 0.080 mol A⁻ and 0.12 mol HA in a total volume of 1.0 L, so the "initial" molarities of A⁻ and HA are 0.080 M and 0.12 M, respectively. The weak acid equilibrium of interest is

$$\text{HA(aq)} \; \rightleftharpoons \; \text{H}^+\text{(aq)} + \text{A}^-\text{(aq)}$$

(a) $K_a = \dfrac{[\text{H}^+][\text{A}^-]}{[\text{HA}]}$; $[\text{H}^+] = 10^{-4.80} = 1.58 \times 10^{-5} = 1.6 \times 10^{-5} \; M$

Assuming [H⁺] is small compared to [HA] and [A⁻],

$$K_a \approx \frac{(1.58 \times 10^{-5})(0.080)}{(0.12)} = 1.06 \times 10^{-5} = 1.1 \times 10^{-5}, pK_a = 4.98$$

(b)   At pH = 5.00, $[H^+] = 1.0 \times 10^{-5} M$. Let b = extra moles NaOH.

[HA] = 0.12 – b, $[A^-]$ = 0.080 + b

$$1.06 \times 10^{-5} \approx \frac{(1.0 \times 10^{-5})(0.080+b)}{(0.12-b)}; \, 2.06 \times 10^{-5}\,b = 4.72 \times 10^{-7};$$

b = 0.023 mol NaOH

17.92   Assume that H_3PO_4 will react with NaOH in a stepwise fashion: (This is not unreasonable, since the three K_a values for H_3PO_4 are significantly different.)

	$H_3PO_4(aq)$	+	NaOH(aq)	$\rightarrow$	$H_2PO_4^-(aq) + Na^+(aq) + H_2O(l)$
before	0.20 mol		0.30 mol		0 mol
after	0 mol		0.10 mol		0.20 mol

	$H_2PO_4^-(aq)$	+	NaOH(aq)	$\rightarrow$	$HPO_4^-(aq) + Na^+(aq) + H_2O(l)$
before	0.20 mol		0.10 mol		0.25 mol
after	0.10 mol		0		0.35 mol

Thus, after all NaOH has reacted, the resulting 1.00 L solution is a buffer containing 0.10 mol $H_2PO_4^-$ and 0.35 mol HPO_4^{2-}. $H_2PO_4^-(aq) \rightleftharpoons H^+(aq) + HPO_4^{2-}(aq)$

$$K_a = 6.2 \times 10^{-8} = \frac{[HPO_4^{2-}][H^+]}{[H_2PO_4^-]}; [H^+] = \frac{6.2 \times 10^{-8}\,(0.10\,M)}{0.35\,M} = 1.77 \times 10^{-8} = 1.8 \times 10^{-8}\,M;$$

$$pH = 7.75$$

17.93   The pH of a buffer system is centered around pK_a for the conjugate acid component. For a diprotic acid, two conjugate acid/conjugate base pairs are possible.

$H_2X(aq) \rightleftharpoons H^+(aq) + HX^-(aq); \ K_{a1} = 2 \times 10^{-2}; \ pK_{a1} = 1.70$

$HX^-(aq) \rightleftharpoons H^+(aq) + X^{2-}(aq); \ \ K_{a2} = 5.0 \times 10^{-7}; \ pK_{a2} = 6.30$

Clearly HX^- / X^{2-} is the more appropriate combination for preparing a buffer with pH = 6.50. The $[H^+]$ in this buffer = $10^{-6.50} = 3.16 \times 10^{-7} = 3.2 \times 10^{-7}\,M$. Using the K_{a2} expression to calculate the $[X^{2-}] / [HX^-]$ ratio:

$$K_{a2} = \frac{[H^+][X^{2-}]}{[HX^-]}; \frac{K_{a2}}{[H^+]} = \frac{[X^{2-}]}{[HX^-]} = \frac{5.0 \times 10^{-7}}{3.16 \times 10^{-7}} = 1.58 = 1.6$$

Since X^{2-} and HX^- are present in the same solution, the ratio of concentrations is also a ratio of moles.

$$\frac{[X^{2-}]}{[HX^-]} = \left(\frac{mol\ X^{2-}/L\ soln}{mol\ HX^-/L\,soln}\right) = \frac{mol\ X^{2-}}{mol\ HX^-} = 1.58; mol\ X^{2-} = (1.58)\ mol\ HX^-$$

In the 1.0 L of 1.0 M H_2X, there is 1.0 mol of material containing X^{2-} .

Thus, mol HX^- + 1.58 (mol HX^-) = 1.0 mol. 2.58 (mol HX^-) = 1.0;

mol HX^- = 1.0 / 2.58 = 0.39 mol HX^-; mol X^{2-} = 1.0 – 0.39 = 0.61 mol X^{2-}.

Thus enough 1.0 M NaOH must be added to produce 0.39 mol HX^- and 0.61 mol X^{2-}.

Considering the neutralization in a step-wise fashion (see discussion of titrations of polyprotic acids in Section 17.3).

	$H_2X(aq)$	+	$NaOH(aq)$	$\rightarrow$	$HX^-(aq) + H_2O(l)$
before	1.0 mol		1 mol		0
after	0		0		1.0 mol

	$HX^-(aq)$	+	$NaOH(aq)$	$\rightarrow$	$X^{2-}(aq) + H_2O(l)$
before	1.0				0.61
change	–0.61		–0.61		+0.61
after	0.39		0		0.61

Starting with 1.0 mol of H_2X, 1.0 mol of NaOH is added to completely convert it to 1.0 mol of HX^-. Of that 1.0 mol of HX^-, 0.61 mol must be converted to 0.61 mol X^{2-}. The total moles of NaOH added is (1.00 + 0.61) = 1.61 mol NaOH.

$$\text{L NaOH} = \frac{\text{mol NaOH}}{M \text{ NaOH}} = \frac{1.61 \text{ mol}}{1.0 \, M} = 1.6 \text{ L of } 1.0 \, M \text{ NaOH}$$

17.94 $CH_3CH(OH)COO^-$ will be formed by reaction $CH_3CH(OH)COOH$ with NaOH.
0.1000 M × 0.02500 L = 2.500 × 10^{-3} mol $CH_3CH(OH)COOH$; b = mol NaOH needed

	$CH_3CH(OH)COOH$	+	NaOH	$\rightarrow$	$CH_3CH(OH)COO^- + H_2O + Na^+$
initial	2.500 × 10^{-3} mol		b mol		
rx	–b mol		–b mol		+b mol
after rx	(2.500 × 10^3 – b) mol		0		b mol

$$K_a = \frac{[H^+][CH_3CH(OH)COO^-]}{[CH_3CH(OH)COOH]}; K_a = 1.4 \times 10^{-4}; [H^+] = 10^{-pH} = 10^{-3.75} = 1.778 \times 10^{-4} = 1.8 \times 10^{-4} \, M$$

Since solution volume is the same for reaction $CH_3CH(OH)COOH$ and $CH_3CH(OH)COO^-$, we can use moles in the equation for $[H^+]$.

$$K_a = 1.4 \times 10^{-4} = \frac{1.778 \times 10^{-4} \, (b)}{(2.500 \times 10^{-3} - b)}; 0.7874 \, (2.500 \times 10^{-3} - b) = b, 1.969 \times 10^{-3} = 1.7874 \, b,$$

b = 1.10 × 10^{-3} = 1.1 × 10^{-3} mol OH^-

(The precision of K_a dictates that the result has 2 sig figs.)

Substituting this result into the K_a expression gives $[H^+]$ = 1.8 × 10^{-4}. This checks and confirms our result. Calculate volume NaOH required from M = mol/L.

$$1.10 \times 10^{-3} \text{ mol } OH^- \times \frac{1 \text{ L}}{1.000 \text{ mol}} \times \frac{1 \, \mu L}{1 \times 10^{-6} \text{ L}} = 1.1 \times 10^3 \, \mu L \, (1.1 \text{ mL})$$

17.95   (a) $H^+(aq) + HCO_3^-(aq) \rightleftharpoons H_2CO_3(aq) \rightleftharpoons H_2O(l) + CO_2(g)$

A person breathing normally exhales $CO_2(g)$. Rapid breathing causes excess $CO_2(g)$ to be removed from the blood. By LeChatelier's principle, this causes both equilibria above to shift right, reducing $[H^+]$ in the blood and raising blood pH.

(b)   Breathing in a paper bag traps the exhaled CO_2; the gas in the bag contains more CO_2 than ambient air. When a person inhales gas from the bag, a greater amount (partial pressure) of $CO_2(g)$ in the lungs shifts the equilibria left, increasing $[H^+]$ and lowering blood pH.

17.96   (a)   CdS: 8.0×10^{-28}; CuS: 6×10^{-37} CdS has greater molar solubility.

(b) $PbCO_3$: 7.4×10^{-14}; $BaCrO_4$: 2.1×10^{-10} $BaCrO_4$ has greater molar solubility.

(c)   Since the stoichiometry of the two complexes is not the same, K_{sp} values can't be compared directly; molar solubilities must be calculated from K_{sp} values.

$Ni(OH)_2$: $K_{sp} = 6.0 \times 10^{-16} = [Ni^{2+}][OH^-]^2$; $[Ni^{2+}] = x$, $[OH^-] = 2x$

$6.0 \times 10^{-16} = (x)(2x)^2 = 4x^3$; $x = 5.3 \times 10^{-6}\, M\, Ni^{2+}$

Note that $[OH^-]$ from the autoionization of water is less than 1% of $[OH^-]$ from $Ni(OH)_2$ and can be neglected.

$NiCO_3$: $K_{sp} = 1.3 \times 10^{-7} = [Ni^{2+}][CO_3^{2-}]$; $[Ni^{2+}] = [CO_3^{2-}] = x$

$1.3 \times 10^{-7} = x^2$; $x = 3.6 \times 10^{-4}\, M\, Ni^{2+}$

$NiCO_3$ has greater molar solubility than $Ni(OH)_2$, but the values are much closer than expected from inspection of K_{sp} values alone.

(d)   Again, molar solubilities must be calculated for comparison.

Ag_2SO_4: $K_{sp} = 1.5 \times 10^{-5} = [Ag^+]^2[SO_4^{2-}]$; $[SO_4^{2-}] = x$, $[Ag^+] = 2x$

          $1.5 \times 10^{-5} = (2x)^2(x) = 4x^3$; $x = 1.6 \times 10^{-2}\, M\, SO_4^{2-}$

AgI: $K_{sp} = 8.3 \times 10^{-17} = [Ag^+][I^-]$; $[Ag^+] = [I^-] = x$

          $8.3 \times 10^{-17} = x^2$; $x = 9.1 \times 10^{-9}\, M\, Ag^+$

Ag_2SO_4 has greater molar solubility than AgI.

17.97   (a) $K_{sp} = 4.5 \times 10^{-9} = [Ca^{2+}][CO_3^{2-}]$; $s = [Ca^{2+}] = [CO_3^{2-}]$

$s^2 = 4.5 \times 10^{-9}$, $s = 6.708 \times 10^{-5} = 6.7 \times 10^{-5}$

(b) $CaCO_3(s) \rightleftharpoons Ca^{2+}(aq) + CO_3^{2-}(aq)$ K_{sp}

$CO_3^{2-}(aq) + H_2O(l) \rightleftharpoons HCO_3^-(aq) + OH^-(aq)$ K_b

---

$CaCO_3(s) + H_2O(l) \rightleftharpoons Ca^{2+}(aq) + HCO_3^-(aq) + OH^-(aq)$ K

$K_b = K_w/K_a$ for HCO_3^-

$$K = K_{sp} \times K_b = \frac{K_{sp} \times K_w}{K_a \text{ for } HCO_3^-} = \frac{4.5 \times 10^{-9} \times 1 \times 10^{-14}}{5.6 \times 10^{-11}} = 8.036 \times 10^{-13} = 8.0 \times 10^{-13}$$

(c) $K = 8.036 \times 10^{-13} = [Ca^{2+}][CO_3^{2-}][OH^-] = s^3$; $s = 9.297 \times 10^{-5} = 9.3 \times 10^{-5}$ M

$[OH^-] = s = 9.297 \times 10^{-5}$ M; $pOH = 4.03165 = 4.03$; $pH = 14 - 4.03 = 9.97$

(d) $pH = 8.2$, $pOH = 14 - 8.2 = 5.8$. $[OH^-] = 10^{-5.8} = 1.585 \times 10^{-6} = 2 \times 10^{-6}$ M

$8.036 \times 10^{-13} = s^2(1.585 \times 10^{-6})$, $s = 7.121 \times 10^{-4} = 7 \times 10^{-4}$ M

(e) $pH = 7.5$, $pOH = 14 - 7.5 = 6.5$. $[OH^-] = 10^{-6.5} = 3.162 \times 10^{-7} = 3 \times 10^{-7}$ M

$8.036 \times 10^{-13} = s^2(3.162 \times 10^{-7})$, $s = 1.549 \times 10^{-3} = 2 \times 10^{-3}$ M

The drop in pH from 8.2 to 7.5 approximately doubles (from 7×10^{-4} M to 15×10^{-4} M) the molar solubility of $CaCO_3(s)$.

17.98   (a)   Hydroxyapatite: $K_{sp} = [Ca^{2+}]^5[PO_4^{3-}]^3[OH^-]$

Fluoroapatite: $K_{sp} = [Ca^{2+}]^5[PO_4^{3-}]^3[F^-]$

(b)   For each mole of apatite dissolved, one mole of OH^- or F^- is formed. Express molar solubility, s, in terms of $[OH^-]$ and $[F^-]$.

Hydroxyapatite: $[OH^-] = s$, $[Ca^{2+}] = 5s$, $[PO_4^{3-}] = 3s$

$K_{sp} = 6.8 \times 10^{-27} = (5s)^5(3s)^3 (s) = 84,375 \, s^9$

$s^9 = 8.059 \times 10^{-32} = 8.1 \times 10^{-32}$.

Use logs to find s. $s = 3.509 \times 10^{-4} = 3.5 \times 10^{-4}$ M $Ca_5(PO_4)_3OH$.

Fluoroapatite: $[F^-] = s$, $[Ca^{2+}] = 5s$, $[PO_4^{3-}] = 3s$

$K_{sp} = 1.0 \times 10^{-60} = (5s)^5(3s)^3 (s) = 84,375 \, s^9$

$s^9 = 1.185 \times 10^{-65} = 1.2 \times 10^{-65}$; $s = 6.109 \times 10^{-8} = 6.1 \times 10^{-8}$ M $Ca_5(PO_4)_3F$

17.99

$$Cr(OH)_3(s) \rightleftharpoons Cr^{3+}(aq) + 3OH^-(aq) \qquad\qquad K_{sp}$$
$$Cr^{3+}(aq) + 4OH^-(aq) \rightleftharpoons Cr(OH)_4^-(aq) \qquad\qquad K_f$$

$$Cr(OH)_3(s) + OH^-(aq) \rightleftharpoons Cr(OH)_4^-(aq) \qquad\qquad K$$

$K = K_{sp} \times K_f = (6.7 \times 10^{-31})(8 \times 10^{29}) = 0.536 = 0.5$

$K = \dfrac{[Cr(OH)_4^-]}{[OH^-]}$; $pOH = 14 - pH = 14 - 10.0 = 4.0$; $[OH^-] = 1 \times 10^{-4}$ M

$[Cr(OH)_4^-] = K \times [OH^-] = 0.536(1 \times 10^{-4}) = 5.36 \times 10^{-5} = 5 \times 10^{-5}$ M

(The K_{sp} value for $Cr(OH)_3$ listed in Appendix D is different from the value given in this exercise.)

17.100   *Analyze/Plan.* Calculate the solubility of $Mg(OH)_2$ in 0.50 M NH_4Cl. Find K_{sp} for $Mg(OH)_2$ in Appendix D. NH_4^+ is a weak acid, which will increase the solubility of $Mg(OH)_2$. Combine the various interacting equilibibria to obtain an overall reaction. Calculate K for this reaction and use it to calculate solubility (s) for $Mg(OH)_2$ in 0.50 M NH_4Cl. *Solve.*

$$Mg(OH)_2(s) \rightleftharpoons Mg^{2+}(aq) + 2\,OH^-(aq) \qquad K_{sp}$$

$$2NH_4^+(aq) \rightleftharpoons 2NH_3(aq) + 2H^+(aq) \qquad K_a$$

$$2H^+(aq) + 2OH^-(aq) \rightleftharpoons 2H_2O(l) \qquad 1/K_w$$

$$Mg(OH)_2(s) + 2NH_4^+(aq) + 2H^+(aq) + 2OH^-(aq) \rightleftharpoons Mg^{2+}(aq) + 2NH_3(aq)$$
$$+ 2OH^-(aq) + 2H^+(aq) + 2H_2O(l)$$

$$Mg(OH)_2(s) + 2NH_4^+(aq) \rightleftharpoons Mg^{2+}(aq) + 2NH_3(aq) + 2H_2O(l)$$

$$K = \frac{[Mg^{2+}][NH_3]^2}{[NH_4^+]^2} = \frac{K_{sp} \times K_a^2}{K_w^2}$$

$$K_a \text{ for } NH_4^+ = \frac{K_w}{K_b \text{ for } NH_3}; \quad \frac{K_a}{K_w} = \frac{1}{K_b}$$

$$K = \frac{K_{sp} \times K_a^2}{K_w^2} = \frac{K_{sp}}{K_b^2} = \frac{1.8 \times 10^{-11}}{(1.8 \times 10^{-5})^2} = 5.556 \times 10^{-2} = 5.6 \times 10^{-2}$$

Let $[Mg^{2+}] = s$, $[NH_3] = 2s$, $[NH_4^+] = 0.50 - 2s$

$$K = 5.6 \times 10^{-2} = \frac{[Mg^{2+}][NH_3]^2}{[NH_4^+]^2} = \frac{s\,(2s)^2}{(0.5 - 2s)^2} = \frac{4s^3}{0.25 - 2s + 4s^2}$$

$5.6 \times 10^{-2}(0.25 - 2s + 4s^2) = 4s^3$; $4s^3 - 0.222s^2 + 0.111s - 1.39 \times 10^{-2} = 0$

Clearly, 2s is not small relative to 0.50. Solving the third-order equation, s = 0.1054 = 0.11 M. The solubility of $Mg(OH)_2$ in 0.50 M NH_4Cl is 0.11 mol/L.

Check. Substitute s = 0.1054 into the K expression.

$$K = \frac{4(0.1054)^3}{[0.50 - 2(0.1054)]^2} = 5.6 \times 10^{-2}.$$

The solubility and K value are consistent, to the precision of the K_{sp} and K_b values.

17.101 $K_{sp} = [Ba^{2+}][MnO_4^-]^2 = 2.5 \times 10^{-10}$

$[MnO_4^-]^2 = 2.5 \times 10^{-10} / 2.0 \times 10^{-8} = 0.0125$; $[MnO_4^-] = \sqrt{0.0125} = 0.11\ M$

17.102 $[Ca^{2+}][CO_3^{2-}] = 4.5 \times 10^{-9}$; $[Fe^{2+}][CO_3^{2-}] = 2.1 \times 10^{-11}$

Since $[CO_3^{2-}]$ is the same for both equilibria:

$$[CO_3^{2-}] = \frac{4.5 \times 10^{-9}}{[Ca^{2+}]} = \frac{2.1 \times 10^{-11}}{[Fe^{2+}]}; \text{ rearranging } \frac{[Ca^{2+}]}{[Fe^{2+}]} = \frac{4.5 \times 10^{-9}}{2.1 \times 10^{-11}} = 214 = 2.1 \times 10^2$$

17.103 $PbSO_4(s) \rightleftharpoons Pb^{2+}(aq) + SO_4^{2-}(aq)$; $K_{sp} = 6.3 \times 10^{-7} = [Pb^{2+}][SO_4^{2-}]$

$SrSO_4(s) \rightleftharpoons Sr^{2+}(aq) + SO_4^{2-}(aq)$; $K_{sp} = 3.2 \times 10^{-7} = [Sr^{2+}][SO_4^{2-}]$

Let x = $[Pb^{2+}]$, y = $[Sr^{2+}]$, x + y = $[SO_4^{2-}]$

$$\frac{x(x+y)}{y(x+y)} = \frac{6.3 \times 10^{-7}}{3.2 \times 10^{-7}}; \frac{x}{y} = 1.9688 = 2.0; x = 1.969\ y = 2.0\ y$$

$$y(1.969\ y+y) = 3.2 \times 10^{-7}; 2.969\ y^2 = 3.2 \times 10^{-7}; y = 3.283 \times 10^{-4} = 3.3 \times 10^{-4}$$

$$x = 1.969\ y; x = 1.969(3.283 \times 10^{-4}) = 6.464 \times 10^{-4} = 6.5 \times 10^{-4}$$

$[Pb^{2+}] = 6.5 \times 10^{-4}\ M, [Sr^{2+}] = 3.3 \times 10^{-4}\ M, [SO_4{}^{2-}] = (3.283 + 6.464) \times 10^{-4} = 9.7 \times 10^{-4}\ M$

17.104 $MgC_2O_4(s) \rightleftharpoons Mg^{2+}(aq) + C_2O_4{}^{2-}(aq)$

$K_{sp} = [Mg^{2+}][C_2O_4{}^{2-}] = 8.6 \times 10^{-5}$

If $[Mg^{2+}]$ is to be $3.0 \times 10^{-2}\ M, [C_2O_4{}^{2-}] = 8.6 \times 10^{-5}/3.0 \times 10^{-2} = 2.87 \times 10^{-3} = 2.9 \times 10^{-3}\ M$

The oxalate ion undergoes hydrolysis:

$C_2O_4{}^{2-}(aq) + H_2O(l) \rightleftharpoons HC_2O_4{}^-(aq) + OH^-(aq)$

$$K_b = \frac{[HC_2O_4{}^-][OH^-]}{[C_2O_4{}^{2-}]} = 1.0 \times 10^{-14}/6.4 \times 10^{-5} = 1.56 \times 10^{-10} = 1.6 \times 10^{-10}$$

$[Mg^{2+}] = 3.0 \times 10^{-2}\ M, [C_2O_4{}^{2-}] = 2.87 \times 10^{-3} = 2.9 \times 10^{-3}\ M$

$[HC_2O_4{}^-] = (3.0 \times 10^{-2} - 2.87 \times 10^{-3})\ M = 2.71 \times 10^{-2} = 2.7 \times 10^{-2}\ M$

$$[OH^-] = 1.56 \times 10^{-10} \times \frac{[C_2O_4{}^{2-}]}{[HC_2O_4{}^-]} = 1.56 \times 10^{-10} \times \frac{(2.87 \times 10^{-3})}{(2.71 \times 10^{-2})} = 1.652 \times 10^{-11}$$

$[OH^-] = 1.7 \times 10^{-11}\ M;\ pOH = 10.78, pH = 3.22$

17.105 The student failed to account for the hydrolysis of the $AsO_4{}^{3-}$ ion. If there were no hydrolysis, $[Mg^{2+}]$ would indeed be 1.5 times that of $[AsO_4{}^{3-}]$. However, as the reaction $AsO_4{}^{3-}(aq) + H_2O(l) \rightleftharpoons HAsO_4{}^{2-}(aq) + OH^-(aq)$ proceeds, the ion product $[Mg^{2+}]^3[AsO_4{}^{3-}]^2$ falls below the value for K_{sp}. More $Mg_3(AsO_4)_2$ dissolves, more hydrolysis occurs, and so on, until an equilibrium is reached. At this point $[Mg^{2+}]$ in solution is much greater than 1.5 times free $[AsO_4{}^{3-}]$. However, it is exactly 1.5 times the **total** concentration of all arsenic-containing species. That is,

$[Mg^{2+}] = 1.5\ ([AsO_4{}^{3-}] + [HAsO_4{}^{2-}] + [H_2AsO_4{}^-] + [H_3AsO_4])$

17.106
$$Zn(OH)_2(s) \rightleftharpoons Zn^{2+}(aq) + 2OH^-(aq) \qquad K_{sp} = 3.0 \times 10^{-16}$$

$$Zn^{2+}(aq) + 4OH^-(aq) \rightleftharpoons Zn(OH)_4{}^{2-}(aq) \qquad K_f = 4.6 \times 10^{17}$$

$$Zn(OH)_2(s) + 2OH^-(aq) \rightleftharpoons Zn(OH)_4{}^{2-}(aq) \qquad K = K_{sp} \times K_f = 138 = 1.4 \times 10^2$$

$$K = 138 = 1.4 \times 10^2 = \frac{[Zn(OH)_4^{2-}]}{[OH^-]^2}$$

If 0.015 mol $Zn(OH)_2$ dissolves, 0.015 mol $Zn(OH)_4{}^{2-}$ should be present at equilibrium.

$$[OH^-]^2 = \frac{(0.015)}{138}; [OH^-] = 1.043 \times 10^{-2}\ M; [OH^-] \geq 1.0 \times 10^{-2}\ M\ or\ pH \geq 12.02$$

17.107 (a) $Cd(OH)_2(s) \rightleftharpoons Cd^{2+}(aq) + 2OH^-(aq)$; $K_{sp} = 2.5 \times 10^{-14} = [Cd^{2+}][OH^-]^2$.

$[Cd^{2+}] = s$; $[OH^-] = 2s$; $K_{sp} = 2.5 \times 10^{-14} = 4s^3$. $s = 1.8 \times 10^{-5}$ M.

(b)

$Cd(OH)_2(s) \rightleftharpoons Cd^{2+}(aq) + 2OH^-(aq)$		$K_{sp} = 2.5 \times 10^{-14}$
$Cd^{2+}(aq) + 4Br^-(aq) \rightleftharpoons CdBr_4^{2-}(aq)$		$K_f = 5 \times 10^3$

$Cd(OH)_2(s) + 4Br^-(aq) \rightleftharpoons CdBr_4^{2-}(aq) + 2OH^-(aq)$ K

$K = K_{sp} \times K_f = (2.5 \times 10^{-14})(5 \times 10^3) = 1.25 \times 10^{-10} = 1 \times 10^{-10}$

The desired molar solubility of $Cd(OH)_2$ is 1.0×10^{-3}. Assume all soluble Cd^{2+} is present as $CdBr_4^{2-}$. $[CdBr_4^{2-}] = 1.0 \times 10^{-3}$; $[OH^-] = 2(1.0 \times 10^{-3}) = 2.0 \times 10^{-3}$.

Let c = initial [NaBr] = initial $[Br^-]$; $[Br^-]$ at equilibrium = $c - 4(1.0 \times 10^{-3}) = (c - 4.0 \times 10^{-3})$.

$$K = 1.25 \times 10^{-10} = \frac{[CdBr_4^{2-}][OH^-]^2}{[Br^-]^4} = \frac{(1.0 \times 10^{-3})(2.0 \times 10^{-3})^2}{(c - 4.0 \times 10^{-3})^4}$$

Assume c is large relative to 4.0×10^{-3}.

$(1.25 \times 10^{-10})c^4 = 4.0 \times 10^{-9}$; $c = (32)^{1/4} = 2.378 = 2$ M. The approximation is valid. 4.0×10^{-3} is about 0.2% of 2 M. Check this result in the equilibrium expression.

$$K = \frac{(1.0 \times 10^{-3})(2.0 \times 10^{-3})^2}{(2.378 - 4.0 \times 10^{-3})^4} = 1.26 \times 10^{-10}. \text{ Our calculations are consistent.}$$

Integrative Exercises

17.108 (a) Complete ionic ($CHO_2^- = HCOO^-$)

$H^+(aq) + Cl^-(aq) + Na^+(aq) + HCOO^-(aq) \rightarrow HCOOH(aq) + Na^+(aq) + Cl^-(aq)$

Na^+ and Cl^- are spectator ions.

Net ionic: $H^+(aq) + HCOO^-(aq) \rightleftharpoons HCOOH(aq)$

(b) The net ionic equation in part (a) is the reverse of the dissociation of HCOOH.

$$K = \frac{1}{K_a} = \frac{1}{1.8 \times 10^{-4}} = 5.55 \times 10^3 = 5.6 \times 10^3$$

(c) For Na^+ and Cl^-, this is just a dilution problem.

$M_1V_1 = M_2V_2$; V_2 is 50.0 mL + 50.0 mL = 100.0 mL

Cl^-: $\dfrac{0.15\ M \times 50.0\ mL}{100.0\ mL} = 0.075\ M$; Na^+: $\dfrac{0.15\ M \times 50.0\ mL}{100.0\ mL} = 0.075\ M$

H^+ and $HCOO^-$ react to form HCOOH. Since $K \gg 1$, the reaction essentially goes to completion.

$$0.15 \, M \times 0.0500 \, mL = 7.5 \times 10^{-3} \, mol \, H^+$$

$$\frac{0.15 \, M \times 0.0500 \, mL = 7.5 \times 10^{-3} \, mol \, HCOO^-}{= 7.5 \times 10^{-3} \, mol \, HCOOH}$$

Solve the weak acid problem to determine $[H^+]$, $[HCOO^-]$ and $[HCOOH]$ at equilibrium.

$$K_a = \frac{[H^+][HCOO^-]}{[HCOOH]}; [H^+] = [HCOO^-] = x \, M; [HCOOH] = \frac{(7.5 \times 10^{-3} - x) \, mol}{0.100 \, L}$$

$$= (0.075 - x) \, M$$

$$1.8 \times 10^{-4} = \frac{x^2}{(0.075 - x)} \approx \frac{x^2}{0.075}; x = 3.7 \times 10^{-3} \, M \, H^+ \text{ and } HCOO^-$$

$$[HCOOH] = (0.075 - 0.0037) = 0.071 \, M$$

$$\frac{[H^+]}{[HCOOH]} \times 100 = \frac{3.7 \times 10^{-3}}{0.075} \times 100 = 4.9\% \text{ dissociation}$$

In summary:

$$[Na^+] = [Cl^-] = 0.075 \, M, [HCOOH] = 0.071 \, M, [H^+] = [HCOO^-] = 0.0037 \, M$$

17.109   (a)   For a monoprotic acid (one H^+ per mole of acid), at the equivalence point

moles OH^- added = moles H^+ originally present

$M_B \times V_B = $ g acid/molar mass

$$MM = \frac{g \, acid}{M_B \times V_B} = \frac{0.1044 \, g}{0.0500 \, M \times 0.02210 \, L} = 94.48 = 94.5 \, g/mol$$

(b)   11.05 mL is exactly half-way to the equivalence point (22.10 mL). When half of the unknown acid is neutralized, $[HA] = [A^-]$, $[H^+] = K_a$ and $pH = pK_a$.

$$K_a = 10^{-4.89} = 1.3 \times 10^{-5}$$

(c)   From Appendix D, Table D.1, acids with K_a values close to 1.3×10^{-5} are

name	K_a	formula	molar mass
propionic	1.3×10^{-5}	C_2H_5COOH	74.1
butanoic	1.5×10^{-5}	C_3H_7COOH	88.1
acetic	1.8×10^{-5}	CH_3COOH	60.1
hydroazoic	1.9×10^{-5}	HN_3	43.0

Of these, butanoic has the closest match for K_a and molar mass, but the agreement is not good.

17.110 $n = \dfrac{PV}{RT} = 735 \text{ torr} \times \dfrac{1 \text{ atm}}{760 \text{ torr}} \times \dfrac{7.5 \text{ L}}{295 \text{ K}} \times \dfrac{\text{K} \cdot \text{mol}}{0.08206 \text{ L} \cdot \text{atm}} = 0.300 = 0.30 \text{ mol NH}_3$

$0.40 \, M \times 0.50 \text{ L} = 0.20 \text{ mol HCl}$

	$HCl(aq)$ +	$NH_3(g)$ →	$NH_4^+(aq)$ +	$Cl^-(aq)$
Before	0.20 mol	0.30 mol		
after	0	0.10 mol	0.20 mol	0.20 mol

The solution will be a buffer because of the substantial concentrations of NH_3 and NH_4^+ present. Use K_a for NH_4^+ to describe the equilibrium.

$$NH_4^+(aq) \;\rightleftharpoons\; NH_3(aq) + H^+(aq)$$

equil. $0.20 - x$ $0.10 + x$ x

$$K_a = \dfrac{1.0 \times 10^{-14}}{1.8 \times 10^{-5}} = 5.56 \times 10^{-10} = 5.6 \times 10^{-10}; K_a = \dfrac{[NH_3][H^+]}{[NH_4^+]}; [H^+] = \dfrac{K_a[NH_4^+]}{[NH_3]}$$

Since this expression contains a ratio of concentrations, volume will cancel and we can substitute moles directly. Assume x is small compared to 0.10 and 0.20.

$$[H^+] = \dfrac{5.56 \times 10^{-10} \, (0.20)}{(0.10)} = 1.111 \times 10^{-9} = 1.1 \times 10^{-9} \, M, \text{ pH} = 8.95$$

17.111   Calculate the initial M of aspirin in the stomach and solve the equilibrium problem to find equilibrium concentrations of $C_8H_7O_2COOH$ and $C_8H_7O_2COO^-$. At pH = 2, $[H^+] = 1 \times 10^{-2}$.

$$\dfrac{325 \text{ mg}}{\text{tablet}} \times 2 \text{ tablets} \times \dfrac{1 \text{ g}}{1000 \text{ mg}} \times \dfrac{1 \text{ mol } C_8H_7O_2COOH}{180.2 \text{ g } C_8H_7O_2COOH} \times \dfrac{1}{1 \text{ L}} = 3.61 \times 10^{-3} = 4 \times 10^{-3} \, M$$

	$C_8H_7O_2COOH(aq)$	$\rightleftharpoons$ $C_8H_7O_2COO^-$ +	$H^+(aq)$
initial	$3.61 \times 10^{-3} \, M$	0	$1 \times 10^{-2} \, M$
equil	$(3.61 \times 10^{-3} - x) \, M$	$x \, M$	$(1 \times 10^{-2} + x) \, M$

$$K_a = 3 \times 10^{-5} = \dfrac{[H^+][C_8H_7O_2COO^-]}{[C_8H_7O_2COOH]} = \dfrac{(0.01 + x)(x)}{(3.61 \times 10^{-3} - x)} \approx \dfrac{0.01 \, x}{3.61 \times 10^{-3}}$$

$$x = [C_8H_7O_2COO^-] = 1.08 \times 10^{-5} = 1 \times 10^{-5} \, M$$

$$\% \text{ ionization} = \dfrac{1.08 \times 10^{-5} \, M \, C_8H_7O_2COO^-}{3.61 \times 10^{-3} \, M \, C_8H_7O_2COOH} \times 100 = 0.3\%$$

(% ionization is small, so the approximation was valid.)

% aspirin molecules = 100.0% − 0.3% = 99.7% molecules

17.112   According to Equation [13.4], $S_g = kP_g$

$$S_{CO_2} = 3.1 \times 10^{-2} \frac{mol}{L-atm} \times 1.10 \, atm = 0.0341 = \frac{0.034 \, mol}{L} = 0.034 \, M \, CO_2$$

$CO_2(g) + H_2O(l) \rightarrow H_2CO_3(aq); \, 0.0341 \, M \, CO_2 = 0.0341 \, M \, H_2CO_3$

Consider the stepwise dissociation of $H_2CO_3(aq)$.

	$H_2CO_3(aq)$	$\rightleftharpoons$	$H^+(aq)$	+	$HCO_3^-(aq)$
initial	0.0341 M		0		0
equil.	(0.0341-x) M		x		x

$$K_{a1} = \frac{[H^+][HCO_3^-]}{[H_2CO_3]} = \frac{x^2}{(0.0341-x)} \approx \frac{x^2}{0.0341} \approx 4.3 \times 10^{-7}$$

$x^2 = 1.47 \times 10^{-8}; \, x = 1.2 \times 10^{-4} \, M \, H^+; \, pH = 3.92$

$K_{a2} = 5.6 \times 10^{-11}$; assume the second ionization does not contribute significantly to $[H^+]$.

17.113 $Ca(OH)_2(aq) + 2HCl(aq) \rightarrow CaCl_2(aq) + 2H_2O$

mmol HCl = $M \times mL = 0.0983 \, M \times 11.23 \, mL = 1.1039 = 1.10$ mmol HCl

mmol $Ca(OH)_2$ = mmol HCl/2 = 1.1039/2 = 0.55195 = 0.552 mmol $Ca(OH)_2$

$$[Ca^{2+}] = \frac{0.55195 \, mmol}{50.00 \, mL} = 0.01104 = 0.0110 \, M$$

$[OH^-] = 2[Ca^{2+}] = 0.02208 = 0.0221 \, M$

$K_{sp} = [Ca^{2+}][OH^-]^2 = (0.01104)(0.02208)2 = 5.38 \times 10^{-6}$

The value in Appendix D is 6.5×10^{-6}, a difference of 17%. Since a change in temperature does change the value of an equilibrium constant, the solution may not have been kept at 25 °C. It is also possible that experimental errors led to the difference in K_{sp} values.

17.114 $\Pi = MRT, M = \frac{\Pi}{RT} = \frac{21 \, torr}{298 \, K} \times \frac{1 \, atm}{760 \, torr} \times \frac{K-mol}{0.08206 \, L-atm} = 1.13 \times 10^{-3} = 1.1 \times 10^{-3} \, M$

$SrSO_4(s) \rightleftharpoons Sr^{2+}(aq) + SO_4^{2-}(aq); \, K_{sp} = [Sr^{2+}][SO_4^{2-}]$

The total particle concentration is $1.13 \times 10^{-3} \, M$. Each mole of $SrSO_4$ that dissolves produces 2 mol of ions, so $[Sr^{2+}] = [SO_4^{2-}] = 1.13 \times 10^{-3} \, M/2 = 5.65 \times 10^{-4} = 5.7 \times 10^{-4} \, M$.

$K_{sp} = (5.65 \times 10^{-4})^2 = 3.2 \times 10^{-7}$

17.115   For very dilute aqueous solutions, assume the solution density is 1 g/mL.

$$ppb = \frac{g \, solute}{10^9 \, g \, solution} = \frac{1 \times 10^{-6} \, g \, solute}{1 \times 10^3 \, g \, solution} = \frac{\mu g \, solute}{L \, solution}$$

(a) $K_{sp} = [Ag^+][Cl^-] = 1.8 \times 10^{-10}$; $[Ag^+] = (1.8 \times 10^{-10})^{1/2} = 1.34 \times 10^{-5} = 1.3 \times 10^{-5}\,M$

$$\frac{1.34 \times 10^{-5}\,\text{mol Ag}^+}{L} \times \frac{107.9\,\text{g Ag}^+}{1\,\text{mol Ag}^+} \times \frac{1\,\mu g}{1 \times 10^{-6}\,g} = \frac{1.4 \times 10^3\,\mu g\,\text{Ag}^+}{L}$$

$$= 1.4 \times 10^3\,\text{ppb} = 1.4\,\text{ppm}$$

(b) $K_{sp} = [Ag^+][Br^-] = 5.0 \times 10^{-13}$; $[Ag^+] = (5.0 \times 10^{-13})^{1/2} = 7.07 \times 10^{-7} = 7.1 \times 10^{-7}\,M$

$$\frac{7.07 \times 10^{-7}\,\text{mol Ag}^+}{L} \times \frac{107.9\,\text{g Ag}^+}{1\,\text{mol Ag}^+} \times \frac{1\,\mu g}{1 \times 10^{-6}\,g} = 76\,\text{ppb}$$

(c) $K_{sp} = [Ag^+][I^-] = 8.3 \times 10^{-17}$; $[Ag^+] = (8.3 \times 10^{-17})^{1/2} = 9.11 \times 10^{-9} = 9.1 \times 10^{-9}\,M$

$$\frac{9.11 \times 10^{-9}\,\text{mol Ag}^+}{L} \times \frac{107.9\,\text{g Ag}^+}{1\,\text{mol Ag}^+} \times \frac{1\,\mu g}{1 \times 10^{-6}\,g} = 0.98\,\text{ppb}$$

AgBr(s) would maintain $[Ag^+]$ in the correct range.

17.116   To determine precipitation conditions, we must know K_{sp} for $CaF_2(s)$ and calculate Q under the specified conditions. $K_{sp} = 3.9 \times 10^{-11} = [Ca^{2+}][F^-]^2$

$[Ca^{2+}]$ and $[F^-]$. The term 1 ppb means 1 part per billion or 1 g solute per billion g solution. Assume that the density of this very dilute solution is the density of water.

$$1\,\text{ppb} = \frac{1\,\text{g solute}}{1 \times 10^9\,\text{g solution}} \times \frac{1\,\text{g solution}}{1\,\text{mL solution}} \times \frac{1 \times 10^3\,\text{mL}}{1\,L} = \frac{1 \times 10^{-6}\,\text{g solute}}{1\,\text{L solution}}$$

$$\frac{1 \times 10^{-6}\,\text{g solute}}{1\,\text{L solution}} \times \frac{1\,\mu g}{1 \times 10^{-6}\,g} = 1\,\mu g/1\,L$$

$$8\,\text{ppb Ca}^{2+} \times \frac{1\,\mu g}{1\,L} = \frac{8\,\mu g\,\text{Ca}^{2+}}{1\,L} = \frac{8 \times 10^{-6}\,g\,\text{Ca}^{2+}}{1\,L} \times \frac{1\,\text{mol Ca}^{2+}}{40\,g} = 2 \times 10^{-7}\,M\,\text{Ca}^{2+}$$

$$1\,\text{ppb F}^- \times \frac{1\,\mu g}{1\,L} = \frac{1\,\mu g\,\text{F}^-}{1\,L} = \frac{1 \times 10^{-6}\,g\,\text{F}^-}{1\,L} \times \frac{1\,\text{mol F}^-}{19.0\,g} = 5 \times 10^{-8}\,M\,\text{F}^-$$

$$Q = [Ca^{2+}][F^-]^2 = (2 \times 10^{-7})(5 \times 10^{-8})^2 = 5 \times 10^{-22}$$

$5 \times 10^{-22} < 3.9 \times 10^{-11}$, $Q < K_{sp}$, no CaF_2 will precipitate

18 Chemistry of the Environment

Visualizing Concepts

18.1 *Analyze.* Given that one mole of an ideal gas at 1 atm and 298 K occupies 22.4 L, is the volume of one mole of ideal gas in the middle of the stratosphere greater than, equal to, or less than 22.4 L?

Plan. Consider the relationship between pressure, temperature, and volume of an ideal gas. Use Figure 18.1 to estimate the pressure and temperature in the middle of the stratosphere, and compare the two sets of temperature and pressure.

Solve. According to the ideal gas law, $PV = nRT$, so $V = nRT/P$. Since n and R are constant for this exercise, V is proportional to T/P.

(a) The stratosphere ranges from 10 to 50 km, so the middle is at approximately 30 km. At this altitude, $T \approx 230$ K, $P \approx 40$ torr (from Figure 18.1). Since we are comparing T/P ratios, either atm or torr can be used as pressure units; we will use torr.

At sea level: $T/P = 298$ K/760 torr = 0.39

At 30 km: $T/P = 230$ K/40 torr = 5.75

The proportionality constant (T/P) is much greater at 30 km than sea level, so the volume of 1 mol of an ideal gas is greater at this altitude. The decrease in temperature at 30 km is more than offset by the substantial decrease in pressure.

(b) Volume is proportional to T/P, not simply T. The relative volumes of one mole of an ideal gas at 50 km and 85 km depend on the temperature and pressure at the two altitudes. From Figure 18.1,

50 km: $T \approx 270$ K, $P \approx 20$ torr, $T/P = 270$ K/20 torr = 13.5

85 km: $T \approx 190$ K, $P < 0.01$ torr, $T/P = 190$ K/0.01 torr = 19,000

Again, the slightly lower temperature at 85 km is more than offset by a much lower pressure. One mole of an ideal gas will occupy a much larger volume at 85 km than 50 km.

(c) Gases behave most ideally at high temperature and low pressure. Pressure is minimum and temperature is high in the thermosphere. The stratopause (the boundary between the stratosphere and mesosphere) and the troposphere at low altitude are other regions with temperature maxima and relatively low pressures.

18.2 Molecules in the upper atmosphere tend to have multiple bonds because they have sufficiently high bond dissociation enthalpies (Table 8.4) to survive the incoming high energy radiation from the sun. According to Table 8.4, for the same two bonded atoms, multiple bonds have higher bond dissociation enthalpies than single bonds. Molecules with single bonds are likely to undergo photodissociation in the presence of the high energy, short wavelength solar radiation present in the upper atmosphere.

18.3   (a)   A= troposphere, 0–10 km; B= stratosphere, 12–50 km; C= mesosphere, 50–85 km

            (b)   Ozone is a pollutant in the troposphere and filters UV radiation in the stratosphere.

            (c)   Infrared radiation from Earth is most strongly reflected back in the troposphere.

            (d)   Assuming the "boundary" between the stratosphere and mesosphere is at 50 km, only region C in the diagram is involved in an aurora borealis.

            (e)   The concentration of water vapor is greatest near Earth's surface in region A and decreases with altitude. Water's single bonds are susceptible to photodissociation in regions B and C, so it's concentration is likely to be very low in these regions. The relative concentration of CO_2, with strong double bonds, increases in regions B and C, because it is less susceptible to photodissociation.

18.4   *Analyze.* Given granite, marble, bronze, and other solid materials, what observations and measurements indicate whether the material is appropriate for an outdoor sculpture? If the material changes (erodes) over time, what chemical processes are responsible?

       Plan. An appropriate material resists chemical and physical changes when exposed to environmental conditions. An inappropriate material undergoes chemical reactions with substances in the troposphere, degrading the structural strength of the material and the sculpture.   *Solve.*

       (a)   The appearance and mass of the material upon environmental exposure are both indicators of chemical and physical changes. If the appearance and mass of the material are unchanged after a period of time, the material is well-suited for the sculpture because it is inert to chemical and physical changes. Changes in the color or texture of the material's surface indicate that a chemical reaction has occurred, because a different substance with different properties has formed. A decrease in mass indicates that some of the material has been lost, either by chemical reaction or physical change. An increase in mass indicates corrosion. If the mass of the material is unchanged, it is probably inert to chemical and physical environmental changes and suitable for sculpture.

       (b)   The two main chemical processes that lead to erosion are reaction with acid rain and corrosion or air oxidation, which is encouraged by acid conditions (see Section 20.8).

               Acid rain is primarily H_2SO_3 and/or H_2SO_4, which reacts directly with carbonate minerals such as marble and limestone. Acidic conditions created by acid rain encourage corrosion of metals such as iron, steel, and bronze. Corrosion produces metal oxides which may or may not cling to the surface of the material. If the oxides are washed away, the material will lose mass after corrosion. Physical erosion due to the effects of wind and rain on soft materials such as sandstone also causes mass to decrease.

18.5   The Sun

18.6   *Saltwater*, *freshwater* and *groundwater* differ in salt content, location and percentage of Earth's total water.

    Saltwater contains high concentrations of dissolved salts and solids and includes the world ocean (97.2% of all water) and brackish or salty water (0.1% of all water) in places such as the Great Salt Lake and the Chesapeake Bay. The world ocean averages about 35 g of dissolved salts per kg of water, or 35,000 ppm.

    Freshwater (0.6% of all water on earth) refers to natural waters that have low concentrations (less than 500 ppm) of dissolved salts and solids. Freshwater includes the waters of lakes, rivers, ponds, and streams.

    Groundwater is freshwater that is under the soil. It resides in aquifers, porous rock that holds water, and composes 20% of the world's freshwater.

18.7 $CO_2(g)$ dissolves in seawater to form $H_2CO_3(aq)$. The basic pH of the ocean encourages ionization of $H_2CO_3(aq)$ fo form $HCO_3^-(aq)$ and $CO_3^{2-}(aq)$. Under the correct conditions, carbon is removed from the ocean as $CaCO_3(s)$ (sea shells, coral, chalk cliffs). As carbon is removed, more $CO_2(g)$ dissolves to maintain the balance of complex and interacting acid-base and precipitation equilibria.

18.8   *Analyze/Plan.* Explain how an ion-exchange column "softens" water. See the Closer Look box on "Water Softening" in Section 18.4.

    Solve. The plastic beads in an ion-exchange column contain covalently bound anionic groups such as $R-COO^-$ and $R-SO_3^-$. These groups have Na^+ cations associated with them for charge balance. When "hard" water containing Ca^{2+} and other divalent cations passes over the beads, the 2+ cations are attracted to the anionic groups and Na^+ is displaced. The higher charge on the divalent cations leads to greater electrostatic attractions, which promote the cation exchange. The "soft" water that comes out of the column contains two Na^+ ions in place of each divalent cation, mostly Ca^{2+} and Mg^{2+}, that remains in the column associated with the plastic beads.

18.9   The guiding principle of green chemistry is that "an ounce of prevention is worth a pound of cure." Processes should be designed to minimize or eliminate solvents and waste, generate nontoxic waste, be energy efficient, employ renewable starting materials, and take advantage of catalysts that enable the use of safe and common reagents.

18.10   Some of the missing CO_2 is absorbed by "land plants" (vegetation other than trees) and incorporated into the soil. Soil is the largest land-based carbon reservoir. The amount of carbon-storing capacity of soil is affected by erosion, soil fertility, and other complex factors. For more details, search the internet for "carbon budget."

Earth's Atmosphere (section 18.1)

18.11   (a)   The temperature profile of the atmosphere (Figure 18.1) is the basis of its division into regions. The center of each peak or trough in the temperature profile corresponds to a new region.

(b) Troposphere, 0–12 km; stratosphere, 12–50 km; mesosphere, 50–85 km; thermosphere, 85–110 km.

18.12 (a) Boundaries between regions of the atmosphere are at maxima and minima (peaks and valleys) in the atmospheric temperature profile. For example, in the troposphere, temperature decreases with altitude, while in the stratosphere, it increases with altitude. The temperature minimum is the tropopause boundary.

(b) From Figure 18.1, atmospheric pressure in the troposphere ranges from 760 torr to 200 torr, while pressure in the stratosphere ranges from 200 torr to 20 torr. Gas density (g/L) is directly proportional to pressure. The much lower density of the stratosphere means it has the smaller mass, despite having a larger volume than the troposphere.

18.13 *Analyze/Plan.* Given O_3 concentration in ppm, calculate partial pressure. Use the definition of ppm to get mol fraction O_3. For gases mole fraction = pressure fraction. Use the ideal-gas law to find mol O_3/L air and Avogadro's number to get molecules/L.

$$P_{O_3} = \chi_{O_3} \times P_{atm}; \quad 0.441 \text{ ppm } O_3 = \frac{0.441 \text{ mol } O_3}{1 \times 10^6 \text{ mol air}} = 4.41 \times 10^{-7} = \chi_{O_3} \quad Solve.$$

(a) $P_{O_3} = \chi_{O_3} \times P_{atm} = 4.41 \times 10^{-7} (0.67 \text{ atm}) = 2.955 \times 10^{-7} = 3.0 \times 10^{-7}$ atm

(b) $n = \dfrac{PV}{RT} = \dfrac{2.955 \times 10^{-7} \text{ atm} \times 1.0 \text{ L}}{298 \text{ K}} \times \dfrac{\text{mol-K}}{0.08206 \text{ L-atm}} = 1.208 \times 10^{-8} = 1.2 \times 10^{-8}$ mol O_3

1.208×10^{-8} mol $O_3 \times \dfrac{6.022 \times 10^{23} \text{ molecules}}{\text{mol}} = 7.277 \times 10^{15} = 7.3 \times 10^{15}$ O_3 molecules

18.14 $P_{Ar} = \chi_{Ar} \times P_{atm}; \quad P_{Ar} = 0.00934 (1.05 \text{ bar}) = 0.009807 = 9.81 \times 10^{-3}$ bar

$P_{Ar} = 0.009807 \text{ bar} \times \dfrac{10^5 \text{ Pa}}{\text{bar}} \times \dfrac{760 \text{ torr}}{101{,}325 \text{ Pa}} = 7.3559 = 7.36$ torr

$P_{CO_2} = \chi_{CO_2} \times P_{atm}; \quad P_{CO_2} = 0.000382 (1.05 \text{ bar}) = 0.0004011 = 4.01 \times 10^{-4}$ bar

$P_{CO_2} = 0.0004011 \text{ bar} \times \dfrac{10^5 \text{ Pa}}{\text{bar}} \times \dfrac{760 \text{ torr}}{101{,}325 \text{ Pa}} = 0.30085 = 0.301$ torr

18.15 *Analyze/Plan.* Given CO concentration in ppm, calculate number of CO molecules in 1.0 L air at given conditions. ppm CO $\to \chi_{O_3} \to$ atm CO $\to$ mol CO $\to$ molecules CO. Use the ideal gas law to change atm CO to mol CO, then Avogadro's number to get molecules. *Solve.*

$$3.5 \text{ ppm CO} = \frac{3.5 \text{ mol CO}}{1 \times 10^6 \text{ mol air}} = 3.5 \times 10^{-6} = \chi_{CO}$$

$P_{CO} = \chi_{CO} \times P_{atm} = 3.5 \times 10^{-6} \times 759 \text{ torr} \times \dfrac{1 \text{ atm}}{760 \text{ torr}} = 3.495 \times 10^{-6} = 3.5 \times 10^{-6}$ atm

$n_{CO} = \dfrac{P_{CO}V}{RT} = \dfrac{3.495 \times 10^{-6} \text{ atm} \times 1.0 \text{ L}}{295 \text{ K}} \times \dfrac{\text{mol-K}}{0.08206 \text{ L-atm}} = 1.444 \times 10^{-7} = 1.4 \times 10^{-7}$ mol CO

1.444×10^{-7} mol CO $\times \dfrac{6.022 \times 10^{23} \text{ molecules}}{\text{mol}} = 8.695 \times 10^{16} = 8.7 \times 10^{16}$ molecules CO

18.16   (a)   ppm Ne = mol Ne/1 × 10^6 mol air; χ_{Ne} = 1.818 × 10^{-5} mol Ne/mol air

$$\frac{1.818 \times 10^{-5} \text{ mol Ne}}{1 \text{ mol air}} = \frac{x \text{ mol Ne}}{1 \times 10^6 \text{ mol air}}; x = 18.18 \text{ ppm Ne}$$

(b) $P_{Ne} = \chi_{Ne} \times P_{atm} = 1.818 \times 10^{-5} \times 730 \text{ torr} \times \dfrac{1 \text{ atm}}{760 \text{ torr}} = 1.7462 \times 10^{-5} = 1.75 \times 10^{-5} \text{ atm}$

T = 296 K

$$\frac{n_{Ne}}{V} = \frac{P_{Ne}}{RT} = \frac{1.7462 \times 10^{-5} \text{ atm}}{296 \text{ K}} \times \frac{\text{mol-K}}{0.08206 \text{ L-atm}} = 7.1892 \times 10^{-7} = 7.19 \times 10^{-7} \text{ mol/L}$$

$$\frac{7.1892 \times 10^{-7} \text{ mol Ne}}{L} \times \frac{6.022 \times 10^{23} \text{ atoms}}{\text{mol}} = 4.3293 \times 10^{17}$$

$$= 4.33 \times 10^{17} \text{ Ne atoms/L}$$

18.17   *Analyze/Plan.* Given bond dissociation energy in kJ/mol, calculate the wavelength of a single photon that will rupture a C–Br bond. kJ/mol $\rightarrow$ J/molecule. λ = hc/E. (λ = hc/E describes the energy/wavelength relationship of a single photon.)   *Solve.*

(a) $\dfrac{210 \times 10^3 \text{ J}}{1 \text{ mol}} \times \dfrac{1 \text{ mol}}{6.022 \times 10^{23} \text{ molecules}} = 3.487 \times 10^{-19} = 3.49 \times 10^{-19}$ J/molecule

$\lambda = c/\nu$ We also have that E = hν, so ν = E/h. Thus,

$$\lambda = \frac{hc}{E} = \frac{(6.626 \times 10^{-34} \text{ J-sec})(3.00 \times 10^8 \text{ m/sec})}{3.487 \times 10^{-19} \text{ J}} = 5.70 \times 10^{-7} \text{ m} = 570 \text{ nm}$$

(b)   This 570 nm wavelength is visible electromagnetic radiation.

18.18 $\dfrac{339 \times 10^3 \text{ J}}{1 \text{ mol}} \times \dfrac{1 \text{ mol}}{6.022 \times 10^{23} \text{ molecules}} = 5.6294 \times 10^{-19} = 5.63 \times 10^{-19}$ J/molecule

$$\lambda = \frac{hc}{E} = \frac{(6.626 \times 10^{-34} \text{ J-sec})(3.00 \times 10^8 \text{ m/sec})}{5.6294 \times 10^{-19} \text{ J}} = 3.53 \times 10^{-7} \text{ m} = 353 \text{ nm}$$

$\dfrac{293 \times 10^3 \text{ J}}{1 \text{ mol}} \times \dfrac{1 \text{ mol}}{6.022 \times 10^{23} \text{ molecules}} = 4.8655 \times 10^{-19} = 4.87 \times 10^{-19}$ J/molecule

$$\lambda = \frac{(6.626 \times 10^{-34} \text{ J-sec})(3.00 \times 10^8 \text{ m/sec})}{4.8655 \times 10^{-19} \text{ J}} = 4.09 \times 10^{-7} \text{ m} = 409 \text{ nm}$$

Photons of wavelengths longer than 409 nm cannot cause rupture of the C–Cl bond in either CF_3Cl or CCl_4.   Photons with wavelengths between 409 and 353 nm can cause C–Cl bond rupture in CCl_4, but not in CF_3Cl.

18.19   (a)   *Photodissociation* is cleavage of the O=O bond such that two neutral O atoms are produced: $O_2(g) \rightarrow 2O(g)$

Photoionization is absorption of a photon with sufficient energy to eject an electron from an O_2 molecule: $O_2(g) + h\nu \rightarrow O_2^+ + e^-$

(b)　Photoionization of O_2 requires 1205 kJ/mol. Photodissociation requires only 495 kJ/mol. At lower elevations, solar radiation with wavelengths corresponding to 1205 kJ/mol or shorter has already been absorbed, while the longer wavelength radiation has passed through relatively well. Below 90 km, the increased concentration of O_2 and the availability of longer wavelength radiation cause the photodissociation process to dominate.

18.20　Photodissociation of N_2 is relatively unimportant compared to photodissociation of O_2 for two reasons. The bond dissociation energy of N_2, 941 kJ/mol, is much higher than that of O_2, 495 kJ/mol. Photons with a wavelength short enough to photodissociate N_2 are not as abundant as the ultraviolet photons that lead to photodissociation of O_2. Also, N_2 does not absorb these photons as readily as O_2 so even if a short-wavelength photon is available, it may not be absorbed by an N_2 molecule.

Human Activities and Earth's Atmosphere (section 18.2)

18.21　The oxidation state of oxygen in O_3 , O_2 and O is zero (0). Reactions in which oxygen changes only from one of these species to another do not involve changes in oxidation state. Examples: $O(g) + O(g) \rightarrow O_2(g)$;　$2 O_3(g) \rightarrow 3 O_2(g)$.

Ozone depletion reactions which involve a halogen oxide such as ClO do involve a change in oxidation state for oxygen. In ClO, the oxidation state of oxygen is either +1 or +2, but it is not zero. A reaction involving ClO and one of the oxygen species with a zero oxidation state does involve a change in the oxidation state of oxygen atoms.

18.22　It's those star* reactions, equations [18.3-18.5]. The reaction of $O_2(g) + O(g)$ is exothermic and produces a high energy $O_3*(g)$ molecule with 105 kJ of energy to disperse. This energy is transferred through collisions, primarily to $N_2(g)$ and $O_2(g)$ molecules. The overall kinetic energy (translational, vibrational and rotational energy) of these molecules (M*) increases and the temperature of the stratosphere is kept relatively high. (Recall that the temperature of a gas is directly proportional to its average kinetic energy.)

18.23　(a)　A *chlorofluorocarbon* is a compound tha contains chlorine, fluorine and carbon. A *hydrofluorocarbon* contains hydrogen, fluorine, and carbon; it contains hydrogen in place of chlorine.

　　　(b)　CFCs are harmful because they undergo photodissociation to produce Cl atoms that catalyze the destructions of ozone. HFCs are potentially less harmful because they contain no C—Cl bonds. Their relatively stronger C—F bonds require more energy to undergo photodissociation, energy that is unlikely to be available in the stratosphere.

18.24　$32\,e^-$, $16\,e^-$ pr

$$:\ddot{F}:$$
$$|$$
$$:\ddot{C}l—C—\ddot{C}l:$$
$$|$$
$$:\ddot{C}l:$$

CFC–11, $CFCl_3$, contains C–Cl bonds that can be cleaved by UV light in the stratosphere to produce Cl atoms. It is chlorine in atomic form that catalyzes the destruction of stratospheric ozone. CFC–11 is chemically inert and resists decomposition in the troposphere, so that it eventually reaches the stratosphere in molecular form.

18.25   (a)   In order to catalyze ozone depletion, the halogen must be present as single halogen atoms. These halogen atoms are produced in the stratosphere by photo-dissociation of a carbon-halogen bond. According to Table 8.4, the C–F average bond dissociation energy is 485 kJ/mol, while that of C–Cl is 328 kJ/mol. The C–F bond requires more energy for dissociation and is not readily cleaved by the available wavelengths of UV light.

      (b)   Chlorine is present as chlorine atoms and chlorine oxide molecules, Cl and ClO.

18.26   Yes. Assuming $CFBr_3$ reaches the stratosphere intact, it contains C–Br bonds that are even more susceptible to cleavage by UV light than C–Cl bonds. According to Table 8.4, the average C–Br bond dissociation energy is 276 kJ/mol, compared to 328 kJ/mol for C–Cl bonds. Once in atomic form, Br atoms catalyze the destruction of ozone by a mechanism similar to that of Cl atoms.

18.27   (a)   Methane, CH_4, arises from decomposition of organic matter by certain microorganisms; it also escapes from underground gas deposits.

      (b) SO_2 is released in volcanic gases, and also is produced by bacterial action on decomposing vegetable and animal matter.

      (c)   Nitric oxide, NO, results from oxidation of decomposing organic matter, and is formed in lightning flashes.

18.28   Rainwater is naturally acidic due to the presence of $CO_2(g)$ in the atmosphere. All oxides of nonmetals produce acidic solutions when dissolved in water. Even in the absence of polluting gases such as SO_2, SO_3, NO, and NO_2, CO_2 causes rainwater to be acidic. The important equilibria are:

$$CO_2(g) + H_2O(l) \rightleftharpoons H_2CO_3(aq) \rightleftharpoons H^+(aq) + HCO_3^-(aq).$$

18.29   (a)   Acid rain is primarily $H_2SO_4(aq)$.

$$H_2SO_4(aq) + CaCO_3(s) \rightarrow CaSO_4(s) + H_2O(l) + CO_2(g)$$

      (b)   The $CaSO_4(s)$ would be much less reactive with acidic solution, since it would require a strongly acidic solution to shift the relevant equilibrium to the right.

$$CaSO_4(s) + 2H^+(aq) \rightleftharpoons Ca^{2+}(aq) + 2HSO_4^-(aq)$$

           Note, however, that $CaSO_4(s)$ is brittle and easily dislodged; it provides none of the structural strength of limestone.

18.30   (a) $Fe(s) + O_2(g) + 4H_3O^+(aq) \rightarrow Fe^{2+}(aq) + 6H_2O(l)$

      (b)   No. Silver is a "noble" metal. It is relatively resistant to oxidation, and much more resistant than iron. In Table 4.5, The Activity Series of Metals in Aqueous Solution, Ag is much, much lower than Fe and it is below hydrogen, while Fe is above hydrogen. This means that Fe is susceptible to oxidation by acid, while Ag is not.

18.31   *Analyze/Plan.* Given wavelength of a photon, place it in the electromagnetic spectrum, calculate its energy in kJ/mol, and compare it to an average bond dissociation energy. Use Figure 6.4; $E(J/photon) = hc/\lambda$. J/photon $\rightarrow$ kJ/mol.   *Solve.*

(a)   Ultraviolet (Figure 6.4)

(b) $E_{photon} = hc/\lambda = \dfrac{6.626 \times 10^{-34} \text{ J-s} \times 3.00 \times 10^8 \text{ m/s}}{335 \times 10^{-9} \text{ m}} = 5.934 \times 10^{-19}$

$$= 5.93 \times 10^{-19} \text{ J/photon}$$

$$\frac{5.934 \times 10^{-19} \text{ J}}{1 \text{ photon}} \times \frac{6.022 \times 10^{23} \text{ photons}}{1 \text{ mol}} \times \frac{1 \text{ kJ}}{1000 \text{ J}} = 357 \text{ kJ/mol}$$

(c)   The average C–H bond energy from Table 8.4 is 413 kJ/mol. The energy calculated in part (b), 357 kJ/mol, is the energy required to break 1 mol of C–H bonds in formaldehyde, CH_2O. The C–H bond energy in CH_2O must be less than the "average" C–H bond energy.

(d) $H\!-\!\overset{\displaystyle :\!O\!:}{\overset{\|}{C}}\!-\!H + h\nu \longrightarrow H\!-\!\overset{\displaystyle :\!O\!:}{\overset{\|}{C}}\!\cdot + H$

18.32   (a)   Visible (Figure 6.4)

(b) $E_{photon} = hc/\lambda = \dfrac{6.626 \times 10^{-34} \text{ J-s} \times 3.00 \times 10^8 \text{ m/s}}{420 \times 10^{-9} \text{ m}} = 4.733 \times 10^{-19}$

$$= 4.73 \times 10^{-19} \text{ J/photon}$$

$$\frac{4.733 \times 10^{-19} \text{ J}}{1 \text{ photon}} \times \frac{6.022 \times 10^{23} \text{ photons}}{1 \text{ mol}} \times \frac{1 \text{ kJ}}{1000 \text{ J}} = 285 \text{ kJ/mol}$$

(c) $\ddot{O}\!=\!\dot{N}\!-\!\ddot{O}\!: + h\nu \longrightarrow \ddot{O}\!=\!\ddot{N}\!\cdot + :\!\ddot{O}\!\cdot$

18.33   Most of the energy entering the atmosphere from the sun is in the form of visible radiation, while most of the energy leaving the earth is in the form of infrared radiation. CO_2 is transparent to the incoming visible radiation, but absorbs the outgoing infrared radiation.

18.34   (a)   A *greenhouse gas* absorbs energy in the 10,000–30,000 nm or infrared region. It absorbs wavelengths of radiation emitted by earth and returns it as heat. A non-greenhouse gas is transparent to radiation in this wavelength range.

(b) $CH_4(g)$ contains 4 C–H bonds, while N_2 has one strong triple bond. Infrared radiation has insufficient energy to cause electron transitions or bond cleavage; but it has an appropriate amount of energy to cause molecular deformations, bond stretching, and angle bending. The CH_4 molecule absorbs infrared radiation while undergoing these deformations, but symmetrical diatomic gases such as N_2 cannot "use" infrared radiation and are transparent to it.

Earth's Water (section 18.3)

18.35   *Analyze/Plan.* Given salinity and density, calculate molarity. A salinity of 5.6 denotes that there are 5.6 g of dry salt per kg of water.   *Solve.*

$$\frac{5.6 \text{ g NaCl}}{1 \text{ kg soln}} \times \frac{1.03 \text{ kg soln}}{1 \text{ L soln}} \times \frac{1 \text{ mol NaCl}}{58.44 \text{ g NaCl}} \times \frac{1 \text{ mol Na}^+}{1 \text{ mol NaCl}} = 0.0987 = 0.099 \; M \text{ Na}^+$$

18.36   If the phosphorous is present as phosphate, there is a 1:1 ratio between the molarity of phosphorus and molarity of phosphate. Thus, we can calculate the molarity based on the given mass of P.

$$\frac{0.07 \text{ g P}}{1 \times 10^6 \text{ g H}_2\text{O}} \times \frac{1 \text{ mol P}}{31 \text{ g P}} \times \frac{1 \text{ mol PO}_4{}^{3-}}{1 \text{ mol P}} \times \frac{1 \times 10^3 \text{ g H}_2\text{O}}{1 \text{ L H}_2\text{O}} = 2.26 \times 10^{-6} = 2 \times 10^{-6} \, M \text{ PO}_4{}^{3-}$$

18.37   *Analyze/Plan.* Given the power of sunlight per square meter striking Earth's surface, the enthalpy of evaporation of water and specific heat capacity of water, calculate the amount of energy delivered by the Sun over a 12-hour day. Use this amount of energy to calculate: (a) how many grams of water can be evaporated and (b) the temperature of a 10.0 cm by 1 square meter volume of water after 12 hours in the sunlight, assuming no evaporation. Calculate the mass of this volume of water using density at 25 °C. *Solve.*

(a) $\dfrac{168 \text{ W}}{\text{m}^2} \times \dfrac{1 \text{ J/s}}{1 \text{ W}} = \dfrac{168 \text{ J}}{\text{m}^2 \text{-s}}$

$$\frac{168 \text{ J}}{\text{m}^2\text{-s}} \times 1.00 \text{ m}^2 \times 12 \text{ hr} \times \frac{60 \text{ min}}{1 \text{ hr}} \times \frac{60 \text{ s}}{1 \text{ min}} \times \frac{1 \text{ kJ}}{1000 \text{ J}} = 7257.6 = 7.26 \times 10^3 \text{ kJ}$$

$$7257.6 \text{ kJ} \times \frac{1 \text{ mol H}_2\text{O}}{40.67 \text{ kJ}} \times \frac{18.02 \text{ g H}_2\text{O}}{1 \text{ mol H}_2\text{O}} = 3215.7 = 3.22 \times 10^3 \text{ g H}_2\text{O}$$

(b) $1.00 \text{ m}^2 \times 10.0 \text{ cm} \times \dfrac{(100)^2 \text{ cm}^2}{1 \text{ m}^2} \times \dfrac{0.99707 \text{ g}}{1 \text{ cm}^3} = 99{,}707 = 9.97 \times 10^4 \text{ gH}_2\text{O}$

$$7257.6 \text{ kJ} \times \frac{1000 \text{ J}}{1 \text{ kJ}} \times \frac{1 \text{ g-}^\circ\text{C}}{4.184 \text{ J}} \times \frac{1}{99{,}707 \text{ g H}_2\text{O}} = 17.397 = 17.4 \, ^\circ\text{C}$$

The final temperature is 26 °C + 17.4 °C = 43.4 °C.

18.38   (a) $\dfrac{168 \text{ W}}{\text{m}^2} \times \dfrac{1 \text{ J/s}}{1 \text{ W}} = \dfrac{168 \text{ J}}{\text{m}^2 \text{-s}}$

$$\frac{168 \text{ J}}{\text{m}^2\text{-s}} \times 1.00 \text{ m}^2 \times 12 \text{ hr} \times \frac{60 \text{ min}}{1 \text{ hr}} \times \frac{60 \text{ s}}{1 \text{ min}} \times \frac{1 \text{ kJ}}{1000 \text{ J}} = 7257.6 = 7.26 \times 10^3 \text{ kJ}$$

$$7257.6 \text{ kJ} \times \frac{1 \text{ mol H}_2\text{O}}{6.01 \text{ kJ}} \times \frac{18.02 \text{ g H}_2\text{O}}{1 \text{ mol H}_2\text{O}} = 21{,}761 = 2.18 \times 10^4 \text{ g H}_2\text{O (ice)}$$

(b) $1.00 \text{ m}^2 \times 1.00 \text{ cm} \times \dfrac{(100)^2 \text{ cm}^2}{1 \text{ m}^2} \times \dfrac{0.99987 \text{ g}}{1 \text{ cm}^3} = 9998.7 = 1.00 \times 10^4 \text{ g H}_2\text{O (ice at 0 }^\circ\text{C)}$

$$7257.6 \text{ kJ} \times \frac{1000 \text{ J}}{1 \text{ kJ}} \times \frac{1 \text{ g-}^\circ\text{C}}{2.032 \text{ J}} \times \frac{1}{9998.7 \text{ g H}_2\text{O}} = 357.21 = 357.2 \, ^\circ\text{C}$$

Assuming no phase changes, the final temperature is −5 °C + 357 °C = 352 °C. Clearly the ice melts. This agrees with the result from part (a), which shows that sunlight striking 1.00 square meter of ice for 12 hr provides enough energy to melt 2.18×10^4 g ice, twice the mass in the first cm of a square meter of ice.

18.39   *Analyze/Plan.* g Mg(OH)$_2$ → mol Mg(OH)$_2$ → mol ratio → mol CaO → g CaO.   *Solve.*

$$1000 \text{ lb Mg(OH)}_2 \times \frac{453.6 \text{ g}}{\text{lb}} \times \frac{1 \text{ mol Mg(OH)}_2}{58.33 \text{ g Mg(OH)}_2} \times \frac{1 \text{ mol CaO}}{1 \text{ mol Mg(OH)}_2} \times \frac{56.08 \text{ g CaO}}{1 \text{ mol CaO}}$$

$$= 4.361 \times 10^5 \text{ g CaO}$$

18.40   0.05 ppb Au = 0.05 g Au/1 × 10⁹ g seawater

$$\$1,000,000 \times \frac{1 \, troy \, oz \, Au}{\$800} \times \frac{31.1035 \, g}{troy \, oz} = 3.8879 \times 10^4 \, g = 3.89 \times 10^4 \, g \, Au \, needed$$

$$3.8879 \times 10^4 \, g \, Au \times \frac{1 \times 10^9 \, g \, seawater}{0.05 \, g \, Au} \times \frac{1 \, mL \, seawater}{1.03 \, g \, seawater} \times \frac{1 \, L}{1000 \, mL} = 7.5494 \times 10^{11}$$

$$= 8 \times 10^{11} \, L \, seawater$$

8×10^{11} L seawater are needed if the process is 100% efficient; since it is only 50% efficient, twice as much seawater is needed.

$7.5494 \times 10^{11} \times 2 = 1.5099 \times 10^{12} = 2 \times 10^{12}$ L seawater

Note that the 1 sig fig in 0.05 ppb Au limits the precision of the calculation.

18.41   (a)   *Groundwater* is freshwater (less than 500 ppm total salt content) that is under the soil; it composes 20% of the world's freshwater.

       (b)   An *aquifer* is a layer of porous rock that holds groundwater.

18.42   (a)   Assume the 18 billion gal used for irrigation is 75% of the water withdrawn. Then, 100% of the water is (18 billion/0.75) 24 billion gal. One billion is 1×10^9.

$$\frac{24 \times 10^9 \, gal}{d} \times \frac{365 \, d}{yr} \times 25 \, yr \times \frac{3.7854 \, L}{gal} \times \frac{1 \, dm^3}{L} \times \frac{1 \, km^3}{(10^4)^3 \, dm^3} = 829.0 \, km^3$$

$$= 8.3 \times 10^2 \, km^3 \, H_2O$$

       (b)   In general, an aquifer is recharged from water flowing through the soil. The water withdrawn for irrigation directly recharges the aquifer. Water withdrawn for human use eventually finds its way to rivers and the ocean, evaporates and is redelivered to the soil as precipitation, mostly rain.

Human Activities and Earth's Water (Section 18.4)

18.43   *Analyze/Plan.* Given temperature and the concentration difference between the two solutions, (ΔM = 0.22 – 0.01 = 0.21 M), calculate the minimum pressure for reverse osmosis. Use the relationship $\Pi = MRT$ from Section 13.5. This is the pressure required to halt osmosis from the more dilute (0.01 M) to the more concentrated (0.22 M) solution. Slightly more pressure will initiate reverse osmosis.   *Solve.*

$$\Pi = \Delta MRT = \frac{0.21 \, mol}{L} \times \frac{0.08206 \, L \text{-} atm}{mol \text{-} K} \times 298 \, K = 5.135 = 5.1 \, atm$$

The minimum pressure required to initiate reverse osmosis is greater than 5.1 atm.

18.44   Calculate the total ion concentration of sea water by summing the molarities given in Table 18.5. Then use $\Pi = \Delta MRT$ to calculate pressure.

$$M_{total} = 0.55 + 0.47 + 0.028 + 0.054 + 0.010 + 0.010 + 2.3 \times 10^{-3} + 8.3 \times 10^{-4}$$

$$+ 4.3 \times 10^{-4} + 9.1 \times 10^{-5} + 7.0 \times 10^{-5} = 1.1257 = 1.13 \, M$$

$$\Pi = \frac{(1.1257 - 0.02) \, mol}{L} \times \frac{0.08206 \, L \times atm}{mol \text{-} K} \times 297 \, K = 26.948 = 26.9 \, atm$$

Check. The largest numbers in the molarity sum have 2 decimal places, so M_{total} has 2 decimal places and 3 sig figs. ΔM also has 2 decimal places and 3 sig figs so the calculated pressure has 3 sig figs. Units are correct.

18.45   *Analyze/Plan.* Under aerobic conditions, excess oxygen is present and decomposition leads to oxidized products, the element in its maximum oxidation state combined with oxygen. Under anaerobic conditions, little or no oxygen is present so decomposition leads to reduced products, the element in its minimum oxidation state combined with hydrogen.   *Solve.*

(a) CO_2, HCO_3^-, H_2O, SO_4^{2-}, NO_3^-

(b) $CH_4(g)$, $H_2S(g)$, $NH_3(g)$

18.46   (a)   Decomposition of organic matter by aerobic bacteria depletes dissolved O_2. A low dissolved oxygen concentration indicates the presence of organic pollutants.

(b)   According to Section 13.3, the solubility of $O_2(g)$ (or any gas) in water decreases with increasing temperature.

18.47   *Analyze/Plan.* Given the balanced equation, calculate the amount of one reactant required to react exactly with a certain amount of the other reactants. Solve the stoichiometry problem. $g\ C_{18}H_{29}SO_3^- \rightarrow mol \rightarrow mol$ ratio $\rightarrow mol\ O_2 \rightarrow g\ O_2$.   *Solve.*

$$10.0\ g\ C_{18}H_{29}SO_3^- \times \frac{1\ mol\ C_{18}H_{29}SO_3^-}{325\ g\ C_{18}H_{29}SO_3^-} \times \frac{51\ mol\ O_2}{2\ mol\ C_{18}H_{29}SO_3^-} \times \frac{32.0\ g\ O_2}{1\ mol\ O_2} = 25.1\ g\ O_2$$

Notice that the mass of O_2 required is 2.5 times greater than the mass of biodegradable material.

18.48 $1{,}200{,}000\ persons \times \dfrac{59\ g\ O_2}{1\ person} \times \dfrac{1 \times 10^6\ g\ H_2O}{9\ g\ O_2} \times \dfrac{1\ L\ H_2O}{1 \times 10^3\ g\ H_2O} = 7.08 \times 10^{10} = 7 \times 10^{10}\ L\ H_2O$

18.49   *Analyze/Plan.* Slaked lime is $Ca(OH)_2(s)$. The reaction is metathesis.   *Solve.*

$Mg^{2+}(aq) + Ca(OH)_2(s) \rightarrow Mg(OH)_2(s) + Ca^{2+}(aq)$

The excess $Ca^{2+}(aq)$ is removed as $CaCO_3$ by naturally occurring bicarbonate or added Na_2CO_3.

18.50   (a) Ca^{2+}, Mg^{2+}, Fe^{2+}

(b)   Divalent cations (ions with 2+ charges) contribute to water hardness. These ions react with soap to form scum on surfaces or leave undesirable deposits on surfaces, particularly inside pipes, upon heating.

18.51   *Analyze/Plan.* Given $[Ca^{2+}]$ and $[HCO_3^-]$ calculate mole $Ca(OH)_2$ and Na_2CO_3 needed to remove the Ca^{2+} and HCO_3^-. Consider the chemical equations and reaction stoichiometry in the stepwise process.   *Solve.*

$Ca(OH)_2$ is added to remove Ca^{2+} as $CaCO_3(s)$, and Na_2CO_3 removes the remaining Ca^{2+}.

$Ca^{2+}(aq) + 2HCO_3^-(aq) + [Ca^{2+}(aq) + 2OH^-(aq)] \rightarrow 2CaCO_3(s) + 2H_2O(l)$.

One mole $Ca(OH)_2$ is needed for each 2 moles of $HCO_3^-(aq)$ present.

$$\frac{7.0 \times 10^{-4} \text{ mol HCO}_3^-}{L} \times \frac{1 \text{ mol Ca(OH)}_2}{2 \text{ mol HCO}_3^-} \times 1.200 \times 10^3 \text{ L H}_2\text{O} = 0.42 \text{ mol Ca(OH)}_2$$

$$1.200 \times 10^3 \text{ L H}_2\text{O} \times \frac{5.0 \times 10^{-4} \text{ mol Ca}^{2+}}{L} = 0.60 \text{ mol Ca}^{2+}\text{(aq) total}$$

0.42 mol $Ca(OH)_2$ removes 0.42 mol of the 0.60 mol Ca^{2+}(aq) in the sample. This leaves 0.18 mol Ca^{2+}(aq) to be removed by Na_2CO_3.

$$Ca^{2+}(aq) + Na_2CO_3(aq) \rightarrow CaCO_3(s) + 2Na^+(aq)$$

0.18 mol of Na_2CO_3 is needed to remove the remaining Ca^{2+}(aq).

18.52 $Ca(OH)_2$ is added to remove Ca^{2+} as $CaCO_3$(s), and Na_2CO_3 removes the remaining Ca^{2+}.

$$Ca^{+2}(aq) + 2HCO_3^-(aq) + [Ca^{2+}(aq) + 2OH^-(aq)] \rightarrow 2CaCO_3(s) + 2H_2O(l).$$

One mole $Ca(OH)_2$ is needed for each 2 moles of HCO_3^-(aq) present.

$$5.0 \times 10^7 \text{ L H}_2\text{O} \times \frac{1.7 \times 10^{-3} \text{ mol HCO}_3^-}{1 \text{ L H}_2\text{O}} \times \frac{1 \text{ mol Ca(OH)}_2}{2 \text{ mol HCO}_3^-} \times \frac{74 \text{ g Ca(OH)}_2}{1 \text{ mol Ca(OH)}_2}$$
$$= 3.1 \times 10^6 \text{ g Ca(OH)}_2$$

Half of the native HCO_3^- precipitates the added Ca^{2+} so this operation reduces the Ca^{2+} concentration from 5.7×10^{-3} M to $(5.7 \times 10^{-3} - 8.5 \times 10^{-4})$ $M = 4.85 \times 10^{-3} = 4.9 \times 10^{-3}$ M. Next we must add sufficient Na_2CO_3 to further reduce [Ca^{2+}] to 1.1×10^{-3} M (20% of the original [Ca^{2+}]). We thus need to reduce [Ca^{2+}] by $(4.85 \times 10^{-3} - 1.1 \times 10^{-3})$ $M = 3.75 \times 10^{-3} = 3.8 \times 10^{-3}$ M

$$Ca^{2+}(aq) + CO_3^{-2}(aq) \rightarrow CaCO_3(s).$$

$$5.0 \times 10^7 \text{ L H}_2\text{O} \times \frac{3.75 \times 10^{-3} \text{ mol Ca}^{2+}}{1 \text{ L H}_2\text{O}} \times \frac{1 \text{ mol Na}_2\text{CO}_3}{1 \text{ mol Ca}^{2+}} \times \frac{106 \text{ g Na}_2\text{CO}_3}{1 \text{ mol Na}_2\text{CO}_3}$$
$$= 2.0 \times 10^7 \text{ g Na}_2\text{CO}_3$$

18.53 $4FeSO_4(aq) + O_2(aq) + 2H_2O(l) \rightarrow 4Fe^{3+}(aq) + 4OH^-(aq) + 4SO_4^{2-}(aq)$

SO_4^{2-} is a spectator, so the net ionic equation is

$4Fe^{2+}(aq) + O_2(aq) + 2H_2O(l) \rightarrow 4Fe^{3+}(aq) + 4OH^-(aq).$

$Fe^{3+}(aq) + 3HCO_3^-(aq) \rightarrow Fe(OH)_3(s) + 3CO_2(g)$

In this reaction, Fe^{3+} acts as a Lewis acid, and HCO_3^- acts as a Lewis base.

18.54 $Al_2(SO_4)_3$ is a typical coagulant in municipal water purification. It reacts with OH^- in a slightly basic solution to form a gelatinous precipitate that occludes very small particles and bacteria. The precipitate settles slowly and is removed by sand filtration.

Properties of $Al_2(SO_4)_3$ and other useful coagulants are:

- They react with low concentrations of OH^-(aq). That is, K_{sp} of the hydroxide precipitate is very small. The capacity to form a hydroxide precipitates means that no extra salts must be added to form the precipitate. Also, the [OH^-] can be easily adjusted by $Ca(OH)_2$ and other reagents that are part of the purification process.

- The hydroxide precipitate is composed of very small, evenly dispersed particles that do not settle quickly. This is required to remove very small bacteria and viruses from all parts of the liquid, not just the sites of solid formation.

18.55   (a)   *Trihalomethanes* are a class of molecules with one central carbon atom bound to one hydrogen and three halogen atoms. They are produced by the reaction of dissolved chlorine with organic matter naturally present in water, and are byproducts of water disinfection via chlorination.

       (b)

18.56   If THMs are easily removed from water by aeration, this implies that, at a given temperature, their vapor pressure is greater than that of water. Air bubbles provide a vehicle to carry THM vapor away from the liquid water.

Green Chemistry (section 18.5)

18.57   The fewer steps in a process, the less waste (solvents as well as unusable by-products) is generated. It is probably true that a process with fewer steps requires less energy at the site of the process, and it is certainly true that the less waste the process generates, the less energy is required to clean or dispose of the waste.

18.58   Catalysts increase the rate of a reaction by lowering activation energy, E_a. For an uncatalyzed reaction that requires extreme temperatures and pressures to generate product at a viable rate, finding a suitable catalyst reduces the required temperature and/or pressure, which reduces the amount of energy used to run the process. A catalyst can also increase rate of production, which would reduce the net time and thus energy required to generate a certain amount of product.

18.59   (a)

       (b)

- **Prevention (1).** The alternative process eliminates production of 3-chlorobenzoic acid by-product, chlorine-containing waste that must be treated.

- **Atom Economy (2).** Most of the starting atoms are in the final product.

- **Less hazardous chemical synthesis (3)** and **Inherently safer for accident prevention (12).** The starting material of the alternative process is not shock-sensitive, and the by-product is nontoxic water. The low molar mass of water means that a small amount of "waste" is generated.

- **Catalysis (9)** and **Design for energy efficiency(6)**. The alternative process is catalyzed, which could mean that the process will be more energy efficient than the Baeyer-Villiger reaction (see Solution 18.58).

- **Raw materials should be renewable (7)**. The catalyst can be recovered from the reaction mixture and reused. We don't have information about solvents or other auxiliary substances.

18.60   • In either solvent, the reaction is catalyzed, which usually leads to decreased processing temperatures and times, and greater energy efficiency.

• $scCO_2$ is the preferred solvent. It achieves maximum conversion much faster than CH_2Cl_2 solvent. $scCO_2$ reduces processing time, temperature, and energy requirements. It also results in fewer unwanted by-products to be separated and processed. While use of $scCO_2$ increases the amount of a greenhouse gas released to the environment, it eliminates use of CH_2Cl_2, which is implicated in stratospheric ozone depletion. Use of $scCO_2$ rather than CH_2Cl_2 is a good green trade-off.

18.61   (a)   Water as a solvent is much "greener" than benzene, which is a known carcinogen. Water fits criteria: (5) safer solvent, (7) renewable feedstock and (12) inherently safer for accident prevention.

(b)   Reaction temperature of 500 K rather than 1000 K is "greener", according to criteria (6) design for energy efficiency and (12) inherently safer chemistry for accident prevention. Also, low temperature is less likely to produce undesireable byproducts that have to be separated and treated as waste, which fits criterium (1).

(c)   Sodium chloride as a byproduct rather than chloroform ($CHCl_3$) is "greener", according to criteria: (1) prevention, (3) less hazardous chemical systems, and (12) inherently safer ($CHCl_3$ is flammable, while NaCl is not).

18.62   (a)   The catalyzed reaction that can be run close to room temperature and for a shorter time is definitely greener, according to criteria (6) design for energy efficiency and (9) catalysis.

(b)   The reagent obtained from corn husks is greener, by criteria (7) use of renewable feedstocks.

(c)   Neither process is totally "ungreen", because recycling of unavoidable byproducts is always desirable. However, by criterium (2) atom economy, the process that produces no by-products is greener.

Additional Exercises

18.63   (a)   *Acid rain* is rain with a larger $[H^+]$ and thus a lower pH than expected. The additional H^+ is produced by the dissolution of sulfur and nitrogen oxides such as $SO_3(g)$ and $NO_2(g)$ in rain droplets to form sulfuric and nitric acid, $H_2SO_4(aq)$ and $HNO_3(aq)$.

(b)   A *greenhouse gas* absorbs infrared or "heat" radiation emitted from Earth's surface and serves to maintain a relatively constant temperature on the surface. These include $H_2O(g)$, CH_4, and CO_2. A significant buildup of greenhouse gases in the atmosphere could cause a corresponding increase in the average surface temperature and stimulate global climate.

(c)   *Photochemical smog* is an unpleasant collection of atmospheric pollutants initiated by photochemical dissociation of NO_2 to form NO and O atoms. The major components are $NO(g)$, $NO_2(g)$, $CO(g)$, and unburned hydrocarbons, all produced by automobile engines, and $O_3(g)$, ozone.

(d)   *Ozone depletion* is the reduction of O_3 concentration in the stratosphere, most notably over Antarctica. It is caused by reactions between O_3 and Cl atoms originating from chlorofluorocarbons (CFC's), CF_xCl_{4-x}. Depletion of the ozone layer allows damaging ultraviolet radiation disruptive to the plant and animal life in our ecosystem to reach earth.

18.64 MM_{avg} at the surface = $83.8(0.17) + 16.0(0.38) + 32.0(0.45) = 34.73 = 35$ g/mol.

Next, calculate the percentage composition at 200 km. The fractions can be "normalized" by saying that the 0.45 fraction of O_2 is converted into **two** 0.45 fractions of O atoms, then dividing by the total fractions, $0.17 + 0.38 + 0.45 + 0.45 = 1.45$:

$$MM_{avg} = \frac{83.8(0.17) + 16.0(0.38) + 16.0(0.90)}{1.45} = 23.95 = 24 \text{ g/mol}$$

18.65   Stratospheric ozone is formed and destroyed in a cycle of chemical reactions. The decomposition of O_3 to O_2 and O produces oxygen atoms, an essential ingredient for the production of ozone. While single O_3 molecules exist for only a few seconds, new O_3 molecules are constantly reformed. This cyclic process ensures a finite concentration of O_3 in the stratosphere available to absorb ultraviolet radiation. (This explanation assumes that the cycle is not disrupted by outside agents such as CFCs.)

18.66
$$2[Cl(g) + O_3(g) \rightarrow ClO(g) + O_2(g)] \qquad [18.7]$$
$$2[ClO(g) + h\nu \rightarrow O(g) + Cl(g)] \qquad [18.9]$$
$$\underline{O(g) + O(g) \rightarrow O_2(g)}$$
$$2Cl(g) + 2O_3(g) + 2ClO(g) + 2O(g) \rightarrow 2ClO(g) + 3O_2(g) + 2Cl(g)$$
$$2O_3(g) \xrightarrow{Cl} 3O_2(g) \qquad [18.10]$$

Note that $Cl(g)$ fits the definition of a catalyst in this reaction.

18.67   Chlorofluorocarbons (CFCs), primarily $CFCl_3$ and CF_2Cl_2, are chemically inert and water insoluble. These properties make them valuable as propellants, refrigerants and foaming agents because they are virtually unreactive in the *troposphere* (lower atmosphere) and do not initiate or propagate undesirable reactions. Further, they are water-insoluble and not removed from the atmosphere by rain; they do not end up in the fresh water supply.

These properties render CFCs a long-term problem in the *stratosphere*. Because CFCs are inert and water-insoluble, they are not removed from the troposphere by reaction or dissolution and have very long lifetimes. Virtually the entire mass of released CFCs eventually diffuses into the stratosphere where conditions are right for photo-dissociation and the production of Cl atoms. Cl atoms catalyze the destruction of ozone, O_3.

18.68   (a)   The production of Cl atoms in the stratosphere is the result of the photodissociation of a C–Cl bond in the chlorofluorocarbon molecule.

$$CF_2Cl_2(g) \xrightarrow{h\nu} CF_2Cl(g) + Cl(g)$$

According to Table 8.4, the bond dissociation energy of a C–Br bond is 276 kJ/mol, while the value for a C–Cl bond is 328 kJ/mol. Photodissociation of $CBrF_3$ to form Br atoms requires less energy than the production of Cl atoms and should occur readily in the stratosphere.

     (b) $CBrF_3(g) \xrightarrow{h\nu} CF_3(g) + Br(g)$

        $Br(g) + O_3(g) \rightarrow BrO(g) + O_2(g)$

        Also, under certain conditions

        $BrO(g) + BrO(g) \rightarrow Br_2O_2(g)$

        $Br_2O_2(g) + h\nu \rightarrow O_2(g) + 2Br(g)$

18.69   In an HFC, C–Cl bonds are replaced by C–F bonds. The bond dissociation enthalpy of a C–F bond is 485 kJ/mol, much more than for a C–Cl bond, 328 kJ/mol (Table 8.4). Although HFCs have long lifetimes in the stratosphere, it is infrequent that light with energy sufficient to dissociate a C–F bond will reach an HFC molecule. F atoms, the bad actors in ozone destruction, are much less likely than Cl atoms to be produced by photodissociation in the stratosphere.

18.70   (a) $\cdot\ddot{O}\!-\!H$

     (b) HNO_3 is a major component in acid rain.

     (c)   While it removes CO, the reaction produces NO_2. The photodissociation of NO_2 to form O atoms is the first step in the formation of tropospheric ozone and photochemical smog.

     (d)   Again, NO_2 is the initiator of photochemical smog. Also, methoxyl radical, OCH_3, is a reactive species capable of initiating other undesirable reactions.

     (e)   Beer's law is $A = \varepsilon bc$, where A is measured absorbance, b is path length and c is concentration of analyte. Measured absorbance is directly proportional to both path length and concentration. Since concentration of hydroxyl radical in the troposphere is quite small, a long path length compensates and makes observation of absorbance possible.

18.71   From section 18.2:

     $N_2(g) + O_2(g) \rightleftharpoons 2NO(g)$ $\Delta H = +180.8$ kJ   [18.11]

     $2\,NO(g) + O_2(g) \rightleftharpoons 2NO_2(g)$ $\Delta H = -113.1$ kJ   [18.12]

In an endothermic reaction, heat is a reactant. As the temperature of the reaction increases, the addition of heat favors formation of products and the value of K increases. The reverse is true for exothermic reactions; as temperature increases, the value of K decreases. Thus, K for reaction [18.11], which is endothermic, increases with increasing temperature and K for reaction [18.12], which is exothermic, decreases with increasing temperature.

18.72   (a) $CH_4(g) + 2O_2(g) \rightarrow CO_2(g) + 2H_2O(g)$

(b) $2CH_4(g) + 3O_2(g) \rightarrow 2CO(g) + 4H_2O(g)$

(c)   vol $CH_4 \rightarrow$ vol $O_2 \rightarrow$ volume air ($\chi_{O_2} = 0.20948$)

Equal volumes of gases at the same temperature and pressure contain equal numbers of moles (Avogadro's law). If 2 moles of O_2 are required for 1 mole of CH_4, 2.0 L of pure O_2 are needed to burn 1.0 L of CH_4.

$$\text{vol } O_2 = \chi_{O_2} \times \text{vol}_{air} = \frac{\text{vol } O_2}{\chi_{O_2}} = \frac{2.0\,L}{0.20948} = 9.5\,L \text{ air}$$

18.73   (a)   According to Section 13.3, the solubility of gases in water decreases with increasing temperature. Thus, the solubility of $CO_2(g)$ in the ocean would decrease if the temperature of the ocean increased.

(b)   If the solubility of $CO_2(g)$ in the ocean decreased because of global warming, more $CO_2(g)$ would be released into the atmosphere, perpetuating a cycle of increasing temperature and concomitant release of $CO_2(g)$ from the ocean.

18.74   Most of the 390 watts/m^2 radiated from Earth's surface is in the infrared region of the spectrum. Tropospheric gases, particularly $H_2O(g)$, $CH_4(g)$, and $CO_2(g)$, absorb much of this radiation and prevent it from escaping into space (Figures 18.11 and 18.12). The energy absorbed by these so-called "greenhouse gases" warms the atmosphere close to Earth's surface and makes the planet livable.

18.75   Given 168 watts/m^2 at 10% efficiency, find the land area needed to produce 12,000 megawatts. 12,000 megawatts = 12,000 $\times 10^6$ = 1.2 $\times 10^{10}$ watts.

168 watts/m^2 (0.10) = 16.8 watts/m^2 solar energy possible with current technology.

$$1.2 \times 10^{10} \text{ watts} \times \frac{1\,m^2}{16.8\,watts} = 7.143 \times 10^8 = 7.1 \times 10^8 \ m^2$$

The land area of New York City is 830 km^2, which is 830 $\times 10^6$ m^2. The area needed for solar energy harvesting to provide peak power would then be $\dfrac{7.143 \times 10^8 \ m^2}{830 \times 10^6 \ m^2} = 0.86$

times the land area of New York City.

18.76   (a) $NO(g) + h\nu \rightarrow N(g) + O(g)$

(b) $NO(g) + h\nu \rightarrow NO^+(g) + e^-$

(c) $NO(g) + O_3(g) \rightarrow NO_2(g) + O_2(g)$

(d) $3NO_2(g) + H_2O(l) \rightarrow 2HNO_3(aq) + NO(g)$

18.77   (a) CO_3^{2-} is a relatively strong Brønsted-Lowry base and produces OH^- in aqueous solution according to the hydrolysis reaction:

$$CO_3^{2-}(aq) + H_2O(l) \ \rightleftharpoons \ HCO_3^-(aq) + OH^-(aq), \quad K_b = 1.8 \times 10^{-4}$$

If [$OH^-(aq)$] is sufficient for the reaction quotient, Q, to exceed K_{sp} for $Mg(OH)_2$, the solid will precipitate.

(b) $\dfrac{125 \text{ mg Mg}^{2+}}{1 \text{ kg soln}} \times \dfrac{1 \text{ g Mg}^{2+}}{1000 \text{ mg Mg}^{2+}} \times \dfrac{1.00 \text{ kg soln}}{1.00 \text{ L soln}} \times \dfrac{1 \text{ mol Mg}^{2+}}{24.305 \text{ g Mg}^{2+}} = 5.143 \times 10^{-3}$

$$= 5.14 \times 10^{-3} \ M \text{ Mg}^{2+}$$

$$\dfrac{4.0 \text{ g Na}_2\text{CO}_3}{1.0 \text{ L soln}} \times \dfrac{1 \text{ mol CO}_3^{2-}}{106.0 \text{ g Na}_2\text{CO}_3} = 0.03774 = 0.038 \ M \text{ CO}_3^{2-}$$

$$K_b = 1.8 \times 10^{-4} = \dfrac{[\text{HCO}_3^-][\text{OH}^-]}{[\text{CO}_3^{2-}]} \approx \dfrac{x^2}{0.03774}; \ x = [\text{OH}^-] = 2.606 \times 10^{-3}$$

$$= 2.6 \times 10^{-3} \ M$$

(This represents 6.9% hydrolysis, but the result will not be significantly different using the quadratic formula.)

$$Q = [\text{Mg}^{2+}][\text{OH}^-]^2 = (5.143 \times 10^{-3})(2.606 \times 10^{-3})^2 = 3.5 \times 10^{-8}$$

K_{sp} for $\text{Mg(OH)}_2 = 1.6 \times 10^{-12}$; $Q > K_{sp}$, so Mg(OH)_2 will precipitate.

18.78   Because NO has an odd electron, like Cl(g), it could act as a catalyst for decomposition of ozone in the stratosphere. The increased destruction of ozone by NO would result in less absorption of short wavelength UV radiation now being screened out primarily by the ozone. Radiation in this wavelength range is known to be harmful to humans; it causes skin cancer. There is evidence that many plants don't tolerate it very well either, though more research is needed to test this idea.

In Chapter 22 the oxidation of NO to NO_2 by oxygen is described. On dissolving in water, NO_2 disproportionates into NO_3^-(aq) and NO(g). Thus, over time the NO in the troposphere will be converted into NO_3^-, which is in turn incorporated into soils.

18.79   *Plan.* Calculate the volume of air above Los Angeles and the volume of pure O_3 that would be present at the 84 ppb level. For gases at the same temperature and pressure, volume fractions equal mole fractions.   *Solve.*

$$V_{air} = 4000 \text{ mi}^2 \times \dfrac{(1.6093)^2 \text{ km}^2}{\text{mi}^2} \times \dfrac{(1000)^2 \text{ m}^2}{1 \text{ km}^2} \times 10 \text{ m} \times \dfrac{1 \text{ L}}{1 \times 10^{-3} \text{ m}^3} = 1.036 \times 10^{14}$$

$$= 1.0 \times 10^{14} \text{ L air}$$

$$84 \text{ ppb O}_3 = \dfrac{84 \text{ mol O}_3}{1 \times 10^9 \text{ mol air}} = 8.4 \times 10^{-8} = \chi_{\text{O}_3}$$

$$V \text{ (pure O}_3) = 8.4 \times 10^{-8} (1.036 \times 10^{14} \text{ L air}) = 8.702 \times 10^6 = 8.7 \times 10^6 \text{ L O}_3$$

Values for P and T are required to calculate mol O_3 from volume O_3, using the ideal-gas law. Since these are not specified in the exercise, we will make a reasonable assumption for a sunny April day in Los Angeles. The city is near sea level and temperatures are moderate throughout the year, so P = 1 atm and T = 25°C (78°F) are reasonable values.

PV = nRT, n = PV/RT

$$n = 1.000 \text{ atm} \times \dfrac{8.702 \times 10^6 \text{ L}}{298 \text{ K}} \times \dfrac{\text{mol-K}}{0.08206 \text{ L-atm}} = 3.558 \times 10^5 = 3.6 \times 10^5 \text{ mol O}_3$$

Check. Using known conditions to make reasonable estimates and assumptions is a valuable skill for problem solving. Knowing when assumptions are required is an important step in the learning process.

Integrative Exercises

18.80   (a) $0.016 \text{ ppm NO}_2 = \dfrac{0.016 \text{ mol NO}_2}{1 \times 10^6 \text{ mol air}} = 1.6 \times 10^{-8} = \chi_{NO_2}$

$P_{NO_2} = \chi_{NO_2} \times P_{atm} = 1.6 \times 10^{-8} (755 \text{ torr}) = 1.208 \times 10^{-5} = 1.2 \times 10^{-5} \text{ torr}$

(b) $n = \dfrac{PV}{RT}; \text{ molecules} = n \times \dfrac{6.022 \times 10^{23} \text{ molecules}}{\text{mol}} = \dfrac{PV}{RT} \times \dfrac{6.022 \times 10^{23} \text{ molecules}}{\text{mol}}$

$V = 15 \text{ ft} \times 14 \text{ ft} \times 8 \text{ ft} \times \dfrac{12^3 \text{ in}^3}{\text{ft}^3} \times \dfrac{2.54^3 \text{ cm}^3}{\text{in}^3} \times \dfrac{1 L}{1000 \text{ cm}^3} = 4.757 \times 10^4 = 5 \times 10^4 \text{ L}$

$1.208 \times 10^{-5} \text{ torr} \times \dfrac{1 \text{ atm}}{760 \text{ torr}} \times \dfrac{4.757 \times 10^4 \text{ L}}{293 \text{ K}} \times \dfrac{\text{mol-K}}{0.08206 \text{ L-atm}}$

$\times \dfrac{6.022 \times 10^{23} \text{ molecules}}{\text{mol}} = 1.894 \times 10^{19} = 2 \times 10^{19} \text{ molecules}$

18.81   (a) $8{,}376{,}726 \text{ tons coal} \times \dfrac{83 \text{ ton C}}{100 \text{ ton coal}} \times \dfrac{44.01 \text{ ton CO}_2}{12.01 \text{ ton C}} = 2.5 \times 10^7 \text{ ton CO}_2$

$8{,}376{,}726 \text{ tons coal} \times \dfrac{2.5 \text{ ton S}}{100 \text{ ton coal}} \times \dfrac{64.07 \text{ ton SO}_2}{32.07 \text{ ton S}} = 4.2 \times 10^5 \text{ ton SO}_2$

(b) $CaO(s) + SO_2(g) \rightarrow CaSO_3(s)$

$4.18 \times 10^5 \text{ ton SO}_2 \times \dfrac{55 \text{ ton SO}_2 \text{ removed}}{100 \text{ ton SO}_2 \text{ produced}} \times \dfrac{120.15 \text{ ton CaSO}_3}{64.07 \text{ ton SO}_2}$

$= 4.3 \times 10^5 \text{ ton CaSO}_3$

18.82   *Coarse sand* is removed by coarse sand filtration. *Finely divided particles* and some *bacteria* are removed by precipitation with aluminum hydroxide. Remaining *harmful bacteria* are removed by ozonation. *Trihalomethanes* are removed by either aeration or activated carbon filtration; use of activated carbon might be preferred because it does not involve release of TCMs into the atmosphere. *Dissolved organic substances* are oxidized (and rendered less harmful, but not removed) by both aeration and ozonation. Dissolved *nitrates* and *phosphates* are not removed by any of these processes, but are rendered less harmful by adequate aeration.

18.83   Calculate the molar concentration of impurity that would have an absorbance of 0.0001. This is the minimum concentration of the impurity detectable by absorption spectroscopy.

$A = \varepsilon bc$; A = absorbance, ε = extinction coefficient, b = path length, c = molarity. The common path length is 1 cm.

$c = \dfrac{A}{\varepsilon b} = 0.0001 \times \dfrac{M \times \text{cm}}{3.45 \times 10^3} \times \dfrac{1}{1 \text{ cm}} = 2.8986 \times 10^{-8} = 3 \times 10^{-8} \, M$

Since we do not have the identity of the impurity, we cannot calculate the corresponding concentration in ppb. We can calculate a maximum molar mass for the impurity, such that a $3 \times 10^{-3} \, M$ solution is 50 ppb. A concentration of 50 ppb corresponds to 50 g impurity per 10^9 L solution.

$$\frac{50 \text{ g impurity}}{10^9 \text{ g solution}} \times \frac{1000 \text{ g solution}}{\text{L solution}} \times \frac{1 \text{ L solution}}{2.8986 \times 10^{-8} \text{ mol impurity}} = 1725 \text{ g impurity/mol}$$

In this calculation, molar mass is directly proportional to ppm concentration. This means that a 50 ppm solution or any impurity with a molar mass less than or equal to 1725 g/mol will be observable by absorption spectroscopy. Concentrations less than 50 ppm are probably observable, since 1725 is a large molar mass. (The calculated molar mass is more correctly represented with one sig fig as 2×10^{-3} g/mol).

18.84   (a) $H - \ddot{O} - H \longrightarrow H\cdot + \cdot\ddot{O} - H$

(b) $\Delta H = 2D(O - H) - D(O - H) = D(O - H) = 463$ kJ/mol

$$\frac{463 \text{ kJ}}{\text{mol } H_2O} \times \frac{1 \text{ mol } H_2O}{6.022 \times 10^{23} \text{ molecules}} \times \frac{1000 \text{ J}}{\text{kJ}} = 7.688 \times 10^{-19}$$

$$= 7.69 \times 10^{-19} \text{ J/}H_2O \text{ molecule}$$

$$\lambda = \frac{hc}{\Delta E} = \frac{6.626 \times 10^{-34} \text{ J-sec} \times 2.998 \times 10^8 \text{ m/s}}{7.688 \times 10^{-19} \text{ J}} = 2.58 \times 10^{-7} \text{ m} = 258 \text{ nm}$$

This wavelength is in the UV region of the spectrum, close to the visible.

(c)

$$OH(g) + O_3(g) \rightarrow HO_2(g) + O_2(g)$$
$$HO_2(g) + O(g) \rightarrow OH(g) + O_2(g)$$
$$\overline{OH(g) + O_3(g) + HO_2(g) + O(g) \rightarrow HO_2(g) + 2O_2(g) + OH(g)}$$
$$O_3(g) + O(g) \rightarrow 2O_2(g)$$

OH(g) is the catalyst is this overall reaction, another pathway for the destruction of ozone.

18.85   According to Equation [14.12], $\ln([A]_t / [A]_o) = -kt.$ $[A]_t = 0.10 [A]_o$

$\ln(0.10 [A]_o / [A]_o) = \ln(0.10) = -(2 \times 10^{-6} \text{ s}^{-1}) \text{ t}$

$t = -\ln(0.10) / 2 \times 10^{-6} \text{ s}^{-1} = 1.151 \times 10^6 \text{ s}$

$$1.151 \times 10^6 \text{ s} \times \frac{1 \text{ min}}{60 \text{ s}} \times \frac{1 \text{ hr}}{60 \text{ min}} \times \frac{1 \text{ day}}{24 \text{ hr}} = 13.3 \text{ days } (1 \times 10 \text{ days})$$

The value of the rate constant limits the result to 1 sig fig. This implies that there is minimum uncertainty of ± 1 in the tens place of our answer. Realistically, the remediation could take anywhere from 1 to 20 days.

18.86   (i) $ClO(g) + O_3(g) \rightarrow ClO_2(g) + O_2(g)$

$\Delta H_i = \Delta H_f^\circ ClO_2(g) + \Delta H_f^\circ O_2(g) - \Delta H_f^\circ ClO(g) - \Delta H_f^\circ O_3(g)$

$\Delta H_i = 102 + 0 - 101 - (142.3) = -141$ kJ

(ii) $ClO_2(g) + O(g) \rightarrow ClO(g) + O_2(g)$

$\Delta H_{ii} = \Delta H_f^\circ ClO(g) + \Delta H_f^\circ O_2(g) - \Delta H_f^\circ ClO_2(g) - \Delta H_f^\circ O(g)$

$\Delta H_{ii} = 101 + 0 - 102 - (247.5) = -249$ kJ

(overall) $ClO(g) + O_3(g) + ClO_2(g) + O(g) \rightarrow ClO_2(g) + O_2(g) + ClO(g) + O_2(g)$

$$O_3(g) + O(g) \rightarrow 2O_2(g)$$

$$\Delta H = \Delta H_i + \Delta H_{ii} = -141 \text{ kJ} + (-249) \text{ kJ} = -390 \text{ kJ}$$

Because the enthalpies of both (i) and (ii) are distinctly exothermic, it is possible that the $ClO - ClO_2$ pair could be a catalyst for the destruction of ozone.

18.87　(a)　Assume the density of water at 20°C is the same as at 25°C.

$$1.00 \text{ gal} \times \frac{4 \text{ qt}}{1 \text{ gal}} \times \frac{1 \text{ L}}{1.057 \text{ qt}} \times \frac{1000 \text{ mL}}{1 \text{ L}} \times \frac{0.99707 \text{ g H}_2\text{O}}{1 \text{ mL}} = 3773$$

$$= 3.77 \times 10^3 \text{ g H}_2\text{O}$$

The $H_2O(l)$ must be heated from 20°C to 100°C and then vaporized at 100°C.

$$3.773 \times 10^3 \text{ g H}_2\text{O} \times \frac{4.184 \text{ J}}{\text{g °C}} \times 80 \text{ °C} \times \frac{1 \text{ kJ}}{1000 \text{ J}} = 1263 = 1.3 \times 10^3 \text{ kJ}$$

$$3.773 \times 10^3 \text{ g H}_2\text{O} \times \frac{1 \text{ mol H}_2\text{O}}{18.02 \text{ g H}_2\text{O}} \times \frac{40.67 \text{ kJ}}{\text{mol H}_2\text{O}} = 8516 = 8.52 \times 10^3 \text{ kJ}$$

energy = 1263 kJ + 8516 kJ = 9779 = 9.8×10^3 kJ/gal H_2O

(b)　According to Solution 5.18, 1 kwh = 3.6×10^6 J.

$$\frac{9779 \text{ kJ}}{\text{gal H}_2\text{O}} \times \frac{1000 \text{ J}}{\text{kJ}} \times \frac{1 \text{ kwh}}{3.6 \times 10^6 \text{ J}} \times \frac{\$0.085}{\text{kwh}} = \$0.23/\text{gal}$$

(c)　$\dfrac{\$0.23}{\$1.26} \times 100 = 18\%$ of the total cost is energy

18.88　(a)　A rate constant of $M^{-1}s^{-1}$ is indicative of a reaction that is second order overall. For the reaction given, the rate law is probably rate = k[O][O_3]. (Although rate = k[O]^2 or k[O_3]^2 are possibilities, it is difficult to envision a mechanism consistent with either one that would result in two molecules of O_2 being produced.)

(b)　Yes. Most atmospheric processes are initiated by collision. One could imagine an activated complex of four O atoms collapsing to form two O_2 molecules. Also, the rate constant is large, which is less likely for a multistep process. The reaction is analogous to the destruction of O_3 by Cl atoms (Equation [18.7]), which is also second order with a large rate constant.

(c)　According to the Arrhenius equation, k = $Ae^{-E_a/RT}$. Thus, the larger the value of k, the smaller the activation energy, E_a. The value of the rate constant for this reaction is large, so the activation energy is small.

(d)　$\Delta H° = 2\Delta H_f° \, O_2(g) - \Delta H_f° \, O(g) - \Delta H_f° \, O_3(g)$

$\Delta H° = 0 - 247.5 \text{ kJ} - 142.3 \text{ kJ} = -389.8 \text{ kJ}$

The reaction is exothermic, so energy is released; the reaction would raise the temperature of the stratosphere.

18.89   (a) $17\ e^-,\ 8.5\ e^-$ pairs

$$\ddot{O}=\dot{N}-\ddot{O}: \longleftrightarrow :\ddot{O}-\dot{N}=\ddot{O}$$

Owing to its lower electronegativity, N is more likely to be electron deficient and to accommodate the odd electron.

(b)   The fact that NO_2 is an electron deficient molecule indicates that it will be highly reactive. Dimerization results in formation of a N—N single bond which completes the octet of both N atoms. NO_2 and N_2O_4 exist in equilibrium in a closed system. The reaction is exothermic, Equation [22.48]. In an urban environment, NO_2 is produced from hot automobile combustion. At these temperatures, equilibrium favors the monomer because the reaction is exothermic.

(c) $2NO_2(g) + 4CO(g) \rightarrow N_2(g) + 4CO_2(g)$

$NO_2(g) + CO(g) \rightarrow NO(g) + CO_2(g)$

NO_2 is an oxidizing agent and CO is a reducing agent, so we expect products to contain N in a more reduced form, NO or N_2, and C in a more oxidized form, CO_2.

(d)   No. Because it is an odd-electron molecule, NO_2 is very reactive. We expect it to undergo chemical reactions or photodissociate before it can migrate to the stratosphere. The expected half-life of an NO_2 molecule is short.

18.90   (a)   Holding one reactant concentration constant and changing the other, evaluate the effect this has on the initial rate. Use these observations to write the rate law.

Compare Experiments 1 and 3. $[O_3]$ is constant, [H] doubles, initial rate doubles. The reaction is first order in [H].

Compare Experiments 2 and 1. [H] is constant, $[O_3]$ doubles, initial rate doubles. The reaction is first order in $[O_3]$.

rate = $k[O_3]$[H]

(b)   Calculate a value for the rate constant for each experiment, then average them to obtain a single representative value.

rate = $k[O_3]$[H]; k = rate/$[O_3]$[H]

$$k_1 = \frac{1.88 \times 10^{-14}\ M/s}{(5.17 \times 10^{-33}\ M)(3.22 \times 10^{-26}\ M)} = 1.1293 \times 10^{44} = 1.13 \times 10^{44}$$

$$k_2 = \frac{9.44 \times 10^{-15}\ M/s}{(2.59 \times 10^{-33}\ M)(3.25 \times 10^{-26}\ M)} = 1.1215 \times 10^{44} = 1.12 \times 10^{44}$$

$$k_3 = \frac{3.77 \times 10^{-14}\ M/s}{(5.19 \times 10^{-33}\ M)(6.46 \times 10^{-26}\ M)} = 1.1245 \times 10^{44} = 1.12 \times 10^{44}$$

$k_{avg} = (1.1293 \times 10^{44} + 1.1215 \times 10^{44} + 1.1245 \times 10^{44})/3 = 1.1251 \times 10^{44} =$

$1.13 \times 10^{44}\ M^{-1}\ s^{-1}$

18.91   rate = $k[CF_3CH_2F][OH]$. $k = 1.6 \times 10^8 \ M^{-1} \ s^{-1}$ at 4°C.

$[CF_3CH_2F] = 6.3 \times 10^8$ molecules/cm^3, $[OH] = 8.1 \times 10^5$ molecules/cm^3

Change molecules/cm^3 to mol/L (M) and substitute into the rate law.

$$\frac{6.3 \times 10^8 \ \text{molecules}}{cm^3} \times \frac{1 \ \text{mol}}{6.022 \times 10^{23} \ \text{molecules}} \times \frac{1000 \ cm^3}{1 \ L} =$$

$$1.0462 \times 10^{-12} = 1.0 \times 10^{-12} \ M \ CF_3CH_2F$$

$$\frac{8.1 \times 10^5 \ \text{molecules}}{cm^3} \times \frac{1 \ \text{mol}}{6.022 \times 10^{23} \ \text{molecules}} \times \frac{1000 \ cm^3}{1 \ L} =$$

$$1.3451 \times 10^{-15} = 1.3 \times 10^{-15} \ M \ OH$$

rate $= \dfrac{1.6 \times 10^8}{M \cdot s} \times 1.0462 \times 10^{-12} \ M \times 1.3451 \times 10^{-15} \ M = 2.2515 \times 10^{-19} = 2.3 \times 10^{-19} \ M/s$

18.92   (a)   According to Table 18.1, the mole fraction of CO_2 in air is 0.000375.

$P_{CO_2} = \chi_{CO_2} \times P_{atm} = 0.000375 \,(1.00 \ atm) = 3.75 \times 10^{-4}$ atm

$C_{CO_2} = kP_{CO_2} = 3.1 \times 10^{-2} \ M/atm \times 3.75 \times 10^{-4} \ atm = 1.16 \times 10^{-5} = 1.2 \times 10^{-5} \ M$

(b) H_2CO_3 is a weak acid, so the $[H^+]$ is regulated by the equilibria:

$H_2CO_3(aq) \ \rightleftharpoons \ H^+(aq) + HCO_3^-(aq) \ K_{a1} = 4.3 \times 10^{-7}$

$HCO_3^-(aq) \ \rightleftharpoons \ H^+(aq) + CO_3^{2-}(aq) \ \ K_{a2} = 5.6 \times 10^{-11}$

Since the value of K_{a2} is small compared to K_{a1}, we will assume that most of the $H^+(aq)$ is produced by the first dissociation.

$K_{a1} = 4.3 \times 10^{-7} = \dfrac{[H^+][HCO_3^-]}{[H_2CO_3]}; [H^+] = [HCO_3^-] = x, [H_2CO_3] = 1.2 \times 10^{-5} - x$

Since K_{a1} and $[H_2CO_3]$ have similar values, we cannot assume x is small compared to 1.2×10^{-5}.

$4.3 \times 10^{-7} = \dfrac{x^2}{(1.2 \times 10^{-5} - x)}; 5.00 \times 10^{-12} - 4.3 \times 10^{-7} \ x = x^2$

$0 = x^2 + 4.3 \times 10^{-7} \ x - 5.00 \times 10^{-12}$

$x = \dfrac{-4.3 \times 10^{-7} \pm \sqrt{(4.3 \times 10^{-7})^2 - 4(1)(-5.00 \times 10^{-12})}}{2(1)}$

$x = \dfrac{-4.3 \times 10^{-7} \pm \sqrt{1.85 \times 10^{-13} + 2.00 \times 10^{-11}}}{2} = \dfrac{-4.3 \times 10^{-7} \pm 4.49 \times 10^{-6}}{2}$

The negative result is meaningless; $x = 2.03 \times 10^{-6} = 2.0 \times 10^{-6} \ M \ H^+$; pH = 5.69

Since this $[H^+]$ is quite small, the $[H^+]$ from the autoionization of water might be significant. Calculation shows that for $[H^+] = 2.0 \times 10^{-6} \ M$ from H_2CO_3, $[H^+]$ from $H_2O = 5.2 \times 10^{-9} \ M$, which we can ignore.

18.93   Calculate $[H_2SO_4]$ required to produce a solution with pH = 3.5. From the volume of rainfall, calculate the amount of H_2SO_4 present.

$[H^+] = 10^{-3.5} = 3.16 \times 10^{-4} = 3 \times 10^{-4} \, M$

Assume initially that both ionization steps are complete.

$$H_2SO_4(aq) \rightleftharpoons H^+(aq) + HSO_4^-(aq)$$
$$ x\,M x\,M$$

$$HSO_4^-(aq) \rightleftharpoons H^+(aq) + SO_4^{2-}(aq)$$
$$ +2x\,M x\,M$$

Since $[HSO_4^-]$ at equilibrium is small but finite, let $[HSO_4^-] = y$.

$$HSO_4^-(aq) \rightleftharpoons H^+(aq) + SO_4^{2-}(aq) \qquad K_a = 0.012$$

equil $y\,M$ $(2x - y)\,M$ $(x - y)\,M$

$$K_a = 0.012 = \frac{[H^+][SO_4^{2-}]}{[HSO_4^-]} = \frac{(2x-y)(x-y)}{y}$$

But we know that $[H^+]$ at equilibrium = $3.16 \times 10^{-4} \, M$.

$2x - y = 3.16 \times 10^{-4}$; $y = 2x - 3.16 \times 10^{-4}$; $(x - y) = [x - (2x - 3.16 \times 10^{-4})] = 3.16 \times 10^{-4} - x$

$$K_a = 0.012 = \frac{(3.16 \times 10^{-4})(3.16 \times 10^{-4} - x)}{2x - 3.16 \times 10^{-4}}$$

$(0.012)(2x - 3.16 \times 10^{-4}) = 1.00 \times 10^{-7} - 3.16 \times 10^{-4}x$;

$0.024x - 3.795 \times 10^{-6} = 1.00 \times 10^{-7} - 3.16 \times 10^{-4}x$;

$0.024316x = 3.895 \times 10^{-6}$; $x = 1.60 \times 10^{-4} = 2 \times 10^{-4} \, M \, H_2SO_4$

Check. This result is reasonable, since it is just slightly greater than $[H^+]/2$. The amount of HSO_4^- at equilibrium, $y = 4.1 \times 10^{-6} \, M$.

$$\frac{[H^+][SO_4^{2-}]}{[HSO_4^-]} = \frac{(3.16 \times 10^{-4})(1.60 \times 10^{-4} - 4.1 \times 10^{-6})}{4.1 \times 10^{-6}} = 0.012$$

The calculated results are reasonable and self-consistent.

Now proceed to find the volume of rainfall and corresponding mass of H_2SO_4 if $[H_2SO_4] = 1.60 \times 10^{-4} = 2 \times 10^{-4} \, M$.

$$V = 1.0 \, in \times 1500 \, mi^2 \times \frac{5280^2 \, ft^2}{mi^2} \times \frac{12^2 \, in^2}{ft^2} \times \frac{2.54^3 \, cm^3}{in^3} \times \frac{1\,L}{1000 \, cm^3} = 9.868 \times 10^{10}$$

$$= 9.9 \times 10^{10} \, L$$

$$\frac{1.60 \times 10^{-4} \, mol \, H_2SO_4}{1 \, L \, rainfall} \times 9.868 \times 10^{10} \, L \times \frac{98.1 g \, H_2SO_4}{1 \, mol \, H_2SO_4} \times \frac{1 \, kg}{1000 \, g} = 1.55 \times 10^6$$

$$= 2 \times 10^6 \, kg \, H_2SO_4$$

18.94 (a) $Al(OH)_3(s) \rightleftharpoons Al^{3+}(aq) + 3OH^-(aq)$ $K_{sp} = 1.3 \times 10^{-33} = [Al^{3+}][OH^-]^3$

This is a precipitation conditions problem. At what $[OH^-]$ (we can get pH from $[OH^-]$) will $Q = 1.3 \times 10^{-33}$, the requirement for the onset of precipitation?

$Q = 1.3 \times 10^{-33} = [Al^{3+}][OH^-]^3$. Find the molar concentration of $Al_2(SO_4)_3$ and thus $[Al^{3+}]$.

$$\frac{5.0 \text{ lb } Al_2(SO_4)_3}{2000 \text{ gal } H_2O} \times \frac{453.6 \text{ g}}{1 \text{ lb}} \times \frac{1 \text{ mol } Al_2(SO_4)_3}{342.2 \text{ g } Al_2(SO_4)_3} \times \frac{1 \text{ gal}}{4 \text{ qt}} \times \frac{1 \text{ qt}}{0.946 \text{ L}}$$

$$= 8.758 \times 10^{-4} M \ Al_2(SO_4)_3 = 1.752 \times 10^{-3} = 1.8 \times 10^{-3} M \ Al^{3+}$$

$Q = 1.3 \times 10^{-33} = (1.752 \times 10^{-3})[OH^-]^3; [OH^-]^3 = 7.42 \times 10^{-31}$

$[OH^-] = 9.054 \times 10^{-11} = 9.1 \times 10^{-11} M$; pOH = 10.04; pH = 14 − 10.04 = 3.96

(b) $CaO(s) + H_2O(l) \rightarrow Ca^{2+}(aq) + 2OH^-(aq)$; $[OH^-] = 9.054 \times 10^{-11}$ mol/L

$$\text{mol } OH^- = \frac{9.054 \times 10^{-11} \text{ mol}}{1 L} \times 2000 \text{ gal } \times \frac{4 \text{ qt}}{1 \text{ gal}} \times \frac{0.946 \text{ L}}{1 \text{ qt}} = 6.852 \times 10^{-7}$$

$$= 6.9 \times 10^{-7} \text{ mol } OH^-$$

$$6.852 \times 10^{-7} \text{ mol } OH^- \times \frac{1 \text{ mol } CaO}{2 \text{ mol } OH^-} \times \frac{56.1 \text{ g } CaO}{1 \text{ mol } CaO} \times \frac{1 \text{ lb}}{453.6 \text{ g}} = 4.2 \times 10^{-8} \text{ lb } CaO$$

This is a **very** small amount of CaO, about 20 μg.

18.95 (a) Process (i) is greener, because it does not involve the toxic reactant phosgene ($COCl_2$) and the by-product is water, not HCl.

(b) Reaction (i): C in CO_2 is linear with sp hybridization; C in R—N=C=O is linear with sp hybridization; C in the urethane monomer is trigonal planar with sp^2 hybridization. Reaction (ii): C in $COCl_2$ is trigonal planar with sp^2 hybridization; C in R—N=C=O is linear with sp hybridization; C in the urethane monomer is trigonal planar with sp^2 hybridization.

(c) Traditionally, industrial processes are conducted at higher temperatures to speed up reactions and encourage formation of product. However, this is not a green solution, because it requires additional energy. Using Le Chatelier's principle, we could either "push" or "pull" the reaction toward products. The "push" requires that we increase the amount of reactants, again not a green approach. The greenest way to promote formation of the isocyanate is to "pull" the reaction forward by removing by-product from the reaction mixture. In reaction (i), remove water; in reaction (ii), remove HCl.

18.96 (a) The various forms of carbonate in water are related by the following equilibria:

$H_2CO_3(aq) \rightleftharpoons H^+(aq) + HCO_3^-(aq)$ $K_{a1} = 4.3 \times 10^{-7}$

$HCO_3^-(aq) \rightleftharpoons H^+(aq) + CO_3^{2-}(aq)$ $K_{a2} = 5.6 \times 10^{-11}$

$$K_{a1} = 4.3 \times 10^{-7} = \frac{[H^+][HCO_3^-]}{[H_2CO_3]}; \quad K_{a2} = 5.6 \times 10^{-11} = \frac{[H^+][CO_3^{2-}]}{[HCO_3^-]}$$

$[H^+] = 10^{-pH} = 10^{-5.6} = 2.5119 \times 10^{-6} = 3 \times 10^{-6} \, M$

Also, $[H_2CO_3] + [HCO_3^-] + [CO_3^{2-}] = 1.0 \times 10^{-5} \, M$

We now have 3 equations in 3 unknowns, so we can solve explicitly for one. Solve for $[HCO_3^-]$ (since it appears in both K_a expressions), then substitute to find $[H_2CO_3]$ and $[CO_3^{2-}]$.

$$1.0 \times 10^{-5} = \frac{[H^+][HCO_3^-]}{K_{a1}} + [HCO_3^-] + \frac{K_{a2}[HCO_3^-]}{[H^+]}$$

$$1.0 \times 10^{-5} = \frac{2.5119 \times 10^{-6}[HCO_3^-]}{4.3 \times 10^{-7}} + [HCO_3^-] + \frac{5.6 \times 10^{-11}[HCO_3^-]}{2.5119 \times 10^{-6}}$$

$$1.0 \times 10^{-5} = 5.8416[HCO_3^-] + [HCO_3^-] + 2.2294 \times 10^{-5}[HCO_3^-]$$

$$[HCO_3^-] = \frac{1.0 \times 10^{-5}}{6.8416} = 1.4616 \times 10^{-6} = 1.5 \times 10^{-6} \, M$$

Note that $[CO_3^{2-}]$ is very small compared to $[H_2CO_3]$ and $[HCO_3^-]$.

$$[H_2CO_3] = \frac{(2.5119 \times 10^{-6})(1.4616 \times 10^{-6})}{4.3 \times 10^{-7}} = 8.5383 \times 10^{-6} = 8.5 \times 10^{-6} \, M$$

$$[CO_3^{2-}] = \frac{(5.6 \times 10^{-11})(1.4616 \times 10^{-6})}{2.5119 \times 10^{-6}} = 3.2586 \times 10^{-11} = 3.3 \times 10^{-11} \, M$$

Check. $1.5 \times 10^{-6} \, M + 8.5 \times 10^{-6} \, M + 3.3 \times 10^{-11} \, M = 1.0 \times 10^{-5} \, M$

(b) In order to test for sulfur-containing species, we must first remove the various forms of carbonate. One method is to exploit the solubility differences between carbonate and sulfate salts. Most sulfates are soluble, while most carbonates are not. However, K_{sp} values for carbonates are relatively large, and $[CO_3^{2-}]$ in the raindrop is very small. Precipitating insoluble carbonates will shift the acid dissociation equilibria to the right, but precipitation may not be the best method for effectively removing carbonates.

A different method involves removing carbonates as $CO_2(g)$. Heating the rainwater will decrease the solubility of $CO_2(g)$, which will bubble off as a gas. Slightly acidifying the solution will encourage this process, by shifting the acid dissociation equilibria toward H_2CO_3 and $CO_2(g)$.

After removal of carbonates, sulfates are precipitated with $Ba^{2+}(aq)$. The amount of precipitate is small, but it does cause turbidity in the solution. Turbidity is detected by instrumental methods which measure light scattering by colloids.

19 Chemical Thermodynamics

Visualizing Concepts

19.1   (a)

    (b) ΔS is positive, because the disorder of the system increases. Each gas has greater motional freedom as it expands into the second bulb, and there are many more possible arrangements for the mixed gases.

         By definition, ideal gases experience no attractive or repulsive intermolecular interactions, so ΔH for the mixing of ideal gases is zero, assuming heat exchange only between the two bulbs.

    (c)   The process is spontaneous and therefore irreversible. It is inconceivable that the gases would reseparate.

    (d)   The entropy change of the surroundings is related to ΔH for the system. Since we are mixing ideal gases and $\Delta H = 0$, ΔH_{surr} is also zero, assuming heat exchange only between the two bulbs.

19.2   (a)   Based on experience, the process is spontaneous. We know that 1,1-difluoroethane is a gas at atmospheric pressure, so the pressure inside the can must be much greater than atmospheric in order for the substance to be liquefied. When the nozzle is pressed and the system is open to the lower pressure of the atmosphere, the liquid vaporizes spontaneously. The 1,1-difluoroethane gas escapes the nozzle without external assistance.

    (b)   We expect q_{sys} to be positive. We know that ΔH is positive for the vaporization of a gas. Since the change does not occur at constant pressure, q_{sys} and ΔH are not equal, but the sign of q_{sys} is still positive.

    (c) ΔS is definitely positive for this process, owing to the larger volume occupied and greater motional freedom of the system, the 1,1-difluoroethane molecules.

    (d)   The operation of the keyboard cleaner definitely depends more on entropy change than heat flow.

19.3   (a)   The process depicted is a change of state from a solid to a gas. ΔS is positive because of the greater motional freedom of the particles. ΔH is positive because both melting and boiling are endothermic processes.

    (b)   Since $\Delta G = \Delta H - T\Delta S$, and both ΔH and ΔS are positive, the sign of ΔG depends on temperature. This is true for all phase changes. If the temperature of the system is greater than the boiling point of the substance, the process is spontaneous and ΔG is negative. If the temperature is lower than the boiling point, the process is not spontaneous and ΔG is positive.

(c) If the process is spontaneous, the second law states that $\Delta S_{univ} \geq 0$. Since ΔS_{sys} is positive, ΔS_{surr} must be negative. If the change occurs via a reversible pathway, $\Delta S_{univ} = 0$ and $\Delta S_{surr} = -\Delta S_{sys}$. If the pathway is irreversible, the magnitude of ΔS_{sys} is greater than the magnitude of ΔS_{surr}, but the sign of ΔS_{surr} is still negative.

19.4   In the depicted reaction, both reactants and products are in the gas phase (they are far apart and randomly placed). There are twice as many molecules (or moles) of gas in the products, so ΔS is positive for this reaction.

19.5   *Analyze/Plan.* Consider the physical changes that occur when a substance is heated. How do these changes affect the entropy of the substance?

(a) Both 1 and 2 represent changes in entropy at constant temperature; these are phase changes. Since 1 happens at a lower temperature, it represents melting (fusion), and 2 represents vaporization.

(b) The substance changes from solid to liquid in 1, from liquid to gas in 2. The larger volume and greater motional freedom of the gas phase causes ΔS for vaporization to (always) be larger than ΔS for fusion.

19.6   (a) We expect the enthalpy of combustion of the two isomers to be very similar. The molecular formulas of the two molecules are the same, so the balanced chemical equations for the two combustion reactions are identical. In the calculation of combustion enthalpy from standard enthalpies of formation of products and reactants, the only difference will be in the standard enthalpies of formation of the two isomers.

(b) We expect n-pentane to have the higher standard molar entropy. The rod-shaped n-pentane has more possible vibrational and rotational motions than the almost-spherical neopentane. That is, n-pentane has greater motional energy, which results in a higher standard molar entropy than that of neopentane.

19.7   (a) At 300 K, $\Delta H = T\Delta S$. Since $\Delta G = \Delta H - T\Delta S$, $\Delta G = 0$ at this point. When $\Delta G = 0$, the system is at equilibrium.

(b) The reaction is spontaneous when ΔG is negative. This condition is met when $T\Delta S > \Delta H$. From the diagram, $T\Delta S > \Delta H$ when $T > 300$ K. The reaction is spontaneous at temperatures above 300 K.

19.8   (a) At equilibrium, $\Delta G = 0$. On the diagram, $\Delta G = 0$ at 250 K. The system is at equilibrium at 250 K.

(b) A reaction is spontaneous when ΔG is negative. The reaction is spontaneous at temperatures greater than 250 K.

(c) $\Delta G = \Delta H - T\Delta S$, in the form of $y = b + mx$. ΔH is the y intercept of the graph (where $T = 0$) and is positive.

(d) The slope of the graph is $-\Delta S$. The slope is negative, so ΔS is positive. [Also, ΔG decreases as T increases, so the $T\Delta S$ term must become more negative and ΔS is positive.]

19.9   (a)   *Analyze.* The boxes depict three different mixtures of reactants and products for the reaction $A_2 + B_2 \rightleftharpoons 2AB$.

Plan. $K_c = 1 = \dfrac{[AB]^2}{[A][B]}$. Calculate Q for each box, using number of molecules as a measure of concentration. If Q = 1, the system is at equilibrium. *Solve.*

Box 1: $K = \dfrac{(3)^2}{(3)(3)} = 1$.

Box 2: $Q = \dfrac{(1)^2}{(4)(4)} = \dfrac{1}{16} = 0.0625 = 0.06$

Box 3: $Q = \dfrac{(7)^2}{(1)(1)} = \dfrac{49}{1} = 49$

Box 1 is at equilibrium.

(b)   All nonequilibrium systems move spontaneously to achieve equilibrium. As the reaction is written, the sign of ΔG indicates the direction in which the reaction is spontaneous. If ΔG is negative, the reaction is spontaneous in the forward direction, toward products. This is the case for Box 2. If ΔG is positive, the reaction is spontaneous in the reverse direction, toward reactants. This is the case for Box 3.

(c)   Qualitatively, Box 3 is farthest from equilibrium, so it has the largest magnitude of ΔG (driving force to reach equilibrium), then Box 2, then Box 1, where $\Delta G = 0$. Box 1 < Box 2 < Box 3.

Quantitatively, $\Delta G = \Delta G° - RT\ln Q$. For Box 1, $\Delta G = 0$ and K = 1, so $\Delta G° = 0$.

Box 2: $\Delta G = 0 - RT\ln(0.0625) = 2.77\ RT$

Box 3: $\Delta G = 0 - RT\ln(49) = -3.89\ RT$

Quantitative treatment confirms the order for magnitude of ΔG as Box 1 < Box 2 < Box 3.

19.10   (a)   The minimum in the plot is the equilibrium position of the reaction, where $\Delta G = 0$.

(b)   The quantity x is the difference in free energy between reactant and products in their standard states, $\Delta G°$.

Spontaneous Processes (section 19.1)

19.11   *Analyze/Plan.* Follow the logic in Sample Exercise 19.1.   *Solve.*

(a)   Spontaneous; at ambient temperature, ripening happens without intervention.

(b)   Spontaneous; sugar is soluble in water, and even more soluble in hot coffee.

(c)   Spontaneous; N_2 molecules are stable relative to isolated N atoms.

(d)   Spontaneous; under certain atmospheric conditions, lightening occurs.

(e) Nonspontaneous; CO_2 and H_2O are in contact continuously at atmospheric conditions in nature and do not form CH_4 and O_2.

19.12 (a) Nonspontaneous; at 1 atm, ice does not melt spontaneously at temperatures below its normal melting point.

(b) Nonspontaneous; a mixture cannot be separated without outside intervention.

(c) Spontaneous.

(d) Spontaneous. The reaction is spontaneous but slow unless encouraged by a catalyst or spark.

(e) Spontaneous; the very polar HCl molecules readily dissolve in water to form concentrated HCl(aq).

19.13 (a) $NH_4NO_3(s)$ dissolves in water, as in a chemical cold pack. Naphthalene (mothballs) sublimes at room temperature.

(b) Melting of a solid is spontaneous above its melting point but nonspontaneous below its melting point.

19.14 Yes. Bertholet postulated that all spontaneous processes are exothermic. The spontaneous endothermic reaction described in this exercise is one of many exceptions to Bertholet's generalization.

19.15 *Analyze/Plan.* Define the system and surroundings. Use the appropriate definition to answer the specific questions. *Solve.*

(a) Water is the system. Heat must be added to the system to evaporate the water. The process is endothermic.

(b) At 1 atm, the reaction is spontaneous at temperatures above 100°C.

(c) At 1 atm, the reaction is nonspontaneous at temperatures below 100°C.

(d) The two phases are in equilibrium at 100°C.

19.16 (a) Exothermic. If melting requires heat and is endothermic, freezing must be exothermic.

(b) At 1 atm (indicated by the term "normal" freezing point), the freezing of *n*-octane is spontaneous at temperatures below –57°C.

(c) At 1 atm, the freezing of *n*-octane is nonspontaneous at temperatures above

–57°C.

(d) At 1 atm and –57°C, the normal freezing point of *n*-octane, the solid and liquid phases are in equilibrium. That is, at the freezing point, *n*-octane molecules escape to the liquid phase at the same rate as liquid *n*-octane solidifies, assuming no heat is exchanged between *n*-octane and the surroundings.

19.17 *Analyze/Plan.* Define the system and surroundings. Use the appropriate definition to answer the specific questions. *Solve.*

(a)   For a *reversible* process, the forward and reverse changes occur by the same path. In a reversible process, both the system and the surroundings are restored to their original condition by exactly reversing the change. A reversible change produces the maximum amount of work.

(b)   If a system is returned to its original state via a reversible path, the surroundings are also returned to their original state. That is, there is no net change in the surroundings.

(c)   The vaporization of water to steam is reversible if it occurs at the boiling temperature of water for a specified external (atmospheric) pressure, and if the required heat is added infinitely slowly.

(d)   No. Natural processes, such as a banana ripening or a lightning strike are spontaneous in the direction they occur and nonspontaneous in the opposite direction. By definition they are irreversible; they do not occur by reversible pathways. Neither the system nor the surroundings can be returned to their original condition by the same pathway that the change occurred. It is impossible to imagine a banana unripening.

19.18   (a)   A process is *irreversible* if the system cannot be returned to its original state by the same path that the forward process took place.

         (b)   Since the system returned to its initial state via a different path (different q_r and w_r than q_f and w_f), there is a net change in the surroundings.

         (c)   The condensation of a liquid will be irreversible if it occurs at any temperature other than the boiling point of the liquid, at a specified pressure.

19.19   *Analyze/Plan.* The related properties of a gas are pressure, volume, temperature and amount.

         (a)   If T decreases while V is unchanged, either P or amount must change. For a closed system (Section 5.1) at constant volume, a decrease in external temperature leads to a decrease in the temperature of the system, in this case an ideal gas, as well as a decrease in pressure of the gas. An example is the decrease in air pressure in a tire or the first cold autumn day.

         (b)   If T decreases while P stays constant, either amount or volume must change. For a closed system at constant pressure, if the temperature of the gas decreases, the volume also decreases.

         (c)   No. ΔE is a state function. $\Delta E = q + w$; q and w are not state functions. Their values do depend on path, but their sum, ΔE, does not.

19.20   (a) $\Delta E\,(1 \rightarrow 2) = -\Delta E\,(2 \rightarrow 1)$

         (b)   We can say nothing about the values of q and w because we have no information about the paths.

         (c)   If the changes of state are reversible, the two paths are the same and $w\,(1 \rightarrow 2) = -w\,(2 \rightarrow 1)$. This is the maximum realizable work from this system.

19.21   *Analyze/Plan.* Define the system and surroundings. Use the appropriate definition to answer the specific questions.   *Solve.*

     (a)   An ice cube can melt reversibly at the conditions of temperature and pressure where the solid and liquid are in equilibrium. At 1 atm external pressure, the normal melting point of water is 0°C.

     (b)   We know that melting is a process that increases the energy of the system, even though there is no change in temperature. ΔE is not zero for the process.

19.22   (a)   The detonation of an explosive is definitely spontaneous, once it is initiated.

     (b)   The quantity q is related to ΔH. Since the detonation is highly exothermic, q is large and negative.

         If only PV-work is done and P is constant, $\Delta H = q$. Although these conditions probably do not apply to a detonation, we can still predict the sign of q, based on ΔH, if not its exact magnitude.

     (c)   The sign (and magnitude) of w depend on the path of the process, the exact details of how the detonation is carried out. It seems clear, however, that work will be done by the system on the surroundings in almost all circumstances (buildings collapse, earth and air are moved), so the sign of w is probably negative.

     (d) $\Delta E = q + w$. If q and w are both negative, then the sign of ΔE is negative, regardless of the magnitudes of q and w.

Entropy and the Second Law of Thermodynamics (section 19.2)

19.23   (a)   For a process that occurs at constant temperature, an isothermal process, $\Delta S = q_{rev}/T$. Here q_{rev} is the heat that would be transferred if the process were reversible. Since ΔS is a state function, it is independent of path, so ΔS for the reversible path must equal ΔS for any path.

     (b)   No. ΔS is a state function, so it is independent of path.

19.24   Both vaporizations are *isothermal*; they occur at constant temperature. For an isothermal process, : $\Delta S = q_{rev}/T$.

     (a)   Assuming that q_{rev} is closely related to enthalpy of vaporization and is about the same at the two temperatures, ΔS is larger at 25°C than at 100°C.

     (b)   No. Because ΔS is a state function, it is independent of path. We can calculate ΔS for a reversible pathway, even if the change does not occur that way.

19.25   (a) $Br_2(l) \rightarrow Br_2(g)$, entropy increases, more mol gas in products, greater motional freedom.

     (b) $\Delta S = \dfrac{\Delta H}{T} = \dfrac{29.6\,kJ}{mol\,Br_2(l)} \times 1.00\,mol\,Br_2(l) \times \dfrac{1}{(273.15+58.8)K} \times \dfrac{1000\,J}{1\,kJ} = 89.2\,J/K$

19.26   (a) $Ga(l) \rightarrow Ga(s)$, ΔS is negative, less motional freedom

(b) $\Delta H = 60.0 \text{ g Ga} \times \dfrac{1 \text{ mol Ga}}{69.723 \text{ g Ga}} \times \dfrac{-5.59 \text{ kJ}}{\text{mol Ga}} = -4.81046 = -4.81 \text{ kJ}$

$\Delta S = \dfrac{\Delta H}{T} = -4.81046 \text{ kJ} \times \dfrac{1000 \text{ J}}{1 \text{ kJ}} \times \dfrac{1}{(273.15 + 29.8) \text{K}} = -15.9 \text{ J/K}$

19.27   (a)   For a spontaneous process, the entropy of the universe increases; for a reversible process, the entropy of the universe does not change.

(b)   In a reversible process, $\Delta S_{sys} + \Delta S_{surr} = 0$. If ΔS_{sys} is positive, ΔS_{surr} must be negative.

(c)   Since ΔS_{univ} must be positive for a spontaneous process, ΔS_{surr} must be greater than -42 J/K.

19.28   (a)   For a spontaneous process, $\Delta S_{univ} > 0$. For a reversible process, $\Delta S_{univ} = 0$.

(b) ΔS_{surr} is positive and greater than the magnitude of the decrease in ΔS_{sys}.

(c) $\Delta S_{sys} = 78$ J/K.

19.29   *Analyze.* Consider ΔS for the isothermal expansion of 0.200 mol of an ideal gas at 27°C and an initial volume of 10.0 L.

(a)   Whenever an ideal gas expands isothermally, we expect an increase in entropy, or positive ΔS, owing to the greater volume available for motion of the particles.

(b)   *Plan.* Use the relationship $\Delta S_{sys} = nR \ln(V_2/V_1)$, Equation [19.3].

Solve. $\Delta S_{sys} = 0.200 \, (8.314 \text{ J/mol-K})(\ln [18.5 \text{ L}/10.0 \text{ L}]) = 1.02$ J/K.

Check. We expect ΔS to be positive when the motional freedom of a gas increases, and our calculation agrees with this prediction.

(c)   The temperature at which the expansion occurs is not needed to calculate the entropy change, as long as the process is isothermal.

19.30   (a)   According to Boyle's law, pressure and volume are inversely proportional at constant amount and temperature. If the pressure of an ideal gas increases, volume decreases. We expect a decrease in entropy, or negative ΔS, for the isothermal compression of an ideal gas, owing to the smaller volume available for motion of the particles.

(b)   According to Boyle's law, $P_1 V_1 = P_2 V_2$ at constant n and T.

$0.750 \text{ atm} \times V_1 = 1.20 \text{ atm} \times V_2$; $V_2/V_1 = 0.750 \text{ atm}/1.20 \text{ atm} = 0.62500 = 0.625$

$\Delta S_{sys} = nR \ln (V_2/V_1) = 0.600 \text{ mol} \, (8.314 \text{ J/mol-K})(\ln 0.625) = -2.34$ J/K

Check. An increase in pressure results in a decrease in volume at constant T, so we expect ΔS to be negative, and it is.

(c)   The temperature at which the compression (increase in pressure, decrease in volume) occurs is not needed to calculate the entropy change, as long as the process is isothermal.

19 Chemical Thermodynamics

The Molecular Interpretation of Entropy (section 19.3)

19.31   (a)   Yes, the expansion is spontaneous.

         (b)   The ideal gas is the system, and everything else, including the vessel containing the vacuum, is the surroundings. There is literally nothing inside the vessel containing the vacuum, no gas molecules and no physical barriers. As the ideal gas expands into the vacuum, there is nothing for it to "push back", so no work is done. Mathematically, $w = -P_{ext}\Delta V$. Since the gas expands into a vacuum, $P_{ext} = 0$ and $w = 0$.

         (c)   The "driving force" for the expansion of the gas is the increase in entropy associated with greater volume, more motional freedom and more possible positions for the gas particles.

19.32   (a)   A thermodynamic *state* is a set of conditions, usually temperature and pressure, that defines the properties of a bulk material. A *microstate* is a single possibility for all the positions and kinetic energies of all the molecules in a sample; it is a snapshot of positions and speeds at a particular instant.

         (b)   According to Equation [19.5] (Boltzman's Law), the more possible microstates for a macroscopic state, the greater the entropy of the state. If S decreases going from A to B, then A has more microstates than B. Or, if ΔS is negative, the number of microstates decreases.

         (c)   According to part (b), if the number of microstates available to a system decreases, ΔS_{sys} is negative. For a spontaneous process, ΔS_{univ} is positive, so ΔS_{surr} is positive (and the magnitude is greater than that of ΔS_{sys}).

19.33   (a)   The higher the temperature, the broader the distribution of molecular speeds and kinetic energies available to the particles. At higher temperature, the wider range of accessible kinetic energies leads to more microstates for the system.

         (b)   A decrease in volume reduces the number of possible positions for the particles and leads to fewer microstates for the system.

         (c)   Going from liquid to gas, particles have greater translational motion, which increases the number of positions available to the particles and the number of microstates for the system.

19.34   (a) ΔH_{vap} for H_2O at 25°C = 44.02 kJ/mol; at 100°C = 40.67 kJ/mol

$$\Delta S = \frac{q_{rev}}{T} = \frac{44.02\,\text{kJ}}{\text{mol}} \times \frac{1000\,\text{J}}{\text{kJ}} \times \frac{1}{298\,\text{K}} = 148\,\text{J/mol-K}$$

$$\Delta S = \frac{q_{rev}}{T} = \frac{40.67\,\text{kJ}}{\text{mol}} \times \frac{1000\,\text{J}}{\text{kJ}} \times \frac{1}{373\,\text{K}} = 109\,\text{J/mol-K}$$

         (b)   At both temperatures, the liquid → gas phase transition is accompanied by an increase in entropy, as expected. That the magnitude of the increase is greater at the lower temperature requires some explanation.

            In the liquid state, there are significant hydrogen bonding interactions between H_2O molecules. This reduces the number of possible molecular positions and the number of microstates. Liquid water at 100° has sufficient kinetic energy to have broken many hydrogen bonds, so the number of microstates for $H_2O(l)$ at 100° is greater than the number of microstates for $H_2O(l)$ at 25°C. The difference in the number of microstates upon vaporization at 100°C is smaller, and the magnitude of ΔS is smaller.

19.35   *Analyze/Plan.* Consider the conditions that lead to an increase in entropy: more mol gas in products than reactants, increase in volume of sample and, therefore, number of possible arrangements, more motional freedom of molecules, etc.   *Solve.*

    (a)   More gaseous particles means more possible arrangements and greater disorder; ΔS is positive.

    (b) S_{sys} may increase slightly in 19.11 (a), where the sample softens; this is not definitive.

          S_{sys} clearly increases in Exercise 19.11 (b), where there is an increase in volume and possible arrangements for the sample.

          In 19.11 (c), the system goes from two moles of gaseous reactants to one mole of gaseous products, and S_{sys} decreases.

          In 19.11 (d), the entropy of the universe clearly increases, but the definition of the system in a lightning strike is more problematic.

          In 19.11 (e), the state is specified as room temperature and 1 atm pressure. This means that H_2O is present as a liquid; there is then one mol of gaseous reactants (CO_2) and three mol of gaseous products (CH_4 and $2\,O_2$), so S_{sys} increases. (The reaction is not spontaneous because of the very large positive ΔH_{sys} for the reaction as written.)

19.36   (a)   Solids are much more ordered than gases, so ΔS is negative.

    (b)   The entropy of the system increases in Exercise 19.12 (a) and (e). There is more motional freedom for the system in both cases. In (b), (c) and (d), there is less motional freedom after the change and the entropy of the system decreases.

19.37   *Analyze/Plan.* Consider the conditions that lead to an increase in entropy: more mol gas in products than reactants, increase in volume of sample and, therefore, number of possible arrangements, more motional freedom of molecules, etc.   *Solve.*

    (a)   S increases; translational motion is greater in the liquid than the solid.

    (b)   S decreases; volume and translational motion decrease going from the gas to the liquid.

    (c)   S increases; volume and translational motion are greater in the gas than the solid.

19.38   (a)   When temperature increases, the range of accessible molecular speeds and kinetic energies increases. This produces more microstates and an increase in entropy.

    (b)   When the volume of a gas increases (even at constant T), there are more possible positions for the particles, more microstates, and greater entropy.

(c)   When equal volumes of two miscible liquids are mixed, the volume of the sample and therefore the number of possible arrangements increases. This produces more microstates and an increase in entropy.

19.39   (a)   The entropy of a pure crystalline substance at absolute zero is zero.

(b)   In *translational* motion, the entire molecule moves in a single direction; in *rotational* motion, the molecule rotates or spins around a fixed axis. *Vibrational* motion is reciprocating motion. The bonds within a molecule stretch and bend, but the average position of the atoms does not change.

(c)

H—Cl $\xrightarrow{\text{translational}}$ H—Cl

H—|—Cl   H—Cl ↔ H——Cl ↔ H—Cl
rotational   vibrational

19.40   (a)   In order for the entropy of a system to be zero, the system must be a pure crystalline (exactly ordered in three dimensions) solid, and the temperature must be absolute zero.

(b)   Since CO_2 has more than one atom, the thermal energy can be distributed as translational, vibrational, or rotational motion.

O=C=O → O=C=O   O=C=O
      translational   rotational
O=C=O

O=C=O ↔ O=C=O ↔ O=C=O ↔ O=C=O
symmetric   asymmetric   bend
stretch   stretch

vibrational

(c)   At a given temperature, $CO_2(g)$ has more microstates and thus greater entropy than $Ar(g)$. Because $CO_2(g)$ is a triatomic molecule, it has multiple rotational and vibrational microstates not available to monatomic $Ar(g)$.

19.41   *Analyze/Plan.* Consider the factors that lead to higher entropy: more mol gas in products than reactants, increase in volume of sample and, therefore, number of possible arrangements, more motional freedom of molecules, etc.   *Solve.*

(a) $Ar(g)$ (gases have higher entropy due primarily to much larger volume)

(b) $He(g)$ at 1.5 atm (larger volume and more motional freedom)

(c)   1 mol of $Ne(g)$ in 15.0 L (larger volume provides more motional freedom)

(d) $CO_2(g)$ (more motional freedom)

19.42   (a)   1 mol of $As_4(g)$ at 300°C, 0.01 atm (As_4 has more massive atoms in a comparable system at the same temperature.)

(b)   1 mol $H_2O(g)$ at 100°C, 1 atm (larger volume occupied by $H_2O(g)$)

(c)   0.5 mol $CH_4(g)$ at 298 K, 20-L volume (more complex molecule, more rotational and vibrational degrees of freedom)

(d)   100 g of $Na_2SO_4(aq)$ at 30°C (more motional freedom in aqueous solution)

19.43   *Analyze/Plan.* Consider the markers of an increase in entropy for a chemical reaction: liquids or solutions formed from solids, gases formed from either solids or liquids, increase in moles gas during reaction.   *Solve.*

(a) ΔS negative (moles of gas decrease)

(b) ΔS positive (gas produced, increased disorder)

(c) ΔS negative (moles of gas decrease)

(d) ΔS is small and probably positive (moles of gas same in reactants and products, $H_2O(g)$ is more structurally complex than $H_2(g)$]

19.44   (a) $Au(l) \rightarrow Au(s)$; negative ΔS, less motional freedom in the solid

           (b) $Cl_2(g) \rightarrow 2Cl(g)$; positive ΔS, moles of gas increase

           (c) $CO(g) + 2 H_2(g) \rightarrow CH_3OH(l)$; negative ΔS, moles of gas decrease

           (d) $3 Ca(NO_3)_2(aq) + 2 (NH_4)_3PO_4(aq) \rightarrow Ca_3(PO_4)_2(s) + 6 NH_4NO_3(aq)$; ΔS is negative, less motional freedom, fewer moles of ions in aqueous solution.

Entropy Changes in Chemical Reactions (section 19.4)

19.45   (a)

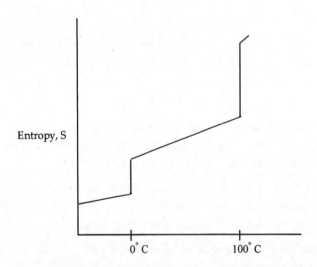

(b)   Boiling water, at 100 °C, has a much larger entropy change than melting ice at 0 °C. Before and after melting, H_2O molecules are touching. And there is actually a small decrease in volume going from solid to liquid water. Boiling drastically increases the distance between molecules and the volume of the sample. The increase in available molecular positions is much greater for boiling than melting, so the entropy change is also greater.

19.46   Melting = –126.5°C; boiling = 97.4°C.

19.47   *Analyze/Plan.* Given two molecules in the same state, predict which will have the higher molar entropy. In general, for molecules in the same state, the more atoms in the molecule, the more degrees of freedom, the greater the number of microstates and the higher the standard entropy, $S°$.

(a) $C_2H_6(g)$ has more degrees of freedom and larger $S°$.

(b) $CO_2(g)$ has more degrees of freedom and larger $S°$.

19.48   Propylene will have a higher $S°$ at 25°C. At this temperature, both are gases, so there are no lattice effects. Since they have the same molecular formula, only the details of their structures are different. In propylene, there is free rotation around the C—C single bond, while in cyclopropane the 3-membered ring severely limits rotation. The greater motional freedom of the propylene molecule leads to a higher absolute entropy.

19.49   *Analyze/Plan.* Consider the conditions that lead to an increase in entropy: more mol gas in products than reactants, increase in volume of sample and, therefore, number of possible arrangements, more motional freedom of molecules, etc. *Solve.*

(a) $Sc(s)$, 34.6 J/mol-K; $Sc(g)$, 174.7 J/mol-K. In general, the gas phase of a substance has a larger $S°$ than the solid phase because of the greater volume and motional freedom of the molecules.

(b) $NH_3(g)$, 192.5 J/mol-K; $NH_3(aq)$, 111.3 J/mol-K. Molecules in the gas phase have more motional freedom than molecules in solution.

(c)   1 mol of $P_4(g)$, 280 J/K; 2 mol of $P_2(g)$, 2(218.1) = 436.2 J/K. More particles have greater motional energy (more available microstates).

(d)   C(diamond), 2.43 J/mol-K; C(graphite) 5.69 J/mol-K. Diamond is a network covalent solid with each C atom tetrahedrally bound to four other C atoms. Graphite consists of sheets of fused planar 6-membered rings with each C atom bound in a trigonal planar arrangement to three other C atoms. The internal entropy in graphite is greater because there is translational freedom among the planar sheets of C atoms while there is very little vibrational freedom within the network covalent diamond lattice.

19.50   (a)   CuO(s), 42.59 J/mol-K; Cu$_2$O(s), 92.36 J/mol-K. Molecules in the solid state have only vibrational motion available to them. The more complex Cu$_2$O molecule has more vibrational degrees of freedom and a larger standard entropy.

        (b)   1 mol N$_2$O$_4$(g), 304.3 J/K; 2 mol NO$_2$(g), 2(240.45) = 480.90 J/K. More particles have a greater number of arrangements.

        (c)   SiO$_2$(s), 41.84 J/mol-K; CO$_2$(g), 213.6 J/mol-K. Molecules in the gas phase have a larger volume and more motional freedom than molecules in the solid state. SiO$_2$ is a covalent network solid so its molecular motion is even more restrained than a typical molecular solid.

        (d)   CO(g), 197.9 J/mol-K; CO$_2$(g), 213.6 J/mol-K. The more complex CO$_2$ molecule has more vibrational degrees of freedom and a slightly higher entropy.

19.51   For elements with similar structures, the heavier the atoms, the lower the vibrational frequencies at a given temperature. This means that more vibrations can be accessed at a particular temperature resulting in a greater absolute entropy for the heavier elements.

19.52   (a)   C(diamond), S° = 2.43 J/mol-K; C(graphite), S° = 5.69 J/mol-K. Diamond is a network covalent solid with each C atom tetrahedrally bound to four other C atoms. Graphite consists of sheets of fused planar 6-membered rings with each C atom bound in a trigonal planar arrangement to three other C atoms. The internal entropy in graphite is greater because there is translational freedom among the planar sheets of C atoms, while there is very little translational or vibrational freedom within the covalent-network diamond lattice.

        (b)   S° for buckminsterfullerene will be ≥ 10 J/mol-K. S° for graphite is twice S° for diamond, and S° for the fullerene should be higher than that of graphite. The 60-atom "bucky" balls have more flexibility than graphite sheets. Also, the balls have translational freedom in three dimensions, while graphite sheets have it in only two directions. Because of the ball structure, there is more empty space in the fullerene lattice than in graphite or diamond; essentially, 60 C-atoms in fullerene occupy a larger volume than 60 C-atoms in graphite or diamond. Thus, the fullerene has additional "molecular" complexity, more degrees of translational freedom, and occupies a larger volume, all features that point to a higher absolute entropy.

19.53   *Analyze/Plan.* Follow the logic in Sample Exercise 19.5.   *Solve.*

        (a)   ΔS° = S° C$_2$H$_6$(g) – S° C$_2$H$_4$(g) – S° H$_2$(g)

                  = 229.5 – 219.4 – 130.58 = –120.5 J/K

        ΔS° is negative because there are fewer moles of gas in the products.

        (b)   ΔS° = 2S° NO$_2$(g) – ΔS° N$_2$O$_4$(g) = 2(240.45) – 304.3 = +176.6 J/K

        ΔS° is positive because there are more moles of gas in the products.

        (c)   ΔS° = ΔS° BeO(s) + ΔS° H$_2$O(g) – ΔS° Be(OH)$_2$(s)

                  = 13.77 + 188.83 – 50.21 = +152.39 J/K

        ΔS° is positive because the product contains more total particles and more moles of gas.

(d) $\Delta S° = 2S° \, CO_2(g) + 4S° \, H_2O(g) - 2S° \, CH_3OH(g) - 3S° \, O_2(g)$

   $= 2(213.6) + 4(188.83) - 2(237.6) - 3(205.0) = +92.3 \, J/K$

$\Delta S°$ is positive because the product contains more total particles and more moles of gas.

19.54   (a) $\Delta S° = S° \, NH_4NO_3(s) - S° \, HNO_3(g) - S° \, NH_3(g)$

   $= 151 - 266.4 - 192.5 = -307.9 = -308 \, J/K$

$\Delta S°$ is large and negative because all reactants are gases (2 moles) and the product is a solid.

(b) $\Delta S° = 4S° \, Fe(s) + 3S° \, O_2(g) - 2 \, S° \, Fe_2O_3(s)$

   $= 4(27.15) + 3(205.0) - 2(89.96) = 543.68 = 543.7 \, J/K$

$\Delta S°$ is large and positive because the reaction produces 3 moles of gas and the reactant is a solid.

(c) $\Delta S° = S° \, CaCl_2(s) + S° \, CO_2(g) + S° \, H_2O(l) - S° \, CaCO_3(s) - 2S° \, HCl(g)$

   $= 104.6 + 213.6 + 69.91 - 92.88 - 2(186.69) = -78.15 \, J/K$

$\Delta S°$ is small and negative because the products contain one fewer mole of gas, but one more mole of liquid. Note the very small standard entropy for $H_2O(l)$, owing to its strength of hydrogen bonding. If the products included one mole of a different liquid, the magnitude of the entropy change would be even smaller.

(d) $\Delta S° = S° \, C_6H_6(l) + 6S° \, H_2(g) - 3S° \, C_2H_6(g)$

   $= 172.8 + 6(130.58) - 3(229.5) = 267.78 = 267.8 \, J/K$

$\Delta S°$ is positive because there are more moles of gas in the products.

Gibbs Free Energy (sections 19.5 and 19.6)

19.55   (a) $\Delta G = \Delta H - T\Delta S$

(b)   If ΔG is positive, the process is nonspontaneous, but the reverse process is spontaneous.

(c)   There is no relationship between ΔG and rate of reaction. A spontaneous reaction, one with a $-\Delta G$, may occur at a very slow rate. For example: $2H_2(g) + O_2(g) \rightarrow 2H_2O(g)$, $\Delta G = -457 \, kJ$ is very slow if not initiated by a spark.

19.56   (a)   The *standard* free energy change, $\Delta G°$, represents the free energy change for the process when all reactants and products are in their standard states. When any or all reactants or products are not in their standard states, the free energy is represented simply as ΔG. The value for ΔG thus depends on the specific states of all reactants and products.

(b)   When $\Delta G = 0$, the system is at equilibrium.

(c)   The sign and magnitude of ΔG give no information about rate; we cannot predict whether the reaction will occur rapidly.

19.57   *Analyze/Plan.* Consider the definitions of $\Delta H°$, $\Delta S°$ and $\Delta G°$, along with sign conventions. $\Delta G° = \Delta H° - T\Delta S°$.   *Solve.*

     (a) $\Delta H°$ is negative; the reaction is exothermic.

     (b) $\Delta S°$ is negative; the reaction leads to decrease in disorder (increase in order) of the system.

     (c) $\Delta G° = \Delta H° - T\Delta S° = -35.4$ kJ $- 298$ K $(-0.0855$ kJ/K$) = -9.921 = -9.9$ kJ

     (d)   At 298 K, $\Delta G°$ is negative. If all reactants and products are present in their standard states, the reaction is spontaneous (in the forward direction) at this temperature.

19.58   (a) $\Delta H°$ is positive; the reaction is endothermic.

     (b) $\Delta S°$ is positive; the reaction leads to an increase in disorder.

     (c) $\Delta G° = \Delta H° - T\Delta S° = 23.7$ kJ $- 298$ K $(0.0524$ kJ/K$) = 8.0848 = 8.08$ kJ

     (d)   At 298 K, $\Delta G°$ is positive. If all reactants and products are present in their standard states, the reaction is spontaneous in the reverse direction at this temperature; it is nonspontaneous in the forward direction.

19.59   *Analyze/Plan.* Follow the logic in Sample Exercise 19.7. Calculate $\Delta H°$ according to Equation [5.31], $\Delta S°$ by Equation [19.8] and $\Delta G°$ by Equation [19.14]. Then use $\Delta H°$ and $\Delta S°$ to calculate $\Delta G°$ using Equation [19.12], $\Delta G° = \Delta H° - T\Delta S°$.   *Solve.*

     (a) $\Delta H° = 2(-268.61) - [0 + 0] = -537.22$ kJ

           $\Delta S° = 2(173.51) - [130.58 + 202.7] = 13.74 = 13.7$ J/K

           $\Delta G° = 2(-270.70) - [0 + 0] = -541.40$ kJ

           $\Delta G° = -537.22$ kJ $- 298(0.01374)$ kJ $= -541.31$ kJ

     (b) $\Delta H° = -106.7 - [0 + 2(0)] = -106.7$ kJ

           $\Delta S° = 309.4 - [5.69 + 2(222.96)] = -142.21 = -142.2$ J/K

           $\Delta G° = -64.0 - [0 + 2(0)] = -64.0$ kJ

           $\Delta G° = -106.7$ kJ $- 298(-0.14221)$ kJ $= -64.3$ kJ

     (c) $\Delta H° = 2(-542.2) - [2(-288.07) + 0] = -508.26 = -508.3$ kJ

           $\Delta S° = 2(325) - [2(311.7) + 205.0] = -178.4 = -178$ J/K

           $\Delta G° = 2(-502.5) - [2(-269.6) + 0] = -465.8$ kJ

           $\Delta G° = -508.26$ kJ $- 298(-0.1784)$ kJ $= -455.097 = -455.1$ kJ

           (The discrepancy in $\Delta G°$ values is due to experimental uncertainties in the tabulated thermodynamic data.)

     (d) $\Delta H° = -84.68 + 2(-241.82) - [2(-201.2) + 0] = -165.92 = -165.9$ kJ

           $\Delta S° = 229.5 + 2(188.83) - [2(237.6) + 130.58] = 1.38 = 1.4$ J/K

           $\Delta G° = -32.89 + 2(-228.57) - [2(-161.9) + 0] = -166.23 = -166.2$ kJ

           $\Delta G° = -165.92$ kJ $- 298(0.00138)$ kJ $= -166.33 = -166.3$ kJ

19.60   (a)   There is no thermodynamic data in Appendix C for CrO_3; we will substitute Cr_2O_3. $4Cr(s) + 3O_2(g) \rightarrow 2Cr_2O_3(s)$

$\Delta H° = 2(-1139.7) - 4(0) + 3(0) = -2279.4$ kJ

$\Delta S° = 2(81.2) - 4(23.6) - 3(205.0) = -547.0$ J/K

$\Delta G° = 2(-1058.1) - 4(0) - 3(0) = -2116.2$ kJ

$\Delta G° = -2279.4$ kJ -298 K$(-0.5470$ kJ/K$) = -2116.4$ kJ

   (b) $\Delta H° = -553.5 - 393.5 - (-1216.3) = 269.3$ kJ

$\Delta S° = 70.42 + 213.6 - 112.1 = 171.92 = 171.9$ J/K

$\Delta G° = -525.1 - 394.4 - (-1137.6) = 218.1$ kJ

$\Delta G° = 269.3$ kJ $- 298$ K $(0.1719$ kJ/K$) = 218.1$ kJ

   (c)   Assume the reactant is $P(g)$, not $P(s)$.

$\Delta H° = 2(-1594.4) + 5(0) - 2(316.4) - 10(-268.61) = -1135.5$ kJ

$\Delta S° = 2(300.8) + 5(130.58) - 2(163.2) - 10(173.51) = -807.0$ J/K

$\Delta G° = 2(-1520.7) + 5(0) - 2(280.0) - 10(-270.70) = -894.4$ kJ

$\Delta G° = -1135.5$ kJ $- 298$ K$(-0.8070$ kJ/K$) = -895.014 = -895.0$ kJ

(The small discrepancy in $\Delta G°$ values is due to experimental uncertainties in tabulated thermodynamic data.)

   (d) $\Delta H° = -284.5 - (0) - (0) = -284.5$ kJ

$\Delta S° = 122.5 - 64.67 - 205.0 = -147.2$ J/K

$\Delta G° = -240.6 - (0) - (0) = -240.6$ kJ

$\Delta G° = -284.5$ kJ $- 298$ K $(-0.1472$ kJ/K$) = -240.634 = -240.6$ kJ

19.61   *Analyze/Plan.* Follow the logic in Sample Exercise 19.7.   *Solve.*

   (a) $\Delta G° = 2\Delta G° \, SO_3(g) - [2\Delta G° \, SO_2(g) + \Delta G° \, O_2(g)]$

$\qquad = 2(-370.4) - [2(-300.4) + 0] = -140.0$ kJ, spontaneous

   (b) $\Delta G° = 3\Delta G° \, NO(g) - [\Delta G° \, NO_2(g) + \Delta G° \, N_2O(g)]$

$\qquad = 3(86.71) - [51.84 + 103.59] = +104.70$ kJ, nonspontaneous

   (c) $\Delta G° = 4\Delta G° \, FeCl_3(s) + 3\Delta G° \, O_2(g) - [6\Delta G° \, Cl_2(g) + 2\Delta G° \, Fe_2O_3(s)]$

$\qquad = 4(-334) + 3(0) - [6(0) + 2(-740.98)] = +146$ kJ, nonspontaneous

   (d) $\Delta G° = \Delta G° \, S(s) + 2\Delta G° \, H_2O(g) - [\Delta G° \, SO_2(g) + 2\Delta G° \, H_2(g)]$

$\qquad = 0 + 2(-228.57) - [(-300.4) + 2(0)] = -156.7$ kJ, spontaneous

19.62   (a) $\Delta G° = 2\Delta G° \, AgCl(s) - [2\Delta G° \, Ag(s) + \Delta G° \, Cl_2(g)]$

$\qquad = 2(-109.7) - 2(0) - 0 = -219.4$ kJ, spontaneous

   (b)   There is no thermodynamic data in Appendix C for $P_4O_6(s)$; we will substitute $P_4O_{10}(s)$. $P_4O_{10}(s) + 16H_2(g) \rightarrow 4PH_3(g) + 10H_2O(g)$

$\Delta G° = 4\Delta G° \, PH_3(g) + 10\Delta G° \, H_2O(g) - [\Delta G° \, P_4O_{10}(s) + 16\Delta G° \, H_2(g)]$

$\qquad = 4(13.4) + 10(-228.57) - [-2675.2] - 16(0) = 443.1$ kJ, nonspontaneous

(c) $\Delta G° = \Delta G° \, CF_4(g) + 4\Delta G° \, HF(g) - [\Delta G° \, CH_4(g) + 4\Delta G° \, F_2(g)]$

   $= -635.1 + 4(-270.70) - (-50.8) - 4(0) = -1667.1$ kJ, spontaneous

(d) $\Delta G° = 2\Delta G° \, H_2O(l) + \Delta G° \, O_2(g) - 2\Delta G° \, H_2O_2(l)$

   $= 2(-237.13) + 0 - 2(-120.4) = -233.5$ kJ, spontaneous

19.63   *Analyze/Plan.* Follow the logic in Sample Exercise 19.8(a).   *Solve.*

(a) $2C_8H_{18}(l) + 25O_2(g) \rightarrow 16CO_2(g) + 18H_2O(l)$

(b)   Because there are more moles of gas in the reactants, $\Delta S°$ is negative, which makes $-T\Delta S$ positive. $\Delta G°$ is less negative than $\Delta H°$. (This argument is true for the reaction as written. If the products are all in the gas phase, there are more moles of gas in the products and $\Delta G°$ is more negative than $\Delta H°$.)

19.64   (a) $\Delta G°$ should be less negative than $\Delta H°$. Products contain fewer moles of gas, so $\Delta S°$ is negative. $\Delta G° = \Delta H° - T\Delta S°$; $-T\Delta S°$ is positive so $\Delta G°$ is less negative than $\Delta H°$.

(b)   We can estimate $\Delta S°$ using a similar reaction and then use $\Delta G° = \Delta H° - T\Delta S°$ (estimate) to get a ballpark figure. There are no sulfite salts listed in Appendix C, so use a reaction such as $CO_2(g) + CaO(s) \rightarrow CaCO_3(s)$ or $CO_2(g) + BaO(s) \rightarrow BaCO_3(s)$. Or calculate both $\Delta S°$ values and use the average as your estimate.

19.65   *Analyze/Plan.* Based on the signs of ΔH and ΔS for a particular reaction, assign a category from Table 19.3 to each reaction.   *Solve.*

(a) ΔG is negative at low temperatures, positive at high temperatures. That is, the reaction proceeds in the forward direction spontaneously at lower temperatures but spontaneously reverses at higher temperatures.

(b) ΔG is positive at all temperatures. The reaction is nonspontaneous in the forward direction at all temperatures.

(c) ΔG is positive at low temperatures, negative at high temperatures. That is, the reaction will proceed spontaneously in the forward direction at high temperature.

19.66 $\Delta G° = \Delta H° - T\Delta S°$

(a) $\Delta G° = -844$ kJ $- 298$ K$(-0.165$ kJ/K$) = -795$ kJ, spontaneous

(b) $\Delta G° = +572$ kJ $- 298$ K$(0.179$ kJ/K$) = +519$ kJ, nonspontaneous

   To be spontaneous, ΔG must be negative ($\Delta G < 0$).

   Thus, $\Delta H° - T\Delta S° < 0$; $\Delta H° < T\Delta S°$; $T > \Delta H°/\Delta S°$; $T > \dfrac{572 \text{ kJ}}{0.179 \text{ kJ/K}} = 3.20 \times 10^3$ K

19.67   *Analyze/Plan.* We are told that the reaction is spontaneous and endothermic, and asked to estimate the sign and magnitude of ΔS. If a reaction is spontaneous, $\Delta G < 0$. Use this information with Equation [19.11] to solve the problem.   *Solve.*

   At 390 K, $\Delta G < 0$; $\Delta G = \Delta H - T\Delta S < 0$

   23.7 kJ $- 390$ K $(\Delta S) < 0$; 23.7 kJ < 390 K (ΔS); $\Delta S > 23.7$ kJ$/390$ K

   $\Delta S > 0.06077$ kJ/K or $\Delta S > 60.8$ J/K

19.68   At 45°C or 318 K, $\Delta G > 0$. $\Delta G = \Delta H - T\Delta S > 0$

$\Delta H - 318$ K $(72 \text{ J/K}) > 0$; $\Delta H > +2.3 \times 10^4$ J; $\Delta H > +23$ kJ

19.69   *Analyze/Plan.* Use Equation [19.11] to calculate T when $\Delta G = 0$. This is similar to calculating the temperature of a phase trasition in Sample Exercise 19.10. Use Table 19.3 to determine whether the reaction is spontaneous or non-spontaneous above this temperature. *Solve.*

(a) $\Delta G = \Delta H - T\Delta S$; $0 = -32$ kJ $- T(-98 \text{ J/K})$; 32×10^3 J $= T(98 \text{ J/K})$

$T = 32 \times 10^3$ J$/(98 \text{ J/K}) = 326.5 = 330$ K

(b)   Nonspontaneous. The sign of ΔS is negative, so as T increases, ΔG becomes more positive.

19.70 ΔG is negative when $T\Delta S > \Delta H$ or $T > \Delta H/\Delta S$.

$\Delta H° = \Delta H° \text{ CH}_3\text{OH} + \Delta H° \text{ CO(g)} - \Delta H° \text{ CH}_3\text{COOH(l)}$

$= -201.2 - 110.5 - (-487.0) = 175.3$ kJ

$\Delta S° = S° \text{ CH}_3\text{OH} + S° \text{ CO(g)} - S° \text{ CH}_3\text{COOH(l)} = 237.6 + 197.9 - 159.8 = 275.7$ J/K

$T > \dfrac{175.3 \text{ kJ}}{0.2757 \text{ kJ/K}} = 635.8$ K

The reaction is spontaneous above 635.8 K (363°C)

19.71   *Analyze/Plan.* Given a chemical equation and thermodynamic data (values of $\Delta H°_f, \Delta G°_f$ and S°) for reactants and products, predict the variation of $\Delta G°$ with temperature and calculate $\Delta G°$ at 800 K and 1000 K. Use Equations [5.31] and [19.8] to calculate $\Delta H°$ and $\Delta S°$, respectively; use these values to calculate $\Delta G°$ at various temperatures, using Equation [19.12]. The signs of $\Delta H°$ and $\Delta S°$ determine the variation of $\Delta G°$ with temperature. *Solve.*

(a)   Calculate $\Delta H°$ and $\Delta S°$ to determine the sign of $T\Delta S°$.

$\Delta H° = 3\Delta H° \text{ NO(g)} - \Delta H° \text{ NO}_2\text{(g)} - \Delta H° \text{ N}_2\text{O(g)}$

$= 3(90.37) - 33.84 - 81.6 = 155.7$ kJ

$\Delta S° = 3S° \text{ NO(g)} - S° \text{ NO}_2\text{(g)} - S° \text{ N}_2\text{O(g)}$

$= 3(210.62) - 240.45 - 220.0 = 171.4$ J/K

$\Delta G° = \Delta H° - T\Delta S°$. Since $\Delta S°$ is positive, $-T\Delta S°$ becomes more negative as T increases and $\Delta G°$ becomes more negative.

(b) $\Delta G° = \Delta H° - T\Delta S° = 155.7$ kJ $- (800 \text{ K})(0.1714 \text{ kJ/K})$

$\Delta G° = 155.7$ kJ $- 137$ kJ $= 19$ kJ

Since $\Delta G°$ is positive at 800 K, the reaction is not spontaneous at this temperature.

(c) $\Delta G° = 155.7$ kJ $- (1000 \text{ K})(0.1714 \text{ kJ/K}) = 155.7$ kJ $- 171.4$ kJ $= -15.7$ kJ

$\Delta G°$ is negative at 1000 K and the reaction is spontaneous at this temperature.

19.72   (a) $\Delta H° = \Delta H_f° \, CH_3OH(g) - \Delta H_f° \, CH_4(g) - 1/2 \, \Delta H_f° \, O_2(g)$

$= -201.2 - (-74.8) - (1/2)(0) = -126.4 \text{ kJ}$

$\Delta S° = S° \, CH_3OH(g) - S° \, CH_4(g) - 1/2 \, S° \, O_2(g)$

$= 237.6 - 186.3 - 1/2(205.0) = -51.2 \text{ J/K} = -0.0512 \text{ kJ/K}$

(b) $\Delta G° = \Delta H° - T\Delta S°$. $-T\Delta S°$ is positive, so $\Delta G°$ becomes more positive as temperature increases.

(c) $\Delta G° = \Delta H° - T\Delta S° = -126.4 \text{ kJ} - 298 \text{ K}(-0.0512 \text{ kJ/K}) = -111.1 \text{ kJ}$

The reaction is spontaneous at 298 K because $\Delta G°$ is negative at this temperature. In this case, $\Delta G°$ could have been calculated from $\Delta G_f°$ values in Appendix C, since these values are tabulated at 298 K.

(d)   The reaction is at equilibrium when $\Delta G° = 0$.

$\Delta G° = \Delta H° - T\Delta S° = 0$. $\Delta H° = T\Delta S°$, $T = \Delta H°/\Delta S°$

$T = -126.4 \text{ kJ}/-0.0512 \text{ kJ/K} = 2469 = 2470 \text{ K}$.

This temperature is so high that the reactants and products are likely to decompose. At standard conditions, equilibrium is functionally unattainable for this reaction.

19.73   *Analyze/Plan.* Follow the logic in Sample Exercise 19.10.   *Solve.*

(a) $\Delta S_{vap}° = \Delta H_{vap}°/T_b$; $T_b = \Delta H_{vap}°/\Delta S_{vap}°$

$\Delta H_{vap}° = \Delta H° \, C_6H_6(g) - \Delta H° \, C_6H_6(l) = 82.9 - 49.0 = 33.9 \text{ kJ}$

$\Delta S_{vap}° = S° \, C_6H_6(g) - S° \, C_6H_6(l) = 269.2 - 172.8 = 96.4 \text{ J/K}$

$T_b = 33.9 \times 10^3 \text{ J}/96.4 \text{ J/K} = 351.66 = 352 \text{ K} = 79°C$

(b)   From the *Handbook of Chemistry and Physics*, 74th Edition, $T_b = 80.1°C$. The values are remarkably close; the small difference is due to deviation from ideal behavior by $C_6H_6(g)$ and experimental uncertainty in the boiling point measurement and the thermodynamic data.

19.74   (a)   As in Sample Exercise 19.10, $T_{sub} = \Delta H_{sub}°/\Delta S_{sub}°$

Use Data from Appendix C to calculate $\Delta H_{sub}°$ and $\Delta S_{sub}°$ for $I_2(s)$.

$I_2(s) \rightarrow I_2(l)$ melting

$I_2(l) \rightarrow I_2(g)$ boiling

$\overline{I_2(s) \rightarrow I_2(g) \text{ sublimation}}$

$\Delta H_{sub}° = \Delta H_f° I_2(g) - \Delta H_f° \, I_2(s) = 62.25 - 0 = 62.25 \text{ kJ}$

$\Delta S_{sub}° = S° \, I_2(g) - S° \, I_2(s) = 260.57 - 116.73 = 143.84 \text{ J/K} = 0.14384 \text{ kJ/K}$

$T_{sub} = \dfrac{\Delta H_{sub}°}{\Delta S_{sub}°} = \dfrac{62.25 \text{ kJ}}{0.14384 \text{ kJ/K}} = 432.8 \text{ K} = 159.6°C$

In making this estimate, we assume that at equilibrium, both $I_2(s)$ and $I_2(g)$ are present in their standard state of pure solid and vapor at 1 atm and consequently,

$\Delta G_{sub} = \Delta G^{o}_{sub} = 0$. We also assume that the values of ΔH^{o}_{sub} and ΔS^{o}_{sub} are the same at 298 K and at the sublimation temperature.

(b)　　T_m for $I_2(s) = 386.85\ K = 113.7°C$; $T_b = 457.4\ K = 184.3°C$

(from WebElements™, 2005)

(c)　　The boiling point of I_2 is closer to the sublimation temperature. Both boiling and sublimation begin with molecules in a condensed phase (little space between molecules) and end in the gas phase (large intermolecular distances). Separation of the molecules is the main phenomenon that determines both ΔH and ΔS, so it is not surprising that the ratio of $\Delta H/\Delta S$ is similar for sublimation and boiling.

19.75　　*Analyze/Plan.* We are asked to write a balanced equation for the combustion of acetylene, calculate $\Delta H°$ for this reaction and calculate maximum useful work possible by the system. Combustion is combination with O_2 to produce CO_2 and H_2O. Calculate $\Delta H°$ using data from Appendix C and Equation [5.31]. The maximum obtainable work is ΔG (Equation [19.18]), which can be calculated from data in Appendix C and Equation [19.14]. 　　*Solve.*

(a)　　$C_2H_2(g) + 5/2\ O_2(g) \rightarrow 2CO_2(g) + H_2O(l)$

(b)　　$\Delta H° = 2\Delta H°\ CO_2(g) + \Delta H°\ H_2O(l) - \Delta H°\ C_2H_2(g) - 5/2\Delta H°\ O_2(g)$

$= 2(-393.5) - 285.83 - 226.77 - 5/2(0)$

$= -1299.6$ kJ produced/mol C_2H_2 burned

(c)　　$w_{max} = \Delta G° = 2\Delta G°\ CO_2(g) + \Delta G°\ H_2O(l) - \Delta G°\ C_2H_2(g) - 5/2\ \Delta G°\ O_2(g)$

$= 2(-394.4) - 237.13 - 209.2 - 5/2(0) = -1235.1$ kJ

The negative sign indicates that the system does work on the surroundings; the system can accomplish a maximum of 1235.1 kJ of work on its surroundings.

19.76　　(a)　　$CH_4(g) + 2O_2(g) \rightarrow CO_2(g) + 2H_2O(l)$

$\Delta H° = \Delta H^{o}_f\ CO_2(g) + 2\Delta H^{o}_f\ H_2O(l) - \Delta H^{o}_f\ CH_4(g) - 2\Delta H^{o}_f\ O_2(g)$

$= (-393.5) + 2(-285.83) - (-74.8) - 2(0) = -890.4$ kJ/mol CH_4 burned

(b)　　$w_{max} = \Delta G° = \Delta G^{o}_f\ CO_2(g) + 2\Delta G^{o}_f\ H_2O(l) - \Delta G^{o}_f\ CH_4(g) - 2\Delta G^{o}_f\ O_2(g)$

$= (-394.4) + 2(-237.13) - (-50.8) - 2(0) = -817.9$ kJ

The system can accomplish at most 817.86 kJ of work per mole of CH_4 on the surroundings.

Free Energy and Equilibrium (section 19.6)

19.77　　*Analyze/Plan.* We are given a chemical reaction and asked to predict the effect of the partial pressure of $O_2(g)$ on the value of ΔG for the system. Consider the relationship $\Delta G = \Delta G° + RT\ lnQ$ where Q is the reaction quotient. 　　*Solve.*

(a)　　$O_2(g)$ appears in the denominator of Q for this reaction. An increase in pressure of O_2 decreases Q and ΔG becomes smaller or more negative. Increasing the concentration or partial pressure of a reactant increases the tendency for a reaction to occur.

(b) $O_2(g)$ appears in the numerator of Q for this reaction. Increasing the pressure of O_2 increases Q and ΔG becomes more positive. Increasing the concentration or partial pressure of a product decreases the tendency for the reaction to occur.

(c) $O_2(g)$ appears in the numerator of Q for this reaction. An increase in pressure of O_2 increases Q and ΔG becomes more positive. Since pressure of O_2 is raised to the third power in Q, an increase in pressure of O_2 will have the largest effect on ΔG for this reaction. Increasing the concentration or partial pressure of a product decreases the tendency for the reaction to occur.

19.78 Consider the relationship $\Delta G = \Delta G° + RT \ln Q$, where Q is the reaction quotient.

(a) $H_2(g)$ appears in the denominator of Q for this reaction. An increase in pressure of H_2 decreases Q and ΔG becomes smaller or more negative. Increasing the concentration or partial pressure of a reactant increases the tendency for a reaction to occur.

(b) $H_2(g)$ appears in the numerator of Q for this reaction. Increasing the pressure of H_2 increases Q and ΔG becomes more positive. Increasing the concentration or partial pressure of a product decreases the tendency for the reaction to occur.

(c) $H_2(g)$ appears in the denominator of Q for this reaction. An increase in pressure of H_2 decreases Q and ΔG becomes smaller or more negative. Increasing the concentration or partial pressure of a reactant increases the tendency for a reaction to occur.

19.79 *Analyze/Plan.* Given a chemical reaction, we are asked to calculate $\Delta G°$ from Appendix C data, and ΔG for a given set of initial conditions. Use Equation [19.14] to calculate $\Delta G°$, and Equation [19.19] to calculate ΔG. Follow the logic in Sample Exercise 19.11 when calculating ΔG. *Solve.*

(a) $\Delta G° = \Delta G° \, N_2O_4(g) - 2\Delta G° \, NO_2(g) = 98.28 - 2(51.84) = -5.40 \text{ kJ}$

(b) $\Delta G = \Delta G° + RT \ln P_{N_2O_4} / P_{NO_2}^2$

$= -5.40 \text{ kJ} + \dfrac{8.314 \times 10^{-3} \text{ kJ}}{\text{mol-K}} \times 298 \text{ K} \times \ln[1.60/(0.40)^2] = 0.3048 = 0.30 \text{ kJ}$

19.80 (a) $\Delta G° = \Delta G° \, C_3H_8(g) + 2\Delta G° \, H_2(g) - 3\Delta G° \, CH_4(g)$

$= -23.47 + 2(0) - 3(-50.8) = 128.9 \text{ kJ}$

(b) $\Delta G = \Delta G° + RT \ln[P_{C_3H_8} \times P_{H_2}^2 / P_{CH_4}^3]$

$= 128.9 + \dfrac{8.314 \times 10^{-3} \text{ kJ}}{\text{mol-K}} \times 298 \text{ K} \times \ln[(0.0100) \times (0.0180)^2 / (40.0)^3]$

$= 128.9 - 58.735 = 70.165 = 70.2 \text{ kJ}$

19.81 *Analyze/Plan.* Given a chemical reaction, we are asked to calculate K using $\Delta G_f°$ data from Appendix C. Calculate $\Delta G°$ using Equation [19.14]. Then $\Delta G° = -RT \ln K$, Equation [19.20]; $\ln K = -\Delta G°/RT$ *Solve.*

(a) $\Delta G° = 2\Delta G° \, HI(g) - \Delta G° \, H_2(g) - \Delta G° \, I_2(g)$

$= 2(1.30) - 0 - 19.37 = -16.77 \text{ kJ}$

$$\ln K = \frac{-(-16.77\text{ kJ}) \times 10^3\text{ J/kJ}}{8.314\text{ J/K} \times 298\text{ K}} = 6.76876 = 6.769; \quad K = 870$$

(b) $\Delta G^\circ = \Delta G^\circ\text{ C}_2\text{H}_4(g) + \Delta G^\circ\text{ H}_2\text{O}(g) - \Delta G^\circ\text{ C}_2\text{H}_5\text{OH}(g)$

$$= 68.11 - 228.57 - (-168.5) = 8.04 = 8.0\text{ kJ}$$

$$\ln K = \frac{-(8.04\text{ kJ}) \times 10^3\text{ J/kJ}}{8.314\text{ J/K} \times 298\text{ K}} = -3.24511 = -3.25; K = 0.039$$

(c) $\Delta G^\circ = \Delta G^\circ\text{ C}_6\text{H}_6(g) - 3\Delta G^\circ\text{ C}_2\text{H}_2(g) = 129.7 - 3(209.2) = -497.9\text{ kJ}$

$$\ln K = \frac{-\Delta G^\circ}{RT} = \frac{-(-497.9\text{ kJ}) \times 10^3\text{ J/KJ}}{8.314\text{ J/K} \times 298\text{ K}} = 200.963 = 201.0; K = 2 \times 10^{87}$$

19.82 $\Delta G^\circ = -RT \ln K; \ln K = -\Delta G^\circ / RT$; at 298 K, RT = 2.4776 = 2.478 kJ

(a) $\Delta G^\circ = \Delta G^\circ\text{ NaOH}(s) + \Delta G^\circ\text{ CO}_2(g) - \Delta G^\circ\text{ NaHCO}_3(s)$

$$= -379.5 + (-394.4) - (-851.8) = +77.9\text{ kJ}$$

$$\ln K = \frac{-\Delta G^\circ}{RT} = \frac{-77.9\text{ kJ}}{2.478\text{ kJ}} = -31.442 = -31.4; \quad K = 2 \times 10^{-14}$$

$$K = P_{\text{CO}_2} = 2 \times 10^{-14}$$

(b) $\Delta G^\circ = 2\Delta G^\circ\text{ HCl}(g) + \Delta G^\circ\text{ Br}_2(g) - 2\Delta G^\circ\text{ HBr}(g) - \Delta G^\circ\text{ Cl}_2(g)$

$$= 2(-95.27) + 3.14 - 2(-53.22) - 0 = -80.96\text{ kJ}$$

$$\ln K = \frac{-(-80.96)}{2.4776} = +32.68; \quad K = 1.6 \times 10^{14}$$

$$K = \frac{P_{\text{HCl}}^2 \times P_{\text{Br}_2}}{P_{\text{HBr}}^2 \times P_{\text{Cl}_2}} = 1.6 \times 10^{14}$$

(c)   From Solution 19.61(a), ΔG° at 298 K = -140.0 kJ.

$$\ln K = \frac{-\Delta G^\circ}{RT} = \frac{-(-140.0)}{2.4776} = 56.51; \quad K = 3.5 \times 10^{24}$$

$$K = \frac{P_{\text{SO}_3}^2}{P_{\text{SO}_2}^2 \times P_{\text{O}_2}} = 3.5 \times 10^{24}$$

19.83   *Analyze/Plan.* Given a chemical reaction and thermodynamic data in Appendix C, calculate the equilibrium pressure of $\text{CO}_2(g)$ at two temperatures. $K = P_{\text{CO}_2}$. Calculate ΔG° at the two temperatures using $\Delta G^\circ = \Delta H^\circ - T\Delta S^\circ$ and then calculate K and P_{CO_2}. *Solve.*

$\Delta H^\circ = \Delta H^\circ\text{ BaO}(s) + \Delta H^\circ\text{ CO}_2(g) - \Delta H^\circ\text{ BaCO}_3(s)$

$$= -553.5 + -393.5 - (-1216.3) = +269.3\text{ kJ}$$

$\Delta S^\circ = S^\circ\text{ BaO}(s) + S^\circ\text{ CO}_2(g) - S^\circ\text{ BaCO}_3(s)$

$$= 70.42 + 213.6 - 112.1 = 171.92\text{ J/K} = 0.1719\text{ kJ/K}$$

(a) ΔG at 298 K = 269.3 kJ – 298 K (0.17192 kJ/K) = 218.07 = 218.1 kJ

$$\ln K = \frac{-\Delta G°}{RT} = \frac{-218.07 \times 10^3 \, J}{8.314 \, J/K \times 298 \, K} = -88.017 = -88.02$$

$K = 6.0 \times 10^{-39}; \quad P_{CO_2} = 6.0 \times 10^{-39} \, atm$

(b) ΔG at 1100 K = 269.3 kJ – 1100 K (0.17192 kJ) = 80.19 = +80.2 kJ

$$\ln K = \frac{-\Delta G°}{RT} = \frac{-80.19 \times 10^3 \, J}{8.314 \, J/K \times 1100 \, K} = -8.768 = -8.77$$

$K = 1.6 \times 10^{-4}; \quad P_{CO_2} = 1.6 \times 10^{-4} \, atm$

19.84 $K = P_{CO_2}$. Calculate $\Delta G°$ at the two temperatures using $\Delta G° = \Delta H° - T\Delta S°$ and then calculate K and P_{CO_2}.

$\Delta H° = \Delta H° \, PbO(s) + \Delta H° \, CO_2(g) - \Delta H° \, PbCO_3(s)$

     = –217.3 – 393.5 + 699.1 = 88.3 kJ

$\Delta S° = S° \, PbO(s) + S° \, CO_2(g) - S° \, PbCO_3(s)$

     = 68.70 + 213.6 – 131.0 = 151.3 J/K or 0.1513 kJ/K

(a) $\Delta G° = \Delta H° - T\Delta S°$. At 673 K, $\Delta G° = 88.3 \, kJ - 673 \, K(0.1513 \, kJ/K) = -13.525$

                                                       = –13.5 kJ

$$\ln K = \frac{-\Delta G°}{RT} = \frac{-(-13.525 \times 10^3) J}{8.314 \, J/K \times 673 \, K} = 2.4172 = 2.42$$

$K = P_{CO_2} = 11.214 = 11 \, atm$

(b) $\Delta G° = \Delta H° - T\Delta S°$. At 453 K, $\Delta G° = 88.3 \, kJ - 453 \, K \, (0.1513 \, kJ) = 19.7611$

                                                       = 19.8 kJ

$$\ln K = \frac{-(19.7611 \times 10^3 \, J)}{8.314 \, J/K \times 453 \, K} = -5.2469 = -5.25; \quad K = P_{CO_2} = 5.3 \times 10^{-3} \, atm$$

19.85   *Analyze/Plan.* Given an acid dissociation equilibrium and the corresponding K_a value, calculate $\Delta G°$ and ΔG for a given set of concentrations. Use Equation [19.20] to calculate $\Delta G°$ and Equation [19.19] to calculate ΔG.   *Solve.*

(a) $HNO_2(aq) \;\rightleftharpoons\; H^+(aq) + NO_2^-(aq)$

(b) $\Delta G° = -RT \ln K_a = -(8.314 \times 10^{-3})(298) \ln (4.5 \times 10^{-4}) = 19.0928 = 19.1 \, kJ$

(c) $\Delta G = 0$ at equilibrium

(d) $\Delta G = \Delta G° + RT \ln Q$

       $= 19.09 \, kJ + (8.314 \times 10^{-3})(298) \ln \dfrac{(5.0 \times 10^{-2})(6.0 \times 10^{-4})}{0.20} = -2.725 = -2.7 \, kJ$

19.86   (a) $CH_3NH_2(aq) + H_2O(l) \;\rightleftharpoons\; CH_3NH_3^+(aq) + OH^-(aq)$

       (b) $\Delta G° = -RT \ln K_b = -(8.314 \times 10^{-3})(298) \ln (4.4 \times 10^{-4}) = 19.148 = 19.1 \, kJ$

(c) $\Delta G = 0$ at equilibrium

(d) $\Delta G = \Delta G° + RT\ \ln Q$; $[OH^-] = 1 \times 10^{-14}/6.7 \times 10^{-9} = 1.4925 \times 10^{-6} = 1.5 \times 10^{-6}$

$$= 19.148 + (8.314 \times 10^{-3})(298)\ \ln\frac{(2.4 \times 10^{-3})(1.4925 \times 10^{-6})}{0.098} = -23.28 = -23.3\ kJ$$

Additional Exercises

19.87   (a)   The thermodynamic quantities T, E, and S are state functions.   T is directly related to the distribution of molecular speeds, which does not depend on the path from one state to another.

        (b)   The quantities q and w do depend on the path taken from one state to another.

        (c)   There is only one *reversible* path between states.

        (d)   Isothermal processes occur at constant T. Since the process is reversible, q is q_{rev} and w is w_{max}.

$$\Delta E = q_{rev} + w_{max}.\quad \Delta S = \frac{q_{rev}}{T}.$$

19.88   (a)   False. The essential question is whether the reaction proceeds far to the right before arriving at equilibrium. The position of equilibrium, which is the essential aspect, is not only dependent on ΔH but on the entropy change as well.

        (b)   True.

        (c)   True.

        (d)   False. **Non**spontaneous processes in general require that work be done to force them to proceed. Spontaneous processes occur without application of work.

        (e)   False. Such a process **might** be spontaneous, but would not necessarily be so. Spontaneous processes are those that are exothermic and/or that lead to increased disorder in the system.

19.89

Process	ΔH	ΔS
(a)	+	+
(b)	−	−
(c)	+	+
(d)	+	+
(e)	−	+

19.90   There is no inconsistency. The second law states that in any spontaneous process there is an increase in the entropy of the universe. While there may be a decrease in entropy of the system, as in the present case, this decrease is more than offset by an increase in entropy of the surroundings.

19.91   (a)   Each of the 4 molecules can be in either the left or the right bulb. Thus, there are $(2)^4 = 16$ arrangements.

        (b)   Only one arrangement has all 4 molecules in the left flask.

(c)   The gas will spontaneously adopt the state with maximum disorder, the state with the most possible arrangements for the molecules.

19.92   (a)   Microstates are possible arrangements for the system. For each die, there are six possibilities for the top face, resulting in (6)(6) = 36 possible arrangements or microstates. (The face that appears on top of one die is not related to or determined by the face on top of the other die.) The two arrangements of top faces shown in the exercise are two of the 36 possible microstates.

       (b)   The left pair of dice belongs to state III; the right pair belongs to state VII.

       (c)   There are eleven possible states (II through XII; I is not a possibility)

       (d)   The state with the most microstates has the highest entropy. State VII has six microstates and the highest entropy. The microstates are (1+6), (2+5), (3+4), (4+3), (5+2) and (6+1). States VI and VIII, on either side of VII, have five microstates. Moving farther away from VII, the number of microstates decreases until we reach the two extremes, II and XII, which each have one microstate.

       (e)   States II and XII, with one microstate each, have the lowest entropy.

19.93   If $NH_4NO_3(s)$ dissolves spontaneously in water, $\Delta G = \Delta H - T\Delta S$. If ΔG is negative and ΔH is positive, the sign of ΔS must be positive. Furthermore, $T\Delta S > \Delta H$ at room temperature.

19.94   (a)   The sign of q for expansion is (+). Vaporization is an endothermic process; the enthaphy of the system increases and q is positive. Our system is the refrigerant. Because the expansion does not occur at constant pressure, q is not exactly equal to ΔH, but it's sign is positive.

       (b)   The sign of q for compression is (−). Compression is the reverse of expansion, and it has the opposite sign.

       (c)   The expansion chamber is inside the house and the compression chamber is outside. During expansion, q_{sys} increases and q_{sur} decreases. The air surrounding the expansion chamber is cooled, and then distributed througout the house to cool it. If expansion occurred outside, the cool air would be wasted. Compression releases heat to the surroundings; it occurs outside so that the released heat can be dissipated by the outside air.

       (d)   No. Heat can flow reversibly between a system and its surroundings only if the two have an infinitesimally small difference in temperature and the amount of heat transferred is infinitesimally small. There is no mechanism in our system to regulate the amount of heat transferred. When the liquid flows into the low pressure chamber, all of the liquid vaporizes, not an infinitesimally small amount.

       (e)   A spontaneous process occurs without outside intervention. In an air conditioner, expansion (vaporization) of the refrigerant is spontaneous, but compression (condensation) to the liquid state is nonspontaneous. Cooling the house from 31 °C to 24 °C is nonspontaneous. [Note that all spontaneous processes are irreversible, but not all irreversible processes are spontaneous.]

19.95   At the normal boiling point of a liquid, $\Delta G = 0$ and $\Delta H_{vap} = T\Delta s S_{vap}$; $T = \Delta H_{vap}/\Delta S_{vap}$. By Trouton's rule, $\Delta S_{vap} = 88$ J/mol-K. The process of vaporization is:

(a) $Br_2(l) \rightleftharpoons Br_2(g)$

$\Delta H_{vap} = \Delta H_f^o\ Br_2(g) - \Delta H_f^o\ Br_2(l) = 30.71\ kJ - 0 = 30.71\ kJ$

$T_b = \dfrac{\Delta H_{vap}}{\Delta S_{vap}} = \dfrac{30.71\ kJ}{88\ J/mol\text{-}K} \times \dfrac{1000\ J}{kJ} = 349 = 3.5 \times 10^2\ K$

(b)   According to WebElements™ 2005, the normal boiling point of $Br_2(l)$ is 332 K. Trouton's rule provides a good "ballpark" estimate.

19.96   (a)   Formation reactions are the synthesis of 1 mole of compound from elements in their standard states.

$1/2\ N_2(g) + 3/2\ H_2(g) \rightarrow NH_3(g)$

$C(s) + 2Cl_2(g) \rightarrow CCl_4(l)$

$K(s) + 1/2\ N_2(g) + 3/2\ O_2(g) \rightarrow KNO_3(s)$

In each of these formation reactions, there are fewer moles of gas in the products than the reactants, so we expect ΔS° to be negative. If $\Delta G_f^o = \Delta H_f^o - T\Delta S^\circ$ and ΔS° is negative, $-T\Delta S^\circ$ is positive and ΔG_f^o is more positive than ΔH_f^o.

(b) $C(s) + 1/2\ O_2(g) \rightarrow CO(g)$

In this reaction, there are more moles of gas in products, ΔS_f^o is positive, $-T\Delta S_f^o$ is negative and ΔG_f^o is more negative than ΔH_f^o.

19.97   (a)   (i) $Ti(s) + 2Cl_2(g) \rightarrow TiCl_4(g)$

$\Delta H^\circ = \Delta H^\circ\ TiCl_4(g) - \Delta H^\circ\ Ti(s) - 2\Delta H^\circ\ Cl_2(g)$

$\quad = -763.2 - 0 - 2(0) = -763.2\ kJ$

$\Delta S^\circ = 354.9 - 30.76 - 2(222.96) = -121.78 = -121.8\ J/K$

$\Delta G^\circ = -726.8 - 0 - 2(0) = -726.8\ kJ$

(ii) $C_2H_6(g) + 7Cl_2(g) \rightarrow 2CCl_4(g) + 6HCl(g)$

$\Delta H^\circ = 2\Delta H^\circ\ CCl_4(g) + 6\Delta H^\circ\ HCl(g) - \Delta H^\circ\ C_2H_6(g) - 7\Delta H^\circ\ Cl_2(g)$

$\quad = 2(-106.7) + 6(-92.30) - (-84.68) - 7(0) = -682.52 = -682.5\ kJ$

$\Delta S^\circ = 2(309.4) + 6(186.69) - 229.5 - 7(222.96) = -51.28 = -51.4\ J/K$

$\Delta G^\circ = 2(-64.0) + 6(-95.27) - (-32.89) - 7(0) = -666.73\ kJ$

(iii) $BaO(s) + CO_2(g) \rightarrow BaCO_3(s)$

$\Delta H^\circ = \Delta H^\circ\ BaCO_3(s) - \Delta H^\circ\ BaO(s) - \Delta H^\circ\ CO_2(g)$

$\quad = -1216.3 - (-553.5) - (-393.5) = -269.3\ kJ$

$\Delta S^\circ = 112.1 - 70.42 - 213.6 = -171.9\ J/K$

$\Delta G^\circ = -1137.6 - (-525.1) - (-394.4) = -218.1\ kJ$

(b) (i), (ii) and (iii) all have negative $\Delta G°$ values and are spontaneous at standard conditions and 25°C.

(c) $\Delta G° = \Delta H° - T\Delta S°$. All three reactions have $-\Delta H°$ and $-\Delta S°$. They all have $-\Delta G°$ at 25°C, and $\Delta G°$ becomes more positive as T increases.

19.98 $\Delta G = \Delta G° + RT \ln Q$

(a) $Q = \dfrac{P_{NH_3}^2}{P_{N_2} \times P_{H_2}^3} = \dfrac{(1.2)^2}{(2.6)(5.9)^3} = 2.697 \times 10^{-3} = 2.7 \times 10^{-3}$

$\Delta G° = 2\Delta G° \, NH_3(g) - \Delta G° \, N_2(g) - 3\Delta G° \, H_2(g)$

$= 2(-16.66) - 0 - 3(0) = -33.32 \text{ kJ}$

$\Delta G = -33.32 \text{ kJ} + \dfrac{8.314 \times 10^{-3} \text{ kJ}}{\text{mol-K}} \times 298 \text{ K} \times \ln(2.69 \times 10^{-3})$

$\Delta G = -33.32 - 14.66 = -47.98 = -48.0 \text{ kJ}$

(b) $Q = \dfrac{P_{N_2}^3 \times P_{H_2O}^4}{P_{N_2H_4}^2 \times P_{NO_2}^2} = \dfrac{(0.5)^3(0.3)^4}{(5.0 \times 10^{-2})^2(5.0 \times 10^{-2})^2} = 162 = 2 \times 10^2$

$\Delta G° = 3\Delta G° \, N_2(g) + 4\Delta G° \, H_2O(g) - 2\Delta G° \, N_2H_4(g) - 2\Delta G° \, NO_2(g)$

$= 3(0) + 4(-228.57) - 2(159.4) - 2(51.84) = -1336.8 \text{ kJ}$

$\Delta G = -1336.8 \text{ kJ} + 2.478 \ln 162 = -1324.2 = -1.32 \times 10^3 \text{ kJ}$

(c) $Q = \dfrac{P_{N_2} \times P_{H_2}^2}{P_{N_2H_4}} = \dfrac{(1.5)(2.5)^2}{0.5} = 18.75 = 2 \times 10^1$

$\Delta G° = \Delta G° \, N_2(g) + 2\Delta G° \, H_2(g) - \Delta G° \, N_2H_4(g)$

$= 0 + 2(0) - 159.4 = -159.4 \text{ kJ}$

$\Delta G = -159.4 \text{ kJ} + 2.478 \ln 18.75 = -152.1 = -152 \text{ kJ}$

19.99

Reaction	(a) Sign of $\Delta H°$	(a) Sign of $\Delta S°$	(b) K > 1?	(c) Variation in K as Temp. Increases
(i)	−	−	yes	decrease
(ii)	+	+	no	increase
(iii)	+	+	no	increase
(iv)	+	+	no	increase

(a) Note that at a particular temperature, positive $\Delta H°$ leads to a smaller value of K, while positive $\Delta S°$ increases the value of K.

19.100 (a) $K = \dfrac{\chi_{CH_3COOH}}{\chi_{CH_3OH} P_{CO}}$

$\Delta G° = -RT \ln K; \ln K = -\Delta G/RT$

$$\Delta G° = \Delta G°\ CH_3COOH(l) - \Delta G°\ CH_3OH(l) - \Delta G°\ CO(g)$$

$$= -392.4 - (-166.23) - (-137.2) = -89.0\ kJ$$

$$\ln K = \frac{-(-89.0\ kJ)}{(8.314 \times 10^{-3}\ kJ/K)(298\ K)} = 35.922 = 35.9;\quad K = 4 \times 10^{15}$$

(b) $\Delta H° = \Delta H°\ CH_3COOH(l) - \Delta H°\ CH_3OH(l) - \Delta H°\ CO(g)$

$$= -487.0 - (-238.6) - (-110.5) = -137.9\ kJ$$

The reaction is exothermic, so the value of K will decrease with increasing temperature, and the mole fraction of CH_3COOH will also decrease. Elevated temperatures must be used to increase the speed of the reaction. Thermodynamics cannot predict the rate at which a reaction reaches equilibrium.

(c) $\Delta G° = -RT \ln K;\ K = 1,\ \ln K = 0,\ \Delta G° = 0$

$\Delta G° = \Delta H° - T\Delta S°;$ when $\Delta G° = 0,\ \Delta H° = T\Delta S°$

$\Delta S° = S°\ CH_3COOH(l) - S°\ CH_3OH(l) - S°\ CO(g)$

$$= 159.8 - 126.8 - 197.9 = -164.9\ J/K = -0.1649\ kJ/K$$

$-137.9\ kJ = T(-0.1649\ kJ/K),\ T = 836.3\ K$

The equilibrium favors products up to 836 K or 563°C, so the elevated temperatures to increase the rate of reaction can be safely employed.

19.101   (a)   First calculate $\Delta G°$ for each reaction:

For $C_6H_{12}O_6(s) + 6O_2(g) \rightleftharpoons 6CO_2(g) + 6H_2O(l)$ (A)

$\Delta G° = 6(-237.13) + 6(-394.4) - (-910.4) + 6(0) = -2878.8\ kJ$

For $C_6H_{12}O_6(s) \rightleftharpoons 2C_2H_5OH(l) + 2CO_2(g)$ (B)

$\Delta G° = 2(-394.4) + 2(-174.8) - (-910.4) = -228.0\ kJ$

For (A), $\ln K = 2879 \times 10^3/(8.314)(298) = 1162;\ K = 5 \times 10^{504}$

For (B), $\ln K = 228 \times 10^3/(8.314)(298) = 92.026 = 92.0;\ K = 9 \times 10^{39}$

(b)   Both these values for K are unimaginably large. However, K for reaction (A) is larger, because $\Delta G°$ is more negative. The magnitude of the work that can be accomplished by coupling a reaction to its surroundings is measured by ΔG. According to the calculations above, considerably more work can in principle be obtained from reaction (A), because $\Delta G°$ is more negative.

19.102   (a) $\Delta G° = -RT \ln K$ (Equation [19.20]); $\ln K = -\Delta G°/RT$

Use $\Delta G° = \Delta H° - T\Delta S°$ to get $\Delta G°$ at the two temperatures. Calculate $\Delta H°$ and $\Delta S°$ using data in Appendix C.

$2CH_4(g) \rightarrow C_2H_6(g) + H_2(g)$

$\Delta H° = \Delta H°\ C_2H_6(g) + \Delta H°\ H_2(g) - 2\Delta H°\ CH_4(g) = -84.68 + 0 - 2(-74.8) = 64.92$

$$= 64.9\ kJ$$

$\Delta S° = S° \, C_2H_6(g) + S° \, H_2(g) - 2S° \, CH_4(g) = 229.5 + 130.58 - 2(186.3) = -12.52$

$$= -12.5 \, J/K$$

at 298 K, $\Delta G = 64.92 \, kJ - 298 \, K(-12.52 \times 10^{-3} \, kJ/K) = 68.65 = 68.7 \, kJ$

$$\ln K = \frac{-68.65 \, kJ}{(8.314 \times 10^{-3} \, kJ/K)(298 \, K)} = -27.709 = -27.7, \, K = 9.25 \times 10^{-13} = 9 \times 10^{-13}$$

at 773 K, $\Delta G = 64.9 \, kJ - 773 \, K(-12.52 \times 10^{-3} \, J/K) = 74.598 = 74.6 \, kJ$

$$\ln K = \frac{-74.598 \, kJ}{(8.314 \times 10^{-3} \, kJ/K)(773 \, K)} = -11.607 = -11.6, \, K = 9.1 \times 10^{-6}$$

Because the reaction is endothermic, the value of K increases with an increase in temperature.

$2CH_4(g) + 1/2 \, O_2(g) \rightarrow C_2H_6(g) + H_2O(g)$

$\Delta H° = \Delta H° \, C_2H_6(g) + \Delta H° \, H_2O(g) - 2\Delta H° \, CH_4(g) - 1/2 \, \Delta H° \, O_2(g)$

$$= -84.68 + (-241.82) - 2(-74.8) - 1/2 \, (0) = -176.9 \, kJ$$

$\Delta S° = S° \, C_2H_6(g) + S° \, H_2O(g) - 2S° \, CH_4(g) - 1/2 \, S° \, O_2(g)$

$$= 229.5 + 188.83 - 2(186.3) - 1/2 \, (205.0) = -56.77 = -56.8 \, J/K$$

at 298 K, $\Delta G = -176.9 \, kJ - 298 \, K(-56.77 \times 10^{-3} \, kJ/K) = -159.98 = -160.0 \, kJ$

$$\ln K = \frac{-(-159.98 \, kJ)}{(8.314 \times 10^{-3} \, kJ/K)(298 \, K)} = 64.571 = 64.57; \, K = 1.1 \times 10^{28}$$

at 773 K, $\Delta G = -176.9 \, kJ - 773 \, K \, (-56.77 \times 10^{-3} \, kJ/K) = -133.02 = -133.0 \, kJ$

$$\ln K = \frac{-(-133.02 \, kJ)}{(8.314 \times 10^{-3} \, kJ/K)(773 \, K)} = 20.698 = 20.70; \, K = 9.750 \times 10^8 = 9.8 \times 10^8$$

Because this reaction is exothermic, the value of K decreases with increasing temperature.

(b)   The difference in $\Delta G°$ for the two reactions is primarily enthalpic; the first reaction is endothermic and the second exothermic. Both reactions have $-\Delta S°$, which inhibits spontaneity.

(c)   This is an example of coupling a useful but nonspontaneous reaction with a spontaneous one to spontaneously produce a desired product.

$$2CH_4(g) \rightarrow C_2H_6(g) + H_2(g) \qquad \Delta G_{298}^o = +68.7 \, kJ, \text{nonspontaneous}$$
$$H_2(g) + 1/2 \, O_2(g) \rightarrow H_2O(g) \qquad \Delta G_{298}^o = -228.57 \, kJ, \text{spontaneous}$$
$$2CH_4(g) + 1/2 \, O_2(g) \rightarrow C_2H_6(g) + H_2O(g) \qquad \Delta G_{298}^o = -159.9 \, kJ, \text{spontaneous}$$

(d). $CH_4(g) + 2O_2(g) \rightarrow CO_2(g) + 2H_2O(g)$

19.103 $\Delta G°$ for the metabolism of glucose is:

$6\Delta G° \, CO_2(g) + 6\Delta G° \, H_2O(l) - \Delta G° \, C_6H_{12}O_6(s) - 6\Delta G° \, O_2(g)$

$\Delta G° = 6(-394.4) + 6(-237.13) - (-910.4) + 6(0) = -2878.8 \, kJ$

moles ATP = –2878.8 kJ × 1 mol ATP / (–30.5 kJ) = 94.4 mol ATP / mol glucose

Note that this calculation is done at standard conditions, not metabolic conditions. A more accurate answer would be obtained using ΔG values that reflect actual concentration, partial pressure, and pH in a cell.

19.104   (a)   The equilibrium of interest here can be written as:

$$K^+ \text{ (plasma)} \rightleftharpoons K^+ \text{ (muscle)}$$

Since an aqueous solution is involved in both cases, assume that the equilibrium constant for the above process is exactly 1, that is, $\Delta G° = 0$. However, ΔG is not zero because the concentrations are not the same on both sides of the membrane. Use Equation [19.16] to calculate ΔG:

$$\Delta G = \Delta G° + RT \ln \frac{[K^+ \text{ (muscle)}]}{[K^+ \text{ (plasma)}]}$$

$$= 0 + (8.314)(310) \ln \frac{(0.15)}{(5.0 \times 10^{-3})} = 8766 \text{ J} = 8.8 \text{ kJ}$$

(b)   Note that ΔG is positive. This means that work must be done on the system (blood plasma plus muscle cells) to move the K^+ ions "uphill," as it were. The minimum amount of work possible is given by the value for ΔG. This value represents the minimum amount of work required to transfer one mole of K^+ ions from the blood plasma at 5×10^{-3} M to muscle cell fluids at 0.15 M, assuming constancy of concentrations. In practice, a larger than minimum amount of work is required.

19.105   (a)   To obtain $\Delta H°$ from the equilibrium constant data, graph $\ln K$ at various temperatures vs $1/T$, being sure to employ absolute temperature. The slope of the linear relationship that should result is $-\Delta H°/R$; thus, $\Delta H°$ is easily calculated.

(b)   Use $\Delta G° = \Delta H° - T\Delta S°$ and $\Delta G° = -RT \ln K$. Substituting the second expression into the first, we obtain

$$-RT \ln K = \Delta H° - T\Delta S°; \quad \ln K = \frac{-\Delta H°}{RT} - \frac{-\Delta S°}{R} = \frac{-\Delta H°}{RT} + \frac{\Delta S°}{R}$$

Thus, the constant in the equation given in the exercise is $\Delta S°/R$.

19.106 $S = k \ln W$ (Equation [19.5]), $k = R/N$, $W \propto V^m$

$\Delta S = S_2 - S_1; S_1 = k \ln W_1, S_2 = k \ln W_2$

$\Delta S = k \ln W_2 - k \ln W_1; W_2 = cV_2^m; W_1 = cV_1^m$

(The number of particles, m, is the same in both states.)

$\Delta S = k \ln cV_2^m - k \ln cV_1^m; \ln a^b = b \ln a$

$\Delta S = k m \ln cV_2 - k m \ln cV_1; \ln a - \ln b = \ln (a/b)$

$$\Delta S = k\, m \ln\left(\frac{cV_2}{cV_1}\right) = k\, m \ln\left(\frac{V_2}{V_1}\right) = \frac{R}{N}\, m \ln\left(\frac{V_2}{V_1}\right)$$

$$\frac{m}{N} = \frac{particles}{6.022 \times 10^{23}} = n(mol);\quad \Delta S = nR \ln\left(\frac{V_2}{V_1}\right)$$

19.107 (a) $(T_{high} - T_{low})/T_{high} = (700 - 288)/700 = 0.58857 = 58.9\%$ efficiency

       (b)   The cooler the exit temperature of the engine or generator, the more efficient the engine. If a body of water can be used to naturally reduce the exit temperature, the efficiency of energy production increases.

       (c)   The closer the exit temperature to 0 K, the more efficient the heat engine.

       (d)   (Refer to Figure 5.10)

Integrative Exercises

19.108 (a)   At the boiling point, vaporization is a reversible process, so $\Delta S^{\circ}_{vap} = \Delta H^{\circ}_{vap}/T$.

          acetone: $\Delta S^{\circ}_{vap} = \Delta H^{\circ}_{vap}/T = (29.1\,\text{kJ/mol}) / 329.25\,\text{K} = 88.4\,\text{J/mol-K}$

          dimethyl ether: $\Delta S^{\circ}_{vap} = (21.5\,\text{kJ/mol}) / 248.35\,\text{K} = 86.6\,\text{J/mol-K}$

          ethanol: $\Delta S^{\circ}_{vap} = (38.6\,\text{kJ/mol}) / 351.6\,\text{K} = 110\,\text{J/mol-K}$

          octane: $\Delta S^{\circ}_{vap} = (34.4\,\text{kJ/mol}) / 398.75\,\text{K} = 86.3\,\text{J/mol-K}$

          pyridine: $\Delta S^{\circ}_{vap} = (35.1\,\text{kJ/mol}) / 388.45\,\text{K} = 90.4\,\text{J/mol-K}$

       (b)   Ethanol is the only liquid listed that doesn't follow *Trouton's rule* and it is also the only substance that exhibits hydrogen bonding in the pure liquid. Hydrogen bonding leads to more ordering in the liquid state and a greater than usual increase in entropy upon vaporization. The rule appears to hold for liquids with London dispersion forces (octane) and ordinary dipole-dipole forces (acetone, dimethyl ether, pyridine), but not for those with hydrogen bonding.

(c)   Owing to strong hydrogen bonding interactions, water probably does not obey Trouton's rule.

From Appendix B, ΔH^o_{vap} at 100°C = 40.67 kJ/mol.

ΔS^o_{vap} = (40.67 kJ/mol) / 373.15 K = 109.0 J/mol-K

(d)   Use ΔS^o_{vap} = 88 J/mol-K, the middle of the range for Trouton's rule, to estimate ΔH^o_{vap} for chlorobenzene.

$\Delta H^o_{vap} = \Delta S^o_{vap} \times T$ = 88 J/mol-K $\times$ 404.95 K = 36 kJ/mol

19.109   The activated complex in Figure 14.15 is a single "particle" or entity that contains four atoms. It is formed from an atom A and a triatomic molecule, ABC, that must collide with exactly the correct energy and orientation to form the single entity. There are many fewer degrees of freedom for the activated complex than the separate reactant particules, so the *entropy of activation* is negative.

19.110   (a) $O_2(g) \xrightarrow{hv} 2O(g)$; S increases because there are more moles of gas in the products.

(b) $O_2(g) + O(g) \rightarrow O_3(g)$, S decreases because there are fewer moles of gas in the products.

(c)   S increases as the gas molecules diffuse into the larger volume of the stratosphere; there are more possible positions and therefore more motional freedom.

(d) $NaCl(aq) \rightarrow NaCl(s) + H_2O(l)$; ΔS decreases as the mixture (seawater, greater disorder) is separated into pure substances (fewer possible arrangements, more order).

19.111   (a)   16 e⁻, 8 e⁻ pairs. The C-S bond order is approximately 2.

$\ddot{\underset{..}{S}}=C=\ddot{\underset{..}{S}}$

(b)   2 e⁻ domains around C, linear e⁻ domain geometry, linear molecular structure

(c) $CS_2(l) + 3O_2(g) \rightarrow CO_2(g) + 2SO_2(g)$

(d) $\Delta H° = \Delta H° \, CO_2(g) + 2\Delta H° \, SO_2(g) - \Delta H° \, CS_2(l) - 3\Delta H° \, O_2(g)$

= –393.5 + 2(–296.9) – (89.7) – 3(0) = –1077.0 kJ

$\Delta G° = \Delta G° \, CO_2(g) + 2\Delta G° \, SO_2(g) - \Delta G° \, CS_2(l) - 3 \Delta G° \, O_2(g)$

= –394.4 + 2(–300.4) – (65.3) – 3(0) = –1060.5 kJ

The reaction is exothermic (–$\Delta H°$) and spontaneous (–$\Delta G°$) at 298 K.

(e)   vaporization: $CS_2(l) \rightarrow CS_2(g)$

$$\Delta G^{\circ}_{vap} = \Delta H^{\circ}_{vap} - T\Delta S^{\circ}_{vap}; \quad \Delta S^{\circ}_{vap} = (\Delta H^{\circ}_{vap} - \Delta G^{\circ}_{vap})/T$$

$$\Delta G^{\circ}_{vap} = \Delta G^{\circ} \ CS_2(g) - \Delta G^{\circ} \ CS_2(l) = 67.2 - 65.3 = 1.9 \ kJ$$

$$\Delta H^{\circ}_{vap} = \Delta H^{\circ} \ CS_2(g) - \Delta H^{\circ} \ CS_2(l) = 117.4 - 89.7 = 27.7 \ kJ$$

$$\Delta S^{\circ}_{vap} = (27.7 - 1.9) \ kJ/298 \ K = 0.086577 = 0.0866 \ kJ/K = 86.6 \ J/K$$

ΔS_{vap} is always positive, because the gas phase occupies a greater volume, has more motional freedom and a larger absolute entropy than the liquid.

(f)   At the boiling point, $\Delta G = 0$ and $\Delta H_{vap} = T_b \Delta S_{vap}$.

$$T_b = \Delta H_{vap}/\Delta S_{vap} = 27.7 \ kJ/0.086577 \ kJ/K = 319.9 = 320 \ K$$

$$T_b = 320 \ K = 47°C. \ CS_2 \text{ is a liquid at 298 K, 1 atm}$$

19.112   (a) $Ag(s) + 1/2 \ N_2(g) + 3/2 \ O_2(g) \rightarrow AgNO_3(s)$; S decreases because there are fewer moles of gas in the product.

(b) $\Delta G^{\circ}_f = \Delta H^{\circ}_f - T\Delta S^{\circ}; \quad \Delta S^{\circ} = (\Delta G^{\circ}_f - \Delta H^{\circ}_f)/(-T) = (\Delta H^{\circ}_f - \Delta G^{\circ}_f)/T$

$$\Delta S^{\circ} = -124.4 \ kJ - (-33.4 \ kJ) / 298 \ K = -0.305 \ kJ/K = -305 \ J/K$$

ΔS° is relatively large and negative, as anticipated from part (a).

(c)   Dissolving of $AgNO_3$ can be expressed as

$$AgNO_3(s) \rightarrow AgNO_3 \ (aq, 1 \ M)$$

$$\Delta H^{\circ} = \Delta H^{\circ} \ AgNO_3(aq) - \Delta H^{\circ} \ AgNO_3(s) = -101.7 - (-124.4) = +22.7 \ kJ$$

$$\Delta H^{\circ} = \Delta H^{\circ} \ MgSO_4(aq) - \Delta H^{\circ} \ MgSO_4(s) = -1374.8 - (-1283.7) = -91.1 \ kJ$$

Dissolving $AgNO_3(s)$ is endothermic $(+\Delta H^{\circ})$, but dissolving $MgSO_4(s)$ is exothermic $(-\Delta H^{\circ})$.

(d) $AgNO_3$: $\Delta G^{\circ} = \Delta G^{\circ}_f \ AgNO_3(aq) - \Delta G^{\circ}_f \ AgNO_3(s) = -34.2 - (-33.4) = -0.8 \ kJ$

$$\Delta S^{\circ} = (\Delta H^{\circ} - \Delta G^{\circ}) / T = [22.7 \ kJ - (-0.8 \ kJ)] / 298 \ K = 0.0789 \ kJ/K = 78.9 \ J/K$$

$MgSO_4$: $\Delta G^{\circ} = \Delta G^{\circ}_f \ MgSO_4(aq) - \Delta G^{\circ}_f \ MgSO_4(s) = -1198.4 - (-1169.6) = -28.8 \ kJ$

$$\Delta S^{\circ} = (\Delta H^{\circ} - \Delta G^{\circ}) / T = [-91.1 \ kJ - (-28.8 \ kJ)] / 298 \ K = -0.209 \ kJ/K = -209 \ J/K$$

(e)   In general, we expect dissolving a crystalline solid to be accompanied by an increase in positional disorder and an increase in entropy; this is the case for $AgNO_3$ ($\Delta S^{\circ} = +78.9$ J/K). However, for dissolving $MgSO_4(s)$, there is a substantial decrease in entropy ($\Delta S = -209$ J/K). According to Section 13.5, ion-pairing is a significant phenomenon in electrolyte solutions, particularly in concentrated solutions where the charges of the ions are greater than 1. According to Table 13.5, a 0.1 m $MgSO_4$ solution has a van't Hoff factor of 1.21. That is, for each mole of $MgSO_4$ that dissolves, there are only 1.21 moles of "particles" in solution instead of 2 moles of particles. For a 1 m solution, the factor is even smaller. Also, the exothermic enthalpy of mixing indicates substantial interactions between solute and solvent. Substantial ion-pairing coupled with ion-dipole interactions with H_2O molecules lead to a decrease in entropy for $MgSO_4(aq)$ relative to $MgSO_4(s)$.

19.113 (a) $K = P_{NO_2}^2 / P_{N_2O_4}$

Assume equal amounts means equal number of moles. For gases, $P = n(RT/V)$. In an equilibrium mixture, RT/V is a constant, so moles of gas are directly proportional to partial pressure. Gases with equal partial pressures will have equal moles of gas present. The condition $P_{NO_2} = P_{N_2O_4}$ leads to the expression $K = P_{NO_2}$. The value of K then depends on P_t for the mixture. For any particular value of P_t, the condition of equal moles of the two gases can be achieved at some temperature. For example, $P_{NO_2} = P_{N_2O_4} = 1.0$ atm, $P_t = 2.0$ atm.

$$K = \frac{(1.0)^2}{1.0} = 1.0; \quad \ln K = 0; \quad \Delta G° = 0 = \Delta H° - T\Delta S°; \quad T = \Delta H°/\Delta S°$$

$$\Delta H° = 2\Delta H° \, NO_2(g) - \Delta H° \, N_2O_4(g) = 2(33.84) - 9.66 = +58.02 \text{ kJ}$$

$$\Delta S° = 2S° \, NO_2(g) - S° \, N_2O_4(g) = 2(240.45) - 304.3 = 0.1766 \text{ kJ/K}$$

$$T = \frac{58.02 \text{ kJ}}{0.1766 \text{ kJ/K}} = 328.5 \text{ K or } 55.5°C$$

(b) $P_t = 1.00$ atm; $P_{N_2O_4} = x$, $P_{NO_2} = 2x$; $x + 2x = 1.00$ atm

$x = P_{N_2O_4} = 0.3333 = 0.333$ atm; $P_{NO_2} = 0.6667 = 0.667$ atm

$$K = \frac{(0.6667)^2}{0.3333} = 1.334 = 1.33; \quad \Delta G° = -RT \ln K = \Delta H° - T\Delta S°$$

$-(8.314 \times 10^{-3} \text{ kJ/K})(\ln 1.334) \, T = 58.02 \text{ kJ} - (0.1766 \text{ kJ/K}) \, T$

$(-0.00239 \text{ kJ/K}) \, T + (0.1766 \text{ kJ/K}) \, T = 58.02 \text{ kJ}$

$(0.1742 \text{ kJ/K}) \, T = 58.02 \text{ kJ}; \, T = 333.0 \text{ K}$

(c) $P_t = 10.00$ atm; $x + 2x = 10.00$ atm

$x = P_{N_2O_4} = 3.3333 = 3.333$ atm; $P_{NO_2} = 6.6667 = 6.667$ atm

$$K = \frac{(6.6667)^2}{3.3333} = 13.334 = 13.33; \quad -RT \ln K = \Delta H° - T\Delta S°$$

$-(8.314 \times 10^{-3} \text{ kJ/K})(\ln 13.334) \, T = 58.02 \text{ kJ} - (0.1766 \text{ kJ/K}) \, T$

$(-0.02154 \text{ kJ/K}) \, T + (0.1766 \text{ kJ/K}) \, T = 58.02 \text{ kJ}$

$(0.15506 \text{ kJ/K}) \, T = 58.02 \text{ kJ}; \, T = 374.2 \text{ K}$

(d)   The reaction is endothermic, so an increase in the value of K as calculated in parts (b) and (c) should be accompanied by an increase in T.

19.114   (a) $\Delta G° = 3\Delta G_f° \, S(s) + 2\Delta G_f° \, H_2O(g) - \Delta G_f° \, SO_2(g) - 2\Delta G_f° \, H_2S(g)$

$= 3(0) + 2(-228.57) - (-300.4) - 2(-33.01) = -90.72 = -90.7 \text{ kJ}$

$\ln K = \dfrac{-\Delta G°}{RT} = \dfrac{-(-90.72 \text{ kJ})}{(8.314 \times 10^{-3} \text{ kJ/K})(298 \text{ K})} = 36.6165 = 36.6; \ K = 7.99 \times 10^{15}$

$= 8 \times 10^{15}$

(b)   The reaction is highly spontaneous at 298 K and feasible in principle. However, use of $H_2S(g)$ produces a severe safety hazard for workers and the surrounding community.

(c) $P_{H_2O} = \dfrac{25 \text{ torr}}{760 \text{ torr/atm}} = 0.033 \text{ atm}$

$K = \dfrac{P_{H_2O}^2}{P_{SO_2} \times P_{H_2S}^2}; \ P_{SO_2} = P_{H_2S} = x \text{ atm}$

$K = 7.99 \times 10^{15} = \dfrac{(0.033)^2}{x(x)^2}; \ x^3 = \dfrac{(0.033)^2}{7.99 \times 10^{15}}$

$x = 5 \times 10^{-7} \text{ atm}$

(d) $\Delta H° = 3\Delta H_f° \, S(s) + 2\Delta H_f° \, H_2O(g) - \Delta H_f° \, SO_2(g) - 2\Delta H_f° \, H_2S(g)$

$= 3(0) + 2(-241.82) - (-296.9) - 2(-20.17) = -146.4 \text{ kJ}$

$\Delta S° = 3S° \, S(s) + 2S° \, H_2O(g) - S° \, SO_2(g) - 2S° \, H_2S(g)$

$= 3(31.88) + 2(188.83) - 248.5 - 2(205.6) = -186.4 \text{ J/K}$

The reaction is exothermic ($-\Delta H$), so the value of K_{eq} will decrease with increasing temperature. The negative $\Delta S°$ value means that the reaction will become nonspontaneous at some higher temperature. The process will be less effective at elevated temperatures.

19.115   (a)   When the rubber band is stretched, the molecules become more ordered, so the entropy of the system decreases, ΔS_{sys} is negative.

(b) $\Delta S_{sys} = q_{rev}/T$. Since ΔS_{sys} is negative, q_{rev} is negative and heat is emitted by the system.

(c)   The unstretched rubber band feels cooler. This confirms our answer to (b). If heat is emitted by the system when it is stretched, the surroundings feel warmer. Upon return to the initial state, heat is absorbed by the system (the rubber band) and the surroundings (your lip) feel cooler.

20 Electrochemistry

Visualizing Concepts

20.1   Consider the Brønsted-Lowry acid-base reaction and the redox reaction below.

$$HA + B \rightarrow BH^+ + A^-$$

$$HA \rightleftharpoons H^+ + A^-$$

$$B + H^+ \rightleftharpoons BH^+$$

$$X(red) + Y^+(ox) \rightarrow X^+(ox) + Y(red)$$

$$X(red) \rightleftharpoons X^+(ox) + e^-$$

$$Y+(ox) + e^- \rightleftharpoons Y(red)$$

Just as acid-base reactions can be viewed as proton-transfer reactions, redox reactions can be viewed as electron-transfer reactions. In the Brønsted-Lowry acid-base reaction, H^+ is transferred from HA to B. In the redox reaction, X(red) loses electrons and Y^+(ox) gains electrons; the number of electrons gained and lost must be equal. The concept of electron transfer from one reactant to the other is clearly applicable to redox reactions. (The path of the transfer may or may not be direct, but ultimately electrons are transferred during redox reactions.)

Furthermore, the species in redox reactions each have an oxidized and reduced form, like a conjugate acid-conjugate base pair. The reduced form has more electrons; the oxidized form has less. The greater the tendency of HA to donate H^+ (the stronger the acid), the lesser the tendency of A^- to gain them (the weaker the conjugate base). Similarly, the greater the tendency of X(red) to donate electrons (the stronger the reducing agent) the lesser the tendency of X^+(ox) to gain electrons (the weaker the oxidizing agent). Similar arguments exist for B, BH^+ and Y^+(ox), Y(red).

20.2   Unintended oxidation reactions in the body lead to unwanted health effects, just as unwanted oxidation of metals leads to corrosion. Antioxidants probably have modes of action similar to anti-corrosion agents. They can preferentially react with oxidizing agents (cathodic protection), create conditions that are unfavorable to the oxidation-reduction reaction, or physically coat or surround the molecule being oxidized to prevent the oxidant from attacking it. The first of these modes of action is likely to be safest in biological systems. Adjusting reaction conditions in our body can be dangerous, and physical protection is unlikely to provide lasting protection against oxidation. Anti-oxidants are likely to be reductants that preferentially react with oxidizing agents.

20.3   *Analyze/Plan.* Apply the definitions of oxidation, reduction, anode and cathode to the diagram. Recall relationship between atomic and ionic size from Chapter 7. *Solve.*

(a)   Oxidation. The gray spheres are uniformly sized and closely aligned; they represent an elemental solid. The diagram shows atoms from the surface of the solid going into solution. In a voltaic cell, this happens when metal atoms on an electrode surface are oxidized. They lose electrons, form cations and move into solution.

(b)   Anode. Oxidation occurs at the anode.

(c)   When a neutral atom loses a valence electron, Z_{eff} for the remaining electrons increases, and the radius of the resulting cation is smaller than the radius of the neutral atom. The neutral atoms in the electrode are represented by larger spheres than the cations moving into solution.

20.4   *Analyze/Plan.* Consider the voltaic cell pictured in Figure 20.5 as a model. The reaction in a voltaic cell is spontaneous. To generate a <u>standard</u> emf, substances must be present in their standard states.

(a)   A concentration of 1 M is the standard state for ions in solution. Ions, but not solution, must be able to flow between compartments in order to complete the circuit so that the cell can develop an emf. Add 1 M A^{2+}(aq) to the beaker with the A(s) electrode. Add 1 M B^{2+}(aq) to the beaker with the B(s) electrode. Add a salt bridge to enable the flow of ions from one compartment to the other.

(b)   Reduction occurs at the cathode. In order for the reaction to occur spontaneously (and thus generate an emf), the half-reaction with the greater E°_{red} will be the reduction half-reaction. In this cell, it is the half-reaction involving A(s) and A^{2+}(aq). The A electrode functions as the cathode.

(c)   According to Figure 20.5, electrons flow through the external circuit from the anode to the cathode. In this example, B is the anode and A is the cathode, so electrons flow from B to A through the external circuit.

(d) $E^{\circ}_{cell} = E^{\circ}_{red}(\text{cathode}) - E^{\circ}_{red}(\text{anode})$

        $E^{\circ}_{cell} = -0.10 \text{ V} - (-1.10 \text{ V}) = 1.00 \text{ V}$

20.5 $A(aq) + B(aq) \rightarrow A^{-}(aq) + B^{+}(aq)$

(a)   A gains electrons and is being reduced; it is the cathode. B loses electrons and is being oxidized; it is the anode.

(a)   Reduction occurs at the cathode; oxidation occurs at the anode.

        $A(aq) + 1e^{-} \rightarrow A^{-}(aq)$ occurs at the cathode.

        $B(aq) \rightarrow B^{+}(aq) + 1e^{-}$ occurs at the anode.

(b)   In a voltaic cell, the anode is at higher potential energy than the cathode. The anode reaction, $B(aq) \rightarrow B^{+}(aq) + 1e^{-}$, is higher in potential energy.

(d) $\Delta G^{\circ} = -nFE^{\circ}$; the signs of ΔG° and E° (or ΔG and E) are opposite. Since this is a spontaneous reaction, ΔG° is negative and E° is positive.

20.6   *Analyze.* Given a series of reduction half-reactions and their standard electrode potentials (E^o_{red}), draw conclusions about their relative strengths as oxidizing and reducing agents.   *Plan.* The reactant with the largest E^o_{red} is the easiest to reduce and the strongest oxidizing agent. The reduced form of this substance, the product of the reduction half-reaction, is the most difficult to oxidize and the weakest reducing agent. Conversely, the reactant with the smallest E^o_{red} is the hardest to reduce and the weakest oxidizing agent. The reduced form of this substance, the product of the reduction half-reaction, is the easiest to oxidize and the strongest reducing agent.   *Solve.*

(a) $A^+(aq)$ is the strongest oxidizing agent, and D^{3+} is the weakest oxidizing agent.

(b)   D(s) is the strongest reducing agent, and A(s) is the weakest reducing agent.

(c)   Reactants with more positive E^o_{red} than $C^{3+}(aq)$ will oxidize $C^{2+}(aq)$. Both $A^+(aq)$ and $B^{2+}(aq)$ will oxidize $C^{2+}(aq)$

20.7   *Analyze.* Given a redox reaction with a negative $E°$, answer questions regarding $\Delta G°$, the equilibrium constant (K), and work (w). *Plan.* $\Delta G° = -nFE°$; $\Delta G° = -RTlnK$; $w_{max} = -nFE$.   *Solve.*

(a)   The signs of $\Delta G°$ and $E°$ are opposite. If $E°$ is negative, $\Delta G°$ is positive. (The reaction is not spontaneous in the forward direction.)

(b)   If $\Delta G°$ is positive, lnK is negative and K < 1. Also, K is less than one for a nonspontaneous reaction.

(c)   No. If $E°$ is negative, the sign of w is positive. A positive value for w means that work is done on the system by the surroundings. An electrochemical cell based on this reaction cannot accomplish work on its surroundings.

20.8   *Analyze.* Given the voltaic cell shown in the diagram, answer questions about the cell and the effect of solution concentration on cell potential, E. *Plan.* Use the definition of a voltaic cell and standard emf, along with the Nernst equation, $E = \Delta E° - (0.0592 \text{ V}/n)\log Q$, to answer the questions. *Solve.*

(a)   A voltaic cell involves a spontaneous redox reaction, one with positive E^o_{cell}. In order to achieve a positive E^o_{cell}, the half-reaction with the more positive E^o_{red} occurs at the cathode. For this cell the two half reactions are

$$Ag^+(aq) + e^- \rightarrow Ag(s), \quad E^o_{red} = 0.799V$$

$$Fe^{2+}(aq) + 2e^- \rightarrow Fe(s), \quad E^o_{red} = -0.440 \text{ V}$$

The Ag(s) electrode is the cathode.

(b)   The standard emf is just E^o_{cell}.

$$E^o_{cell} = E^o_{red}(\text{cathode}) - E^o_{red}(\text{anode}) = 0.799V - (-0.440V) = 1.239V$$

The cell in the diagram is at standard conditions, with solid metal electrodes and 1 M aqueous solutions, so the potential on the meter in the circuit is the standard emf.

(c) $2Ag^+(aq) + Fe(s) \rightarrow 2Ag(s) + Fe^{2+}(aq); \; n = 2; \quad E = E° - \dfrac{0.0592}{2}\log\dfrac{[Fe^{2+}]}{[Ag^+]^2}$

The solution in the cathode half-cell is $Ag^+(aq)$. If $[Ag^+(aq)]$ increases by a factor of 10, the change in cell voltage is $E - E° = -\dfrac{0.0592}{2}\log\dfrac{[1]}{[10]^2} = 0.0592$ V.

(d) The solution in the anode half-cell is $Fe^{2+}(aq)$. If $[Fe^{2+}(aq)]$ increases by a factor of 10, the change in cell voltage is $E - E° = -\dfrac{0.0592}{2}\log\dfrac{[10]}{[1]^2} = -0.0296$ V.

20.9 *Analyze/Plan.* Consider the Nernst equation, which describes the variation of potential (emf) with respect to changes in concentration.

Solve. $E = E° - \dfrac{0.0592}{n}\log Q$.

(a) For this half-reaction, $E^o_{red} = 0.799$ V; $Q = 1/[Ag^+]$

$$E = 0.80 - \dfrac{0.0592}{1}\log\dfrac{1}{[Ag^+]}; \quad E = 0.80 + \dfrac{0.0592}{1}\log[Ag^+]$$

The y-intercept of the graph is $E°$. The slope of the line is $+0.0592$. So, as $[Ag^+]$ and $\log[Ag^+]$ increase, E increases. The line that describes this behavior is line 1.

(b) When $\log[Ag^+] = 0$, $[Ag^+] = 1$ M; this is the standard state for $Ag^+(aq)$, so $E_{red} = E^o_{red} = 0.799$V.

20.10

The main difference between a fuel cell and a battery is that a fuel cell is not self-contained. That is, there is a continuous supply of fuel (reductant) and oxidant to the cell, and continuous exhaust of products. The fuel cell produces electrical current as long as reactants are supplied. It never goes "dead."

20.11 Zinc, $E^o_{red} = -0.763$ V, is more easily oxidized than iron, $E^o_{red} = -0.440$ V. If conditions are favorable for oxidation, zinc will be preferentially oxidized, preventing iron from corroding. The protection lasts until all the Zn coating has reacted.

20.12 (a) $MgCl_2(l)$

(b) Oxidation occurs at the anode. Formation of $Cl_2(g)$ from $2Cl^-(l)$ is oxidation, so the carbon electrode is the anode.

Reduction occurs at the cathode. Formation of Mg(l) from $Mg^{2+}(l)$ is reduction, so the steel electrode is the cathode.

Check. Note that this electrolysis cell does not comply with the convention of drawing anode on the left and cathode on the right.

    (c) $MgCl_2(l) \rightarrow Mg(l) + Cl_2(g)$ overall

                    $2Cl^- \rightarrow Cl_2(g) + 2e^-$ anode (oxidation)

            $Mg^{2+} + 2e^- \rightarrow Mg(l)$ cathode (reduction)

    (d)   Magnesium is an active metal. It must be separated from the $Cl_2(g)$ that is also formed by electrolysis (see screen in diagram) or $MgCl_2$ will spontaneously reform. Also, the Mg(l) and Mg(g) should not come in contact with air (O_2) or moisture (H_2O).

Oxidation - Reduction Reactions (section 20.1)

20.13   (a)   *Oxidation* is the loss of electrons.

          (b)   The electrons appear on the products side (right side) of an oxidation half-reaction.

          (c)   The *oxidant* is the reactant that is reduced; it gains the electrons that are lost by the substance being oxidized.

          (d)   An *oxidizing agent* is the substance that promotes oxidation. That is, it gains electrons that are lost by the substance being oxidized. It is the same as the oxidant.

20.14   (a)   *Reduction* is the gain of electrons.

          (b)   The electrons appear on the reactants side (left side) of a reduction half-reaction.

          (c)   The *reductant* is the reactant that is oxidized; it provides the electrons that are gained by the substance being reduced.

          (d)   A *reducing agent* is the substance that promotes reduction. It donates the electrons gained by the substance that is reduced. It is the same as the reductant.

20.15   (a)   True.

          (b)   False. Fe^{3+} is reduced to Fe^{2+}, so it is the oxidizing agent, and Co^{2+} is the reducing agent.

          (c)   True.

20.16   (a)   False. If something is reduced, it gains electrons.

          (b)   True.

          (c)   True. Oxidation can be thought of as a gain of oxygen atoms. Looking forward, this view will be useful for organic reactions, Chapter 24.

20.17   *Analyze/Plan.* Given a chemical equation, we are asked to indicate which elements undergo a change in oxidation number and the magnitude of the change. Assign oxidation numbers according to the rules given in Section 4.4. Note the changes and report the magnitudes.   *Solve.*

          (a)   I is reduced from +5 to 0; C is oxidized from +2 to +4.

          (b)   Hg is reduced from +2 to 0; N is oxidized from –2 to 0.

    (c)   N is reduced from +5 to +2; S is oxidized from –2 to 0.

    (d)   Cl is reduced from +4 to +3; O is oxidized from –1 to 0.

20.18   (a)   No oxidation-reduction

    (b)   I is oxidized from –1 to +5; Cl is reduced from +1 to –1.

    (c)   S is oxidized from +4 to +6; N is reduced from +5 to +2.

    (d)   S is reduced from +6 to +4; Br is oxidized from –1 to 0.

Balancing Oxidation-Reduction Reactions (section 20.2)

20.19   *Analyze/Plan.* Write the balanced chemical equation and assign oxidation numbers. The substance oxidized is the reductant and the substance reduced is the oxidant.   *Solve.*

    (a) $TiCl_4(g) + 2Mg(l) \rightarrow Ti(s) + 2MgCl_2(l)$

    (b) $Mg(l)$ is oxidized; $TiCl_4(g)$ is reduced.

    (c) $Mg(l)$ is the reductant; $TiCl_4(g)$ is the oxidant.

20.20   (a) $2N_2H_4(g) + N_2O_4(g) \rightarrow 3N_2(g) + 4H_2O(g)$

    (b) $N_2H_4(g)$ is oxidized; $N_2O_4(g)$ is reduced.

    (c) $N_2H_4(g)$ serves as the reducing agent; it is itself oxidized. $N_2O_4(g)$ serves as the oxidizing agent; it is itself reduced.

20.21   *Analyze/Plan.* Follow the logic in Sample Exercises 20.2 and 20.3. If the half-reaction occurs in basic solution, balance as in acid, then add OH^- to each side.   *Solve.*

    (a) $Sn^{2+}(aq) \rightarrow Sn^{4+}(aq) + 2e^-$, oxidation

    (b) $TiO_2(s) + 4H^+(aq) + 2e^- \rightarrow Ti^{2+}(aq) + 2H_2O(l)$, reduction

    (c) $ClO_3^-(aq) + 6H^+(aq) + 6e^- \rightarrow Cl^-(aq) + 3H_2O(l)$, reduction

    (d) $N_2(g) + 8H^+(aq) + 6e^- \rightarrow 2NH_4^+(aq)$, reduction

    (e) $4OH^-(aq) \rightarrow O_2(g) + 2H_2O(l) + 4e^-$, oxidation

    (f) $SO_3^{2-}(aq) + 2OH^-(aq) \rightarrow SO_4^{2-}(aq) + H_2O(l) + 2e^-$, oxidation

    (g) $N_2(g) + 6H_2O + 6e^- \rightarrow 2NH_3(g) + 6OH^-(aq)$, reduction

20.22   (a) $Mo^{3+}(aq) + 3e^- \rightarrow Mo(s)$, reduction

    (b) $H_2SO_3(aq) + H_2O(l) \rightarrow SO_4^{2-}(aq) + 4H^+(aq) + 2e^-$, oxidation

    (c) $NO_3^-(aq) + 4H^+(aq) + 3e^- \rightarrow NO(g) + 2H_2O(l)$, reduction

    (d) $O_2(g) + 4H^+(aq) + 4e^- \rightarrow 2H_2O(l)$, reduction

    (e) $O_2(g) + 2H_2O(l) + 4e^- \rightarrow 4OH^-(aq)$, reduction

        (O_2 is reduced to OH^-, not H_2O, in basic solution)

    (f) $Mn^{2+}(aq) + 4OH^-(aq) \rightarrow MnO_2(s) + 2H_2O(l) + 2e^-$, oxidation

    (g) $Cr(OH)_3(s) + 5OH^-(aq) \rightarrow CrO_4^{2-}(aq) + 4H_2O(l) + 3e^-$, oxidation

20.23   *Analyze/Plan.* Follow the logic in Sample Exercises 20.2 and 20.3 to balance the given equations. Use the method in Sample Exercise 20.1 to identify oxidizing and reducing agents.   *Solve.*

(a) $Cr_2O_7^{2-}(aq) + I^-(aq) + 8H^+ \rightarrow 2Cr^{3+}(aq) + IO_3^-(aq) + 4H_2O(l)$

oxidizing agent, $Cr_2O_7^{2-}$; reducing agent, I^-

(b)   The half-reactions are:

$$4[MnO_4^-(aq) + 8H^+(aq) + 5e^- \rightarrow Mn^{2+}(aq) + 4H_2O(l)]$$
$$5[CH_3OH(aq) + H_2O(l) \rightarrow HCO_2H(aq) + 4H^+(aq) + 4e^-]$$
$$\overline{4MnO_4^-(aq) + 5CH_3OH(aq) + 12H^+(aq) \rightarrow 4Mn^{2+}(aq) + 5HCO_2H(aq) + 11H_2O(l)}$$

oxidizing agent, MnO_4^-; reducing agent, CH_3OH

(c) $$I_2(s) + 6H_2O(l) \rightarrow 2IO_3^-(aq) + 12H^+(aq) + 10e^-$$
$$\underline{5[OCl^-(aq) + 2H^+(aq) + 2e^- \rightarrow Cl^-(aq) + H_2O(l)}$$
$$I_2(s) + 5OCl^-(aq) + H_2O(l) \rightarrow 2IO_3^-(aq) + 5Cl^-(aq) + 2H^+(aq)]$$

oxidizing agent, OCl^-; reducing agent, I_2

(d) $$As_2O_3(s) + 5H_2O(l) \rightarrow 2H_3AsO_4(aq) + 4H^+(aq) + 4e^-$$
$$\underline{2NO_3^-(aq) + 6H^+(aq) + 4e^- \rightarrow N_2O_3(aq) + 3H_2O(l)}$$
$$As_2O_3(s) + 2NO_3^-(aq) + 2H_2O(l) + 2H^+(aq) \rightarrow 2H_3AsO_4(aq) + N_2O_3(aq)$$

oxidizing agent, NO_3^-; reducing agent, As_2O_3

(e) $$2[MnO_4^-(aq) + 2H_2O(l) + 3e^- \rightarrow MnO_2(s) + 4OH^-]$$
$$\underline{Br^-(aq) + 6OH^-(aq) \rightarrow BrO_3^-(aq) + 3H_2O(l) + 6e^-}$$
$$2MnO_4^-(aq) + Br^-(aq) + H_2O(l) \rightarrow 2MnO_2(s) + BrO_3^-(aq) + 2OH^-(aq)$$

oxidizing agent, MnO_4^-; reducing agent, Br^-

(f) $Pb(OH)_4^{2-}(aq) + ClO^-(aq) \rightarrow PbO_2(s) + Cl^-(aq) + 2OH^-(aq) + H_2O(l)$

oxidizing agent, ClO^-; reducing agent, $Pb(OH)_4^{2-}$

20.24   (a) $$3[NO_2^-(aq) + H_2O(l) \rightarrow NO_3^-(aq) + 2H^+(aq) + 2e^-]$$
$$\underline{Cr_2O_7^{2-}(aq) + 14H^+(aq) + 6e^- \rightarrow 2Cr^{3+}(aq) + 7H_2O(l)}$$
Net: $3NO_2^-(aq) + Cr_2O_7^{2-}(aq) + 8H^+(aq) \rightarrow 3NO_3^-(aq) + 2Cr^{3+}(aq) + 4H_2O(l)$

oxidizing agent, $Cr_2O_7^{2-}$; reducing agent, NO_2^-

(b)   The oxidation half-reaction involves S, and is listed in Appendix E. The reduction half-reaction involves N, and must be written and balanced, according to the procedure in Section 20.2.

$$HNO_3(aq) \rightarrow N_2O(g)$$

$$2HNO_3(aq) \rightarrow N_2O(g)$$

$$2HNO_3(aq) \rightarrow N_2O(g) + 5H_2O(l)$$

$$2HNO_3(aq) + 8H^+(aq) \rightarrow N_2O(g) + 5H_2O(l)$$

$$2HNO_3(aq) + 8H^+ + 8e^- \rightarrow N_2O(g) + 5H_2O(l)$$

$$2[S(s) + 3H_2O(l) \rightarrow H_2SO_3(aq) + 4H^+ + 4e^-]$$

$$\underline{2HNO_3(aq) + 8H^+ + 8e^- \rightarrow N_2O(g) + 5H_2O(l)}$$

$$2HNO_3(aq) + 2S(s) + H_2O(l) \rightarrow 2H_2SO_3(aq) + N_2O(g)$$

oxidizing agent, HNO_3; reducing agent, S.

(c) $$2[Cr_2O_7{}^{2-}(aq) + 14H^+(aq) + 6e^- \rightarrow 2Cr^{3+}(aq) + 7H_2O(l)]$$

$$\underline{3[CH_3OH(aq) + H_2O(l) \rightarrow HCO_2H(aq) + 4H^+(aq) + 4e^-]}$$

Net: $$2Cr_2O_7{}^{2-}(aq) + 3CH_3OH(aq) + 16H^+(aq) \rightarrow 4Cr^{3+}(aq) + 3HCO_2H(aq) + 11H_2O(l)$$

oxidizing agent, $Cr_2O_7{}^{2-}$; reducing agent, CH_3OH

(d)   The half-reaction involving N_2H_4 is given in Appendix E in base. We add $4H^+(aq)$ to each side and reverse the reaction to obtain oxidation half-reaction shown below.

$$2[2BrO_3{}^-(aq) + 12H^+(aq) + 10e^- \rightarrow Br_2(l) + 6H_2O(l)]$$

$$\underline{5[N_2H_4(aq) \rightarrow N_2(g) + 4H^+(aq) + 4e^-]}$$

Net: $$4BrO_3{}^-(aq) + 5N_2H_4(aq) + 4H^+(aq) \rightarrow 2Br_2(l) + 5N_2(g) + 12H_2O(l)$$

oxidizing agent, $BrO_3{}^-$; reducing agent, N_2H_4

(e)   Write and balance each half-reaction, and then sum to get the overall reaction. Follow the procedure in Sample Exercise 20.3 for reactions in basic solution.

oxidation: $$Al(s) \rightarrow AlO_2{}^-(aq)$$

$$Al(s) + 2H_2O(l) \rightarrow AlO_2{}^-(aq) + 4H^+(aq) + 3e^-$$

$$Al(s) + 4OH^-(aq) \rightarrow AlO_2{}^-(aq) + 2H_2O(l) + 3e^-$$

reduction: $$NO_2{}^-(aq) \rightarrow NH_4{}^+(aq)$$

$$NO_2{}^-(aq) + 8H^+(aq) + 6e^- \rightarrow NH_4{}^+(aq)) + 2H_2O(l)$$

$$NO_2{}^-(aq) + 6H_2O(l) + 6e^- \rightarrow NH_4{}^+(aq) + 8OH^-(aq)$$

$$NO_2{}^-(aq) + 6H_2O(l) + 6e^- \rightarrow NH_4{}^+(aq) + 8OH^-(aq)$$

$$2[Al(s) + 4OH^-(aq) \rightarrow AlO_2{}^-(aq) + 2H_2O(l) + 3e^-]$$

$$NO_2{}^-(aq) + 6H_2O(l) + 6e^- \rightarrow NH_4{}^+(aq) + 8OH^-(aq)$$

$$NO_2{}^-(aq) + 2Al(s) + 2H_2O(l) \rightarrow NH_4{}^+(aq) + 2AlO_2{}^-(aq)$$

oxidizing agent, $NO_2{}^-$; reducing agent, Al

(f) $$H_2O_2(aq) + 2e^- \rightarrow O_2(g) + 2H^+(aq)$$

Since the reaction is in base, the H^+ can be "neutralized" by adding $2OH^-$ to each side of the equation to give $H_2O_2(aq) + 2OH^-(aq) + 2e^- \rightarrow O_2(g) + 2H_2O(l)$. The other half reaction is $2[ClO_2(aq) + e^- \rightarrow ClO_2{}^-(aq)]$.

Net: $H_2O_2(aq) + 2ClO_2(aq) + 2OH^-(aq) \rightarrow O_2(g) + 2ClO_2^-(aq) + 2H_2O(l)$

oxidizing agent, ClO_2; reducing agent, H_2O_2

Voltaic Cells (section 20.3)

20.25   (a)   The reaction $Cu^{2+}(aq) + Zn(s) \rightarrow Cu(s) + Zn^{2+}(aq)$ is occurring in both figures. In Figure 20.3, the reactants are in contact, and the concentrations of the ions in solution aren't specified. In Figure 20.4 the oxidation half-reaction and reduction half-reaction are occurring in separate compartments, joined by a porous connector. The concentrations of the two solutions are initially 1.0 M. In Figure 20.4, electrical current is isolated and flows through the voltmeter. In Figure 20.3, the flow of electrons cannot be isolated or utilized.

(b)   In the cathode compartment of the voltaic cell in Figure 20.5, Cu^{2+} cations are reduced to Cu atoms, decreasing the number of positively charged particles in the compartment. Na^+ cations are drawn into the compartment to maintain charge balance as Cu^{2+} ions are removed.

20.26   (a)   The porous glass dish in Figure 20.4 provides a mechanism by which ions not directly involved in the redox reaction can migrate into the anode and cathode compartments to maintain charge neutrality of the solutions. Ionic conduction within the cell, through the glass disk, completes the cell circuit.

(b)   In the anode compartment of Figure 20.5, Zn atoms are oxidized to Zn^{2+} cations, increasing the number of positively charged particles in the compartment. NO_3^- anions migrate into the compartment to maintain charge balance as Zn^{2+} ions are produced.

20.27   *Analyze/Plan.* Follow the logic in Sample Exercise 20.4. *Solve.*

(a)   Fe(s) is oxidized, $Ag^+(aq)$ is reduced.

(b) $Ag^+(aq) + 1e^- \rightarrow Ag(s)$; $Fe(s) \rightarrow Fe^{2+}(aq) + 2e^-$

(c)   Fe(s) is the anode, Ag(s) is the cathode.

(d)   Fe(s) is negative; Ag(s) is positive.

(e)   Electrons flow from the Fe(–) electrode toward the Ag(+) electrode.

(f)   Cations migrate toward the Ag(s) cathode; anions migrate toward the Fe(s) anode.

20.28   (a)   Al(s) is oxidized, $Ni^{2+}(aq)$ is reduced.

(b) $Al(s) \rightarrow Al^{3+}(aq) + 3e^-$; $Ni^{2+}(aq) + 2e^- \rightarrow Ni(s)$

(c)   Al(s) is the anode; Ni(s) is the cathode.

(d)   Al(s) is negative (–); Ni(s) is positive (+).

(e)   Electrons flow from the Al(–) electrode toward the Ni(+) electrode.

(f)   Cations migrate toward the Ni(s) cathode; anions migrate toward the Al(s) anode.

Cell Potentials under Standard Conditions (section 20.4)

20.29   (a)   *Electromotive force*, emf, is the driving force that causes electrons to flow through the external circuit of a voltaic cell. It is the potential energy difference between an electron at the anode and an electron at the cathode.

       (b)   One *volt* is the potential energy difference required to impart 1 J of energy to a charge of 1 coulomb. $1\,V = 1\,J/C$.

       (c)   *Cell potential*, E_{cell}, is the emf of an electrochemical cell.

20.30   (a)   In a voltaic cell, the anode has the higher potential energy for electrons. To achieve a lower potential energy, electrons flow from the anode to the cathode.

       (b)   The units of electrical potential are volts. A potential of one volt imparts one joule of energy to one coulomb of charge.

       (c)   A *standard* cell potential describes the potential of an electrochemical cell where all components are present at standard conditions: elements in their standard states, gases at 1 atm pressure and 1 M aqueous solutions.

20.31   (a) $2H^+(aq) + 2e^- \rightarrow H_2(g)$

       (b)   A *standard* hydrogen electrode is a hydrogen electrode where the components are at standard conditions, 1 M $H^+(aq)$ and $H_2(g)$ at 1 atm.

       (c)   The platinum foil in an SHE serves as an inert electron carrier and a solid reaction surface.

20.32   (a) $H_2(g) \rightarrow 2H^+(aq) + 2e^-$

       (b)   The platinum electrode serves as a reaction surface; the greater the surface area, the more H_2 or H^+ that can be adsorbed onto the surface to facilitate the flow of electrons.

       (c)

20.33   (a)   A *standard reduction potential* is the relative potential of a reduction half-reaction measured at standard conditions, 1 M aqueous solution and 1 atm gas pressure.

       (b) $E^{\circ}_{red} = 0\,V$ for a standard hydrogen electrode.

20.34   (a)   It is not possible to measure the standard reduction potential of a single half-reaction because each voltaic cell consists of two half-reactions and only the potential of a complete cell can be measured.

(b)   The standard reduction potential of a half-reaction is determined by combining it with a reference half-reaction of known potential and measuring the cell potential. Assuming the half-reaction of interest is the reduction half-reaction:

$$E^o_{cell} = E^o_{red}(\text{cathode}) - E^o_{red}(\text{anode}) = E^o_{red}(\text{unknown}) - E^o_{red}(\text{reference});$$

$$E^o_{red}(\text{unknown}) = E^o_{cell} + E^o_{red}(\text{reference}).$$

20.35   *Analyze/Plan.* Follow the logic in Sample Exercise 20.5.   *Solve.*

(a)   The two half-reactions are:

$$\text{Tl}^{3+}(aq) + 2e^- \rightarrow \text{Tl}^+(aq) \qquad\qquad \text{cathode } E^o_{red} = ?$$

$$2[\text{Cr}^{2+}(aq) \rightarrow \text{Cr}^{3+}(aq) + e^-] \qquad \text{anode } E^o_{red} = -0.41\text{ V}$$

(b) $E^o_{cell} = E^o_{red}(\text{cathode}) - E^o_{red}(\text{anode}); 1.19\text{ V} = E^o_{red} - (-0.41\text{ V});$

$E^o_{red} = 1.19\text{ V} - 0.41\text{ V} = 0.78\text{ V}$

(c)

Note that because $\text{Cr}^{2+}(aq)$ is readily oxidized, it would be necessary to keep oxygen out of the left-hand cell compartment.

20.36   (a) $\text{PdCl}_4{}^{2-}(aq) + 2e^- \rightarrow \text{Pd}(s) + 4\text{Cl}^-$ cathode $E^o_{red} = ?$

                $\text{Cd}(s) \rightarrow \text{Cd}^{2+}(aq) + 2e^-$ anode $E^o_{red} = -0.403\text{ V}$

(b) $E^o_{cell} = E^o_{red}(\text{cathode}) - E^o_{red}(\text{anode}); 1.03\text{ V} = E^o_{red} - (-0.403\text{ V});$

$E^o_{red} = 1.03\text{ V} - 0.403 = 0.63\text{ V}$

(c)

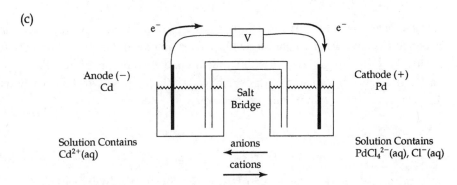

20.37   *Analyze/Plan.* Follow the logic in Sample Exercise 20.6.   *Solve.*

(a) $Cl_2(g) \rightarrow 2Cl^-(aq) + 2e^-$ $E^o_{red} = 1.359 \text{ V}$

       $I_2(s) + 2e^- \rightarrow 2I^-(aq)$ $E^o_{red} = 0.536 \text{ V}$

       $E^\circ = 1.359 \text{ V} - 0.536 \text{ V} = 0.823 \text{ V}$

(b) $Ni(s) \rightarrow Ni^{2+}(aq) + 2e^-$ $E^o_{red} = -0.28 \text{ V}$

       $2[Ce^{4+}(aq) + 1e^- \rightarrow Ce^{3+}(aq)]$ $E^o_{red} = 1.61 \text{ V}$

       $E^\circ = 1.61 \text{ V} - (-0.28 \text{ V}) = 1.89 \text{ V}$

(c) $Fe(s) \rightarrow Fe^{2+}(aq) + 2e^-$ $E^o_{red} = -0.440 \text{ V}$

       $2[Fe^{3+}(aq) + 1e^- \rightarrow Fe^{2+}(aq)]$ $E^o_{red} = 0.771 \text{ V}$

       $E^\circ = 0.771 \text{ V} - (-0.440 \text{ V}) = 1.211 \text{ V}$

(d) $2[NO_3^-(aq) + 4H^+ + 3e^- \rightarrow NO(g) + 2H_2O(l)]$ $E^o_{red} = 0.96 \text{ V}$

                  $3[Cu(s) \rightarrow Cu^{2+}(aq) + 2e^-]$ $E^o_{red} = 0.337 \text{ V}$

       $E^\circ = 0.96 \text{ V} - (0.337 \text{ V}) = 0.623 = 0.62 \text{ V}$

20.38   (a) $F_2(g) + 2e^- \rightarrow 2F^-(aq)$ $E^o_{red} = 2.87 \text{ V}$

           $H_2(g) \rightarrow 2H^+(aq) + 2e^-$ $E^o_{red} = 0.00 \text{ V}$

           $E^\circ = 2.87 \text{ V} - 0.00 \text{ V} = 2.87 \text{ V}$

(b) $Cu^{2+}(aq) + 2e^- \rightarrow Cu(s)$ $E^o_{red} = 0.337 \text{ V}$

             $Ca(s) \rightarrow Ca^{2+}(aq) + 2e^-$ $E^o_{red} = -2.87 \text{ V}$

           $E^\circ = 0.337 \text{ V} - (-2.87 \text{ V}) = 3.21 \text{ V}$

(c) $Fe^{2+}(aq) + 2e^- \rightarrow Fe(s)$ $E^o_{red} = -0.440 \text{ V}$

          $2[Fe^{2+}(aq) \rightarrow Fe^{3+}(aq) + 1e^-]$ $E^o_{red} = 0.771 \text{ V}$

           $E^\circ = -0.440 \text{ V} - 0.771 \text{ V} = -1.211 \text{ V}$

(d) $2ClO_3^-(aq) + 12H^+ + 10e^- \rightarrow Cl_2(g) + 6H_2O(l)$ $E^o_{red} = 1.47 \text{ V}$

              $5[2Br^-(aq) \rightarrow Br_2(l) + 2e^-]$ $E^o_{red} = 1.065 \text{ V}$

           $E^\circ = 1.47 \text{ V} - 1.065 \text{ V} = 0.405 = 0.41 \text{ V}$

20.39   *Analyze/Plan.* Given four half-reactions, find E^o_{red} from Appendix E and combine them to obtain a desired E_{cell}. (a) The largest E_{cell} will combine the half-reaction with the most positive E^o_{red} as the cathode reaction and the one with the most negative E^o_{red} as the anode reaction. (b) The smallest positive E^o_{cell} will combine two half-reactions whose E^o_{red} values are closest in magnitude **and** sign.   *Solve.*

(a) $3[Ag^+(aq) + 1e^- \rightarrow Ag(s)]$ $E^o_{red} = 0.799$

             $\underline{Cr(s) \rightarrow Cr^{3+}(aq) + 3e^- \qquad\qquad\quad E^o_{red} = -0.74}$

       $3Ag^+(aq) + Cr(s) \rightarrow 3Ag(s) + Cr^{3+}(aq)$ $E^\circ = 0.799 - (-0.74) = 1.54 \text{ V}$

(b)   Two of the combinations have essentially equal E° values.

$$2[Ag^+(aq) + 1e^- \rightarrow Ag(s)] \qquad E^o_{red} = 0.799 \text{ V}$$

$$\underline{Cu(s) \rightarrow Cu^{2+}(aq) + 2e^- \qquad E^o_{red} = 0.337 \text{ V}}$$

$$2Ag^+(aq) + Cu(s) \rightarrow 2Ag(s) + Cu^{2+}(aq) \quad E^o = 0.799 \text{ V} - 0.337 \text{ V} = 0.462 \text{ V}$$

$$3[Ni^{2+}(aq) + 2e^- \rightarrow Ni(s)] \qquad E^o_{red} = -0.28 \text{ V}$$

$$\underline{2[Cr(s) \rightarrow Cr^{3+}(aq) + 3e^-] \qquad E^o_{red} = -0.74 \text{ V}}$$

$$3Ni^{2+}(aq) + 2Cr(s) \rightarrow 3Ni(s) + 2Cr^{3+}(aq) \quad E^o = -0.28 \text{ V} - (-0.74 \text{ V}) = 0.46 \text{ V}$$

20.40   (a) $2[Au(s) + 4Br^-(aq) \rightarrow AuBr_4^-(aq) + 3e^-] \qquad E^o_{red} = -0.858 \text{ V}$

$$\underline{3[2e^- + IO^-(aq) + H_2O(l) \rightarrow I^-(aq) + 2OH^-(aq)] \qquad E^o_{red} = 0.49 \text{ V}}$$

$$2Au(s) + 8Br^-(aq) + 3IO^-(aq) + 3H_2O(l) \rightarrow 2AuBr_4^-(aq) + 3I^-(aq) + 6OH^-(aq)$$

$$E^o = 0.49 - (-0.858) = 1.35 \text{ V}$$

(b) $2[Eu^{2+}(aq) \rightarrow Eu^{3+}(aq) + 1e^-] \qquad E^o_{red} = -0.43 \text{ V}$

$$\underline{Sn^{2+}(aq) + 2e^- \rightarrow Sn(s) \qquad E^o_{red} = -0.14 \text{ V}}$$

$$2Eu^{2+}(aq) + Sn^{2+}(aq) \rightarrow 2Eu^{3+}(aq) + Sn(s) \qquad E^o = -0.14 - (-0.43) = 0.29 \text{ V}$$

20.41   *Analyze/Plan.* Given the description of a voltaic cell, answer questions about this cell. Combine ideas in Sample Exercises 20.4 and 20.7. The reduction half-reactions are:

$$Cu^{2+}(aq) + 2e^- \rightarrow Cu(s) \qquad E^o = 0.337 \text{ V}$$

$$Sn^{2+}(aq) + 2e^- \rightarrow Sn(s) \qquad E^o = -0.136 \text{ V}$$

Solve.

(a)   It is evident that Cu^{2+} is more readily reduced. Therefore, Cu serves as the cathode, Sn as the anode.

(b)   The copper electrode gains mass as Cu is plated out, the Sn electrode loses mass as Sn is oxidized.

(c)   The overall cell reaction is $Cu^{2+}(aq) + Sn(s) \rightarrow Cu(s) + Sn^{2+}(aq)$

(d) $E^o = 0.337 \text{ V} - (-0.136 \text{ V}) = 0.473 \text{ V}$

20.42   (a)   The two half-reactions are:

$$Cd^{2+}(aq) + 2e^- \rightarrow Cd(s) \qquad E^o = -0.403 \text{ V}$$

$$Cl_2(g) + 2e^- \rightarrow 2Cl^-(aq) \qquad E^o = 1.359 \text{ V}$$

Because E° for the reduction of Cl_2 is greater, Cl_2 is reduced at the cathode, the Pt electrode. Cd(s) is oxidized at the anode, the Cd electrode.

(b)   The Cd anode loses mass as $Cd^{2+}(aq)$ is produced.

(c) $Cl_2(g) + Cd(s) \rightarrow Cd^{2+}(aq) + 2Cl^-(aq)$

(d) $E^o = 1.359 \text{ V} - (-0.403 \text{ V}) = 1.762 \text{ V}$

Strengths of Oxidizing and Reducing Agents (section 20.4)

20.43   *Analyze/Plan.* The more readily a substance is oxidized, the stronger it is as a reducing agent. In each case choose the half-reaction with the more negative reduction potential and the given substance on the right. *Solve.*

(a) $Mg(s)$ (–2.37 V vs. –0.440 V)

(b) $Ca(s)$ (–2.87 V vs. –1.66 V)

(c) $H_2(g, acidic)$ (0.000 V vs. 0.141 V)

(d) $IO_3^-(aq)$ [Both $IO_3^-(aq)$ and $BrO_3^-(aq)$ are good oxidizing agents, but $IO_3^-(aq)$ has the smaller positive reduction potential. (1.195 V vs. 1.52 V)]

20.44   Follow the logic in Sample Exercise 20.8. In each case, choose the half-reaction with the more positive reduction potential and with the given substance on the left.

(a) $Cl_2(g)$ (1.359 V vs. 1.065 V)

(b) $Cd^{2+}(aq)$ (–0.403 V vs. –0.763 V)

(c) $ClO_3^-(aq)$ ($Cl^-(aq)$ is in its minimum oxidation state and cannot act as an oxidizing agent)

(d) $O_3(g)$ (2.07 V vs. 1.776 V)

20.45   *Analyze/Plan.* If the substance is on the left of a reduction half-reaction, it will be an oxidant; if it is on the right, it will be a reductant. The sign and magnitude of the E_{red}^o determines whether it is strong or weak.   *Solve.*

(a) $Cl_2(aq)$: strong oxidant (on the left, $E_{red}^o = 1.359 \, V$)

(b) $MnO_4^-(aq, acidic)$: strong oxidant (on the left, $E_{red}^o = 1.51 \, V$)

(c) $Ba(s)$: strong reductant (on the right, $E_{red}^o = -2.90 \, V$)

(d) $Zn(s)$: reductant (on the right, $E_{red}^o = -0.763 \, V$)

20.46   If the substance is on the left of a reduction half-reaction, it will be an oxidant; if it is on the right, it will be a reductant. The sign and magnitude of the E_{red}^o determine whether it is strong or weak.

(a) $Ce^{3+}(aq)$: very weak reductant (on the right, $E_{red}^o = 1.61 \, V$)

(b) $Ca(s)$: strong reductant (on the right, $E_{red}^o = -2.87 \, V$)

(c) $ClO_3^-(aq)$: strong oxidant (on the left, $E_{red}^o = 1.47 \, V$)

(d) $N_2O_5(g)$: oxidant (N has maximum oxidation number, +5; can only be reduced and act as oxidant.)

20.47   *Analyze/Plan.* Follow the logic in Sample Exercise 20.8. *Solve.*

(a)   Arranged in order of increasing strength as oxidizing agents (and increasing reduction potential):

$Cu^{2+}(aq) < O_2(g) < Cr_2O_7^{2-}(aq) < Cl_2(g) < H_2O_2(aq)$

(b)   Arranged in order of increasing strength as reducing agents (and decreasing reduction potential):

$H_2O_2(aq) < I^-(aq) < Sn^{2+}(aq) < Zn(s) < Al(s)$

20 Electrochemistry

Solutions to Exercises

20.48   (a)   The strongest oxidizing agent is the species most readily reduced, as evidenced by a large, positive reduction potential. That species is H_2O_2. The weakest oxidizing agent is the species that least readily accepts an electron. We expect that it will be very difficult to reduce Zn(s); indeed, Zn(s) acts as a comparatively strong **reducing** agent. No potential is listed for reduction of Zn(s), but we can safely assume that it is less readily reduced than any of the other species present.

(b)   The strongest reducing agent is the species most easily oxidized (the largest negative reduction potential). Zn, $E^{o}_{red} = -0.76\,V$, is the strongest reducing agent and F^-, $E^{o}_{red} = 2.87\,V$, is the weakest.

20.49   *Analyze/Plan.* In order to reduce Eu^{3+} to Eu^{2+}, we need an oxidizing agent, one of the reduced species from Appendix E. It must have a greater tendency to be oxidized than Eu^{3+} has to be reduced. That is, E^{o}_{red} must be more negative than –0.43 V. *Solve.*

Any of the **reduced** species in Appendix E from a half-reaction with a reduction potential more negative than –0.43 V will reduce Eu^{3+} to Eu^{2+}. From the list of possible reductants in the exercise, Al and $H_2C_2O_4$ will reduce Eu^{3+} to Eu^{2+}.

20.50   Any oxidized species from Appendix E with a reduction potential greater than 0.59 V will oxidize RuO_4^{2-} to RuO_4^{-}. From the list of possible oxidants in the exercise, $Br_2(l)$ and $BrO_3^-(aq)$ will definitely oxidize RuO_4^{2-} to RuO_4^{-}. $Sn^{2+}(aq)$ will not, and $O_2(g)$ depends on conditions. In base, it will not, but in strongly acidic solution, it will.

Free Energy and Redox Reactions (section 20.5)

20.51   *Analyze/Plan.* In each reaction, $Fe^{2+} \rightarrow Fe^{3+}$ will be the oxidation half-reaction and one of the other given half-reactions will be the reduction half-reaction. Follow the logic in Sample Exercise 20.10 to calculate E° and $\Delta G°$ for each reaction.   *Solve.*

(a) $2Fe^{2+}(aq) + S_2O_6^{2-}(aq) + 4H^+(aq) \rightarrow 2Fe^{3+}(aq) + 2H_2SO_3(aq)$

$E° = 0.60\,V - 0.77\,V = -0.17\,V$

$2Fe^{2+}(aq) + N_2O(aq) + 2H^+(aq) \rightarrow 2Fe^{3+}(aq) + N_2(g) + H_2O(l)$

$E° = -1.77\,V - 0.77\,V = -2.54\,V$

$Fe^{2+}(aq) + VO_2^+(aq) + 2H^+(aq) \rightarrow Fe^{3+}(aq) + VO^{2+}(aq) + H_2O(l)$

$E° = 1.00\,V - 0.77\,V = +0.23\,V$

(b) $\Delta G° = -nFE°$ For the first reaction,

$$\Delta G° = -2\,mol \times \frac{96,485\,J}{1\,V\text{-}mol} \times (-0.17\,V) = 3.280 \times 10^4 = 3.3 \times 10^4\,J\ or\ 33\,kJ$$

For the second reaction, $\Delta G° = -2(96,485)(-2.54) = 4.901 \times 10^5 = 4.90 \times 10^2\,kJ$

For the third reaction, $\Delta G° = -1(96,485)(0.23) = -2.22 \times 10^4\,J = -22\,kJ$

(c) $\Delta G° = -RT\,lnK$; $lnK = -\Delta G°/RT$; $K = e^{-\Delta G°/RT}$

For the first reaction,

$$lnK = \frac{-3.281 \times 10^4\,J}{(8.314\,J/mol\text{-}K)(298\,K)} = -13.243 = -13;\ K = e^{-13.2428} = 1.78 \times 10^{-6} = 2 \times 10^{-6}$$

[Convert ln to log; the number of decimal places in the log is the number of sig figs in the result.]

For the second reaction,

$$\ln K = \frac{-4.902 \times 10^5 \text{ J}}{8.314 \text{ J/mol-K} \times 298 \text{ K}} = -197.86 = -198; \quad K = e^{-198} = 1.23 \times 10^{-86} = 10^{-86}$$

For the third reaction,

$$\ln K = \frac{-(-2.22 \times 10^4 \text{ J})}{8.314 \text{ J/mol-K} \times 298 \text{ K}} = 8.958 = 9.0; \quad K = e^{9.0} = 7.77 \times 10^3 = 8 \times 10^3$$

Check. The equilibrium constants calculated here are indicators of equilibrium position, but are not particularly precise numerical values.

20.52   (a)

$$2I^-(aq) \rightarrow I_2(s) + 2e^- \qquad E^\circ_{red} = 0.536 \text{ V}$$

$$\underline{Hg_2^{2+}(aq) + 2e^- \rightarrow 2Hg(l) \qquad E^\circ_{red} = 0.789 \text{ V}}$$

$$2I^-(aq) + Hg_2^{2+}(aq) \rightarrow I_2(s) + 2Hg(l) \qquad E^\circ = 0.789 - 0.536 = 0.253 \text{ V}$$

$$\Delta G^\circ = -nFE^\circ = -2 \text{ mol e}^- \times \frac{96.5 \text{ kJ}}{\text{V-mol e}^-} \times 0.253 \text{ V} = -48.829 = -48.8 \text{ kJ}$$

$$\ln K = \frac{-(-4.8829 \times 10^4 \text{ J})}{(8.314 \text{ J/mol-K})(298 \text{ K})} = 19.708 = 19.7; \quad K = e^{19.7} = 3.61 \times 10^8 = 3.6 \times 10^8$$

(b)

$$3[Cu^+(aq) \rightarrow Cu^{2+}(aq) + 1e^-] \qquad E^\circ_{red} = 0.153 \text{ V}$$

$$\underline{NO_3^-(aq) + 4H^+(aq) + 3e^- \rightarrow NO(g) + H_2O(l) \qquad E^\circ_{red} = 0.96 \text{ V}}$$

$$3Cu^+(aq) + NO_3^-(aq) + 4H^+(aq) \rightarrow 3Cu^{2+}(aq) + NO(g) + 2H_2O(l)$$

$$E^\circ = 0.96 - 0.153 = 0.81 \text{ V}; \quad \Delta G^\circ = -3(96.5)(0.81) = -2.345 \times 10^2 \text{ kJ} = -2.3 \times 10^5 \text{ J}$$

$$\ln K = \frac{-(-2.345 \times 10^5 \text{ J})}{(8.314 \text{ J/mol-K})(298 \text{ K})} = 94.65 = 95; \quad K = e^{95} = 1.3 \times 10^{41} = 10^{41}$$

(c)

$$2[Cr(OH)_3(s) + 5OH^-(aq) \rightarrow CrO_4^{2-}(aq) + 4H_2O(l) + 3e^-] \quad E^\circ_{red} = -0.13 \text{ V}$$

$$\underline{3[ClO^-(aq) + H_2O(l) + 2e^- \rightarrow Cl^-(aq) + 2OH^-(aq)] \qquad E^\circ_{red} = 0.89 \text{ V}}$$

$$2Cr(OH)_3(s) + 3ClO^-(aq) + 4OH^-(aq) \rightarrow 2CrO_4^{2-}(aq) + 3Cl^-(aq) + 5H_2O(l)$$

$$E^\circ = 0.89 - (-0.13) = 1.02 \text{ V}; \quad \Delta G^\circ = -6(96.5)(1.02) = -590.58 \text{ kJ} = -5.91 \times 10^5 \text{ J}$$

$$\ln K = \frac{-(-5.9058 \times 10^5 \text{ J})}{(8.314 \text{ J/mol-K})(298 \text{ K})} = 238.37 = 238; \quad K = 3.3 \times 10^{103} = 10^{103}$$

This is an unimaginably large number.

20.53   *Analyze/Plan.* Given K, calculate ΔG° and E°. Reverse the logic in Sample Exercise 20.10. According to Equation [19.20], $\Delta G^\circ = -RT \ln K$. According to Equation [20.12], $\Delta G^\circ = -nFE^\circ$, $E^\circ = -\Delta G^\circ/nF$. *Solve.*

$$K = 1.5 \times 10^{-4}$$

$$\Delta G^\circ = -RT \ln K = -(8.314 \text{ J/mol-K})(298) \ln (1.5 \times 10^{-4}) = 2.181 \times 10^4 \text{ J} = 21.8 \text{ kJ}$$

$$E^\circ = -\Delta G^\circ/nF; \quad n = 2; \quad F = 96.5 \text{ kJ/mol e}^-$$

$$E^\circ = \frac{-21.81 \text{ kJ}}{2 \text{ mol e}^- \times 96.5 \text{ kJ/V-mol e}^-} = -0.113 \text{ V}$$

Check. The unit of $\Delta G°$ is actually kJ/mol, which means kJ per 'mole of reaction', or for the reaction as written. Since we don't have a specific reaction, we interpret the unit as referring to the overall reaction.

20.54 $K = 8.7 \times 10^4$; $\Delta G° = -RT \ln K$; $E° = -\Delta G°/nF$; $n = 1$; $T = 298$ K

$\Delta G° = -8.314 \text{ J/mol-K} \times 298 \text{ K} \times \ln(8.7 \times 10^4) = -2.818 \times 10^4 \text{ J} = -28.2 \text{ kJ}$

$E° = -\Delta G°/nF = \dfrac{-(-28.18 \text{ kJ})}{1e^- \times 96.5 \text{ kJ/V-mol } e^-} = 0.292 \text{ V}$

20.55   *Analyze.* Given $E^°_{red}$ values for half reactions, calculate the value of K for a given redox reaction.

Plan. Combine the relationships involving $E°$, $\Delta G°$ and K to get a direct relationship between $E°$ and K. For each reaction, calculate $E°$ from $E^°_{red}$, then apply the relationship to calculate K.

Solve. $\Delta G° = -nFE°$, $\Delta G° = -RT \ln K$; $\ln K = 2.303 \log K$

$-nFE° = -RT \ln K,\ E° = \dfrac{RT}{nF} \ln K = \dfrac{2.303\,RT}{nF} \log K$

From Equation [20.17] and [20.18], $2.303\,RT/F = 0.0592$.

$E° = \dfrac{0.0592}{n} \log K;\ \log K = \dfrac{nE°}{0.0592};\ K = 10^{\log K}$

(a) $E° = -0.28 - (-0.440) = 0.16$ V, $n = 2$ ($Ni^{2+} + 2e^- \rightarrow Ni$)

$\log K = \dfrac{2(0.16)}{0.0592} = 5.4054 = 5.4;\ K = 2.54 \times 10^5 = 3 \times 10^5$

(b) $E° = 0 - (-0.277) = 0.277$ V; $n = 2$ ($2H^+ + 2e^- \rightarrow H_2$)

$\log K = \dfrac{2(0.277)}{0.0592} = 9.358 = 9.36;\ K = 2.3 \times 10^9$

(c) $E° = 1.51 - 1.065 = 0.445 = 0.45$ V; $n = 10$ ($2MnO_4^- + 10e^- \rightarrow 2Mn^{+2}$)

$\log K = \dfrac{10(0.445)}{0.0592} = 75.169 \approx 75;\ K = 1.5 \times 10^{75} = 10^{75}$

Check. Note that small differences in $E°$ values lead to large changes in the magnitude of K. Sig fig rules limit precision of K values; using log instead of ln leads to more sig figs in the K value. This result is strictly numerical and does not indicate any greater precision in the data.

20.56 $E° = \dfrac{0.0592 \text{ V}}{n} \log K;\ \log K = \dfrac{nE°}{0.0592 \text{ V}}.$ See Solution 20.55 for a more complete explanation.

(a) $E° = 0.799$ V $- 0.337$ V $= 0.462$ V; $n = 2$ ($2Ag^+ + 2e^- \rightarrow 2Ag$)

$\log K = \dfrac{2(0.462 \text{ V})}{0.0592 \text{ V}} = 15.6081 = 15.6;\ K = 4.056 \times 10^{15} = 4 \times 10^{15}$

(b) $E° = 1.61\ V - 0.32\ V = 1.29\ V;\ n = 3\ (3Ce^{4+} + 3e^- \rightarrow 3Ce^{3+})$

$$\log K = \frac{3(1.29)}{0.0592} = 65.372 = 65.4;\ K = 2.35 \times 10^{65} = 2 \times 10^{65}$$

(c) $E° = 0.36\ V - (-0.23\ V) = 0.59\ V;\ n = 4\ (4Fe(CN)_6{}^{3-} + 4e^- \rightarrow 4Fe(CN)_6{}^{4-})$

$$\log K = \frac{4(0.59)}{0.0592} = 39.865 = 40;\ K = 7.3 \times 10^{39} = 10^{40}$$

20.57   *Analyze/Plan.* $E° = \dfrac{0.0592\ V}{n} \log K.$ See Solution 20.55 for a more complete

development. $\log K = \dfrac{nE°}{0.0592\ V}.$ *Solve.*

(a) $\log K = \dfrac{1(0.177\ V)}{0.0592\ V} = 2.9899 = 2.99;\ K = 9.8 \times 10^2$

(b) $\log K = \dfrac{2(0.177\ V)}{0.0592\ V} = 5.9797 = 5.98;\ K = 9.5 \times 10^5$

(c) $\log K = \dfrac{3(0.177\ V)}{0.0592\ V} = 8.9696 = 8.97;\ K = 9.32 \times 10^8 = 9.3 \times 10^8$

20.58 $E° = \dfrac{0.0592\ V}{n} \log K;\ n = \dfrac{0.0592\ V}{E°} \log K.$ See Solution 20.55 for a more complete

development.

$$n = \frac{0.0592\ V}{0.17\ V} \log(5.5 \times 10^5);\ n = 2$$

20.59   *Analyze/Plan.* Given a spontaneous chemical reaction, calculate the maximum possible
work for a given amount of reactant at standard conditions. Separate the equation into
half-reactions and calculate cell emf. Use Equation [20.14], $w_{max} = -nFE$, to calculate
maximum work. At standard conditions, $E = E°$.   *Solve.*

$$I_2(s) + 2e^- \rightarrow 2I^-(aq) \qquad\qquad E_{red}^{o} = \ \ 0.536\ V$$
$$\underline{\ Sn(s) \rightarrow Sn^{2+}(aq) + 2e^- \qquad\qquad E_{red}^{o} = -0.136\ V}$$
$$I_2(s) + Sn(s) \rightarrow 2I^-(aq) + Sn^{2+}(aq) \qquad E° = 0.536 - (-0.136) = 0.672\ V$$

$w_{max} = -2(96.5)(0.672) = -129.7 = -130\ kJ/mol\ Sn$

$$\frac{-129.7\ kJ}{mol\ Sn(s)} \times \frac{1\ mol\ Sn}{118.71\ g\ Sn} \times 75.0\ g\ Sn \times \frac{1000\ J}{kJ} = -8.19 \times 10^4\ J$$

Check. The (–) sign indicates that work is done by the cell.

20.60   For this cell at standard conditions, $E° = 1.10\ V$.

$w_{max} = \Delta G° = -nFE° = -2(96.5)(1.10) = -212.3 = -212\ kJ/mol\ Cu$

$$50.0\ g\ Cu \times \frac{1\ mol\ Cu}{63.55\ g\ Cu} \times \frac{-212.3\ kJ}{mol\ Cu} = -167\ kJ = -1.67 \times 10^5\ J$$

Cell EMF under Nonstandard Conditions (section 20.6)

20.61   (a)   The *Nernst equation* is applicable when the components of an electrochemical cell
are at nonstandard conditions.

(b) $Q = 1$ if all reactants and products are at standard conditions.

(c) If concentration of reactants increases, Q decreases, and E increases.

20.62   (a) No. As the spontaneous chemical reaction of the voltaic cell proceeds, the concentrations of products increase and the concentrations of reactants decrease, so standard conditions are not maintained.

(b) Yes. The Nernst equation is applicable to cell emf at nonstandard conditions, so it must be applicable at temperatures other than 298 K. There are two terms in the Nernst Equation. First, values of $E°$ at temperatures other than 298 K are required. Then, in the form of Equation [20.16], there is a variable for T in the second term. In the short-hand form of Equation [20.18], the value 0.0592 assumes 298 K. A different coefficient would apply to cells at temperatures other than 298 K.

(c) If concentration of products increases, Q increases, and E decreases.

20.63   *Analyze/Plan.* Given a circumstance, determine its effect on cell emf. Each circumstance changes the value of Q. An increase in Q reduces emf; a decrease in Q increases emf. *Solve.*

$$Zn(s) + 2H^+(aq) \rightarrow Zn^{2+}(aq) + H_2(g); \quad E = E° - \frac{0.0592}{n}\log Q; \quad Q = \frac{[Zn^{2+}]P_{H_2}}{[H^+]^2}$$

(a) P_{H_2} increases, Q increases, E decreases

(b) $[Zn^{2+}]$ increases, Q increases, E decreases

(c) $[H^+]$ decreases, Q increases, E decreases

(d) No effect; does not appear in the Nernst equation

20.64 $$Al(s) + 3Ag^+(aq) \rightarrow Al^{3+}(aq) + 3Ag(s); \quad E = E° - \frac{0.0592}{n}\log Q; \quad Q = \frac{[Al^{3+}]}{[Ag^+]^3}$$

Any change that causes the reaction to be less spontaneous (that causes Q to increase and ultimately shifts the equilibrium to the left) will result in a less positive value for E.

(a) Increases E by decreasing $[Al^{3+}]$ on the right side of the equation, which decreases Q.

(b) No effect; the "concentrations" of pure solids and liquids do not influence the value of K for a heterogeneous equilibrium.

(c) No effect; the concentration of Ag^+ and the value of Q are unchanged.

(d) Decreases E; forming $AgCl(s)$ decreases the concentration of Ag^+, which increases Q.

20.65   *Analyze/Plan.* Follow the logic in Sample Exercise 20.11.   *Solve.*

(a)

$Ni^{2+}(aq) + 2e^- \rightarrow Ni(s)$	$E^o_{red} = -0.28$ V
$Zn(s) \rightarrow Zn^{2+}(aq) + 2e^-$	$E^o_{red} = -0.763$ V

$$\overline{Ni^{2+}(aq) + Zn(s) \rightarrow Ni(s) + Zn^{2+}(aq) \quad\quad E° = -0.28 - (-0.763) = 0.483 = 0.48 \text{ V}}$$

(b) $E = E^\circ - \dfrac{0.0592}{n} \log \dfrac{[Zn^{2+}]}{[Ni^{2+}]}; \quad n = 2$

$E = 0.483 - \dfrac{0.0592}{2} \log \dfrac{(0.100)}{(3.00)} = 0.483 - \dfrac{0.0592}{2} \log (0.0333)$

$E = 0.483 - \dfrac{0.0592\,(-1.477)}{2} = 0.483 + 0.0437 = 0.527 = 0.53 \text{ V}$

(c) $E = 0.483 - \dfrac{0.0592}{2} \log \dfrac{(0.900)}{(0.200)} = 0.483 - 0.0193 = 0.464 = 0.46 \text{ V}$

20.66 (a)

$$3[Ce^{4+}(aq) + 1e^- \rightarrow Ce^{3+}(aq)] \qquad\qquad E^\circ_{red} = 1.61 \text{ V}$$

$$\underline{\quad Cr(s) \rightarrow Cr^{3+}(aq) + 3e^- \qquad\qquad\qquad E^\circ_{red} = -0.74 \text{ V} \quad}$$

$$3Ce^{4+}(aq) + Cr(s) \rightarrow 3Ce^{3+}(aq) + Cr^{3+}(aq) \qquad E^\circ = 1.61 - (-0.74) = 2.35 \text{ V}$$

(b) $E = E^\circ - \dfrac{0.0592}{n} \log \dfrac{[Ce^{3+}]^3[Cr^{3+}]}{[Ce^{4+}]^3}; \quad n = 3$

$E = 2.35 - \dfrac{0.0592}{3} \log \dfrac{(0.10)^3(0.010)}{(3.0)^3} = 2.35 - \dfrac{0.0592}{3} \log (3.704 \times 10^{-7})$

$E = 2.35 - \dfrac{0.0592\,(-6.431)}{3} = 2.35 + 0.127 = 2.48 \text{ V}$

(c) $E = 2.35 - \dfrac{0.0592}{3} \log \dfrac{(2.0)^3(1.5)}{(0.010)^3} = 2.35 - 0.1397 = 2.21 \text{ V}$

20.67 *Analyze/Plan.* Follow the logic in Sample Exercise 20.11.   *Solve.*

(a)

$$4[Fe^{2+}(aq) \rightarrow Fe^{3+}(aq) + 1e^-] \qquad\qquad E^\circ_{red} = 0.771 \text{ V}$$

$$\underline{\quad O_2(g) + 4H^+(aq) + 4e^- \rightarrow 2H_2O(l) \qquad\qquad E^\circ_{red} = 1.23 \text{ V} \quad}$$

$$4Fe^{2+}(aq) + O_2(g) + 4H^+(aq) \rightarrow 4Fe^{3+}(aq) + 2H_2O(l) \quad E^\circ = 1.23 - 0.771 = 0.459 = 0.46$$

(b) $E = E^\circ - \dfrac{0.0592}{n} \log \dfrac{[Fe^{3+}]^4}{[Fe^{2+}]^4[H^+]^4 P_{O_2}}; \quad n = 4, \; [H^+] = 10^{-3.50} = 3.2 \times 10^{-4} \text{ M}$

$E = 0.459 \text{ V} - \dfrac{0.0592}{4} \log \dfrac{(0.010)^4}{(1.3)^4 (3.2\times 10^{-4})^4 (0.50)} = 0.459 - \dfrac{0.0592}{4} \log (7.0 \times 10^5)$

$E = 0.459 - \dfrac{0.0592}{4}(5.845) = 0.459 - 0.0865 = 0.3725 = 0.37 \text{ V}$

20.68 (a)

$$2[Fe^{3+}(aq) + 1e^- \rightarrow Fe^{2+}(aq)] \qquad\qquad E^\circ_{red} = 0.771 \text{ V}$$

$$\underline{\quad H_2(g) \rightarrow 2H^+(aq) + 2e^- \qquad\qquad\qquad E^\circ_{red} = 0.000 \text{ V} \quad}$$

$$2Fe^{3+}(aq) + H_2(g) \rightarrow 2Fe^{2+}(aq) + 2H^+(aq) \qquad E^\circ = 0.771 - 0.000 = 0.771 \text{ V}$$

(b)

$$E = E° - \frac{0.0592}{n} \log \frac{[Fe^{2+}]^2[H^+]^2}{[Fe^{3+}]^2 P_{H_2}}; \ [H^+] = 10^{-pH} = 1.0 \times 10^{-4}, \ n = 2$$

$$E = 0.771 - \frac{0.0592}{2} \log \frac{(0.0010)^2 (1.0 \times 10^{-4})^2}{(3.50)^2 (0.95)} = 0.771 - \frac{0.0592}{2} \log(8.6 \times 10^{-16})$$

$$E = 0.771 - \frac{0.0592(-15.066)}{2} = 0.771 + 0.446 = 1.217 \text{ V}$$

20.69   *Analyze/Plan.* We are given a concentration cell with Zn electrodes. Use the definition of a concentration cell in Section 20.6 to answer the stated questions. Use Equation [20.18] to calculate the cell emf. For a concentration cell, Q = [dilute]/[concentrated].   *Solve.*

(a)   The compartment with the more dilute solution will be the anode. That is, the compartment with $[Zn^{2+}] = 1.00 \times 10^{-2} \ M$ is the anode.

(b)   Since the oxidation half-reaction is the opposite of the reduction half-reaction, E° is zero.

(c) $$E = E° - \frac{0.0592}{n} \log Q; \ Q = [Zn^{2+}, \text{dilute}]/[Zn^{2+}, \text{conc.}]$$

$$E = 0 - \frac{0.0592}{2} \log \frac{(1.00 \times 10^{-2})}{(1.8)} = 0.0668 \text{ V}$$

(d)   In the anode compartment, $Zn(s) \rightarrow Zn^{2+}(aq)$, so $[Zn^{2+}]$ increases from $1.00 \times 10^{-2} \ M$. In the cathode compartment, $Zn^{2+}(aq) \rightarrow Zn(s)$, so $[Zn^{2+}]$ decreases from 1.8 M.

20.70   (a)   The compartment with 0.0150 M Cl^- (aq) is the cathode.

(b)   E° = 0 V

(c) $$E = E° - \frac{0.0592}{n} \log Q; \ Q = [Cl^-, \text{dilute}]/[Cl^-, \text{conc.}]$$

$$E = 0 - \frac{0.0592}{1} \log \frac{(0.0150)}{(2.55)} = -0.13204 = -0.1320 \text{ V}$$

(d)   In the anode compartment, $[Cl^-]$ will decrease from 2.55 M. In the cathode, $[Cl^-]$ will increase from 0.0150 M.

20.71   *Analyze/Plan.* Follow the logic in Sample Exercise 20.12.   *Solve.*

$$E = E° - \frac{0.0592}{2} \log \frac{[P_{H_2}][Zn^{2+}]}{[H^+]^2}; \ E° = 0.0 \text{ V} - (-0.763 \text{ V}) = 0.763 \text{ V}$$

$$0.684 = 0.763 - \frac{0.0592}{2} \times (\log [P_{H_2}][Zn^{2+}] - 2 \log [H^+])$$

$$= 0.763 - \frac{0.0592}{2} \times (-0.5686 - 2 \log [H^+])$$

$$0.684 = 0.763 + 0.0168 + 0.0592 \log [H^+]; \ \log [H^+] = \frac{0.684 - 0.0168 - 0.763}{0.0592}$$

$$\log [H^+] = -1.6188 = -1.6; \ [H^+] = 0.0241 = 0.02 \ M; \ pH = 1.6$$

20.72   (a) $E° = -0.136 V - (-0.126 V) = -0.010 V; n = 2$

$$0.22 = -0.010 - \frac{0.0592}{2} \log \frac{[Pb^{2+}]}{[Sn^{2+}]} = -0.010 - \frac{0.0592}{2} \log \frac{[Pb^{2+}]}{1.00}$$

$$\log [Pb^{2+}] = \frac{-0.23 (2)}{0.0592} = -7.770 = -7.8; [Pb^{2+}] = 1.7 \times 10^{-8} = 2 \times 10^{-8} \, M$$

(b)   For $PbSO_4 (s)$, $K_{sp} = [Pb^{2+}] [SO_4^{2-}] = (1.0)(1.7 \times 10^{-8}) = 1.7 \times 10^{-8}$

Batteries and Fuel Cells (section 20.7)

20.73   (a)   The emf of a battery decreases as it is used. This happens because the concentrations of products increase and the concentrations of reactants decrease. According to the Nernst equation, these changes increase Q and decrease E_{cell}.

(b)   The major difference between AA- and D-size batteries is the amount of reactants present. The additional reactants in a D-size battery enable it to provide power for a longer time.

20.74   (a)   First, H_2O is a reactant in the cathodic half-reaction, so it must be present in some form. Additionally, liquid water enhances mobility of the hydroxide ion in the alkaline battery. OH^- is produced in the cathode compartment and consumed in the anode compartment. It must be available at all points where Zn(s) is being oxidized. If the Zn(s) near the separator is mostly reacted, OH^- must diffuse through the gel until it reaches fresh Zn(s). A small amount of $H_2O(l)$ mobilizes OH^- so that redox can continue until reactants throughout the battery are depleted.

(b)   Highly concentrated or solid reactants offer a large amount of reactant in a small sample volume. The more available reactant, the longer the cell produces a voltage. A voltaic cell with solid or highly concentrated reactants has the advantages of small size and long operational lifetime.

20.75   *Analyze/Plan.* Given mass of a reactant (Pb), calculate mass of product (PbO_2), and coulombs of charge transferred. This is a stoichiometry problem; we need the balanced equation for the chemical reaction that occurs in the lead-acid battery.

The overall cell reaction is:

$Pb(s) + PbO_2(s) + 2H^+ (aq) + 2HSO_4^- (aq) \rightarrow 2PbSO_4(s) + 2H_2O(l)$ *Solve.*

(a) $g \, Pb \rightarrow mol \, Pb \rightarrow mol \, PbO_2 \rightarrow g \, PbO_2$

$$402 \, g \, Pb \times \frac{1 \, mol \, Pb}{207.2 \, g \, Pb} \times \frac{1 \, mol \, PbO_2}{1 \, mol \, Pb} \times \frac{239.2 \, g \, PbO_2}{1 \, mol \, PbO_2} = 464 \, g \, PbO_2$$

(b)   From the half-reactions for the lead-acid battery, 2 mol electrons are transferred for each mol of Pb reacted. From section 20.5, 96,485 C/mol e^-.

$$402 \, g \, Pb \times \frac{1 \, mol \, Pb}{207.2 \, g \, Pb} \times \frac{2 \, mol \, e^-}{1 \, mol \, Pb} \times \frac{96,485 \, C}{1 \, mol \, e^-} = 374,392 = 3.74 \times 10^5 \, C$$

20.76   (a)   The overall cell reaction is:

$$2MnO_2(s) + Zn(s) + 2H_2O(l) \rightarrow 2MnO(OH)(s) + Zn(OH)_2(s)$$

$$4.50 \text{ g Zn} \times \frac{1 \text{ mol Zn}}{65.39 \text{ g Zn}} \times \frac{2 \text{ mol } MnO_2}{1 \text{ mol Zn}} \times \frac{86.94 \text{ g } MnO_2}{1 \text{ mol } MnO_2} = 12.0 \text{ g } MnO_2$$

(b)   Two mol e^- are transferred for every mol of Zn reacted. 96,485 C/mol e^-

$$4.50 \text{ g Zn} \times \frac{1 \text{ mol Zn}}{65.39 \text{ g Zn}} \times \frac{2 \text{ mol } e^-}{1 \text{ mol Zn}} \times \frac{96,485 \text{ C}}{1 \text{ mol } e^-} = 13,280 = 1.32 \times 10^4 \text{ C}$$

20.77   *Analyze/Plan.* We are given a redox reaction and asked to write half-reactions, calculate E°, and indicate whether Li(s) is the anode or cathode. Determine which reactant is oxidized and which is reduced. Separate into half-reactions, find E_{red}^o for the half-reactions from Appendix E and calculate E°.   *Solve.*

(a)   Li(s) is oxidized at the anode.

(b)
$$Ag_2CrO_4(s) + 2e^- \rightarrow 2Ag(s) + CrO_4^{2-}(aq) \qquad E_{red}^o = 0.446 \text{ V}$$
$$\underline{2[Li(s) \rightarrow Li^+(aq) + 1e^-] \qquad\qquad\qquad E_{red}^o = -3.05 \text{ V}}$$
$$Ag_2CrO_4(s) + 2Li(s) \rightarrow 2Ag(s) + CrO_4^-(aq) + 2Li^+(aq)$$

E° = 0.446 V – (–3.05 V) = 3.496 = 3.50 V

(c)   The emf of the battery, 3.5 V, is exactly the standard cell potential calculated in part (b).

(d)   For this battery at ambient conditions, E ≈ E°, so log Q ≈ 0. This makes sense because all reactants and products in the battery are solids and thus present in their standard states. Assuming that E° is relatively constant with temperature, the value of the second term in the Nernst equation is ≈ 0 at 37°C, and E ≈ 3.5 V.

20.78   (a) $HgO(s) + Zn(s) \rightarrow Hg(l) + ZnO(s)$

(b) $E_{cell}^o = E_{red}^o \text{ (cathode)} - E_{red}^o \text{ (anode)}$

$E_{red}^o \text{ (anode)} = E_{red}^o - E_{cell}^o = 0.098 - 1.35 = -1.25 \text{ V}$

(c) E_{red}^o is different from $Zn^{2+}(aq) + 2e^- \rightarrow Zn(s)$ (–0.76 V) because in the battery the process happens in the presence of base and Zn^{2+} is stabilized as ZnO(s). Stabilization of a reactant in a half-reaction decreases the driving force, so E_{red}^o is more negative.

20.79   *Analyze/Plan.* (a) Consider the function of Zn in an alkaline battery. What effect would it have on the redox reaction and cell emf if Cd replaces Zn? (b) Both batteries contain Ni. What is the difference in environmental impact between Cd and the metal hydride? *Solve.*

(a) E_{red}^o for Cd (–0.40 V) is less negative than E_{red}^o for Zn (–0.76 V), so E_{cell} will have a smaller (less positive) value.

(b)   NiMH batteries use an alloy such as $ZrNi_2$ as the anode material. This eliminates the use and concomitant disposal problems associated with Cd, a toxic heavy metal.

20.80   (a)   The alkali metal Li has much greater metallic character than Zn, Cd, Pb or Ni. The reduction potential for Li is thus more negative, leading to greater overall cell emf for the battery. Also, Li is less dense than the other metals, so greater total energy for a battery can be achieved for a given total mass of material. One disadvantage is that Li is very reactive and the cell reactions are difficult to control.

         (b)   Li has a much smaller molar mass (6.94 g/mol) than Ni (58.69 g/mol). A Li-ion battery can have many more charge-carrying particles than a Ni-based battery with the same mass. That is, Li-ion batteries have a greater *energy density* than Ni-based batteries.

20.81   The main advantage of a H_2–O_2 fuel cell over an alkaline battery is that the fuel cell is not a closed system. Fuel, H_2, and oxidant, O_2 are continuously supplied to the fuel cell, so that it can produce electrical current for a time limited only by the amount of available fuel. An alkaline battery contains a finite amount of reactant and produces current only until the reactants are spent, or reach equilibrium.

        Alkaline batteries are much more convenient, because they are self-contained. Fuel cells require a means to acquire and store volatile and explosive $H_2(g)$. Disposal of spent alkaline batteries, which contain zinc and manganese solids, is much more problematic. H_2–O_2 fuel cells produce only $H_2O(l)$, which is not a disposal problem.

20.82   (a)   Both batteries and fuel cells are electrochemical power sources. Both take advantage of spontaneous oxidation-reduction reactions to produce a certain voltage. The difference is that batteries are self-contained (all reactants and products are present inside the battery casing) while fuel cells require continuous supply of reactants and exhaust of products.

         (b)   No. The fuel in a fuel cell must be fluid, either gas or liquid. Because fuel must be continuously supplied to the fuel cell, it must be capable of flow; the fuel cannot be solid.

Corrosion (section 20.8)

20.83   *Analyze/Plan.* (a) Decide which reactant is oxidized and which is reduced. Write the balanced half-reactions and assign the appropriate one as anode and cathode. (b) Write the balanced half-reaction for $Fe^{2+}(aq) \rightarrow Fe_2O_3 \cdot 3H_2O$. Use the reduction half-reaction from part (a) to obtain the overall reaction.   *Solve.*

         (a)   anode: $Fe(s) \rightarrow Fe^{2+}(aq) + 2e^-$

                cathode: $O_2(g) + 4H^+(aq) + 4e^- \rightarrow 2H_2O(l)$

         (b) $2Fe^{2+}(aq) + 6H_2O(l) \rightarrow Fe_2O_3 \cdot 3H_2O(s) + 6H^+(aq) + 2e^-$

                $O_2(g) + 4H^+(aq) + 4e^- \rightarrow 2H_2O(l)$

                (Multiply the oxidation half-reaction by two to balance electrons and obtain the overall balanced reaction.)

20.84   (a)   Calculate E_{cell}^{o} for the given reactants at standard conditions.

$$O_2(g) + 4H^+(aq) + 4e^- \rightarrow 2H_2O(l) \qquad\qquad E_{red}^{o} = 1.23\ V$$
$$\underline{\quad\quad 2[Cu(s) \rightarrow Cu^{2+}(aq) + 2e^-] \qquad\qquad E_{red}^{o} = 0.337\ V\quad}$$
$$2Cu(s) + O_2(g) + 4H^+(aq) \rightarrow 2Cu^{2+}(aq) + 2H_2O(l) \qquad E^{\circ} = 1.23 - 0.337 = 0.89\ V$$

At standard conditions with $O_2(g)$ and $H^+(aq)$ present, the oxidation of Cu(s) has a positive E° value and is spontaneous. Cu(s) will oxidize (corrode) in air in the presence of acid.

   (b) Fe^{2+} has a more negative reduction potential (–0.440 V) than Cu^{2+} (+0.337 V), so Fe(s) is more readily oxidized than Cu(s). If the two metals are in contact, Fe(s) would act as a sacrificial anode and oxidize (corrode) in preference to Cu(s); this would weaken the iron support skeleton of the statue. The teflon spacers prevent contact between the two metals and insure that the iron skeleton doesn't corrode when the Cu(s) skin comes in contact with atmospheric $O_2(g)$ and $H^+(aq)$.

20.85   (a)   A "sacrificial anode" is a metal that is oxidized in preference to another when the two metals are coupled in an electrochemical cell; the sacrificial anode has a more negative E_{red}^{o} than the other metal. In this case, Mg acts as a sacrificial anode because it is oxidized in preference to the pipe metal; it is sacrificed to preserve the pipe.

   (b) E_{red}^{o} for Mg^{2+} is –2.37 V, more negative than most metals present in pipes, including Fe $(E_{red}^{o} = -0.44\ V)$ and Zn $(E_{red}^{o} = -0.763\ V)$.

20.86   No. To afford cathodic protection, a metal must be more difficult to reduce (have a more negative reduction potential) than Fe^{2+}. $E_{red}^{o}\ Co^{2+} = -0.28\ V$, $E_{red}^{o}\ Fe^{2+} = -0.44\ V$.

20.87   *Analyze/Plan.* Given the materials brass, composed of Zn and Cu, and galvanized steel, determine the possible spontaneous redox reactions that could occur when the materials come in contact. Calculate E° values for these reactions.

   Solve. The main metallic component of steel is Fe. Galvanized steel is steel plated with Zn. The three metals in question are Fe, Zn, and Cu; their E_{red}^{o} values are shown below.

$$E_{red}^{o}\ Fe^{2+}(aq) = -0.440\ V$$
$$E_{red}^{o}\ Zn^{2+}(aq) = -0.763\ V$$
$$E_{red}^{o}\ Cu^{2+}(aq) = 0.337\ V$$

Zn, with the most negative E_{red}^{o} value, can act as a sacrificial anode for either Fe or Cu. That is, Zn(s) will be preferentially oxidized when in contact with Fe(s) or Cu(s). For environmental corrosion, the oxidizing agent is usually $O_2(g)$ in acidic solution, $E_{red}^{o} = 1.23\ V$. The pertinent reactions and their E° values are:

$$2Zn(s) + O_2(g) + 4H^+(aq) \rightarrow 2Zn^{2+}(aq) + 2H_2O(l)$$
$$E^{\circ} = 1.23\ V - (-0.763\ V) = 1.99\ V$$

$$2Fe(s) + O_2(g) + 4H^+(aq) \rightarrow 2Fe^{2+}(aq) + 2H_2O(l)$$

$$E° = 1.23 \text{ V} - (-0.440 \text{ V}) = 1.67 \text{ V}$$

$$2Cu(s) + O_2(g) + 4H^+(aq) \rightarrow 2Cu^{2+}(aq) + 2H_2O(l)$$

$$E° = 1.23 \text{ V} - (0.337 \text{ V}) = 0.893 \text{ V}$$

Note, however, that Fe has a more negative E_{red}^o than Cu so when the two are in contact Fe acts as the sacrificial anode, and corrosion (of Fe) occurs preferentially. This is verified by the larger E° value for the corrosion of Fe, 1.67 V, relative to the corrosion of Cu, 0.893 V. When the three metals Zn, Fe, and Cu are in contact, oxidation of Zn will happen first, followed by oxidation of Fe, and finally Cu.

20.88   The principal metallic component of steel is Fe. E_{red}^o for Fe, –0.763 V, is more negative than that of Cu, 0.337 V. When the two are in contact, Fe acts as the sacrificial anode and corrodes (oxidizes) preferentially in the presence of $O_2(g)$.

$$2Fe(s) + O_2(g) + 4H^+(aq) \rightarrow 2Fe^{2+}(aq) + 2H_2O(l)$$

$$E° = 1.23 \text{ V} - (-0.440 \text{ V}) = 1.67 \text{ V}$$

$$2Cu(s) + O_2(g) + 4H^+(aq) \rightarrow 2Cu^{2+}(aq) + 2H_2O(l)$$

$$E° = 1.23 \text{ V} - (0.337 \text{ V}) = 0.893 \text{ V}$$

Both reactions are spontaneous, but the corrosion of Fe has the larger E° value and happens preferentially.

Electrolysis; Electrical Work (section 20.9)

20.89   (a)   *Electrolysis* is an electrochemical process driven by an outside energy source.

(b)   Electrolysis reactions are, by definition, nonspontaneous.

(c) $2Cl^-(l) \rightarrow Cl_2(g) + 2e^-$

(d)   When an aqueous solution of NaCl undergoes electrolysis, H_2O is preferentially reduced to form $H_2(g)$.

20.90   (a)   An *electrolytic cell* is the vessel in which electrolysis occurs. It consists of a power source and two electrodes in a molten salt or aqueous solution.

(b)   It is the cathode. In an electrolysis cell, as in a voltaic cell, electrons are consumed (via reduction) at the cathode. Electrons flow from the negative terminal of the voltage source and then to the cathode.

(c)   A small amount of $H_2SO_4(aq)$ present during the electrolysis of water acts as a change carrier, or supporting electrolyte. This facilitates transfer of electrons through the solution and at the electrodes, speeding up the reaction. (Considering $H^+(aq)$ as the substance reduced at the cathode changes the details of the half-reactions, but not the overall E° for the electrolysis. $SO_4^{2-}(aq)$ cannot be oxidized.)

(d)   If the active metal salt is present as an aqueous solution during electrolysis, water is reduced [to $H_2(g)$] rather than the metal ion being reduced to the metal. This is true for any active metal with an E_{red}^o value more negative than –0.83 V.

20.91   *Analyze/Plan.* Follow the logic in Sample Exercise 20.14, paying close attention to units. Coulombs = **amps-s**; since this is a 3e⁻ reduction, each mole of Cr(s) requires 3 Faradays.   *Solve.*

(a) $7.60 \text{ A} \times 2.00 \text{ d} \times \dfrac{24 \text{ hr}}{1 \text{ d}} \times \dfrac{60 \text{ min}}{1 \text{ hr}} \times \dfrac{60 \text{ s}}{1 \text{ min}} \times \dfrac{1 \text{ C}}{1 \text{ amp-s}} \times \dfrac{1 \text{ F}}{96,485 \text{ C}}$

$\times \dfrac{1 \text{ mol Cr}}{3 \text{ F}} \times \dfrac{52.00 \text{ g Cr}}{1 \text{ mol Cr}} = 236 \text{ g Cr(s)}$

(b) $0.250 \text{ mol Cr} \times \dfrac{3 \text{ F}}{1 \text{ mol Cr}} \times \dfrac{96,485 \text{ C}}{\text{F}} \times \dfrac{1 \text{ amp-s}}{1 \text{ C}} \times \dfrac{1}{8.00 \text{ hr}} \times \dfrac{1 \text{ hr}}{60 \text{ min}} \times \dfrac{1 \text{ min}}{60 \text{ s}}$

$= 2.51 \text{ A}$

20.92   Coulombs = **amps-s**; since this is a 2e⁻ reduction, each mole of Mg(s) requires 2 Faradays.

(a) $4.55 \text{ A} \times 4.50 \text{ d} \times \dfrac{24 \text{ h}}{1 \text{ d}} \times \dfrac{60 \text{ min}}{1 \text{ h}} \times \dfrac{60 \text{ s}}{1 \text{ min}} \times \dfrac{1 \text{ C}}{1 \text{ amp-s}} \times \dfrac{1 \text{ F}}{96,485 \text{ C}}$

$\times \dfrac{1 \text{ mol Mg}}{2 \text{ F}} \times \dfrac{24.31 \text{ g Mg}}{1 \text{ mol Mg}} = 223 \text{ g Mg}$

(b) $25.00 \text{ g Mg} \times \dfrac{1 \text{ mol Mg}}{24.31 \text{ g Mg}} \times \dfrac{2 \text{ F}}{1 \text{ mol Mg}} \times \dfrac{96,485 \text{ C}}{\text{F}} \times \dfrac{1 \text{ amp-s}}{\text{C}} \times \dfrac{1 \text{ min}}{60 \text{ s}} \times \dfrac{1}{3.50 \text{ A}}$

$= 945 \text{ min}$

20.93   *Analyze/Plan.* Combine the ideas in Sample Exercises 20.14 and 20.15, paying close attention to units. Li⁺ is reduced at the anode; Cl⁻ is oxidized at the anode.   *Solve.*

(a)   If the cell is 85% efficient, $\dfrac{96,485 \text{ C}}{\text{F}} \times \dfrac{1 \text{ F}}{0.85 \text{ mol}} = 1.13512 \times 10^5$

$= 1.1 \times 10^5 \text{ C/mol Li required}$

$7.5 \times 10^4 \text{ A} \times 24 \text{ h} \times \dfrac{3600 \text{ s}}{1 \text{ h}} \times \dfrac{1 \text{ C}}{1 \text{ amp-s}} \times \dfrac{1 \text{ mol Li}}{1.13512 \times 10^5 \text{ C}} \times \dfrac{6.94 \text{ g Li}}{1 \text{ mol Li}}$

$= 3.962 \times 10^5 = 4.0 \times 10^5 \text{ g Li}$

(b) $E^{\circ}_{\text{cell}} = E^{\circ}_{\text{red}}(\text{cathode}) - E^{\circ}_{\text{red}}(\text{anode}) = -3.05 \text{ V} - (1.359 \text{ V}) = -4.409 = -4.41 \text{ V}$

The minimum voltage required to drive the reaction is the magnitude of E°_{cell}, 4.41 V.

20.94   (a) $7.5 \times 10^3 \text{ A} \times 48 \text{ h} \times \dfrac{3600 \text{ s}}{1 \text{ h}} \times \dfrac{1 \text{ C}}{1 \text{ amp-s}} \times \dfrac{1 \text{ F}}{96,485 \text{ C}} \times \dfrac{1 \text{ mol Ca}}{2 \text{ F}} \times 0.68 \times \dfrac{40.0 \text{ g Ca}}{1 \text{ mol Ca}}$

$= 1.830 \times 10^5 = 1.8 \times 10^5 \text{ g Ca}$

(b) $E^{\circ}_{\text{cell}} = E^{\circ}_{\text{red}}(\text{cathode}) - E^{\circ}_{\text{red}}(\text{anode}) = -2.87 \text{ V} - (1.359 \text{ V}) = -4.229 = -4.23 \text{ V}$

The minimum voltage required to drive the reaction is the magnitude of E°_{cell}, 4.23 V.

20.95   Table 4.5 is "The Activity Series of the Metals". Gold is the least active metal on this table, less active than copper. This means that gold is more difficult to oxidize than copper (and that E_{red}^{o} for Au^{3+} is more positive than E_{red}^{o} for Cu^{2+}). When crude copper is refined by electrolysis, Cu is oxidized from the crude anode, but any metallic gold present in the crude copper is not oxidized, so it accumulates near the anode, along with other impurities less active than copper.

20.96   The standard reduction potential for Te^{4+}, 0.57 V, is more positive than that of Cu^{2+}, 0.34 V. This means the Te^{4+} is "easier" to reduce than Cu^{2+}, but Te is harder to oxidize and less active than Cu. During electrorefining, while Cu is oxidized from the crude anode, Te will not be oxidized. It is likely to accumulate along with other impurities less active than Cu, in the so-called anode sludge.

Additional Exercises

20.97   (a) $Ni^{+}(aq) + 1e^{-} \rightarrow Ni(s)$

$$\frac{Ni^{+}(aq) \qquad \rightarrow Ni^{2+}(aq) + 1e^{-}}{2Ni^{+}(aq) \qquad \rightarrow Ni(s) + Ni^{2+}(aq)}$$

(b) $MnO_4^{2-}(aq) + 4H^{+}(aq) + 2e^{-} \rightarrow MnO_2(s) + 2H_2O(l)$

$$\frac{2[MnO_4^{2-}(aq) \rightarrow MnO_4^{-}(aq) + 1e^{-}]}{3MnO_4^{2-}(aq) + 4H^{+}(aq) \rightarrow 2MnO_4^{-}(aq) + MnO_2(s) + 2H_2O(l)}$$

(c) $H_2SO_3(aq) + 4H^{+}(aq) + 4e^{-} \rightarrow S(s) + 3H_2O(l)$

$$\frac{2[H_2SO_3(aq) + H_2O(l) \rightarrow HSO_4^{-}(aq) + 3H^{+}(aq) + 2e^{-}]}{3H_2SO_3(aq) \rightarrow S(s) + 2HSO_4^{-}(aq) + 2H^{+}(aq) + H_2O(l)}$$

(d) $Cl_2(aq) + 2H_2O(l) \rightarrow 2ClO^{-}(aq) + 4H^{+}(aq) + 2e^{-}$
          $4OH^{-}(aq) \qquad + 4OH^{-}(aq)$

$$\frac{}{Cl_2(aq) + 4OH^{-}(aq) \rightarrow 2ClO^{-}(aq) + 2H_2O(l) + 2e^{-}}$$

$$\frac{Cl_2(aq) + 2e^{-} \rightarrow 2Cl^{-}(aq)}{1/2[2Cl_2(aq) + 4OH^{-}(aq) \rightarrow 2Cl^{-}(aq) + 2ClO^{-}(aq) + 2H_2O(l)]}$$

$$Cl_2(aq) + 2OH^{-}(aq) \rightarrow Cl^{-}(aq) + ClO^{-}(aq) + H_2O(l)$$

20.98   (a)

(b)

(c) $MnO_4^-(aq) + 8H^+(aq) + 5e^- \rightarrow Mn^{2+}(aq) + 4H_2O(l)$ $E_{red}^o = 1.51\ V$

$5[Fe^{2+}(aq) \rightarrow Fe^{3+}(aq) + 1e^-]$ $E_{red}^o = 0.771\ V$

$E^\circ = 1.51\ V - 0.771\ V = 0.74\ V$

(d) $E = E^\circ - \dfrac{0.0592}{5} \log \dfrac{[Fe^{3+}]^5[Mn^{2+}]}{[Fe^{2+}]^5[MnO_4^-][H^+]^8}$; $pH = 0.0, [H^+] = 1.0$

$E = 0.74\ V - \dfrac{0.0592}{5} \log \dfrac{(2.5 \times 10^{-4})^5(0.001)}{(0.10)^5(1.50)(1.0)^8}$; $Q = 6.510 \times 10^{-17} = 6.5 \times 10^{-17}$

$E = 0.74\ V - \dfrac{0.0592(-16.1864)}{5} = 0.74\ V + 0.19\ V = 0.93\ V$

20.99   (a)

Anode   Cathode

Fe(s)   Ag(s)

Fe^{2+} Ag$^+$

Porous
separator

$Fe(s) \rightarrow Fe^{2+}(aq) + 2e^-$

$2Ag^+(aq) + 2e^- \rightarrow 2Ag(s)$

$\overline{Fe(s) + 2Ag^+(aq) \rightarrow Fe^{2+}(aq) + 2Ag(s)}$

(b) $Zn(s) \rightarrow Zn^{2+}(s) + 2e^-$

$2H^+(aq) + 2e^- \rightarrow H_2(g)$

$\overline{Zn(s) + 2H^+(aq) \rightarrow Zn^{2+}(aq) + H_2(g)}$

Zn(s)

Pt

Zn^{2+} H$^+$

Porous
separator

(c) $Cu\,|\,Cu^{2+}\,||\,ClO_3^-, Cl^-\,|\,Pt$ Here, both the oxidized and reduced forms of the cathode solution are in the same phase, so we separate them by a comma, and then indicate an inert electrode.

20.100 We need in each case to determine whether E° is positive (spontaneous) or negative (nonspontaneous).

(a)
$$I_2(s) + 2e^- \rightarrow 2I^-(aq) \qquad E^\circ_{red} = 0.536 \text{ V}$$
$$\underline{Sn(s) \rightarrow Sn^{2+}(aq) + 2e^- \qquad E^\circ_{red} = -0.136}$$
$$Sn(s) + I_2(s) \rightarrow Sn^{2+}(aq) + 2I^-(aq) \quad E^\circ = 0.536 - (-0.136) = 0.672 \text{ V, spontaneous}$$

(b)
$$Ni^{2+}(aq) + 2e^- \rightarrow Ni(s) \qquad E^\circ_{red} = -0.28 \text{ V}$$
$$\underline{2I^-(aq) \rightarrow I_2(s) + 2e^- \qquad E^\circ_{red} = 0.536 \text{ V}}$$
$$Ni^{2+}(aq) + 2I^-(aq) \rightarrow Ni(s) + I_2(s) \quad E^\circ = -0.28 - 0.536 = -0.82 \text{ V, nonspontaneous}$$

(c)
$$2[Ce^{4+}(aq) + 1e^- \rightarrow Ce^{3+}(aq)] \qquad E^\circ_{red} = 1.61 \text{ V}$$
$$\underline{H_2O_2(aq) \rightarrow O_2(g) + 2H^+(aq) + 2e^- \qquad E^\circ_{red} = 0.68 \text{ V}}$$
$$2Ce^{4+}(aq) + H_2O_2(aq) \rightarrow 2Ce^{3+}(aq) + O_2(g) + 2H^+(aq) \quad E^\circ = 1.61 - 0.68 = 0.93 \text{ V, spontaneous}$$

(d)
$$Cu^{2+}(aq) + 2e^- \rightarrow Cu(s) \qquad E^\circ_{red} = 0.337 \text{ V}$$
$$\underline{Sn^{2+}(aq) \rightarrow Sn^{4+}(aq) + 2e^- \qquad E^\circ_{red} = 0.154 \text{ V}}$$
$$Cu^{2+}(aq) + Sn^{2+}(aq) \rightarrow Cu(s) + Sn^{4+}(aq) \quad E^\circ = 0.337 - 1.54 = 0.183 \text{ V, spontaneous}$$

20.101 (a) The reduction potential for $O_2(g)$ in the presence of acid is 1.23 V. $O_2(g)$ cannot oxidize Au(s) to $Au^+(aq)$ or $Au^{3+}(aq)$, even in the presence of acid.

(b) The possible oxidizing agents need a reduction potential greater than 1.50 V. These include $Co^{3+}(aq)$, $F_2(g)$, $H_2O_2(aq)$, and $O_3(g)$. Marginal oxidizing agents (those with reduction potential near 1.50 V) from Appendix E are $BrO_3^-(aq)$, $Ce^{4+}(aq)$, HClO(aq), $MnO_4^-(aq)$, and $PbO_2(s)$.

(c) $4Au(s) + 8NaCN(aq) + 2H_2O(l) + O_2(g) \rightarrow 4Na[Au(CN)_2](aq) + 4NaOH(aq)$

$$Au(s) + 2CN^-(aq) \rightarrow [Au(CN)_2]^- + 1e^-$$

$$O_2(g) + 2H_2O(l) + 4e^- \rightarrow 4OH^-(aq)$$

Au(s) is being oxidized and $O_2(g)$ is being reduced.

(d)
$$2[Na[Au(CN)_2](aq) + 1e^- \rightarrow Au(s) + 2CN^-(aq) + Na^+(aq)]$$
$$\underline{Zn(s) \rightarrow Zn^{2+}(aq) + 2e^-}$$
$$2Na[Au(CN)_2](aq) + Zn(s) \rightarrow 2Au(s) + Zn^{2+}(aq) + 2Na^+(aq) + 4CN^-(aq)$$

Zn(s) is being oxidized and $[Au(CN)_2]^-(aq)$ is being reduced. While $OH^-(aq)$ is not included in the redox reaction above, its presence in the reaction mixture probably causes $Zn(OH)_2(s)$ to form as the product. This increases the driving force (and E°) for the overall reaction.

20.102 (a)

$$2[Ag^+(aq) + 1e^- \rightarrow Ag(s)] \qquad\qquad E^\circ_{red} = 0.80 \text{ V}$$

$$\underline{Ni(s) \rightarrow Ni^{2+}(aq) + 2e^- \qquad E^\circ_{red} = -0.28 \text{ V}}$$

$$2Ag^+(aq) + Ni(s) \rightarrow 2Ag(s) + Ni^{2+}(aq) \quad E^\circ = 0.80 - (-0.28) = 1.08 \text{ V}$$

(b) As the reaction proceeds, $Ni^{2+}(aq)$ is produced, so $[Ni^{2+}]$ increases as the cell operates.

(c) $E = E^\circ - \dfrac{0.0592}{n}\log K; \; 1.12 = 1.08 - \dfrac{0.0592}{2}\log\dfrac{[Ni^{2+}]}{[Ag^+]^2}$

$-\dfrac{0.04(2)}{0.0592} = \log(0.0100) - \log[Ag^+]^2; \; \log[Ag^+]^2 = \log(0.0100) + \dfrac{0.04(2)}{0.0592}$

$\log[Ag^+]^2 = -2.000 + 1.351 = -0.649; \; [Ag^+]^2 = 0.255 \; M; \; [Ag^+] = 0.474 = 0.5 \; M$
(Strictly speaking, $[E - E^\circ]$ having only one sig fig leads (after several steps) to the answer having only one sig fig. This is not a very precise or useful result.)

20.103 (a)

$$I_2(s) + 2e^- \rightarrow 2I^-(aq) \qquad\qquad E^\circ_{red} = 0.536 \text{ V}$$

$$\underline{2[Cu(s) \rightarrow Cu^+(aq) + 1e^-] \qquad E^\circ_{red} = 0.521 \text{ V}}$$

$$I_2(s) + 2Cu(s) \rightarrow 2Cu^+(aq) + 2I^-(aq) \quad E^\circ = 0.536 - 0.521 = 0.015 \text{ V}$$

$E = E^\circ - \dfrac{0.0592}{n}\log Q = 0.015 - \dfrac{0.0592}{2}\log [Cu^+]^2 [I^-]^2$

$E = +0.015 - \dfrac{0.0592}{2}\log (0.25)^2(3.5)^2 = +0.015 + 0.0034 = 0.018 \text{ V}$

(b) Since the cell potential is positive at these concentration conditions, the reaction as written in part (a) is spontaneous in the forward direction. Cu is oxidized and Cu(s) is the anode.

(c) Yes. E° is positive, so Cu is oxidized and Cu(s) is the anode at standard conditions.

(d) $E = 0; \;\; +0.015 = \dfrac{0.0592}{2}\log (0.15)^2 [I^-]^2; \;\; \dfrac{2(0.015)}{0.0592} = \log (0.15)^2 + 2\log [I^-];$

$\log[I^-] = 1.0773 = 1.08; \; [I^-] = 10^{1.08} = 11.95 = 12 \; M \; I^-$

20.104 Use the relationship developed in Solution 20.101 to calculate K from E°. Use data from Appendix E to calculate E° for the disproportionation.

$$Cu^+(aq) + 1e^- \rightarrow Cu(s) \qquad\qquad E^\circ_{red} = 0.521 \text{ V}$$

$$\underline{Cu^+(aq) \rightarrow Cu^{2+}(aq) + 1e^- \qquad E^\circ_{red} = 0.153 \text{ V}}$$

$$2Cu^+(aq) \rightarrow Cu(s) + Cu^{2+}(aq) \qquad E^\circ = 0.521 \text{ V} - 0.153 \text{ V} = 0.368 \text{ V}$$

$E^\circ = \dfrac{0.0592}{n}\log K, \log K = \dfrac{nE^\circ}{0.0592} = \dfrac{1 \times 0.368}{0.0592} = 6.216 = 6.22$

$K = 10^{6.216} = 1.6 \times 10^6$

20.105 (a) In discharge: $Cd(s) + 2NiO(OH)(s) + 2H_2O(l) \rightarrow Cd(OH)_2(s) + 2Ni(OH)_2(s)$
In charging, the reverse reaction occurs.

(b)   E° = 0.49 V – (–0.76 V) = 1.25 V

(c)   The 1.25 V calculated in part (b) is the standard cell potential, E°. The concentrations of reactants and products inside the battery are adjusted so that the cell output is greater than E°. Note that most of the reactants and products are pure solids or liquids, which do not appear in the Q expression. It must be [OH⁻] that is other than 1.0 M, producing an emf of 1.30 rather than 1.25.

(d) $E° = \dfrac{0.0592}{n}\log K; \log k = \dfrac{nE°}{0.0592}$

$\log K = \dfrac{2 \times 1.30}{0.0592} = 43.92 = 43.9; \; K = 8.3 \times 10^{43} = 8 \times 10^{43}$

20.106 (a)   The battery capacity expressed in units of mAh indicates the total amount of electrical charge that can be delivered by the battery.

(b)   Quantity of electrical charge is measured in coulombs, C. C = A - s

$2850 \text{ mAh} \times \dfrac{1\text{ A}}{1000\text{ mA}} \times \dfrac{3600\text{ s}}{\text{h}} \times \dfrac{1\text{ C}}{1\text{ A-s}} = 10{,}260 \text{ C}$

The battery can deliver 10,260 C. Work, electrical or otherwise, is measured in J. J = V × C. If the battery voltage decreases linearly from 1.55 V to 0.80 V, assume an average voltage of 1.175 = 1.2 V.

10, 260 C × 1.175 V = 12,055.5 = 12 × 10³ J = 12 kJ

The total maximum electrical work of the battery is 12 kJ.

(This is 3.3 × 10⁻³ kWh or 3.3 Wh.)

20.107 The ship's hull should be made negative. By keeping an excess of electrons in the metal of the ship, the tendency for iron to undergo oxidation, with release of electrons, is diminished. The ship, as a negatively charged "electrode," becomes the site of reduction, rather than oxidation, in an electrolytic process.

20.108 (a)   Total volume of Cr = 2.5×10^{-4} m × 0.32 m² = 8.0×10^{-5} m³

$\text{mol Cr} = 8.0 \times 10^{-5} \text{ m}^3 \text{ Cr} \times \dfrac{100^3 \text{ cm}^3}{1\text{ m}^3} \times \dfrac{7.20\text{ g Cr}}{1\text{ cm}^3} \times \dfrac{1\text{ mol Cr}}{52.0\text{ g Cr}} = 11.077$

$= 11 \text{ mol Cr}$

The electrode reaction is:

$CrO_4^{2-}(aq) + 4H_2O(l) + 6e^- \rightarrow Cr(s) + 8OH^- (aq)$

$\text{Coulombs required} = 11.077 \text{ mol Cr} \times \dfrac{6\text{ F}}{1\text{ mol Cr}} \times \dfrac{96{,}485\text{ C}}{1\text{ F}} = 6.41 \times 10^6$

$= 6.4 \times 10^6 \text{ C}$

(b) $6.41 \times 10^6 \text{ C} \times \dfrac{1\text{ amp-s}}{1\text{ C}} \times \dfrac{1}{10.0\text{ s}} = 6.4 \times 10^5 \text{ amp}$

(c)   If the cell is 65 efficient, $(6.41 \times 10^6/0.65) = 9.867 \times 10^6 = 9.9 \times 10^6$ C are required to plate the bumper.

$6.0 \text{ V} \times 9.867 \times 10^6 \text{ C} \times \dfrac{1\text{ J}}{1\text{ C-V}} \times \dfrac{1\text{ kWh}}{3.6 \times 10^6 \text{ J}} = 16.445 = 16 \text{ kWh}$

20.109 (a) The standard reduction potential for $H_2O(l)$ is much greater than that of $Mg^{2+}(aq)(-0.83$ V vs. -2.37 V). In aqueous solution, $H_2O(l)$ would be preferentially reduced and no Mg(s) would be obtained.

(b) $97,000 \text{ A} \times 24 \text{ hr} \times \dfrac{3600 \text{ s}}{1 \text{ hr}} \times \dfrac{1 \text{ C}}{1 \text{ A-s}} \times \dfrac{1 \text{ F}}{96,485 \text{ C}} \times \dfrac{1 \text{ mol Mg}}{2 \text{ F}} \times \dfrac{24.31 \text{ g Mg}}{1 \text{ mol Mg}} \times 0.96$

$= 1.0 \times 10^6 \text{ g Mg} = 1.0 \times 10^3 \text{ kg Mg}$

20.110 *Analyze.* Given mass of aluminum desired, applied voltage and electrolysis efficiency, calculate kWh of electricity required. *Plan.* Beginning with mass Al and paying attention to units, calculate coulombs required if the process is 100% efficient. Then, take efficiency into account and then use V, C and the relationship between J and kWh to calculate kWh required. *Solve.*

$1.0 \times 10^3 \text{ kg Al} \times \dfrac{1000 \text{ g}}{1 \text{ kg}} \times \dfrac{1 \text{ mol Al}}{26.98 \text{ g Al}} \times \dfrac{3 \text{ F}}{1 \text{ mol Al}} \times \dfrac{96,485 \text{ C}}{\text{F}} = 1.073 \times 10^{10} = 1.1 \times 10^{10} \text{ C}$

If the cell is 45 efficient, $(1.073 \times 10^{10}/0.45) = 2.384 \times 10^{10} = 2.4 \times 10^{10}$ C are required to plate the bumper.

$4.50 \text{ V} \times 2.384 \times 10^{10} \text{ C} \times \dfrac{1 \text{ J}}{1 \text{ C-V}} \times \dfrac{1 \text{ kWh}}{3.6 \times 10^6 \text{ J}} = 29,801 = 3.0 \times 10^4 \text{ kWh}$

20.111 (a) $7 \times 10^8 \text{ mol } H_2 \times \dfrac{2 \text{ F}}{1 \text{ mol } H_2} \times \dfrac{96,485 \text{ C}}{1 \text{ F}} = 1.35 \times 10^{14} = 1 \times 10^{14} \text{ C}$

(b)
$$2H_2O(l) \rightarrow O_2(g) + 4H^+(aq) + 4e^- \qquad E^o_{red} = 1.23 \text{ V}$$
$$\dfrac{2[2H^+(aq) + 2e^- \rightarrow H_2(g)]}{2H_2O(l) \rightarrow O_2(g) + 2H_2(g)} \qquad \dfrac{E^o_{red} = 0 \text{ V}}{E^o = 0.00 - 1.23 = -1.23 \text{ V}}$$

$P_t = 300 \text{ atm} = P_{O_2} + P_{H_2}$. Since $H_2(g)$ and $O_2(g)$ are generated in a 2:1 mole ratio, $P_{H_2} = 200 \text{ atm}$ and $P_{O_2} = 100 \text{ atm}$.

$E = E^o - \dfrac{0.0592}{4} \log (P_{O_2} \times P_{H_2}^2) = -1.23 \text{ V} - \dfrac{0.0592}{4} \log [100 \times (200)^2]$

$E = -1.23 \text{ V} - 0.100 \text{ V} = -1.33 \text{ V}; E_{min} = 1.33 \text{ V}$

(c) $\text{Energy} = nFE = 2(7 \times 10^8 \text{ mol}) (1.33 \text{ V}) \dfrac{96,485 \text{ J}}{\text{V-mol}} = 1.80 \times 10^{14} = 2 \times 10^{14} \text{ J}$

(d) $1.80 \times 10^{14} \text{ J} \times \dfrac{1 \text{ kWh}}{3.6 \times 10^6 \text{ J}} \times \dfrac{\$0.85}{\text{kWh}} = \$4.24 \times 10^7 = \$4 \times 10^7$

It would cost more than \$40 million for the electricity alone.

Integrative Exercises

20.112 $N_2(g) + 3H_2(g) \rightarrow 2NH_3(g)$

(a) The oxidation number of $H_2(g)$ and $N_2(g)$ is 0. The oxidation number of N in NH_3 is -3, H in NH_3 is $+1$. H_2 is being oxidized and N_2 is being reduced.

(b)   Calculate $\Delta G°$ from $\Delta G_f^°$ values in Appendix C. Use $\Delta G° = -RT \ln K$ to calculate K.

$$\Delta G° = 2\Delta G_f^° \, NH_3(g) - \Delta G_f^° \, N_2(g) - 3\Delta G_f^° \, H_2(g)$$

$$\Delta G° = 2(-16.66 \text{ kJ}) - 0 - 3(0) = -33.32 \text{ kJ}$$

$$\Delta G° = -RT\ln K, \ln K = \frac{-\Delta G°}{RT} = \frac{-(-33.32 \times 10^3 \text{ J})}{(8.314 \text{ J/mol-K})(298 \text{ K})} = 13.4487 = 13.45$$

$$K = e^{13.4487} = 6.9 \times 10^5$$

(c) $\Delta G° = -nfE°; \quad E° = \dfrac{-\Delta G°}{nF}; \quad n = ?$

2 N atoms change from 0 to –3, or 6 H atoms change from 0 to +1.
Either way, $n = 6$.

$$E° = \frac{-(-33.32 \text{ kJ})}{6 \times 96.5 \text{ kJ/V}} = 0.05755 \text{ V}$$

20.113   The redox reaction is: $2Ag^+(aq) + H_2(g) \rightarrow 2Ag(s) + 2H^+(aq)$. $n = 2$ for this reaction.

$$E_{cell}^o = E_{red}^o \text{ cathode} - E_{red}^o \text{ anode} = 0.799 \text{ V} - 0 \text{ V} = 0.799$$

$$E = E° - \frac{0.0592}{n} \log \frac{[H^+]^2}{[Ag^+]^2 \, P_{H_2}}$$

$[H^+]$ in the cell is held essentially constant by the benzoate buffer.

$$C_6H_5COOH(aq) \rightleftharpoons H^+(aq) + C_6H_5COO^-(aq) \quad K_a = ?$$

$$K_a = \frac{[H^+][C_6H_5COO^-]}{[C_6H_5COOH]}; [H^+] = \frac{K_a[C_6H_5COOH]}{[C_6H_5COO^-]} = \frac{0.10 \text{ M}}{0.050 \text{ M}} \times K_a = 2K_a$$

Solve the Nernst expression for $[H^+]$ and calculate K_a and pK_a as shown above.

$$1.030 \text{ V} = 0.799 \text{ V} - \frac{0.0592}{n} \log \frac{[H^+]^2}{(1.00)^2(1.00)}$$

$$0.231 \times \frac{2}{0.0592} = -\log [H^+]^2 = -2 \log[H^+]$$

$$\frac{0.231}{0.0592} = -\log [H^+] = pH; pH = 3.9020 = 3.90; [H^+] = 10^{-3.902} = 1.253 \times 10^{-4} = 1.3 \times 10^{-4};$$

$$[H^+] = 2K_a; K_a = [H^+]/2 = 6.265 \times 10^{-5} = 6.3 \times 10^{-5}; pK_a = 4.20$$

Check. According to Appendix D, K_a for benzoic acid is 6.3×10^{-5}.

20.114   (a)   The oxidation potential of A is equal in magnitude but opposite in sign to the reduction potential of A^+.

(b)   Li(s) has the highest oxidation potential, Au(s) the lowest.

(c)   The relationship is reasonable because both oxidation potential and ionization energy describe removing electrons from a substance. Ionization energy is a property of gas phase atoms or ions, while oxidation potential is a property of the bulk material.

20.115 (a)

$$Ag^+(aq) + e^- \rightarrow Ag(s) \qquad\qquad E^o_{red} = 0.799\ V$$

$$\dfrac{Fe^{2+}(aq) \rightarrow Fe^{3+}(aq) + 1e^- \qquad E^o_{red} = 0.771\ V}{Ag^+(aq) + Fe^{2+}(aq) \rightarrow Ag(s) + Fe^{3+}(aq) \qquad E^o = 0.799\ V - 0.771\ V = 0.028\ V}$$

(b) $Ag^+(aq)$ is reduced at the cathode and $Fe^{2+}(aq)$ is oxidized at the anode.

(c) $\Delta G^o = -nFE^o = -(1)(96.5)(0.028) = -2.7\ kJ$

$\Delta S^o = S^o\ Ag(s) + S^o\ Fe^{3+}(aq) - S^o Ag^+(aq) - S^o\ Fe^{2+}(aq)$

$\qquad = 42.55\ J + 293.3\ J - 73.93\ J - 113.4\ J = 148.5\ J$

$\Delta G^o = \Delta H^o - T\Delta S^o$ Since ΔS^o is positive, ΔG^o will become more negative and E^o will become more positive as temperature is increased.

20.116 (a) $\Delta H^o = 2\Delta H^o\ H_2O(l) - 2\Delta H^o\ H_2(g) - \Delta H^o\ O_2(g) = 2(-285.83) - 2(0) - 0 = -571.66\ kJ$

$\Delta S^o = 2S^o\ H_2O(l) - 2S^o\ H_2(g) - \Delta S^o\ O_2(g)$

$\qquad = 2(69.91) - 2(130.58) - (205.0) = -326.34\ J$

(b) Since ΔS^o is negative, $-T\Delta S$ is positive and the value of ΔG will become more positive as T increases. The reaction will become nonspontaneous at a fairly low temperature, because the magnitude of ΔS^o is large.

(c) $\Delta G = w_{max}$. The larger the negative value of ΔG, the more work the system is capable of doing on the surroundings. As the magnitude of ΔG decreases with increasing temperature, the usefulness of H_2 as a fuel decreases.

(d) The combustion method increases the temperature of the system, which quickly decreases the magnitude of the work that can be done by the system. Even if the effect of temperature on this reaction could be controlled, only about 40% of the energy from any combustion can be converted to electrical energy, so combustion is intrinsically less efficient than direct production of electrical energy via a fuel cell.

20.117 First balance the equation:

$4CyFe^{2+}(aq) + O_2(g) + 4H^+(aq) \rightarrow 4CyFe^{3+}(aq) + 2H_2O(l);\ E = +0.60\ V;\ n = 4$

(a) From Equation [20.11] we can calculate ΔG for the process under the conditions specified for the measured potential E:

$$\Delta G = -nFE = -(4\ mol\ e^-) \times \dfrac{96.485\ kJ}{1\ V\text{-}mol\ e^-}(0.60\ V) = -231.6 = -232\ kJ$$

(b) The moles of ATP synthesized per mole of O_2 is given by:

$$\dfrac{231.6\ kJ}{O_2\ molecule} \times \dfrac{1\ mol\ ATP\ formed}{37.7\ kJ} = \text{approximately 6 mol ATP/mol } O_2$$

20.118 $AgSCN(s) + e^- \rightarrow Ag(s) + SCN^-(aq)$ $E^o_{red} = 0.0895$ V

$\underline{\qquad Ag(s) \rightarrow Ag^+(aq) + e^- \qquad\qquad E^o_{red} = 0.799 \text{ V} \qquad}$

$AgSCN(s) \rightarrow Ag^+(aq) + SCN^-(aq)$ $E^o = 0.0895 - 0.799 = -0.710$ V

$$E^o = \frac{0.0592}{n} \log K_{sp}; \; \log K_{sp} = \frac{(-0.710)(1)}{0.0592} = -11.993 = -12.0$$

$$K_{sp} = 10^{-11.993} = 1.02 \times 10^{-12} = 1 \times 10^{-12}$$

20.119   The reaction can be written as a sum of the steps:

$Pb^{2+}(aq) + 2e^- \rightarrow Pb(s)$ $E^o_{red} = -0.126$ V

$\underline{\qquad PbS(s) \rightarrow Pb^{2+}(aq) + S^{2-}(aq) \qquad\qquad "E^o" = ? \qquad}$

$PbS(s) + 2e^- \rightarrow Pb(s) + S^{2-}(aq)$ $E^o_{red} = ?$

"E^o" for the second step can be calculated from K_{sp}.

$$E^o = \frac{0.0592}{n} \log K_{sp} = \frac{0.0592}{2} \log(8.0 \times 10^{-28}) = \frac{0.0592}{2}(-27.10) = -0.802 \text{ V}$$

E^o for the half-reaction = -0.126 V + $(-0.802$ V) = -0.928 V

Calculating an imaginary E^o for a nonredox process like step 2 may be a disturbing idea. Alternatively, one could calculate K for step 1 (5.4×10^{-5}), K for the reaction in question (K = $K_1 \times K_{sp} = 4.4 \times 10^{-32}$) and then E^o for the half-reaction. The result is the same.

20.120   The two half-reactions in the electrolysis of $H_2O(l)$ are:

$2[2H_2O(l) + 2e^- \rightarrow H_2(g) + 2OH^-]$

$\underline{2H_2O(l) \rightarrow O_2(g) + 4H^+ + 4e^-}$

$2H_2O(l) \rightarrow 2H_2(g) + O_2(g)$

4 mol e^-/2 mol $H_2(g)$ or 2 mol e^-/mol $H_2(g)$

Using partial pressures and the ideal-gas law, calculate the mol $H_2(g)$ produced, and the current required to do so.

$P_t = P_{H_2} + P_{H_2O}$. From Appendix B, P_{H_2O} at 25.5 °C is approximately 24.5 torr.

$P_{H_2} = 768 \text{ torr} - 24.5 \text{ torr} = 743.5 = 744$ torr

$$n = PV/RT = \frac{(743.5/760) \text{ atm} \times 0.0123 \text{ L}}{298.5 \text{ K} \times 0.08206 \text{ L-atm/mol-K}} = 4.912 \times 10^{-4} = 4.91 \times 10^{-4} \text{ mol } H_2$$

$$4.912 \times 10^{-4} \text{ mol } H_2 \times \frac{2 \text{ mol } e^-}{\text{mol } H_2} \times \frac{96,485 \text{ C}}{1 \text{ mol } e^-} \times \frac{1 \text{ amp-s}}{1 \text{ C}} \times \frac{1 \text{ min}}{60 \text{ s}} \times \frac{1}{2.00 \text{ min}} = 0.790 \text{ amp}$$

21 Nuclear Chemistry

Visualizing Concepts

21.1 *Analyze.* Given the name and mass number of a nuclide, decide if it lies within the belt of stability. If not, suggest a process that moves it toward the belt.

Plan. Calculate the number of protons and neutrons in each nuclide. Locate this point on Figure 21.2. If the point is above the belt, β-decay increases protons and decreases neutrons, decreasing the neutron-to-proton ratio. If the point is below the belt, either positron emission or neutron capture decreases protons and increases neutrons, increasing the neutron-to-proton ratio. *Solve.*

(a) ^{24}Ne: 10 p, 14 n, just above the belt of stability. Reduce the neutron-to proton ratio via β-decay.

(b) ^{32}Cl: 17 p, 15 n, just below the belt of stability. Increase the neutron-to-proton ratio via positron emission or orbital electron capture.

(c) ^{108}Sn: 50 p, 58 n, just below the belt of stability. Increase the neutron-to-proton ratio via positron emission or orbital electron capture.

(d) ^{216}Po: 84 p, 132 n, just beyond the belt of stability. Nuclei with atomic numbers ≥ 84 tend to decay via alpha emission, which decreases both protons and neutrons.

21.2 *Analyze/Plan.* From the diagram, determine the atomic number (number of protons) and mass number (number of protons plus neutrons) of the two nuclides involved. Based on the relationship between the two nuclides, decide whether the reaction is α or β-decay, positron emission or electron capture. Complete the nuclear reaction, balancing atomic numbers and mass numbers.

Solve. The two nuclides in the diagram are $^{109}_{46}$Pd and $^{109}_{47}$Ag so the second product is a β-particle. The balanced reaction is:

$$^{109}_{46}\text{Pd} \rightarrow {}^{109}_{47}\text{Ag} + {}^{0}_{-1}\text{e}$$

Check. Atomic number and mass number balance.

21.3 *Analyze/Plan.* Determine the number of protons and neutrons present in the two heavy nuclides in the reaction. Draw a graph with appropriate limits and plot the two points. Draw an arrow from reactant to product. *Solve.*

Bi: 83 p, 128 n; Tl: 81 p, 126 n.

Check. An α-particle has 2 p and 2 n. The diagram shows a decrease in 2 p and 2 n for the reaction.

21.4   *Analyze/Plan.* Write the balanced equation for the decay. Nuclear decay is a first-order process; use appropriate relationships for first-order processes to determine $t_{1/2}$, k and remaining ^{88}Mo after 12 minutes.   *Solve.*

     (a) $t_{1/2}$ is the time required for half of the original nuclide to decay. Relative to the graph, this is the time when the amount of ^{88}Mo is reduced from 1.0 to 0.5. This time is 7 minutes.

     (b)   For a first-order process, $t_{1/2} = 0.693/k$ or $k = 0.693/t_{1/2}$.

           $k = 0.693/7 \text{ min} = 0.0990 = 0.1 \text{ min}^{-1}$

     (c)   From the graph, the fraction of ^{88}Mo remaining after 12 min is 0.3/1.0 = 0.3

           Check. $\ln(N_t/N_o) = -kt = -(0.099)(12) = -1.188$; $N_t/N_o = e^{-1.188} = 0.30$.

     (d) $^{88}_{42}\text{Mo} \rightarrow {}^{88}_{41}\text{Nb} + {}^{0}_{1}\text{e}$

21.5   *Analyze/Plan.* Atomic number is number of protons, mass number is (protons + neutrons). Chemical symbol is determined by atomic number. Beta decay increases the number of protons while mass number stays constant. Positron emission decreases the number of protons while mass number stays constant. Half-life, $t_{1/2}$, is the time required to reduce the amount of radioactive material by half. *Solve.*

     (a) $^{10}_{5}\text{B}, {}^{11}_{5}\text{B}; \quad {}^{12}_{6}\text{C}, {}^{13}_{6}\text{C}; \quad {}^{14}_{7}\text{N}, {}^{15}_{7}\text{N}; \quad {}^{16}_{8}\text{O}, {}^{17}_{8}\text{O}, {}^{18}_{8}\text{O}; \quad {}^{19}_{9}\text{F}$

     (b)   On the diagram, $^{14}_{6}\text{C}$ is the only radioactive nuclide above and left of the band of stable red nuclides. $^{14}_{6}\text{C}$ will reduce its neutron-to-proton ratio by β-decay.

           $^{14}_{6}\text{C} \rightarrow {}^{14}_{7}\text{N} + {}^{0}_{-1}\text{e}$

     (c)   On the diagram, radioactive nuclides right and below the band of stable red nuclides are likely to increase their neutron-to-proton ratio via positron emission. In order to be useful for positron emission tomography, the nuclides must have a half-life on the order of minutes. (Nuclides with very fast decay disappear before they can be imaged. Those with longer half-lives linger in the patient.) Four radioactive nuclides fit these criteria: $^{11}_{6}\text{C}$, $^{13}_{7}\text{N}$, $^{15}_{8}\text{O}$, $^{18}_{9}\text{F}$

(d)   A reduction of 12.5% in amount or concentration of a radionuclide amounts to three half-lives. If the total decay time is 1 hour, 1/3 of this time is 20 min. The radionuclide with a half-life of 20 min is $^{11}_{6}C$.

21.6   *Analyze/Plan.* Express the particles in the diagram as a nuclear reaction. Determine the mass number and atomic number of the unknown particle by balancing these quantities in the nuclear reaction.   *Solve.*

(a) $^{239}_{94}Pu + ^{1}_{0}n \rightarrow ^{95}_{40}Zr + ? + 2\,^{1}_{0}n$

The unidentified particle has an atomic number of $(94 - 40) = 54$; it is Xe. The mass number of the nuclide is $[(239 + 1) - (95 + 2)] = 143$. The unknown particle is $^{143}_{54}Xe$.

(b) ^{95}Zr: 40 p, 55 n is stable. ^{143}Xe: 54 p, 89 n is above the belt of stability and is not stable; it will probably undergo β-decay.

Radioactivity (section 21.1)

21.7   *Analyze/Plan.* Given various nuclide descriptions, determine the number of protons and neutrons in each nuclide. The left superscript is the mass number, protons plus neutrons. If there is a left subscript, it is the atomic number, the number of protons. Protons can always be determined from chemical symbol; all isotopes of the same element have the same number of protons. A number following the element name, as in part (c) is the mass number.   *Solve.*

p = protons, n = neutrons, e = electrons; number of protons = atomic number; number of neutrons = mass number – atomic number

(a) $^{55}_{25}Mn$: 25p, 30n   (b) ^{201}Hg: 80p, 121n   (c) ^{39}K: 19p, 20n

21.8   p = protons, n = neutrons, e = electrons; number of protons = atomic number; number of neutrons = mass number – atomic number

(a) $^{124}_{52}Te$: 52p, 72n   (b) ^{37}Cl: 17p, 20n   (c) ^{232}Th: 90p, 142n

21.9   *Analyze/Plan.* See definitions in Section 21.1. In each case, the left superscript is mass number, the left subscript is related to atomic number.   *Solve.*

(a) $^{1}_{0}n$ (b) $^{4}_{2}He$ or α (c) $^{0}_{0}\gamma$ or γ

21.10   (a) $^{1}_{1}p$ or $^{1}_{1}H$ (b) $^{0}_{-1}e$ or $^{0}_{-1}\beta$ (c) $^{0}_{1}e$

21.11   *Analyze/Plan.* Follow the logic in Sample Exercises 21.1 and 21.2. Pay attention to definitions of decay particles and conservation of mass and charge.   *Solve.*

(a) $^{90}_{37}Rb \rightarrow ^{90}_{38}Sr + ^{0}_{-1}e$ (b) $^{72}_{34}Se + ^{0}_{-1}e$ (orbital electron) $\rightarrow ^{72}_{33}As$

(c) $^{76}_{36}Kr \rightarrow ^{76}_{35}Br + ^{0}_{1}e$ (d) $^{226}_{88}Ra \rightarrow ^{222}_{86}Rn + ^{4}_{2}He$

21.12   (a) $^{213}_{83}Bi \rightarrow ^{209}_{81}Tl + ^{4}_{2}He$ (b) $^{13}_{7}N + ^{0}_{-1}e$ (orbital electron) $\rightarrow ^{13}_{6}C$

(c) $^{98}_{43}Tc + ^{0}_{-1}e$ (orbital electron) $\rightarrow ^{98}_{42}Mo$ (d) $^{188}_{79}Au \rightarrow ^{188}_{78}Pt + ^{0}_{1}e$

21.13   *Analyze/Plan.* Using definitions of the decay processes and conservation of mass number and atomic number, work backwards to the reactants in the nuclear reactions.

Solve.

(a) $^{211}_{82}Pb \rightarrow ^{211}_{83}Bi + ^{0}_{-1}\beta$

(b) $^{50}_{25}Mn \rightarrow ^{50}_{24}Cr + ^{0}_{1}e$

(c) $^{179}_{74}W + ^{0}_{-1}e \rightarrow ^{179}_{73}Ta$

(d) $^{230}_{90}Th \rightarrow ^{226}_{88}Ra + ^{4}_{2}He$

21.14   (a) $^{24}_{11}Na \rightarrow ^{24}_{12}Mg + ^{0}_{-1}e$; a β particle is produced

(b) $^{188}_{80}Hg \rightarrow ^{188}_{79}Au + ^{0}_{1}e$; a positron is produced

(c) $^{122}_{53}I \rightarrow ^{122}_{54}Xe + ^{0}_{-1}e$; a β particle is produced

(d) $^{242}_{94}Pu \rightarrow ^{238}_{92}U + ^{4}_{2}He$; an α particle is produced

21.15   *Analyze/Plan.* Given the starting and ending nuclides in a nuclear decay sequence, we are asked to determine the number of alpha and beta emissions. Use the total change in A and Z, along with definitions of alpha and beta decay, to answer the question. *Solve.*

The total mass number change is (235–207) = 28. Since each α particle emission decreases the mass number by four, whereas emission of a β particle does not correspond to a mass change, there are 7 α particle emissions. The change in atomic number in the series is 10. Each α particle results in an atomic number lower by two. The 7 α particle emissions alone would cause a decrease of 14 in atomic number. Each β particle emission raises the atomic number by one. To obtain the observed lowering of 10 in the series, there must be 4 β emissions.

21.16   This decay series represents a change of (232–208 =) 24 mass units. Since only alpha emissions change the nuclear mass, and each changes the mass by four, there must be a total of 6 α emissions. Each alpha emission causes a decrease of two in atomic number.

Therefore, the 6 alpha emissions, by themselves, would cause a decrease in atomic number of 12. The series as a whole involves a decrease of 8 in atomic number. Thus, there must be a total of 4 β emissions, each of which increases atomic number by one. Overall, there are 6 α emissions and 4 β emissions.

Nuclear Stability (section 21.2)

21.17   *Analyze/Plan.* Follow the logic in Sample Exercise 21.3, paying attention to the guidelines for neutron-to-proton ratio. *Solve.*

(a) $^{8}_{5}B$ - low neutron/proton ratio, positron emission (for low atomic numbers, positron emission is more common than orbital electron capture)

(b) $^{68}_{29}Cu$ - high neutron/proton ratio, beta emission

(c) $^{32}_{15}P$ - slightly high neutron/proton ratio, beta emission

(d) $^{39}_{17}Cl$ - high neutron/proton ratio, beta emission

21.18   (a) $^{3}_{1}H$ - high neutron/proton ratio, beta emission

(b) $^{89}_{38}Sr$ - (slightly) high neutron/proton ratio, beta emission

(c) $^{120}_{53}$I - low neutron/proton ratio, positron emission

(d) $^{102}_{47}$Ag - low neutron/proton ratio, positron emission

21.19   *Analyze/Plan.* Use the criteria listed in Table 21.4.   *Solve.*

(a)   Stable: $^{39}_{19}$K   odd proton, even neutron more abundant than odd proton, odd neutron; 20 neutrons is a magic number.

(b)   Stable: $^{209}_{83}$Bi   odd proton, even neutron more abundant than odd proton, odd neutron; 126 neutrons is a magic number.

(c)   Stable: $^{58}_{28}$Ni   even proton, even neutron more likely to be stable than even proton, odd neutron; $^{65}_{28}$Ni has high neutron/proton ratio

21.20   Use criteria listed in Table 21.4.

(a) $^{40}_{20}$Ca ; stable, magic numbers of protons and neutrons

        $^{45}_{20}$Ca , radioactive, high neutron/proton ratio.

(b) $^{12}_{6}$C , stable, even proton, even neutron

        $^{14}_{6}$C , radioactive, high neutron/proton ratio

(c) $^{206}_{82}$Pb , stable, magic number of protons, even proton, even neutron

        $^{230}_{90}$Th , radioactive, atomic number greater than 84

21.21   *Analyze/Plan.* For each nuclide, determine the number of protons and neutrons and decide if they are magic numbers.   *Solve.*

(a) $^{4}_{2}$He , both   (b) $^{18}_{8}$O has a magic number of protons, but not neutrons

(c) $^{40}_{20}$Ca , both   (d) $^{66}_{30}$Zn has neither   (e) $^{208}_{82}$Pb , both

21.22   The high points on the graph all correspond to elements with even atomic numbers. Stable isotopes of elements with even numbers of protons are much more abundant than isotopes of elements with odd atomic numbers. If radioactive isotopes of elements with odd atomic numbers were once abundant, they would have decayed to more stable nuclides.

21.23   Consider the stability of the two emitted particles. The alpha particle, $^{4}_{2}$He , has a magic number of both protons and neutrons. The proton bas no magic numbers, and is an odd proton – even neutron particle. The alpha is a very stable emitted particle, Twhich makes alpha emission a favorable process. The proton is not a stable emitted particle and its formation does not encourage proton emission as a process.

21.24   The criterion employed in judging whether the nucleus is likely to be radioactive is the position of the nucleus on the plot shown in Figure 21.2. If the neutron/proton ratio is too high or low, or if the atomic number exceeds 83, the nucleus will be radioactive.

Radioactive: $^{58}_{29}\text{Cu}$ — odd proton, odd neutron, low neutron/proton ratio

^{206}Po — high atomic number

Stable: $^{62}_{28}\text{Ni}$ — even proton, even neutron, stable neutron/proton ratio

$^{108}_{47}\text{Ag}$ — stable neutron/proton ratio, (one of 5 stable odd proton/odd neutron nuclides)

^{184}W — even proton, even neutron, stable neutron/proton ratio

Nuclear Transmutations (section 21.3)

21.25   Protons and alpha particles are positively charged and must be moving very fast to overcome electrostatic forces which would repel them from the target nucleus. Neutrons are electrically neutral and not repelled by the nucleus.

21.26   The element is technetium, Tc. $^{96}_{42}\text{Mo} + ^{2}_{1}\text{H} \rightarrow ^{98}_{43}\text{Tc}$

21.27   *Analyze/Plan.* Determine A and Z for the missing particle by conservation principles. Find the appropriate symbol for the particle.   *Solve.*

     (a) $^{252}_{98}\text{Cf} + ^{10}_{5}\text{B} \rightarrow 3\,^{1}_{0}\text{n} + ^{259}_{103}\text{Lr}$ (b) $^{2}_{1}\text{H} + ^{3}_{2}\text{He} \rightarrow ^{4}_{2}\text{He} + ^{1}_{1}\text{H}$

     (c) $^{1}_{1}\text{H} + ^{11}_{5}\text{B} \rightarrow 3\,^{4}_{2}\text{He}$ (d) $^{122}_{53}\text{I} \rightarrow ^{122}_{54}\text{Xe} + ^{0}_{-1}\text{e}$

     (e) $^{59}_{26}\text{Fe} \rightarrow ^{0}_{-1}\text{e} + ^{59}_{27}\text{Co}$

21.28   (a) $^{14}_{7}\text{N} + ^{4}_{2}\text{He} \rightarrow ^{17}_{8}\text{O} + ^{1}_{1}\text{H}$ (b) $^{40}_{19}\text{K} + ^{0}_{-1}\text{e (orbital electron)} \rightarrow ^{40}_{18}\text{Ar}$

          (c) $^{27}_{13}\text{Al} + ^{4}_{2}\text{He} \rightarrow ^{30}_{14}\text{Si} + ^{1}_{1}\text{H}$ (d) $^{58}_{26}\text{Fe} + 2\,^{1}_{0}\text{n} \rightarrow ^{0}_{-1}\text{e} + ^{60}_{27}\text{Co}$

          (e) $^{235}_{92}\text{U} + ^{1}_{0}\text{n} \rightarrow ^{135}_{54}\text{Xe} + ^{99}_{38}\text{Sr} + 2\,^{1}_{0}\text{n}$

21.29   *Analyze/Plan.* Follow the logic in Sample Exercise 21.5, paying attention to conservation of A and Z.   *Solve.*

     (a) $^{238}_{92}\text{U} + ^{4}_{2}\text{He} \rightarrow ^{241}_{94}\text{Pu} + ^{1}_{0}\text{n}$ (b) $^{14}_{7}\text{N} + ^{4}_{2}\text{He} \rightarrow ^{17}_{8}\text{O} + ^{1}_{1}\text{H}$

     (c) $^{56}_{26}\text{Fe} + ^{4}_{2}\text{He} \rightarrow ^{60}_{29}\text{Cu} + ^{0}_{-1}\text{e}$

21.30   (a) $^{238}_{92}\text{U} + ^{1}_{0}\text{n} \rightarrow ^{239}_{92}\text{U} + ^{0}_{0}\gamma$ (b) $^{14}_{7}\text{N} + ^{1}_{1}\text{H} \rightarrow ^{11}_{6}\text{C} + ^{4}_{2}\text{He}$

          (c) $^{18}_{8}\text{O} + ^{1}_{0}\text{n} \rightarrow ^{19}_{9}\text{F} + ^{0}_{-1}\text{e}$

Rates of Radioactive Decay (section 21.4)

21.31   (a)   True. $k = 0.693/t_{1/2}$. The decay rate constant, k, and half-life, $t_{1/2}$ are inversely related.

          (b)   False. If X is not radioactive, it does not spontaneously decay and its half-life is essentially infinity.

(c) True. Changes in the amount of A would be measurable over the 40-year time frame, while changes in the amount of X would be very small and difficult to detect.

21.32 (a) The suggestion is not reasonable. The energies of nuclear states are very large relative to ordinary temperatures. Thus, merely changing the temperature by less than 100 K would not be expected to significantly affect the behavior of nuclei with regard to nuclear decay rates.

(b) No. Radioactive decay has no activation energy like a chemical reaction. Activation energy is the minimum amount of energy required to initiate a chemical reaction. Radioactive decay is a spontaneous nuclear transformation from a less stable to a more stable nuclear configuration. Radioisotopes are by definition in a "transition state," prone to nuclear change or decay. Changes in external conditions such as temperature, pressure or chemical state provide insufficient energy to either excite or relax an unstable nucleus.

21.33 *Analyze/Plan.* The half-life is 12.3 yr. Use $t_{1/2}$ to calculate k and the mass fraction (N_t/N_0) remaining after 50 yr.

Solve. $k = 0.693 / t_{1/2} = 0.693/12.3 \text{ yr} = 0.056341 = 0.0563 \text{ yr}^{-1}$

$\ln\dfrac{N_t}{N_0} = -kt; \quad \ln\dfrac{N_t}{N_0} = -0.056341 \text{ yr}^{-1}(50\text{yr}) = -2.81707 = -2.8; \quad \dfrac{N_t}{N_0} = 0.05978 = 0.06$

When the watch is 50 years old, only 6% (or 6.0%) of the tritium remains. The dial will be dimmed by 94%.

21.34 Calculate the decay constant, k, and then $t_{1/2}$.

$k = \dfrac{-1}{t}\ln\dfrac{N_t}{N_o} = \dfrac{-1}{5.2 \text{ min}}\ln\dfrac{0.250 \text{ g}}{1.000 \text{ g}} = 0.2666 = 0.27 \text{ min}^{-1}$

Using Equation [21.20], $t_{1/2} = 0.693/k = 0.693/0.02666 \text{ min}^{-1} = 2.599 = 2.6 \text{ min}$

21.35 *Analyze/Plan.* We are given half-life of cobalt-60, and replacement time when the activity of the sample is 75% of the initial value. Consider the rate law for (first-order) nuclear decay: $\ln(N_t/N_o) = -kt$. *Solve.*

$k = 0.693 / t_{1/2} = 0.693/5.26 \text{ yr} = 0.1317 = 0.132 \text{ yr}^{-1}; \quad N_t/N_o = 0.75$

$t = \dfrac{-1}{k}\ln\dfrac{N_t}{N_o} = -(1/0.1317 \text{ yr}^{-1})\ln(0.75) = 2.18 \text{ yr} = 26.2 \text{ mo} = 797 \text{ d}.$

The source would have been replaced sometime in the summer of 2012, probably in August.

21.36 Follow the logic in Sample Exercise 21.7. In this case, we are given initial sample mass as well as mass at time t, so we can proceed directly to calculate k (Equation [21.20], and then t (Equation [21.19]). *Solve.*

$k = 0.693 / t_{1/2} = 0.693/27.8 \text{ d} = 0.02493 = 0.0249 \text{ d}^{-1}$

$t = \dfrac{-1}{k}\ln\dfrac{N_t}{N_o} = \dfrac{-1}{0.02493 \text{ d}^{-1}}\ln\dfrac{0.75}{6.25} = 85.06 = 85 \text{ d}$

21.37 (a) *Analyze/Plan.* $^{226}_{88}\text{Ra} \rightarrow {}^{222}_{86}\text{Rn} + {}^{4}_{2}\text{He}$

1 α particle is produced for each ^{226}Ra that decays. Rate = kN. Calculate the number of ^{226}Ra particles in the 10.0 mg sample. Calculate $t_{1/2}$ and k in min, then rate in dis/min, then the number of disintegrations in 5.0 min. *Solve.*

$$10.0 \text{ mg Ra} \times \frac{1\text{ g}}{1000\text{ mg}} \times \frac{1\text{ mol Ra}}{226\text{ g Ra}} \times \frac{6.022 \times 10^{23}\text{ Ra atoms}}{1\text{ mol Ra}} = 2.6646 \times 10^{19} = 2.66 \times 10^{19} \text{ atoms}$$

Calculate k in min^{-1}. $1600 \text{ yr} \times \frac{365\text{ d}}{1\text{ yr}} \times \frac{24\text{ hr}}{1\text{ d}} \times \frac{60\text{ min}}{1\text{ hr}} = 8.410 \times 10^8 \text{ min}^{-1}$

$$k = \frac{0.693}{t_{1/2}} = \frac{0.693}{8.410 \times 10^8 \text{ min}} = 8.241 \times 10^{-10} \text{ min}^{-1}$$

Rate = kN = $(8.241 \times 10^{-10} \text{ min}^{-1})(2.6646 \times 10^{19} \text{ atoms}) = 2.20 \times 10^{10} \text{ atoms/min}$

$(2.20 \times 10^{10} \text{ atoms/min})(5.0 \text{ min}) = 1.1 \times 10^{11} \; {}^{226}\text{Ra atoms decay in 5.0 min}$

1.1×10^{11} α particles emitted in 5.0 min

(b) *Plan.* From part (a), the rate is 2.20×10^{10} disintegrations/min. Change this to dis/s and apply the definition 1 Ci = 3.7×10^{10} dis/s.

$$\frac{2.20 \times 10^{10} \text{ dis}}{1\text{ min}} \times \frac{1\text{ min}}{60\text{ s}} \times \frac{1\text{ Ci}}{3.7 \times 10^{10}\text{ dis/s}} \times \frac{1000\text{ mCi}}{\text{Ci}} = 9.891 = 9.9 \text{ mCi}$$

21.38 (a) Proceeding as in Solution 21.37, calculate number of ^{60}Co atoms and k in s^{-1}.

$$3.75 \text{ mg Co} \times \frac{1\text{ g}}{1000\text{ mg}} \times \frac{1\text{ mol Co}}{60\text{ g Co}} \times \frac{6.022 \times 10^{23}\text{ Co atoms}}{1\text{ mol Co}} = 3.76375 \times 10^{19} = 3.76 \times 10^{19}$$

$$5.26 \text{ yr} \times \frac{365\text{ d}}{1\text{ yr}} \times \frac{24\text{ hr}}{1\text{ d}} \times \frac{3600\text{ sec}}{1\text{ hr}} = 1.659 \times 10^8 = 1.66 \times 10^8 \text{ s}$$

$$k = \frac{0.693}{t_{1/2}} = \frac{0.693}{1.659 \times 10^8} = 4.178 \times 10^{-9} = 4.18 \times 10^{-9} \text{ s}^{-1}$$

Rate = kN = $(4.178 \times 10^{-9} \text{ s}^{-1})(3.76375 \times 10^{19} \text{ atoms}) = 1.57 \times 10^{11} \text{ atoms/s}$

$(1.57 \times 10^{11} \text{ atoms/s})(600 \text{ s}) = 9.43 \times 10^{13} \; {}^{60}\text{Co atoms decay in 600 s}$

9.43×10^{13} β particles emitted by a 3.75 mg sample in 600 s

(b) $\dfrac{1.57 \times 10^{11} \text{ dis}}{\text{s}} \times \dfrac{1\text{ Bq}}{1\text{ dis/s}} = 1.57 \times 10^{11} \text{ Bq}$

The activity of the sample is 1.57×10^{11} Bq.

21.39 *Analyze/Plan.* Calculate k in yr^{-1} and solve Equation [21.19] for t. $N_o = 16.3/min/g$, $N_t = 9.7/min/g$. *Solve.*

$k = 0.693/t_{1/2} = 0.693/5715$ yr $= 1.213 \times 10^{-4} = 1.21 \times 10^{-4}$ yr^{-1}

$t = \dfrac{-1}{k} \ln \dfrac{N_t}{N_o} = \dfrac{-1}{1.213 \times 10^{-4} \ yr^{-1}} \ln \dfrac{9.7}{16.3} = 4.280 \times 10^3 = 4.3 \times 10^3$ yr

21.40 Follow the logic in Sample Exercise 21.7.

$t = \dfrac{-1}{k} \ln \dfrac{N_t}{N_o}; k = 0.693/5715$ yr $= 1.213 \times 10^{-4}$ yr^{-1}

$t = \dfrac{-1}{1.213 \times 10^{-4} \ yr^{-1}} \ln \dfrac{38.0}{58.2} = 3.52 \times 10^3$ yr

21.41 *Analyze/Plan.* Follow the procedure outlined in Sample Exercise 21.7. If the mass of ^{40}Ar is 4.2 times that of ^{40}K, the original mass of ^{40}K must have been 4.2 + 1 = 5.2 times the amount of ^{40}K present now. *Solve.*

$k = 0.693/1.27 \times 10^9$ yr $= 5.457 \times 10^{-10} = 5.46 \times 10^{-10}$ yr^{-1}

$t = \dfrac{-1}{5.457 \times 10^{-10} \ yr^{-1}} \times \ln \dfrac{1}{(5.2)} = 3.0 \times 10^9$ yr

21.42 Follow the procedure outlined in Sample Exercise 21.7. The original quantity of ^{238}U is 75.0 mg plus the amount that gave rise to 18.0 mg of ^{206}Pb. This amount is 18.0(238/206) = 20.8 mg.

$k = 0.693/4.5 \times 10^9$ yr $= 1.54 \times 10^{-10} = 1.5 \times 10^{-10}$ yr^{-1}

$t = \dfrac{-1}{k} \ln \dfrac{N_t}{N_o} = \dfrac{-1}{1.54 \times 10^{-10} \ yr^{-1}} \ln \dfrac{75.0}{95.8} = 1.59 \times 10^9$ yr

Energy Changes (section 21.6)

21.43 *Analyze/Plan.* Given a particle reaction, calculate Δm and ΔE. An α particle is ^4_2He. Use Equation [21.22], $E = mc^2$. Compare the calculated energy to the energy given off by the thermite reaction. *Solve.*

$2 \, ^1_1p + 2 \, ^1_0n \rightarrow \, ^4_2He$

Δm = mass of individual protons and neutrons – mass of ^4_2He

$\Delta m = 2(1.0072765 \text{ amu}) + 2(1.0086649 \text{ amu}) - 4.0015 \text{ amu} = 0.030383 = 0.0304$ amu

The mass change for the formation of 1 mol of ^4_2He can be expressed as 0.0304 g.

$\Delta E = c^2 \Delta m$; $1 J = kg \text{-} m^2/s^2$

$\Delta E = 0.030383 \text{ g} \times \dfrac{1 \, kg}{1000 \, g} \times (2.9979 \times 10^8 \text{ m/s})^2 = \dfrac{2.73 \times 10^{12} \, kg \text{-} m^2}{s^2} = 2.73 \times 10^{12}$ J

The energy released when one mole of Fe_2O_3 reacts is or 8.515×10^5 J. The energy released when one mole of ^4_2He is formed from protons and neutrons is 2.73×10^{12} J. This is 3×10^6 or 3 million times as much energy as the thermite reaction.

21.44 $\Delta E = c^2 \Delta m = (2.9979246 \times 10^8 \text{ m/s})^2 \times 0.1 \text{ mg} \times \dfrac{1 \text{ g}}{1000 \text{ mg}} \times \dfrac{1 \text{ kg}}{1000 \text{ g}} \times \dfrac{1 \text{ kJ}}{1000 \text{ J}} = 9 \times 10^6 \text{ kJ}$

21.45   *Analyze/Plan.* Given the mass of an ^{27}Al atom, subtract the mass of 13 electrons to get the mass of an ^{27}Al nucleus. Calculate the mass difference between the ^{27}Al nucleus and the separate nucleons, convert this to energy using Equation [21.22]. Use the molar mass of ^{27}Al to calculate the energy required for 100 g of ^{27}Al. *Solve.*

The mass of an electron is 5.485799×10^{-4} amu (inside back cover of the text). The mass of a ^{27}Al nucleus is then 26.9815386 amu $-13(5.485799 \times 10^{-4}$ amu $) = 26.9744071$ amu. $\Delta m = 13(1.0072765 \text{ amu}) + 14(1.0086649 \text{ amu}) - 26.9744071 \text{ amu} = 0.2414960$ amu.

$$\Delta E = (2.9979246 \times 10^8 \text{ m/s})^2 \times 0.2414960 \text{ amu} \times \frac{1 \text{ g}}{6.0221421 \times 10^{23} \text{ amu}} \times \frac{1 \text{ kg}}{1 \times 10^{23} \text{ g}}$$

$= 3.604129 \times 10^{-11} = 3.604129 \times 10^{-11}$ J/^{27}Al nucleus required

If the mass change for a single ^{27}Al nucleus is 0.2414960 amu, the mass change for 1 mole of ^{27}Al is 0.2414960 g.

$$\Delta E = 100 \text{ g } ^{27}\text{Al} \times \frac{1 \text{ mol } ^{27}\text{Al}}{26.9815386 \text{ g } ^{27}\text{Al}} \times \frac{0.241960}{\text{mol } ^{27}\text{Al}} \times \frac{1 \text{ kg}}{1000 \text{ g}} \times (2.9979246 \times 10^8 \text{ m/s})^2$$

$= 8.044234 \times 10^{13} \text{ J} = 8.044234 \times 10^{10} \text{ kJ}/100 \text{ g } ^{27}\text{Al}$

21.46 Δm = mass of individual protons and neutrons – mass of nucleus

$\Delta m = 10(1.0072765 \text{ amu}) + 11(1.0086649 \text{ amu}) - 20.98846 \text{ amu} = 0.1796189 = 0.17962$ amu

$$\Delta E = (2.9979246 \times 10^8 \text{ m/s})^2 \times 0.1796189 \text{ amu} \times \frac{1 \text{ g}}{6.0221421 \times 10^{23} \text{ amu}} \times \frac{1 \text{ kg}}{1000 \text{ g}}$$

$= 2.680664 \times 10^{-11} = 2.6807 \times 10^{-11}$ J/^{21}Ne nucleus required

$$2.680664 \times 10^{-11} \frac{\text{J}}{\text{nucleus}} \times \frac{6.0221421 \times 10^{23} \text{ nuclei}}{\text{mol}}$$

$$= 1.6143 \times 10^{13} \text{ J/mol } ^{21}\text{Ne binding energy}$$

21.47   *Analyze/Plan.* Given atomic mass, subtract mass of the electrons to get nuclear mass. Calculate the nuclear binding energy by finding the mass difference between the nucleus and the separate nucleons and converting this to energy using Equation [21.22]. Divide by the total number of nucleons to find binding energy per nucleon. *Solve.*

(a)   Nuclear mass

     ^{2}H: 2.014102 amu $- 1(5.485799 \times 10^{-4}$ amu) $= 2.013553$ amu

     ^{4}He: 4.002602 amu $- 2(5.485799 \times 10^{-4}$ amu) $= 4.001505$ amu

     ^{6}Li: 6.0151228 amu $- 3(5.4857991 \times 10^{-4}$ amu) $= 6.0134771$ amu

(b)   Nuclear binding energy

     ^{2}H: $\Delta m = 1(1.0072765) + 1(1.0086649) - 2.013553 = 0.002388$ amu

$$\Delta E = 0.002388 \text{ amu} \times \frac{1 \text{ g}}{6.022142 \times 10^{23} \text{ amu}} \times \frac{1 \text{ kg}}{1000 \text{ g}} \times \frac{8.987551 \times 10^{16} \text{ m}^2}{\text{s}^2}$$

$$= 3.564490 \times 10^{-13} = 3.564 \times 10^{-13} \text{ J}$$

^{4}He: $\Delta m = 2(1.0072765) + 2(1.0086649) - 4.001505 = 0.030378$ amu

$$\Delta E = 0.030378 \text{ amu} \times \frac{1 \text{ g}}{6.022142 \times 10^{23} \text{ amu}} \times \frac{1 \text{ kg}}{1000 \text{ g}} \times \frac{8.987551 \times 10^{16} \text{ m}^2}{\text{s}^2}$$

$$= 4.533636 \times 10^{-12} = 4.5336 \times 10^{-12} \text{ J}$$

^{6}Li: $\Delta m = 3(1.0072765) + 3(1.0086649) - 6.0134771 = 0.0343471$ amu

$$\Delta E = 0.0343471 \text{ amu} \times \frac{1 \text{ g}}{6.022142 \times 10^{23} \text{ amu}} \times \frac{1 \text{ kg}}{1000 \text{ g}} \times \frac{8.987551 \times 10^{16} \text{ m}^2}{\text{s}^2}$$

$$= 5.126021 \times 10^{-12} = 5.12602 \times 10^{-12} \text{ J}$$

(c) Binding energy per nucleon

^{2}H: 3.564490×10^{-13} J/2 nucleons $= 1.782 \times 10^{-13}$ J/nucleon

^{4}He: 4.533636×10^{-12} J/4 nucleons $= 1.1334 \times 10^{-12}$ J/nucleon

^{6}Li: 5.126021×10^{-12} J/6 nucleons $= 8.54337 \times 10^{-13}$ J/nucleon

This trend in binding energy/nucleon agrees with the curve in Figure 21.12, which shows an irregular increase in binding energy/nucleon up to atomic number 56. The anomalously high value for ^{4}He calculated above is also apparent on the figure.

21.48 Nuclear mass is atomic mass minus mass of electrons. Nuclear binding energy is nuclear mass minus mass of the separate nucleons, converted to energy using Equation [21.22]. Divide by the total number of nucleons to find binding energy per nucleon.

(a) Nuclear mass

^{14}N: $13.999234 - 7(5.485799 \times 10^{-4} \text{ amu}) = 13.995394$

^{48}Ti: $47.935878 - 22(5.485799 \times 10^{-4} \text{ amu}) = 47.923809$

^{129}Xe: $128.904779 - 54(5.485799 \times 10^{-4} \text{ amu}) = 128.875156$ amu

(b) Nuclear binding energy

^{14}N: $\Delta m = 7(1.0072765) + 7(1.0086649) - 13.995394 = 0.1161959 = 0.116196$ amu

$$\Delta E = 0.1161959 \text{ amu} \times \frac{1 \text{ g}}{6.0221421 \times 10^{23} \text{ amu}} \times \frac{1 \text{ kg}}{1000 \text{ g}} \times \frac{8.987551 \times 10^{16} \text{ m}^2}{\text{s}^2}$$

$$= 1.734127 \times 10^{-11} = 1.73413 \times 10^{-11} \text{ J}$$

^{48}Ti: $\Delta m = 22(1.0072765) + 26(1.0086649) - 47.923809 = 0.4615614 = 0.461561$ amu

$$\Delta E = 0.4615614 \text{ amu} \times \frac{1 \text{ g}}{6.0221421 \times 10^{23} \text{ amu}} \times \frac{1 \text{ kg}}{1000 \text{ g}} \times \frac{8.987551 \times 10^{16} \text{ m}^2}{\text{s}^2}$$

$$= 6.888428 \times 10^{-11} = 6.88843 \times 10^{-11} \text{ J}$$

^{129}Xe: $\Delta m = 54(1.0072765) + 75(1.0086649) - 128.875156 = 1.1676425 = 1.167643$ amu

$$\Delta E = 1.1676425 \text{ amu} \times \frac{1\,\text{g}}{6.0221421 \times 10^{23}\,\text{amu}} \times \frac{1\,\text{kg}}{1000\,\text{g}} \times \frac{8.987551 \times 10^{16}\,\text{m}^2}{\text{s}^2}$$

$$= 1.742610 \times 10^{-10}\,\text{J}$$

(c)   Binding energy per nucleon

      ^{14}N: 1.73413×10^{-11} J / 14 nucleons $= 1.23866 \times 10^{-12}$ J/nucleon

      ^{48}Ti: 6.888428×10^{-11} J / 48 nucleons $= 1.43509 \times 10^{-12}$ J/nucleon

      ^{129}Xe: 1.742610×10^{-10} J/129 nucleons $= 1.350860 \times 10^{-12}$ J/nucleon

21.49   *Analyze/Plan.* Use Equation [21.22] to calculate the mass equivalence of the solar radiation.   *Solve.*

(a) $\dfrac{1.07 \times 10^{16}\,\text{kJ}}{1\,\text{min}} \times \dfrac{60\,\text{min}}{1\,\text{h}} \times \dfrac{24\,\text{h}}{1\,\text{d}} = 1.541 \times 10^{19}\,\dfrac{\text{kJ}}{\text{d}} = 1.54 \times 10^{22}$ J/d

      $\Delta m = \dfrac{1.541 \times 10^{22}\,\text{kg-m}^2/\text{s}^2/\text{d}}{(2.998 \times 10^8\,\text{m/s})^2} = 1.714 \times 10^5 = 1.71 \times 10^5$ kg/d

(b)   *Analyze/Plan.* Calculate the mass change in the given nuclear reaction, then a conversion factor for g ^{235}U to mass equivalent.   *Solve.*

      $\Delta m = 140.8833 + 91.9021 + 2(1.0086649) - 234.9935 = -0.19077 = -0.1908$ amu

      Converting from atoms to moles and amu to grams, it requires 1.000 mol or 235.0 g ^{235}U to produce energy equivalent to a change in mass of 0.1908 g.

      0.10% of 1.714×10^5 kg is 1.714×10^2 kg $= 1.714 \times 10^5$ g

      $1.714 \times 10^5\,\text{g} \times \dfrac{235.0\,\text{g}\ ^{235}\text{U}}{0.1908\,\text{g}} = 2.111 \times 10^8 = 2.1 \times 10^8$ g ^{235}U

      (This is about 230 tons of ^{235}U **per day.**)

21.50   First, calculate nuclear masses from atomic masses. Then, the calculated Δm is for one group of single nuclides involved in a reaction, labeled Δm/'atomic reaction'. Multiplying by Avogadro's number changes the quantity to 'mol of reaction'. Since energy is released, the sign of ΔE is negative.

      ^{1}H: 1.00782 amu $- 1(5.485799 \times 10^{-4}$ amu$) = 1.0072714 = 1.00727$ amu

      ^{2}H: 2.01410 amu $- 1(5.485799 \times 10^{-4}$ amu$) = 2.0135514 = 2.01355$ amu

      ^{3}H: 3.10605 amu $- 1(5.485799 \times 10^{-4}$ amu$) = 3.1055014 = 3.10550$ amu

      ^{3}He: 3.10603 amu $- 2(5.485799 \times 10^{-4}$ amu$) = 3.1049328 = 3.10493$ amu

      ^{4}He: 4.00260 amu $- 2(5.485799 \times 10^{-4}$ amu$) = 4.0015028 = 4.00150$ amu

(a)   Δm = 4.0015028 + 1.0086649 – 3.1055014 – 2.0135514 = –0.1088851 = –0.10889 amu

$$\Delta E = \frac{-0.1088851 \text{ amu}}{\text{'atomic reaction'}} \times \frac{1\,g}{6.022 \times 10^{23}\text{ amu}} \times \frac{6.022 \times 10^{23}\text{ 'atomic reaction'}}{\text{mol of reaction}}$$

$$\times \frac{1\,kg}{10^3\,g} \times (2.99792458 \times 10^8 \text{ m/sec})^2 = -9.7861 \times 10^{12}\text{ J/mol}$$

(b)   Δm = 3.1049328 + 1.0086649 – 2(2.0135514) = –0.0864949 = –0.08649 amu

ΔE = –7.774 × 10^{12} J/mol

(c)   Δm = 4.0015028 + 1.0072714 – 2.0135514 – 3.1049328 = –0.1097100 = –0.10971 amu

ΔE = –9.8602 × 10^{12} J/mol

21.51   We can use Figure 21.12 to see that the binding energy per nucleon (which gives rise to the mass defect) is greatest for nuclei of mass numbers around 50. Thus (a) $^{59}_{27}$Co should possess the greatest mass defect per nucleon.

21.52   Nuclear mass = 61.928345 amu – 28(5.485799 × 10^{-4} amu) = 61.912985

Binding energy = 28(1.0072765) + 34(1.0086649) – 61.912985 = 0.585363 amu

$$\Delta E = 0.585363 \text{ amu} \times \frac{1\,g}{6.0221421 \times 10^{23}\text{ amu}} \times \frac{1\,kg}{1000\,g} \times \frac{8.987551 \times 10^{16}\text{ m}^2}{s^2}$$

= 8.73606 × 10^{-11} J

Binding energy/nucleon = 8.73606 × 10^{-11} J / 62 = 1.40904 × 10^{-12} J/nucleon

The value given for iron-56 in Table 21.7 is 1.41 × 10^{-12} J/nucleon. These values are the same, to three significant figures.

Effects and Uses of Radioisotopes (sections 21.7-21.9)

21.53   (a)   NaI is a good source of iodine, because it is a strong electrolyte and completely dissociated into ions in aqueous solution. The I$^-$(aq) are mobile and immediately available for bio-uptake. They do not need to be digested or processed in the body before uptake can occur. Also, iodine is a large percentage of the total mass of NaI.

(b)   After ingestion, I$^-$(aq) must enter the bloodstream, travel to the thyroid and then be absorbed. This requires a finite amount of time. A Geiger counter placed near the thyroid immediately after ingestion will register background, then gradually increase in signal until the concentration of I$^-$(aq) in the thyroid reaches a maximum. Then, over time, iodine-131 decays, and the signal decreases.

(c)   *Analyze/Plan.* The half-life of iodine-131 is 8.02 days. Use t$_{1/2}$ to calculate the decay rate constant, k. Then solve Equation [21.19] for t. N$_o$ = 0.12 (12% of ingested iodine absorbed); N$_t$ = 0.0001 (0.01% of the original ingested amount).

Solve.   k = 0.693 t$_{1/2}$ = 0.693/8.02 d = 0.086409 = 0.0864 d^{-1}

ln(N$_t$/N$_o$) = –kt; t = –ln(N$_t$/N$_o$)/k

$$t = \frac{-\ln(0.0001 / 0.12)}{0.086409 \text{ d}^{-1}} = 82.05 = 82 \text{ d}$$

Check. N_t is given to 1 sig fig, so 8×10^1 (70 – 90) days is a more correct representation of the time frame for decay.

21.54   Radioisotopes used as diagnostic tools are introduced into the body and carried to the point where imaging or some other diagnostic data is needed. We want the decay products of these radioisotopes to leave the body and do as little damage as possible on the way. Gamma rays are penetrating radiation and can escape the body more easily than other radioactive decay products. Also, gamma rays leaving the body can be easily detected using scintillation counters. This is particularly important when imaging is the goal of the procedure.

         Alpha emitters are never used as diagnostic tools because alpha particles are ionizing but do not move easily through the body. Trapped inside the body, alpha particles initiate the ionization of water, which ultimately produces free radicals that disrupt the normal operation of cells.

21.55 ^{235}U

21.56   Enriched uranium is a uranium-containing substance that has had its natural amount of uranium-235 increased. It is different from natural uranium because it contains more than 0.7% uranium-235.

21.57   The *control rods* in a nuclear reactor regulate the flux of neutrons to keep the reaction chain self-sustaining and also prevent the reactor core from overheating. They are composed of materials such as boron or cadmium that absorb neutrons.

21.58   (a)   A moderator slows neutrons so that they are more easily captured by fissioning nuclei.

       (b)   Water is the moderator in a pressurized water generator.

       (c)   Graphite is used as a moderator in gas-cooled reactors, and D_2O is used in heavy-water reactors.

21.59   (a) $^{2}_{1}\text{H} + {}^{2}_{1}\text{H} \rightarrow {}^{3}_{2}\text{He} + {}^{1}_{0}\text{n}$

       (b) $^{239}_{92}\text{U} + {}^{1}_{0}\text{n} \rightarrow {}^{133}_{51}\text{Sb} + {}^{98}_{41}\text{Nb} + 9\,{}^{1}_{0}\text{n}$

21.60   *Analyze/Plan.* Use conservation of A and Z to complete the equations, keeping in mind the symbols and definitions of various decay products.   *Solve.*

       (a) $^{235}_{92}\text{U} + {}^{1}_{0}\text{n} \rightarrow {}^{160}_{62}\text{Sm} + {}^{72}_{30}\text{Zn} + 4\,{}^{1}_{0}\text{n}$

       (b) $^{239}_{94}\text{Pu} + {}^{1}_{0}\text{n} \rightarrow {}^{144}_{58}\text{Ce} + {}^{94}_{36}\text{Kr} + 2\,{}^{1}_{0}\text{n}$

21.61   (a)   *Analyze/Plan.* At these temperatures, assume the reaction occurs between nuclei rather than atoms. From Table 21.7, the nuclear mass of $^{4}_{2}\text{He}$ is 4.00150. The nuclear mass of $^{1}_{1}\text{H}$ is simply the mass of a proton, 1.007276467 amu. Note that $^{0}_{1}\text{e}$ is a positron, which has the same mass as an electron, 5.4857991×10^{-4} amu. Calculate the difference in mass between product and reactant nuclei, and the energy released by this mass change. Do the calculation in terms of moles and grams, rather than nuclei and amu. 1 mol amu = 1 g. *Solve.*

$\Delta m = 4.00150 + 2(5.4857991 \times 10^{-4}) - 4(1.007276467) = -0.0265087 = -0.02651$ g

If the reaction is run with 1 mol of ^1_1H, the mass change is $(0.0265087/4) = 0.0066272 = 0.006627$ g

$$\Delta E = c^2 \Delta m = 0.0066272 \text{ g} \times \frac{1 \text{ kg}}{1000 \text{ g}} \times \frac{8.987551 \times 10^{16} \text{ m}^2}{\text{s}^2} = 5.95621 \times 10^{11}$$

$$= 5.956 \times 10^{11} \text{ J} = 5.956 \times 10^8 \text{ kJ}$$

(b) The extremely high temperature is required to overcome the electrostatic charge repulsions between the nuclei so that they come together to react.

21.62 (a) If the spent fuel rods are more radioactive than the original rods, the products of fission must lie outside the belt of stability and be radioactive themselves.

(b) The heavy (Z > 83) nucleus has a high neutron/proton ratio. The lighter radioactive fission products, (e.g., barium-142 and krypton-91) also have high neutron/proton ratios, since only 2 or 3 free neutrons are produced during fission. The preferred decay mode to reduce the neutron/proton ratio is β decay, which has the effect of converting a neutron into a proton. Both barium-142 (86 n, 56 p) and krypton-91 (55 n, 36 p) undergo β decay.

21.63 (a) A *boiling water reactor* does not use a secondary coolant.

(b) A *fast breeder reactor* creates more fissionable material than it consumes.

(c) A *gas-cooled reactor* uses a gas as a primary coolant.

21.64 (a) A *heavy water reactor* and a *gas-cooled rector* can use natural uranium as a fuel.

(b) A *fast breeder reactor* does not use a moderator.

(c) A *high temperature pebble-bed reactor* can be refueled without shutting down.

21.65 *Analyze/Plan.* Hydroxyl radical is electrically neutral but has an unpaired electron, •OH. Hydroxide is an anion, OH⁻. *Solve.*

Hydrogen abstraction: $RCOOH + \cdot OH \rightarrow RCOO\cdot + H_2O$

Deprotonation: $RCOOH + OH^- \rightarrow RCOO^- + H_2O$

Hydroxyl radical is more toxic to living systems, because it produces other radicals when it reacts with molecules in the organism. This often starts a disruptive chain of reactions, each producing a different free radical.

Hydroxide ion, OH⁻, on the other hand, will be readily neutralized in the buffered cell environment. Its most common reaction is ubiquitous and innocuous: $H^+ + OH^- \rightarrow H_2O$. The acid-base reactions of OH⁻ are usually much less disruptive to the organism than the chain of redox reactions initiated by •OH radical.

21.66 X-rays, alpha particles and gamma rays are classified as ionizing radiation.

21.67 *Analyze/Plan.* Use definitions of the various radiation units and conversion factors to calculate the specified quantities. Pay particular attention to units.   *Solve.*

(a) $1 \, Ci = 3.7 \times 10^{10}$ disintegrations(dis)/s; $1 \, Bq = 1$ dis/s

$$14.3 \, mCi \times \frac{1 \, Ci}{1000 \, m \, Ci} \times \frac{3.7 \times 10^{10} \, dis/s}{Ci} = 5.29 \times 10^8 = 5.3 \times 10^8 \, dis/s = 5.3 \times 10^8 \, Bq$$

(b) $1 \, rad = 1 \times 10^{-2} \, J/kg$; $1 \, Gy = 1 \, J/kg = 100$ rad. From part (a), the activity of the source is 5.3×10^8 dis/s.

$$5.29 \times 10^8 \, dis/s \times 14.0 \, s \times 0.35 \times \frac{9.12 \times 10^{-13} \, J}{dis} \times \frac{1}{0.385 \, kg} = 6.14 \times 10^{-3} = 6.1 \times 10^{-3} \, J/kg$$

$$6.1 \times 10^{-3} \, J/kg \times \frac{1 \, rad}{1 \times 10^{-2} \, J/kg} \times \frac{1000 \, mrad}{rad} = 6.1 \times 10^2 \, mrad$$

$$6.1 \times 10^{-3} \, J/kg \times \frac{1 \, Gy}{1 \, J/kg} = 6.1 \times 10^{-3} \, Gy$$

(c)   rem = rad (RBE); Sv = Gy (RBE) , where 1 Sv = 100 rem

mrem = 6.14×10^2 mrad $(9.5) = 5.83 \times 10^3 = 5.8 \times 10^3$ mrem (or 5.8 rem)

Sv = 6.14×10^{-3} Gy $(9.5) = 5.83 \times 10^{-2} = 5.8 \times 10^{-2}$ Sv

21.68   (a) $1 \, Ci = 3.7 \times 10^{10}$ dis/s; $1 \, Bq = 1$ dis/s

$$15 \, mCi \times \frac{1 \, Ci}{1000 \, mCi} \times 3.7 \times 10^{10} \, dis/s = 5.55 \times 10^8 = 5.6 \times 10^8 \, dis/s = 5.6 \times 10^8 \, Bq$$

(b) $1 \, Gy = 1 \, J/kg$; $1 \, Gy = 100$ rad

$$5.55 \times 10^8 \, dis/s \times 240 \, s \times 0.075 \times \frac{8.75 \times 10^{-14} \, J}{dis} \times \frac{1}{65 \, kg} = 1.345 \times 10^{-5} = 1.3 \times 10^{-5} \, J/kg$$

$$1.3 \times 10^{-5} \, J/kg \times \frac{1 \, Gy}{1 \, J/kg} = 1.3 \times 10^{-5} \, Gy; \; 1.3 \times 10^{-5} \, Gy \times \frac{100 \, rad}{1 \, Gy} = 1.3 \times 10^{-3} \, rad$$

(c)   rem = rad (RBE); Sv = Gy (RBE)

$$1.3 \times 10^{-3} \, rad \, (1.0) = 1.3 \times 10^{-3} \, rem \times \frac{1000 \, mrem}{1 \, rem} = 1.3 \, mrem$$

$$1.3 \times 10^{-5} \, Gy \, (1.0) = 1.3 \times 10^{-5} \, Sv$$

(d)   The mammogram dose of 300 mrem is ~230 times as much radiation as the dose absorbed by the 65 kg person described above.

Additional Exercises

21.69 $^{222}_{86}Rn \rightarrow X + 3 \, ^4_2He + 2 \, ^0_{-1}\beta$

This corresponds to a reduction in mass number of $(3 \times 4 =) \, 12$ and a reduction in atomic number of $(3 \times 2 - 2) = 4$. The stable nucleus is $^{210}_{82}Pb$. (This is part of the sequence in Figure 21.5.)

21.70 $^3_2He + \, ^3_2He \rightarrow \, ^4_2He + 2 \, ^1_1H$. Use nuclear masses calculated in Solution 21.50.

$\Delta m = 4.00150 + 2(1.00727) - 2(3.10493) = -0.19382$ amu

$$\Delta E = \frac{-0.19382 \text{ amu}}{\text{'atomic reaction'}} \times \frac{1\,g}{6.022 \times 10^{23}\,\text{amu}} \times \frac{6.022 \times 10^{23}\,\text{'atomic reaction'}}{\text{mol of reaction}}$$

$$\times \frac{1\,kg}{10^3\,g} \times (2.99792458 \times 10^8\,\text{m/sec})^2 = -1.7420 \times 10^{13}\,\text{J/mol}$$

21.71   (a) $^{36}_{17}Cl \rightarrow {}^{36}_{18}Ar + {}^{0}_{-1}e$

        (b)   According to Table 21.3, nuclei with even numbers of both protons and neutrons, or an even number of one kind of nucleon, are more stable. ^{35}Cl and ^{37}Cl both have an odd number of protons **but** an even number of neutrons. ^{36}Cl has an odd number of protons and neutrons (17 p, 19 n), so it is less stable than the other two isotopes. Also, ^{37}Cl has 20 neutrons, a nuclear closed shell.

21.72   A ^{2}He nucleus has 2 protons and no neutrons. Electrostatic repulsion between two positively charged protons in very close proximity causes ^{2}He to be unstable.

21.73   (a) $^{6}_{3}Li + {}^{56}_{28}Ni \rightarrow {}^{62}_{31}Ga$

        (b) $^{40}_{20}Ca + {}^{248}_{96}Cm \rightarrow {}^{147}_{62}Sm + {}^{141}_{54}Xe$

        (c) $^{88}_{38}Sr + {}^{84}_{36}Kr \rightarrow {}^{116}_{46}Pd + {}^{56}_{28}Ni$

        (d) $^{40}_{20}Ca + {}^{238}_{92}U \rightarrow {}^{70}_{30}Zn + 4\,{}^{1}_{0}n + 2\,{}^{102}_{41}Nb$

21.74

Time (hr)	N_t (dis/min)	$\ln N_t$
0	180	5.193
2.5	130	4.868
5.0	104	4.644
7.5	77	4.34
10.0	59	4.08
12.5	46	3.83
17.5	24	3.18

The plot on the left is a graph of activity (disintegrations per minute) vs. time. Choose $t_{1/2}$ at the time where $N_t = 1/2\,N_o = 90$ dis/min. $t_{1/2} \approx 6.0$ hr.

Rearrange Equation [21.19] to obtain the linear relationship shown on the right.

$\ln(N_t / N_o) = -kt$; $\ln N_t - \ln N_o = -kt$; $\ln N_t = -kt + \ln N_o$

The slope of this line = $-k = -0.11$; $t_{1/2} = 0.693/0.11 = 6.3$ hr.

21.75 1×10^{-6} curie $\times \dfrac{3.7 \times 10^{10} \text{ dis/s}}{\text{curie}} = 3.7 \times 10^4$ dis/s

rate $= 3.7 \times 10^4$ nuclei/s $= kN$

$k = \dfrac{0.693}{t_{1/2}} = \dfrac{0.693}{28.8 \text{ yr}} \times \dfrac{1 \text{ yr}}{365 \times 24 \times 3600 \text{ sec}} = 7.630 \times 10^{-10} = 7.63 \times 10^{-10} \text{ s}^{-1}$

3.7×10^4 nuclei/s $= (7.63 \times 10^{-10}/\text{s}) N$; $N = 4.849 \times 10^{13} = 4.8 \times 10^{13}$ ^{90}Sr nuclei

mass ^{90}Sr $= 4.849 \times 10^{13}$ nuclei $\times \dfrac{89.907738 \text{ g Sr}}{6.022 \times 10^{23} \text{ nuclei}} = 7.2 \times 10^{-9}$ g Sr

(mass of ^{90}Sr from webelements.com)

21.76   First calculate k in s^{-1}

$k = \dfrac{0.693}{2.4 \times 10^4 \text{ yr}} \times \dfrac{1 \text{ yr}}{365 \times 24 \times 3600 \text{ s}} = 9.16 \times 10^{-13} = 9.2 \times 10^{-13} \text{ s}^{-1}$

Now calculate N:

$N = 0.385$ g Pu $\times \dfrac{1 \text{ mol Pu}}{239.052 \text{ g Pu}} \times \dfrac{6.022 \times 10^{23} \text{ Pu atoms}}{1 \text{ mol Pu}} = 9.699 \times 10^{20}$

$= 9.7 \times 10^{20}$ Pu atoms

rate $= (9.16 \times 10^{-13} \text{ s}^{-1})(9.699 \times 10^{20} \text{ Pu atoms}) = 8.880 \times 10^8 = 8.9 \times 10^8$ dis/s

(mass of ^{239}Pu from webelements.com)

21.77   The C—OH bond of the acid and the O—H bond of the alcohol break in this reaction. Initially, ^{18}O is present in the C—^{18}OH group of the alcohol. In order for ^{18}O to end up in the ester, the ^{18}O—H bond of the alcohol must break. This requires that the C—OH bond in the acid also breaks. The unlabeled O from the acid ends up in the H_2O product.

21.78   Assume that no depletion of iodide from the water due to plant uptake has occurred. Then the activity after 30 days would be:

$k = 0.693/t_{1/2} = 0.693/8.02$ d $= 0.0864$ d^{-1}

$\ln \dfrac{N_t}{N_o} = -(0.0864 \text{ d}^{-1})(30 \text{ d}) = -2.592 = -2.6$; $\dfrac{N_t}{N_o} = 0.07485 = 0.07$

We thus expect $N_t = 0.07485(214) = 16.0 = 2 \times 10^1$ counts/min. The measured value of 15.7 counts/min is within experimental uncertainty of the expected value, 2×10^1 (16.0) counts/minute, for no iodine uptake by the plant. We conclude that no iodine is absorbed by the plant.

21.79   Because of the relationship $\Delta E = \Delta mc^2$, the mass defect (Δm) is directly related to the binding energy (ΔE) of the nucleus.

^{7}Be: 4p, 3n; 4(1.0072765) + 3(1.0086649) = 7.05510 amu

Total mass defect = 7.0551 – 7.0147 = 0.0404 amu

0.0404 amu/7 nucleons = 5.77 × 10^{-3} amu/nucleon

$$\Delta E = \Delta m \times c^2 = \frac{5.77 \times 10^{-3} \text{ amu}}{\text{nucleon}} \times \frac{1 \text{g}}{6.022 \times 10^{23} \text{ amu}} \times \frac{1 \text{ kg}}{1 \times 10^3 \text{ g}} \times \frac{8.988 \times 10^{16} \text{ m}^2}{\text{sec}^2}$$

$$= \frac{5.77 \times 10^{-3} \text{ amu}}{\text{nucleon}} \times \frac{1.4925 \times 10^{-10} \text{ J}}{1 \text{amu}} = 8.612 \times 10^{-13} = 8.61 \times 10^{-13} \text{ J/nucleon}$$

^{9}Be: 4p, 5n; 4(1.0072765) + 5(1.0086649) = 9.07243 amu

Total mass defect = 9.0724 – 9.0100 = 0.06243 = 0.0624 amu

0.0624 amu/9 nucleons = 6.937 × 10^{-3} = 6.94 × 10^{-3} amu/nucleon

6.937 × 10^{-3} amu/nucleon × 1.4925 × 10^{-10} J/amu = 1.035 × 10^{-12} = 1.04 × 10^{-12} J/nucleon

^{10}Be: 4p, 6n; 4(1.0072765) + 6(1.0086649) = 10.0811 amu

Total mass defect = 10.0811 – 10.0113 = 0.0698 amu

0.0698 amu/10 nucleons = 6.98 × 10^{-3} amu/nucleon

6.98 × 10^{-3} amu/nucleon × 1.4925 × 10^{-10} J/amu = 1.042 × 10^{-12} = 1.04 × 10^{-12} J/nucleon

The binding energies/nucleon for ^{9}Be and ^{10}Be are very similar; that for ^{10}Be is slightly higher.

21.80   First, calculate k in s^{-1}

$$k = \frac{0.693}{12.3 \text{ yr}} \times \frac{1 \text{yr}}{365 \text{d}} \times \frac{1 \text{d}}{24 \text{ hr}} \times \frac{1 \text{ hr}}{3600 \text{ sec}} = 1.7866 \times 10^{-9} = 1.79 \times 10^{-9} \text{ s}^{-1}$$

From Equation [21.18], 1.50 × 10^3 s^{-1} = (1.7866 × 10^{-9} s^{-1})(N);

N = 8.396 × 10^{11} = 8.40 × 10^{11}. In 26.00 g of water, there are

$$26.00 \text{ g H}_2\text{O} \times \frac{1 \text{ mol H}_2\text{O}}{18.02 \text{ g H}_2\text{O}} \times \frac{6.022 \times 10^{23} \text{ H}_2\text{O}}{1 \text{ mol H}_2\text{O}} \times \frac{2 \text{ H}}{1 \text{H}_2\text{O}} = 1.738 \times 10^{24} \text{ H atoms}$$

The mole fraction of $^3_1$H atoms in the sample is thus

8.396 × 10^{11}/1.738 × 10^{24} = 4.831 × 10^{-13} = 4.83 × 10^{-13}

21.81   (a) $\Delta m = \Delta E/c^2$; $\Delta m = \dfrac{3.9 \times 10^{26} \text{ J/s}}{(2.9979246 \times 10^8 \text{ m/s})^2} \times \dfrac{1 \text{ kg-m}^2/\text{s}^2}{1 \text{ J}} = 4.3 \times 10^9$ kg/s

            The rate of mass loss is 4.3 × 10^9 kg/s. (Fewer sig figs in the value of c produce the same result.)

     (b)   The mass loss arises from fusion reactions that produce more stable nuclei from less stable ones, e.g., Equations [21.26-21.29].

     (c)   Express the mass lost by the sun in terms of protons per second consumed in fusion reactions like Equations [21.26], [21.27] and [21.29].

$$\frac{4.3 \times 10^9 \text{ kg}}{\text{s}} \times \frac{1 \text{ proton}}{1.673 \times 10^{-24} \text{ g}} \times \frac{1000 \text{ g}}{1 \text{ kg}} = 2.594 \times 10^{36} = 3 \times 10^{36} \text{ protons/s}$$

21.82 $\quad 1000 \text{ Mwatts} \times \dfrac{1 \times 10^6 \text{ watts}}{1 \text{ Mwatt}} \times \dfrac{1 \text{J}}{1 \text{ watt-s}} \times \dfrac{1 \text{ } ^{235}\text{U atom}}{3 \times 10^{-11} \text{ J}} \times \dfrac{1 \text{ mol U}}{6.02214 \times 10^{23} \text{ atoms}}$

$$\times \frac{235 \text{ g U}}{1 \text{ mol}} \times \frac{3600 \text{ s}}{1 \text{ hr}} \times \frac{24 \text{ hr}}{1 \text{ d}} \times \frac{365 \text{ d}}{1 \text{ yr}} \times \frac{100}{40} (\text{efficiency}) = 1.03 \times 10^6 = 1 \times 10^6 \text{ g U/yr}$$

21.83 $\quad 2 \times 10^{-12} \text{ curies} \times \dfrac{3.7 \times 10^{10} \text{ dis/s}}{1 \text{ curie}} = 7.4 \times 10^{-2} = 7 \times 10^{-2} \text{ dis/s}$

$$\frac{7.4 \times 10^{-2} \text{ dis/s}}{75 \text{ kg}} \times \frac{8 \times 10^{-13} \text{ J}}{\text{dis}} \times \frac{1 \text{ rad}}{1 \times 10^{-2} \text{ J/g}} \times \frac{3600 \text{ s}}{\text{hr}} \times \frac{24 \text{ hr}}{1 \text{ d}}$$

$$\times \frac{365 \text{ d}}{1 \text{ yr}} = 2.49 \times 10^{-6} = 2 \times 10^{-6} \text{ rad/yr}$$

Recall that there are 10 rem/rad for alpha particles.

$$\frac{2.49 \times 10^{-6} \text{ rad}}{1 \text{ yr}} \times \frac{10 \text{ rem}}{1 \text{ rad}} = 2.49 \times 10^{-5} = 2 \times 10^{-5} \text{ rem/yr}$$

Integrative Exercises

21.84 Calculate the molar mass of $NaClO_4$ that contains 29.6% ^{36}Cl. Atomic mass of the enhanced Cl is $0.296(36.0) + 0.704(35.453) = 35.615 = 35.6$. The molar mass of $NaClO_4$ is then $(22.99 + 35.615 + 64.00) = 122.605 = 122.6$. Calculate N, the number of ^{36}Cl nuclei, the value of k in s^{-1}, and the activity in dis/s.

$$53.8 \text{ mg NaClO}_4 \times \frac{1 \text{g}}{1000 \text{ mg}} \times \frac{1 \text{ mol NaClO}_4}{122.605 \text{ g NaClO}_4} \times \frac{1 \text{ mol Cl}}{1 \text{ mol NaClO}_4} \times \frac{6.022 \times 10^{23} \text{ Cl atoms}}{\text{mol Cl}}$$

$$\times \frac{29.6 \text{ }^{36}\text{Cl atoms}}{100 \text{ Cl atoms}} = 7.822 \times 10^{19} = 7.82 \times 10^{19} \text{ }^{36}\text{Cl atoms}$$

$$k = 0.693 / t_{1/2} = \frac{0.693}{3.0 \times 10^5 \text{ yr}} \times \frac{1 \text{ yr}}{365 \times 24 \times 3600 \text{ s}} = 7.32 \times 10^{-14} = 7.3 \times 10^{-14} \text{ s}^{-1}$$

rate $= kN = (7.32 \times 10^{-14} \text{ s}^{-1})(7.822 \times 10^{19} \text{ nuclei}) = 5.729 \times 10^6 = 5.7 \times 10^6 \text{ dis/s}$

21.85 Calculate the amount of energy produced by the nuclear fusion reaction, the enthalpy of combustion, $\Delta H°$, of C_8H_{18}, and then the mass of C_8H_{18} required.

Δm for the reaction $\quad 4 \, ^1_1\text{H} \rightarrow \, ^4_2\text{He} + 2 \, ^0_1\text{e} \quad$ is:

$4(1.00782) - 4.00260 \text{ amu} - 2(5.4858 \times 10^{-4} \text{ amu}) = 0.027583 = 0.02758 \text{ amu}$

$$\Delta E = \Delta mc^2 = 0.027583 \text{ amu} \times \frac{1 \text{g}}{6.02214 \times 10^{23} \text{ amu}} \times \frac{1 \text{ kg}}{1000 \text{ g}} \times (2.9979246 \times 10^8 \text{ m/s})^2$$

$$= 4.11654 \times 10^{-12} = 4.117 \times 10^{-12} \text{ J/4 } ^1\text{H nuclei}$$

$$1.0 \text{ g } {}^1\text{H} \times \frac{1 \text{ }{}^1\text{H nucleus}}{1.00782 \text{ amu}} \times \frac{6.02214 \times 10^{23} \text{ amu}}{\text{g}} \times \frac{4.11654 \times 10^{-12} \text{ J}}{4 \text{ }{}^1\text{H nuclei}}$$

$$= 6.1495 \times 10^{11} \text{ J} = 6.1 \times 10^8 \text{ kJ produced by the fusion of } 1.0 \text{ g } {}^1\text{H}.$$

$$C_8H_{18}(l) + 25/2 O_2(g) \rightarrow 8CO_2(g) + 9H_2O(g)$$

$$\Delta H° = 8(-393.5 \text{ kJ}) + 9(-241.82 \text{ kJ}) - (-250.1 \text{ kJ}) = -5074.3 \text{ kJ}$$

$$6.1495 \times 10^8 \text{ kJ} \times \frac{1 \text{ mol C}_8H_{18}(l)}{5074.3 \text{ kJ}} \times \frac{114.231 \text{ g C}_8H_{18}}{\text{mol C}_8H_{18}} = 1.384 \times 10^7 \text{ g} = 1.4 \times 10^4 \text{ kg C}_8H_{18}$$

14,000 kg $C_8H_{18}(l)$ would have to be burned to produce the same amount of energy as fusion of 1.0 g ^{1}H.

21.86   (a) $0.18 \text{ Ci} \times \dfrac{3.7 \times 10^{10} \text{ dis/s}}{\text{Ci}} \times \dfrac{3600 \text{ s}}{\text{hr}} \times \dfrac{24 \text{ hr}}{\text{d}} \times 245 \text{ d} = 1.41 \times 10^{17} = 1.4 \times 10^{17} \text{ } \alpha \text{ particles}$

        (b) $P = nRT/V = 1.41 \times 10^{17} \text{ He atoms} \times \dfrac{1 \text{ mol He}}{6.022 \times 10^{23} \text{ atoms}} \times \dfrac{295 \text{ K}}{0.0250 \text{ L}} \times \dfrac{0.08206 \text{ L-atm}}{\text{mol-K}}$

$$= 2.27 \times 10^{-4} = 2.3 \times 10^{-4} \text{ atm} = 0.17 \text{ torr}$$

21.87   Calculate N_t in dis/min/g C from 1.5×10^{-2} dis/0.788 g $CaCO_3$. $N_o = 15.3$ dis/min/g C. Calculate k from $t_{1/2}$, calculate t from $\ln(N_t / N_o) = -kt$.

$$C(s) + O_2(g) \rightarrow CO_2(g) + Ca(OH_2)(aq) \rightarrow CaCO_3(s) + H_2O(l)$$

1 C atom $\rightarrow$ 1 $CaCO_3$ molecule

$$\frac{1.5 \times 10^{-2} \text{ Bq}}{0.788 \text{ g CaCO}_3} \times \frac{1 \text{ dis/s}}{1 \text{ Bq}} \times \frac{60 \text{ s}}{1 \text{ min}} \times \frac{100.1 \text{ g CaCO}_3}{12.01 \text{ g C}} = 9.52 = 9.5 \text{ dis/min/g C}$$

$$k = 0.693/t_{1/2} = 0.693/5.715 \times 10^3 \text{ yr} = 1.213 \times 10^{-4} = 1.21 \times 10^{-4} \text{ yr}^{-1}$$

$$t = -\frac{1}{k} \ln \frac{N_t}{N_o} = \frac{-1}{1.213 \times 10^{-4} \text{ yr}^{-1}} \ln \frac{9.52 \text{ dis/min/g C}}{15.3 \text{ dis/min/g C}} = 3.91 \times 10^3 \text{ yr}$$

21.88   (a) $Ba(NO_3)_2(aq) + Na_2SO_4(aq) \rightarrow BaSO_4(s) + 2NaNO_3(aq)$

        (b) $1.25 \text{ mmol Ba}^{2+} + 1.25 \text{ mmol SO}_4{}^{2-} \rightarrow 1.25 \text{ mmol BaSO}_4$

           Neither reactant is in excess, so the activity of the filtrate is due entirely to $[SO_4{}^{2-}]$ from dissociation of $BaSO_4(s)$. Calculate $[SO_4{}^{2-}]$ in the filtrate by comparing the activity of the filtrate to the activity of the reactant.

$$\frac{0.050 \text{ } M \text{ SO}_4^{2-}}{1.22 \times 10^6 \text{ Bq/mL}} = \frac{x \text{ } M \text{ filtrate}}{250 \text{ Bq/mL}}$$

$[SO_4{}^{2-}]$ in the filtrate $= 1.0246 \times 10^{-5} = 1.0 \times 10^{-5}$ M

$K_{sp} = [Ba^{2+}][SO_4{}^{2-}]; [SO_4{}^{2-}] = [Ba^{2+}]$

$K_{sp} = (1.0246 \times 10^{-5})^2 = 1.0498 \times 10^{-10} = 1.0 \times 10^{-10}$

22 Chemistry of the Nonmetals

Visualizing Concepts

22.1   (a) C_2H_4, the structure on the left, is the stable compound. Carbon, with a relatively small covalent radius owing to its location in the second row of the periodic chart, is able to closely approach other atoms. This close approach enables significant π overlap, so carbon can form strong multiple bonds to satisfy the octet rule. Silicon, in the third row of the periodic table, has a covalent radius too large for significant π overlap. Si does not form stable multiple bonds and Si_2H_4 is unstable.

(b)   There are 3 electron domains about each central C atoms in C_2H_4. The geometry about these atoms is trigonal planar.

22.2   (a)   Acid-base (Brønsted)

(b)   Charges on species from left to right in the reaction: 0, 0, 1+, 1–

(c) $NH_3(aq) + H_2O(l) \rightleftharpoons NH_4^+(aq) + OH^-(aq)$

22.3   *Analyze.* The structure is a trigonal bipyramid where one of the five positions about the central atom is occupied by a lone pair, often called a see-saw.

Plan A: Count the valence electrons in each molecule, draw a correct Lewis structure, and count the electron domains about the central atom.

Plan B: Molecules (a)–(d) each contain four F atoms bound to a central atom through a single bond (F is unlikely to form multiple bonds because of its high electronegativity). This represents 16 electron pairs; the fifth position is occupied by a lone pair, for a total of 17 e$^-$ pairs. A valence e$^-$ count for (a)–(d) will tell us which molecules are likely to have the designated structure. Molecule (e), $HClO_4$, is not exactly of the type AX_4, so a Lewis structure will be required.   *Solve.*

(a) XeF_4 36 e$^-$, 16 e$^-$ pairs. Plan B predicts that this molecule **will not** adopt the see-saw structure.

6 e$^-$ domains about the Xe
octahedral domain geometry
square planar structure

(b) BrF_4^+ 34 e$^-$, 17 e$^-$ pairs; structure **will** be see-saw.

5 e$^-$ domains about Br trigonal
bipyramidal domain geometry
see-saw structure

(c)   SiF$_4$ 32 e$^-$, 16 e$^-$ pairs; structure **will not** be see-saw

$$\begin{array}{c} :\!\ddot{F}\!: \\ | \\ :\!\ddot{F}\!-\!Si\!-\!\ddot{F}\!: \\ | \\ :\!\ddot{F}\!: \end{array}$$

4 e$^-$ domains about Si
tetrahedral domain geometry and structure

(d)   TeCl$_4$ 34 e$^-$, 17 e$^-$ pairs; structure **will be** see-saw

$$\begin{array}{c} :\!\ddot{F}\!: \\ \ddot{F}\diagdown \!| \\ Te\!: \\ \ddot{F}\diagup\!| \\ :\!\ddot{F}\!: \end{array}$$

5 e$^-$ domains about Te
trigonal bipyramidal domain geometry
see-saw structure

(e)   HClO$_4$ 32 e$^-$, 16 e$^-$ pairs; structure **will not be** see-saw

$$\begin{array}{c} :\!\ddot{O}\!: \\ | \\ :\!\ddot{O}\!-\!Cl\!-\!\ddot{O}\!-\!H \\ | \\ :\!\ddot{O}\!: \end{array}$$

(HClO$_4$ is an oxyacid, so H is bound to O, not Cl.
Other Lewis structures that optimize formal charges
are possible; structure predictions are the same.)

22.4   Since ozone is "pale blue" and oxygen is colorless. If the bottles contain samples of the pure gases, this difference might be visible to the naked eye. If the bottles are not visibly different, the visible spectrum of ozone should have an absorption peak, while the oxygen spectrum should be featureless.

Molecular oxygen is odorless, while ozone has a sharp, irritating odor. Very carefully waft a bit of each gas toward your nose, and let it be your guide. (This is the easiest, but perhaps not the safest method.) Finally, there are test strips for the detection of ozone, which rely on its greater strength as an oxidizing agent.

22.5   *Analyze.* Given: space-filling models of molecules containing nitrogen and oxygen atoms.

Find: molecular formulas and Lewis structures.

Plan. Nitrogen atoms are blue, and oxygen atoms are red. Count the number of spheres of each color to determine the molecular formula. From each molecular formula, count the valence electrons (N = 5, O = 6) and draw a correct Lewis structure. Resonance structures are likely.

Solve.

(a)   N$_2$O$_5$ 40 valence electrons, 20 e$^-$ pairs

Many other resonance structures are possible. Those with double bonds to the central oxygen (like the right-hand structure above) do not minimize formal charge and are less significant in the net bonding model.

(b)　N_2O_4　　34 e$^-$, 17 e$^-$ pairs

Other equivalent resonance structures with different arrangement of the double bonds are possible.

(c)　NO_2　　17 e$^-$, 8.5 e$^-$ pairs

We place the odd electron on N because of electronegativity arguments.

(d)　N_2O_3　　28 e$^-$, 14 e$^-$ pairs

(e)　NO　　11 e$^-$, 5.5 e$^-$ pairs

We place the odd electron on N because of electronegativity arguments.

(f)　N_2O　　16 e$^-$, 8 e$^-$ pairs

:N≡N—Ö: ⟷ :N̈=N=Ö: ⟷ :N̈—N≡O:

The right-most structure above does not minimize formal charge and makes smaller contribution to the net bonding model.

22.6　The graph is applicable only to (c) density. Density depends on both atomic mass and volume (radius). Both increase going down a family, but atomic mass increases to a greater extent. Density, the ratio of mass to volume, increases going down the family; this trend is consistent with the data in the figure.

According to periodic trends, (a) electronegativity and (b) first ionization energy both decrease rather than increase going down the family. According to Table 22.5 both (d) X—X single bond enthalpy and (e) electron affinity are somewhat erratic, with the trends decreasing from S to Po, and anomalous values for the properties of O, probably owing to its small covalent radius.

22.7　(a)　Atomic radius increases moving downward in a group because the principal quantum number (n) of the valence electrons increases. As n increases, the average distance of an electron from the nucleus increases and so does atomic radius.

(b)　Anionic radii are greater than atomic radii because of increased electrostatic repulsions among electrons. Additional electrons in the same principle quantum level lead to additional electrostatic repulsion. This increases the energy of the electrons, and their average distance from the nucleus; the anionic radii are thus greater than the atomic radii.

(c) The anion that is the strongest base in water is the conjugate base of the weakest conjugate acid. The conjugate acids are OH^-, SH^-, and SeH^-. According to trends in binary hydrides, the acid with the longest X—H bond will be the most readily ionized and the strongest acid. SeH^- is thus the strongest acid and OH^- the weakest. Therefore O^{2-} is the strongest base in water.

22.8 *Analyze/Plan.* Evaluate the graph, describe the trend in data, recall the general trend for each of the properties listed, and use details of the data to discriminate between possibilities.

Solve. The general trend is an increase in value moving from left to right across the period, with a small discontinuity at S. Considering just this overall feature, both (a) first ionization energy and (c) electronegativity increase moving from left to right, so these are possibilities. (b) Atomic radius decreases, and can be eliminated. Since Si is a solid and Cl and Ar are gases at room temperature, melting points must decrease across the row; (d) melting point can be eliminated. According to data in Tables 22.2, 22.5, 22.7, and 22.8, (e) X-X single bond enthalpies show no consistent trend. Furthermore, there is no known Ar-Ar single bond, so no value for this property can be known; (e) can be eliminated.

Now let's examine trends in (a) first ionization energy and (c) electronegativity more closely. From electronegativity values in Chapter 8, we see a continuous increase with no discontinuity at S, and no value for Ar. Values in (a) first ionization energy from Chapter 7 do match the pattern in the figure. The slightly lower value of I_1 for S is due to a decrease in repulsion by removing an electron from a fully occupied orbital. In summary, only (a) first ionization energy fits the property depicted in the graph.

22.9 The compound on the left, with the strained three-membered ring, will be the most generally reactive. For central atoms with four electron domains*, idealized bond angles are 109°. From left to right, the bond angles in the three molecules pictured are 60°, 90° and 108°. The larger the deviation from ideal bond angles, the more strain in the molecule and the more generally reactive it is.

*For the stick structures shown in the exercise, each line represents a C—C single bond and the intersection of two lines is a C atom. To determine the number of electron domains about each atom, visualize or draw the hydrogen atoms and nonbonded electron pairs in each molecule. Alternatively, note that both C and O atoms form only single bonds, so hybridization must be sp^3 and idealized bond angles are 109°.

22.10 *Analyze/Plan.* The structure shown is a diatomic molecule or ion, depending on the value of n. Each species has 10 valence electrons and 5 electron pairs. *Solve.*

(a) Only second row elements are possible, because of the small covalent radius required for multiple bonding. Likely candidates are CO, N_2, NO^+, CN^-, and C_2^{2-}.

:C≡O: :N≡N: $[:N≡O:]^+$ $[:C≡N:]^-$ $[:C≡C:]^{2-}$

(b) Since C_2^{2-} has the highest negative charge, it is likely to be the strongest H^+ acceptor and strongest Brønsted base. This is confirmed in Section 22.9 under "Carbides."

Periodic Trends and Chemical Reactions (section 22.1)

22.11   *Analyze/Plan.* Use the color-coded periodic chart on the front-inside cover of the text to classify the given elements.   *Solve.*

Metals: (b) Sr, (c) Mn, (e) Na;   nonmetals: (a) P, (d) Se, (f) Kr;   metalloids: none

22.12   Metals: (a) Ga, (b) Mo, (f) Ru   nonmetals: (e) Xe   metalloid: (c) Te, (d) As

22.13   *Analyze/Plan.* Follow the logic in Sample Exercise 22.1.   *Solve.*

(a)   O   (b)   Br   (c)   Ba

(d)   O   (e)   Co   (f)   Br

22.14   (a)   Cl   (b)   K

(c)   K in the gas phase (lowest ionization energy), Li in aqueous solution (most positive $E°$ value)

(d)   Ne; Ne and Ar are difficult to compare to the other elements because they do not form compounds and their radii are not measured in the same way as other elements. However, Ne is several rows to the right of C and surely has a smaller atomic radius. The next smallest is C.

(e)   C

(f)   C (graphite, diamond, fullerenes, carbon nanotubes, and graphene)

22.15   *Analyze/Plan.* Use the position of the specified elements on the periodic chart, periodic trends, and the arguments in Sample Exercise 22.1 to explain the observations.   *Solve.*

(a)   Nitrogen is too small to accommodate five fluorine atoms about it. The P and As atoms are larger. Furthermore, P and As have available 3d and 4d orbitals, respectively, to form hybrid orbitals that can accommodate more than an octet of electrons about the central atom.

(b)   Si does not readily form π bonds, which would be necessary to satisfy the octet rule for both atoms in SiO.

(c)   A reducing agent is a substance that readily loses electrons. As has a lower electronegativity than N; that is, it more readily gives up electrons to an acceptor and is more easily oxidized.

22.16   (a)   Nitrogen is a highly electronegative element. In HNO_3 it is in its highest oxidation state, +5, and thus is more readily reduced than phosphorus, which forms stable P—O bonds.

(b)   The difference between the third row element and the second lies in the smaller size of C as compared with Si, and the fact that Si has additional orbitals available to accommodate more than an octet of electrons.

(c)   Two of the carbon compounds, C_2H_4 and C_2H_2, contain C—C π bonds. Si does not readily form π bonds (to itself or other atoms), so Si_2H_4 and Si_2H_2 are not known as stable compounds.

22.17   *Analyze/Plan.* Follow the logic in Sample Exercise 22.2.   *Solve.*

     (a) $NaOCH_3(s) + H_2O(l) \rightarrow NaOH(aq) + CH_3OH(aq)$

     (b) $CuO(s) + 2HNO_3(aq) \rightarrow Cu(NO_3)_2(aq) + H_2O(l)$

     (c) $WO_3(s) + 3H_2(g) \rightarrow W(s) + 3H_2O(g)$

     (d) $4NH_2OH(l) + O_2(g) \rightarrow 6H_2O(l) + 2N_2(g)$

     (e) $Al_4C_3(s) + 12H_2O(l) \rightarrow 4Al(OH)_3(s) + 3CH_4(g)$

22.18   (a) $Mg_3N_2(s) + 6H_2O(l) \rightarrow 2NH_3(g) + 3Mg(OH)_2(s)$

                 Because $H_2O(l)$ is a reactant, the state of NH_3 in the products could be expressed as $NH_3(aq)$.

     (b) $2C_3H_7OH(l) + 9O_2(g) \rightarrow 6CO_2(g) + 8H_2O(l)$

     (c) $MnO_2(s) + C(s) \xrightarrow{\Delta} CO(g) + MnO(s)$ or

                 $MnO_2(s) + 2C(s) \xrightarrow{\Delta} 2CO(g) + Mn(s)$ or

                 $MnO_2(s) + C(s) \xrightarrow{\Delta} CO_2(g) + Mn(s)$

     (d) $AlP(s) + 3H_2O(l) \rightarrow PH_3(g) + Al(OH)_3(s)$

     (e) $Na_2S(s) + 2HCl(aq) \rightarrow H_2S(g) + 2NaCl(aq)$

Hydrogen, the Noble Gases, and the Halogens (sections 22.2-22.4)

22.19   *Analyze/Plan.* Use information on the isotopes of hydrogen in Section 22.2 to list their symbols, names, and relative abundances.   *Solve.*

     (a) ^1_1H - protium; ^2_1H - deuterium; ^3_1H - tritium

     (b)   The order of abundance is proteum > deuterium > tritium.

     (c) ^3_1H - tritium is radioactive.

     (d) $^3_1H \rightarrow ^3_2He + ^{0}_{-1}e$

22.20   Yes, the physical properties of H_2O are different than those of D_2O. Deuterium atoms have a neutron, while protium atoms do not, so deuterium is almost twice as heavy as protium. We expect physical properties influenced by mass to be different for the two isotopes of hydrogen. In fact, D_2O has higher melting and boiling points, and a greater density than H_2O.

22.21   *Analyze/Plan.* Consider the electron configuration of hydrogen and the Group 1A elements. *Solve.*

     Like other elements in group 1A, hydrogen has only one valence electron and its most common oxidation number is +1.

22.22   In its standard state, hydrogen is a gas, and thus a nonmetal, like the halogens. Hydrogen can gain an electron to form an anion with a 1– charge. Chemically, hydrogen can combine with group 1A metals to form ionic compounds, where H^- is the anion.

22.23   *Analyze/Plan.* Use information on the descriptive chemistry of hydrogen in Section 22.2 to formulate the required equations. Steam is $H_2O(g)$.   *Solve.*

(a) $Mg(s) + 2H^+(aq) \rightarrow Mg^{2+}(aq) + H_2(g)$

(b) $C(s) + H_2O(g) \xrightarrow{1000°C} CO(g) + H_2(g)$

(c) $CH_4(g) + H_2O(g) \xrightarrow{1100°C} CO(g) + 3H_2(g)$

22.24   (a)   Electrolysis of brine; reaction of carbon with steam; reaction of methane with steam; by-product in petroleum refining

(b)   Synthesis of ammonia; synthesis of methanol; reducing agent; hydrogenation of unsaturated vegetable oils

22.25   *Analyze/Plan.* Use information on the descriptive chemistry of hydrogen given in Section 22.2 to complete and balance the equations.   *Solve.*

(a) $NaH(s) + H_2O(l) \rightarrow NaOH(aq) + H_2(g)$

(b) $Fe(s) + H_2SO_4(aq) \rightarrow Fe^{2+}(aq) + H_2(g) + SO_4^{2-}(aq)$

(c) $H_2(g) + Br_2(g) \rightarrow 2HBr(g)$

(d) $2Na(l) + H_2(g) \rightarrow 2NaH(s)$

(e) $PbO(s) + H_2(g) \xrightarrow{\Delta} Pb(s) + H_2O(g)$

22.26   (a) $2Al(s) + 6H^+(aq) \rightarrow 2Al^{3+}(aq) + 3H_2(g)$

(b) $Mg(s) + H_2O(g) \rightarrow MgO(s) + H_2(g)$

(c) $MnO_2(s) + H_2(g) \rightarrow MnO(s) + H_2O(g)$

(d) $CaH_2(s) + 2H_2O(l) \rightarrow Ca(OH)_2(aq) + 2H_2(g)$

22.27   *Analyze/Plan.* If the element bound to H is a nonmetal, the hydride is molecular. If H is bound to a metal with integer stoichiometry, the hydride is ionic; with noninteger stoichiometry, the hydride is metallic.   *Solve.*

(a)   ionic (metal hydride)

(b)   molecular (nonmetal hydride)

(c)   metallic (nonstoichiometric transition metal hydride)

22.28   (a)   molecular   (b)   ionic   (c)   metallic

22.29   Vehicle fuels produce energy via combustion reactions. The reaction $H_2(g) + 1/2\ O_2(g) \rightarrow H_2O(g)$ is very exothermic, producing 242 kJ per mole of H_2 burned. The only product of combustion is H_2O, a nonpollutant (but like CO_2, a greenhouse gas).

22.30   Electrolysis of water is the cleanest way to produce hydrogen, but it is energy intensive. In order to make this process sustainable, the energy must come from renewable sources, such as hydroelectric or nuclear power plants, wind generators, or solar cells. The biomass production of fuel for electric power generation would also be a sustainable energy source.

22.31   *Analyze/Plan.* Consider the periodic properties of Xe and Ar.   *Solve.*

Xenon is larger, and can more readily accommodate an expanded octet. More important is the lower ionization energy of xenon; because the valence electrons are a greater average distance from the nucleus, they are more readily promoted to a state in which the Xe atom can form bonds with fluorine.

22.32   Your friend cannot be correct. In general, noble gas elements have very stable electron configurations with complete s and p subshellls. They have very large positive ionization energies; they do not lose electrons easily. They have positive electron affinities; they do not attract electrons to themselves. They do not easily gain, lose or share electrons, so they do not readily form the chemical bonds required to create compounds. To date, the only known compounds of noble gases involve Xe and Kr bound to other nonmetals. Specifically, there are no known compounds of Ne.

22.33   *Analyze/Plan.* Follow the rules for assigning oxidation numbers in Section 4.4 and the logic in Sample Exercise 4.8.   *Solve.*

    (a) $Ca(OBr)_2$, Br, +1   (b) $HBrO_3$, Br, +5   (c) XeO_3, Xe, +6

    (d) ClO_4^-, Cl, +7   (e) HIO_2, I, +3   (f) IF_5; I, +5; F, –1

22.34   (a) ClO_3^-, Cl +5   (b)   HI, I, –1   (c) ICl_3; I, +3; Cl, –1

    (d)   NaOCl, Cl, +1   (e) $HClO_4$, Cl, +7   (f) XeF_4; Xe, +4; F, –1

22.35   *Analyze/Plan.* Review the nomenclature rules and ion names in Section 2.8, as well as the rules for assignming oxidation numbers in Section 4.4.   *Solve.*

    (a)   iron(III) chlorate, Cl, +5   (b)   chlorous acid, Cl, +3

    (c)   xenon hexafluoride, F, –1   (d)   bromine pentafluoride; Br, +5; F, –1

    (e)   xenon oxide tetrafluoride, F, –1 (f)   iodic acid, I, +5

22.36   (a)   potassium chlorate, Cl, +5   (b)   calcium iodate, I, +5

    (c)   aluminum chloride, Cl, –1   (d)   bromic acid, Br, +5

    (e)   paraperiodic acid, I, +7   (f)   xenon tetrafluoride, F, –1

22.37   *Analyze/Plan.* Consider intermolecular forces and periodic properties, including oxidizing power, of the listed substances.   *Solve.*

    (a)   Van der Waals intermolecular attractive forces increase with increasing numbers of electrons in the atoms.

    (b) F_2 reacts with water: $F_2(g) + H_2O(l) \rightarrow 2HF(aq) + 1/2\ O_2(g)$. That is, fluorine is too strong an oxidizing agent to exist in water.

    (c)   HF has extensive hydrogen bonding.

    (d)   Oxidizing power is related to electronegativity. Electronegativity decreases in the order given.

22.38   (a)   The more electronegative the central atom, the greater the extent to which it withdraws charge from oxygen, in turn making the O—H bond more polar, and enhancing ionization of H^+.

(b)   HF reacts with the silica which is a major component of glass:

$$6HF(aq) + SiO_2(s) \rightarrow SiF_6^{2-}(aq) + 2H_2O(l) + 2H^+(aq)$$

(c)   Iodide is oxidized by sulfuric acid, as shown in Figure 22.10.

(d)   The major factor is size; there is not room about Br for the three chlorides plus the two unshared electron pairs that would occupy the bromine valence shell orbitals.

Oxygen and the Group 6A Elements (sections 22.5 and 22.6)

22.39   *Analyze/Plan.* Use information on the descriptive chemistry of oxygen given in Section 22.5 to complete and balance the equations.   *Solve.*

(a) $2HgO(s) \overset{\Delta}{\rightarrow} 2Hg(l) + O_2(g)$

(b) $2Cu(NO_3)_2(s) \overset{\Delta}{\rightarrow} 2CuO(s) + 4NO_2(g) + O_2(g)$

(c) $PbS(s) + 4O_3(g) \rightarrow PbSO_4(s) + 4O_2(g)$

(d) $2ZnS(s) + 3O_2(g) \overset{\Delta}{\rightarrow} 2ZnO(s) + 2SO_2(g)$

(e) $2K_2O_2(s) + 2CO_2(g) \rightarrow 2K_2CO_3(s) + O_2(g)$

(f) $3O_2(g) \overset{h\nu}{\rightarrow} 2O_3(g)$

22.40   (a) $CaO(s) + H_2O(l) \rightarrow Ca^{2+}(aq) + 2OH^-(aq)$

(b) $Al_2O_3(s) + 6H^+(aq) \rightarrow 2Al^{3+}(aq) + 3H_2O(l)$

(c) $Na_2O_2(s) + 2H_2O(l) \rightarrow 2Na^+(aq) + 2OH^-(aq) + H_2O_2(aq)$

(d) $N_2O_3(g) + H_2O(l) \rightarrow 2HNO_2(aq)$

(e) $2KO_2(s) + 2H_2O(l) \rightarrow 2K^+(aq) + 2OH^-(aq) + O_2(g) + H_2O_2(aq)$

(f) $NO(g) + O_3(g) \rightarrow NO_2(g) + O_2(g)$

22.41   *Analyze/Plan.* Oxides of metals are bases, oxides of nonmetals are acids, oxides that act as both acids and bases are amphoteric and oxides that act as neither acids nor bases are neutral.   *Solve.*

(a)   acidic (oxide of a nonmetal)

(b)   acidic (oxide of a nonmetal)

(c)   amphoteric

(d)   basic (oxide of a metal)

22.42   (a) Mn_2O_7 (higher oxidation state of Mn)

(b) SnO_2 (higher oxidation state of Sn)

(c) SO_3 (higher oxidation state of S)

(d) SO_2 (more nonmetallic character of S)

(e) Ga_2O_3 (more nonmetallic character of Ga)

(f) SO_2 (more nonmetallic character of S)

22.43   *Analyze/Plan.* Follow the rules for assigning oxidation numbers in Section 4.4 and the logic in Sample Exercise 4.8.   *Solve.*

(a) H_2SeO_3, +4   (b) $KHSO_3$, +4   (c) H_2Te, –2   (d) CS_2, –2

(e) $CaSO_4$, +6   (f) CdS, –2   (g) $ZnTe$, –2

Oxygen (a group 6A element) is in the –2 oxidation state in compounds (a), (b), and (e).

22.44   (a) SCl_4, +4   (b) SeO_3, +6   (c) $Na_2S_2O_3$, +2   (d) H_2S, –2

(e) H_2SO_4, +6   (f) SO_2, +4   (g) $HgTe$, –2

Oxygen (a group 6A element) is in the –2 oxidation state in compounds (b), (c), (e) and (f).

22.45   *Analyze/Plan.* The half-reaction for oxidation in all these cases is:

$H_2S(aq) \rightarrow S(s) + 2H^+ + 2e^-$ (The product could be written as $S_8(s)$, but this is not necessary. In fact it is not necessarily the case that S_8 would be formed, rather than some other allotropic form of the element.) Combine this half-reaction with the given reductions to write complete equations. The reduction in (c) happens only in acid solution. The reactants in (d) are acids, so the medium is acidic.   *Solve.*

(a) $2Fe^{3+}(aq) + H_2S(aq) \rightarrow 2Fe^{2+}(aq) + S(s) + 2H^+(aq)$

(b) $Br_2(l) + H_2S(aq) \rightarrow 2Br^-(aq) + S(s) + 2H^+(aq)$

(c) $2MnO_4^-(aq) + 6H^+(aq) + 5H_2S(aq) \rightarrow 2Mn^{2+}(aq) + 5S(s) + 8H_2O(l)$

(d) $2NO_3^-(aq) + H_2S(aq) + 2H^+(aq) \rightarrow 2NO_2(aq) + S(s) + 2H_2O(l)$

22.46   An aqueous solution of SO_2 contains H_2SO_3 and is acidic. Use H_2SO_3 as the reducing agent and balance assuming acid conditions.

(a)

$$2[MnO_4^-(aq) + 8H^+(aq) + 5e^- \rightarrow Mn^{2+}(aq) + 4H_2O(l)]$$
$$\underline{5[H_2SO_3(aq) + H_2O(l) \rightarrow SO_4^{2-}(aq) + 4H^+(aq) + 2e^-]}$$
$$2MnO_4^-(aq) + 5H_2SO_3(aq) \rightarrow 2MnSO_4(aq) + 3SO_4^{2-}(aq) + 3H_2O(l) + 4H^+(aq)$$

(b)

$$Cr_2O_7^{2-}(aq) + 14H^+(aq) + 6e^- \rightarrow 2Cr^{3+}(aq) + 7H_2O(l)$$
$$\underline{3[H_2SO_3(aq) + H_2O(l) \rightarrow SO_4^{2-}(aq) + 4H^+(aq) + 2e^-]}$$
$$Cr_2O_7^{2-}(aq) + 3H_2SO_3(aq) + 2H^+(aq) \rightarrow 2Cr^{3+}(aq) + 3SO_4^{2-}(aq) + 4H_2O(l)$$

(c)

$$Hg_2^{2+}(aq) + 2e^- \rightarrow 2Hg(l)$$
$$\underline{H_2SO_3(aq) + H_2O(l) \rightarrow SO_4^{2-}(aq) + 4H^+(aq) + 2e^-}$$
$$Hg_2^{2+}(aq) + H_2SO_3(aq) + H_2O(l) \rightarrow 2Hg(l) + SO_4^{2-}(aq) + 4H^+(aq)$$

22.47   *Analyze/Plan.* For each substance, count valence electrons, draw the correct Lewis structure, and apply the rules of VSEPR to decide electron domain geometry and geometric structure.   *Solve.*

(a) trigonal pyramidal   (b) bent (free rotation around S-S bond)   (c) tetrahedral

22.48 SF_4, 34 e$^-$ SF_5^-, 42 e$^-$

(lone pairs on F atoms omitted for clarity)

trigonal bipyramidal	octahedral
electron pair geometry	electron pair geometry
see-saw	square pyramidal
molecular geometry	molecular geometry

22.49   *Analyze/Plan.* Use information on the descriptive chemistry of sulfur given in Section 22.6 to complete and balance the equations.   *Solve.*

(a) $SO_2(s) + H_2O(l) \rightarrow H_2SO_3(aq) \rightleftharpoons H^+(aq) + HSO_3^-(aq)$

(b) $ZnS(s) + 2HCl(aq) \rightarrow ZnCl_2(aq) + H_2S(g)$

(c) $8SO_3^{2-}(aq) + S_8(s) \rightarrow 8S_2O_3^{2-}(aq)$

(d) $SO_3(aq) + H_2SO_4(l) \rightarrow H_2S_2O_7(l)$

22.50   (a) $Al_2Se_3(s) + 6H^+(aq) \rightarrow 2Al^{3+}(aq) + 3H_2Se(g)$

(b) $Cl_2(aq) + S_2O_3^{2-}(aq) + H_2O(l) \rightarrow 2Cl^-(aq) + S(s) + SO_4^{2-}(aq) + 2H^+(aq)$

Nitrogen and the Group 5A Elements (sections 22.7 and 22.8)

22.51   *Analyze/Plan.* Follow the rules for assigning oxidation numbers in Section 4.4 and the logic in Sample Exercise 4.8.   *Solve.*

(a) $NaNO_2$, +3   (b) NH_3, –3   (c) N_2O, +1 (d) $NaCN$, –3

(e) HNO_3, +5   (f) NO_2, +4   (g) N_2, 0   (h) BN, –3

22.52   (a) NO, +2   (b) N_2H_4, –2   (c) KCN, –3

(d) $NaNO_2$, +3   (e) NH_4Cl, –3   (f) Li_3N, –3

22.53   *Analyze/Plan.* For each substance, count valence electrons, draw the correct Lewis structure, and apply the rules of VSEPR to decide electron domain geometry and geometric structure.   *Solve.*

(a)   :Ö=N̈—Ö̈—H ⟷ :Ö̈—N̈=Ö—H

The molecule is bent around the central oxygen and nitrogen atoms; the four atoms need not lie in a plane. The right-most form does not minimize formal charges and is less important in the actual bonding model. The oxidation state of N is +3.

(b)   [:N̈=N=N̈:]$^-$ ⟷ [:N≡N—N̈:]$^-$ ⟷ [:N̈—N≡N:]$^-$

The molecule is linear. The oxidation state of N is −1/3.

(c)

$$\left[\begin{array}{c} \overset{\displaystyle H \quad H}{\underset{\displaystyle H \quad H}{H-N-N:}} \end{array} \right]^{+}$$

(d)

$$\left[\begin{array}{c} :\ddot{O}: \\ | \\ :\ddot{O}-N=\ddot{O} \end{array} \right]^{-}$$

The geometry is tetrahedral around the left nitrogen, trigonal pyramidal around the right. The oxidation state of N is −2.

(three equivalent resonance forms) The ion is trigonal planar. The oxidation state of N is +5.

22.54　(a)

$$\left[\begin{array}{c} H \\ | \\ H-N-H \\ | \\ H \end{array} \right]^{+}$$

The ion is tetrahedral. The oxidation state of N is −3.

(b) $\left[\ddot{O}=N-\ddot{O}: \right]^{-} \longleftrightarrow \left[:\ddot{O}-N=\ddot{O} \right]^{-}$

The ion is bent with a 120° O−N−O angle. The oxidation state of N is +3.

(c) $:\ddot{N}=N=\ddot{O}: \longleftrightarrow :N\equiv N-\ddot{O}: \longleftrightarrow :\ddot{N}-N\equiv O:$

The molecule is linear. Again, the third resonance form makes less contribution to the structure because of the high formal charges involved. The oxidation state of N is +1.

(d) $\ddot{O}=\dot{N}-\ddot{O}: \longleftrightarrow :\ddot{O}-\dot{N}=\ddot{O}:$

The molecule is bent (nonlinear). The odd electron resides on N because it is less electronegative than O. The oxidation state of N is +4.

22.55　*Analyze/Plan.* Use information on the descriptive chemistry of nitrogen given in Section 22.7 to complete and balance the equations.　*Solve.*

(a)　$Mg_3N_2(s) + 6H_2O(l) \rightarrow 2NH_3(g) + 3Mg(OH)_2(s)$

Because $H_2O(l)$ is a reactant, the state of NH_3 in the products could be expressed as $NH_3(aq)$.

(b)　$2NO(g) + O_2(g) \rightarrow 2NO_2(g)$, redox reaction

(c)　$N_2O_5(g) + H_2O(l) \rightarrow 2H^+(aq) + 2NO_3^-(aq)$

(d)　$NH_3(aq) + H^+(aq) \rightarrow NH_4^+(aq)$

(e)　$N_2H_4(l) + O_2(g) \rightarrow N_2(g) + 2H_2O(g)$, redox reaction

22.56　(a)　$4Zn(s) + 2NO_3^-(aq) + 10H^+(aq) \rightarrow 4Zn^{2+}(aq) + N_2O(g) + 5H_2O(l)$

(b) $4NO_3^-(aq) + S(s) + 4H^+(aq) \rightarrow 4NO_2(g) + SO_2(g) + 2H_2O(l)$

     (or $6NO_3^-(aq) + S(s) + 4H^+(aq) \rightarrow 6NO_2(g) + SO_4^{2-}(aq) + 2H_2O(l)$

(c) $2NO_3^-(aq) + 3SO_2(g) + 2H_2O(l) \rightarrow 2NO(g) + 3SO_4^{2-}(aq) + 4H^+(aq)$

(d) $N_2H_4(g) + 5F_2(g) \rightarrow 2NF_3(g) + 4HF(g)$

(e) $4CrO_4^{2-}(aq) + 3N_2H_4(aq) + 4H_2O(l) \rightarrow 4Cr(OH)_4^-(aq) + 4OH^-(aq) + 3N_2(g)$

22.57   *Analyze/Plan.* Follow the method for writing balanced half-reactions given in Section 20.2 and Sample Exercises 20.2 and 20.3   *Solve.*

(a) $HNO_2(aq) + H_2O(l) \rightarrow NO_3^-(aq) + 3H^+(aq) + 2e^-,\ E^\circ_{red} = 0.96$ V

(b) $N_2(g) + H_2O(l) \rightarrow N_2O(g) + 2H^+(aq) + 2e^-,\ E^\circ_{red} = 1.77$ V

22.58   (a) $NO_3^-(aq) + 4H^+(aq) + 3e^- \rightarrow NO(g) + 2H_2O(l)$

         (b) $HNO_2(aq) \rightarrow NO_2(g) + H^+(aq) + 1e^-$

22.59   *Analyze/Plan.* Follow the rules for assigning oxidation numbers in Section 4.4 and the logic in Sample Exercise 4.8.   *Solve.*

(a) H_3PO_3, +3	(b) $H_4P_2O_7$, +5	(c) $SbCl_3$, +3
(d) Mg_3As_2, –3	(e) P_2O_5, +5	(f) Na_3PO_4, +5

22.60

(a) PO_4^{3-}, +5	(b) H_3AsO_3, +3	(c) Sb_2S_3, +3
(d) $Ca(H_2PO_4)_2$, +5	(e) K_3P, –3	(f) $GaAs$, –3

22.61   *Analyze/Plan.* Consider the structures of the compounds of interest when explaining the observations.   *Solve.*

(a)   Phosphorus is a larger atom and can more easily accommodate five surrounding atoms and an expanded octet of electrons than nitrogen can. Also, P has energetically "available" 3d orbitals which participate in the bonding, but nitrogen does not.

(b)   Only one of the three hydrogens in H_3PO_2 is bonded to oxygen. The other two are bonded directly to phosphorus and are not easily ionized because the P—H bond is not very polar.

(c) PH_3 is a weaker base than H_2O (PH_4^+ is a stronger acid than H_3O^+). Any attempt to add H^+ to PH_3 in the presence of H_2O merely causes protonation of H_2O.

(d)   Refer to the structures of white and red phosphorus in Figure 22.27. White phosphorus consists of P_4 molecules, with P—P—P bond angles of 60°. Each P atom has four VSEPR pairs of electrons, so the predicted electron pair geometry is tetrahedral and the preferred bond angle is 109°. Because of the severely strained bond angles in P_4 molecules, white phosphorus is highly reactive. Red phosphorus is a chain of groups of four P atoms. It has fewer severely strained P—P—P bond angles and is less reactive than white phosphorus.

22.62   (a)   Only two of the hydrogens in H_3PO_3 are bound to oxygen. The third is attached directly to phosphorus, and not readily ionized, because the H—P bond is not very polar.

(b)   The smaller, more electronegative nitrogen withdraws more electron density from the O—H bond, making it more polar and more likely to ionize.

(c)   Phosphate rock consists of $Ca_3(PO_4)_2$, which is only slightly soluble in water. The phosphorus is unavailable for plant use.

(d) N_2 can form stable π bonds to complete the octet of both N atoms. Because phosphorus atoms are larger than nitrogen atoms, they do not form stable π bonds with themselves and must form σ bonds with several other phosphorus atoms (producing P_4 tetrahedral or chain structures) to complete their octets.

(e)   In solution Na_3PO_4 is completely dissociated into Na^+ and PO_4^{3-}. PO_4^{3-}, the conjugate base of the very weak acid HPO_4^{2-}, has a K_b of 2.4×10^{-2} and produces a considerable amount of OH^- by hydrolysis of H_2O.

22.63   *Analyze/Plan.* Use information on the descriptive chemistry of phosphorus given in Section 22.8 to complete and balance the equations.   *Solve.*

(a) $2Ca_3(PO_4)_2(s) + 6SiO_2(s) + 10C(s) \xrightarrow{\Delta} P_4(g) + 6CaSiO_3(l) + 10CO(g)$

(b) $PBr_3(l) + 3H_2O(l) \rightarrow H_3PO_3 (aq) + 3HBr(aq)$

(c) $4PBr_3 (g) + 6H_2(g) \rightarrow P_4 (g) + 12HBr(g)$

22.64   (a) $PCl_5(l) + 4H_2O(l) \rightarrow H_3PO_4 (aq) + 5HCl(aq)$

(b) $2H_3PO_4(aq) \xrightarrow{\Delta} H_4P_2O_7(aq) + H_2O(l)$

(c) $P_4O_{10}(s) + 6H_2O(l) \rightarrow 4H_3PO_4 (aq)$

Carbon, the Other Group 4A Elements, and Boron (sections 22.9-22.11)

22.65   *Analyze/Plan.* Review the nomenclature rules and ion names in Section 2.8.   *Solve.*
(a)   HCN   (b) $Ni(CO)_4$ (c) $Ba(HCO_3)_2$ (d) CaC_2 (e) K_2CO_3

22.66   (a) H_2CO_3 (b) NaCN   (c) $KHCO_3$ (d) C_2H_2 (f) $Fe(CO)_5$

22.67   *Analyze/Plan.* Use information on the descriptive chemistry of carbon given in Section 22.9 to complete and balance the equations.   *Solve.*

(a) $ZnCO_3(s) \xrightarrow{\Delta} ZnO(s) + CO_2(g)$

(b) $BaC_2(s) + 2H_2O(l) \rightarrow Ba^{2+}(aq) + 2OH^-(aq) + C_2H_2(g)$

(c) $2C_2H_2(g) + 5O_2(g) \rightarrow 4CO_2(g) + 2H_2O(g)$

(d) $CS_2(g) + 3O_2(g) \rightarrow CO_2(g) + 2SO_2(g)$

(e) $Ca(CN)_2(s) + 2HBr(aq) \rightarrow CaBr_2(aq) + 2HCN(aq)$

22.68   (a) $CO_2(g) + OH^-(aq) \rightarrow HCO_3^-(aq)$

(b) $NaHCO_3(s) + H^+(aq) \rightarrow Na^+(aq) + H_2O(l) + CO_2(g)$

(c) $2CaO(s) + 5C(s) \xrightarrow{\Delta} 2CaC_2(s) + CO_2(g)$

(d) $C(s) + H_2O(g) \xrightarrow{\Delta} H_2(g) + CO(g)$

(e) $CuO(s) + CO(g) \rightarrow Cu(s) + CO_2(g)$

22.69 *Analyze/Plan.* Use information on the descriptive chemistry of carbon given in Section 22.9 to complete and balance the equations. *Solve.*

(a) $2CH_4(g) + 2NH_3(g) + 3O_2(g) \xrightarrow[\text{cat}]{800°C} 2HCN(g) + 6H_2O(g)$

(b) $NaHCO_3(s) + H^+(aq) \rightarrow CO_2(g) + H_2O(l) + Na^+(aq)$

(c) $2BaCO_3(s) + O_2(g) + 2SO_2(g) \rightarrow 2BaSO_4(s) + 2CO_2(g)$

22.70 (a) $2Mg(s) + CO_2(g) \rightarrow 2MgO(s) + C(s)$

(b) $6CO_2(g) + 6H_2O(l) \xrightarrow{h\nu} C_6H_{12}O_6(aq) + 6O_2(g)$

(c) $CO_3^{2-}(aq) + H_2O(l) \rightarrow HCO_3^-(aq) + OH^-(aq)$

22.71 *Analyze/Plan.* Follow the rules for assigning oxidation numbers in Section 4.4 and the logic in Sample Exercise 4.8. *Solve.*

(a) H_3BO_3, +3   (b) $SiBr_4$, +4   (c) $PbCl_2$, +2

(d) $Na_2B_4O_7 \cdot 10H_2O$, +3   (e) B_2O_3, +3   (f) GeO_2, +4

22.72 (a) SiO_2, +4   (b) $GeCl_4$, +4   (c) $NaBH_4$, +3

(d) $SnCl_2$, +2   (e) B_2H_6, +3   (f) BCl_3, +3

22.73 *Analyze/Plan.* Consider periodic trends within a family, particularly metallic character, as well as descriptive chemistry in Sections 22.9 and 22.10. *Solve.*

(a) Tin; see Table 22.8. The filling of the 4f subshell at the beginning of the sixth row of the periodic table increases Z and Z_{eff} for later elements. This causes the ionization energy of Pb to be greater than that of Sn.

(b) Carbon, silicon, and germanium; these are the nonmetal and metalloids in group 4A. They form compounds ranging from XH_4 (–4) to XO_2 (+4). The metals tin and lead are not found in negative oxidation states.

(c) Silicon; silicates are the main component of sand.

22.74 (a) carbon   (b) lead   (c) germanium

22.75 *Analyze/Plan.* Consider the structural chemistry of silicates discussed in Section 22.10 and shown in Figure 22.34. *Solve.*

(a) Tetrahedral

(b) Metasilicic acid will probably adopt the single-strand silicate chain structure shown in Figure 22.34(b). The empirical formula shows 3 O and 2 H atoms per Si atom. The chain has the same Si to O ratio as metasilicic acid. Furthermore, in the chain structure, there are two terminal (not bridging) O atoms on each Si. These can accommodate the 2 H atoms associated with each Si atom of the acid. The sheet structure does not fulfill these requirements.

22.76 Carbon forms carbonates rather than silicates to take advantage of its ability to form pi bonds. Because of its relatively compact 2p valence orbitals, carbon can engage in effective pi-type overlap and form multiple bonds with itself and other elements.

Carbonate, CO_3^{2-}, the anion present in carbonates, takes advantage of this ability to form stable pi bonds, and is additionally stabilized by resonance. In silicates, silicon atoms form only single bonds and are tetrahedral.

22.77   (a)   Diborane (Figure 22.36 and below) has bridging H atoms linking the two B atoms. The structure of ethane shown below has the C atoms bound directly, with no bridging atoms.

(b) B_2H_6 is an electron deficient molecule. It has 12 valence electrons, while C_2H_6 has 14 valence electrons. The 6 valence electron pairs in B_2H_6 are all involved in B—H sigma bonding, so the only way to satisfy the octet rule at B is to have the bridging H atoms shown in Figure 22.36.

(c)   A hydride ion, H^-, has two electrons while an H atom has one. The term *hydridic* indicates that the H atoms in B_2H_6 have more than the usual amount of electron density for a covalently bound H atom.

22.78   (a) $B_2H_6(g) + 6H_2O(l) \rightarrow 2H_3BO_3(aq) + 6H_2(g)$

(b) $4H_3BO_3(s) \xrightarrow{\Delta} H_2B_4O_7(s) + 5H_2O(g)$

(c) $B_2O_3(s) + 3H_2O(l) \rightarrow 2H_3BO_3(aq)$

Additional Exercises

22.79   (a)   *Allotropes* are different structural forms of the same element. They are composed of atoms of a single element bound into different structures. For example, graphite, diamond, and buckey balls are all allotropes of carbon.

(b)   *Disproportionation* is an oxidation-reduction process where the same element is both oxidized and reduced.

(c)   *Interhalogen* is a compound formed from atoms of two or more halogens.

(d)   An *acidic anhydride* is a neutral molecule that is the oxide of a nonmetal. It reacts with water to produce an acid.

(e)   A *condensation reaction* is the combination of two molecules to form a large molecule and a small one such as H_2O or HCl.

(f)   *Protium* is the isotope of hydrogen with a mass number of 1. The nucleus of protium contains one proton and no neutrons.

22.80   (a) $BrO_3^-(aq) + XeF_2(aq) + H_2O(l) \rightarrow Xe(g) + 2HF(aq) + BrO_4^-(aq)$

(b) $BrO_3^-, +5; \quad BrO_4^-, +7$

22.81   (a) $SO_2(g) + H_2O(l) \rightleftharpoons H_2SO_3(aq)$

(b) $Cl_2O_7(g) + H_2O(l) \rightleftharpoons 2HClO_4(aq)$

(c) $Na_2O_2(s) + 2H_2O(l) \rightarrow H_2O_2(aq) + 2NaOH(aq)$

(d) $\quad BaC_2(s) + 2H_2O(l) \rightarrow Ba^{2+}(aq) + 2OH^-(aq) + C_2H_2(g)$

(e) $\quad 2RbO_2(s) + 2H_2O(l) \rightarrow 2Rb^+(aq) + 2OH^-(aq) + O_2(g) + H_2O_2(aq)$

(f) $\quad Mg_3N_2(s) + 6H_2O(l) \rightarrow 3Mg(OH)_2(s) + 2NH_3(g)$

(g) $\quad NaH(s) + H_2O(l) \rightarrow NaOH(aq) + H_2(g)$

22.82 (a) $\quad H_2SO_6 - H_2O \rightarrow SO_3$

(b) $\quad 2HClO_3 - H_2O \rightarrow Cl_2O_5$

(c) $\quad 2HNO_2 - H_2O \rightarrow N_2O_3$

(d) $\quad H_2CO_3 - H_2O \rightarrow CO_2$

(e) $\quad 2H_3PO_6 - 3H_2O \rightarrow P_2O_5$

22.83 Sulfur has a total of six valence electrons; its possible oxidation states range from −2 to +6. SO_3 has sulfur in its maximum +6 oxidation state; it cannot lose electrons and serve as a reducing agent. SO_2 has sulfur in the +4 oxidation state. It can lose electrons, be oxidized and serve as a reducing agent.

22.84

$$\begin{array}{lll} S(g) + O_2(g) \rightarrow SO_2(g) & \Delta H = -296.9 \text{ kJ} & (1) \\ SO_2(g) + 1/2\, O_2(g) \rightarrow SO_3(g) & \Delta H = -98.3 \text{ kJ} & (2) \\ SO_3(g) + H_2O(l) \rightarrow H_2SO_4(aq) & \Delta H = -130 \text{ kJ} & (3) \\ \hline S(g) + 3/2\, O_2(g) + H_2O(l) \rightarrow H_2SO_4(aq) & \Delta H = -525 \text{ kJ} & \end{array}$$

$$5000 \text{ lb } H_2SO_4 \times \frac{453.6 \text{ g}}{1 \text{ lb}} \times \frac{1 \text{ mol } H_2SO_4}{98.09 \text{ g}} \times \frac{-525 \text{ kJ}}{\text{mol } H_2SO_4} = -1.21 \times 10^7 \text{ kJ}$$

One mole of H_2SO_4 produces 525 kJ of heat, 5000 lb of H_2SO_4 produces 1.21×10^7 kJ.

22.85 (a) $\quad PO_4^{3-}, +5; NO_3^-, +5$

(b) The Lewis structure for NO_4^{3-} would be:

$$\left[\begin{array}{c} \ddot{O}: \\ | \\ :\ddot{O}-N-\ddot{O}: \\ | \\ :\ddot{O}: \end{array} \right]^{3-}$$

The formal charge on N is +1 and on each O atom is −1. The four electronegative oxygen atoms withdraw electron density, leaving the nitrogen deficient. Since N can form a maximum of four bonds, it cannot form a π bond with one or more of the O atoms to regain electron density, as the P atom in PO_4^{3-} does. Also, the short N—O distance would lead to a tight tetrahedron of O atoms subject to steric repulsion.

22.86 (a) Although P_4, P_4O_6 and P_4O_{10} all have four P atoms in a tetrahedral arrangement, the bonding **between** P atoms and **by** P atoms is not the same in the three molecules. In P_4, the 4 P atoms are bound only to each other by P—P single bonds with strained bond angles of approximately 60°. In the two oxides, the 4 P atoms are directly bound to oxygen atoms, not to each other. Bonding by P atoms in P_4O_6 and P_4O_{10} is very similar. Each contains the P_6O_6 cage, formed by four

P_3O_3 rings which share a P—O—P edge. Phosphorus bonding to oxygen maintains the overall P_4 tetrahedron but allows the P atoms to move away from each other so that the angle strain is relieved relative to molecular P_4. The P—O—P and O—P—O angles in both oxides are near the ideal 109°. In P_4O_6, each P is bound to 3 O atoms and has a lone pair completing its octet. In P_4O_{10}, the lone pair is replaced by a terminal O atom and each P is bound to 3 bridging and 1 terminal O atom.

(b)

In both structures there are unshared pairs on all oxygens to give octets and the geometry around each P is approximately tetrahedral.

22.87 $GeO_2(s) + C(s) \xrightarrow{\Delta} Ge(l) + CO_2(g)$

$Ge(l) + 2Cl_2(g) \rightarrow GeCl_4(l)$

$GeCl_4(l) + 2H_2O(l) \rightarrow GeO_2(s) + 4HCl(g)$

$GeO_2(s) + 2H_2(g) \rightarrow Ge(s) + 2H_2O(l)$

22.88   Assume that the reactions occur in acidic solution. The half-reaction for reduction of H_2O_2 is in all cases $H_2O_2(aq) + 2H^+(aq) + 2e^- \rightarrow 2H_2O(aq)$.

(a) $N_2H_4(aq) + 2H_2O_2(aq) \rightarrow N_2(g) + 4H_2O(l)$

(b) $SO_2(g) + H_2O_2(aq) \rightarrow SO_4{}^{2-}(aq) + 2H^+(aq)$

(c) $NO_2{}^-(aq) + H_2O_2(aq) \rightarrow NO_3{}^-(aq) + H_2O(l)$

(d) $H_2S(g) + H_2O_2(aq) \rightarrow S(s) + 2H_2O(l)$

(e) $2H^+(aq) + H_2O_2(aq) + 2e^- \rightarrow 2H_2O(l)$

$$\underline{\hspace{3cm} 2[Fe^{2+}(aq) \rightarrow Fe^{3+}(aq) + e^-] \hspace{3cm}}$$
$$2Fe^{2+}(aq) + H_2O_2(aq) + 2H^+(aq) \rightarrow 2Fe^{3+}(aq) + 2H_2O(l)$$

Integrative Exercises

22.89   (a) $100.0 \times 10^3 \, g \, FeTi \times \dfrac{1 \, mol \, FeTi}{103.7 \, g \, FeTi} \times \dfrac{1 \, mol \, H_2}{1 \, mol \, FeTi} \times \dfrac{2.016 \, g \, H_2}{1 \, mol \, H_2} = 1944.1 = 1.94 \times 10^3 \, g \, H_2$

(b) $V = \dfrac{1944.1 \, g \, H_2}{2.016 \, g/mol \, H_2} \times \dfrac{0.08206 \, L\text{-}atm}{mol\text{-}K} \times \dfrac{273 \, K}{1 \, atm} = 21,603 = 2.16 \times 10^4 \, L \, H_2$

(c) $2H_2(g) + O_2(g) \rightarrow 2H_2O(l)$

$\Delta H° = 2 \Delta H_f° \, H_2O(l) - 2 \Delta H_f° \, H_2(g) - \Delta H_f° \, O_2(g)$

$\Delta H° = 2(-285.83) - 2(0) - (0) = -571.66 \, kJ$

$$1944.1 \, g \, H_2 \times \frac{1 \, mol \, H_2}{2.016 \, g \, H_2} \times \frac{-571.66 \, kJ}{2 \, mol \, H_2} = -275,636 = -2.76 \times 10^5 \, kJ$$

The minus sign indicates that energy is produced.

22.90   From Appendix C, we need only ΔH_f° for $F(g)$, so that we can estimate ΔH for the process:

$$\begin{aligned} F_2(g) &\rightarrow F(g) + F(g); & \Delta H^\circ &= 160 \, kJ \\ XeF_2(g) &\rightarrow Xe(g) + F_2(g) & -\Delta H_f^\circ &= 109 \, kJ \\ \hline XeF_2(g) &\rightarrow Xe(g) + 2F(g) & \Delta H^\circ &= 269 \, kJ \end{aligned}$$

The average Xe—F bond enthalpy is thus 269/2 = 134 kJ. Similarly,

$$\begin{aligned} XeF_4(g) &\rightarrow Xe(g) + 2F_2(g) & -\Delta H_f^\circ &= 218 \, kJ \\ 2F_2(g) &\rightarrow 4F(g) & \Delta H^\circ &= 320 \, kJ \\ \hline XeF_4(g) &\rightarrow Xe(g) + 4F(g) & \Delta H^\circ &= 538 \, kJ \end{aligned}$$

Average Xe—F bond energy = 538/4 = 134 kJ

$$\begin{aligned} XeF_6(g) &\rightarrow Xe(g) + 3F_2(g) & -\Delta H_f^\circ &= 298 \, kJ \\ 3F_2(g) &\rightarrow 6F(g) & \Delta H^\circ &= 480 \, kJ \\ \hline XeF_6(g) &\rightarrow Xe(g) + 6F(g) & \Delta H^\circ &= 778 \, kJ \end{aligned}$$

Average Xe—F bond energy = 778/6 = 130 kJ

The average bond enthalpies are: XeF_2, 134 kJ; XeF_4, 134 kJ; XeF_6, 130 kJ. They are remarkably constant in the series.

22.91   (a) $H_2(g) + 1/2 \, O_2(g) \rightarrow H_2O(l)$; $\Delta H = -285.83 \, kJ/mol \, H_2$

                $CH_4(g) + 2O_2(g) \rightarrow CO_2(g) + 2H_2O(l)$

                $\Delta H = 2(-285.83) - 393.5 - (-74.8) = -890.4 \, kJ/mol \, CH_4$

     (b)   for H_2: $\dfrac{-285.83 \, kJ}{1 \, mol \, H_2} \times \dfrac{1 \, mol \, H_2}{2.0159 \, g \, H_2} = -141.79 \, kJ/g \, H_2$

                 for CH_4: $\dfrac{-890.4 \, kJ}{1 \, mol \, CH_4} \times \dfrac{1 \, mol \, CH_4}{16.043 \, g \, CH_4} = -55.50 \, kJ/g \, CH_4$

     (c)   Find the number of moles of gas that occupy $1 \, m^3$ at STP:

$$n = \frac{1 \, atm \times 1 \, m^3}{273 \, K} \times \frac{1 \, mol \text{-} K}{0.08206 \, L \text{-} atm} \times \left[\frac{100 \, cm}{1 \, m}\right]^3 \times \frac{1 \, L}{10^3 \, cm^3} = 44.64 \, mol$$

                 for H_2: $\dfrac{-285.83 \, kJ}{1 \, mol \, H_2} \times \dfrac{44.64 \, mol \, H_2}{1 \, m^3 \, H_2} = -1.276 \times 10^4 \, kJ/m^3 \, H_2$

                 for CH_4: $\dfrac{-890.4 \, kJ}{1 \, mol \, CH_4} \times \dfrac{44.64 \, mol \, CH_4}{1 \, m^3 \, CH_4} = -3.975 \times 10^4 \, kJ/m^3 \, CH_4$

22.92 (a) First calculate the molar solubility of Cl_2 in water.

$$n = \frac{1\,atm\,(0.310\,L)}{\dfrac{0.08206\,L\text{-}atm}{1\,mol\text{-}K} \times 273\,K} = 0.01384 = 0.0138\,mol\,Cl_2$$

$$M = \frac{0.01384\,mol}{0.100\,L} = 0.1384 = 0.138M$$

$[Cl^-] = [HOCl] = [H^+]$ Let this quantity = x. Then, $\dfrac{x^3}{(0.1384 - x)} = 4.7 \times 10^{-4}$

Assuming that x is small compared with 0.1384:

$x^3 = (0.1384)(4.7 \times 10^{-4}) = 6.504 \times 10^{-5}$; $x = 0.0402 = 0.040\,M$

We can correct the denominator using this value, to get a better estimate of x:

$$\frac{x^3}{0.1384 - 0.0402} = 4.7 \times 10^{-4}; x = 0.0359 = 0.036\,M$$

One more round of approximation gives x = 0.0364 = 0.036 M. This is the equilibrium concentration of HClO.

(b) From the equilibrium reaction in part (a), $[H^+] = 0.036\,M$. $pH = -\log[H^+] = 1.4$

The HOCl produced by this equilibrium will ionize slightly to produce additional $H^+(aq)$. However, the K_a value for HOCl is small, 3.0×10^{-8}, and the acid ionization will be suppressed by the presence of $H^+(aq)$ from the solubility equilibrium. $[H^+]$ from ionization of HOCl will be small compared to 0.036 M and will not significantly impact the pH.

22.93 (a) $2NH_4ClO_4(s) \xrightarrow{\Delta} N_2(g) + 2HCl(g) + 3H_2O(g) + 5/2\,O_2(g)$

$NH_4ClO_4(s) \xrightarrow{\Delta} 1/2\,N_2(g) + HCl(g) + 3/2\,H_2O(g) + 5/4\,O_2(g)$

(b) $\Delta H° = \Sigma\,\Delta H_f° \text{ prod} - \Sigma\,\Delta H \text{ react}$

$\Delta H° = \Delta H_f°\,HCl(g) + 3/2\,\Delta H_f°\,H_2O(g) + 1/2\,\Delta H_f°\,N_2(g) + 5/4\,\Delta H_f°\,O_2(g) - \Delta H_f°\,NH_4ClO_4\Delta H°$

$= -92.30\,kJ + 3/2(-241.82\,kJ) + 1/2\,(0\,kJ) + 5/4\,(0\,kJ) - (-295.8\,kJ)$

$= -159.2\,kJ/mol\,NH_4ClO_4$

(c) The aluminum reacts exothermically with $O_2(g)$ and HCl(g) produced in the decomposition, providing additional heat and thrust.

(d) There are (1/2 + 1 + 3/2 + 5/4) = 4.25 mol gas per mol NH_4ClO_4 decomposed

$$1\,lb\,NH_4ClO_4 \times \frac{453.6\,g}{1\,lb} \frac{1\,mol\,NH_4ClO_4}{117.49\,g\,NH_4ClO_4} \times \frac{4.25\,mol\,gas}{1\,mol\,NH_4ClO_4} = 16.408 = 16.4\,mol\,gas$$

$$V = \frac{nRT}{P} = 16.408\,mol\,gas \times \frac{0.08206\,L\text{-}atm}{mol\text{-}K} \times \frac{273\,K}{1\,atm} = 367.57 = 368\,L$$

22.94 (a) $N_2H_4(g) + O_2(g) \rightarrow N_2(g) + 2H_2O(l)$

(b) $\Delta H° = \Delta H_f°\,N_2(g) + 2\Delta H_f°\,H_2O(l) - \Delta H_f°\,N_2H_4(aq) - \Delta H_f°\,O_2(g)$

$= 0 + 2(-285.83) - 95.40 - 0 = -667.06\,kJ$

(c) $\dfrac{9.1 \text{ g O}_2}{1 \times 10^6 \text{ g H}_2\text{O}} \times \dfrac{1.0 \text{ g H}_2\text{O}}{1 \text{ mL H}_2\text{O}} \times \dfrac{1000 \text{ mL}}{1 \text{ L}} \times 3.0 \times 10^4 \text{ L} = 273 = 2.7 \times 10^2 \text{ g O}_2$

$2.73 \times 10^2 \text{ g O}_2 \times \dfrac{1 \text{ mol O}_2}{32.00 \text{ g O}_2} \times \dfrac{1 \text{ mol N}_2\text{H}_4}{1 \text{ mol O}_2} \times \dfrac{32.05 \text{ g N}_2\text{H}_4}{1 \text{ mol N}_2\text{H}_4} = 2.7 \times 10^2 \text{ g N}_2\text{H}_4$

22.95 (a) $SO_2(g) + 2H_2S(aq) \rightarrow 3S(s) + 2H_2O(g)$ or, if we assume S_8 is the product,

$8SO_2(g) + 16H_2S(aq) \rightarrow 3S_8(s) + 16H_2O(g)$.

(b)   Assume that all S in the coal becomes SO_2 upon combustion, so that

1 mol S (coal) = 1 mol SO_2; 1 ton = 2000 lb; 760 torr = 1.00 atm

$4000 \text{ lb coal} \times \dfrac{0.035 \text{ lb S}}{1 \text{ lb coal}} \times \dfrac{453.6 \text{ g S}}{1 \text{ lb S}} \times \dfrac{1 \text{ mol S (coal)}}{32.07 \text{ g S}} \times \dfrac{1 \text{ mol SO}_2}{1 \text{ mol S (coal)}} \times \dfrac{2 \text{ mol H}_2\text{S}}{1 \text{ mol SO}_2}$

$= 3960 = 4.0 \times 10^3 \text{ mol H}_2\text{S}$

$V = \dfrac{3960 \text{ mol} \times (0.08206 \text{ L-atm/mol-K}) \times 300 \text{ K}}{1.00 \text{ atm}} = 97{,}496 = 9.7 \times 10^4 \text{ L}$

(c) $3960 \text{ mol H}_2\text{S} \times \dfrac{3 \text{ mol S}}{2 \text{ mol H}_2\text{S}} \times \dfrac{32.07 \text{ g S}}{1 \text{ mol S}} = 1.9 \times 10^5 \text{ g S}$

This is about 210 lb S per ton of coal combusted. (However, two-thirds of this comes from the H_2S, which presumably at some point was also obtained from coal.)

22.96   *Plan.* vol air $\rightarrow$ kg air $\rightarrow$ g H_2S $\rightarrow$ g FeS. Use the ideal-gas equation to change volume of air to mass of air, (assuming 1.00 atm, 298 K and an average molar mass (MM) for air of 29.0 g/mol. Use (20 mg H_2S/kg) air to find the mass of H_2S in the given mass of air.

Solve.

$V_{air} = 12 \text{ ft} \times 20 \text{ ft} \times 8 \text{ ft} \times \dfrac{12^3 \text{ in}^3}{\text{ft}^3} \times \dfrac{2.54^3 \text{ cm}^3}{1^3 \text{ in}^3} \times \dfrac{1 \text{ L}}{1000 \text{ cm}^3} = 5.4368 \times 10^4 = 5 \times 10^4 \text{ L}$

$g_{air} = \dfrac{PV \text{ MM}}{RT}$; assume $P = 1.00$ atm, $T = 298$ K, $MM_{air} = 29.0$ g/mol

$g_{air} = \dfrac{1.00 \text{ atm} \times 5.4368 \times 10^4 \text{ L} \times 29.0 \text{ g/mol}}{298 \text{ K}} \times \dfrac{\text{mol-K}}{0.08206 \text{ L-atm}} = 64{,}476 = 6 \times 10^4 \text{ g air}$

$6.4476 \times 10^4 \text{ g air} \times \dfrac{1 \text{ kg}}{1000 \text{ g}} \times \dfrac{20 \text{ mg H}_2\text{S}}{1 \text{ kg air}} \times \dfrac{1 \text{ g}}{1000 \text{ mg}} = 1.2895 = 1 \text{ g H}_2\text{S}$

$FeS(s) + 2HCl(aq) \rightarrow FeCl_2(aq) + H_2S(g)$

$1.2895 \text{ g H}_2 \times \dfrac{1 \text{ mol H}_2}{34.08 \text{ g H}_2\text{S}} \times \dfrac{1 \text{ mol FeS}}{1 \text{ mol H}_2\text{S}} \times \dfrac{87.91 \text{ g FeS}}{1 \text{ mol FeS}} = 3.3263 = 3 \text{ g FeS}$

22.97   The reactions can be written as follows:

$$H_2(g) + X(\text{std state}) \rightarrow H_2X(g) \qquad \Delta H_f^\circ$$
$$2H(g) \rightarrow H_2(g) \qquad \Delta H_f^\circ(H{-}H)$$
$$X(g) \rightarrow X(\text{std state}) \qquad \Delta H_3$$
$$\overline{\text{Add}: 2H(g) + X(g) \rightarrow H_2X(g) \qquad \Delta H = \Delta H_f^\circ + \Delta H_f^\circ (H{-}H) + \Delta H_3}$$

These are all the necessary ΔH values. Thus,

Compound	$\underline{\Delta H}$	$\underline{D\ H{-}X}$
H_2O	$\Delta H = -241.8\ \text{kJ} - 436\ \text{kJ} - 248\ \text{kJ} = -926\ \text{kJ}$	463 kJ
H_2S	$\Delta H = -20.17\ \text{kJ} - 436\ \text{kJ} - 277\ \text{kJ} = -733\ \text{kJ}$	367 kJ
H_2Se	$\Delta H = +29.7\ \text{kJ} - 436\ \text{kJ} - 227\ \text{kJ} = -633\ \text{kJ}$	317 kJ
H_2Te	$\Delta H = +99.6\ \text{kJ} - 436\ \text{kJ} - 197\ \text{kJ} = -533\ \text{kJ}$	267 kJ

The average $H{-}X$ bond energy in each case is just half of ΔH. The $H{-}X$ bond energy decreases steadily in the series. The origin of this effect is probably the increasing size of the orbital from X with which the hydrogen 1s orbital must overlap.

22.98   (a)   MnSi: more than one element, so not metallic; high melting, so not molecular; insoluble in water, so not ionic; therefore covalent network.

(b) $MnSi(s) + HF(aq) \rightarrow SiH_4(g) + MnF_4(s)$

Reduction of Mn(IV) to Mn(II) is unlikely, because F^- is an extremely weak reducing agent. E_{red}° for $F_2(g) + 2\,e^- \rightarrow 2F^-(aq) = 2.87$ V

22.99   The most definitive experiment is X-ray crystallography to determine the Si–Si bond length. Compare the experimentally determined bond length to the Si–Si lengths in elemental Si, which is a covalent-network solid with only single bonds. If the length from the new compound is shorter than the bonds in elemental Si, the bond in the new compound has at least some double bond character. The difference in bond lengths must be greater than the uncertainty in the experimentally determined Si–Si bond length in the new compound. (We assume the structure of elemental Si has been determined with high precission.)

Visible absorption spectroscopy might be useful if the compound is colored. Otherwise, infrared absorption spectroscopy might give some useful information, but the intensity of double bond stretching frequencies is often small, and the peaks can be difficult to assign.

22.100 $N_2H_5^+(aq) \rightarrow N_2(g) + 5H^+(aq) + 4e^- \qquad E_{red}^\circ = -0.23$ V

Reduction of the metal should occur when E_{red}° of the metal ion is more positive than about –0.15 V. This is the case for (b) Sn^{2+} (marginal), (c) Cu^{2+}, (d) Ag^+ and (f) Co^{3+}

22.101　First write the balanced equation to give the number of moles of gaseous products per mole of hydrazine.

(A)　$(CH_3)_2NNH_2 + 2N_2O_4 \rightarrow 3N_2(g) + 4H_2O(g) + 2CO_2(g)$

(B)　$(CH_3)HNNH_2 + 5/4\,N_2O_4 \rightarrow 9/4\,N_2(g) + 3H_2O(g) + CO_2(g)$

In case (A) there are nine moles gas per one mole $(CH_3)_2NNH_2$ plus two moles N_2O_4. The total mass of reactants is $60 + 2(92) = 244$ g. Thus, there are

$$\frac{9 \text{ mol gas}}{244 \text{ g reactants}} = \frac{0.0369 \text{ mol gas}}{1 \text{ g reactants}}$$

In case (B) there are 6.25 moles of gaseous product per one mole $(CH_3)HNNH_2$ plus 1.25 moles N_2O_4. The total mass of this amount of reactants is $46.0 + 1.25(92.0) = 161$ g.

$$\frac{6.25 \text{ mol gas}}{161 \text{ g reactants}} = \frac{0.0388 \text{ mol gas}}{1 \text{ g reactants}}$$

Thus the methylhydrazine (B) has marginally greater thrust.

22.102　(a)　$HOOC{-}CH_2{-}COOH \xrightarrow{P_2O_5} C_3O_2 + 2H_2O$

(b)　$20.0 \text{ g } C_3H_4O_4 \times \dfrac{1 \text{ mol } C_3H_4O_4}{104.06 \text{ g } C_3H_4O_4} \times \dfrac{1 \text{ mol } C_3O_2}{1 \text{ mol } C_3H_4O_4} \times \dfrac{68.03 \text{ g } C_3O_2}{1 \text{ mol } C_3O_2} = 13.1 \text{ g } C_3O_2$

(c)　24 valence e$^-$, 12 e$^-$ pair　$\ddot{O}{=}C{=}C{=}C{=}\ddot{O}$

(d)　$C{=}O$, about 1.23 Å; $C{=}C$, 1.34 Å or less. Since consecutive $C{=}C$ bonds require sp hybrid orbitals on C (as in allene, C_3H_4), we might expect the orbital overlap requirements of this bonding arrangement to require smaller than usual $C{=}C$ distances.

(e)　The product has the formula $C_3H_4O_2$.

28 valence e$^-$, 14 e$^-$ pr

Three possibilities are shown above. The $O{=}C{=}C$ group on the lower structure is uncommon and less likely than the two symmetrical structures.

22.103　(a)　$3B_2H_6(g) + 6NH_3(g) \rightarrow 2(BH)_3(NH)_3(l) + 12H_2(g)$

$3LiBH_4(s) + 3NH_4Cl(s) \rightarrow 2(BH)_3(NH)_3(l) + 9H_2(g) + 3LiCl(s)$

(b)   30 valence e^-, 15 e^- pairs

The structure with nonbonded pairs minimizes formal charge, but these electrons are almost certainly delocalized about the six-membered ring, mimicking the bonding in benzene.

(c) $n = \dfrac{PV}{RT} = \dfrac{1.00 \text{ atm} \times 2.00 \text{ L}}{273 \text{ K}} \times \dfrac{\text{mol-K}}{0.08206 \text{ L-atm}} = 0.08929 = 8.93 \times 10^{-2} \text{ mol NH}_3$

$0.08929 \text{ mol NH}_3 \times \dfrac{2 \text{ mol (BH)}_3(\text{NH})_3}{6 \text{ mol NH}_3} \times \dfrac{80.50 \text{ g (BH)}_3(\text{NH})_3}{1 \text{ mol (BH)}_3(\text{NH})_3}$

$$= 2.3956 = 2.40 \text{ g (BH)}_3(\text{NH})_3$$

22.104   (a) $\text{As}_2\text{O}_3(s) + 6\text{Zn}(s) + 6\text{H}_2\text{SO}_4(l) \rightarrow 2\text{AsH}_3(g) + 6\text{ZnSO}_4(s) + 3\text{H}_2\text{O}(l)$

                  $2\text{AsH}_3(g) + 3\text{O}_2(g) \rightarrow 2\text{As}(s) + 3\text{H}_2\text{O}(l)$

(b) $3[\text{OCl}^-(aq) + \text{H}_2\text{O} + 2e^- \rightarrow \text{Cl}^-(aq) + 2\text{OH}^-(aq)]$

                    $\dfrac{2[\text{As}(s) \rightarrow \text{As}^{3+}(aq) + 3e^-]}{2\text{As}(s) + 3\text{OCl}^-(aq) + 3\text{H}_2\text{O} \rightarrow 2\text{As}^{3+}(aq) + 3\text{Cl}^-(aq) + 6\text{OH}^-(aq)}$

(Na+ is a spectator ion in this reaction)

(c) $\text{As}_2\text{O}_3(s) + \text{H}_2\text{S}(g) \xrightarrow{\text{HCl}} \text{As}_2\text{S}_3(s) + 3\text{H}_2\text{O}(l)$

HCl can be thought of as a catalyst in this reaction. It is necessary for the reactions to proceed, and is probably consumed and then reformed.

23 Transition Metals and Coordination Chemistry

Visualizing Concepts

23.1   *Analyze/Plan.* Given the diagram of a trend moving across the fourth period of the chart, decide which atomic property the trend represents.   *Solve.*

Periodic properties are explained in terms of effective nuclear charge, Z_{eff}. Moving from left to right in a period, Z_{eff} increases because the increase in Z is not offset by a significant increase in shielding. Increasing Z_{eff} leads to increasing ionization energy and electronegativity, but decreasing atomic radius.

The chart shows a general decrease in magnitude of the property from K to Ge, so the property must be atomic radius.

23.2   *Analyze.* Given the formula of a coordination compound, determine the coordination geometry, coordination number, and oxidation state of the metal.

Plan. From the formula, determine the identity of the ligands and the number of coordination sites they occupy. From the total coordination number, decide on a likely geometry. Use ligand and overall complex charges to calculate the oxidation number of the metal.

Solve.

(a)   The ligands are 2Cl⁻, one coordination site each, and en, ethylenediamine, two coordination sites, for a coordination number of 4. This coordination number has two possible geometries, tetrahedral and square planar. Pt is one of the metals known to adopt square planar geometry when CN = 4.

(b)   CN = 4, coordination geometry = square planar

(c) $Pt(en)Cl_2$ is a neutral compound, the en ligand is neutral, and the 2Cl⁻ ligands are each –1, so the oxidation state of Pt must be +2, Pt(II).

23.3   *Analyze.* Given a ball-and-stick figure of a ligand, write the Lewis structure and answer questions about the ligand.

Plan. Assume that each atom in the Lewis structure obeys the octet rule. Complete each octet with unshared electron pairs or multiple bonds, depending on the bond angles in the ball-and-stick model. Black = C, blue = N, red = O, gray = H.

There is a second resonance structure with the double bond drawn to the second O atom.

Check. Write the molecular formula, count the valence electron pairs and see if it matches your structure. $[C_4H_9N_2O_2]^-$ (16 + 9 + 10 + 12 + 1) = 48 valence e^-, 24 e^- pair Our Lewis structure also has 24 e^- pairs.

(a) Donor atoms have unshared electron pairs. The potential donors in this structure are the two N and two O atoms.

The ligand is tridentate. (Even though there are four possible donor atoms, the structure would be strained if all four were bound to one metal center. It is likely that only one of the two O atoms binds to the same metal as the two N atoms.)

(b) An octahedral complex has 6 coordination sites. A single ligand has only 4 possible donors, so two ligands are needed. From a steric perspective, the likely donors would be the 2 N atoms and 1 of the carbonyl oxygen atoms. The chelate bite of a carboxyl group is relatively small and would require an O—M—O angle of less than 90°.

23.4 *Analyze.* Given a ball-and-stick structure, name the complex ion, which has a 1– charge.

Plan. Write the chemical formula of the complex ion, determine the oxidation state of the metal, and name the complex.

Solve. $[Pt(NH_3)Cl_3]^-$. Oxidation numbers: [Pt + 0 + 3(–1) = –1, Pt = +2, Pt(II)

Arrange the ligands alphabetically, followed y the metal. Since the complex is an anion, add the suffix -ate, then the oxidation state of the metal: aminotrichloroplatinate(II)

23.5 *Analyze.* Given 5 structures, visualize which are identical to (1) and which are geometric isomers of (1).

Plan. There are two possible ways to arrange MA_3X_3. The first has bond angles of 90° between all similar ligands; this is structure (1). The second has one 180° angle between similar ligands. Visualize which description fits each of the five structures.

Solve. (1) has all 90° angles between similar ligands.

(2) has a 180° angle between similar ligands (see the blue ligands in the equatorial plane of the octahedron)

(3) has all 90° angles between similar ligands

(4) has all 90° angles between similar ligands

(5) has a 180° angle between similar ligands (see the blue axial ligands)

Structures (3) and (4) are identical to (1); (2) and (5) are geometric isomers.

23.6 *Analyze.* Given four structures, decide which are chiral.

Plan. Chiral molecules have nonsuperimposable mirror images. Draw the mirror image of each molecule and visualize whether it can be rotated into the original molecule. If so, the complex is not chiral. If the original orientation cannot be regenerated by rotation, the complex is chiral. *Solve.*

(1)   (1) mirror

The two orientations are not superimposable and molecule (1) is chiral.

The two orientations are superimposible. Rotate the right-most structure 90° counterclockwise about the B–M–B axis to align the G's; the bidentate ligands then also overlap. Molecule (2) is not chiral.

The two orientations are not superimposable and molecule (3) is chiral.

The two orientations are not superimposable and molecule (4) is chiral.

23.7   *Analyze.* Given the visible colors of two solutions, determine the colors of light absorbed by each solution.

Plan. Apparent color is transmitted or reflected light, absorbed color is basically the complement of apparent color. Use the color wheel in Figure 23.25 to obtain the complementary absorbed color for the solutions.

Solve. Moving from left to right, the solutions appear blue-green (cyan), yellow, green and red. The solutions absorb red-orange, violet, red and green.

23.8   *Analyze.* Fit the crystal field splitting diagram to the complex description in each part.

Plan. Determine the number of d-electrons in each transition metal. On the splitting diagrams match the d-orbital splitting patterns to complex geometry and electron pairing to the definition of high-spin and low-spin.

Solve. Octahedral complexes have the 3 lower, 2 higher splitting pattern, while tetrahedral complexes have the opposite 2 lower, 3 higher pattern. Low spin complexes favor electron pairing because of large d-orbital splitting. High-spin complexes have maximum occupancy because of small orbital splitting.

(a) Fe^{3+}, 5d-electrons; weak field: spins unpaired; octahedral: 3 lower, 2 higher d-splitting ∴ diagram (4)

(b) Fe^{3+}, 5 d-electrons; strong field: spins paired; octahedral: 3 lower, 2 higher d-splitting ∴ diagram (1)

(c) Fe^{3+}, 5 d-electrons; tetrahedral: 2 lower, 3 higher d-splitting ∴ diagram (3)

(d) Ni^{2+}, 8 d-electrons; tetrahedral: 2 lower, 3 higher d-splitting ∴ diagram (2)

Check. Diagram (2) was the remaining choice for (d) and it fits the description.

23.9 *Analyze/Plan.* Given the linear diagram and axial labels, answer the questions and predict crystal field splitting. Orbitals with lobes nearest ligand charges (or partial charges) will be highest in energy; orbitals with lobes away from charges are lowest in energy.

Solve. d_{z^2} has lobes nearest the charges. $d_{x^2-y^2}$ and d_{xy} have lobes in the xy-plane farthest from the charges. d_{xz} and d_{yz} point between the respective axes and are intermediate in energy.

$$
\begin{array}{ll}
\underline{\hspace{3cm}} & d_{z^2} \\[1em]
\underline{\hspace{2cm}} \quad \underline{\hspace{2cm}} & d_{xz},\, d_{yz} \\[1em]
\underline{\hspace{2cm}} \quad \underline{\hspace{2cm}} & d_{xz},\, d_{x^2-y^2}
\end{array}
$$

23.10 *Analyze.* Given the colors of two low spin Fe(II) complexes, determine which complex contains the stronger field ligand. *Plan.* We can make this direct comparison because the two solutions both contain low spin d^6 ions. A solution that appears one color absorbs visible light of the complementary color. Use the color wheel in Figure 23.25 to decide which color and approximate wavelength of visible light is absorbed by the two solutions. The stronger-field ligand causes a larger d-orbital splitting and absorbs light with the shorter wavelength.

Solve. The green solution absorbs red light, in the 650-750 nm range. The red solution absorbs green light, in the 490-560 nm range. The complex that produces the red solution has the larger d-orbital splitting and the stronger-field ligand.

The Transition Metals (section 23.1)

23.11 *Analyze/Plan.* Define lanthanide contraction. Based on the definition, describe how it affects properties of the transition elements. *Solve.*

The *lanthanide contraction* is the name given to the decrease in atomic size due to the build-up in effective nuclear charge as we move through the lanthanides (elements 58–71) and beyond them. This effect offsets the expected increase in atomic size, decrease in

ionization energy and increase in electron affinity going from period 5 to period 6
transition elements; it causes density to increase more dramatically than expected.
Because of its effect on size, ionization energy and electron affinity, it causes the
chemical properties of period 5 and period 6 elements in the same family to have
chemical properties even more similar than we would expect.

23.12

Number of d electrons

The trends on the sketch are a combination of the effects of increasing effective nuclear
charge moving across the row and increasing strength of metallic bonding up to the
middle of the row. The two effects cooperate to cause a rapid decrease in atomic radius
for metals with up to 4 d-electrons. From 5 to 10 d-electrons, they oppose each other to
slow the decrease in radius and eventually produce a gradual increase.

23.13   All transition metal atoms have two s-electrons in their valence shell. Because these s-
electrons are, on average, farther from the nucleus, they are the first electrons lost to
ionization. Loss of these two s-electrons leads to the +2 oxidation state common for
most of the transition metals.

23.14 Sc^{2+}, $[Ar]3d^1$; Sc^{3+}, $[Ar]$. The single d-electron in Sc^{2+} is effectively shielded by the $[Ar]$
core of electrons. Because Sc is the first element in the d-series, nuclear charge has not
built up, and the d-electron experiences a relatively small Z_{eff}. Experiencing no strong
electrostatic attraction to the nucleus, the single d-electron is readily lost and Sc^{2+} is not
a stable ion. (To verify this conclusion, we can calculate shielding values using a set of
Slater's rules modified for d- and f-electrons. The calculation produces the same
shielding value for both 3d- and 4s-electrons in Sc, and thus the same Z_{eff}. The 3d
electron will be lost as readily as the 4s electrons, confirming that Sc^{2+} is not a stable
ion.)

23.15   (a) Ti^{3+}, $[Ar]3d^1$ (b) Ru^{2+}, $[Kr]4d^6$ (c) Au^{3+}, $[Xe]4f^{14}5d^8$ (d) Mn^{4+}, $[Ar]3d^3$

23.16   (a) Co^{3+}, $[Ar]3d^6$; 6 valence d-electrons   (b) Cu^+; $[Ar]3d^{10}$; 10 valence d-electrons

         (c) Cd^{2+}, $[Kr]4d^{10}$; 10 valence d-electrons   (d) Os^{3+}: $[Xe]$ $4f^{14}5d^5$; 5 valence d-electrons

23.17   *Analyze/Plan.* Consider the definitions of paramagnetic and diamagnetic.   *Solve.*

         The unpaired electrons in a *paramagnetic* material cause it to be weakly attracted into a
         magnetic field. A *diamagnetic* material, where all electrons are paired, is very weakly
         repelled by a magnetic field.

23.18   Ferromagnetic, antiferromagnetic and ferrimagnetic materials all have atoms or ions with unpaired electrons. Furthermore, the spins of these electrons are influenced by (coupled with) the electron spins at neighboring atoms or ions. In *ferromagnetic* materials, coupled electron spins are aligned in the same direction. In *antiferromagnetic* materials, coupled spins are aligned in opposite directions and the opposing spins exactly cancel. In ferrimagnetic materials coupled spins are aligned in opposite directions (like antiferromagnets) but the opposing spins do <u>not</u> cancel.

23.19   *Analyze/Plan.* Consider the orientation of spins in various types of magnetic materials as shown in Figure 23.5.

The diagram shows a material with misaligned spins that become aligned in the direction of an applied magnetic field. This is a paramagnetic material.

23.20   (a) Fe_2O_3 has all Fe atoms in the +3 oxidation state, while Fe_3O_4 contains Fe atoms in both the +2 and +3 states. Each Fe_3O_4 formula unit has one Fe(II) and two Fe(III).

   (b)   In an antiferromagnetic material, spins on coupled atoms are oppositely aligned, producing a net spin of zero. This is only possible for Fe_2O_3, where all Fe atoms have the same oxidation state, d-electron configuration and number of unpaired electrons. In Fe_3O_4, Fe(II) and Fe(III) atoms have different d-electron configurations and different numbers of unpaired electrons. Assuming an Fe(II) is coupled to an Fe(III), even if spins on coupled centers are oppositely aligned, their spins do not fully cancel and the material is ferrimagnetic.

Transition-Metal Complexes (section 23.2)

23.21   (a)   In Werner's theory, *primary valence* is the charge of the metal cation at the center of the complex. *Secondary valence* is the number of atoms bound or coordinated to the central metal ion. The modern terms for these concepts are oxidation state and coordination number, respectively. (Note that "'oxidation state" is a broader term than ionic charge, but Werner's complexes contain metal ions where cation charge and oxidation state are equal.)

   (b)   Ligands are the Lewis base in metal-ligand interactions. As such, they must possess at least one unshared electron pair. NH_3 has an unshared electron pair but BH_3, with less than 8 electrons about B, has no unshared electron pair and cannot act as a ligand. In fact, BH_3 acts as a Lewis acid, an electron pair acceptor, because it is electron-deficient.

23.22   (a)   *Coordination number* is the number of atoms bound directly to the metal in a metal complex.

   (b)   Ligands in a metal complex usually have a lone (unshared, nonbonding) pair of electrons. NH_3 is neutral, CN^- is negatively charged.

   (c)   No, ligands with positive charges are not common. Metal atoms in a complex usually have a positive charge, so a positively charged ligand would neither be electrostatically attracted to the metal nor provide the electron density required to form a metal-ligand bond.

(d)   In $Co(NH_3)_6Cl_3$, there are two types of chemical bonds. The bonds formed between Co^{3+} and $:NH_3$ are covalent. They are the result of Lewis acid-Lewis base interactions, where $:NH_3$ is the electron pair donor (Lewis base) and Co^{3+} is the electron pair acceptor (Lewis acid). The interactions between the $[Co(NH_3)_6]^{3+}$ complex cation and the three Cl^- anions are ionic bonds.

(e)   The most common coordination numbers for metal complexes are six and four. (Coordination numbers of two, three and five are less common, but not unknown.)

23.23   *Analyze/Plan.* Follow the logic in Sample Exercises 23.1 and 23.2. *Solve.*

(a)   This compound is electrically neutral, and the NH_3 ligands carry no charge, so the charge on Ni must balance the –2 charge of the 2 Br^- ions. The charge and oxidation state of Ni is +2.

(b)   Since there are 6 NH_3 molecules in the complex, the likely coordination number is 6. In some cases Br^- acts as a ligand, so the coordination number could be other than 6.

(c)   Assuming that the 6 NH_3 molecules are the ligands, 2 Br^- ions are not coordinated to the Ni^{2+}, so 2 mol AgBr(s) will precipitate. (If one or both of the Br^- act as a ligand, the mol AgBr(s) would be different.)

23.24   (a)   Yes. Conductivity is directly related to the number of ions in a solution. The lower the conductivity, the more Cl^- ions that act as ligands. Conductivity measurements on a set of standard solutions with various moles of ions per mole of complex would provide a comparative method for quantitative determination of the number of free and bound Cl^- ions.

(b)   In using conductivity measurements to test which ligands are bound to the metal atom, the assumption is that the total number of ions in solution is constant. This requires that either the Cl^- in the coordination sphere are so tightly bound that exchange with ions in solution is extremely slow, or that the rates at which they leave and enter are equal.

(c)   For coordination number 6, an octahedral complex with 3 H_2O and 3 Cl^- ligands; all ligands are monodentate. For coordination number 4, a tetrahedral complex with varying amounts of H_2O and Cl^- ligands are possible. Since there is a single species in solution, the octahedral complex is more likely.

23.25   *Analyze/Plan.* Count the number of donor atoms in each complex, taking the identity of polydentate ligands into account. Follow the logic in Sample Exercise 23.2 to obtain oxidation numbers of the metals. Use Tables 23.4 and 23.5 to determine the number and kinds of donor atoms in the ligands of the complexes.

(a)   Coordination number = 4, oxidation number = +2; 4 Cl^-

(b)   5, +4; 4 Cl^-, 1 O^{2-}

(c)   6, +3; 4 N, 2 Cl^-

(d)   5, +2; 5 C. In CN^-, both C and N have an unshared electron pair. C is less electronegative and more likely to donate its unshared pair.

(e)   6, +3; 6 O. $C_2O_4^{2-}$ is a bidentate ligand; each ion is bound through 2 O atoms for a total of 6 O donor atoms.

(f)   4, +2; 4 N. en is a bidentate ligand bound through 2 N atoms.

23.26   (a)   Coordination number = 6, oxidation number = +3; 6 C (see Solution 23.25(d))

(b)   4, +2; 4 Br^-

(c)   6, +4; 6 N. en is a bidentate ligand bound through N, for a total of 6 N donors.

(d)   6, +3 ; 4 N, 2 O. en is a bidentate ligand bound through N, for a total of 4 N donors. $C_2O_4^{2-}$ is bidentate with 2 O donors.

(e)   6, +3; 6 N. When thiocyanate is written "NCS," it is bound through N. This makes a total of 6 N donors.

(f)   5, +2; 4 N, 1 I. bipy is bidentate bound through N, for a total of 4 N donors.

Common Ligands in Coordination Chemistry (section 23.3)

23.27   (a)   A monodendate ligand binds to a metal in through one atom; a bidendate ligand binds through two atoms.

(b)   If a bidentate ligand occupies two coordination sites, three bidentate ligands fill the coordination sphere of a six-coordinate complex.

(c)   A tridentate ligand has at least three atoms with unshared electron pairs in the correct orientation to simultanously bind one or more metal ions.

23.28   (a)   2 coordination sites, 2 N donor atoms

(b)   2 coordination sites, 2 N donor atoms

(c)   2 coordination sites, 2 O donor atoms (Although there are four potential O donor atoms in $C_2O_4^{2-}$, it is geometrically impossible for more than two of these to be bound to a single metal ion.)

(d)   4 coordination sites, 4 N donor atoms

(e)   6 coordination sites, 2 N and 4 O donor atoms

23.29   *Analyze/Plan.* Given the formula of a coordination compound, determine the number of coordination sites occupied by the polydentate ligand. The coordination number of the complexes is either 4 or 6. Note the number of monodentate ligands and determine the number of coordination sites occupied by the polydentate ligands.   *Solve.*

(a)   *ortho*-phenanthroline, *o*-phen, is bidentate

(b)   oxalate, $C_2O_4^{2-}$, is bidentate

(c)   ethylenediaminetetraacetate, EDTA, is pentadentate

(d)   ethylenediamine, en, is bidentate

23.30   (a)   6   (b)   6   (c)   6   (d)   6

23.31 (a) The term *chelate effect* means there is a special stability associated with formation of a metal complex containing a polydentate (chelate) ligand relative to a complex containing only monodentate ligands.

(b) When a single chelating ligand replaces two or more monodendate ligands, the number of free molecules in the system increases and the entropy of the system increases. Chemical reactions with $+\Delta S$ tend to be spontaneous, have negative ΔG, and large positive values of K.

(c) Polydentate ligands can be used to bind metal ions and prevent them from undergoing unwanted chemical reactions without removing them from solution. The polydentate ligand thus hides or *sequesters* the metal ion.

23.32 (a) Pyridine is a **mono**dentate ligand because it has one N donor atom and therefore occupies one coordination site in a metal complex.

(b) K for this reaction will be less than one. Two free pyridine molecules are replaced by one free bipy molecule. There are more moles of particles in the reactants than products, so ΔS is predicted to be negative. Processes with a net decrease in entropy are usually nonspontaneous, have positive ΔG, and values of K less than one. This equilibrium is likely to be spontaneous in the reverse direction.

23.33 *Analyze/Plan.* Consider the structural or steric requirements for chelating ligands. Analyze the structure of the ligand in the figure to determine whether it meets these requirements. *Solve.*

The ligand shown in the figure is not typically a chelate. The entire molecule is planar; there is no "bend" in the central 6-membered ring that includes the two N atoms. The benzene rings on either side of the two N atoms inhibit their approach in the correct orientation for chelation.

23.34 The complex in the figure has tetrahedral geometry about the metal. The ligands are neutral molecules and the metal is a cation, so the complex will have a positive charge and there will be negatively charged counterions.

Nomenclature and Isomerism in Coordination Chemistry (section 23.4)

23.35 *Analyze/Plan.* Given the name of a coordination compound, write the chemical formula. Refer to Tables 23.4 and 23.5 to find ligand formulas. Place the metal complex (metal ion + ligands) inside square brackets and the counter ion (if there is one) outside the brackets. *Solve.*

(a) $[Cr(NH_3)_6](NO_3)_3$ (b) $[Co(NH_3)_4CO_3]_2SO_4$ (c) $[Pt(en)_2Cl_2]Br_2$

(d) $K[V(H_2O)_2Br_4]$ (e) $[Zn(en)_2][HgI_4]$

23.36 (a) $[Mn(H_2O)_4Br_2]ClO_4$ (b) $[Cd(bipy)_2]Cl_2$

(c) $K[Co(o\text{-}phen)Br_4]$ (d) $Cs[Cr(NH_3)_2(CN)_4]$

(e) $[Rh(en)_3][Co(ox)_3]$

23.37 *Analyze/Plan.* Follow the logic in Sample Exercise 23.4, paying attention to naming rules in Section 23.4. *Solve.*

    (a)   tetraamminedichlororhodium(III) chloride

    (b)   potassium hexachlorotitanate(IV)

    (c)   tetrachlorooxomolybdenum(VI)

    (d)   tetraaqua(oxalato)platinum(IV) bromide

23.38   (a)   dichloroethylenediamminecadmium(II)

    (b)   potassium hexacyanomanganate(II)

    (c)   pentaamminecarbonatochromium(III) chloride

    (d)   tetraamminediaquairidium(III) nitrate

23.39 *Analyze/Plan.* Consider the definitions of the various types of isomerism, and which of the complexes could exhibit isomerism of the specified type. *Solve.*

    (a)

    (b) $[Pd(NH_3)_2(ONO)_2]$, $[Pd(NH_3)_2(NO_2)_2]$

    (c)

    (d) $[Co(NH_3)_4Br_2]Cl$, $[Co(NH_3)_4BrCl]Br$

23.40   (a)

    (b)

    (c)

coordination sphere isomerism

23.41 Yes. A tetrahedral complex of the form MA_2B_2 would have neither structural nor stereoisomers. For a tetrahedral complex, no differences in connectivity are possible for a single central atom, so the terms *cis* and *trans* do not apply. No optical isomers with tetrahedral geometry are possible because M is not bound to four different groups. The complex must be square planar with *cis* and *trans* geometric isomers.

23.42 Two geometric isomers are possible for an octahedral MA_3B_3 complex (see below). All other arrangements, including mirror images, can be rotated into these two structures. Neither isomer is optically active.

(i)   (ii)

23.43 *Analyze/Plan.* Follow the logic in Sample Exercise 23.5 and 23.6.   *Solve.*

(a)

OH_2

H_2O Cd ''Cl

Cl

(b) $\left[\begin{array}{c} Cl \quad PH_3 \\ Ir \\ Cl \quad PH_3 \end{array}\right]^{-}$ $\left[\begin{array}{c} Cl \quad PH_3 \\ Ir \\ H_3P \quad Cl \end{array}\right]^{-}$

cis   trans

(c)

cis   cis

optical isomers

trans

(The three isomeric complex ions in part (c) each have a 1+ charge.)

23.44

(a)

optical isomers

(b)

(c)

Color and Magnetism in Coordination Chemistry; Crystal-Field Theory
(sections 23.5 and 23.6)

23.45 (a) Visible light has wavelengths between 400 and 700 nm. We cannot see the light with 300 nm wavelength, but we can see the 500 nm light.

(b) *Complementary* colors are opposite each other on a color wheel such as Figure 23.25.

(c) A colored metal complex absorbs visible light of its complementary color. For example, a red complex absorbs green light.

(d) $E(J/photon) = h\nu = hc/\lambda$. Change J/photon to kJ/mol.

$$E = \frac{6.626 \times 10^{-34} \, J\text{-}s}{610 \, nm} \times \frac{3.00 \times 10^{8} \, m}{s} \times \frac{1 \, nm}{1 \times 10^{-9} \, m} = 3.259 \times 10^{-19} = 3.26 \times 10^{-19} \, J$$

$$\frac{3.259 \times 10^{-19} \, J}{photon} \times \frac{1 \, kJ}{1000 \, J} \times \frac{6.022 \times 10^{23} \, photons}{mol} = 196 \, kJ/mol$$

23.46 (a) No. The complex absorbs light with a range of wavelengths not in the visible range, so all visible light is transmitted and the complex appears white.

(b) No. A solution can appear green by transmitting or reflecting only green light (the situation stated in the exercise) **or** by absorbing red light, the complementary color of green.

(c) A visible absorption spectrum shows the amount of light absorbed at a given wavelength. It is a plot of absorbance (dependent variable, y-axis) vs. wavelength (independent variable, x-axis).

(d) $E(J/photon) = h\nu = hc/\lambda$. Change J/photon to kJ/mol.

$$E = \frac{6.626 \times 10^{-34} \text{ J-s}}{440 \text{ nm photon}} \times \frac{3.00 \times 10^{8} \text{ m}}{\text{s}} \times \frac{1 \text{nm}}{1 \times 10^{-9} \text{ m}} = 4.5177 \times 10^{-19} = 4.52 \times 10^{-19} \text{ J/photon}$$

$$\frac{4.5177 \times 10^{-19} \text{ J}}{\text{photon}} \times \frac{1 \text{ kJ}}{1000 \text{ J}} \times \frac{6.022 \times 10^{23} \text{ photons}}{\text{mol}} = 272 \text{ kJ/mol}$$

23.47 No. The Fe^{2+} ion has 6 d-electrons. In an octahedral crystal field, the energies of the d orbitals are split three and two. That is, the d_{xy}, d_{xz} and d_{yz} orbitals are lower in energy than the free ion, and the $d_{x^2-y^2}$ and d_{z^2} orbitals are higher in energy. In a low-spin complex, the d-electrons are paired to the maximum possible extent. All 6 d-electrons in a low-spin octahedral complex will pair and occupy the low energy d_{xy}, d_{xz} and d_{yz} orbitals. With no unpaired electrons, the complex cannot be paramagnetic.

23.48 No. The d-electrons of a transition metal complex will occupy orbitals with equal energy singly before they pair in any single orbital. The possibilities for unpaired electrons depends on the geometry of the complex and the nature (high- or low-spin) of the ligands.

23.49 Most of the electrostatic interaction between a metal ion and a ligand is the attractive interaction between a positively charged metal cation and the full negative charge of an anionic ligand or the partial negative charge of a polar covalent ligand. Whether the interaction is ion-ion or ion-dipole, the ligand is strongly attracted to the metal center and can be modeled as a point negative charge.

23.50 Six ligands in an octahedral arrangement are oriented along the x, y, and z axes of the metal. These negatively charged ligands (or the negative end of ligand dipoles) have greater electrostatic repulsion with valence electrons in metal orbitals that also lie along these axes, the d_{z^2}, and $d_{x^2-y^2}$. The d_{xy}, d_{xz} and d_{yz} metal orbitals point between the x, y, and z axes, and electrons in these orbitals experience less repulsion with ligand electrons. Thus, in the presence of an octahedral ligand field, the d_{xy}, d_{xz} and d_{xy} metal orbitals are lower in energy than the $d_{x^2-y^2}$ and d_{z^2}.

23.51 (a)

$$\begin{array}{c} \overline{}\ \ \overline{} \qquad d_{x^2-y^2}, d_{z^2} \\ \\ \Updownarrow \ \Delta \\ \\ \underline{}\ \ \underline{}\ \ \underline{} \qquad d_{xy}, d_{xz}, d_{yz} \end{array}$$

(b) The magnitude of Δ and the energy of the d-d transition for a d^1 complex are equal.

(c)

$$\frac{6.626 \times 10^{-34} \text{ J-s}}{545 \text{ nm}} \times \frac{3.00 \times 10^{8} \text{ m}}{\text{s}} \times \frac{1 \text{nm}}{1 \times 10^{-9} \text{ m}} \times \frac{1 \text{ kJ}}{1000 \text{ J}} \times \frac{6.022 \times 10^{23} \text{ photons}}{\text{mol}}$$

$$= 220 \text{ kJ/mol}$$

23.52 (a) $\Delta E = hc/\lambda = \dfrac{6.626 \times 10^{-34} \text{ J-s} \times 2.998 \times 10^{8} \text{ m/s}}{500 \times 10^{-9} \text{ m photon}} = 3.973 \times 10^{-19} = 3.97 \times 10^{-19} \text{ J/photon}$

$\Delta = 3.973 \times 10^{-19} \text{ J/photon} \times \dfrac{6.022 \times 10^{23} \text{ photons}}{1 \text{ mol}} \times \dfrac{1 \text{ kJ}}{1000 \text{ J}} = 239.25 = 239 \text{ kJ/mol}$

(b) The *spectrochemical* series is an ordering of ligands according to their ability to increase the energy gap, Δ. If H_2O is replaced by NH_3 in the complex, the magnitude of Δ would increase because NH_3 is higher in the spectrochemical series and creates a stronger ligand field.

23.53 *Analyze/Plan.* Consider the relationship between the color of a complex, the wavelength of absorbed light, and the position of a ligand in the spectrochemical series. *Solve.*

A yellow color corresponds to absorption of a photon in the violet region of the visible spectrum, between 430 and 400 nm. The blue or green colors of aqua complexes correspond to absorptions in the region of 620 nm. The shorter wavelength corresponds to a higher-energy electron transition and larger Δ value. Cyanide is a stronger-field ligand, and its complexes are expected to have larger Δ values than aqua complexes. These are very general comparisons; other factors are involved, including whether the complex is high spin or low spin.

23.54 (a) $[Ni(H_2O)_6]^{2+}$ absorbs 725 nm red light and appears as the complementary color, green. $[Ni(NH_3)_6]^{2+}$ absorbs 570 nm yellow light and appears as the complementary color, violet.

(b) The shorter the wavelength of light absorbed, the greater the value of Δ, and the stronger the ligand field. The order of increasing ligand field strength is the order of decreasing wavelength absorbed.

$H_2O < NH_3 <$ en $<$ bipy

23.55 *Analyze/Plan.* Determine the charge on the metal ion, subtract it from the row number (3-12) of the transition metal, and the remainder is the number of d-electrons. *Solve.*

(a) Ti^{3+}, d^1 (b) Co^{3+}, d^6 (c) Ru^{3+}, d^5

(d) Mo^{5+}, d^1 (e) Re^{3+}, d^4

23.56 (a) Fe^{3+}, d^5 (b) Mn^{2+}, d^5 (c) Ag^+, d^{10}

(d) Cr^{3+}, d^3 (e) Sr^{2+}, d^0

23.57 Yes. A weak-field ligand leads to a small Δ value and a small d-orbital splitting energy. If the splitting energy of a complex is smaller than the energy required to pair electrons in an orbital, the complex is high-spin.

23.58 No. A strong-field ligand is one that interacts strongly with d-electrons of the metal, creating a large Δ splitting. However, the valence d-electrons of the metal are not directly involved in metal-ligand bonding. The field strength of the ligand is not directly related to the strength of metal-ligand bonding.

23.59   *Analyze/Plan.* Follow the logic in Sample Exercise 23.9.   *Solve.*

(a)   Mn: $[Ar]4s^2 3d^5$ (b)   Ru: $[Kr]5s^1 4d^7$ (c)   Rh: $[Kr]5s^1 4d^8$

     Mn^{2+}: $[Ar]3d^5$ Ru^{2+}: $[Kr]4d^6$ Rh^{2+}: $[Kr]4d^7$

1 unpaired electron   0 unpaired electrons   1 unpaired electron

23.60   (a)   Ru: $[Kr]5s^1 4d^7$ (b)   Mo: $[Kr]5s^1 4d^5$ (c)   Co: $[Ar]4s^2 3d^7$

     Ru^{3+}: $[Kr]4d^5$ Mo^{3+}: $[Kr]3d^3$ Co^{3+}: $[Ar]3d^6$

5 unpaired electrons   3 unpaired electrons   4 unpaired electrons

23.61   *Analyze/Plan.* All complexes in this exercise are six-coordinate octahedral. Use the definitions of high-spin and low-spin along with the orbital diagram from Sample Exercise 23.9 to place electrons for the various complexes.   *Solve.*

(a) d^4, high spin   (b) d^5, high spin   (c) d^6, low spin

(d) d^5, low spin   (e) d^3 (f) d^8

23.62   (a) d^2 (b) d^5, high spin   (c) d^5, low spin

(d) d^8 (e) d^8 (f) d^2

23.63 *Analyze/Plan.* Follow the ideas but reverse the logic in Sample Exercise 24.9. *Solve.*

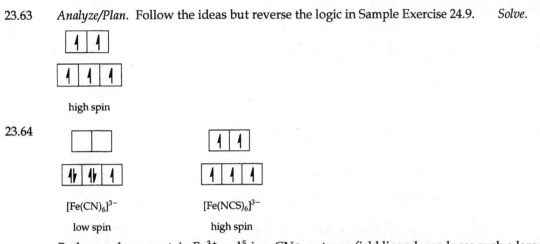

high spin

23.64

[Fe(CN)$_6$]$^{3-}$

low spin

[Fe(NCS)$_6$]$^{3-}$

high spin

Both complexes contain Fe^{3+}, a d^5 ion. CN^-, a strong field ligand, produces such a large Δ that the splitting energy is greater than the pairing energy, and the complex is low spin. NCS^- produces a smaller Δ, so it is energetically favorable for d-electrons to be unpaired in the higher energy d-orbitals. NCS^- is a much weaker-field ligand than CN^-. It is probably weaker than NH_3 and near H_2O in the spectrochemical series.

Additional Exercises

23.65 The paper clip must contain a significant amount of Ni, a ferromagnetic metal. At ambient temperature, the paper clip is below its Curie temperature, behaves ferromagnetically and is strongly attracted to the permanent magnet. The lighter heats the left paperclip above its Curie temperature (354 °C), and it switches from from ferromagnetic to paramagnetic behavior. That is, below its Curie temperature, the spins of the unpaired electrons in Ni are perfectly aligned and the clip is strongly attracted to the permanent magnet. Above the Curie temperature, the unpaired spins become randomly aligned, and the paper clip loses most of its attraction for the permanent magnet.

23.66 We expect radii in a group to increase moving down the periodic table as principle quantum number increases. However, the nuclear build-up associated with filling of the 4f subshell at the beginning of period 6 counteracts this trend. The increased nuclear charge for transition metals of period 6 means that the valence electrons experience a Z_{eff} large enough to offset the increase in principle quantum number. The increased Z_{eff} causes the radii of the metals in group 6 to be smaller than expected, and period 5 and 6 metals in the same group to have very similar radii.

23.67 [Pt(NH$_3$)$_6$]Cl$_4$; [Pt(NH$_3$)$_4$Cl$_2$]Cl$_2$; [Pt(NH$_3$)$_3$Cl$_3$]Cl; [Pt(NH$_3$)$_2$Cl$_4$]; K[Pt(NH$_3$)Cl$_5$]

23.68 (a)

$$\left[\begin{array}{c} \text{Cl} \\ H_2O \diagdown \quad \diagup OH_2 \\ Ru \\ H_2O \diagup \quad \diagdown OH_2 \\ H_2O \end{array} \right]^{2+} + 2Cl^-$$

(b)

$$\left[\begin{array}{c} H_2O \\ H_2O \diagdown \quad \diagup OH_2 \\ Ru \\ H_2O \diagup \quad \diagdown OH_2 \\ H_2O \end{array} \right]^{3+} + 3Cl^-$$

[Ru(H$_2$O)$_5$Cl]Cl$_2$ $\longrightarrow$ [Ru(H$_2$O)$_6$]Cl$_3$

23.69   (a)

$$\left[\begin{array}{c} NH_3 \\ H_2O \,\text{—} \, Co \, \text{—} \, NH_3 \\ H_2O \qquad NH_3 \\ NH_3 \end{array} \right]^{2+}$$

octahedral

(b)

$$\left[\begin{array}{c} H_2O \\ Cl \, \text{—} \, Ru \, \text{—} \, Cl \\ Cl \qquad Cl \\ Cl \end{array} \right]^{2-}$$

octahedral

(c)

$$\left[\begin{array}{c} H_2O \\ O \text{—} Co \text{—} O \\ O \qquad O \\ H_2O \end{array} \right]^{-}$$

octahedral

(d)

$$\begin{array}{c} N \\ N \, \text{—} \, Ru \, \text{—} \, Cl \\ N \qquad Cl \\ N \end{array}$$

octahedral

     (a)   *cis*-tetraamminediaquacobalt(II) nitrate

     (b)   sodium aquapentachlororuthenate(III)

     (c)   ammonium *trans*-diaquabisoxalatocobaltate(III)

     (d)   *cis*-dichlorobisethylenediammineruthenium(II)

23.70   (a)   In these octahedral complex ions, a mirror plane contains the central metal ion, and reflects the part of the ion on one side of the plane into the part on the other side of the plane. In all cases, assume ligands can be rotated so that H atoms either sit on the mirror plane, or are reflected across the mirror plane into another H atom. The complex ions in (a), (b) and (c) above all have multiple mirror planes. Below we describe one mirror plane in each complex ion; it is possible to visualize other correct planes in each complex.

                In complex (a), one mirror contains the Co, two NH_3 and two H_2O ligands; it reflects one of the remaining NH_3 ligands into the other. In complex (b), one plane contains the Ru, H_2O, and 3 Cl^- ligands; it reflects the other two Cl^- ligands into each other. In complex (c), one plane contains the Co and both oxalate ligands; it reflects the two H_2O ligands into each other. Complex (d) does not have a mirror plane; the orientation of the en ligands precludes the presence of a mirror plane.

     (b)   Only the complex in 23.69(d) is optically active. The mirror images of (a)-(c) can be superimposed on the original structure. The chelating ligands in (d) prevent its mirror images (enantiomers) from being superimposable.

23.71   (a)   Valence electrons: $2P + 6C + 16H = 10 + 24 + 16 = 50$ e$^-$, 25 e$^-$ pr

$$\begin{array}{c} H \qquad\quad H \;\; H \qquad\quad H \\ | \qquad\quad\; | \;\;\; | \qquad\quad\; | \\ H\text{—}C\text{—}\ddot{P}\text{—}C\text{—}C\text{—}\ddot{P}\text{—}C\text{—}H \\ | \qquad\quad\; | \;\;\; | \qquad\quad\; | \\ H \quad\; | \;\; H \;\; H \;\; | \quad\; H \\ H\text{—}C\text{—}H \quad H\text{—}C\text{—}H \\ | \qquad\qquad\quad | \\ H \qquad\qquad\quad H \end{array}$$

                Both dmpe and en are bidentate ligands. The dmpe ligand binds through P, while en binds through N. Phosphorus is less electronegative than N, so dmpe is a stronger electron pair donor and Lewis base than en. Dmpe creates a stronger ligand field and is higher on the spectrochemical series.

Structurally, P has a larger covalent radius than N, so M–P bonds are longer than M–N bonds. This is convenient because the two –CH_3 groups on each P atom in dmpe create more steric hindrance (bumping with adjacent atoms) than the H atoms on N in en.

(b) CO and dmpe are neutral, $2CN^- = 2-$, $2Na^+ = 2+$. The ion charges balance, so the oxidation state of Mo is zero.

(c) The symbol P⌢P represents the bidentate dmpe ligand.

optical isomers

23.72 (a) In a square planar complex such as [Pt(en)Cl_2], if one pair of ligands is trans, the remaining two coordination sites are also trans to each other. Ethylenediamine is a relatively short bidentate ligand that cannot occupy trans coordination sites, so the trans isomer is unknown.

(b) The minimum steric requirement for a bidentate ligand is a medium-length chain between the two coordinating atoms that will occupy the trans positions. In terms of reaction rate theory, it is unlikely that a flexible bidentate ligand will be in exactly the right orientation to coordinate trans. The ligand with the four-carbon chain is more able to occupy trans positions, although four carbons may still not be long enough. And, the flexibility of its backbone means that it is still an unlikely trans bidentate ligand.

23.73 We will represent the end of the bidentate ligand containing the CF_3 group by a shaded oval, the other end by an open oval:

23.74 (a) Hemoglobin is the iron-containing protein that transports O_2 in human blood.

(b) Chlorophylls are magnesium-containing porphyrins in plants. They are the key components in the conversion of solar energy into chemical energy that can be used by living organisms.

(c) Siderophores are iron-binding compounds or ligands produced by a microorganism. They compete on a molecular level for iron in the medium outside the organism and carry needed iron into the cells of the organism.

23.75 (a) $AgCl(s) + 2NH_3(aq) \rightarrow [Ag(NH_3)_2]^+(aq) + Cl^-(aq)$

(b) $[Cr(en)_2Cl_2]Cl(aq) + 2H_2O(l) \rightarrow [Cr(en_2)(H_2O)_2]^{3+}(aq) + 3Cl^-(aq)$
   green   brown-orange

$3Ag^+(aq) + 3Cl^-(aq) \rightarrow 3AgCl(s)$

$[Cr(en)_2(H_2O)_2]^{3+}$ and $3NO_3^-$ are spectator ions in the second reaction.

(c) $Zn(NO_3)_2(aq) + 2NaOH(aq) \rightarrow Zn(OH)_2(s) + 2NaNO_3(aq)$

$Zn(OH)_2(s) + 2NaOH(aq) \rightarrow [Zn(OH)_4]^{2-}(aq) + 2Na^+(aq)$

(d) $Co^{2+}(aq) + 4Cl^-(aq) \rightarrow [CoCl_4]^{2-}(aq)$

23.76 (a) pentacarbonyliron(0)

(b) Since CO is a neutral molecule, the oxidation state of iron must be zero.

(c) $[Fe(CO)_4CN]^-$ has two geometric isomers. In a trigonal bipyramid, the axial and equatorial positions are not equivalent and not superimposable. One isomer has CN in an axial position and the other has it in an equatorial position.

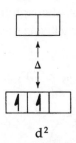

23.77 (a) left shoe

(c) wood screw

(e) a typical golf club

23.78 (a)

d^2

(b) These complexes are colored because the crystal-field splitting energy, Δ, is in the visible portion of the electromagnetic spectrum. Visible light with $\lambda = hc/\Delta$ is absorbed, promoting one of the d-electrons into a higher energy d-orbital. The remaining wavelengths of visible light are reflected or transmitted; the combination of these wavelengths is the color we see.

(c) $[V(H_2O)_6]^{3+}$ will absorb light with higher energy. H_2O is in the middle of the spectrochemical series, and causes a larger Δ than F^-, a weak-field ligand. Since Δ and λ are inversely related, larger Δ corresponds to higher energy and shorter λ.

23.79 (a) Formally, the two Ru centers have different oxidation states; one is +2 and the other is +3.

(b) Ru^{2+}, d^6 Ru^{3+}, d^5

(c) There is extensive bonding-electron delocalization in the isolated pyrazine molecule. When pyrazine acts as a bridging ligand, its delocalized molecular orbitals provide a pathway for delocalization of the "odd" d-electron in the Creutz-Taube ion. The two metal ions appear equivalent because the odd d-electron is delocalized across the pyrazine bridge.

23.80 According to the spectrochemical series, the order of increasing Δ for the ligands is $Cl^- < H_2O < NH_3$. (The tetrahedral Cl^- complex will have an even smaller Δ than an octahedral one.) The smaller the value of Δ, the longer the wavelength of visible light absorbed. The color of light absorbed is the complement of the observed color. A blue complex absorbs orange light (580–650 nm), a pink complex absorbs green light (490–560 nm) and a yellow complex absorbs violet light (400–430 nm). Since $[CoCl_4]^{2-}$ absorbs the longest wavelength, it appears blue. $[Co(H_2O)_6]^{2+}$ absorbs green and appears pink, and $[Co(NH_3)_6]^{3+}$ absorbs violet and appears yellow.

23.81 (a) oxyhemoglobin   deoxyhemoglobin

$Fe^{2+} : d^6$ $Fe^{2+} : d^6$

low spin,   high spin,
no unpaired electrons   4 unpaired electrons

(b) In deoxyhemoglobin, H_2O is bound to Fe in place of O_2.

(c) The two forms of hemoglobin have different colors because they absorb different wavelengths of visible light. They differ by just the H_2O or O_2 ligand, which means that the two ligands have slightly different ligand fields. Oxyhemoglobin appears red and absorbs green light, while deoxyhemoglobin appears bluish and absorbs longer wavelength yellow-green light. O_2 has a stronger ligand field than H_2O.

(d) According to Table 18.1, air is 20.948 mole percent O_2. This translates to 209,480 ppm O_2. This is approximately 500 times the 400 ppm concentration of CO in the experiment. If air with a CO concentration 1/500th that of O_2 converts

1/10 of the oxyhemoglobin to carboxyhemoglobin, the equilibrium constant for binding CO is much larger than that for binding O_2.

(e) If CO is a stronger field ligand than O_2, carboxyhemoglobin will absorb shorter wavelengths than hemoglobin. It will absorb blue-green light and appear orange-red.

23.82 (a) The term *isoelectronic* means that the three ions have the same number of electrons.

(b) In each ion, the metal is in its maximum oxidation state and has a d^0 electron configuration. That is, the metal ions have no *d*-electrons, so there should be no *d-d* transitions.

(c) A *ligand-metal charge transfer* transition occurs when an electron in a filled ligand orbital is excited to an empty d-orbital of the metal.

(d) Absorption of 565 nm yellow light by MnO_4^- causes the compound to appear violet, the complementary color. CrO_4^{2-} appears yellow, so it is absorbing violet light of approximately 420 nm. The wavelength of the LMCT transition for chromate, 420 nm, is shorter than the wavelength of LCMT transition in permanganate, 565 nm. This means that there is a larger energy difference between filled ligand and empty metal orbitals in chromate than in permanganate.

(e) UV. A white compound indicates that no visible light is absorbed. Going left on the periodic chart from Mn to Cr, the absorbed wavelength got shorter and the energy difference between ligand and metal orbitals increased. The 420 nm absorption by CrO_4^- is at the short wavelength edge of the visible spectrum. It is not surprising that the ion containing V, further left on the chart, absorbs at a still shorter wavelength in the ultraviolet region and that VO_4^{3-} appears white.

23.83 The oxidation states of the metals in the tetrahedral oxoanions are: Mn, +7; Cr, +6; V, +5. From Solution 23.82, the energy separation between the ligand orbitals and the empty d-orbitals on the metals increases in the order Mn < Cr < V. The lower the oxidation state of the metal, the greater the energy separation between the ligand orbitals and the empty d-orbitals on the metals.

23.84 Application of pressure would result in shorter metal ionoxide distances. This would have the effect of increasing the ligand-electron repulsions, and would result in a larger splitting in the d-orbital energies. Thus, application of pressure should result in a shift in the absorption to a higher energy and shorter wavelength.

23.85   (a)

$$\left[\begin{array}{c} \text{NC} \quad \overset{\displaystyle \text{CO}}{\underset{\displaystyle \text{CO}}{\overset{\displaystyle |}{\underset{\displaystyle |}{\text{Fe}}}}} \quad \text{CN} \\ \text{NC} \qquad\qquad \text{CN} \end{array}\right]^{2-}$$

(b)   sodium dicarbonyltetracyanoferrate(II)

(c)   +2, 6 d-electrons

(d)   We expect the complex to be low spin. Cyanide (and carbonyl) are high on the spectrochemical series, which means the complex will have a large Δ splitting characteristic of low spin complexes.

23.86

23.87   A large part of the metal-ligand interaction is electrostatic attraction between the positively charged metal and the fully or partially negatively charged ligand. For the same ligand, the greater the charge on the metal or the shorter the M−L separation, the stronger the interaction and the more stable the complex. The greater positive charge and smaller ionic radius of a metal in the 3+ oxidation state means that, for the same ligand, complexes with metals in the 3+ state are more stable than those with metals in the 2+ state.

23.88   (a)   Only one   (b)   Two

(c)   Four; two are geometric, the other two are stereoisomers of each of these.

23.89

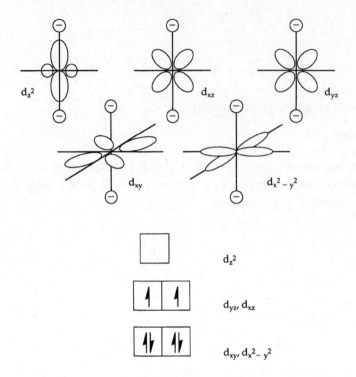

For a d^6 metal ion in a strong ligand field, there would be two unpaired electrons.

Integrative Exercises

23.90   (a)

(b)   The pK_a of pure water is 14, that of carbonic anhydrase is 7.5. The active site of carbonic anhydrase is much more acidic than the bulk water. In carbonic anhydrase, the Zn^{2+} ion withdraws electron density from the O atom of water. The electronegative oxygen atom compensates by withdrawing electron-density from the O—H bond. The O—H bond is polarized and H becomes more ionizable, more acidic than in the bulk solvent. This is similar to the effect of an electronegative central atom in an oxyacid such as H_2SO_4.

(c)   When the water molecule is deprotonated, the ligand coordinated to water becomes hydroxide ion, OH^-. The three N atoms are unaffected.

(d)   In $[Zn(H_2O)_6]^{2+}$, the Zn^{2+} ion has six bound O atoms from which to withdraw electron density. Each O atom donates less electron density than the single O atom in carbonic anhydrase and each O atom withdraws less electron density from its O—H bonds. The O—H bonds in $[Zn(H_2O)_6]^{2+}$ are less polarized and less acidic than those in carbonic anhydrase. $[Zn(H_2O)_6]^{2+}$ is a weaker acid and has a higher pK_a than carbonic anydrase.

(e) No, we do not expect carbonic anydrase to have a deep color like hemoglobin. The Zn^{2+} ion is a d^{10} metal center. Its d-orbitals are completely occupied and there is no possibility for the d-d transitions that lead to colored complexes.

23.91 (a) Both compounds have the same general formulation, so Co is in the same (+3) oxidation state in both complexes.

(b) Cobalt(III) complexes are generally inert; that is, they do not rapidly exchange ligands inside the coordination sphere. Therefore, the ions that form precipitates in these two cases are probably outside the coordination sphere. The dark violet compound A forms a precipitate with $BaCl_2(aq)$ but not $AgNO_3(aq)$, so it has SO_4^{2-} outside the coordination sphere and coordinated Br^-, $[Co(NH_3)_5Br]SO_4$. The red-violet compound B forms a precipitate with $AgNO_3(aq)$ but not $BaCl_2(aq)$ so it has Br^- outside the coordination sphere and coordinated SO_4^{2-}, $[Co(NH_3)_5SO_4]Br$.

Compound A, dark violet   Compound B, red-violet

$$\left[\begin{array}{c} NH_3 \\ NH_3 \underset{\underset{NH_3}{|}}{\overset{|}{\underset{Co}{}}} NH_3 \\ NH_3 \quad Br \end{array}\right]^{2+} SO_4^{2-} \qquad \left[\begin{array}{c} NH_3 \\ NH_3 \underset{\underset{NH_3}{|}}{\overset{|}{\underset{Co}{}}} NH_3 \\ NH_3 \quad SO_4 \end{array}\right]^{+} Br^-$$

(c) Compounds A and B have the same formula but different properties (color, chemical reactivity), so they are isomers. They vary by which ion is inside the coordination sphere, so they are *coordination sphere isomers*.

(d) Compound A is an ionic sulfate and compound B is an ionic bromide, so both are strong electrolytes. According to the solubility rules in Table 4.1, both should be water-soluble.

23.92 Determine the empirical formula of the complex, assuming the remaining mass is due to oxygen, and a 100 g sample.

$$10.0 \text{ g Mn} \times \frac{1 \text{ mol Mn}}{54.94 \text{ g Mn}} = 0.1820 \text{ mol Mn}; 0.182 / 0.182 = 1$$

$$28.6 \text{ g K} \times \frac{1 \text{ mol K}}{39.10 \text{ g K}} = 0.7315 \text{ mol K}; 0.732 / 0.182 = 4$$

$$8.8 \text{ g C} \times \frac{1 \text{ mol C}}{12.0 \text{ g C}} = 0.7327 \text{ mol C}; 0.733 / 0.182 = 4$$

$$29.2 \text{ g Br} \times \frac{1 \text{ mol Br}}{79.904 \text{ g Br}} = 0.3654 \text{ mol Br}; 0.365 / 0.182 = 2$$

$$23.4 \text{ g O} \times \frac{1 \text{ mol O}}{16.00 \text{ g O}} = 1.463 \text{ mol O}; 1.46 / 0.182 = 8$$

There are 2 C and 4 O per oxalate ion, for a total of two oxalate ligands in the complex. To match the conductivity of $K_4[Fe(CN)_6]$, the oxalate and bromide ions must be in the coordination sphere of the complex anion. Thus, the compound is $K_4[Mn(ox)_2Br_2]$.

23.93   (a) $\Delta G^\circ = -nFE^\circ$. The positive E° values for both sets of complexes correspond to $-\Delta G^\circ$ values. Negative values of ΔG° mean that both processes are spontaneous. For both o-phen and CN^- ligands, the Fe(II) complex is more thermodynamically favorable than the Fe(III) complex.

   (b)   The CN^- complex, with the smaller positive E° value, is more difficult to reduce.

   (c)   That both the Fe(II) complexes are low spin means that both CN^- and o-phen are strong-field ligands. The negatively charged CN^- has a stronger electrostatic interaction with Fe^{3+} than the neutral o-phen has. This stabilizes the Fe(III) complex of CN^- relative to the Fe(III) complex of o-phen, which reduces the driving force for reduction of $[Fe(CN)_6]^{3-}$ relative to reduction of $[Fe(o\text{-phen})_3]^{3+}$. The E° value and magnitude of ΔG° for the reduction of the CN^- complex are thus smaller than those values for the o-phen complex.

23.94   First determine the empirical formula, assuming that the remaining mass of complex is Pd.

$$37.6 \text{ g Br} \times \frac{1 \text{ mol Br}}{79.904 \text{ g Br}} = 0.4706 \text{ mol Br}; 0.4706 / 0.2361 = 2$$

$$28.3 \text{ g C} \times \frac{1 \text{ mol C}}{12.01 \text{ g C}} = 2.356 \text{ mol C}; 2.356 / 0.2361 = 10$$

$$6.60 \text{ g N} \times \frac{1 \text{ mol N}}{14.01 \text{ g N}} = 0.4711 \text{ mol N}; 0.4711 / 0.2361 = 2$$

$$2.37 \text{ g H} \times \frac{1 \text{ mol H}}{1.008 \text{ g H}} = 2.351 \text{ mol H}; 2.351 / 0.2361 = 10$$

$$25.13 \text{ g Pd} \times \frac{1 \text{ mol Pd}}{106.42 \text{ g Pd}} = 0.2361 \text{ mol Pd}; 0.2361 / 0.2361 = 1$$

The chemical formula is $[Pd(NC_5H_5)_2Br_2]$. This should be a neutral square-planar complex of Pd(II), a nonelectrolyte. Because the dipole moment is zero, we can infer that it must be the trans isomer.

23.95   (a)   The reaction that occurs increases the conductivity of the solution by producing a greater number of charged particles, particles with higher charges, or both. It is likely that H_2O from the bulk solvent exchanges with a coordinated Br^- according to the reaction below. This reaction would convert the 1:1 electrolyte, $[Co(NH_3)_4Br_2]Br$, to a 1:2 electrolyte, $[Co(NH_3)_3(H_2O)Br]Br_2$.

(b) $[Co(NH_3)_4Br_2]^+(aq) + H_2O(l) \rightarrow [Co(NH_3)_4(H_2O)Br]^{2+}(aq) + Br^-(aq)$

(c) Before the exchange reaction, there is one mole of free Br^- per mole of complex.
mol $Br^- =$ mol Ag^+

$M =$ mol/L; L $AgNO_3 =$ mol $AgNO_3 / M$ $AgNO_3$

$$\frac{3.87 \text{ g complex}}{0.500 \text{ L soln}} \times \frac{1 \text{ mol complex}}{366.77 \text{ g complex}} \times 0.02500 \text{ L soln used} =$$

$$5.276 \times 10^{-4} = 5.28 \times 10^{-4} \text{ mol complex}$$

$$5.276 \times 10^{-4} \text{ mol complex} \times \frac{1 \text{ mol Br}^-}{1 \text{ mol complex}} \times \frac{1 \text{ mol Ag}^+}{1 \text{ mol Br}^-} \times \frac{1 \text{ L Ag}^+(\text{aq})}{0.0100 \text{ mol Ag}^+(\text{aq})}$$

$$= 0.05276 \text{ L} = 52.8 \text{ mL AgNO}_3(\text{aq})$$

(d) After the exchange reaction, there are 2 mol free Br^- per mol of complex. Since M $AgNO_3(aq)$ and volume of complex solution are the same for the second experiment, the titration after conductivity changes will require twice the volume calculated in part (c), 105.52 = 106 mL of 0.0100 M $AgNO_3(aq)$.

23.96 Calculate the concentration of Mg^{2+} alone, and then the concentration of Ca^{2+} by difference. $M \times L =$ mol

$$\frac{0.0104 \text{ mol EDTA}}{1 \text{ L}} \times 0.0187 \text{L} \times \frac{1 \text{ mol Mg}^{2+}}{1 \text{ mol EDTA}} \times \frac{24.31 \text{ g Mg}^{2+}}{1 \text{ mol Mg}^{2+}} \times \frac{1000 \text{ mg}}{\text{g}}$$

$$\times \frac{1}{0.100 \text{ L H}_2\text{O}} = 47.28 = 47.3 \text{ mg Mg}^{2+}/\text{L}$$

0.0104 M EDTA $\times$ 0.0315 L = mol $(Ca^{2+} + Mg^{2+})$

$\underline{0.0104 \text{ } M \text{ EDTA} \times 0.0187 \text{ L} = \text{mol Mg}^{2+}}$

0.0104 M EDTA $\times$ 0.0128 L = mol Ca^{2+}

$$0.0104 \text{ M EDTA} \times 0.0128 \text{ L} \times \frac{1 \text{ mol Ca}^{2+}}{1 \text{mol EDTA}} \times \frac{40.08 \text{ g Ca}^{2+}}{1 \text{ mol Ca}^{2+}} \times \frac{1000 \text{ mg}}{\text{g}} \times \frac{1}{0.100 \text{ L H}_2\text{O}}$$

$$= 53.35 = 53.4 \text{ mg Ca}^{2+}/\text{L}$$

23.97 Use Hess' law to calculate $\Delta G°$ for the desired equilibrium. Then $\Delta G° = -RT\ln K$ to calculate K.

$Hb + CO \rightarrow HbCO$	$\Delta G° = -80$ kJ
$\underline{HbO_2 \rightarrow Hb + O_2}$	$\Delta G° = 70$ kJ
$HbO_2 + Hb + CO \rightarrow HbCO + Hb + O_2$	
$HbO_2 + CO \rightarrow HbCO + O_2$	$\Delta G° = -10$ kJ

$$\Delta G° = -RT\ln K, \ln K = \frac{-\Delta G°}{RT} = \frac{-(-10 \text{ kJ})}{8.314 \text{ J/K-mol} \times 298 \text{ K}} \times \frac{1000 \text{ J}}{\text{kJ}} = 4.036 = 4.04$$

$K = e^{4.04} = 56.61 = 57$

23.98 (a)
$$[Cd(CH_3NH_2)_4]^{2+} \rightleftharpoons Cd^{2+}(aq) + 4CH_3NH_2(aq) \qquad \Delta G° = 37.2 \text{ kJ}$$
$$Cd^{2+}(aq) + 2en(aq) \rightleftharpoons [Cd(en)_2]^{2+}(aq) \qquad \Delta G° = -60.7 \text{ kJ}$$

$$Cd(CH_3NH_2)_4]^{2+} + 2en(aq) \rightleftharpoons [Cd(en)_2]^{2+}(aq) + 4CH_3NH_2(aq) \qquad \Delta G° = -23.5 \text{ kJ}$$

$\Delta G° = -RT\ln K; -23.5 \text{ kJ} = -2.35 \times 10^4 \text{ J}$

$$-2.35 \times 10^4 \text{ J} = \frac{-8.314 \text{ J}}{K\text{-mol}} \times 298 \text{ K} \times \ln K; \ln K = 9.485, K = 1.32 \times 10^4$$

The magnitude of K is large, so the reaction favors products. The bidentate chelating ligand en will spontaneously replace the monodentate ligand CH_3NH_2. This is an illustration of the chelate effect.

(b) Using the stepwise construction from part (a),

$\Delta H° = 57.3 \text{ kJ} - 56.5 \text{ kJ} = 0.8 \text{ kJ}$

$\Delta S° = 67.3 \text{ J/K} + 14.1 \text{ J/K} = 81.4 \text{ J/K}$

$-T\Delta S = -298 \text{ K} \times 81.4 \text{ J/K} = -2.43 \times 10^4 \text{ J} = -24.3 \text{ kJ}$

The chelate effect is mainly the result of entropy. The reaction is spontaneous due to the increase in the number of free particles and corresponding increase in entropy going from reactants to products. The enthalpic contribution is essentially zero because the bonding interactions of the two ligands are very similar and the reaction is not "downhill" in enthalpy.

(c) $\Delta H°$ will be very small and negative. When NH_3 replaces H_2O in a complex (Closer Look Box), the tighter bonding of the NH_3 ligand causes a substantial negative $\Delta H°$ for the substitution reaction. When a bidentate amine ligand replaces a monodentate amine ligand of similar bond strength, $\Delta H°$ is very small and either positive (part (c)) or negative (Closer Look Box). In the case of NH_3 replacing CH_3NH_2, the bonding characteristics are very similar. The presence of CH_3 groups in CH_3NH_2 produces some steric hindrance in $[Cd(CH_3NH_2)_4]^{2+}$. This complex is at a slightly higher energy than $[Cd(NH_3)_4]^{2+}$, which experiences no steric hindrance, so $\Delta H°$ will have a negative sign but a very small magnitude. Relief of steric hindrance leads to a very small negative $\Delta H°$ for the substitution reaction.

23.99
$$\frac{182 \times 10^3 \text{ J}}{1 \text{ mol}} \times \frac{1 \text{ mol}}{6.022 \times 10^{23} \text{ molecules}} = 3.022 \times 10^{-19} = 3.02 \times 10^{-19} \text{ J/photon}$$

$\Delta E = h\nu = 3.02 \times 10^{-19} \text{ J}; \nu = \Delta E/h$

$\nu = 3.022 \times 10^{-19} \text{ J}/6.626 \times 10^{-34} \text{ J-s} = 4.561 \times 10^{14} = 4.56 \times 10^{14} \text{ s}^{-1}$

$$\lambda = \frac{2.998 \times 10^8 \text{ m/s}}{4.561 \times 10^{14} \text{ s}^{-1}} = 6.57 \times 10^{-7} \text{ m} = 657 \text{ nm}$$

We expect that this complex will absorb in the visible, at around 660 nm. It will thus exhibit a blue-green color (Figure 23.25).

23.100 The process can be written:

$$H_2(g) + 2e \rightarrow 2H^+(aq) \qquad\qquad E^{\circ}_{red} = 0.0 \text{ V}$$

$$Cu(s) \rightarrow Cu^{2+} + 2e^- \qquad\qquad E^{\circ}_{red} = 0.337 \text{ V}$$

$$\underline{Cu^{2+}(aq) + 4NH_3(aq) \rightarrow [Cu(NH_3)_4]^{2+}(aq)} \qquad "E^{\circ}_f" = ?$$

$$H_2(g) + Cu(s) + 4NH_3(aq) \rightarrow 2H^+(aq) + [Cu(NH_3)_4]^{2+}(aq) \qquad E = 0.08 \text{ V}$$

$$E = E^{\circ} - RT \ln K; K = \frac{[H^+]^2 [Cu(NH_3)_4^{2+}]}{P_{H_2}[NH_3]^4}$$

$$P_{H_2} = 1 \text{ atm}, \ [H^+] = 1 \ M, [NH_3] = 1 \ M, [Cu(NH_3)_4]^{2+} = 1 \ M, Q = 1$$

$$E = E^{\circ} - RT \ln(1); E = E^{\circ} - RT(0); E = E^{\circ} = 0.08 \text{ V}$$

Since we know E° values for two steps and the overall reaction, we can calculate "E°" for the formation reaction and then K_f, using $E^{\circ} = \dfrac{0.0592}{n} \log K_f$ for the step.

$$E_{cell} = 0.08 \text{ V} = 0.0 \text{ V} - 0.337 \text{ V} + "E^{\circ}_f" \quad "E^{\circ}_f" = 0.08 \text{ V} + 0.337 \text{ V} = 0.417 \text{ V} = 0.42 \text{ V}$$

$$"E^{\circ}_f" = \frac{0.0592}{n} \log K_f; \log K_f = \frac{n(E^{\circ}_f)}{0.0592} = \frac{2(0.417)}{0.0592} = 14.0878 = 14$$

$$K_f = 10^{14.0878} = 1.2 \times 10^{14} = 10^{14}$$

23.101 (a) The units of the rate constant and the rate dependence on the identity of the second ligand show that the reaction is second order. Therefore, the rate-determining step cannot be the dissociation of water, since that would be independent of the concentration and identity of the incoming ligand. The alternative mechanism, a bimolecular association of the incoming ligand with the complex, is indicated.

(b) The larger the value of the rate constant, the faster the exchange reaction, the stronger the donor ability of the nitrogen-containing ligand toward Ru(III). The rate constants indicate that the order of nitrogen-donor strength is: pyridine > SCN^- > CH_3CN.

(c) Ru(III) is a d^5 ion. In a low-spin d^5 octahedral complex, there is one unpaired electron.

24 The Chemistry of Life: Organic and Biological Chemistry

Visualizing Concepts

24.1 *Analyze/Plan.* Follow the logic in Sample Exercise 24.1 to name each compound. Decide which structures are the same compound. *Solve.*

(a)   2,2,4-trimethylpentane

(b)   3-ethyl-2-methylpentane

(c)   2,3,4-trimethylpentane

(d)   2,3,4-trimethylpentane

Structures (c) and (d) are the same molecule.

24.2 *Analyze/Plan.* Given structural formulas, specify which molecules are unsaturated. Consider the definition of unsaturated and apply it to the molecules in the exercise. *Solve.*

Unsaturated molecules contain one or more multiple bonds. Saturated molecules contain only single bonds. Molecules (c) and (d) are unsaturated.

24.3 *Analyze/Plan.* Given structural formulas, decide which molecule will undergo addition. Consider which functional groups are present in the molecules, and which are most susceptible to addition. *Solve.*

Addition reactions are characteristic of alkenes. Molecule (c), an alkene, will readily undergo addition.

Molecule (a) is an aromatic hydrocarbon, which does not typically undergo addition because the delocalized electron cloud is too difficult to disrupt. Molecules (b) and (d) contain carbonyl groups (actually carboxylic acid groups) that do not typically undergo addition, except under special conditions.

24.4 *Analyze/plan.* Given structural formulas, predict which molecule will have the highest boiling point. Boiling point is determined by strength of intermolecular forces; for neutral molecules with similar molar masses, the strongest intermolecular force is hydrogen bonding. The molecule that experiences hydrogen bonding will have the highest boiling point. *Solve.*

Only F—H, O—H, and N—H bonds fit the strict definition of hydrogen bonding. Molecule (b), an alcohol, forms hydrogen bonds with like molecules; it has the highest boiling point.

[Molecules (a) and (d) have dipole-dipole and dispersion forces. The greater molar mass of (d) probably means it has stronger dispersion forces and a slightly higher boiling point than molecule (a). Molecule (c) has only dispersion forces and the lowest boiling point. The probable order of strength of forces and boiling points is: (b) > (d) > (a) > (c).]

24.5   *Analyze.* Given structural formulas, decide which molecules are capable of isomerism, and what type. *Plan.* Analyze each molecule for possible structural, geometric, and optical isomers/enantiomers.   *Solve.*

(a) $C_5H_{11}NO_2$, structural, geometric and optical. There are many ways to arrange the atoms in molecules with this empirical formula, so there are many structural isomers. There is one point of unsaturation in the given molecule, the C=O group; structural isomers with their point of unsaturation at a C=C group could have geometric isomers as well.   The C atom to which the —NH_3^+ group is bound is a chiral center, so there are enantiomers. All amino acids except glycine have two possible enantiomers.

(b) $C_7H_5O_2Cl$, structural and geometric.   The most obvious isomers for this aromatic compound are ortho, meta, and para geometric isomers. Because the molecule has several points of unsaturation, the number of structural isomers is limited, but there are a few possibilities with two triple bonds. Switching the —OH and —Cl groups also generates a structural isomer.   There are no chiral centers, so no optical isomers.

(c) C_5H_{10}, structural and geometric (cis-trans). There are many structural isomers for this empirical formula. The straight-chain alkene shown also has geometric (cis-trans) isomers.

(d) C_3H_8. There are no other structural, geometric, or optical isomers for this molecule.

24.6   *Analyze/Plan.* Given ball-and-stick models, select the molecule that fits the description given. From the models, decide the type of molecule or functional group represented.

Solve. Molecule (i) is a sugar, (ii) is an ester with a long hydrocarbon chain, (iii) is an organic base and a component of nucleic acids, (iv) is an amino acid, and (v) is an alcohol.

(a)   Molecule (i) is a disaccharide composed of galactose (left) and glucose (right); it can be hydrolyzed to form a solution containing glucose. Since it is the only sugar molecule depicted, it was not necessary to know the exact structure of glucose to answer the question.

(b)   Amino acids form zwitterions, so the choice is molecule (iv).

(c)   Molecule (iii) is an organic base present in DNA (again, the only possible choice).

(d)   Molecule (v) because alcohols react with carboxylic acids to form esthers.

(e)   Molecule (ii), because it has a long hydrocarbon chain and an ester functional group.

Introduction to Organic Compounds; Hydrocarbons
(sections 24.1 and 24.2)

24.7   (a) sp^3 (b) sp^2 (c) sp^2 (d) sp

24.8   (a) 109°   (b) 120°   (c) 180°

24.9   *Analyze/Plan.* Given a condensed structural formula, determine the bond angles and hybridization about each carbon atom in the molecule. Visualize the number of electron domains about each carbon. State the bond angle and hybridization based on electron domain geometry.   *Solve.*

C1 has triangonal planar electron domain geometry, 120° bond angles and sp^2 hybridization. C3 and C4 have linear electron domain geometry, 180° bond angles and sp hybridization. C2 and C5 both have tetrahedral electron domain geometry, 109° bond angles and sp^3 hybridization.

24.10

(a)   C2, C5 and C6 have sp^3 hybridization (4 e⁻ domains around C)

(b)   C7 has sp hybridization (2 e⁻ domains around C)

(c)   C1, C3, and C4 have sp^2 hybridization (3 e⁻ domains around C)

24.11   Ammonia, NH_3, contains no carbon, so it is not, strictly speaking, considered an organic molecule. Carbon monoxide contains a carbon atom that does not form four bonds, so it certainly is not a typical organic molecule.

24.12   From Table 8.4, the bond enthalpies in kJ/mol are: C—H, 413; C—C, 348; C—O, 358; C—Cl, 328. The bond enthalpes indicate that C—H bonds are most difficult to break, and C—Cl bonds least difficult. However, they do not explain the reactivity of C—O bonds, or stability of C—C bonds.

The reactivity of molecules containing C—O and C—Cl bonds is a result of their unequal charge distribution, which attracts reactants that are either electron deficient (electrophilic) or electron rich (nucleophilic).

24.13   (a)   A *straight-chain alkane* has all carbon atoms connected in a continuous chain; no carbon atom is bound to more than two other carbon atoms. Carbon forms only single (sigma) bonds to other carbon or hydrogen atoms. A *branched-chain alkane* has a branch; at least one carbon atom is bound to three or more carbon atoms.

(b)   An *alkane* is a complete molecule composed of carbon and hydrogen in which all bonds are single (sigma) bonds. An *alkyl group* is a substituent formed by removing a hydrogen atom from an alkane.

24.14   All the classifications listed are hydrocarbons; they contain only the elements hydrogen and carbon.

(a)   *Alkanes* are hydrocarbons that contain only single bonds.

(b)   *Cycloalkanes* contain at least one ring of three or more carbon atoms joined by single bonds. Because it is a type of alkane, all bonds in a cycloalkane are single bonds.

(c)   *Alkenes* contain at least one $C{=}C$ double bond.

(d)   *Alkynes* contain at least one $C{\equiv}C$ triple bond.

(e)   A *saturated hydrocarbon* contains only single bonds. Alkanes and cycloalkanes fit this definition.

(f)   An *aromatic hydrocarbon* contains one or more planar, six-membered rings of carbon atoms with delocalized π-bonding throughout the ring.

24.15   *Analyze/Plan.* Follow the rules for naming alkanes given in Section 24.2 and illustrated in Sample Exercise 24.1.   *Solve.*

(a)   2-methylhexane

(b)   4-ethyl-2,4-dimethyldecane

(c)

$$CH_3CH_2CH_2CH_2CH_2\underset{\displaystyle |}{\overset{\displaystyle CH_3}{CH}}{-}CH_3$$

(d)

$$CH_3CH_2CH_2CH_2{-}\underset{\displaystyle \underset{\displaystyle |}{CH_2}}{\overset{\displaystyle CH_3}{CH}}{-}\underset{\displaystyle |}{\overset{\displaystyle CH_3}{CH}}{-}\underset{\displaystyle |}{\overset{\displaystyle CH_3}{CH}}{-}CH_3$$

(e)

24.16   (a)   3,3,5-trimethylheptane

(b)   3,4,4-trimethylheptane

(c)

$$CH_3CH_2CH_2{-}\underset{\displaystyle |}{\overset{\displaystyle CH_3}{CH}}{-}\underset{\displaystyle |}{\overset{\displaystyle CH_3}{CH}}{-}CH_2{-}CH_2{-}\underset{\displaystyle |}{\overset{\displaystyle CH_3}{CH}}{-}CH_3$$

(d)

$$CH_3CH_2CH_2CH_2CH_2-\underset{\underset{CH_3}{|}}{CH}-\underset{\underset{CH_3}{|}}{CH}-\underset{\underset{\underset{\underset{CH_2}{|}}{CH_2}}{\overset{|}{CH_2}}}{CH}-CH_2-CH_3$$

(e)

24.17 *Analyze/Plan.* Follow the rules for naming alkanes given in Section 24.2 and illustrated in Sample Exercise 24.1.   *Solve.*

(a) 2,3-dimethylheptane

(b)
$$CH_3CH_2CH_2-\underset{\underset{CH_3}{|}}{\overset{\overset{CH_3}{|}}{C}}-CH_3$$

(c)

(d) 2,2,5-trimethylhexane

(e) 3-ethylheptane

24.18 (a)

CH_3CH_2CHCH_2CH_3

(b)
$$CH_3CH_2CH_2\underset{\underset{CH_3}{|}}{CH}\underset{\underset{CH_3}{|}}{CH}CH_3$$

(c)
$$CH_3CH_2CH_2CH_2CH_2\underset{\underset{\underset{CH_2CH_3}{|}}{|}}{\overset{\overset{CH_3}{|}}{C}}CH_3$$

(A more correct name for this compound is 3,3-dimethyloctane.)

(d)   2,4-dimethylhexane

(e)   methylcyclobutane

24.19   Assuming that each component retains its effective octane number in the mixture (and this isn't always the case), we obtain: octane number = 0.35(0) + 0.65(100) = 65.

24.20   Octane number can be increased by increasing the fraction of branched-chain alkanes or aromatics, since these have high octane numbers. This can be done by cracking. The octane number also can be increased by adding an anti-knock agent such as tetraethyl lead, $Pb(C_2H_5)_4$ (no longer legal); methyl t-butyl ether (MTBE); or an alcohol, methanol, or ethanol.

Alkenes, Alkynes, and Aromatic Hydrocarbons (section 24.3)

24.21   (a)   Alkanes are said to be *saturated* because they contain only single bonds. Multiple bonds that enable addition of H_2 or other substances are absent. The bonding capacity of each carbon atom is fulfilled with single bonds to C or H.

(b)   No, C_4H_6 is not saturated. Alkanes are saturated hydrocarbons. The maximum number of hydrogen atoms for 4 C atoms in an alkane is [(2×4)+2] = 10. C_4H_6 does not contain the maximum possible hydrogen atoms and is unsaturated.

24.22   (a)   The molecule $CH_3CH=C H_3$ is unsaturated because it contains a double bond. It is possible to add more hydrogen to the molecule.

(b)   The formula $CH_3CH_2CH=CH_3$ has too many H atoms bound to the right-most C atom; the formula as it stands implies 5 bonds to this atom. A correct formula is $CH_3CH_2CH=CH_2$, with 2 H atoms on the right-most C atom.

24.23   *Analyze/Plan.* Consider the definition of the stated classification and apply it to a compound containing five C atoms.   *Solve.*

(a) $CH_3CH_2CH_2CH_2CH_3$, C_5H_{12}

(b)

, C_5H_{12}

(c) $CH_2=CHCH_2CH_2CH_3$, C_5H_{10}

(d) $HC\equiv CCH_2CH_2CH_3$, C_5H_8 saturated: (a), (b); unsaturated: (c), (d)

24.24   cycloalkane,

, C_6H_{12}, saturated

cycloalkene,

, C_6H_{10}, unsaturated

alkyne, $CH_3-CH_2-C\equiv C-CH_2-CH_3$, C_6H_{10}, unsaturated

aromatic hydrocarbon,

C_6H_6, unsaturated

24.25 *Analyze/Plan.* We are given the class of compounds "enediyne". Based on organic nomenclature, determine the structural features of an enediyne. Construct a molecule with 6 C atoms that has these features. *Solve.*

The term "enediyne" contains the suffixes –ene and –yne. The suffix –ene is used to name alkenes, molecules with one double bond. The suffix –yne is used to name alkynes, molecules with one triple bond. An enediyne then features one double and two triple bonds. Possible arrangements of these bonds involving 6 C atoms are:

$$CH_2=CH-C\equiv C-C\equiv CH \qquad CH\equiv C-CH=CH-C\equiv CH$$

Check. The formula of a saturated alkane is C_nH_{2n+2}. For each double bond subtract 2 H atoms, for each triple bond subtract 4 H atoms. A saturated 6 C alkane has 14 H atoms. For the enediyne, subtract (2 + 4 + 4 =) 10 H atoms. The molecular formula is C_6H_4. That is the molecular formula of each structure above.

24.26 C_nH_{2n-2}

24.27 *Analyze/Plan.* Follow the logic in Sample Exercise 24.3. *Solve.*

$CH_3CH_2CH_2CH_2C\equiv CH$ \qquad $CH_3CH_2CH_2C\equiv CCH_3$

$CH_3CH_2C\equiv CCH_2CH_3$

$$CH_3CH_2CH_2\overset{\displaystyle CH_3}{\underset{\displaystyle |}{C}}HCH_2C\equiv CH$$

$$CH_3CH_2\overset{\displaystyle CH_3}{\underset{\displaystyle |}{C}}HC\equiv CH$$

$$CH_3\overset{\displaystyle CH_3}{\underset{\displaystyle |}{C}}HC\equiv CCH_3$$

$$CH_3CH_2\overset{\displaystyle H}{\underset{\displaystyle |}{C}}=\overset{\displaystyle H}{\underset{\displaystyle |}{C}}-CH=CH_2$$

$$CH_3CH_2\overset{\displaystyle H}{\underset{\displaystyle |}{C}}=C-CH=CH_2 \atop \underset{\displaystyle |}{\underset{\displaystyle H}{}}$$

$$CH_3\overset{\displaystyle H}{\underset{\displaystyle |}{C}}=\overset{\displaystyle H}{\underset{\displaystyle |}{C}}-CH_2CH=CH_2$$

$$CH_3\overset{\displaystyle H}{\underset{\displaystyle |}{C}}=C-CH_2CH=CH_2 \atop \underset{\displaystyle |}{\underset{\displaystyle H}{}}$$

$$CH_2=CHCH_2CH_2CH=CH_2 \qquad CH_3\overset{\displaystyle H}{\underset{\displaystyle |}{C}}=\overset{\displaystyle H}{\underset{\displaystyle |}{C}}-\overset{\displaystyle H}{\underset{\displaystyle |}{C}}=\overset{\displaystyle H}{\underset{\displaystyle |}{C}}-CH_3$$

$$CH_3C{=}C{-}C{=}C{-}CH_3$$
(with H above CH3C, H above second C, H above third C, H above fourth C, and H below the C)

$$CH_3C{=}C{-}C{=}C{-}CH_3$$
(with H's above and below)

$$CH_2{=}CHCHCH{=}CH_2$$
with CH_3 above

$$CH_2{=}CCH_2CH{=}CH_2$$
with CH_3 above

$$CH_2{=}CHC{=}CH$$
with CH_3 CH_3 above

$$CH_2{=}CHC{=}CCH_3$$
with CH_3 H above

$$CH_2{=}CC{=}CCH_3$$
with CH_3 H above, H below

$$CH_2{=}CC{=}CCH_3$$
with CH_3 above, H H below

$$CH_2{=}CHCH{=}CCH_3$$
with CH_3 above

$$CH_2{=}CHC{=}CH_2$$
with CH_2CH_3 above

$$CH_2{=}C{-}C{=}CH_2$$
with CH_3 CH_3 above

$$CH_3,H{\,}C{=}C{=}C{\,}CH_3,CH_3$$

$$CH_3,H{\,}C{=}C{=}C{\,}CH_2CH_3,H$$

$$H,H{\,}C{=}C{=}C{\,}CH_2CH_2CH_3,H$$

$$H,H{\,}C{=}C{=}C{\,}CH_2CH_3,CH_3$$

(ring structures)

$$\begin{array}{c} HC{\,}CH\\ \| \quad \\ H_2C \quad CH_2\\ \quad CH_2 \end{array}$$

$$\begin{array}{c} CH{=}C{-}CH_3\\ H_2C \quad CH_2\\ CH_2 \end{array}$$

$$\begin{array}{c} CH{=}CH\\ H_2C \quad C{-}CH_3,H\\ CH_2 \end{array}$$

$$\begin{array}{c} CH{=}CH\\ H_2C \quad CH_2\\ C{-}H,CH_3 \end{array}$$

$$\begin{array}{c} H_2C{-}C{-}CH_3\\ H_2C{-}C{-}CH_3 \end{array}$$

$$\begin{array}{c} H\\ C{-}CH\\ H\\ C\\ CH_3,CH_3 \end{array}$$

$$\begin{array}{c} CH_3\\ C{-}CH\\ H\\ H_2C{-}C\\ CH_3 \end{array}$$

$$\begin{array}{c} CH_3\\ C{-}CH\\ CH_3\\ H_2C{-}CH \end{array}$$

$$\begin{array}{c} CH_3\\ CH_3 C{-}CH\\ H\\ C{-}CH\\ H \end{array}$$

$$\begin{array}{c} CH_3\\ C{-}CH\\ H,H\\ C{-}CH\\ CH_3 \end{array}$$

$$\begin{array}{c} H_2C{-}C{-}CH_2CH_3\\ H_2C{-}CH \end{array}$$

$$\begin{array}{c} CH_2CH_3\\ C{-}CH\\ H\\ H_2C{-}CH \end{array}$$

$$\underset{H_2C \longrightarrow CCH_2CH_2CH_3}{\overset{CH}{\triangle}}$$
$$\underset{H_2C \longrightarrow CCH_2CH_3}{\overset{CH_3}{\overset{C}{\triangle}}}$$
$$\underset{CH_3 - CH \longrightarrow CCH_2CH_3}{\overset{CH}{\triangle}}$$

$$\underset{CH_3CH_2CH_2CH \longrightarrow CH}{\overset{CH}{\triangle}}$$
$$\underset{CH_3CH_2CH \longrightarrow C - CH_3}{\overset{CH}{\triangle}}$$
$$\underset{CH_3CH \longrightarrow CCH_3}{\overset{\overset{CH_3}{C}}{\triangle}}$$

$$\underset{\underset{CH_3}{\overset{CH_3}{\diagdown}} C \longrightarrow CCH_3}{\overset{CH}{\triangle}}$$

24.28 $CH_3 - CH_2 - CH_2 - CH = CH_2$
     pentene

$CH_3 - CH_2 - CH = CH - CH_3$ $\underset{CH_2 = CH - \overset{\overset{\displaystyle CH_3}{|}}{CH} - CH_3}{}$
   2-pentene   3-methyl-1-butene

$\underset{CH_2 = \overset{\overset{\displaystyle CH_3}{|}}{C} - CH_2 - CH_3}{}$ $\underset{CH_3 - \overset{\overset{\displaystyle CH_3}{|}}{C} = CH - CH_3}{}$
   2-methyl-1-butene   2-methyl-2-butene

24.29   *Analyze/Plan.* Follow the logic in Sample Exercises 24.1 and 24.4.   *Solve.*

(a) $$\underset{CH_3CH_2}{\overset{H}{\diagdown}} C = C \underset{H}{\overset{CH_3}{\diagup}}$$

(b) $$CH_3CH_2CH_2\overset{\overset{\displaystyle CH_3}{|}}{C} = CHCH_2CH_2 - \overset{\overset{\displaystyle CH_3}{|}}{\underset{\underset{\displaystyle CH_3}{|}}{CH}}$$

(c)   *cis*-6-methyl-3-octene

(d)   *para*-dibromobenzene

(e)   4,4-dimethyl-1-hexyne

24.30   (a) $$\underset{CH_3CH_2CH = CHCH_3}{\overset{\overset{\displaystyle CH_3}{|}}{}}$$

(b) $$\underset{H_3C - \overset{\underset{\displaystyle CH_3}{|}}{CH}}{\overset{H}{\diagdown}} C = C \underset{\overset{\displaystyle CH - CH_3}{\underset{\displaystyle CH_3}{|}}}{\overset{H}{\diagup}}$$

(c) a benzene ring with two CH_3 groups (ortho)

(d)   1-butyne

(e)   *trans*-2-heptene

24.31   Each doubly bound carbon atom in an alkene has two unique sites for substitution. These sites cannot be interconverted because rotation about the double bond is restricted; *geometric isomerism* results. In an alkane, carbon forms only single bonds, so the three remaining sites are interchangeable by rotation about the single bond. Although there is also restricted rotation around the triple bond of an alkyne, there is only one additional bonding site on a triply bound carbon, so no isomerism results.

24.32   Butene is an alkene, C_4H_8. There are two possible placements for the double bond:

$$CH_2=CHCH_2CH_3 \text{ or } CH_3CH=CHCH_3$$

    1-butene   2-butene

These two compounds are *structural isomers*. For 2-butene, there are two different, noninterchangeable ways to construct the carbon skeleton (owing to the absence of free rotation around the double bond). These two compounds are *geometric isomers*.

            cis-2-butene   *trans*-2-butene

24.33   *Analyze/Plan.* In order for geometrical isomerism to be possible, the molecule must be an alkene with two different groups bound to each of the alkene C atoms.   *Solve.*

(a)   , no

(b)

(c)   no, not an alkene

(d)   no, not an alkene

24.34

24.35   (a)   An *addition reaction* is the addition of some reagent to the two atoms that form a multiple bond. In a *substitution reaction*, one atom or group of atoms replaces (substitutes for) another atom or group of atoms. In an addition reaction, two atoms and a multiple bond on the target molecule are altered; in a substitution reaction, the environment of one atom in the target molecule changes. Alkenes typically undergo addition, while aromatic hydrocarbons usually undergo substitution.

(b) *Plan.* Consider the general form of addition across a double bond. The π bond is broken and one new substituent (in this case two Br atoms) adds to each of the C atoms involved in the π bond. *Solve.*

$$CH_3CH_2CH=CH-CH_3 + Br_2 \rightarrow CH_3CH_2CH(Br)CH(Br)CH_3$$

2-pentene   2,3-dibromopentane

(c) *Plan.* Consider the general form of a *substitution* reaction. Two Cl atoms will replace two of the H atoms on the benzene ring. The term *para* means the Cl atoms will be opposite each other across the benzene ring in the product. *Solve.*

$$C_6H_6 + Cl_2 \xrightarrow{FeCl_3} C_6H_4Cl_2$$

24.36

(a)

(b)

$$\cdots \xrightarrow{H_2SO_4} CH_3CH(OH)CH_2CH_2CH_3 + CH_3CH_2CH(OH)CH_2CH_3$$

(c)

24.37 (a) *Plan.* Consider the structures of cyclopropane, cyclopentane, and cyclohexane. *Solve.*

The small 60° C—C—C angles in the cyclopropane ring cause strain that provides a driving force for reactions that result in ring opening. There is no comparable strain in the five- or six-membered rings.

(b) *Plan.* First form an alkyl halide: $C_2H_4(g) + HBr(g) \rightarrow CH_3CH_2Br(l)$; then carry out a Friedel-Crafts reaction. *Solve.*

24.38 (a) The reaction of Br_2 with an alkene to form a colorless halogenated alkane is an addition reaction. Aromatic hydrocarbons do not readily undergo addition reactions, because their π-electrons are stabilized by delocalization.

(b)   *Plan.* Use a Friedel-Crafts reaction to substitute a —CH_2CH_3 onto benzene. Do a second substitution reaction to get *para*-bromoethylbenzene.   *Solve.*

It appears that ortho, meta, and para geometric isomers of bromoethylbenzene would be possible. However, because of electronic effects beyond the scope of this chapter, the ethyl group favors formation of ortho and para isomers, but not the meta. The ortho and para products must be separated by distillation or some other technique.

24.39   Not necessarily. That the rate laws are both first order in both reactants and second order overall indicates that the activated complex in the rate-determining step in each mechanism is bimolecular and contains one molecule of each reactant. This is usually an indication that the mechanisms are the same, but it does not rule out the possibility of different fast steps, or a different order of elementary steps.

24.40   The partially positive end of the hydrogen halide, $\overset{\delta^+ \;\; \delta^-}{H-X}$, is attached to the π electron cloud of the alkene cyclohexene. The electrons that formed the π bond in cyclohexene form a sigma bond to the H atom of HX, leaving a halide ion, X^-. The intermediate is a carbocation; one of the C atoms formerly involved in the π bond is now bound to a second H atom. The other C atom formerly involved in the π bond carries a full positive charge and forms only three sigma bonds, two to adjacent C atoms and one to H.

24.41   *Analyze/Plan.* Both combustion reactions produce CO_2 and H_2O:

$C_3H_6(g) + 9/2\,O_2(g) \rightarrow 3CO_2(g) + 3H_2O(l)$

$C_5H_{10}(g) + 15/2\,O_2(g) \rightarrow 5CO_2(g) + 5H_2O(l)$

Thus, we can calculate the ΔH_{comb} / CH_2 group for each compound.   *Solve.*

$$\frac{\Delta H_{comb}}{CH_2 \text{ group}} = \frac{2089 \text{ kJ/mol } C_3H_6}{3 \text{ } CH_2 \text{ groups}} = \frac{696.3 \text{ kJ}}{\text{mol } CH_2}; \frac{3317 \text{ kJ/mol } C_5H_{10}}{5 \text{ } CH_2 \text{ groups}} = 663.4 \text{ kJ/mol } CH_2$$

$\Delta H_{comb}/CH_2$ group for cyclopropane is greater because C_3H_6 contains a strained ring. When combustion occurs, the strain is relieved and the stored energy is released during the reaction.

24.42

$$
\begin{array}{ll}
 & \underline{\Delta H} \\
C_{10}H_8(l)+12O_2(g) \rightarrow 10CO_2(g)+4H_2O(l) & -5157 \text{ kJ} \\
-[C_{10}H_{18}(l)+29/2\,O_2(g) \rightarrow 10CO_2(g)+9H_2O(l) & -(-6286)\text{ kJ} \\
\hline
C_{10}H_8(l)+5H_2O(l) \rightarrow C_{10}H_{18}(l)+5/2\,O_2(g) & +1129\text{ kJ} \\
5/2\,O_2(g)+5H_2(g) \rightarrow 5H_2O(l) & 5(-285.8)\text{ kJ} \\
\hline
C_{10}H_8(l)+5H_2(g) \rightarrow C_{10}H_{18}(l) & -300\text{ kJ}
\end{array}
$$

Compare this with the heat of hydrogenation of ethylene:

$C_2H_4(g) + H_2(g) \rightarrow C_2H_6(g)$; $\Delta H = -84.7 - (52.3) = -137$ kJ. This value applies to just one double bond. For five double bonds, we would expect about –685 kJ. The fact that hydrogenation of napthalene yields only –300 kJ indicates that the overall energy of the napthalene molecule is lower than expected for five isolated double bonds and that there must be some special stability associated with the aromatic system in this molecule.

Functional Groups and Chirality (sections 24.4 and 24.5)

24.43   *Analyze/Plan.* Match the structural features of various functional groups shown in Table 24.6 to the molecular structures in this exercise. *Solve.*

(a)   –OH, alcohol

(b)   –NH– , amine; –C=C–, alkene

(c)   –O–, ether

(d) $\underset{\text{C}}{\overset{\text{O}}{\|}}$, ketone; –C=C–, alkene

(e) $\underset{\text{CH}}{\overset{\text{O}}{\|}}$ (–CHO), aldehyde

(f)   –C≡C–(–CC–), alkyne; –COOH, carboxylic acid

24.44   (a) $\underset{\text{C}}{\overset{\text{O}}{\|}}$—O, ester

(b)   –Cl, halocarbon; –OH, alcohol (aromatic alcohols are phenols)

(c) $\underset{\text{C}}{\overset{\text{O}}{\|}}$–NH— , amide

(d)   alkane

(e)   –C=C– , alkene; $\underset{\text{CH}}{\overset{\text{O}}{\|}}$, aldehyde

(f) $\underset{\text{C}}{\overset{\text{O}}{\|}}$— , ketone

24.45   *Analyze/Plan.* Given the name of a molecule, write the structural formula of an isomer molecular formula of the given molecule, draw the structural formula of a molecule with the same formula that contains the specified functional group.   *Solve.*

(a)   The formula of acetone is C_3H_6O. An aldehyde contains the group $-C\!\!\overset{\displaystyle O}{\underset{\displaystyle H}{\diagdown}}$

An aldehyde that is an isomer of acetone is propionaldehyde (or propanal):

$$H-\overset{\displaystyle H}{\underset{\displaystyle H}{\overset{|}{\underset{|}{C}}}}-\overset{\displaystyle H}{\underset{\displaystyle H}{\overset{|}{\underset{|}{C}}}}-C\!\!\overset{\displaystyle O}{\underset{\displaystyle H}{\diagdown}}$$

(b)   The formula of 1-propanol is C_3H_8O. An ether contains the group $-O-$. An ether that is an isomer of 1-propanol is ethylmethyl ether:

$$H-\overset{\displaystyle H}{\underset{\displaystyle H}{\overset{|}{\underset{|}{C}}}}-\overset{\displaystyle H}{\underset{\displaystyle H}{\overset{|}{\underset{|}{C}}}}-O-\overset{\displaystyle H}{\underset{\displaystyle H}{\overset{|}{\underset{|}{C}}}}-H$$

24.46   (a) C_4H_8O, $\overset{\displaystyle H_2C}{}\overset{O}{\diagup\diagdown}\overset{\displaystyle CH_2}{}$
                  H_2C-CH_2

(b) $CH_3CH_2\overset{\displaystyle O}{\overset{\|}{C}}CH_3$, $CH_3CH_2CH_2\overset{\displaystyle O}{\overset{\|}{C}}-H$

$CH_2{=}CH_2CH_2CH_2OH$, $CH_3CH{=}CHCH_2OH$,   (cis and trans)
$CH_2{=}CHCH(OH)CH_3$ (enantiomers)

(Structures with the $-OH$ group attached to an alkene carbon atom are not included. These molecules are called "vinyl alcohols" and are not the major form at equilibrium.)

24.47   Analyze/Plan. From the hydrocarbon name, deduce the number of C atoms in the acid; one carbon atom is in the carboxyl group. *Solve.*

(a)   meth = 1 C atom

$$H-\overset{\displaystyle O}{\overset{\|}{C}}-OH$$

(b)   pent = 5 C atoms

$CH_3CH_2CH_2CH_2\overset{\displaystyle O}{\overset{\|}{C}}-OH$ or   [structure: pentanoic acid skeletal with $\overset{O}{\|}$ and OH]

(c)   dec = 10 C atoms in backbone

$CH_3CH_2CH_2CH_2CH_2CH_2CH_2CH-\underset{}{\overset{\displaystyle CH_3}{|}}\;\;CH-\underset{}{\overset{\displaystyle Cl}{|}}\;\;\overset{\displaystyle O}{\overset{\|}{C}}-OH$

or

[skeletal structure with CH₃ branch, Cl, and carboxylic acid group]

24.48   (a)

$$CH_3CH_2\overset{\displaystyle O}{\overset{\|}{C}}\!\!-\!\!H$$

(b)

$$CH_3CH_2CH_2\overset{\displaystyle O}{\overset{\|}{C}}CH_3$$

(c)

$$CH_3\underset{\underset{\displaystyle CH_3}{|}}{CH}\overset{\displaystyle O}{\overset{\|}{C}}CH_3$$

(d)

$$CH_3CH_2\underset{\underset{\displaystyle CH_3}{|}}{CH}\overset{\displaystyle O}{\overset{\|}{C}}\!\!-\!\!H$$

24.49   *Analyze/Plan.* In a condensation reaction between an alcohol and a carboxylic acid, the alcohol loses its —OH hydrogen atom and the acid loses its —OH group. The alkyl group from the acid is attached to the carbonyl group and the alkyl group from alcohol is attached to the ether oxygen of the ester. The name of the ester is the alkyl group from the alcohol plus the alkyl group from the acid plus the suffix *-oate.*   *Solve.*

(a)

$$CH_3CH_2O\!\!-\!\!\overset{\displaystyle O}{\overset{\|}{C}}\!\!-\!\!\bigcirc$$

ethylbenzoate

(b)

$$CH_3\underset{\underset{\displaystyle }{}}{\overset{\displaystyle H}{\overset{|}{N}}}\!\!-\!\!\overset{\displaystyle O}{\overset{\|}{C}}CH_3$$

N-methylethanamide
or N-methylacetamide

(c)

$$\bigcirc\!\!-\!\!O\!\!-\!\!\overset{\displaystyle O}{\overset{\|}{C}}CH_3$$

phenylacetate

24.50   (a)

$$CH_3CH_2CH_2\overset{\displaystyle O}{\overset{\|}{C}}\!\!-\!\!O\!\!-\!\!CH_3$$

methylbutanoate

(b)

$$\bigcirc\!\!-\!\!\overset{\displaystyle O}{\overset{\|}{C}}\!\!-\!\!O\!\!-\!\!\underset{\underset{\displaystyle CH_3}{|}}{\overset{\overset{\displaystyle CH_3}{|}}{C}}\!\!-\!\!H$$

2-propylbenzoate

(c)

$$CH_3CH_2\overset{\displaystyle O}{\overset{\|}{C}}\!\!-\!\!\underset{\underset{\displaystyle CH}{|}}{N}\!\!-\!\!CH_3$$

N, N-dimethylpropanamide

24.51   *Analyze/Plan.* Follow the logic in Sample Exercise 24.6.   *Solve.*

(a)

$$CH_3CH_2\overset{\displaystyle O}{\overset{\|}{C}}\!\!-\!\!O\!\!-\!\!CH_3 + NaOH \longrightarrow \left[CH_3CH_2C\!\!\overset{\nearrow O}{\underset{\searrow O}{}}\right]^- + Na^+ + CH_3OH$$

(b)

$$CH_3\overset{\displaystyle O}{\overset{\|}{C}}\!\!-\!\!O\!\!-\!\!\bigcirc + 2NaOH \longrightarrow \left[CH_3C\!\!\overset{\nearrow O}{\underset{\searrow O}{}}\right]^- + 2Na^+ + \left[\bigcirc\!\!-\!\!O\right]^-$$

24.52 (a)

$$CH_3CH_2CH_2CH_2OH + HO\overset{\overset{O}{\|}}{C}CH_2CH_3 \longrightarrow CH_3CH_2CH_2CH_2O\overset{\overset{O}{\|}}{C}CH_2CH_3$$

1-butanol   propionic acid   butyl proprionate

(propanoic acid)

(b)

24.53 Yes, we expect acetic acid to be a strongly hydrogen-bonded substance. The carboxyl group has —OH , which acts as a donor, and —C=O , which acts as an acceptor in hydrogen bonding. The boiling point of acetic acid is higher than that of water (118°C vs. 100°C), indicating that hydrogen-bonding in acetic acid is even stronger than that of water (Figure 11.11). The melting points, 16.7°C for acetic acid and 0°C for water, show a similar trend.

24.54 $2 CH_3COOH(l) \longrightarrow CH_3\overset{\overset{O}{\|}}{C}O\overset{\overset{O}{\|}}{C}H_3(l) + H_2O(l)$

24.55 *Analyze/Plan.* Follow the logic in Sample Exercise 24.2, incorporating functional group information from Table 24.6. *Solve.*

(a) $CH_3CH_2CH_2CH(OH)CH_3$ (b) $CH_3CH(OH)CH_2OH$

(c) $CH_3\overset{\overset{O}{\|}}{C}OCH_2CH_3$ (d)

(e) $CH_3OCH_2CH_3$

24.56 (a) $CH_3CH_2CH_2CH_2CH(C_2H_5)CH_2OH$

(b)

(c)

(d) $CH_3CH_2OCH_2CH_2CH_2CH_3$

(e)

24.57 *Analyze/Plan.* Review the rules for naming alkanes and haloalkanes; draw the structures. That is, draw the carbon chain indicated by the root name, place substituents, fill remaining positions with H atoms. Each C atom attached to four different groups is chiral.   *Solve.*

$$\begin{array}{ccccccccc} & H & & H & & CH_3 & Br & & H \\ & | & & | & & | & | & & | \\ H- & C & - & C & - & C^* & - C^* & - & C -H \\ & | & & | & & | & | & & | \\ & H & & H & & H & Cl & & H \end{array}$$

˙ chiral C atoms

C2 is obviously attached to four different groups. C3 is chiral because the substituents on C2 render the C1-C2 group different than the C4-C5 group.

24.58

$$\begin{array}{cccccccccccc} & H & & H & & H & & Cl & & H & & H \\ & | & & | & & | & & | & & | & & | \\ H- & C & - & C & - & C & - & C^* & - & C & - & C -H \\ & | & & | & & | & & | & & | & & | \\ & H & & H & & H & & CH_3 & & H & & H \end{array}$$

Yes, the molecule has optical isomers. The chiral carbon atom is attached to chloro, methyl, ethyl, and propyl groups. (If the root was a 5-carbon chain, the molecule would not have optical isomers because two of the groups would be ethyl groups.)

Proteins (section 24.7)

24.59 (a) An α-amino acid contains an NH_2 group attached to the carbon that is bound to the carbon of the carboxylic acid function.

(b) In forming a protein, amino acids undergo a condensation reaction between the amino group and carboxylic acid:

$$\begin{array}{c} O \\ \| \\ -C \boxed{-OH + H-} N-CH_2C-OH \\ | \\ H \end{array} \longrightarrow \begin{array}{c} O \qquad O \\ \| \qquad \| \\ -C-N-CH_2-C-OH + H_2O \\ | \\ H \end{array}$$

(c) The bond that links amino acids in proteins is called the *peptide* bond.

$$\begin{array}{c} O \\ \| \\ -C-N- \\ | \\ H \end{array}$$

24.60 The side chains possess three characteristics that may be of importance. They may be bulky (e.g., the phenyl group in phenylalanine) and thus impose restraints on where and how the amino acid can undergo reaction. Secondly, the side chain will be either hydrophobic, containing mostly nonpolar groups such as $(CH_3)_2 CH-$ in valine, or hydrophilic, containing a polar group such as $-OH$ in serine. The hydrophobic or hydrophilic nature of the side chain definitely influences solubility and other intermolecular interactions. Finally, the side chain may contain an acidic (e.g., the $-COOH$ group in glutamic acid) or basic (e.g., the $-NH_2$ group in lysine) functional group. These groups will be protonated or deprotonated, depending on the pH of the solution, and determine the variation of properties (including solubility) over a range of pH values. Acidic or basic side chains may also become involved in hydrogen-bonding with other amino acids.

24.61   *Analyze/Plan.* Two dipeptides are possible. Either peptide can have the terminal carboxyl group or the terminal amino group.   *Solve.*

leucyltryptophan, Leu-Trp, LW

tryptophanylleucine, Trp-Leu, WL

24.62

methionine   glycine   methionylglycine

24.63   *Analyze/Plan.* Follow the logic in Sample Exercise 24.7.   *Solve.*

(a)

Gly-Gly-His

(b)   Three tripeptides are possible: Gly-Gly-His, GGH; Gly-His-Gly, GHG; His-Gly-Gly, HGG

24.64   (a)   Valine, serine, glutamic acid

(b)   Six (assuming the tripeptide contains all three amino acids):

Gly-Ser-Glu, GSE; Gly-Glu-Ser, GES; Ser-Gly-Glu, SGE; Ser-Glu-Gly, SEG; Glu-Ser-Gly, ESG; Glu-Gly-Ser, EGS

24.65   (a)   The *primary structure* of a protein refers to the sequence of amino acids in the chain. Along any particular section of the protein chain the configuration may be helical, may be an open chain, or arranged in some other way. This is called the *secondary structure*. The overall shape of the protein molecule is determined by the way the segments of the protein chain fold together, or pack. The interactions which determine the overall shape are referred to as the *tertiary structure*.

        (b)   X-ray crystallography is the primary and preferred technique for determining protein structure.

24.66   The α-helix and β-sheet are examples of regular orientations in protein chains that are termed protein secondary structures. Both patterns are formed by hydrogen bonding. The main difference is that an α-helix is formed by hydrogen bonds between amino acids in the same chain, while a β-sheet is formed by hydrogen bonds between two chains (or a chain with a flexible loop that has bent back on itself to form hydrogen bonds).

An α-helix is a column, with hydrogen bonds between a particular amino acid and a different amino acid several groups away. A β-sheet has a hydrogen-bonding pattern that zippers together two uncoiled protein strands to form a "pleated" sheet. These two secondary structures are enabled by different amino acid sequences. And, many sequences form neither an α-helix nor a β-sheet.

Carbohydrates and Lipids (sections 24.8 and 24.9)

24.67   (a)   *Carbohydrates*, or sugars, are composed of carbon, hydrogen, and oxygen. From a chemical viewpoint, they are polyhydroxyaldehydes or ketones. Carbohydrates are primarily derived from plants and are a major food source for animals.

        (b)   A *monosaccharide* is a simple sugar molecule that cannot be decomposed into smaller sugar molecules by (acid) hydrolysis.

        (c)   A *disaccharide* is a carbohydrate composed of two simple sugar units. Hydrolysis breaks the disaccharides into two monosaccharides.

        (d)   A *polysaccharide* is a polymer composed of many simple sugar units.

24.68   Glucose exists in solution as a cyclic structure in which the aldehyde function on carbon 1 reacts with the OH group of carbon 5 to form what is called a hemiacetal, Figure 24.22. Carbon atom 1 carries an OH group in the hemiacetal form; in α-glucose this OH group is on the opposite side of the ring as the CH_2OH group on carbon atom 5. In the β (beta) form the OH group on carbon 1 is on the same side of the ring as the CH_2OH group on carbon 5.

The condensation product of two glucose units looks like this:

α-linkage   β-linkage

24.69 The empirical formula of cellulose is $C_6H_{10}O_5$. As in glycogen, the six-membered ring form of glucose forms the monomer unit that is the basis of the polymer cellulose. In cellulose, glucose monomer units are joined by β linkages.

24.70 The empirical formula of glycogen is $C_6H_{10}O_5$. The six-membered ring form of glucose is the unit that forms the basis of glycogen. The monomeric glucose units are joined by α linkages.

24.71 (a) In the linear form of mannose, the aldehydic carbon is C1. Carbon atoms 2, 3, 4, and 5 are chiral because they each carry four different groups. Carbon 6 is not chiral because it contains two H atoms.

(b) Both the α (left) and β (right) forms are possible.

24.72 (a) In the linear form of galactose, the aldehydic carbon is C1. Carbon atoms 2, 3, 4, and 5 are chiral because they each carry four different groups. Carbon 6 is not chiral because it contains two H atoms.

(b) The structure is best deduced by comparing galactose with glucose, and inverting the configurations at the appropriate carbon atoms. Recall from Solution 25.68 that both the β-form (shown here) and the α-form (OH on carbon 1 on the opposite side of ring as the CH_2OH on carbon 5) are possible.

galactose

24.73 The term *lipid* refers to the broad class of naturally-occurring molecules that are soluble in nonpolar solvents. Two important subgroups are fats and fatty acids. Structurally, fatty acids are carboxylic acids with a hydrocarbon chain of more than four carbon atoms (typically 16-20 carbon atoms). Fats are esters formed by condensation of an alcohol and a fatty acid. In animals, the alcohol is the triol glycerol; three fatty acid molecules condense with one glycerol molecule to form a large, nonpolar molecule. For both fatty acids and fats it is the long hydrocarbon chains that define the polarity, solubility and other physical properties of the molecules.

Phospholipids are glycerol esters formed from one phosphoric acid (RPO(OH)$_2$ and two fatty acid (RCOOH) molecules. At body pH, the phosphate group is deproned and has a negative charge. It is the juxtaposition of two long, nonpolar hydrocarbon chains with the charged phosphate "head" that causes phospholipids to form bilayers in water. The nonpolar chains do not readily mix with polar water. They do interact with the nonpolar chains of other phospholipids molecules on the inside of the bilayer. The charged phosphate heads interact with polar water molecules on the outsides of the bilayer.

24.74   Consider the fuels ethane, C_2H_6, and ethanol, C_2H_5OH, where one C–H bond has been replaced by C–O–H, a C–O and an O–H bond. Combustion reactions for the two fuels follow.

$C_2H_6 + 7/2\,O_2 \rightarrow 2CO_2 + 3H_2O$; $C_2H_5OH + 3O_2 \rightarrow 2CO_2 + 3H_2O$

Both reactions have the same products, so the exothermic (negative) parts of the reaction enthalpies are the same. The difference is in the endothermic (positive) part, the energy required to break bonds of the reactants. According to Table 8.4, the energies required to break bonds in the two sets of reactants follow.

C_2H_6: 6D(C–H) + D(C –C) + 7/2D(O$_2$) = 6(413) + 348 + 3.5(495) = 4558.5 = 4559 kJ

C_2H_5OH: 5D(C–H) + D(C–C) + D(C–O) + D(O–H) + 3D(O$_2$) =

5(413) + 348 + 358 + 463 + 3(495) = 4719 kJ

Since more energy is required to break bonds in the combustion of one mole of ethanol, the reaction is less exothermic overall. Because C_2H_6 has a more exothermic combustion reaction, we say that more energy is "stored" in C_2H_6 than in C_2H_5OH.

Nucleic Acids (section 24.10)

24.75   Dispersion forces increase as molecular size (and molar mass) increases. The larger purines (2 rings vs. 1 ring for pyrimidines) have larger dispersion forces.

24.76

24.77   *Analyze/Plan.* Consider the structures of the organic bases in Section 24.10. The first base in the sequence is attached to the sugar with the free phosphate group in the 5' position. The last base is attached to the sugar with a free –OH group in the 3' position. *Solve.*

The DNA sequence is 5'–TACG–3'.

24.78   In the helical structure for DNA, the strands of the polynucleotides are held together by hydrogen-bonding interactions between particular pairs of bases. It happens that adenine and thymine form an especially effective base pair, and that guanine and cytosine are similarly related. Thus, each adenine has a thymine as its opposite number in the other strand, and each guanine has a cytosine as its opposite number. In the overall analysis of the double strand, total adenine must then equal total thymine, and total guanine equals total cytosine.

24.79   *Analyze/Plan.* Recall that there is complimentary base pairing in nucleic acids because of hydrogen bond geometry. The DNA pairs are A–T and G–C. (The RNA pairs are A–U and G–C.)

Solve. From the single strand sequence, formulate the complimentary strand. Note that 3' of the complimentary strand aligns with 5' of the parent strand.

5'–GCATTGGC–3'

3'–CGTAACCG–5'

24.80   In terms of the "small molecule" components of DNA and RNA, there are two main differences. Both DNA and RNA contain 5-membered ring sugars. In RNA, the sugar is ribose; in DNA the substituent at C2 is –H instead of –OH, and the sugar is deoxyribose. Both include four nitrogen-containing organic bases. Three of these, adenine, guanine and cytosine, occur in both DNA and RNA. The fourth base is thymine in DNA and uracil in RNA; thymine and uracil differ by a single –CH_3 substituent.

In terms of macromolecular structure, DNA is double-stranded and exists as the famous "double helix", while RNA is single-stranded. The seemingly minor structural differences in small-molecule components results in a major difference between the macromolecular structures of DNA and RNA.

Additional Exercises

24.81

$$H_2C{=}CH{-}\overset{\overset{\textstyle O}{\|}}{C}{-}H$$

$$H{-}C\overset{\overset{\textstyle H}{|}}{\underset{\underset{\textstyle H}{|}}{{=}}}C{-}OH$$ (with $H{-}C$ at left)

$$H{-}C{\equiv}C{-}CH_2OH$$

$$O{=}C{=}CH{-}CH_3$$

$$HC{\equiv}COCH_3$$

$$\overset{\overset{\textstyle O}{\|}}{C}\;\;H_2C{-}CH_2$$

Structures with the —OH group attached to an alkene carbon atom are not included. These molecules are called "vinyl alcohols" and are not the major form at equilibrium.

24.82   *Analyze/Plan.* We are asked the number of structural isomers for two specified carbon chain lengths and a certain number of double bonds. Structural isomers have different connectivity. Since the chain length is specified, we can ignore structural isomers created by branching. We are not asked about geometrical isomers, so we ignore those as well. The resulting question is: How many ways are there to place the specified number of double bonds along the specified C chain? *Solve.*

5 C chain with one double bond: 2 structural isomers

C=C—C—C—C   C—C=C—C—C

6 C chain with two double bonds: 6 structural isomers

C=C—C=C—C—C   C=C—C—C=C—C   C=C—C—C—C=C

C—C=C—C=C—C   C=C=C—C—C—C   C—C=C=C—C—C

24.83

Cyclopentene does not show cis-trans isomerism because the existence of the ring demands that the C—C bonds be cis to one another.

24.84   The suffic −ene signifies an alkene, −one a ketone. The molecule has alkene and ketone functional groups.

24.85

$$H_2C=CH—CH_2OH \qquad H_2C—\overset{\displaystyle CH_2}{\underset{\displaystyle OH}{C}}—H$$

(Structures with the −OH group attached to an alkene carbon atom are not included. These molecules are called "vinyl alcohols" and are not the major form at equilibrium.)

24.86   (a)

, aldehyde;   , *trans*-alkene;   , *cis*-alkene

     (b)   —O— , ether;   —OH , alcohol;   C≡C , alkene;

           —N— , amine (two of these, one aliphatic and one aromatic);

           , aromatic (phenyl) ring

     (c)

           , ketone (2 of these);   —N— , amine (2 of these)

           , aromatic (phenyl) ring (2 of these)

(d)

$$-\overset{\overset{\displaystyle O}{\|}}{C}-\overset{|}{N}- \text{ , amide;}$$, aromatic (phenyl) ring;

—OH , alcohol (aromatic alcohol, phenol)

24.87

(a)

$$CH_3CH_2CH_2\overset{\overset{\displaystyle O}{\|}}{C}OH \text{ or } (CH_3)_2CH\overset{\overset{\displaystyle O}{\|}}{C}OH$$

(b)

(c)

$$CH_3-\overset{\overset{\displaystyle OH}{|}}{CH}-\overset{\overset{\displaystyle OH}{|}}{CH_2} \text{ or } \overset{\overset{\displaystyle OH}{|}}{CH_2}-CH_2-\overset{\overset{\displaystyle OH}{|}}{CH_2}$$

(d)

24.88   The difference between an alcoholic hydrogen and a carboxylic acid hydrogen is two-fold. First, the electronegative carbonyl oxygen in a carboxylic acid withdraws electron density from the O—H bond, rendering the bond more polar and the H more ionizable. Second, the conjugate base of a carboxylic acid, carboxylate anion, exhibits resonance. This stabilizes the conjugate base and encourages ionization of the carboxylic acid. In an alcohol no electronegative atoms are bound to the carbon that holds the —OH group, and the H is tightly bound to the O.

24.89   In order for indole to be planar, the N atom must be sp^2 hybridized. The nonbonded electron pair on N is in a pure p orbital perpendicular to the plane of the molecule. The electrons that form the π bonds in the molecule are also in pure p orbitals perpendicular to the plane of the molecule. Thus, each of these p orbitals is in the correct orientation for π overlap; the delocalized π system extends over the entire molecule and includes the "nonbonded" electron pair on N. The reason that indole is such a weak base (H$^+$ acceptor) is that the nonbonded electron pair is delocalized and a H$^+$ ion does not feel the attraction of a full localized electron pair.

24.90   (a)   None

(b)   The carbon bearing the secondary —OH has four different groups attached, and is thus chiral.

(c)   The carbon bearing the —NH$_2$ group and the carbon bearing the CH$_3$ group are both chiral.

24.91   In the zwitterion form of a tripeptide present in aqueous solution near pH 7, the terminal carboxyl group is deprotonated and the terminal amino group is protonated, resulting in a net zero charge. The molecule has a net charge only if a side (R) group contains a charged (protonated or deprotonated) group. The tripeptide is positively charged if a side group contains a protonated amine. According to Figure 24.18, the only amino acids with protonated amines in their side groups are histidine (His), lysine (Lys), and arginine (Arg). Of the tripeptides listed, only (a) Gly-Ser-Lys will have a net positive charge at pH 7.

[Note that aspartic acid (Asp) has a deprotonated carboxyl in its side group, so (c) Phe-Tyr-Asp will have a net negative charge at pH 7.]

24.92   Glu-Cys-Gly is the only possible order. Glutamic acid has two carboxyl groups that can form a peptide bond with cysteine, so there are two possible structures.

24.93   Both glucose and fructose contain six C atoms, so both are hexoses. Glucose contains an aldehyde group at C1, so it is an aldohexose. Fructose has a ketone at C2, so it is a ketohexose.

24.94   DNA and RNA have the bases guanine, cytosine and adenine in common, but DNA contains thymine while RNA contains uracil. Thymine and uracil differ by a single methyl group, so both have a similar hydrogen bonding pattern with the complementary base adenine. This means that there is the possibility of a DNA strand binding to a "complementary" RNA strand.

Given this possibility, RNA is not involved in DNA replication. However, during the process of transcription and in the presence of the enzyme RNA polymerase, a complementary strand of mRNA is assembled along a segment of the backbone of a single DNA strand. During transcription, when there is adenine (A) in the DNA strand, uracil (U) is added to the RNA strand.

Integrative Exercises

24.95 CH_3CH_2OH CH_3-O-CH_3
         ethanol   dimethyl ether

Ethanol contains $-O-H$ bonds which form strong intermolecular hydrogen bonds, while dimethyl ether experiences only weak dipole-dipole and dispersion forces.

difluoromethane   methane

CH_2F_2 has much greater molar mass and is a polar molecule, while CH_4 is lighter and nonpolar. CH_2F_2 experiences dipole-dipole and stronger dispersion forces, while CH_4 experiences only weaker dispersion forces.

In both cases, stronger intermolecular forces lead to the higher boiling point.

24.96   Determine the empirical formula of the unknown compound and its oxidation product. Use chemical properties to propose possible structures.

$$68.1 \, g \, C \times \frac{1 \, mol \, C}{12.01 \, g \, C} = 5.6703; \, 5.6703/1.1375 = 4.98 \approx 5$$

$$13.7 \, g \, H \times \frac{1 \, mol \, H}{1.008 \, g \, H} = 13.5913; \, 13.5913/1.1375 = 11.95 \approx 12$$

$$18.2 \, g \, P \times \frac{1 \, mol \, O}{16.00 \, g \, O} = 1.1375; \, 1.1375/1.1375 = 1$$

The empirical formula of the unknown is $C_5H_{12}O$.

$$69.7 \, g \, C \times \frac{1 \, mol \, C}{12.01 \, g \, C} = 5.8035; \, 5.8035/1.1625 = 4.99 \approx 5$$

$$11.7 \, g \, H \times \frac{1 \, mol \, H}{1.008 \, g \, H} = 11.6071; \, 11.6071/1.1625 = 9.99 \approx 10$$

$$18.6 \, g \, O \times \frac{1 \, mol \, O}{16.00 \, g \, O} = 1.1625; \, 1.1625/1.1625 = 1$$

The empirical formula of the oxidation product is $C_5H_{10}O$.

The compound is clearly an alcohol. Its slight solubility in water is consistent with the properties expected of a secondary alcohol with a five-carbon chain. The fact that oxidation results in a ketone, rather than an aldehyde or a carboxylic acid, tells us that it is a secondary alcohol. Some reasonable structures for the unknown secondary alcohol are:

$$\begin{array}{ccc} CH_3CHCH_2CH_2CH_3 & CH_3CHCHCH_2CH_3 & CH_3CHCH(CH_3)_2 \\ | & | & | \\ OH & OH & OH \end{array}$$

24.97   Determine the empirical formula, molar mass, and thus molecular formula of the compound. Confirm with physical data.

$$66.7 \, g \, C \times \frac{1 \, mol \, C}{12.01 \, g \, C} = 5.554 \, \, mol \, C; \, 5.554/1.381 = 4.021 = 4$$

$$11.2 \, g \, H \times \frac{1 \, mol \, H}{1.008 \, g \, H} = 11.11 \, \, mol \, H; \, 11.11/1.381 = 8.043 = 8$$

$$22.1 \, g \, O \times \frac{1 \, mol \, O}{16.00 \, g \, O} = 1.381 \, \, mol \, O; \, 1.381/1.381 = 1$$

The empirical formula is C_4H_8O. Using Equation 10.11 (MM = molar mass):

$$MM = \frac{(2.28g/L)(0.08206 \, L\text{-}atm/mol\text{-}K)(373K)}{0.970\text{-}atm} = 71.9 \, g/mol$$

The formula weight of C_4H_8O is 72, so the molecular formula is also C_4H_8O. Since the compound has a carbonyl group and cannot be oxidized to an acid, the only possibility is 2-butanone.

$$\underset{CH_3CCH_2CH_3}{\overset{O}{\overset{\|}{}}}$$

The boiling point of 2-butanone is 79.6°C, confirming the identification.

24.98   Determine the empirical formula, molar mass, and thus molecular formula of the compound. Confirm with physical data.

$$85.7 \text{ g C} \times \frac{1 \text{ mol C}}{12.01 \text{ g C}} = 7.136 \text{ mol C}; \; 7.136/7.136 = 1$$

$$14.3 \text{ g H} \times \frac{1 \text{ mol H}}{1.008 \text{ g H}} = 14.19 \text{ mol H}; \; 14.19/7.136 \approx 2$$

Empirical formula is CH_2. Using Equation 10.11 (MM = molar mass):

$$MM = \frac{(2.21 \text{ g/L})(0.08206 \text{ L-atm/mol-K})(373K)}{(735/760) \text{ atm}} = 69.9 \text{ g/mol}$$

The molecular formula is thus C_5H_{10}. The absence of reaction with aqueous Br_2 indicates that the compound is not an alkene, so the compound is probably the cycloalkane cyclopentane. According to the *Handbook of Chemistry and Physics*, the boiling point of cyclopentane is 49°C at 760 torr. This confirms the identity of the unknown.

24.99   The reaction is: $2NH_2CH_2COOH(aq) \rightarrow NH_2CH_2CONHCH_2COOH(aq) + H_2O(l)$

$\Delta G° = (-488) + (-237.13) - 2(-369) = 12.87 = 13 \text{ kJ}$

24.100   (a)   At low pH, the amine and carboxyl   At high pH, the amine and carboxyl
groups are protonated.   groups are deprotonated.

$$\underset{H}{\overset{H_3N^+}{OH-CH_2-\overset{|}{\underset{|}{C}}-\overset{O}{\overset{\|}{C}}-OH}} \qquad \underset{H}{\overset{H_2N}{OH-CH_2-\overset{|}{\underset{|}{C}}-\overset{O}{\overset{\|}{C}}-O^-}}$$

(b) $CH_3\overset{O}{\overset{\|}{C}}-OH(aq) \longrightarrow CH_3\overset{O}{\overset{\|}{C}}-O^-(aq) + H^+(aq)$

$K_a = 1.8 \times 10^{-5}$, $pK_a = -\log(1.8 \times 10^{-5}) = 4.74$

The conjugate acid of NH_3 is NH_4^+.

$NH_4^+(aq) \rightleftharpoons NH_3(aq) + H^+(aq)$

$K_a = K_w/K_b = 1.0 \times 10^{-14} / 1.8 \times 10^{-5} = 5.55 \times 10^{-10} = 5.6 \times 10^{-10}$

$pK_a = -\log(5.55 \times 10^{-10}) = 9.26$

In general, a $-COOH$ group is stronger acid than a $-NH_3^+$ group. The lower pK_a value for amino acids is for the ionization (deprotonation) of the $-COOH$ group and the higher pK_a is for the deprotonation of the $-NH_3^+$ group.

(c)

By analogy to serine, the carboxyl group near the amine will have pK_a ~2 and the amino group will have pKa ~9. By elimination, the carboxyl group in the side chain has pK_a ~4.

24.101 (a) Because the native form is most stable, it has a lower, more negative free energy than the denatured form. Another way to say this is that ΔG for the process of denaturing the protein is positive.

(b) ΔS is negative in going from the denatured form to the folded (native) form; the native protein is more ordered.

(c) The four S—S linkages are strong covalent links holding the chain in place in the folded structure. A folded structure without these links would be less stable (higher G) and have more motional freedom (more positive entropy).

(d) After reduction, the eight S—H groups will form hydrogen-bond-like interations with acceptors along the protein backbone, but these will be weaker and less specifically located than the S—S covalent bonds of the native protein. Overall, the tertiary structure of the reduced protein will be looser and less compact due to the loss of the S—S linkages; the entropy will be higher.

(e) The amino acid cysteine must be present in order for $-SH$ bonds to be found in ribonuclease A. (Methionine contains S, but no $-SH$ functional group.)

24.102 $AMPOH^-(aq) \rightleftharpoons AMPO^{2-}(aq) + H^+(aq)$

$pK_a = 7.21; K_a = 10^{-pK_a} = 6.17 \times 10^{-8} = 6.2 \times 10^{-8}$

$K_a = \dfrac{[AMPO^{2-}][H^+]}{[AMPOH^-]} = 6.2 \times 10^{-8}$. When pH = 7.40, $[H^+] = 3.98 \times 10^{-8} = 4 \times 10^{-8}$.

Then $\dfrac{[AMPOH^-]}{[AMPO^{2-}]} = 3.98 \times 10^{-8} / 6.17 \times 10^{-8} = 0.6457 = 0.6$